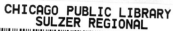

PRIZE STORIES 1954

The O. Henry Awards

PRIZE STORIES 1954: *The O. Henry Awards*

Selected and Edited by

PAUL ENGLE *and* HANSFORD MARTIN

Doubleday & Company, Inc., Garden City, N.Y. 1954

Library of Congress Catalog Card Number 21-9372 Rev. 3
Copyright, 1954, by Doubleday & Company, Inc.
All Rights Reserved
Printed in the United States
At the Country Life Press, Garden City, N.Y.
First Edition
Designed by Diana Klemin

To the memory of Herschel Brickell

PUBLISHER'S NOTE

This is the thirty-fourth appearance of the O. Henry Memorial Award Prize Stories, which until 1951 had been published annually. The continuity of the series was broken by the sudden death in May 1952 of its late editor, Herschel Brickell. No collection appeared in 1952 or 1953.

For its first years this series remained under the auspices of its founders, the Society of Arts and Sciences, which met in 1918 to vote upon a monument to O. Henry. They decided to offer two prizes for the best short stories published by American authors in American magazines in 1919. This memorial was extended almost at once into an annual collection of the best short stories. It was published from the beginning by Doubleday, which later took over sole responsibility for it. Blanche Colton Williams, one of the founders of the awards, was editor from 1919 until 1932; Harry Hansen took over from 1933 to 1940; and Herschel Brickell edited the collection from 1941 to 1951.

The stories chosen for this volume were published between August 1952 and July 1953. Subsequent volumes will also cover the period from August through July. A list of the magazines consulted appears at the back of the book. The choice of stories and the selection of prize winners is exclusively the responsibility of the editors.

CONTENTS

After the three prize stories the order is alphabetical by author

INTRODUCTION

It is the editors' conviction that the only thing a short story *should be* is a brief fictional narrative that achieves an aesthetic effect of emotional depth which, at first glance, would seem to be out of proportion to the apparently simple scope of the work.

The good short story does not merely fulfill the announcement of its superficial intent, it exceeds it; and it is this extended accomplishment which moves the short story from the realm of entertainment into that of literature.

American magazines today are serviced by a great number of competent craftsmen who are able to deliver the goods they promise. It is our hope that the yearly O. Henry Prize Stories collection, in the future as it has in the past, will represent the much smaller number of present-day writers who are equally competent as workmen, but who are predominantly concerned with the discovery and presentation of those values beyond the reach or interest of the professional entertainer. It is neither ironic nor accidental that it is precisely the smaller group, rather than the larger, which succeeds in permanently entertaining us after all.

Certainly some such similar criterion must have guided the late Herschel Brickell in his compilation of this series through so many years, and it is the wish of the new editors to continue that tradition of service to the short story which distinguished his career. As a tribute to his accomplishment, this volume is dedicated to him.

THE AWARDS FOR 1954

First prize of $500 for the best short story: To Thomas Mabry, for "The Indian Feather," published in the *Sewanee Review*.

Second prize of $400: To Clay Putman for "The News from Troy," published in *Furioso*.

Third prize of $300: To Richard Wilbur for "A Game of Catch," published in *The New Yorker*.

In a time when too many short stories are growing longer, more verbose and more diffuse, and thus losing that explosive capacity of aesthetic excitement which characterizes the best short fiction, the most striking impression offered by Thomas Mabry's "The Indian Feather" lies in its rich sense of complexity and compression. The author has utilized most of the techniques available to the modern writer in order to construct a thick-textured and dimensional piece of work.

The story's basic situation—its subject matter—is the primal theme of initiation. Mr. Mabry has been careful to create a tangible world, peopled with living characters, and vivid with a sense of felt life, for his protagonist to come into. Dialogue serves the dual function of characterization and exposition in his treatment of the more important persons of the story; but even his minor figures are brought to quick life by a conversational phrase, a simile, or a physical detail. Ellen Alice, whose "high smooth pompadour gleamed yellow like glue," or the anonymous farmer in mud-dry shoes have a solidity of being against which the boy, his parents, and Mr. Kirk are highlighted as persons involved in a world of other living individuals.

Similarly, Mr. Mabry's careful attention to naturalistic fact creates a visible sensuous physical world, the properties of which are perceived through the nerve ends. The town, the river, the countryside are more than backdrops for an action; they are physical factors which help to constitute the problems of the story's people.

It is the rich substance of this background which supports and extends the symbolic elements of the narrative. The Indian feather itself is not a mere prop; its symbolic function is not imposed upon the reader, but arises from its proper physical place in the natural environment, and from the varying degrees of comprehension with which both the boy and Mr. Kirk regard it as both a natural object and a symbolic one. The climactic confrontation of the story—the stare of Mr. Kirk through the darkened glass in the warehouse—is an effective image of evil in its own terms, but its impact is reinforced because the earlier encounter of the boy with the copperhead has convinced the reader of its particular reality. The equation of the human and the animal evil is not an arbitrary act of the author; it is an inevitable conjunction arising from the physical facts of the story's milieu and action. Just so, Mabry's rich and intricate use of color remains unobtrusive and right because it is natural; the play of light and shadow that haunts the story, and which correlates the ambiguity of the boy's awareness, passes beyond ornament or device into an inescapable element of the scene.

Finally, the author has not hesitated to exploit language to its fullest extent, when justified by the emotional intensity of situation. It is for this rich texture of style, incident, and created character, growing out of the most carefully observed physical environment and culminating in a complex awareness, that the editors chose "The Indian Feather" as the most outstanding short story of the year.

In somewhat the same way, though in an entirely different setting and with a distinctive narrative tone, Clay Putman's "The News from Troy" drives through the particular to the universal. In fact, Mr. Putman's direct presentation is so successful in its implication that one feels the timelessness of the theme to be needlessly labored by occasional comment. However that may be, the family in Mr. Putman's story, in its relation to the soldier son, is presented with all the vivid impact of dense emotion that arises from private relationships shattered by public disaster. Mr. Putman's story builds impressively to his final heartbreaking image, an image that fuses love and helplessness in an unforgettable, compassionate grotesquerie.

Richard Wilbur's "A Game of Catch" is a slighter story, but also one that mounts to a final moment of memorable tension. As carefully constructed as a sonnet, it is an example of the clean economy of the short story at its best; an apparently casual construction which leaves nonetheless an indelible impression of inevitability. Scho's last cry, haunting as any classical curse, continues to reverberate in the reader's mind long after he has laid the story down.

There were other close contestants for prize honors. Donald Justice's "Vineland's Burning" offered a style which was as rich as good verse, but never fell into the trap of "poetic prose." James B. Hall's *jeu d'esprit* "Estate and Trespass" completely fulfilled its intention of being a modern gothic tale; it was the rather limited specialness of that intention which somewhat diminished the editors' general admiration for the story. But Hall is one of the most rewarding of the young short-story writers, and "Estate and Trespass" was the most outstanding experimental story of the year.

On the level of realism, a field in which the American short story has achieved some of its most notable permanent successes, Stanford Whitmore's "Lost Soldier" was a demonstration of the sheer dramatic power of direct narration. Corporal Wolfe is a specific soldier in a specific war, confronted by a specific enemy, but Whitmore has so clearly and forcefully concentrated his presentation of Wolfe's problem, practical as well as moral, that while avoiding allegory the incident becomes a deeply moving comment on the nature of the individual soldier's predicament in any war.

R. V. Cassill's mixture of psychological fantasy and mundane reality in "The War in the Air" also excited the appreciation of the editors. If our final conclusion was that the story's opening suggested a realm of fantasy beyond the psychological which was never fully explored, the skill with which the elements of the real and the imagined achieved a delicately shifting position in the mind of the reader as well as in the mind of Jimmy Stark was worthy of genuine respect.

But each of the stories in this volume is possessed of its striking individual merits. Although it is a truism, the difficulty of picking the best is one of the most harrowing of editorial labors. This is especially the case in a year that offers so many stories of nearly uniform merit; the better the harvest, the harder the chores.

THE SHORT-STORY SCENE

Yet, superficially, the present landscape of the short story offers a certain barrenness of aspect. There is no one undisputed dominant master, as Hemingway seemed to be during the twenties; nor is there any school close-knit by a common ideology, as was the case with the social-protest writers of the early thirties. Even the exuberant high stylists of the recent past seem considerably depressed; the exciting verbal fireworks that spangled the pages of American periodicals at the close of the forties are at least temporarily dampened, and the literary air is no longer illuminated by the Roman candles and Catherine wheels of rich full-flaring prose that formerly dazzled the reader, particularly of the glossier-quality magazines.

Yet beneath the quieter literary surface of the present period the editors feel that contemporary writers are working determinedly in a certain definite direction toward a definite goal. This goal might be defined as a consolidation and reconciliation of the two chief historical trends in the American short story.

In our country the first and longest-lasting contribution to the theory of the short story, arising out of the tale, was the concept of the short story as a deliberately artificial construct. This had its roots in "Once upon a time . . ." the sense of short fiction as a work of art which beguiled or instructed through obvious art.

Poe was its foremost early practitioner, and the two dominating elements in his work, plot and fantasy, are permanent characteristics of the popular short story. The former element reached a certain apogee in the works of the writer after whom this collection is named, and today the plotted story is still the staple of the magazine business;

the latter element of fantasy has permeated all branches of literature, popular or serious, and representations of its effect can be found in the whole range of contemporary fiction, from *Astounding Stories* to the work of our latest Nobel Prize winner.

But it is not often remarked that the reportorial element in Poe was also very strong, and in such pieces as "The Premature Burial," "The Mystery of Marie Rogêt," and his hoaxes, he erected prototypes for a second kind of fiction: the fiction which disdained the obvious employment of artifice, which pretended to the direct presentation of "truth," and which was to be extensively developed in the work of the naturalists, in the French- and Russian-influenced "slice of life" writers of the twenties, and in the social protest, clinical-history short stories of the thirties. The social documentation and regionalism of that era placed a continual emphasis upon the reportorial element of the short story, its ability to represent life undistorted by the admitted use of conscious style or manipulation of event.

Each school had its merits, and the masters of each school used, of course, factors from both; but in the theory and practice of many able young writers the schism resulted in a genuine division of aesthetic. If the editors may be permitted to generalize upon the chief structural contribution being made in the short story today, they would suggest that the work of our present writers is a conscious attempt to reconcile these two schools.

The past few years have seen a revival of the consciously artistic story, the story devoted to the fullest exploitation of language, and to the obvious arrangement of action and event. But in the most able writers, at least, this has not been merely a return to the romance; for today's authors, though they may call upon conscious style and contrived incident with considerable frankness, are generally careful to root their artifice in a specific environment and social context.

Of this year's prize winners only Richard Wilbur's could claim to be a realistic story in the most exact meaning of the term. Both Thomas Mabry and Clay Putman have, in different ways, intervened between the story and the reader, and the kind of truth we accept from their works is the truth of fiction, not that of fact. Yet in each story this fictional truth is imbedded in a context of carefully observed and selected fact, and the complex power each story generates arises from this artistic combination.

The private crisis of the heroine in Ruth Harnden's "Rebellion" occurs in a highly particularized social set, and the public activities of this group provide the final metaphor, which moves the story into the realm of general experience. In P. H. Lowrey's "Too Young to Have a Gun," as in Herbert Wilner's "Whistle and the Heroes," the

emotional drama is (literally) played out in public arenas, and in
each case the sense of locale and personnel reinforces the central emotional problem of the protagonist. Even in the field of fantasy Herbert
Gold's "The Witch" and Augusta Walker's "The Day of the Cipher"
rest solidly upon a foundation of concrete detail.

It is in this kind of conjunction, the connection of artifice and
reality, the union of personal emotion and realized physical environment, that today's writers seem to be finding a strong base for a fiction that will be able to manifest both realistic scope and spiritual
precision. If such an effort does not produce the most immediately
exciting kind of writing, it does suggest a solid and heartening advance toward aesthetic maturity and a literature supple and complex
enough to reflect without simplification or falsification the private
and public dilemmas of our times.

A NOTE ON PROCEDURE

It is with a great deal of pleasure and a certain sense of fitness that
the editors welcome the O. Henry Prize Stories to the State University
of Iowa, and to the Writers' Workshop there. Henceforth the collection will be edited from the campus, with a staff of readers selected
from graduate writing students representing all sections of the country.

During the past decade authors who have been associated with
the Iowa Writers' Workshop, either as students or members of the
faculty, have had continual representation in the various American
anthologies. Herschel Brickell commented in these pages a few years
ago upon the excellence of the *Western Review*, published at the
State University of Iowa; Martha Foley, in her *Best American Short
Stories 1953*; listed twenty-three stories by past and present members
of the Iowa Workshop on her honor roll, and reprinted two. The
eight novels by recent Iowa Workshop students accepted or published
in the past year are further evidence that it is appropriate to edit the
O. *Henry* Prize Stories from a community so congenial to fiction.

For these reasons the editors felt that in compiling the annual
O. Henry Prize Stories it would be unjust to the collection to exclude
short stories because of connections their authors may have had with
the State University of Iowa. It was our decision to stand by our
definition of the good short story, to attempt to find its most distinguished representatives yearly, and to reprint them regardless of their
source of origin.

Our editorial associate, Donald Justice, offers a case in point. Mr.
Justice was reprinted in the O. Henry collection some time before
he came to the University of Iowa. His excellent story, "Vineland's

Burning," in this year's volume, was written and published, and chosen by the editors as a definite entry before he assumed any connection with the anthology. To deny ourselves the services of one of the country's most able young writers and one of its most promising editorial critics because he happened to be on the premises would have been absurd. We are extremely glad that Mr. Justice was present and able to work with us; and we would like to take this opportunity to thank him for his assistance in all the branches of editorial labor connected with the compiling of this year's collection. An even harder problem was the decision to award First Prize to Thomas Mabry. "The Indian Feather" was written before Mr. Mabry came to the University of Iowa to join the staff of the Fiction Workshop. At the risk of seeming to favor Iowa City writers, the editors decided that they had only one obligation; to honor genuine talent, which they did in Mr. Mabry's case.

We would like also to thank those other graduate writing students who contributed their time and talents toward making the present volume possible: Marie Finney, Eugene Lichtenstein, Sheldon Tannenbaum, and Richard G. Stern. We also wish to thank the University of Iowa, which, with a care for the creative in all the arts hardly existing in many universities, but constant in it, has welcomed the O. Henry Prize Stories. Particular thanks are due to President Virgil M. Hancher, Provost Harvey H. Davis, and Professors Baldwin Maxwell and Bartholow Crawford, who have generously made facilities for editing available.

Finally, our appreciation to Miss Marjorie Piera and Mr. Ken McCormick of Doubleday and Company, and to Mr. Frank Taylor of Dell Books for their friendly and uninterfering advice, which made the composition of the collection a genuine pleasure from the technical as well as the critical standpoint. Thanks are also due to Dell Books and Western Printing and Lithographing Company for their considerable contribution to our editorial overhead as well as for their doubling the prize money.

Paul Engle
Hansford Martin

PRIZE STORIES 1954

The O. Henry Awards

THOMAS DABNEY MABRY *"greatly desires to live below the Mason and Dixon Line, longs for some Southern College to offer him a job, and invites correspondence."* Mr. Mabry is a graduate of Harvard College, has a master's degree from Vanderbilt, is married, with two children aged eight and ten. He was formerly executive director of the Museum of Modern Art, New York; was originator and director of Life magazine's photographic exhibits and film strips; now teaches at the State University of Iowa in the Writers' Workshop. He is a member of the First Baptist Church of Clarksville, Tennessee.

THE INDIAN FEATHER

FROM THE SEWANEE REVIEW

"You may as well go on and go," his father said, sitting up a little and shoving another pillow behind him. "I'm not all that sick."

At the other end of the room his mother was pulling down the ivory-colored shades one by one. She looked at him over her shoulder and her eyes said he is very sick indeed and if you had any consideration for me you would not be going off somewhere.

"It's just for the afternoon," he said quickly, turning his face away from the tall windows that were closed against the spring sunshine. In the dimmed room his father's bed had resumed its consequential air. An extra quilt lay folded over the sturdy foot and the carvings of the high headboard twisted and turned in fixed and sculptured ambiguity.

His mother came back and stood beside the bed and her fingers smoothed a pillow's white monogram.

He watched her small hand finally come to rest on his father's arm. Then he said, "But I'll be glad to stay if you want me to . . . if there's anything you want me to do for you down at the factory."

His father smiled. "No sense in your sitting around down there on a sunny Saturday afternoon," he said, "without a blame thing to do."

The room's even light warmed, burgeoned to yellow and paused. It glowed intensely for a moment and sank back suddenly to grey again, and he felt the whole outside rush of shadow against the drawn shades. ". . . Besides," his father was saying, "Kirk is more likely to stay sober if he's with you. And I'll need him bad Monday if it rains and we have a good season."

"Yes sir," he said, and hoped the clouds he had noticed that morning were the usual kind, and not rain clouds.

Again the shades went luminous with the shifting sunlight and the walnut bed in front of him turned gold. Against the wall the sculptured wood shone for an instant in the travelling light like an ancient and beneficent face.

The smile lingered: "I'll need you too," his father said. "No telling how much tobacco'll come pouring in next week." The expression darkened. "But I'll be up from here by Monday," he added, and put his hand under the pillow for his watch. "Go on and have a good time."

His mother relaxed into her wicker rocking chair and looked forlornly at him through her glasses. He tried not to understand the look. From the distant dining-room he could hear Stella clearing off the table. He glanced at the tray of uneaten food that still weighted his father's legs into two straight sticks under the sheets.

He backed to the open door. Through his sneakers the sill was hard against the arch of his foot and from the hall floor behind him a coolness crept up under his pants and caressed the calves of his legs behind his knees. He kept his eyes on his father's face. "Are you sure there's nothing I can do for you?" he asked again, and when a faint "No" formed on the grey lips he said, "I hope you'll feel better, Father."

He let his foot slip off the sill into the hall, and backed away not looking at his mother. But from the closing crack of the door he saw her pretty arm reach out to the tray, saw his father turn his head toward the curtained windows and the unseen spring trees.

The front door was open; the May air filled the dark hall. He took his cap off the hat-rack—the one he called his hunting cap—and pulled his rifle out of the umbrella stand where he had stored it before lunch, took a handful of cartridges from the hat-rack drawer, and went out into the driveway and climbed into his old Ford.

Mr. Kirk was waiting outside the gate when he drove up, leaning against the wire fence in front of the one-story brick house that he rented from the boy's father for $10 a month. Mr. Kirk's wife and his three daughters were sitting on the porch silently looking out at the afternoon. He tipped his hat to them. The two younger girls and Mrs. Kirk were barefooted, but the eldest daughter wore high-heeled shoes.

"How's J.J. today, J.D.?" Mr. Kirk asked, opening the car door.

"Better, I think," he said.

"Would you mind dropping my Ellen Alice up town?" Mr. Kirk asked. "It won't be out of our way none."

"Glad to," he said.

Mr. Kirk raised his voice and without looking back called out, "Come on here, girl."

She came running, her heels clicking on the brick walk. She opened the door and squeezed into the narrow space beside her father. "I don't want to crowd you," she said as the car moved forward. Her high smooth pompadour gleamed yellow like glue and the smell of her perfume filled the space between them, its heavy fugitive odor lingering in little waves even after the car had gathered speed.

At the corner of First and Franklin he slowed down and stopped at the newly installed traffic light in front of the Lillian Theatre. The electric bulbs that studded the theatre entrance and that at night seemed to pierce the sky with their brilliance now struggled weakly in the dry white sunlight. Ellen Alice leaned out to gaze. "I'll just get out here," she said, and got out. "I'm certainly much obliged."

The traffic light changed and he started to pull away from the curb.

"Hold on, J.D.," Mr. Kirk said suddenly in a low voice.

He put on the brakes again and as he did so a man in worn blue overalls and mud-dry shoes leaned into the car and slowly placed his hand over Mr. Kirk's knee.

"Hi, friend," Mr. Kirk said with composure.

The man stood waiting, as if certain Mr. Kirk had more to say. Mr. Kirk looked up. "You class that tobacco clean before you bring it in to me, you hear?" he said, and felt in his coat pocket for a match and stuck the end of it in his ear. He twisted it around, pulled it out and threw it away. It landed at the feet of the man who still stood close beside him. "You class it clean, mister," Mr. Kirk said, thrusting his head out through the car door, "or I'll dock you so much you won't have enough gimmie left to take your old lady a sack of candy."

The man's lips smiled around his teeth that were clenched on a chew of tobacco. His eyes, under the red hairs of his eyebrows, narrowed in the sunlight. "You can't take nothing from nothing," he said, and turned away, still smiling, to touch the arm of another acquaintance and move with him slowly down the street.

Mr. Kirk spat on the curb and pulled his head back in.

"If I had half what that old feller's got salted away," he said, "I'd have me a Christmas dinner every Sunday. Let's go, J.D."

They rolled away from the curb and along Franklin and up to the Square. At the Square they turned down the rocky hill behind the tobacco warehouses. When they reached the bottom of the hill he drove across the Tennessee Central tracks (rusty and abandoned except for a weekly freight from Kentucky) and parked on the cinder gravel in the hot treeless glare of the sun. Below them, forty feet down the sloping bank, stretched the river: silent and deep, shining with the pale yellow of suspended mud. At the water's edge a narrow unpainted skiff lay almost beached, dry at one end and half full of water at the other. It was tied to a stake and over the stake an upside-down tin can, glittering silver, jabbed their eyes as they walked down the steep incline.

"We'll have to bail her out," Mr. Kirk said.

"I'll do it," J.D. said, and knelt on the weathered board. An empty minnow bucket lay on its side and a dead minnow sloshed back and forth in the warm muddy water. A few dried fish scales speckled the narrow plank seats, and along the edges of the seats were black pencil-like scars where burning cigarettes had lain too long.

After a few minutes he said, "I'd like to have a boat like this."

Mr. Kirk was sitting down carefully on the bank. "We'll make you one out at the factory when things slow down," he said. "We'll get a nigger to help us and it won't take no time with all them hogshead staves lying around out there doing nobody no good."

"You mean you made this one?" he asked, and raised his head.

"Ten years ago," Mr. Kirk said, flipping away a cigarette butt and looking down at him from above, "and it's still holding up."

He dipped in the can and poured out the pale water—in and out, in and out. The smell filled him with a deep excitement: a smell of mud and warmth and wetness, a smell from the roots of plants.

"I'd sure appreciate your helping me build one," he said.

Mr. Kirk stood up and brushed the dust off his pants. "That'll do," he said. "Now you get up there in front."

J.D. sat down on the bow seat and they were quickly out in the middle of the river. Nothing was in sight on the smooth surface. The skiff moved silently with the unseen current. Above them, rich bottom land full of new corn stretched away on both sides until far, far down at the bend the river narrowed, and a line of bluff rose in chalky haze. From where he sat, close to the water, it looked a long way.

He hoped his father was asleep by now. He wondered if they would get back by dark. Maybe if Mr. Kirk didn't take too long they would get back in time for him to see his father a little while before supper. But the bluff was miles in the distance. They would hardly reach it much before sundown, and it might be night before Mr. Kirk got ready for the long pull home. If he could turn around now, immediately, and start back, before the current had carried them out of sight . . .

He heard Mr. Kirk say, "Well, how do you like the tobacco business, J.D.?"

"All right," he answered, "but I don't know much about it yet. But I like it fine."

"You've learned a lot for a young feller that just works in the afternoons after school," Mr. Kirk said.

He looked back toward town. Most of it had already disappeared. Even the high courthouse tower had sunk below the green crowding tree-tops, and the Presbyterian Church steeple as well. Only the tall smokestacks of the outlying water-works rose in lonely isolation against the cloudless sky and he could still tell, by the sprinkling of tiny white dots far out on the edge of town, where a corner of the City Graveyard came over the hill. He turned and faced forward, and the sun glistened on the water in front of him.

"I told J.J. the other day," Mr. Kirk was saying. "I said, 'J.J., you've got a boy what'll make a better tobacco man than you and me both.' "

"Did you, sure enough?" he said.

"Yes sir, I did. And you know what J.J. said? He said, 'Well, Kirk, teach him all you know. I'm building it up so he can take it over.' "

"Did he, sure enough?" he said, and shivered and suddenly felt warm again.

The banks of the river were thick with willows. The green spears of canes grew rank close to the water's edge, but between the canes and the river lay a narrow band of cracked mud, treacherous and barren, a place for cottonmouths to lie in the sun and shed their last year's skins. He was surprised to see how wide the river was, now that the small boat was out in the middle of it. It occurred to him that he couldn't have recognized anybody standing on the bank. His fingers closed over the rifle across his knees.

The soft thrust of Mr. Kirk's paddle sent them forward at a good speed. Alone in the low flat trough of water they smelled but could not see the new corn in the endless fields above them. It was a little after two o'clock and no shade anywhere. But the bend of the river was getting nearer. By the time they would reach it there would be shade close to the bluff side.

"Yes sir," Mr. Kirk said, "you'll be better'n your daddy and me both if you keep on like you started. You're a pretty good judge of tobacco already." The skiff slowed for a moment while he lit a cigarette. "You have to watch them farmers, though."

"Why?" he asked.

"They'll cheat you every time if you give them half a chance."

He was silent for a minute. Then he said, "How can they cheat you?"

"They'll class their lugs with their seconds and their seconds with their prime leaf," Mr. Kirk said. "Then they'll wet it all down till it looks like first-class tobacco." He jabbed his paddle deep into the yellow water. "And what's more," he said, "they'll set up nights thinking up new ways to skin you."

He made no reply to this but kept his eyes on the smooth expanse in front of them. He doubted if he'd ever be able to dock a farmer the way Mr. Kirk could do it. His mind went back to the long line of wagons at the factory door, the four-mule team wagons standing all day in line, waiting to be unloaded. His job had been to help unload, and he remembered how often he had climbed up on the wagon and knelt on the great mound of tobacco—his knees crowding those of the farmer and of the farmer's sons and his Negro sharecroppers, lifting it down to the waiting dollies at the door—he remembered how Mr. Kirk would step up and pull out from the middle of the load below them an armful of the sweet odorous leaf. He would hold it up to the light in brief and critical appraisal, the farmer meanwhile still kneeling on the unloaded part, darting a quick glance down at Mr. Kirk, who, turning round and jerking his chin up in a beckoning command, would say, "Come here, my friend. Let me see you a minute, please sir." The crouched figure would rise, wordless, and slide down from the top of the load, hands slowly falling to his sides, and Mr. Kirk would look at him for a minute in thoughtful silence. "I can't accept this, my friend," he would then say with soft solicitude. "Here, feel this here. It's as wet as a new-born kitten. Smell it," and Mr. Kirk would stick it under his nose. "It's as high as a kite; I can't bulk it in this condition, and it will cost me big money to spread it out. Twon't be no good anyhow after what you done to it. I'll have to dock you." And the farmer would stand silently waiting, or maybe would say in a low whispering voice, "It warn't wet none when we loaded up last night," while above on the brown piled wagon the other faces stared down, the hands having slowed and come to a hesitant stop. "Well, boys, what do you want to do?" the farmer would say. "Take it back home?" And finally out of the silence the muttered reply would come: "Reckon he might as well take it on off the wagon. Ain't no place else to carry it." And the hands would begin again, now moving more slowly, moving this time in bitterness and hate.

The bluff rose in rocky layers above them on their left. Oaks and hickories leaned out along the ledges. Now and then a small spring trickled over the moss and slid without noise from one ledge to another and vanished into the river. This was the place where Mr. Kirk shot squirrels.

"Be right quiet now, J.D.," he said, and headed the boat toward the bluff. He laid his paddle down and they drifted slowly inward, and as the skiff moved noiselessly over the opaque surface of the water he picked up his rifle. "There's plenty of squirrels in them trees," Mr. Kirk said, and raised the rifle to his shoulder.

Almost instantly he fired, and a furry body fell from a high limb, hit another lower one, bounced among still lower branches, and thumped to a rocky slab near the water's edge.

"We'll drift a little farther down now, and pick him up on our way back," Mr. Kirk said.

"I don't see how you'll remember where he is," he said.

Mr. Kirk laughed. "Boy, what are you talking about! I never lost no squirrel yet."

At last there was shade in front of them. They slipped into it and at once the air from the water was cool and fresh. They were so close to the rocks that he could see the maiden's hair fern and the wild sweet-william and the yellow violets that grew in the earthy crevices. Mounting overhead, the arching trees hung out, while the boat, undirected by Mr. Kirk, was pulled fitfully onward by deep and invisible strings. Mr. Kirk fired again; a second squirrel fell upon a mossy ledge, crawled a few feet and was still.

"There's another little bastard; get it, boy, quick!"

"Where?" he asked, looking up into the green forest, turning his head this way and that, his hands gripping his rifle. For answer, Mr. Kirk's shot splintered the air behind him and he was aware of its brittle echo darting back from across the river.

"We might as well pick them two up now," Mr. Kirk said, and laid his gun down on the middle plank and made a few quick thrusts of the paddle.

The skiff nosed the bank and J.D. jumped out and scrambled over the rocks. He picked up one squirrel and shoved it in his pants pocket. He moved up the bank toward the second squirrel. It lay full length yet seemed to crouch a little, its open sightless eyes fixed on something bright caught under the outstretched claws. He paused, curious, and bending over saw that the object was only a feather. Yet it looked as if the squirrel's last faint throb of energy had been spent to reach the bright immaculate blue. He picked up the body by the tail, and as he did so the feather swung in the air, suspended by a single claw. Suddenly it fell; he caught it with his hand as it floated downward, and stuck it in his cap and climbed back into the boat and sat facing Mr. Kirk.

Mr. Kirk winked at him and said, "I used to play with them things when I was a kid. I called them Indian feathers. I'd get me a couple of bluebirds and make a whole Indian hat out of them. Yes sir. . . ." He leaned back, "Youngsters will do anything."

J.D. pulled the feather from his cap and held it in his fingers. The color lifted with the river breeze. Mr. Kirk stopped paddling. "It's right pretty," he said, smiling. Then, as J.D. was about to drop it into the water, he added, "Why don't you keep it?"

J.D. looked up, and thrust the feather back under the band of his cap.

The current, stronger at the bend, caught at the skiff and bore them out toward the middle once more.

"Your daddy likes squirrel meat, don't he?" Mr. Kirk asked suddenly.

"Yes sir, I think so," he said.

"Well, I'll tell you what to do. You give them squirrels to your mamma and tell her to cook them for your daddy's supper."

"Thank you, sir, that's mighty nice," he said, "but I don't think Father could eat but one of them."

"Go ahead and take them," Mr. Kirk said. "Maybe he'll eat with a growing appetite. Besides which," he added, "there ain't nothing I wouldn't do for your daddy."

"Well, I certainly do thank you," he said.

Mr. Kirk looked at the sky. "I guess by the time we pick up that first one it'll be time to start moving along home."

With a deft twist of the paddle he turned the skiff round and they moved with stealth back along the way they'd come, keeping far enough away from the bank to see the tree-tops easily: maybe he would get another shot. But all unkilled squirrels on that part of the bluff had fled, and presently Mr. Kirk bore toward the bank.

The bow of the little boat was like a telescope. Perched in the center of its expanding eye, he watched earth, sky and water shift, blur, turn and focus again; watched gradually appear a fern or flower or fallen rock, a single blade of grass or wandering butterfly. The bluff was thirty feet away but seemed so close he might have touched it with his hand.

"I don't see how you remember the place," he said.

"I mark it with my eyes," said Mr. Kirk. "That little cedar yonder, sticking out crooked from the bluff, you see where it is?"

"Yes sir," he said.

"Well, that's the place."

They reached the spot and J.D. jumped again upon the land, upon the protruding rock, and Mr. Kirk sat in the skiff waiting. The squirrel lay only a few yards away on the flat ledge where it had fallen.

"Do you see him?" Mr. Kirk asked.

He walked forward, stooped and stretched out his hand, and on the instant his exploding heart froze him to stillness.

The dead squirrel lay on its side, its mouth slightly open and its teeth exposed. A little blood had dripped from the nostrils and congealed into a red button on the rock. Just beyond—a foot away—disturbed, jerked crookedly back, and rigid in sunlight, was a copperhead.

"Don't you see the squirrel, J.D.?"

He stood unable to open his lips, his knees half bent and his thin arm aching in slow spasms of recoiling blood. This noiseless confrontation was the evil so often warned against, the dream now suddenly become more real than all the hideous nights of dreaming ever made it.

Back in town, behind the closed windows, his father would be turning his head in restless sleep upon the walnut bed and his mother, opening doors softly, would softly close them and go upstairs and sit whispering in the dark corner at the telephone, and outside, above the roof, the maples would stir and lean against the house, and blocks away the courthouse clock would strike the slow deliberate hour. But here . . . but here . . . the ancient head, the dusty obsidian stare, that long ago had marked his fear and doomed his warm and vulnerable flesh.

If he could cry out through the dry erasure of his lips. If he could cry, "Help me, Help me! . . ." But the cry remained a voiceless echo in the back of his head and, acknowledging already the stinging venomous blow, he fell backward, as the rifle shot cracked behind him, spinning the raised snake in the air, knocking it across the rock where it lay and twisted in harmless subsiding grace. He snatched up the squirrel and ran back down to the river's edge.

Mr. Kirk was standing in the middle of the skiff, still holding his rifle up. His hat had fallen into the water and was floating a few feet from the bank.

"You have to watch out for them copperheads," he said, frowning hard at him. "I should of recollected this old bluff."

Mr. Kirk reached over with his paddle and pulled in his hat and then held the skiff steady while J.D. climbed in. He sat down in the bow as before, his rifle across his knees. He had not had a shot all afternoon. "I guess I'm not much good at shooting squirrels from a boat," he said.

"It's a lazy man's way," said Mr. Kirk.

"Don't you want me to paddle some?" he asked, turning his head back and looking into Mr. Kirk's grey-blue eyes. "I'll be glad to."

"Naw, son, naw. You just set there. I need the exercise."

By this time the whole length of the river was in shade and the drops of water from the paddle that touched his face now and then were cooler than they had been before. A few birds were starting up. Crows called to one another from the invisible corn fields, and a kingfisher spread its wings high over their heads, gently banking against the motionless air.

Mr. Kirk stopped paddling and glanced up toward the sky. "Looking for his supper," he said.

The river still belonged to them. No other craft was in sight. Behind, the bluff was gradually sinking, and far ahead he could just make out the distant smokestacks of the town water-works. In the late high afterlight of the sun, between and all around, the water was turning a pale green. From beyond the new corn, at the edge of an unseen woods, there came three falling sing-song notes, the long seductive drawn-out call of a Negro, walking across the fields to supper and to sleep, the warm-throated sound at the end of day. He shut his eyes and saw the little line of dust rising behind in the path, smelled the supper smell of wood smoke as he neared the cabin, saw the bare feet and beaten ground, and now saw the smoke itself lift above the chimney, stretch out in horizontal veil and fade upward into sky. . . . You couldn't thank anybody for maybe saving your life. You couldn't thank a marksman for his aim. You couldn't thank him for the casual tone, for the grey embracing eyes. All you could do was to swear a silent oath to learn to shoot like that, to train your eye and your hand; to stand beside him in any danger, to be ready if he should ever, someday, need you. . . .

The roofs of the buildings on the Square were still touched with amber light. They climbed up the long bank and as he opened the car door the metal was warm under his hand. He could see the flame now as Mr. Kirk struck a match when he lit a cigarette. He looked down toward the water and as he turned it seemed to him that they had brought a little of the river air back up the hill with them. Mr. Kirk threw the three squirrels on the floor of the car.

"I'll ride on out to the house with you for a minute," Mr. Kirk said, "and see how J.J.'s coming along."

"All right, sir," he said.

The afternoon had altogether faded now. The streets were vacant and only a few empty cars were nosed to the curb. The Capitol Cafe's neon sign and the bubbling electric spelling of LILLIAN announced the end of the day to silent pavements. The town was briefly at supper, and its country visitors, scattered over the roads and hunched together on seats, were heading homeward through the rising dew.

In front of his house they saw the doctor's car. "Aw-aw," said Mr. Kirk, "ain't that Doctor Dan's car?"

"Yes sir, but that don't necessarily mean anything. Uncle Dan is just as liable to be coming to supper as anything else," he said, feeling a glow of family importance: his uncle, so desperately, so constantly sought by the rest of the town, often came to sit and talk and eat the evening meal at his house.

Dr. Dan was standing just inside the screen door in the unlighted hall, holding his black satchel and talking in a low voice. Mr. Kirk took off his hat and stood at the bottom of the porch steps. "You got all three of them squirrels, J.D.?" he whispered.

"Yes sir," he said, and turned toward the half-open door, waiting. Presently his uncle came down the steps. "Aren't you going to stay to supper, Uncle Dan?" he said.

"Not tonight, young feller. I've got to go clear to Kentucky and back before suppertime."

"How's Mr. Bradbury, Doctor?" asked Mr. Kirk.

"Mr. Bradbury's right bad off, Kirk, right bad off."

"I'm mighty sorry to hear that, Doctor," said Mr. Kirk.

His mother did not open the screen door.

"Well, I'll be going on home," said Mr. Kirk. "You give them squirrels to your mamma, J.D., and tell her what I told you."

"All right," he said, hoping his mother was going to open the door and speak to Mr. Kirk. He started up the steps, stopped and turned round. Mr. Kirk was halfway to the street. "Mr. Kirk," he called out, "don't you want me to run you home?"

"You get them squirrels started, J.D. And telephone me if you need me, you hear?"

"Yes sir, I will," he called back, and went on up the steps.

He pushed the screen door open and entered the hall. His mother's hand reached out in the gloom and closed over his bare arm. She stood for a moment leaning silently upon him before she looked up.

"Uncle Dan says John is not going to get well," she whispered.

He glanced beyond her through the dark hallway toward the closed door. "No," he said.

She bent her head again, her soft hair brushing his cheek. "Yes," she said. "Yes, Son."

The blood pumped cold and sodden under his chest, and he tried to swallow the dry pain in his throat. He backed against the door-frame, but she followed and pressed close to him. Pinning his arms at his sides, she leaned out and away to look up into his face, at the hair falling over his forehead, at his flushed cheeks, his eyes, at his open lips. "You will have to take over responsibilities," she said in the same intimate whisper.

He met her gaze at last. "What responsibilities, Mother?" he asked. And when she did not answer he repeated the question. "What responsibilities do you mean?"

She was looking at him in a way he had never seen her look before.

"What responsibilities, Mother?"

Her nails tightened on his flesh. "Many," she said.

He pulled away from her and had got as far as the stairs.

"Son!"

He turned round. She was still standing by the door.

"How can you treat me this way? How can you?" she said in a low vibrant voice.

He went back and picked up his rifle that he had left leaning against the wall beside the screen door, and turned without speaking and went up the stairs and into his room and hung the rifle on the nail above his bureau. He washed his face and combed his wet hair straight back over his forehead. The little mole on his cheek, just under his eye, was surrounded by the pink glow that shone through his smooth, tan skin. He still had the squirrels with him, so he went downstairs again and into the dining-room where he stood looking at the waiting supper table. The swinging door pushed open and Stella put her head in. "Tell your mamma supper's ready," she said.

"Here's some squirrels for Father," he said, holding them out to her. "Mr. Kirk shot them for him."

"Who's gonna clean um for him?" she said, and closed the door.

He followed her out into the kitchen. "I'll leave them here," he said, and laid them tenderly on the marble top of the beaten-biscuit table.

Stella glanced at him and suddenly the kitchen was filled with the sound of her voice: "Don't you leave them things on my table!"

He picked them up and held them to his chest.

"You ought to knowed better than to bring them things home with all I got to do."

She paused, straightened up and turned to stare at him as though she had never seen him before.

"Put um there on the drain board."

He went back into the dining-room and began to eat his supper. After a while his mother came in and sat down at the end of the table. She put her elbows on the white cloth and covered her face with her hands. The coils of her brown, voluptuous hair tilted forward.

He kept his eyes on his plate, and after he had finished eating he rose and went to his father's room. He opened the door gently into the darkness.

"Are you asleep, Father?" he asked in a low voice.

"Come in, Son," his father said, and roused himself to receive the guest. "Glad to see you."

He felt his way over and sat down in his mother's small rocking chair, his knees wedged tight against the hard side of the bed. In the subdued light its massive frame seemed to fill the long room.

"Well, Son," his father said, "it looks like you're going to have to take charge of things for a while."

"Yes sir," he said.

His father reached out and touched him with his hand. After a minute he said, "Your mother forgot to turn on the light. Switch it on, will you, Son?"

He got up and walked to the door, turned on the light and came back to the rocking chair.

"You can ask Kirk anything you want to know," his father said, as if at the end of a long conversation. "He's a right good judge of tobacco. He'll be a help to you."

"Yes sir," he said. He was conscious of a knot under his right buttock, and felt back and pulled his hunting cap out of his back pocket. The feather was bent but still sticking under the band. He smoothed out the rumpled blue.

"You'll make a good tobacco man, Son, if you keep on like you started," he heard his father say.

He looked up, "Yes sir," he said again.

"I wish Kirk was a little more dependable, though," his father said, and laid a strange white hand on the sheet.

"He shot three squirrels this afternoon, Father."

His father closed his eyes.

He leaned closer. "And, Father, besides that, Father, he killed . . ." But his father's eyes had opened again at the sound of the door, and his mother came in carrying a cup on a tray.

"Here's some freshly made chicken broth," she said. "I asked Stella to make it especially for you."

"Thank you," his father said, "I'm not hungry."

"You must try to eat something," his mother said.

He stood up and watched her come over to the chair. She waited to sit down until he held it steady for her. She sat far forward and pushed the cup toward the bed.

He looked over her head at his father's face. "I think I'll walk down to the factory, Father, and see if the doors are locked up all right," he said.

"That's a good idea, Son," his father said. "The keys are there on the bureau."

He went over to the bureau and separated the keys from his father's watch, a thin gold watch with a black silk watch-fob to which was attached a gold pendant. He put the keys in his pocket.

Out on the porch he sat for a moment on the steps and looked down the street. He could not see any farther than the haw tree in the edge of the yard, but the corner street lights, marking the blocks, disappeared in the distance, telling him like a familiar code of all the houses between his own and town. He was still holding his cap so he put it on, spreading out the feather again, and slid down the steps.

From across the black grass, lights gleamed from the houses, and at the edges of the yards the night-filled trees made a dark and fragrant tunnel. He moved through it along the pavement, and as he walked fallen maple wings broke with occasional sound beneath the soles of his sneakers.

He crossed to Commerce Street and stopped at the top of the hill. Halfway down on the right the black expanse of the factory roof reflected the night sky. Low, one-story Negro cabins surrounded the large frame building. From where he stood the roof was a dim lake of tar whose obscure shores twinkled smokily from flickering lamps lit in the single rooms.

His feet lifted with pleasure at the answering movements of his ankles down the long slope. And as he moved the factory took form and shape: the roof disappeared, the clapboard walls appeared: and then he was standing at the office door next to the overhanging roofs of the sheds above the big doors where load after load of tobacco had been handed down, and weighed and wheeled away to bulks and handed up again to mountainous piles, built carefully, a handful at a time.

The factory loomed close above him like a benevolent monster, dark, inactive, silent: its deep interiors bulging with the brown sweet-smelling leaf. He leaned against the door, his hand on the knob, inhaling the smell.

He turned the key and stepped inside and walked through the office to the inner door that opened into the huge storage space. He held this door open and listened. Here the stronger odor of tobacco made his nostrils tingle. He heard nothing except from high overhead the faint cracking of the tin roof, cooling in the night. He smiled in the aromatic darkness. Things would be taken care of properly. He and Mr. Kirk would see to that.

He was about to switch on the lights to find the wooden steps that led to the floor below, but he decided to reach the lower floor from outside, down the hill in the rear. So he went back through the office and out into the street again. It was cool after the close heat of the factory. He stood, feeling the air around him, and heard the court-house clock strike nine. He looked overhead. There were no stars. Heavy clouds had come up since supper.

He walked along the front of the building until he reached the alley that led to the rear. He turned down into this passage on the right and walked somewhat hesitantly until he came to the back corner where he turned right again and passed the big shipping door which opened waist high from the ground. It seemed to be pulled tightly shut so far as he could tell. This was the door where the hogs-heads, full of the steamed and packed tobacco and weighing two thousand pounds each, were loaded behind mule teams and hauled to distant warehouses. Oh, the whole intricate process was there in his mind. He would surprise even Mr. Kirk with his knowledge.

The last thing to check was the small glass door of the prizing-room where during the day Negro girls stood at long tables under the horizontal windows, classing the different grades—the leaf, the sec-onds, and the lugs—all into three neat piles.

He put his hand on the doorknob and pressed his face close against the glass of the door. For an instant he thought he was looking at his own reflection. But the face shifted, its luminous head took form, moved forward, floating, swelling out toward him until, nose pressed to nose and eyes to eyes, it peered out through the vague light with only the thin dirty panes between them.

He could not move, transfixed, turned to stone, by the same fatal stare, poised but this time closer, closer, boring into the center of his brain. And surrounding his skull the tender skin, exposed, began to edge in immemorial response, and his ears pounded with the trebled beating of his heart. Then the door opened and a voice, embarrassed, a new voice, spoke.

"That you, J.D.?"

The fear subsided, leaving him chill. "You kind of scared me," he said.

The door opened wider. "Come on in."

He stepped inside. "Sir?" he asked. "Is anything the matter?"

Mr. Kirk's grey hair was neatly parted and brushed flat slick on his large round head. Even in the dim light that filtered through the prizing-room windows his shirt looked white and clean, his trousers sleekly pressed.

"Ain't nothing the matter," he said, and paused: "I just thought for a minute you was that little gal. . . ."

"Sir?" he said.

Mr. Kirk spat noiselessly into the soft tobacco trash on the floor. ". . . that little high yaller I'm waiting for—the one what classes next to Aunt Emma." He nodded toward the empty classing tables. "Yes, sir," he said, laughing, "I sure thought for a minute you was that little gal."

His father's keys were heavy in his pocket. "I was just seeing if everything was locked up," he said, and glanced at the door.

Mr. Kirk sat down on one of the empty dollies. "Well, now you're here," he said, "set down and rest yourself."

"Father says we'll have to attend to things for a while," he said.

"Unh-huh," Mr. Kirk said.

J.D. walked beyond Mr. Kirk and leaned against a tobacco bulk, his shoulder making a burrow in the soft leaf.

"Father said what you said, Mr. Kirk. He said I'd make a good tobacco man if I keep on like I started." He paused, and swallowed. Then he said, "I've already been upstairs to see if the doors were all locked."

Mr. Kirk struck a match. "That so?" he said, and held out his hand. In the small flare he was holding an object, a Gargantuan rod of rounded, smoothed tobacco, skillfully, unmistakably shaped. He looked up inquiringly, his eyes yellow in the matchlight. "Ever see one of these here things, J.D.?"

Slowly the hot blood climbed all the way up to his cheeks. "No," he said.

The match went out. In the black silence there came from somewhere in the rear the soft swish of falling tobacco, inexpertly bulked, sliding to the floor. It would be stepped on Monday morning probably and the good cigar leaf crushed and ruined.

"Them gals are always making these things," Mr. Kirk said, and struck another match.

"Father doesn't want any doors left unlocked," he said slowly, staring at Mr. Kirk's hand.

There was a pause. Mr. Kirk stood up, thrust the brown rod in his pocket and pinched out the flame. He walked rapidly to the door and stuck his head out.

"What time is it?" he demanded, peering out into the alley.

J.D. followed him to the door. "I just heard the courthouse clock strike nine a few minutes ago," he said. The outside air was soft with the coming rain. It sucked past him into the prizing-room, and he could almost hear the thousands of leaves relaxing from its dampness. His father had been right. Next week would be a good tobacco season. By Monday the leaves would be pliable and easy to work with.

Mr. Kirk stood in the door and looked up at the sky. "It's on the way all right," he said, and pulled a handkerchief from his pocket and blew his nose, and as he flipped the white square back into a neat cone there rose from it an odor of perfume, filling the air between them as it had filled the car that afternoon, yet now mixing also with a faint and acrid smell of whiskey. He turned back into the prizing-room. "Damn that gal," he muttered, and went over to one of the classing-tables where his coat lay folded as neatly as if upon a bed.

A sudden swirl of cinder dust swept in upon them from the path, and the first heavy rain drops clicked against the long rows of window panes that lined the wall above the tables.

Mr. Kirk picked up his coat and looked at the boy. From across the room the words cut through the quiet air: "You're in a pretty big hurry, ain't you, Mister J.D., to close things up?" He paused, and tenderly unfolded his coat. Then he said: "I guess you sort of think you're looking after things around here now."

He met Mr. Kirk's stare. "I just promised Father I'd see if the doors were all locked," he said once more.

Mr. Kirk was shoving his arms into his coat sleeves. "Sure," he said. "Yes siree. And while you're at it you better take a look at all them windows."

"Windows?" J.D. asked.

"Sure," Mr. Kirk said. "Windows need locks, don't they?"

"Father didn't say anything. . . ."

"He must of forgot, then," Mr. Kirk said. "They been needing locks bad all year."

The grey light darkened, and the rain wavered and slowed against the glass and settled to a more regular beat. In the open doorway the form of a woman appeared. It paused for an instant before it slipped into the deeper shadow of the tobacco bulks.

Mr. Kirk's arms stopped in mid air, his sleeves dangling, and the coat slid back and fell to the floor. He leaned over slowly and picked it up, brushed it off with deliberate care and folded it over his arm.

"Sure," he said again, in a different tone. "Sure. . . ."

Then he was hurrying over to J.D., his eyes glittering with impatience. ". . . but them windows can wait now, Son," he whispered hoarsely. "I'll take care of them. And the doors too."

The boy turned and stared at the man. Even in the faint light he could see that Mr. Kirk was queerly smiling. He looked away, toward the waiting tables and the vacant dollies, toward the half-filled hogsheads and shadowy mounds of tobacco, and still turning, his gaze shifted to the door where outside the sharp rain was rapidly changing the cinder path to mud. It was raining harder now. It was raining on the Negro houses across the alley, and on the yard at home. It was raining on the whole town, raining on the little skiff tied at the dark water's edge and on the twisting glassy river itself. And far away, down at the river's bend, it was raining on the long bluff.

He roused himself and turned to speak again to Mr. Kirk. But Mr. Kirk had already disappeared among the bulks of tobacco. He took a step forward and hesitated. Then, as he stood trying to see through the dim light, he heard Mr. Kirk's voice call out to him softly.

"J.D. . . ."

And suddenly, from somewhere back in the shadows, a long sibilant sound that must have been laughter filled the low room.

A second gust of wind swept through the doorway, billowing his shirt and almost lifting his cap from his head. His hand flew up to catch too late at the falling feather. He stooped down in the gloom and felt around him on the littered floor. He leaned farther over to reach a wider circle but his searching fingers still touched only nails and bits of wood and broken tobacco stalks, and he heard again the sound of his name called softly before the door banged shut, closing him into the black and pungent room.

CLAY PUTMAN *was born twenty-eight years ago in Quapaw, Oklahoma. He was educated there and in California. After serving three years in the Army, he entered Stanford University, where he graduated in 1949. He was an instructor in English at Cornell University for two years, and since then has been living and writing in New York. Several of his stories have appeared in previous editions of the* O. Henry Prize Stories, *and in the annual* Martha Foley *collections. He is at work on a novel,* The Ruined City, *for McGraw-Hill, and is the recipient of a Rockefeller Iowa writing fellowship.*

THE NEWS FROM TROY

FROM FURIOSO

My father speaks of time as if it has deserted him, as if it were some favored son who has gone off with the years. "If I had the time," he says, "I'd just take off and begin to look around. If I had the time, Tom, I'd look around for me a good truck. You and I'd go into business; we'd take that truck and see what we could do with it. We'd be in business for ourselves, boy—before you know it we'd have us a living."

"Wait till this war's over," is what he'd used to say. "When old Roy gets back, you and me and him can take some time to look around. I'm not old, Tom, I got a lot of time yet if I can get my hands on it."

But he knows now that it isn't going to come back. He knows that Roy isn't going to bring it back. "I'm a man of forty-eight years of age," he says, "and I've never had me a good watch. A man needs to know the time of day, Tom."

It is evening when my father says these things. Supper is over. We have left the kitchen, we have come back to the living room; no one has drawn the blinds yet. The soft, sudden California dusk comes through the windows; out on the parking strip that edges the boulevard children are playing their old games, screaming under the water from the lawn sprinklers whenever it touches them, as if it were a kind of fire which they must dodge and try. The red and violet neon of the service station next door makes streaks in the sky, ignites the windows of this room. The rubbery whooshing sound of traffic on the asphalt boulevard is always here; in bed at night I know the size and make of all the trucks that pass carrying produce to Los Angeles. Beyond the boulevard the big smooth hills, folded at the bottom like stone in a statue, carry light on their backs. The light is from Los Angeles, and in some way that I don't understand it makes the hills realer.

The radio is going. I am lying on the couch which is placed across a corner with a table behind it that holds the radio and my mother's abalone-shell lamp. My mother is in a chair by the window; she sits bent forward with her light eyes narrowed, reading from the paper which is wet from the lawn sprinklers. She frowns, she finds a column which interests her and quietly she begins to read to my father and me. The news is of the war, and I remember to watch the startled look that my father's face has for a moment. She pauses often in her reading, and her voice is odd, not deep but perilously close to falling, as it always is when she laughs or grows excited. She has lost most of her country accent. It is a strange voice for such a plain woman, full of eagerness and sudden unutterable boredoms, rising and falling like a child's. Except for her hair, which she has hennaed at the beauty parlor, because she is older than my father and some time ago began visibly to age, and her hands which are large and rough for a woman's, she would look rather like an ugly child. Her body is insignificant, her thin face with its groined cheeks is unlined. Always when she sits like this in the evening, reading or speaking in that low, probing voice I am aware that she is searching for something, and that if I remain silent long enough I will know for what. When she looks up from her paper or from her work her glance seems to examine the air between her and my father or myself. The quiet movements of her hands, the knuckles enlarging with the arthritis which she has begun to suffer from, must be meant to brush away the veils, the obstructions which she feels. It is always terrible to watch an ugly woman grow old. Whenever she looks at a thing, no matter if it is a person or merely, as now, the paper in her hands, she appears to memorize it, to want to know it in a way I have seen make my father tremble with anger.

Every night when he comes home from his job my father puts on a clean white shirt. He bathes and dresses himself in a starched shirt, his sharply-creased gabardine pants, his thin black silk socks, and his splendidly polished shoes. This process of bathing, of dressing in those clean, fresh-smelling clothes is a ritual with him. He is proud of his cleanliness and of the feel of silk on his body. I could name you the things he is proud of. He is not quite a tall man, and almost bald now, with a broad chest and big arms. The years have also done their business with my father, making him a kind of abstraction of what he appears to be, and yet of what he would never have become, I think, if he had lived according to that notion of himself. What could you say of him if you should meet him? Say that you travel a lot, he is the kind of man you see getting on and off the buses all over the middle reaches of this country: you think here is a man who has got himself into his best clothes to travel somewhere for a job. The kind of middle-westerner who owns a new Ford and lives in a rooming house. You would not take him for a married man. It is hateful to him that this is the kind of man he seems. He was proud when Roy worked in an office and carried to work a brief case that he, my father, won at a crap game in Gardena.

He lights a match now, its flare rocks and spreads on the wall. My mother looks up, narrowing her gaze across the room. "Rob," she says, "is it time for the news?" and without answering, my father turns up the radio. Its mutter fills the room: that and the hum of the refrigerator, like an invader, are all we hear.

Outside it is beginning to be dark. I like to think of that cold drenched summer darkness falling beyond the windows, and beyond the oleander bushes in the yard and beyond the shriveled hedge, over the rows of stucco houses with their shutters that never close, the boulevard with its streaks of neon, and the brown hills. Those brown hills, I think, dreaming to sleep, hearing the radio speak of death somewhere, of flak and bombs—these brown western hills can serve a winter purpose. And all at once I am with my brother Roy, and we have carried the wooden sleds we have built onto the hills. We wax the runners and tumble belly-down on our sleds and go gliding down the crisp summer grass; there is no snow but we go very fast under the haze-filled summer sky. The wind is everywhere. Roy and I have taken off our shirts and the dry grass is stinging to the skin. Roy is wearing his imitation leather helmet with the isinglass goggles. We carry our sleds once more to the top, where we arrive panting to lie in the shade of the oaks. That sky. Then Roy says, "You stay here, I'm going to try that slope over there." I tell him no, for the slope is steep, dropping sharply at the bottom into a ravine with a dried-up stream like a crease in the gravelly bed. But Roy is on his feet before I can stop him, the blue isinglass goggles are lowered, he flings himself onto the sled, and the sound of the wooden runners against the treacherous grass is like scissors through silk. I watch, seeing the sled go hurtling into that downward shadow over the dead hillside, and I see Roy try to swerve the sled, and his terrible voice moves back to me as if it were permanent in the air. I begin to run as fast as I am able down the slope, sliding and falling, hearing no sound after Roy's first cry. Then I am at the lip of the ravine and I see Roy lying at the bottom beside the broken unseasonal sled. His eyes are closed, the gravel cuts on his cheek look like the smallest of sea things, pink and hollowed-out as if the flesh had been stolen from its shell. On his chest the shell-shaped wound lets blood onto the white gravel bed of the ravine. Down below us moves the sound of traffic, and I stand, there in the hidden place of the hill, powerless to help, powerless to move. I reach to shake him from sleep, and I myself awaken. I awaken to see my mother and my father confronting each other mutely, in a dream of their own, in the sealed-in living room. The light of the bridgelamp splotches their faces.

It is because of Roy that they sit like this. The radio continues in the room, my mother and father sit transfixed, absorbing their own piece of this death, and they will not be surprised out of it. I remember the night of the telegram, a night like this one, with my father fixing to go out and my mother dreaming in her chair. My father has put on his tie and his coat; she watches him, her head is bent, her eyes narrowed, one finger is tracing something—nothing— on the windowpane. He moves before the mirror over the couch and straightens his tie, his handsome ravaged face wavering in the glass, the neon like worms in the mirror around him. He sings a piece of song to himself as he puts the finishing touches to his attire. "Good night, ladies," he sings, "Good night, ladies . . ." The doorbell rings and he goes smiling into the hallway to answer it.

It begins to happen. My mother looks at me when for a long time he does not come back from the door. What does her smile mean? She sits with her high cheekbones molded by the light, the smile hovering about her face. Her long nose shadows the smile. My father does not come back to the room, even after we have heard the sound of the front door closing and a car pulling away from the curb. On this night too the radio talks in the room, and perhaps it is because of what it says that my mother, and then I, rise, rise and walk over the cheap rugs to the hallway and the front door.

What do we find? For a moment I begin to laugh, for my father is there sitting on the floor, his back against the wall. I laugh seeing him like that, dressed to go out—he has even put on his ring—seeing him dropped onto the floor, weeping like a battered child who has been sent to sit in a lonely corner. My mother asks him what is the matter—"Rob, what are you doing on the floor?"—and he does not answer; he raises his eyes and the huge tears roll down his face. Surely he is drunk and my mother has come to undress him and put him to sleep. Then I become angry, believing that he is drunk. My mother picks up the yellow paper from my father's lap; somebody has left it. It is a message, soft and wise in its wording, and I think of a song I have heard my father sing, of a telegram edged in black, which this one is not. It is absurd, my father weeping on the floor, my mother standing pale, holding the paper out to me. This is almost something I might have seen in a picture.

Before I have read the message my mother has gone out the door, I hear her steps across the porch. I do not want to follow her. Neither do I want to stay with this inconsolable man. I concentrate on what the telegram says. Roy is dead, his airplane buried under the sea, and I think no, that is impossible, remembering the hill and the shell-shaped wound, something is wrong here. The only image I meet is of Roy rolled from his sled onto the sun-warmed floor of the ravine where there is never any water except in winter. The man weeping there on the floor buries his head in his arms; the walls of our duplex are thin, and I try to tell him that the neighbors will hear. But that does not stop him. I think, Where do I go? Which of them needs more to be alone? I move to the door to follow my mother into the yard: I can see her in the flickering dark on the sidewalk among the screaming children. I stop and watch my father on the floor. I go to him and try to lift him with my hands under his arms.

I pull him to his feet despite his cries and support him into the living room. All his emotions are saved for his drunkenness, and now that there is one for him to feel he seems to be drunk. The great tears roll down his face. I leave him on the couch resting against the satin pillow he won by throwing baseballs at Long Beach and which is encrusted with embroidery like colored sugar. He puts his head in his hands in so classic a gesture that I stop, halting forever I think in this tideless room with the red and green lights beating at its windows.

His eyes roll toward me when I bring in the whiskey. How grateful he is, how delicately he begins to drink from the glass I pour. It is only to gather his strength, he seems to say. From the table he takes Roy's picture in its chromium frame, and that too he makes into a part of some ceremony. He sits holding the picture on his knee and pulling at the drink; between swallows the grief falls very legitimately over him. No ancient woe could be more authentic. Here is Priam or somebody, I think, with a sport shirt on.

Presently we are both drunk, and he is telling me a story that started out to be about Roy but which ends with himself. "Tom," he says, "when I was a boy your age I thought I couldn't get drunk. Do you know that?"

I remember the summer day and the sledding on the hills, and I try to speak of that. But he will not listen. "Do you think that's funny?" he asks impatiently, pulling me back to his own story. He leans forward, imploring. He seems very eager as he sits there with his hands clenched upon his thighs, his face screwed up into a scowl that everyone likes, his dark head bent to one side and the words coming out of the side of his still boyish mouth. The tears still roll down his cheeks and he raises his hand with the cheap ruby ring to feel them. I lose the beginning of his talk, only after a while do I understand that he is telling me a story. "I thought I couldn't get drunk. Do you know that?" he asks. "I thought I couldn't get drunk. Do you think that's funny, Tom? I'd chase all over the country—I had me a car in those days, boy, and I'd know just how it'd feel to be drunk, and I wanted it."

This private anguish becomes for him like the choruses, ribald and purifying, that primed the Greeks for tragedy. He is kindled to an awful rage. It gives him such a sense of awe and desolation, to remember when he was young and could not get drunk, that he begins to shout with his weeping. "I am forty-eight years of age," he says, "and I don't even own a good watch!" His clenched fist rises in the air, it smashes a metal ashtray to the floor.

It is then that my mother comes back into the room. Seeing her, my father lurches toward her, accusing her of not feeling for his killed son. But the rug slips beneath him and he falls heavily back onto the couch. He holds the cushion to his chest, and the sounds he makes rise above the radio which all this time has been chattering to the room. We have never seen him so drunk before. "Roy!" he shouts. Somebody begins to pound on the wall separating the two halves of the duplex.

There is no quieting him. Once more on his feet, he rocks crazily around the room. He is a strong man and it will take a subtle violence to calm him. He has fought with men half his age in the bars; my mother has gone many times to bring him back bloody and elated from the cocktail lounges and the beachfront gambling rooms.

"Help me, Tom," my mother says, and we go to him. Together we pull him toward the door and support him into their bedroom. He sinks onto the bed, making his murderous sounds. My mother goes stealthily to the windows and closes them. The venetian blinds rattle down. The neon licks at the glass, the heavy trucks roll by and the room shivers with the sound they make in passing.

I have never seen him so drunk and I have never seen her so living. She begins to undress him, her small ugly body moving with precision and passion. Her silent anger matches his. I watch with surprise as she takes a fresh sheet from a drawer of the bureau. But she does not spread it over my father. Without even answering my look she steps past me into the bathroom; I hear the water running.

When she comes back she is carrying the wet sheet and a broom. Then I know. There is no way of stopping her; it is permissible. I watch her enfold him in the wet sheet, see her tie the ends into two careful housewifely knots. It is like a shroud over the drunk and stricken man; his arms are clasped close to his body, his head is partly covered. His cries cease almost as soon as she strikes the first blow with her broom. I make no move to stop it, for I recognize a method and an appropriateness in what is happening. She thrashes him because of something they have done to each other, and because of Roy, and just to winnow my father's grief a little. I only wonder why she had wrapped him in the wet sheet so carefully knotted, and then when I see the look of love on her face, and the look of rage, I know that it is so he will not be bruised.

RICHARD WILBUR. Writer. *"Born 1921 NYC. Brought up on a New Jersey farm. Edited the paper at Amherst. Enlisted 1942, served two years overseas in 36th Infantry. During the war turned to poetry and fiction out of boredom & confusion. M.A. in English, 1947. Assistant Professor of English at Harvard since 1950. Two books of poems:* The Beautiful Changes, *1947;* Ceremony, *1950. Essays, criticism, translation in various periodicals. Residence South Lincoln, Mass. Wife and three children. Passed a Guggenheim in New Mexico 1953. 'A Game of Catch' is my first story in ten years."*

A GAME OF CATCH

FROM THE NEW YORKER

Monk and Glennie were playing catch on the side lawn of the firehouse when Scho caught sight of them. They were good at it, for seventh-graders, as anyone could see right away. Monk, wearing a catcher's mitt, would lean easily sidewise and back, with one leg lifted and his throwing hand almost down to the grass, and then lob the white ball straight up into the sunlight. Glennie would shield his eyes with his left hand and, just as the ball fell past him, snag it with a little dart of his glove. Then he would burn the ball straight toward Monk, and it would spank into the round mitt and sit, like a still-life apple on a plate, until Monk flipped it over into his right hand and, with a negligent flick of his hanging arm, gave Glennie a fast grounder.

They were going on and on like that, in a kind of slow, mannered, luxurious dance in the sun, their faces perfectly blank and entranced, when Glennie noticed Scho dawdling along the other side of the street and called hello to him. Scho crossed over and stood at the front edge of the lawn, near an apple tree, watching.

"Got your glove?" asked Glennie after a time. Scho obviously hadn't.

"You could give me some easy grounders," said Scho. "But don't burn 'em."

"All right," Glennie said. He moved off a little, so the three of them formed a triangle, and they passed the ball around for about five minutes, Monk tossing easy grounders to Scho, Scho throwing to Glennie, and Glennie burning them in to Monk. After a while, Monk began to throw them back to Glennie once or twice before he let Scho have his grounder, and finally Monk gave Scho a fast, bumpy grounder that hopped over his shoulder and went in to the brake on the other side of the street.

"Not so hard," called Scho as he ran across to get it.

"You should've had it," Monk shouted.

It took Scho a little while to find the ball among the ferns and dead leaves, and when he saw it, he grabbed it up and threw it toward Glennie. It struck the trunk of the apple tree, bounced back at an angle, and rolled steadily and stupidly onto the cement apron in front of the firehouse, where one of the trucks was parked. Scho ran hard and stopped it just before it rolled under the truck, and this time he carried it back to his former position on the lawn and threw it carefully to Glennie.

"I got an idea," said Glennie. "Why don't Monk and I catch for five minutes more, and then you can borrow one of our gloves?"

"That's all right with me," said Monk. He socked his fist into his mitt, and Glennie burned one in.

"All right," Scho said, and went over and sat under the tree. There in the shade he watched them resume their skillful play. They threw lazily fast or lazily slow—high, low, or wide—and always handsomely, their expressions serene, changeless, and forgetful. When Monk missed a low backhand catch, he walked indolently after the ball and, hardly even looking, flung it sidearm for an imaginary put-out. After a good while of this, Scho said, "Isn't it five minutes yet?"

"One minute to go," said Monk, with a fraction of a grin.

Scho stood up and watched the ball slap back and forth for several minutes more, and then he turned and pulled himself up into the crotch of the tree.

"Where you going?" Monk asked.

"Just up the tree," Scho said.

"I guess he doesn't want to catch," said Monk.

Scho went up and up through the fat light-gray branches until they grew slender and bright and gave under him. He found a place where several supple branches were knit to make a dangerous chair, and sat there with his head coming out of the leaves into the sunlight. He could see the two other boys down below, the ball going back and forth between them as if they were bowling on the grass, and Glennie's crew-cut head looking like a sea urchin.

"I found a wonderful seat up here," Scho said loudly. "If I don't fall out." Monk and Glennie didn't look up or comment, and so he began jouncing gently in his chair of branches and singing "Yo-ho, heave ho" in an exaggerated way.

"Do you know what, Monk?" he announced in a few moments. "I can make you two guys do anything I want. Catch that ball, Monk! Now you catch it, Glennie!"

"I was going to catch it anyway," Monk suddenly said. "You're not making anybody do anything when they're already going to do it anyway."

"I made you say what you just said," Scho replied joyfully.

"No, you didn't," said Monk, still throwing and catching but now less serenely absorbed in the game.

"That's what I wanted you to say," Scho said.

The ball bounded off the rim of Monk's mitt and plowed into a gladiolus bed beside the firehouse, and Monk ran to get it while Scho jounced in his treetop and sang, "I wanted you to miss that. Anything you do is what I wanted you to do."

"Let's quit for a minute," Glennie suggested.

"We might as well, until the peanut gallery shuts up," Monk said.

They went over and sat crosslegged in the shade of the tree. Scho looked down between his legs and saw them on the dim, spotty ground, saying nothing to one another. Glennie soon began abstractedly spinning his glove between his palms; Monk pulled his nose and stared out across the lawn.

"I want you to mess around with your nose, Monk," said Scho, giggling. Monk withdrew his hand from his face.

"Do that with your glove, Glennie," Scho persisted. "Monk, I want you to pull up hunks of grass and chew on it."

Glennie looked up and saw a self-delighted, intense face staring down at him through the leaves. "Stop being a dope and come down and we'll catch for a few minutes," he said.

Scho hesitated, and then said, in a tentatively mocking voice, "That's what I wanted you to say."

"All right, then, nuts to you," said Glennie.

"Why don't you keep quiet and stop bothering people?" Monk asked.

"I made you say that," Scho replied, softly.

"Shut up," Monk said.

"I made you say that, and I want you to be standing there looking sore. And I want you to climb up the tree. I'm making you do it!"

Monk was scrambling up through the branches, awkward in his haste, and getting snagged on twigs. His face was furious and foolish, and he kept telling Scho to shut up, shut up, shut up, while the other's exuberant and panicky voice poured down upon his head.

"*Now* you shut up or you'll be sorry," Monk said, breathing hard as he reached up and threatened to shake the cradle of slight branches in which Scho was sitting.

"I *want*——" Scho screamed as he fell. Two lower branches broke his rustling, crackling fall, but he landed on his back with a deep thud and lay still, with a strangled look on his face and his eyes clenched. Glennie knelt down and asked breathlessly, "Are you O.K., Scho? Are you O.K.?" while Monk swung down through the leaves crying that honestly he hadn't even touched him, the crazy guy just let go. Scho doubled up and turned over on his right side, and now both the other boys knelt beside him, pawing at his shoulder and begging to know how he was.

Then Scho rolled away from them and sat partly up, still struggling to get his wind but forcing a species of smile onto his face.

"I'm sorry, Scho," Monk said. "I didn't mean to make you fall."

Scho's voice came out weak and gravelly, in gasps. "I meant—you to do it. You—had to. You can't do—anything—unless I want—you to."

Glennie and Monk looked helplessly at him as he sat there, breathing a bit more easily and smiling fixedly, with tears in his eyes. Then they picked up their gloves and the ball, walked over to the street, and went slowly away down the sidewalk, Monk punching his fist into the mitt, Glennie juggling the ball between glove and hand.

From under the apple tree, Scho, still bent over a little for lack of breath, croaked after them in triumph and misery, "I want you to do whatever you're going to do for the whole rest of your life!"

R. V. CASSILL *was born in Cedar Falls, Iowa, in
1911. During World War II he spent four years in
the Army, and the following two years was teaching
in Illinois. He received his M.A. from the University
of Iowa in 1947, and later taught in the Writers'
Workshop there. In 1950 his first novel,* The Eagle
on the Coin, *appeared, and in 1952–53 he was in
Europe on a Fulbright scholarship. He is at present
in New York, completing a second novel.*

THE WAR IN THE AIR

FROM EPOCH

Even when Jimmy Stark was dead his parents had no idea of what
he had been doing that could kill him like this. They went to City
Hospital, when they were summoned, after the police who had found
him in the park had traced his address, and saw his unmarked body
lying loose on the bed as though inside him the bones might have all
been broken into dozens of pieces or been softened by the impact of
death into a substance softer than his ten-year-old muscles.

With awed servile curiosity they asked the doctor what had happened to their son and got only a kind shrug for an answer. There
could be an autopsy if they wished. Perhaps it was a stroke, the doctor
said. Perhaps Jimmy had overexerted himself in play. That happened
sometimes. Not very often of course. Was Jimmy inclined to overdo
things?

"Yes he was," his mother said. "Oh yes. He was an eager little
fellow."

The parents trembled in the shock of seeing the little boy dead
and went home by taxi to sleep in the mediocre suburb where the
need for victory is born but where it becomes acute infrequently,
where the imaginative forms are invented but not understood.

Jimmy had taken his first air victory in June of 1951, at a time
when it was critically necessary to him as a matter of morale. His
world, which was pretty much composed of his mother and father,
had come to depend on him with a weight that could only be relieved

by that swift successful pass of combat more intense than love and
more impersonal than murder. Through the preceding winter and
spring there had been reason to worry—if there had been anyone
able to understand and willing to worry—about the tension building
up in him as he waited for action. The tension had led him frequently
to melancholy and crazy fits of temper at home or at school of the
sort that would have been familiar to anyone who had spent some
time in an Air Corps Junior Officer's Mess, but they were merely
puzzling to his folks.

The first combat took place in the southwestern corner of Lincoln
Park while he was on his way home from swimming. He was thoroughly miserable. On top of other things his nose was stopped up
from the irritation of the water so that he could scarcely breathe. He
disliked very much having to go home. His father would be testing
the lawn mower in the back yard or working on it in his shop in the
garage. Probably his mother would be next door at the Vicos', perhaps sitting in the porch swing behind the vines with Harlan Vico
and Harlan's mother, the clink of ice in their three glasses and the
hard murmur of their laughter coming from the shadow of the porch
like pellets flung from ambush.

If that turned out to be the way it was, Jimmy would go in through
his own front room, dining room, and to the kitchen, and the twilit
rooms would whisper a little to him until he found the cord to turn
on the kitchen light. They would whisper "your own mother" as he
passed the soft shapes of furniture and the lecherous open spaces of
the floor and remembered the doggone things Billy Cornwall had told
him. He would stand in the kitchen with the light from overhead
glinting on the unclean porcelain of the sink and the dishes, wishing
awfully that his mother would keep things clean, wanting to break
something but with nothing in sight that he dared to break.

So, because he had to go home to that and didn't want to, he took
the long way through the park to the streetcar instead of the short
way. This journey brought him to the clearing where the older boys
were flying their model of a jet plane.

The model was attached to long cords that held it in a circle and
at the same time controlled it. When he saw it first it was swinging
in high, fast circles. It was nearly as high as the tree tops, he thought;
at any rate he could see it move above the dark green of the trees
beyond the clearing before he had time to see the boys controlling

it from below. For a stunning second it seemed to be a real plane and to be his.

Seeing it, he stopped in the thrill of recognition. He stood a hundred feet from the boys and the plane passed directly over him at one extreme of its orbit. Time after time he watched it go over. Each time it passed him was like a touch and he grew dizzy with the excitement and with keeping his eyes on its fast circle. He could feel his hands tighten like claws and all the muscles in his trunk contract. It hurt. He crouched a little and let the pure spasm of hate possess him. "Vico," he whispered. The plane swung in two more intense circles. "Vico," he whispered again through his bared teeth.

The model, controlled by an ingenious rigging of cord, was built to perform a number of manoeuvres besides level flight. As he kept repeating the name like an incantation, some unseen tug of the controls sent it diving, and like a real plane, the sound of its motor changed pitch, and in the rising whistle all at once Jimmy felt himself confirmed, safe, as though a door behind him, opening formerly on danger, had been swung to and bolted.

As though he could breathe now—only now—he threw back his head and drew in the damp lake shore air in big gasps. It was like coming up from swimming underwater, he thought, and the images of his afternoon at the beach blent with the present moment. Holding his breath underwater he might have felt like saying, "Vico." Then the air could have come miraculously into his lungs.

"Vico," he said quietly now, and the name was both relief and requiem, the amazed acknowledgement of intimacy so fierce that it could never be glimpsed except in its own light, like a welder's work, illumined by his working torch beyond the dark glass of his mask.

"Vico," he said to himself in wonder as he walked on across the park to the streetcar stop. He began to laugh and raced on, ripping leaves from the bushes and tossing them over his head.

So he was not surprised when he found at home a scene that was different from the one to which he usually returned, something festive and vaguely scorching. His mother and father were at the table together in the kitchen and they had just finished eating. His mother was sitting stiffly in her chair. She had on a pretty blue and white dress, a cool dress for summer, and her face was pale but very pretty, he thought.

His father was leaning across the table toward her, and he had heard his father's voice rising fast and unusually confident when he came in through the front rooms. His father was bare to the waist and hair on his chest was spotted with bread crumbs.

When he drew his own chair to the table and his mother had passed him food, his father turned to him and said, grinning, "We're having a little old celebration tonight, Jimmy."

"Uh-huh."

"Don't get him in this," his mother said. "Please, Stuart."

"We're having a few drinks to celebrate," his father said. He raised his water glass and Jimmy saw that it was full of whiskey. "Yes, sir, things like this don't happen every day."

"No, sir," Jimmy said, and his father looked at him owl-eyed as though he had expected a question and was thrown off track by his complacent agreement.

"You know what we're celebrating? We're going to have some new neighbors on the other side of the goddamn fence. Old Harlan Vico has decided to move back home—back down Sa-outh where folks are *friendlier*, I hear, but I expect he thought they were pretty goddamn friendly here, some of them."

"Stuart, that's enough, that's enough," his mother said. She dabbed her eyes with her knuckles and left the table. Jimmy heard her go into the bedroom and shut the door.

After a while his father said to him in a gentler voice, "It's true. The Vicos are moving."

"I know," Jimmy said.

"Wasn't he a slimy little mink, though? I knew what he was from the time they moved in. You have to hate a guy like that."

"I hated him," Jimmy said. He helped himself to the pudding which was still cool from the icebox and had large slices of banana, still partly crisp, in it. It was his favorite and he thought his mother must have made it especially for him, as if she had known he would deserve a treat this evening.

His father stared hopefully at him. Between the man and the boy there seemed a strand of hope that the events of this day awakened something slumbering a long time, some demand that had month by month and year by year been buried under the routine of work and home until it was conceivably dead forever. He put out his hand and rumpled Jimmy's hair. He said, "Things are going to be better, kid. Whadda you say? Whadda you *say* . . . ?"

"Sure, Dad." The pudding was awfully good, and Jimmy helped himself to another bowl of it.

His father went in the bedroom and presently came back carrying a large stack of movie magazines, confession, and religious periodicals. "Burn these, will you, kid?" Then in embarrassment, as though he must play a role effeminate and formal—effeminate in its very for-mality, perhaps—said quickly, "I think these were a lot of her trouble You know she would read them so much. Burn them tonight, huh, kid?" Then his father turned, went to the bedroom, and shut the door firmly behind him.

Dreamily, lazily, almost as though something inside himself were trying to laugh but he was too lazy to let it, Jimmy finished eating. He drummed lightly with his spoon on the edge of the empty bowl, listening to the silver and clear sound of its ringing.

But when he carried the magazines through the back yard to the incinerator in the alley he noticed how *feathery* his legs felt, and a headache had begun, a small pain above his eyes.

He ripped the magazines apart so they would burn. In a minute or two the flames were rising higher than the rusty top of the incin-erator. On the blast of hot air, sparks rose and floated between him and the pale stars. It was like watching a Mig burn, he thought, remembering the name Mig without giving it any particular associa-tion, not wondering even from where he remembered it. There goes the fuel tank, he thought, as more pages caught and the fire came up. He felt a proud, melancholy identification with the man he had shot down—not bothering to name the man Vico any longer—and this seemed to justify the pain in his head. He felt that what had happened separated him from other people. He *remembered* that this uprush of fire into the night was the token sign of his manhood and mortality and that properly the sign confirmed his loneliness.

Behind him he heard bicycle wheels on the cinders of the alley, but he did not turn to look until he heard the whisper, "Hey, Jimmy? That you?"

It was Billy Cornwall, the fat kid who lived on the other side of the alley. Billy was thirteen, three years older than he, and he never knew whether Billy was going to pick on him or not. Billy was apt to if he said a word that questioned Billy's opinions or actions. He hated having Billy come up and watch him looking at the fire.

"What are you burning?" Billy asked.

"Nothing."

"O.K.," Billy said. He pushed his bicycle closer so that the front wheel was almost against the wires of the incinerator. He kept one fat leg over the frame of the bicycle and leaned on the handlebars. "Where were you this afternoon, Jimmy? You know what happened at your house?"

"I went swimming," Jimmy said. "I went to Lincoln Park like I always do."

"Wow," Billy said. "Things were really humming for a while. Your Dad and my Dad and Tim Simms beat hell out of this old Vico. Your Dad come home early and he found him and his old woman over at your place, so he got these two and they went back for him. Boy."

The light of the flames in the incinerator was going; only a few black and weightless fragments, rimmed with sparks, came up now from the pile of ashes within the fire-rusted wire frame.

"Your Dad tell you about it?" Billy asked. "Jeez, when I got there old Mrs. Vico came running out of your house in them shorts she wears, yelling for the police—'Poh-leez'—and Tom Simms caught her right by the fence and twisted her arm up behind her and he said, 'You want to call the police, lady?' What they did to Vico! I guess it wasn't what they ought to have done for what he did. I don't think."

Jimmy glanced toward the Vico house and saw that it was without lights. He wondered, though, if the Vicos might not be in there anyway, really, moving about in the dark where they no longer could move in either lamplight or daylight.

He smelled the horseweeds around his gate. He started for his gate but Billy quickly ran the bicycle across his way. "What did your Dad do to your old lady? I bet he slapped her around, didn't he?"

"No, he didn't do that at all," Jimmy said. He tugged at the gate, but Billy wouldn't let him open it.

"I would've, or any real man would've," Billy said. "For what she did? She had it coming to her all right. I told you what I saw that time I hid in the bushes by your porch and Vico went in the kitchen with her."

"Shut up. Shut your mouth," Jimmy said.

Billy let the bicycle drop and grabbed his shoulders. "Who you telling to shut up? Do you mean it? You mean you want me to shut up?"

Jimmy clawed at Billy's face as he half lost his balance. He felt his fingernails hit the fat cheek, but then, almost before he realized that

he was going to fall he was down and Billy was astraddle his chest.
He felt Billy's knees grinding into his arms.

He said, "Get off, you fat dumbbell. Get off."

"Take it back," Billy said, and slapped him.

"You stinking fat dumb . . ."

"All right then," Billy said. "Don't think I didn't hear that." He
fumbled for Jimmy's ears and twisted them. "Now tell me what your
Mom did with old Vico. Say it."

"Nothing," Jimmy said. "Get off me. I won't." Then with a wild
pain in his ears rising to a climax, he felt a calm begin, as though the
pain itself were opening another door and closing it solidly behind
him when he had passed. Strangely he let himself lie inert and the
frightening inertness communicated itself to Billy, who let go his ears.

"Do you want me to say it?" Billy asked. "All right." He leaned
forward and spoke repetitiously into Jimmy's face. Then he took
down Jimmy's trousers, spit on him, got on his bicycle and rode away.

Jimmy felt the cinders through his thin shirt, cutting him, but his
knowledge of them was remote and actually trivial. He looked up at
the black, mastered sky and knew himself borne steadily at the airy
center of things. "Billy," he whispered, and was able to laugh.

2

He was awake before light, before the hour of dawn patrols, and he
lay there for half an hour toying with his illness. There was still a
pain in the back of his head, and if he stirred he felt nausea and a
cramping in his bowels. If he lay absolutely quiet, both these disturbances having something feverish about them were comforting,
like a hot towel or like lying in a hot bath.

As the light came on among the trees and telephone wires that he
could see from where he lay, he played a game with the cord ring
hung from the curtain. It was a ring sight, and through it he searched
the sky for a passing bird or anything alive that would give him
practice in killing. He aimed at leaves, and there was a fly that crawled
up the screen and directly through the cross-hair center of the ring.
That fly was a deader, he thought.

At six-thirty he had to go to the bathroom to throw up. He was as
quiet as he could be, but his mother must have been awake, for she
came in as he was squatted on the floor with his cheek leaned against
the soothing porcelain of the stool.

"Jimmy," she whispered. "What's the matter, honey? Hey, can you

stand up? Let's get you back in bed. Why, you're burning up, honey."
Her hand lay wonderfully cool and limp on his forehead, and he
began to whimper in a mixture of pleasure and solicitation. He stood
up and leaned against her hip as they walked back to his room.

She brought him a poached egg on toast for his breakfast and sat
beside him, stroking his head while he ate. His father came in before
leaving for work and asked if they shouldn't call a doctor.

"I'll take care of him," his mother said shortly.

"Well, then, see that you do for a change," his father said. His
father seemed, this morning, to have fallen back into the old helpless
surliness which for a while last evening he had broken free of. It was
pitiful that he had not known how to hold his victory, had given
it back.

"All right, all right, all right," Jimmy's mother said arrogantly.

When his father had gone out and the room was hushed except
for the endless remote noise of traffic spreading away like a battle
front on an indecisive day of combat, Jimmy turned his face against
the pillow and closed his eyes. His mother must have thought he was
sleeping, because she left him and tiptoed toward the door.

He said, without opening his eyes, having something to hide from
her, "The only thing is, Mom, I've got to be well enough to go swimming this afternoon."

"Oh no you don't," she said. "I'll say you don't, honey. That's
what made you sick today."

"But if I feel good. I may feel swell by then," he said. He knew he
would not and the effort of lying when he didn't want to entirely
forced tears up to burn in his eyes.

"Well, you won't," she said. "You can go another day. The lake
will still be there."

During the endless morning he heard her playing the radio, then
singing, then crying. When he heard her crying he went back to his
killer game with the curtain ring.

Shortly before noon he caught Billy in the ring and held him there
for a full minute, sliding down the bed to keep the fat boy centered
until he disappeared past the end of the block. He had heard Billy's
loud happy voice and had come to immediate cramping attention.
Then he'd caught him all right. Nothing happened. He whispered,
"Billybillybillybilly," and waited for him to fall, but Billy rode his
bike right on past the corner, dodging the trucks on Elm Street in
the smart-alec way he did.

Reflecting on this, Jimmy understood how truly necessary it was for him to get to the park. He spoke about it again to his mother when she came in, but she was wrapped in her own misery by now and answered sarcastically. "From now on no one goes out of this house," she said. "Our happy home. I guess that's how it will be. No one will have any fun or talk to anyone that is any fun. That's the way he wants it." Her eyes glittered hatefully. "Listen, will he ever take us anywhere on Sunday? Will he ever talk? In the spring I wanted him to take you out in the country so you could get some air and sun, but did he? He won't even take us fishing—goes with those mutt friends of his. What will he ever do but go out in that workshop and fiddle with that lawn mower? Does he think he's an inventor like Thomas Edison? Don't you think he could be a little human sometimes if he wanted? You don't know all about how he is either, Jimmy." She threw herself flat on the bed with a grotesque squawk. "Listen," she said with excitement, "what did he tell you about me last night?"

"Nothing," Jimmy said.

She watched him suspiciously. Enduring her stare, knowing that she was getting ready to lie to him, Jimmy wanted to bury his head under the pillow. He held himself quiet and said, "Nothing," and that seemed to convince her.

"He said ugly things to me and said a lot of things I never even thought about doing."

"He didn't tell me anything," Jimmy said, and his mind raced like a steel hammer falling on a pin, Billybillybillybilly. "I want to go to sleep," he said.

She kissed his brow. "You sure sizzle," she said. "Try to sleep now, honey." Then she added before she left, "Those magazines. Did he make you burn them all?" Getting no answer, she left him.

Jimmy waited motionless and without patience. He counted to sixty several times—he could not keep count of how many times. He could not hear her when he quit. He dressed, pushed the screen from his window and dropped to the ground. He went around the yard to the back gate, past the incinerator and down the alley to Elm Street, where he caught the streetcar that would take him to the park.

The ride was a nightmare. It was like riding a dull ship in convoy, annoyance without interest. But in the park itself, among the still flowers and the trees swaying gently up to the point where the highest leaf gave way to the shapeless sky, he became serene. It was then as if he had separated successfully from the other world.

He had a long wait still. Four o'clock passed and the boys with the model plane had not yet appeared where they had been yesterday, but he waited now with certainty.

He sat on a bench a little removed from the clearing. A policeman who had circled past him several times looked as though he wanted to question him but never did.

A dog came and sniffed at his shoes. He patted the dog and made friends with him. Carefully saying nothing, he developed a language of gestures that the dog understood. He would pretend to throw a stick and the dog would race a few steps after the imaginary stick and then return to him with its bright eyes puzzled. A little more urging and the dog would retrieve it, he was sure. He laughed at the dog and the dog cocked its head cutely in a sort of reply.

At five the boys came carrying the model plane and the apparatus for its control, and he was ready. He watched them lay the cords out on the ground and pace off the orbit to make sure there was plenty of space within the trees. He saw one crouch with it to get it airborne. Then he walked closer when it began to circle until he was again standing under its path, and presently he felt the second approach when it would be made to stoop in its killing dive.

Afterward he walked with difficulty to the streetcar. He discovered that he had left the house without bothering to get money for fare, and it was his luck that he found three tokens in his pants' pockets. Just his luck. He gave the next to last token to the conductor for this ride home.

When the car turned onto Elm Street, from a long way off he could hear the purr of a siren running at low speed, and as he approached closer to his own corner he saw the crowd on the curb and the red light turning and flashing in the sunshine on top of the ambulance. He saw the truck slanting up onto the curb, its double wheels resting on the bicycle frame. The frame was bent curiously, like the soft shapes of spaghetti. Jimmy felt a lonely smile shape his lips.

3

Then he was really sick. For two weeks he stayed in bed with a fever and a dark half-awareness of his mother and father coming into his room, and the doctor. It was not time in which he lay, but an uncomfortable timelessness in which he heard things and then lost them so that he did not know any sequence. Once his mother told him about poor Billy Cornwall's accident. Once she asked him if he had burned all the magazines. Once she said, probably to the doctor, maybe to his father, "It's this summer. He hasn't been real well since school was out. Maybe when he goes back in the fall he'll be himself." Then he had drifted down into the red-threaded blackness which was sleep, amused because he knew there was little chance of his returning to where school was, in some country oceanic-distances away.

Once again Billy Cornwall came with a red star on his forehead, the star shining like blood on his fatty skin, and told him again what he had seen from behind the bush in the back yard—the thing that couldn't be true because Billy was a liar—and his mother whined, "He hurt me." Or his father was welding in the shop in the garage and the fire came from his torch like tracers from the guns in movies.

Then in the week when it seemed he was getting better, his mother told him how he had crumpled up on the porch that evening when he got home from wherever he had been.

"Where were you anyway that afternoon?" she asked him. "Boy, was I scared." The question seemed to touch her curiosity sharply. She asked him several times as though she had forgotten his answer.

"In the park," he usually told her. She looked at him skeptically, rumpled his hair and said, "Aw, you don't know where you were. You were delirious or something." She added with passion, "It was his fault, the things he told you."

Once, to his terror, he slipped and told her, "Flying."

"Flying? Judas Priest. Well, I guess you're not going to tell me. If you know, I mean, and I'll bet you don't. What do you mean, flying?"

"I don't know," he said, carefully now. "I don't remember so good."

"We'll get you out in the sun today," she said, "where you can see some sky. You don't have any tan at all. Fishbelly. If your father would get a car and take us somewhere—I guess I could forgive him some other things."

She went on absently arranging things in the chest of drawers and organizing her wishes like plans. "We could have a vacation," she said. "Lots of people with no more money than us have vacations every year."

"All right, Mom," he said. "Don't talk about it." He couldn't stand the note of complaint crying through her voice, though he felt guilty not to listen to it, for not being strong enough to listen and console her. "I have to sleep," he said. When he slept after a session of her complaints, Billy Cornwall would come with the red spot of death on his flesh and in the remote alleys of the sky he would have to kill again.

For the next week he spent most of his time sitting under a tree in the back yard. His father had once built an armchair for the yard, and he sat there through the long afternoons, reading sometimes and sometimes drowsing. His mother bought him a lot of comic books. Most of them were about air battles, because those were the ones he asked for, but she got Jungle Queen and Superman because she liked them herself and thought he would like them too.

It tired him to read. Up to a point he could got interested in these books, but they were full of Spads, Nieuports, Fokkers, and Camels— old-fashioned junk that didn't seem real except for the queer excited feeling they gave him of a familiar anxiety. He wondered if a German had ever spit on Lt. Frank Luke or Capt. Eddie Rickenbacker. He thought this might have happened and that's why they were good aces too. Finally he would let the books fall from his lap and sit looking at the clouds or the leaves against the summer sky.

The doctor came once more and said there was nothing wrong with him now except that he was run down, needed vitamins perhaps to tone him up. His parents talked a little of what might tone him up, but ended in making the discussion their personal battlefield. The argument was nothing new, only more vocal than it ever had been. He for one had work, the father said, and she wanted to cat around for her own sake, not the kid's. Work? What was he doing with the lawn mower he spent his time on? Did he think that was the way things were invented? They had factories with lots of people working in them to invent things nowadays. Why didn't he catch up with the times?

It seemed to Jimmy, listening, that their argument might never be settled. It was somehow up to him to settle it for them. As long as they lived they would fight this way unless he could tip the balance. He didn't know how. He had to get rid of the Vicos for them and got rid of Billy, but nothing was any better, and he felt no longer responsible for them except as a judge feels, waiting to utter a judgment that will not be his own but the Law's, a judgment superior to himself if he can discover what it is.

In the evenings he would sometimes go sit on a stool in the garage workshop where his father was building the lawn mower. There were two masks in the shop, and his father let him watch the welding through one of them. His father was rather pleased to have the boy sit there fascinated beside him.

And Jimmy liked this watching. At such times his sluggish heart would beat faster against his ribs. The tracery of flames, appearing through the complete darkness of the mask, was somehow the real thing. He could breathe easily as he watched, and usually he had to make a tiresome effort to breathe.

Nevertheless, the watching frightened him. He recognized his fear initially in the form of an anxiety that his father's hand would slip and let the torch swing against himself. Be careful, Dad, he thought angrily.

He began to feel that any injury to his father would be no accident; it would be the work of the power he had discovered that day in the park, and he was not ready to use that.

While he watched the dangerous flames, he remembered his father on the night of the Vicos' departure, marching with shabby arrogance to the bedroom where his mother lay, and this memory frightened him, because then he almost felt triggers ready under his fingers, and he believed there was no reason to use them yet, not against his father, who was going to make a lawn mower that would make them rich, maybe.

An occasion had come when he was so close to opening up, though, that in panic he jumped from the stool on which he was sitting, threw the mask off, stared a second at the naked torch and then ran for the house.

He heard his father following him, asking what was the trouble. Having temporarily blinded himself he stumbled on the doorsill and wailed as he dropped to the kitchen floor. His mother jumped to pick him up and before he could explain, both his parents were fighting across him. "Well, did you burn him?" "Can't you see if he's all right before you start shooting your mouth off?" Their voices rang with self-pity and hatred so stupid that they could find no instrument to execute it except their son.

Weighing this, sensing the suffocation to which the three of them were committed, grasping it not in the language but in the war-like images of his education transposed to fit the personal situation as a dull preacher might use the myth of Genesis to illustrate the planting of crops, that night in his bed Jimmy made a decision.

Lying in his bed stiffly, staring toward where no ceiling appeared, almost without passion, in the interests of justice, he thought his father would have to go. He could feel his lips and throat getting ready to whisper. He still held back, hating to whisper the name—then he let go, "Dad," diving past into the security of sleep without troublesome dreams.

In the anxiety of the next morning he wanted to take it back, but he was not at all sure that he could. Of course it was possible to stay away from the park and the model airplane—if he wanted to—but like a hypnosis an impulse thrust him toward them. It might be that he would have to go after such a commitment. He wished for more reasons, though, if it had to be that way.

He went to the workshop in the garage and played thoughtfully with the masks he and his father had worn. He slipped on his father's mask and shuddered at the smell inside and at the sweated headband touching the skin of his forehead. He discovered the dimensions of darkness inside the mask. It was as large as the darkness of a whole night, of his room when it was utterly black, big enough for anything, and this darkness was filled with the hateful smell of his father. "Let him do one more thing to her," Jimmy thought, "and I'll go." He sat there imagining his father's hand lifted to strike, but frozen yet in the gesture for which he waited.

And then one morning he knew why he had waited, why that abstract and superior justice whose servant he had become had obliged him to wait. That morning when he returned from an errand to the corner store carrying a sack of groceries, entering the kitchen, he heard his mother's voice from the back porch and a man's voice, unfamiliar and familiar at the same time, answering her.

Jimmy set the groceries on the table to free his hands. The voices from the porch fumbled viciously, as though on purpose, with the lightly balanced mechanism of his consciousness, and he stood there, taking the shock of their violation and accepting his responsibility for what he heard in those careless, awful, summery voices. He listened to his mother's laughter, and then, surprised but certain of what he thought, he whispered to himself, "They've all got to go."

His mother came into the kitchen for a dishpan. "A man's here selling sweet corn," she explained. "Won't that be good? That will taste good."

To Jimmy the flush in her cheeks was a sign of her guilt, and, more than that, as he looked down from a peak of agelessness, it seemed a sign of some corruption of youth that was intolerable. "Aren't you feeling well again?" she asked jauntily. "Maybe you'd better go to your room and lie down. Go on now."

"No."

"Jimmy . . . Go on."

He stood fixed and then watched from the rear window while she went out with the vendor to his truck parked in the alley. He felt the pity of her going, because in this moment of discovery he knew that he must kill her, along with his father, and that afterward there must be an accelerated pattern of killing to which there was no imaginable limit. He felt also the pity of her sacrificing him to be the agent of this necessity by failing to be good. At the same time he made no attempt to argue the consequences of what he believed to be the truth. Now he could see the steps of a great wrong reaching back to what he did not bother to think of as an Eden.

Where was it the family had lived before they moved here? he asked himself. He had no exact memory of another city, but he felt it. Caught in the vision, it was as though he might have been circling at a great height and seen in the haze which for airmen replaces a horizon some kind of dimple—not quite a form but a potentiality of form—that he recognized as home.

In the moment of his submission to the necessity, as though clutching at one more less human reason for what he had to do, he remembered Billy Cornwall's words about his mother. He imagined Billy waiting behind the door of the next room, ready to knock him down and spit on him. He squared his shoulders and forced himself to walk through the door to see.

Going to the park that afternoon, watching from the streetcar window the blue wink of the sky, he kept thinking to himself, "If she just hadn't of laughed with that man . . ." The improper laughter hissed toward him from the anonymous crowd with whom he rode—all of them condemned now by what he meant to do. Every one of them had to die.

On the park bench he recaptured the vision and certainty he had known in the kitchen. The streetcar had dimmed it, like a flashback of memory where all sorts of trivia creep in—sentimental sounds of voice, promise of store windows, weather compositions, faces reminiscent of jollier times and places back on the other side of the ocean, maybe—but triumphing over these he rose easily again and began circling. The dimple of home appeared first over one wing tip and then the other.

He saw, between home and himself, little black shapes swift as insects rise toward him from the checkered landscape. He recognized their number and their hostility without panicking. It was part of the compact that whatever he needed enough would be provided. There would be time enough.

As on the earlier occasion when he had shot down Billy he had to wait a long time. The black planes hovered in remote perspectives, waiting with him. Then, as the boys appeared carrying their model, the black planes moved in to intercept him.

The model raced on the end of the cords and Jimmy walked toward its orbit. He felt himself go with it, and in the moment of climbing for an attack position was happy enough. This time, better than on any of the earlier occasions, he sensed the moment for his diving pass. "Now," he cried to himself, without hate, without love.

It was a long way down and something seemed to thrust itself against his chest and stomach and drag his breath away. Then, like a blackout from the strain of diving, dark replaced the light and the shapes beyond the cockpit bubble. All together the ground beneath, the insidious planes, the imaginary haze of the horizon, the actual grass, the boys in their T-shirts, vanished.

He did not see the model crash splintering in the grass of the park, nor the boys, its owners, rushing toward it with varied expressions of chagrin and repressed pleasure on their faces.

RICHARD CLAY *has a passion for aviation which begin when he was a boy and used to build models out of steamed bamboo. He was born in Philadelphia in 1915 and brought up there. He went to school in Switzerland and at St. George's in Newport. After a time at Princeton and Harvard, and in the oil business and the advertising business, he found his way back to aviation late in the thirties, and he now works for a builder of helicopters in Bridgeport, Connecticut. Mr. Clay's interest in writing has been lifelong, but he has only recently devoted serious time to it. "Very Sharp for Jagging" was his first story. Two others have since appeared in* The Hudson Review. *He and his family are presently living in Westport, Connecticut.*

VERY SHARP FOR JAGGING

FROM THE HUDSON REVIEW

The midget car went by them, scoot and scatter, spitting gravel as it raced and roared in the opposite direction like a tornado on a tear. It was a red car, not a full size car but a miniature red bolt of lightning, speeding across the Connecticut countryside, ripping up and down farmers' lanes, streaking down gravel drives, bumping over back roads, never daring to go out on the paved highways but invading privacy from behind like a quick red fox on a hunt.

Ben Stroud could still hear the unmuffled splitting roar that issued from the tiny machine that was no more than a toy. He leaned urgently forward and touched the shoulder of Frank's forest green uniform so that Frank stopped the limousine on the drive with a slow easy motion and a quiet crunching of gravel.

"It's them boys," Frank said, turning his round face towards the back seat and grinning. "They all got the devil in them nowadays."

Ben was half up on the seat peering out the rear window and feeling dizzy and short of breath from the sudden exertion of climbing up like this on the soft upholstered seat which he never would have done at his age if he had been fully awake when the red car went by with a thunderous racket like the Twentieth Century Limited at a grade crossing, throbbing so that it woke him from his nap and made him touch Frank's shoulder as if for an emergency and made him climb up on his knees on the seat all in one motion without thinking so that when he did begin to think he found himself peering out the rear window at the small red racer scooting away down his drive and gleaming hotly in the September sunlight as it turned off his private driveway and skidded in a cloud of pink dust on the logging road and bumped and flashed through the trees and disappeared behind clumps of yellow-green bushes and appeared again, flashing red and gleaming, always a bit further away towards the wall at the edge of his property and finally disappeared through the opening in the wall into the deep maple wood on Chris Faith's side of the line. For a moment before it went out of sight some trick of the distance made Ben think that it was a big car like the red Stutz that his son Warren owned before he went to Europe last year. But he knew that was ridiculous because his senses and his memory told him that it was nothing but a midget car such as a boy might drive, such as his only grandson Harold might drive in two years when he would be twelve as Jackie Faith had been twelve in August when he got the red car from Chris Faith for his birthday. The whole neighborhood had heard about the red car and soon learned about it from its eyes and ears and was scandalized, as Ben knew, not just at a boy of twelve having a car but at the sudden unpleasant reminder of restlessness and a heedless tempo from which they had sought refuge here in the country and which was being violated now daily and invaded by the red racer tearing up and down their back lanes and their private drives and across their lawns.

"It's not 'them boys,' Frank," Ben corrected, settling back into the seat. "It's only Jackie Faith with the fire-breathing hounds of Beelzebub burning inside of him or not more than two feet behind his tail."

"I didn't mean that all the boys were in that red car, Mr. Stroud." Frank spoke deliberately and slowly and somewhat grievously like a farmer. "I could see very well that it was only Jackie Faith. But I meant to say that Roy and Master Harold have the same devil's itch as Jackie has, as you might say. Roy told me at supper last night that Master Harold is fair wild to get a midget racer like that for his birthday next week. He's got plans to speak to you about it, sir, so I'd be obliged if you didn't say I told you anything about the scheme."

"Plans to speak to me about it—by Heaven, do you think it's a secret, Frank? Do you think it's a secret when he hasn't talked about anything else for a month? In the name of Jupiter I'm sick of hearing about that car, and I'm twice as sick of hearing it buzz around my place like a hornet all day so that I can't even come home from the city for a quiet Saturday lunch without having the blasted thing almost crash into me on my own drive."

Frank tilted the black visor of his chauffeur's cap upwards like a lifted lid on a pot and scratched the forelock of his ginger hair with the little finger of the same hand that held the cap. "That Jackie Faith is a wild enough youngster, I must admit," he said. He had a slow manner of speaking in a soft uninflected voice which added an air of deliberation and homely wisdom to his words. "He's been known as a wild youngster ever since I first remember hearing that he kicked his biddy on the beach and had to be carried home. But boys like Master Harold and Roy are different; they may be a bit wild but there's no mischief in them, Mr. Stroud. If you were to ask me I would say don't judge Master Harold by what you see of Jackie Faith and don't judge of how Master Harold would treat a nice car of his own by the way Jackie treats—"

"Don't be an ass, man," Ben interrupted irritably. "Look what happened to that brand new bicycle I got him. He had it exactly three days before he smashed it into the wall; an accident, he said. He has too many accidents. Look at the electric train he wrecked just because he wanted to see if the engine could knock the cars off of the track; and before that there was the wagon; and a dozen other things. He can't keep a blessed thing long enough to even let it wear out decently. What would he do with a car, I ask you? He and that Jackie! I can see them racing each other up and down my drive and skidding across my grass. By Heaven, it would be a Roman circus, a regular Roman circus, and he'd wrap the car around one of those damned elm trees the first day, and himself too, God bless him."

Frank's milk blue eyes sparkled. "God bless them all," he said impulsively, and then he grinned so that his plump face looked like a rosy red moon. It was a grin that Ben had loved for its buoyancy when they were both younger but which annoyed him now because it seemed so vapid and foolish as if all you had to do was mention boys and Frank said "God bless them all" and delivered a round grin like a plate at the automat. It was not very rewarding or very helpful, and it seemed particularly sad when Ben reflected that his chauffeur was one of the very few people with whom he could discuss the problems of bringing up Harold, since his partners and the others that he knew intimately in the investment business were all grandfathers, like himself, but with the difference that they saw their grandchildren only on occasional carefree visits and did not have to make the constant tiresome day to day decisions about them.

"God bless them all," Frank said again. "It's a feeling I have about them boys, Mr. Stroud, a religious kind of feeling that God looks after them much better than we mortals can ever do, so it's a bit—what you might call—prezuntious for us to try to do all the planning for them. We have to leave room for God to make his plans, as you might say. Like if God should choose to take one of them boys unto his bosom today or tomorrow or anytime, we could not stop the rotten branch from falling on the boy or hold back the thunderbolt from the sky or watch his steps all the day long to keep him safe from the snakes and the knives and the glass and the loose stones on the wall that would let him fall with a broken neck. Ah, but if God had other plans for him, why the boy could wrap his car around every tree on this drive and walk off without a scratch. That reminds me about my older sister, Mary, down in Norwalk and her youngest boy, Lonnie. She was always worrying—"

"That's all very well to say, Frank," Ben interrupted sharply, "but you're a father, and you know better than that. Would you give Roy one of those infernal machines just because he wanted it? If the money didn't matter, I mean."

Frank frowned, drawing his pale eyebrows down and puckering his big soft mouth in concentration. "I think I would, Mr. Stroud," he nodded his head vigorously. "I think I'd get it for him if Roy wanted it enough. But even if the money didn't matter, I'd make him do some work to earn part of it so he'd have more of a feeling that it was his."

"In the name of Jupiter, man, wouldn't you think of the rest of us? Wouldn't you realize that there are others in the world besides a noisy boy?" Ben yelled, feeling his pulse rise and the beads of sweat on his forehead so he had to mop at it and at his cheeks several times, although it was a cool September day.

"I thought of all that, sir, but a noisy boy is part of the world, too, as you might say, and he has a lot to learn. It may be hard for us older ones to watch and listen while he's doing the learning, but it's twice as hard for him that's going through it. This is an age for machines like that car, and it does a boy like Roy or any boy a lot of good to get the feel of machines in his blood while he's young. The future's going to be his, and he'll need every bit of help that I can give or you can give or anyone else—"

"By Heaven, that's what I mean," Ben bellowed, "that's exactly what I mean. The future's going to be his, Harold's and Roy's and Jackie's. Why the devil can't they wait. The present is mine, and I've fought for it. I fought all my life for peace and quiet and waited a long time for it. By Heaven, it's mine now, and I intend to keep it. I hate that red car. If Jackie's father weren't my oldest friend around here I'd speak to him about it in no uncertain terms. The whole neighborhood is upset. If anyone speaks to Chris it should be me, and maybe I will. He should lay down some rules to keep that boy in check. Those boys can wait. All those youngsters can just stand by and wait a while and leave me and the rest of us a few years of peace and quiet before they push us out of the way."

Ben mopped at his forehead and along his cheeks, although it was a cool lovely day, one of those rare days, he realized, as he looked out the open window across the neatly clipped lawn, one of those rarest of days that is so rare that it only comes once a year and then only in the last half of September so that he woke in the morning of that day knowing at once by the very bite and smell of the air and by the quality and clarity of the lemon colored sunlight that the world around him had been released at last from the long thrall of summer. And now again, as he saw the lemon light strike down through the magnificent elms and bathe the meadows and faraway fields where the corn stalks stood already gathered in bundled shocks pointing to the clean swept sky and as he heard the thrilling songs of birds that had summered in Canada and were now headed south, he remembered this rare gem of a day last year and ten years ago and every important year of his life, each time marking a period in his mind like the end of suffering and suffocation, like that morning in Naples at the end of his long summer honeymoon trip with Jean through India and Africa when the boat had come across from Egypt and into Naples in the night so that he woke in the early light of the day feeling and smelling the sharp bite of the air and seeing the round spot of fresh blue sky through the porthole above him as he lay in his bunk knowing he was home again, home in the north, home away from the tropics and the heat, home in the cool north even in a foreign land thousands of miles from New England, but home even there in Naples because of the day and the air. Jean had died in September when Warren was only two, leaving him to bring up his only son.

And when Warren was grown and was married to Ellen it had been in September; and in September again when Ellen had died giving birth to Harold. For him September was a month of birth and marriage and death, he reflected, as these familiar memories went through his head in less time than it took him to turn his eyes from the window of the limousine to the opposite door that was being wrenched open.

"Hands up or you're dead."

Frank put his hands up quickly in mock fright as Ben looked at the two boys holding pointed sticks raised like javelins. One of the boys had disordered ginger hair like Frank's and the other had blond sandy hair the way Ben's had been before it turned white. He noticed again that Harold was at least half a head taller than Roy, although they were both the same age; or Roy was actually a little older, as a matter of fact, since his tenth birthday had come earlier in the summer while Harold's wouldn't be until next week. Harold was also the handsomer boy of the two; there was no doubt about that, except for his ears which stuck out like butterfly wings.

"Hands up, Gran," Harold ordered, "we're jaggerin you."

He made several jabbing motions with the stick which Ben could see was nothing but an old broom handle with a wicked pointed end. The wood had been turned or sanded to a needle point and a steel nail driven in the end and cut off.

"What's that you're doing to me?" Ben asked peevishly. "And what in thunder is that murderous weapon, boy? Where did you get it?"

"It's my jagger stick, Gran, my best one. It's very good and sharp for jaggin. I made it myself. Roy and me make 'em in his Dad's shop in the garage."

"Do you indeed," Ben said petulantly. "And what's that thing you do with them?"

"We jag things. I'll show you. This is very good and sharp for jaggin."

"I'm sure it is," Ben said acidly. "And now you ought to jag yourself right up to the house and get some clean clothes and wash up. You look like you spent the morning on a coal pile. How on earth do you get so dirty with these games, boy?"

"They're not games," Harold protested in his piping voice. "Games are for babies. What we do, Roy an me, is real jaggin."

"Stop using that silly word," Ben said impatiently. "You know it doesn't mean a blessed thing."

"Yes it does, Gran. Roy an me know about it. It's what bootleggers do to get somethin from each other like when one bootlegger wants somethin that the other bootlegger won't give him he hijaggers it from him. We were playin it with Jackie only he got mad cause we hijaggered his car, and I drove it around back of the garage, an he was so mad he was goin to throw stones at us only he didn't cause it would of scratched the paint on his new car."

"You did what?" Ben spluttered. "Did you say that you drove that infernal machine? Where the devil did you—how in thunder did you learn to drive it?"

"Jackie showed me the other day for a trade for the penknife."

"Penknife? What penknife? You know you're not allowed to have a penknife."

"It's not *mine*, Gran. Please *listen* to me instead of intraruptin me. It's *Roy's* penknife that his Dad gave him for his birthday. It's not mine. Roy traded it to me so I'll let him ride in my car when I get it an I traded it to Jackie to teach me how to drive his car so I'll know what to do when I get my car."

For a moment Ben felt a stirring inside of all the old dreams and certainties. Somehow he had forgotten that they started this young in life, and the discovery annoyed him so unreasonably that he felt he had to set the boy straight at once before matters went any further. "You're not getting a car," he said. "You're not getting a car, do you hear me? Let's have that understood. Let's get that through your thick head once and for all. No car. And you're forbidden to ride in Jackie's car from now on. That's a rule; no riding in Jackie's car. Is that clear?"

Harold looked baffled and stricken. "Yes, Gran," he said, letting the hand with the jagger stick fall to his side.

Ben mopped his cheeks again and stuffed the soggy handkerchief back into his pocket. "All right, Prince Hal," he said, "it's not as bad as all that. You and Roy climb in and we'll take you up to the house for lunch."

But Harold stood unmoving with his smudged cheek against the edge of the door and his eyes cast down studying a scab on his elbow as he picked at it tentatively around the edges.

"Come on, boy, don't sulk."

"I'm not sulkin," Harold looked up with a fierce glare in his blue-green eyes. "It's just that I don't—well, you're just no fun, Gran. You're no fun at all. You just spoil all the fun. We were jaggerin you, an then you made all this fuss, an it isn't any fun any more."

"Stop being a spoiled baby and get in the car, both of you."

Roy opened the front door and climbed in next to his father, and Harold began to follow him into the front seat but stopped when Ben called out: "In here, boy; get in back. This is where you belong."

"I wanta sit with Roy in front."

"Did you hear me, boy?"

"Yes, sir."

"In here, please, at once. No nonsense."

"Why? I don't see why."

"Because I say so. That's enough reason why."

"I wanta sit with Roy."

"I don't care what you want. Get in here at once." Ben spanked his palms together hard with a noise like the crack of a pistol, and then he reached for his soggy handkerchief again as he saw Harold turn towards the back seat and heard him slam the front door and then slam the back door after he was inside.

"It's darn mean,"Harold muttered. "You always have to get the better of me in everythin."

"What? Speak up, boy. How can I hear you when you mumble that way?"

"It's not important, Gran."

"Then keep your mouth shut. You're wasting my time." He picked up the speaking tube and said into it; "All right, Frank, let's go."

As the heavy limousine got under way slowly and smoothly on the gravel, Ben heard a falsetto whisper and saw the freckled moon face, a smaller edition of Frank, leaning over the back of the front seat and looking fixedly at Harold as if the whispered words would follow the intent gaze straight to Harold's ears and would not be heard by his grown up ears at all.

"The mail," Roy whispered. "They must of stopped in Southport. They got the mail." Roy made exaggerated grimaces with his mouth and pumped his right hand up and down rapidly with a finger pointing down at the front seat. "They got it here," he whispered.

Harold's stony face broke into an expression of joy and anticipation. "Is the letter there?" he whispered, and moved forward until he perched on the edge of the seat. "Take a look," he said hopefully.

"What letter?" Ben growled, and saw them turn their shocked young faces to him with their mouths half open as he went on, "What letter? Who would be writing you letters?"

"Nobody, Gran. It's nothin."

"Is it Warren?—your father, I mean? Do you expect to hear from him? Did you write him, Harold?"

"No, Gran. I promised you I wouldn't."

"Humph—let me see the mail, Roy. I was napping when we stopped at the post office."

Roy and Harold exchanged a quick glance before Roy leaned over and handed him the stack of mail. He leafed through the letters rapidly, noting that they were mostly addressed to him except a few for the different servants and an odd shaped envelope larger than legal size and addressed to Harold. He handed it to him.

"Is that what you're expecting?"

Harold nodded and tucked the fat envelope under the jagger stick between his thigh and the upholstery on his far side.

"What's it about?" Ben demanded, mopping at his cheeks and the back of his neck. "Open it up, Hal."

Harold stared straight ahead at Roy without moving a muscle. Roy dropped his eyes and turned around, withdrawing out of sight except for his thatch of ginger hair sticking up above the seat.

"Don't be stubborn, boy. Open it up."

Ben saw his grandson's lips tremble and the tears start brimming from the lower lids of his eyes and roll down his soiled cheeks and drop into space. He took the letter and threw it on the seat between them.

"There," he said, quavering, "you'll get it away from me, anyway."

Ben mopped his forehead and his cheeks as he stared indignantly at the letter and then at Harold.

"I wouldn't open a letter addressed to you," he thundered. "Don't insult me. Do you know what's in it?"

"Yes."

"Tell me at once. Stop all this nonsense."

Harold sucked in his breath and wiped his wet cheeks quickly on the shoulders of his jersey.

"It's nothin but a contest, Gran," he said. "Roy an me saw it in one of his Dad's magazines," he went on more easily and evenly. "You get these points for things an whoever gets the most points wins the special grand prize of ten thousand dollars an the second most points wins five thousand dollars. There's lot of other prizes, so Roy an me thought we could win one of them."

"Roy and I."

"What?"

"Roy and I, damn it."

"Oh, yes, Roy an I."

"How do you get the points?"

"There's lots of ways." Harold's face lighted up with enthusiasm. "You get five hunderd points for neatness an another five hunderd points for prompness, an you get a hunderd points for each thing you sell. They send you perfume an seeds an religious pictures an you're supposed—"

"Perfume and seeds and religious pictures," Ben roared. "Where the devil are you going to sell trash like that?—perfume and seeds and religious pictures—what poppycock."

Harold looked at him in surprise. "That's easy, Gran. Everyone's goin to help us. Roy's Dad will help with the religious pictures through the Father at the Church an his friends at the Catholic Men's Club in Southport. Marie says she and the other ladies in her French Club will help with the perfume. Tony says he'll buy the seeds for our garden, an he knows all the other gardeners around here for Jackie Faith's father an people like that, an he's goin to tell them to buy their seeds from me. Roy an me have it all planned so we oughta get lots and lots of points."

"You ought to get a thrashing for victimizing the servants," Ben exploded. "I won't stand for such nonsense in my own house. I won't stand for your coercing them into buying all that trash from you."

"I don't know what that word means, Gran."

"Coercing? It means forcing them to buy it."

"But I'm not. Everybody's glad to help me. They come an ask me if they can help. They all want me to get the car."

"The what?"

"Oh—"

"What's behind all this, boy? What do you want with the money? Speak up."

Harold bowed his head. "I was goin to buy a car like Jackie's. You said it cost too much money. I thought I could win some money an then—"

"Is that all I said, you nincompoop! Don't you listen to even half the words I say?" Ben mopped furiously at his cheeks. "What else did I say the last time we had this out?"

Harold looked stricken. "I don't know, Gran, I can't remember. You only said it cost too much."

"Damn it, boy," Ben roared. "I said it was dangerous too. You're not old enough. You'll kill yourself on some damn fool tree. Do you remember that?"

"Yes, Gran." Harold squirmed on the seat.

"Well, I forbid it absolutely. No car. You're not to drive a car or even think about driving one or getting one. That's a rule. No car. Put it out of your head for good and all. Is that clear?"

"Yes, Gran." He was bouncing up and down on the seat.

Ben stuffed the hopelessly sodden handkerchief back into his pocket, leaning forward a moment to catch a glimpse, interrupted by the great elms, of his house ahead looking like a giant wedding cake with all its porches spread around it.

"Now, son," said Ben, "we ought to have a sensible talk about plans for your birthday party."

"Tell Frank to stop the car, Gran. I have to get out." Harold's sharp nose looked pinched and white. "I have to wee."

"Hold on till we get to the house, Hal. I want to talk to you."

"I can't."

"Nonsense. A boy of your age. Stop wriggling all over."

"I can't. I have to go now."

"Fiddlesticks."

"I'll just have to wee in my pants an all over the seat," he wailed.

"Oh, damn." Ben leaned forward urgently and touched Frank's shoulder, and the big limousine rolled gently to a stop on the gravel. "Get out," he said. "Hurry up." But his words were wasted because Harold was already out, the door slammed behind him, and Roy was out, the door slammed behind him, and both of them were running across the lawn towards the wall of laurel bushes, carrying their jagger sticks raised like spears and hurling them into the trees as they dove through the bushes like swimmers breasting an ocean wave and disappeared into the woods.

"They're gone," said Frank. "God bless them. They'll take the short cut by the old quarry and come up by the back of the house."

"No, Frank, I don't agree. They'll be back in a minute when Harold's finished his business. The path by the quarry is too dangerous. Harold knows he's forbidden to go that way."

"Yes, sir."

Ben stared at the short sharp ginger hairs on the back of Frank's red neck under the tight edge of his cap. "I suppose you think I'm too severe with the boy," he said.

"That's not for me to say, Mr. Stroud."

"No, it isn't," Ben laughed, "not in so many words anyway. But you'll find a way, Frank. You usually do."

"Yes, sir." Frank turned around in the seat so that his right arm was resting on the top of the seat and his rosy freckled face was leaning on his arm. "I'd like to tell you that story now about my sister's youngest boy, Lonnie. While we're waiting here, as you might say."

"Proceed, Frank, please proceed. You have my fullest attention."

"I know you remember my Da that you knew better than I did in some ways and how he used to say, 'God works in mysterious ways.' It's just as true today, Mr. Stroud; it's the very soul of the truth, sir."

"I remember well, Frank."

"Yes, sir. And the truth of the saying was brought to my mind like a voice from the past when I visited my sister Mary down at Norwalk the other night and found her youngest boy Lonnie home on leave from the Navy. He's been stationed over at Lakehurst with the dridgibles there and had the bad fortune to be on the crew of that one as crashed in the terrible disaster out in Ohio early this month. The Shenandoah was her name, do you remember?"

"Of course I remember. But what about the boy? How did he escape? It must have been terribly dangerous—I mean, was he hurt very badly?"

"Not a scratch, sir, except for his hands where he was holding the wires. It was a miracle, as you might say, and no doubt about it. My sister Mary says it was the hand of God reached down for him. To hear her talk you'd think you were hearing scripture. ' 'Twas the hand of God,' she says, ' 'twas the hand of the angry God reached down and broke the machine of the devil and threw the mighty to the ground, and 'twas the God of mercy in all His love that held my boy and laid him gently down.' "

"You and your sister have a similar view of the power of God," Ben commented wryly. "What does the boy have to say? What happened to him?"

"He doesn't say much, sir, but he did tell us once what it was like, and then he wouldn't speak of it again. He said it was the black storm of them all that caught the dridgible in the night and broke it in half like a dry corn cob being snapped in two. He said he was going along the catwalk between the big gas bags on his way to the control car when he remembered he'd left his watch on his bunk. He said he turned to go back and felt the dridgible lift up under him so steep and so fast that it knocked him down on his knees and almost threw him off the catwalk until he turned and got his legs around it and caught the guy wires and held them with a grip like his hands were frozen tight to them, as you might say. That was when he heard the girders snapping like chicken bones, he says, and he heard the fabric ripping and saw the catwalk twist and tear away not one foot from his eyes so he was looking out into the black storm with half the dridgible behind him that he was holding onto by those wires and riding the catwalk like a bucking horse and the other half of the big thing breaking in two and falling away from him in the dark and the control car with the Commander and all them in it falling free by itself like a stone straight for the ground thousands of feet down so that he lost sight of it in the night and never saw it again but heard the terrible noise when it hit. It was then he says he first felt the cold rain on his shirt and knew he was throwing up all his supper and all he had before supper and even lunch until he had no more to throw up but kept trying to do it anyway, throwing up dry, like you might say. We asked him if he had any particular thoughts that he would tell us, but he doesn't remember any except that he thinks he might have been a lot more frightened if it was daytime and he could have seen how far down it was. It didn't seem very long to him, he says, maybe five or ten minutes at the most that he rode the bucking catwalk as the rear half of the dridgible came floating down like a leaf. And then he saw some lights beneath him and pretty soon some trees rushing under him, and then he felt the hard bump and the bucking stop. He heard everything very quiet except the wind and the crying of the men and the rain whipping his shirt as he climbed down from the broken girders and walked across the field to the light in the farmhouse; and it wasn't until he was inside the farmhouse and saw the blood dripping from his fingers that he knew he'd been hurt at all."

Ben had been staring fixedly at Frank's agitated face. "That's an extraordinary story," he said, shaking his head, "almost unbelievable."

"It's true, every word of it, sir. But the most remarkable part to me is what it did to Mary. She's always fussed and fretted over the boy ever since he could walk. She begged him not to go in the service because he was her youngest, and she was afraid of the danger to him where she couldn't watch over him any more. But he was dead set on it, as you might say, and his father said it would make a man out of him, which it certainly has now with this experience behind him. Ah, but the biggest change is in Mary, to my way of thinking. When she first heard the news of the disaster she was prosterated for the whole night in tears for losing Lonnie, but when the report come through that he was saved she took the dust cloth to the rocker and she said, 'This is where I stay.' And there she is, rocking on the porch and saying it over and over again: ' 'Twas the hand of God, 'twas the hand of God.' Mary's always been a religious soul, as you might say, but she never was willing to turn Lonnie over to God until now."

Ben looked down at his blue veined hands and smiled to himself. He could remember the time that Frank had started work with him when the century had only begun. Even then he had learned that Frank was enough of a realist to accept his station in life but also enough of a man to have his own opinions and let them be known.

"So you think that's the best way, do you, Frank? You think I should sit back on a rocking chair and turn Harold over to God?"

"It's the best way, sir. Look at Lonnie."

Ben shook his head. "It seems like a miracle," he said, "I don't deny it. But look at the Commander and all those in the control car that fell to their death. Even in physical perils God is uncertain. Some are chosen; some are let fall. And Harold's all I have, or will ever have now, from the looks of things. But that's not all, Frank. The physical danger isn't all. There's the much worse peril of cheats and sharpers and confidence men who'll be after Harold's money someday. Look how he already trusts them and their fancy promises with this contest that you and I know is just a confidence game played on children. He must be warned and protected and guarded until he can look out for himself. God can't do that for him."

Frank turned his rosy face away so that he was sitting behind the wheel and looking out the front again. "Even in that my old Da was right when he used to say, 'God helps those as helps themselves.' I'm reminded of the story of my Uncle Danny and the three New York toughs which I'll tell you sometime, sir. But I'm even more reminded, sir, of what happened to that handsome penknife I gave Roy for his birthday."

"Humph," Ben said, looking out the window, knowing he couldn't insult the man by offering to pay him for his birthday present to his son, but secretly feeling proud of the way Harold had handled the older boy. "I'll speak to him severely about it, Frank. I don't approve of that kind of sharp trading for the boy, and I'll make sure he gets the knife back from Jackie."

"He won't get it back, sir, I'm sure of that."

"I think you're wrong, Frank. I'll order him to get it."

"No, sir, it's gone now. Them boys, God bless them, is a law unto themselves. You can order them all you please, but it's gone now, unless you want to break their spirit, which I won't be party to, as you might say."

"Break their spirit?" Ben said gruffly, and looked out the window at the motionless trees where the boys had disappeared. "By Jupiter, their spirit needs a little breaking. Let's go, Frank. It appears that you're right. They've gone up by the quarry."

2

When Ben entered the house across the porch he headed straight for the library, pausing only once in the hall to ask Loomis to bring him a fresh handkerchief and the decanter of brandy.

As he closed the library door with a firm click he looked around him and sighed with the first feeling of relaxation and complete privacy he'd had that day. There was a soothing sense of ease and familiarity in the sun filled room with the well ordered and well known objects that were so very precious to his widower's existence that Loomis himself personally dusted and cleaned them. Loomis was so painstaking in his task that Ben was never able to find a speck of dust even in such unlikely places as the ears of the marble head of his namesake, Benjamin Franklin, or in the folds of the marble toga on the Emperor's shoulder or even in the leaves and buds and curlicues of gold that decorated the frames of the oil paintings hung between the shelves. Loomis always knew when he would be home, and it was a measure of his affection that he never failed to have the small lights above each picture frame turned on so that the paintings glowed with a cheerful welcome when Ben first entered the room at any time of day.

He went to the desk and sat in the chair, gathering the humidor towards him. As he raised the chased silver cover he delicately selected a cigar with great leisure and with a love and enjoyment of every motion of his fingers. He held the cigar one inch under his nostrils, not sniffing it or making any vulgar sound, but sensing and feeling its richness and aroma and the heat of the Cuban sun that had made it and the whole world of ease and gratification that it represented to him.

When this ritual had reached its climax, he sighed and placed the cigar on the green blotter while he reached in his vest pocket for the gold cigar cutter with which he clipped the end of the cigar off like a brown bud, watching the bud as it rolled on the blotter, and then sweeping it from there into the basket. From another vest pocket he drew a small gold box which he flipped open with his thumb nail, taking out one of the blue tipped wooden matches, then closing the top with a snap, and turning the box over as he felt its satiny corners in his fingers. He scratched the blue tip of the match on the serrations on the bottom of the box, baring his teeth as he clamped the cigar between them, and then closed his lips on the cigar as he touched the flame to the tip and drew in at the same time, so that for a moment there was no sign that the cigar was lit until he exhaled the first clouds of blue smoke into the quiet sun streaked air.

As he settled back and watched the smoke he thought briefly that he was setting too much store by a mere cigar, but in the two years since his heart had begun missing a beat now and then, and since he had those dizzy spells and the terrible sweating, he had tried to take better care of himself by rationing all his pleasures, and this was the first of the two cigars he now allowed himself each day.

Loomis knocked and came in to lay the silver tray like an offering on the desk and to withdraw without a word. Ben watched him come and go silently, thankful that Loomis asked nothing of him at this moment when he felt the greatest need of privacy.

For he had a decision to make, and he had nowhere to turn except to himself. Frank had already had his say, and so, at various times, had Loomis and Harold's nurse, Marie, and fat Louis, the chef, and Tony, the gardener. These were all the senior members of what he thought of as his family, gathered under his roof, sustaining and soothing him, all surprisingly different like a family and all like a family in their loyalty to him and to an indefinable entity that was called "Fairlawn," where they had chosen to live, putting down their roots for good, placing themselves in his care.

And now his grandson, a nearly ten year old sprite of a boy, had stirred their sympathies over an utterly foolish question and had created a subtle division in his family so that, while none of them would openly oppose him, none of them were entirely with him any more.

But he had the final decision to make, whether it was about the red car or anything else that concerned all of them. And the decision had to be made now, and it had to be a clear one. Harold was growing quickly out of boyhood and would soon be a young man. Ben remembered how Marie had said last year after a fight with Harold: "Truly he doesn't want a single thing to stop him in his life, all his life. He is most *most* stubborn." That was the problem in a nutshell right there. Whether to prune and clip and trim the boy to hold him down and hold him close or whether to let him grow in any tangled way and run the risk of his becoming thorny and wild and impossible to have around, as Warren had become before he left.

It was not an easy decision.

As he looked up from the cigar smoke at the portrait that had been painted before the war he wondered whether it would have been any easier ten years ago. Certainly he had not changed much in outward appearance from the Ben Stroud who had posed for the portrait, a big man with a big frame and bushy hair and eyebrows that had not altered in their fierceness in those ten years but only in their color, being pure white now. His aquiline nose was just as sharp today, and his face just as pink and round and unlined with age. In fact, the only noticeable physical change was the small protruding stomach that shamed him whenever he had to send his clothes to be let out again. No, the biggest alteration had not been on the outside but on the inside, a corroding away of his confidence and spirit, so that for the last two years he who had never been sick had been in mortal fear of his heart and of death and final oblivion, and had fastened on Harold with a frenzy as his only hope of survival, his only contact with the ages after he was gone.

Ben poured himself some brandy and finished it off in one swallow and poured himself another glass, his second and his final ration for the day. He held the stem between his thumb and his forefinger, moving the crystal goblet slowly across the blotter like the Queen on a chess board, seeing with pleasure the lovely liquid patterns of moving sunlight that it made on the surface of the blotter.

Suddenly he rose, glass in hand, and walked across the quiet room, intent, but not knowing what he was doing, walking jerkily, almost without thinking or with just beginning to think "What am I doing?" as he stopped in front of the garlanded marble head of the Emperor; and then he knew, standing there, that he had come for help, as he had once or twice before in his life.

"Ave Antoninus!" he said.

The sightless eyes stared back at him. He took a sip from the crystal goblet and then, as if at the communion rail, held the goblet to the Emperor's patrician lips in turn, tilting the goblet until some of the brandy ran down and stained the marble chin.

"Ave Aurelius!" he sighed, like a benediction.

He felt for a moment transported into the noble world of the Antoinines in the time when the Pax Romana reached over all the shores of the Mediterranean, a sunny time of peace unlike any that the world has known since, a time when elders were respected and household gods were respected and life had an easy well defined pattern.

He reached to the shelf of the bookcase behind the marble head and picked out the book that was bound in calfskin dyed imperial purple. He opened it to the first page, as familiar as the prayer book.

MARCUS AURELIUS ANTONINUS, THE EMPEROR, TO HIMSELF

1. FROM MY GRANDFATHER VERUS, a kindly disposition and sweetness of temper.
2. FROM WHAT I HEARD OF MY FATHER AND MY MEMORY OF HIM, modesty and manliness.
3. FROM MY MOTHER, respect for the gods, and generosity; and abstention not only from doing ill but even from the very thought of doing it; and furthermore to live the simple life, far removed from the habits of the rich.

There he stopped and looked up at the sightless eyes and whispered, "Ave," for who could read even these few simple words without looking deep inside himself and finding that he fell far short of their measure. He read the words again, moving his lips slowly. Generosity was there, and a kindly disposition, and sweetness of temper. Also the gods were there with a thousand names glimmering beyond the printed page, a multitude of Roman gods each named with a Roman name so that one god protected the shining breastplates of all the legions on guard in foreign lands while another breathed life into the cooking fires in the dwelling places of Rome. There was a god for every household, for every market, for every river and harbor and tree. There was a god for every profession, for every trade, for every wonder that man could see. And then, like a clap of thunder, Ben saw a vision of clouds fading back from the beginning of time to reveal a host of gods for all races and tribes and natures of men, gods of beauty and hate and fear and love, gods of birth and growth and travel and death, gods enough for all men everywhere at all times so that each man everywhere could have his own god to watch over him. And Ben closed his eyes to see the vision better. And he saw that there was nothing outside of him, but that all was inside. And he rested, knowing what he would do now. He would be kind; he would have a sweet temper; he would be generous but not indulgent; he would be such a perfect grandfather and father to the boy that when he was gone Harold would remember him with the fondest—

Crash, the library door flew open.

"Gran, I have it, I have—"

Ben turned away from the marble sightless eyes.

"Hush, child, hush," he said. "Please learn to knock on doors."

"But I have it," the boy gasped, and then Ben saw that he still carried the jagger stick in one hand and now held a blue paper in the other.

"Quiet down, Hal," he said, absorbed in his vision. "You're acting like a wild Indian. Quiet down now. I have something to tell you that I think you'll like. I think you'll be glad to hear that I've reconsidered the whole question of your birthday, and that I now believe that your tenth birthday warrants a special present."

"I have it here, Gran, if you'll—"

The boy waved his hand with the blue paper as Ben looked down on him benignly. "Please try not to interrupt me, Prince Hal. I want to tell you about the present for your birthday. It's the most wonderful thing a boy could have, something I always longed for—"

"I don't—"

"Please, Hal, please," Ben pleaded.

"All right, Gran. You go ahead." The boy dropped his arms to his side.

"When I was your age I—well, I won't bother you with that. But there aren't many big events in anyone's life, and going from the single into the double numbers is certainly one of them. When my father Amos could have changed my whole—well, this is what I'm thinking of, Hal. Would you like a Shetland pony and a real wicker cart?"

"No."

"Oh, think what you're saying, boy. It's a very exciting thing to have a pony with a life that is all your own and the proper rig to go with it."

"No, Gran."

"What's the matter, boy? Don't you like animals?"

"No."

"Stop picking your nose," Ben ordered. "Can't you say anything else but no?"

There was a moment of silence. "I'm not pickin my nose," said Harold.

"You were."

"I'm not now, Gran."

"All right, you aren't now."

Ben walked to the desk and put the empty goblet on the tray, snatching the fresh handkerchief away as he sat down.

"Let's start over again, Harold," he said, blinking his eyes. "I don't believe you understood me. I'm opposed to your having a car because of the cost and the danger involved. That's my final decision, as you well know, and there'll be no change in it. On the other hand, I realize that your tenth birthday is a special event, and I think you should have a special present regardless of cost, something you'll remember all your life. Now, I want to leave the choice entirely up to you in this matter, but I would like to suggest that a pony and a pony cart can be a source of a great deal of pleasure. Ponies are very intelligent animals and also very safe, and they're lots of fun to learn to take care of. A pony is like a pet. You'll grow to be good friends with him, and that will be a wonderful experience for you. You can give him a name, and he'll get to know you as his master."

"Jackie calls his car Blitzen. I heard him when he's startin it. 'Come on, good old Blitzen,' he says."

Ben sighed with a mild feeling of exasperation. "Yes, I wouldn't be surprised at anything from that quarter," he said acidly as he picked up the handkerchief and began to pat his forehead. "Jackie's what is called a late child. His mother's over forty, and his father's nearly my age. When you add to that the fact that he's an only child you can understand that he might be queer about some things. But no normal boy would act that way. No normal boy would give a name to a machine."

"I'm going to name my car Stinger. That's a better name than Blitzen. Blitzen is a sort of baby name from a baby story."

Ben mopped along his cheeks and down his neck. "Now, Harold," he said, raising his voice and feeling that the Pax Romana was slipping forever away from him, "for the hundredth and last time. You are not getting a car. Be a good child and put that thought out of your mind."

"Yes, I am, Gran." He held up the hand with the blue paper. "I have it here an—"

"You're not, absolutely not."

"Yes, Gran. I'm goin to buy it myself an if you won't let me I'll run away an buy it anyway an live with Jackie until Dad comes home."

"Buy it," Ben roared. "How in thunder are *you* going to buy it? With what? With those seeds and perfume and religious pictures, I suppose? You're talking utter rot, boy."

"If you'll let me tell you—I been tryin to tell you all along." He held up the blue paper again. "Look, I got five *hunderd* dollars from Dad for my birthday."

Ben ran the sopping handkerchief across his forehead. "You lie. You're lying to me. Let me see it. How did you get it? Where did it come from?"

"Frank saved it out of the mail for me, a letter from Dad."

"Frank, eh? By Heaven, I'll—let me see it. I don't believe you."

"Here it is, Gran. Five hunderd dollars, it says. Look. An my name. Pay to the order of Harold Stroud. It's for me. It's mine."

Ben put down the wet handkerchief and held the blue paper stretched between his hands. He felt dizzy so that he could hardly focus his eyes on it. Finally he managed to do so and saw that it was an international money order drawn on Barclay's Bank at Nice, A.M., France on September 5, 1925, more than two weeks ago. Ben had no doubt that it was negotiable. He folded it neatly and tucked it in his vest.

"Give it back to me," screamed Harold, shocked. "It's mine. You can't have it. It's my money."

"It's gambling money," Ben roared. "It's dirty filthy gambling money your father won at the casino. It doesn't belong to you or to him or to anyone else. I'll give it to charity. It doesn't belong to you."

"It does, it does." Harold's sharp nose was pinched and white. "It's my money. It has my name on it. I'll tell Frank to tell Judge Bond on you. You're a thief. You stole it from me. Judge Bond'll put you in jail. You'll see, you'll see, if you don't give it back to me." The tears were dripping from his cheeks.

"Damn it," Ben shouted, "Judge Bond appointed me your guardian a year ago when your father left. How can I steal from myself? You can't own anything until you're twenty-one. Get hold of yourself, boy." Ben's head was throbbing, and he could feel the drops of sweat running down his cheeks and neck and wilting his starched collar.

"I don't care," Harold shrieked, "it's mine. Give it back to me. It's mine. Give it to me." His ears trembled like butterfly wings as he raised the jagger stick like a javelin. "I'll jag you. I'll jag you good. I'll jag you dead."

"What?" Ben rose from the chair in wrath. "What?" he bellowed. "Are you threatening me?"

"I'll jag you, I will," Harold sobbed. "I'll jag you dead," he wailed.

Ben started around the corner of the desk towards the boy when his head exploded, and it was like Frank said as he heard the girders snapping like chicken bones and the fabric ripping and felt himself knocked down on the catwalk and looking out into the black storm all around so that he was like a dry corn cob snapped in two and falling into the black storm, falling free like a stone straight for the ground, losing all sight of himself as he fell in the night and fell and fell and fell. And then there was nothing.

After a very long time there were large blue bubbles.

And then, much later, there were orange bubbles and then blood red bubbles floating upwards in a tawny liquid like honey that seemed to be lighted from within.

Sometime later he heard the bubbles making a terrible roar like the thunder of a waterfall.

Several hours passed by and then through the pouring cataract of water he heard a distant piping voice calling to him.

"Gran, Gran, Gran," it called. And as it grew louder it sobbed, "Come back to me, Gran. Don't leave me alone."

Ben opened his eyes and found that he was looking up at the ceiling and feeling that a wide space of years had passed. He was surprised to see Warren leaning over him with tears falling from his boyish cheeks. He wondered how this could be. Certainly Warren was grown now. And yet this boy with the ears sticking out was just like—and then he remembered it all.

"Gran," Harold quavered, "are you all right? I didn't do it. I didn't jag you. Honest I didn't. Are you all right?"

Ben stared up at the boy. It was surprisingly peaceful lying on his back on the rug. In a minute or so he would try to speak to him and would try to move. But just for now it was wonderfully peaceful lying there not involved in anything, coasting, gliding, immobilized as if pinned in some wreckage.

"Are you all right, Gran? I didn't jag you. I just lost my temper. I wouldn't have jagged you ever. Honest I wouldn't. You just fell down in a lump, and I didn't know what happened. I was sort of frightened and lonesome."

"Hal," Ben said in a thin weak scream.

"What, Gran? Is anythin wrong? Why don't you get up, Gran?"

Ben did not move. "Get Loomis—Hal—get Loomis."

"Are you sick?"

Ben closed his eyes. He could hear the sharp windy noise of his own breathing as well as the distant slam of a door in the upstairs hall. Was he sick, indeed, he thought. Not sick, he thought, just brushed lightly and warningly by death, just struck down and gasping. Not sick at all, though they would certainly send for that old quack of a doctor to come and examine him and issue orders prohibiting brandy and cigars and rich foods and going to work and everything worthwhile in life, leaving him all alone rocking on his porch like an invalid husbanding his remaining strength for the few weeks or months or years he had left by himself rocking on his porch like Frank's sister Mary. Only she wasn't an invalid; she chose it that way; and her family came to her; and she was never alone as she rocked, saying, "'Twas the hand of God, 'twas the hand of God," as if she knew better than he did what the Emperor meant when he wrote, "and furthermore to live the simple life, far removed from the habits of the rich." Ben opened his eyes.

"Get Loomis," he said, noticing that his voice was stronger.

"I will, Gran." Harold started away slowly but come back again before he reached the door. "What about my five hunderd dollars, Gran?"

"It's no time for that. I've had a heart attack, Hal. Get Loomis."

"But it's mine, Gran," he said plaintively.

"Now you're jagging me, Hal. This is no time to be asking me about that. Now you're jagging me," Ben said with reproach. His voice was much stronger.

Harold's green-blue eyes stared at him and then down at the scab he was picking at on his elbow.

"I guess you're right, Gran. I guess I *was* jaggin you in a way. I'm sorry. I won't do it again, Gran. Let's forget all about it. Let's forget all about the car an the money an everythin. I won't do it again, Gran."

He turned towards the door with an odd precise stiffness.

Ben rolled his head on the rug to watch him. "Harold," he called, "just a moment."

"Yes?"

"What did you mean—you won't do it again?"

"I won't jag you again, Gran."

"With the stick, you mean? Threatening me, you mean?"

"No, Gran, botherin you about the car and things and not obeyin you an tellin fibs like sayin I had to do wee when I really didn't an—well, just jaggin you to get things from you. That's what I mean."

"I see. Listen, son, have those people sent you any of those things yet—the perfume and seeds and religious pictures?"

"No, Gran. They're waitin for my order."

"Good. Have you and Roy decided how many you can sell?"

"Yes, Gran."

"Very good. Now listen carefully. I want you to make out that order and send it in just as soon as you can, son. And listen, I want you to double it, double the number you decided on, triple it, quadruple it, no, make it tenfold. Order ten times the number. I may spend the rest of my life in a rocking chair, but you and I and the rest of us are going to plaster this county with perfume and seeds and religious pictures. And do you know something else, son? For every dollar's worth you sell I'm going to put five dollars in a box, and when there are enough of them in the box you're going down to buy yourself a car and have its name painted in white on the red door in neat letters one inch high STINGER. That car will be yours because you earned it and not because you got some play money that meant nothing to him who sent it and would mean nothing to you if you spent it. Now what do you think of that?"

"I'll never jag you again," the boy kissed him. "You're my real Gran; you're my very best Gran there is. I'll never jag you again, never, never, never; an if you see me even just beginnin to jag you, you say 'No jaggin today, Harold' an I'll know right away an I'll stop." The boy kissed him again.

"It's your nature, son. You'll always be jagging me. I don't think I'll mind that so much now as long as God gives me the wisdom to prevent you from ever getting as close again to actually jagging me with your jagger stick as you were a few minutes ago."

"Yes, Gran." Harold turned away with embarrassment. "I'm going to get Loomis," he said, running.

"Get Frank, too," Ben called after him, "and Louis and Marie and Tony. I'm going to need them all."

As the door was closed carefully and firmly Ben let his head settle back on the rug so his eyes were staring at the ceiling again. He listened to all the noises of the house, the closing doors and the running on the stairs and the hurried voices as his family gathered its strength. While he was listening intently he heard Jackie's car sputtering in the distance, the noise growing rapidly louder so that he knew the car was coming up his drive.

"Damn it," he roared, raising himself up on his elbow, "damn—damn—damn."

GEORGE P. ELLIOTT *was born on a farm in Indiana in 1918. His family moved to a bare ranch in California where he spent most of the depression, reading. Since 1937 he has lived in Berkeley, obtaining an M.A. in English from the University of California and working at an assortment of jobs. The one he likes best, he says, is teaching at St. Mary's College, which he has done since 1947. His enterprize has for some time been turned toward trying to write theatrically good plays.*

A FAMILY MATTER

FROM QUARTERLY REVIEW OF LITERATURE

In the summer of his thirty-fifth year Bryan Mott, second son of the inventor Gordon Mott, received the following letter from his father.

My dear Bryan,

Ever since Thelma's unhappy death this spring, I have had the growing feeling that her daughter Jessica (I believe I sent you a picture of her, a charming thing) not only does not need me but what is worse does not want me hanging around. In my day, and it is obviously my day no longer, a girl of twenty would have sought the wise counsel of a man like myself in a thousand concerns. There is no reason for her to think I lack wisdom, and I haven't bothered her much; yet everything I say bores her to death (the expression is hers). Now that she's home for the summer vacation, I have been feeling superannuated, and besides I abominate the New York heat.

Therefore I have decided to renew my acquaintance with my sons, beginning with you.

According to the ticket I have before me, I shall arrive at the SP station in Oakland at 8:03 p.m., July 11. If I don't see you in the station I'll take a cab on out.

There's a lot more to say, but since I'll be seeing you so soon I won't bother to write it down.

The check enclosed is to cover any extra expenses you may run on my account. I don't eat much but I do cause a lot of trouble. Which Martha will bear the brunt of, so I've made it out to her.

Give my best to her and the children. I hope she is a little mellowed by having had children. A psychoanalyst told me once—I've tried everything, mineral water, body-building, psychoanalysis—that the reason I've had so many wives was that I was seeking a mother-substitute. Which may be so, and if it is, then Martha as she was when you first married her is not the one for me. Charming, intelligent, companionable, but how unmaternal.

I look forward to getting to know your children—and you too.

Gordon

That flippancy about the psychoanalyst sounds worse than I meant it to sound. I never really went to one; he was just a friend of Diana's. There's nothing more the matter with me than there is with anyone else. It's New York. A dreadful atmosphere.

The letter arrived on a Monday morning ten days before the eleventh. Aylmer fetched the mail to his mother, who was in the midst of washing clothes. At her prolonged wail, Bryan came running out of his writing room to see what had happened, and Roxana sang out from her sand-pile, "What's the matter, Mommy?"

"I won't be able to write a word while he's here," Bryan groaned.

"He's your father," said Martha darkly.

"Grampa Gordon?" asked Aylmer.

"Yes, dear," his mother answered, "Grampa Gordon. Go out and play with Zan."

"And stay out," said Bryan.

"Oh why couldn't this letter have come at any other time?" said Martha belligerently, but not exactly to Bryan.

"Because," he responded, "there was no other time."

"I suppose so."

"Of course," Bryan continued, "it might have arrived the afternoon of the eleventh. Then I could at least have written for the next ten days."

"Oh come on, you sensitive plant. You haven't lived in the same city with your father since you were ten."

"Twelve. But it's the childhood experiences that leave their deepest impress on the soul."

"Carry out this basket of wet clothes, and then go back to your room and do something about it. He's *your* father."

"Laundering seems to dull your razor-like wit, my love."

"Daddy," said Roxana at the back door, "is Grampa going to sleep in the cellar?"

At which there was another wail from Martha, "Where is he going to sleep?" And Bryan ducked back to his room, where he tried to pick up the thread of his thought—he was translating Racine—but failed. He sighed, but to maintain his honor he stayed in his room till lunch-time reading a novel.

For lunch there were peanut butter sandwiches and raw carrots. Bryan did not object in words but he created a ruckus by putting jam on his peanut butter. Their children were not allowed jam except on state occasions—their teeth.

"I suppose," said Martha, "your father will wreck what little discipline you let me keep over the children. The old goat. He probably wouldn't give them a second glance if he didn't think I'd mind."

"The size of the pitcher, my love, has nothing to do with the size of the ear. Caution."

"Do you have to be so coy, Bryan? After all—"

"My maternal little wife," said Bryan, patting her behind as she poured the milk. "I think Gordon will find you as maternal as he could wish."

"And that's another thing," said Martha, whirling so vigorously she kicked the table and knocked Roxana's milk over, "I never read such an insulting letter in my life. If you suppose," she continued while mopping up Roxana and the floor, "that I'm going to coddle a white-haired broken-down old roué, you're thicker than even I thought."

"Well," said Bryan, "where is he going to sleep?"

"He paid *me* to worry about it, darling. So go back to Phèdre and don't fret your poetic soul about such mundane matters."

"You're pretty snippy for a person who opens other people's letters."

"Bryan, really, it was from your father."

"All I have to say is—he does not sleep in my writing room."

He marched out, his pennon ragged but flying.

Racine could not hold his attention, and by two he had finished the novel. He was working on the composition of a literary crossword puzzle—he had had a number published under another name—when the door opened to Martha.

"I know you can't be working, darling," she began, but hesitated when she saw him hunched over his desk. "You could help me, couldn't you?"

He leaned back in his chair but did not turn to face her.

"Un dieu vengeur te suit, tu ne peux l'éviter.
Je t'aimais; et je sens que malgré ton offense
Mes entrailles pour toi se troublent par avance."

"I'm sorry," she said. "I'll take the children down shopping."

His problem was to find a nine-letter name whose first two letters were SH and whose seventh was W. There was none, so he made a name up, Shaddower in this case: "That the sun may not shine in broad day" or "Shamus."

Late in the afternoon of the same day Justin Mott, the third son, returned from work, to have his wife hand him this letter. She told him the peas were nearly cooked, so he read it fast.

My dear Justin,

I have before me a ticket which says I am to arrive in Oakland on July 11 at 8:03 p.m. I bought this ticket because I am getting old and want to see my sons. The truth is no one needs me in New York. Oakland is my home.

I know from Charlene's most daughterly letters that you have an extra room for me. I shan't be more trouble than Charlene can bear, I hope, and I can't tell you how much I want to make the acquaintance of all three of you. Imagine, I have never seen my most beautiful grandson! How fortunate you are in your wife, Justin. Do with her better than I did with your mother. I hope Diana's well. Give Charlene a kiss for me. I haven't seen her since your wedding. Or you either, my dear son.

Your father

"What did he have to say, honey?" asked Charlene as she was taking off her apron.

"Here, baby, get into your high chair," said Justin, picking up Michael.

Michael was well into his second year and not nearly so helpless as his parents supposed. As it was, picked up and stuffed into his high chair, he found it engaging to kick up the tray and poke one foot out through the side. There was more to put down in Michael than there was zeal in his parents for putting it down; they were young too.

"My, smoked pork chops and peas. What could be better? What do you get, baby? Scraped liver and spinach as usual?"

"And he loves it. What did you father say in his letter?"

"Let's not talk about disagreeable subjects while we eat."

"He said he was coming out here to visit," Charlene stated.

"Yes."

"Glube blg wawaffrts cheese," said Michael.

"You see, he wants cheese," said Justin.

"It just means he's feeling good."

"You won't even give my son cheese when he wants it."

"Yackety yackety. Get the cheese yourself if you want to."

He went to the ice-box and got a piece of Cheddar. Michael dunked the Cheddar in his spinach and threw it onto the floor. Justin rather ungraciously mopped up.

"He's getting old and wants to see his sons," said Charlene as she picked a bone.

"So he says," answered Justin with a malevolent glance.

"Oakland is his real home now. No one needs him in New York."

"Look, you've read the letter. Let's not talk about it."

"I did not. When did I have a chance?"

"How do I know? While I was fussing with Mickey."

"But the letter's in your pocket."

"Well, maybe you steamed it open and resealed it."

But Charlene had burst into tears, and Michael was starting up, slowly but ominously, like a fire siren.

Charlene was thought by some of her friends to be psychic: how else could she win at bridge so often? But Justin was a businessman.

"You don't believe me," she sobbed.

"I'm sorry, honey," he said with irritation as he bent over her, hugging her shoulders with one hand and tickling Michael's stomach with the other. "So you didn't read the letter. I still don't see——"

"I wouldn't dream of steaming open a letter."

"Well, I guess it's just a woman's intuition," he said.

"Thassawrai, thassawrai. Mama, mama."

His parents turned on him like heliotropes.

"Did you hear that?"

"He said, 'That's all right.' "

"Cheese, cheese, cheese, cheese."

Michael crowed. His parents embraced.

"I'm sorry, baby," said Justin to his wife. "Here, read it, I'm sorry."

"It's just that you were so rough," she said. She disclaimed any pride in being psychic, but only did what she was prompted to do in these matters.

"Well, I think it's sweet of your father to just come like this. Real family-like. Do you suppose he'll mind if I call him Gordon?"

"I don't suppose he'll mind if you call him Gordon."

"Are you being sarcastic, Justin?"

"Only irritated. Why should he mind?"

"I don't know. I just remembered him as a very courtly old man. Sort of like a nobleman. An earl, say."

Justin did not respond; he was mustering his miscellaneous knowledge of his father so that he might demolish in an orderly and accurate fashion this picture of him as an earl.

"We ought to get an innerspring mattress for the guest bed and a new rug for the guest room. I saw a bargain in rugs just yesterday."

"We ought not. It's a good bed and a good enough rug. Your mother didn't complain of them when she stayed with us when Michael was born."

"Oh, Mother. But we don't know how long your father is going to be with us. He didn't say. Maybe he even wants to settle down with us for the rest of his life."

"Oh no, oh no," said Justin, at first with the inflection of determination and then with that of horror. "Oh no, oh no, no, no."

"Why not? He has no one to take care of him."

"I don't know why not. Just not. He has three sons and two living wives. Why should he stay with us?"

"I like him."

"I don't."

"Justin!"

"He may stay here a couple of weeks, a month even. Then he goes to visit Roscoe or Bryan."

"I don't think Mickey will like firecrackers."

"And why not? He's a boy, isn't he?"

"A baby boy. I was thinking, we ought to get Nancy to stay with him Friday evening."

"Why Nancy? Is she sound-absorbent?"

"We're going to Roscoe's on Friday, to watch the fireworks over Lake Merritt. Can't you even remember your own family?"

"Oh yes . . . Mickey is my son. He can stand a little noise."

"I don't think so," she said lightly. Scowl darkened his face. Seeing this little victory, she added, "You frightened him, Justin."

With the slightest readjustment of muscles his scowl became an anxious frown.

"I don't know how it is, but I manage a factory with 150 men in it with less trouble than I manage you. In fact, I don't manage you at all. You always make me feel in the wrong."

She suppressed a very quiet smile and patted him on the arm.

"Tell me what happened today, dear," she said. "It's harder to manage 150 than one."

Justin, not perceiving the fallacy in this proposition, brightened and gave her an account of his day as he always did. He did not yet know that she was not interested in his factory life; indeed she did not yet know it herself. She would respond to his statements with an occasional polite yes and is that so and really, but her eyes were not in harmony with her voice. He thought it was her way, and talked on.

Roscoe Mott, the eldest son, received no such letter from his father. Roscoe was forty, spare and slightly dandyish. He was in the habit of watching an interlocutor with the air of one who seeks confirmation of his opinion of himself. This opinion fluctuated on the scale of pride rather extremely, and did not always receive confirmation. His wife, for example, did not give it him promiscuously.

"Roscoe," she said, somewhat thickly for she had toothpicks between her lips, "do we have enough seltzer?"

"Hrmph," he answered from the dining room. He was ranging through the house, with hostly eye alert, that he might rectify error.

"You know you should see to it," she said as she rolled another delicacy in a strip of bacon.

"I am sure, Edwa," he called out, "we have enough."

"The last three Fourths we ran out of seltzer," she said as she speared the bacon. "And we ran out when the Tollertons dropped by. You always say you'll take care of the drinks but just look——"

"All right, I'll get it, all right."

"You might as well get John to go."

"All right. John!" There was no response. "I suppose he's around, Edwa? John!"

"There's no use shouting. He went down to the lake to watch them set up the stage for the fireworks."

"You might have told me. I suppose Henry has a date as usual?"

"Oh, Roscoe, how can you talk so harshly about him? This may be the last summer he'll be with us. Who knows when he will love us so much again?"

"Hrmph."

"Well, as long as you're going, dear, you might just as well get another package of cocktail napkins. There are so many of us."

"Yes, yes, yes. That's all?" He put on his hat, an exact, gray Homburg.

"Don't forget, everybody takes seltzer but Martha."

Yet it had been the napkins she had wanted and that had suggested sending him out in the first place.

As he left he met Bryan and his family arriving, and by the time he had returned Justin and Charlene had installed Michael in the baby bed upstairs. There was scarcely time for a highball before dinner was ready.

"We must hurry with dinner," he said serving. "It'll soon be time for the fireworks."

"The children won't want to miss them," said Edwa.

"If the children are the ones who won't want to miss them," said Martha, "then why must we bolt our food?"

"Honey," said Charlene to Justin before Edwa could have responded had she wished to, "do you suppose we ought to go home and get baby's cod liver oil?"

"Can't you give it to him tomorrow morning?"

"Yes."

"Then don't worry."

"And powder his bottom and button his sleepers," said Bryan in a crooning voice to Charlene beside him, "tuck him in tight and kiss him and tell him you love him, leave the door open just a crack and sing him good-night."

She looked at him sentimentally, put her hand on his arm, and said, "You and Martha ought to have another baby."

"Ah, but it's not as simple as all that."

"It should be, for you. Really."

Bryan watched her a moment.

And Martha and Edwa were both watching him watch her, though he didn't notice it. Bryan had so many internal eyes, some like Edwa's and more like Martha's, scrutinizing him day and night that he paid very little attention to watchful eyes outside himself. Which accounted, among other things, for his attire as of a workingman at a ball game, in contrast to Roscoe's gray flannels and Justin's soft, expensive, sporty clothes.

"You know," said Bryan, remembering Roscoe's injunction to hurry, "here we are, the assembled sons of Gordon." He held forth his glass of wine and drained it as though drinking a toast. "Sons of the famous Mott. True, Roscoe is known in the best real estate circles of the Bay Area, and I am known to critics and editors of literary magazines, and Justin is making his mark in the realm of tubes and condensers and frequency modulation. But essentially we are the three who are identified at a party, should someone want to know, as the sons of Gordon Mott. That at least we have in common, the shuddering loin."

He paused to pour himself another glass of wine and drink it. During the interval, Martha said, "Pass the beets, please," and Edwa urged Justin to have some more cold tongue. Bryan went on.

"He has set us an example which we have not followed, encumbered as we are by charming and devoted wives." He saluted each; only Charlene liked it. "Yet I propose that each of us, since we are not apt to live them out as he has done, tells a love-story on occasions of our forgathering like this."

"Really, Bryan," said his wife.

"I hardly think we have time now," said Roscoe.

"You are the senior brother," said Bryan. "Why don't you start off?"

"No," said Charlene before Roscoe could object, "you must start. You thought of it and anyway you have one to tell or you wouldn't have brought the subject up."

"That's true," Bryan said, "that's perfectly true. I am seen through." Martha snorted and Edwa stirred in her chair. "Very well, my story. I was down in the book section of the Good Will store one day. You know, down on Broadway and Fifth or Sixth."

"We know," said Martha.

"I was just looking around rather aimlessly, at Winston Churchill and F. Marion Crawford and Somebody Canfield. I noticed, only because she was in my way, a young woman also looking at books. She was perfectly unnoteworthy, perfectly. Hair-colored hair and eye-colored eyes and clothes that were a perfection of the ordinary. I doubt if I would recognize her again. She had good wrists, though, very delicate and supple, only with listless, chapped hands."

"It takes a queen," said Charlene, "to look like anything in the Good Will."

"Yes, yes, that's it. That's what I was trying to get at," he said, turning to her and addressing the rest of his story to her. "Nothing was happening when presently a young man, her gray counterpart, walked in and came up to her. She started a little when he touched her shoulder. 'Peter!' she said. 'How did you know I was here?' He smiled at her with a tenderness I cannot describe. His ordinary face suddenly shone with a love so little ordinary, so pure and true, that I held my breath to hear what he would reply. Her face reflected some of his radiance, very quietly. They had halos—You understand, they were not touching each other at all. He stooped a little, and she still held a copy of some novel or other. They just looked into each other's eyes, smiling a little, aware of me and indifferent to my presence as though I had been another book. There was only a moment of this before he replied: 'How do I know my foot is in my shoe?' That was all the answer she needed. They walked out with little fingers linked, not talking, as ordinary as ever, and I have never forgotten them."

Bryan looked about the table commandingly: there was to be a moment of respectful, not to say reverent, contemplation following this apologue.

Charlene seemed sunk deepest of all, chin in hand, eyes in nether space, when dreamily she said, "How did you remember his name was Peter?"

"What difference does it make?" he snapped.

The sound of jaws in motion returned to the room.

"Well, how?"

"Who cares what his real name was?"

"If you don't even know his real name, how do we know it was a real story?"

"Reality is of the essence, not the detail," he said, intending to silence her and nearly succeeding.

"I don't see," Martha put in, "anything so wonderful about what he said. Anybody knows where his foot is."

"How stupid can you get?" said Bryan wrathfully to Martha.

"It was really a very sweet story," said Charlene to him sweetly, making amends.

"Thank you, my dear, for those few kind words.—Come on, Justin, you must have one to tell."

"I don't want to."

"Honey," said Charlene.

"Well, all right. I'm no good at it, but the PBX operator down at the plant fell in love with the stationary engineer. He used to flirt with her, and he flirted too much. Well, he took her out a couple of times and when she found out he was married she ran off to Reno with the truck driver in the company pick-up. He'd been in love with her for months but he had a birthmark on his neck."

"Not a bad situation," said Bryan.

"I think it's too bad for the truck driver," said Edwa.

"Justin," said Charlene, gazing at him intently, "you never told me this story. When did it happen?"

"Last month, and I told you." His eyes opened wider. "At dinner once."

"There should be at least one more complication," said Bryan. "Pregnancy, relationship, threat, misunderstanding, something."

"I like it," said Martha, "just as it is."

"I forgot to say," said Justin, wrenching his eyes from Charlene, "the truck driver is the brother of the engineer's wife."

"Ah, now we're getting someplace," said Bryan.

"Really, honey," said Charlene, her eyes on the table, "I don't remember."

"You said at the time what a terrible way to get married it was."

"I must have been thinking of baby at the time you told it."

But she didn't believe herself, and no one else who was paying any real attention believed her either. Martha perceived that Justin and Charlene were making some unhappy discovery about themselves; therefore, having a profound trust in decorum as the lubricant of life, she began clearing table, to create stir and bustle that would restore the young couple to their social selves.

"No story, Roscoe?" said Bryan.

"Well, you know," said Roscoe with a condescending smile, "there's hardly time."

"Roscoe," said Bryan, not without malice, "you looked remarkably like Gordon just then—the way you took out your watch and peered down your nose at it."

"Hrmph," said Roscoe, who viewed his character as being essentially an inversion of his father's.

"Gordon, Gordon, Gordon," said Edwa as she poured cream over her pudding. "Why all this talk about Gordon, Bryan? If you've mentioned him once you've mentioned him a dozen times."

"Bryan wants to see him," said Charlene in her automatic way.

"Come, my little oracle," he said as though she were dear to him, but weak in the head, "wants to or expects to?"

"Wants to," she said defiantly.

"Maybe she's right," said Bryan to himself, only aloud, "maybe that's what I really want. She's an odd one—My sweet, my pure, my apple-cheeked Cassandra, can you tell me why——"

"Justin!" she cried out. "You can't just sit there and let him insult me even if he is your brother."

"Oh, Charlene," said Justin.

"What in the world!" said Bryan.

Martha was gagging her laughter with her napkin.

"I won't sit by him another minute." Charlene got up, pudding in hand, and made for herself a place beside Justin. Once there, she pressed his foot with hers, and whispered to him how horrible Bryan was, and paid no attention to Bryan's rather stiff-necked explanation of himself.

So love filled up the gap that Justin had found, and after that Charlene would not ask him much about his day at the plant and he would volunteer her very little; and there would be less to talk about when he came home from work, Michael chiefly, so they would talk even more about him.

Roscoe, who had gathered from Charlene's shift that some sort of realignment was going on, turned to Bryan with a rather stately motion and said, "What have you heard from Father recently?"

"He's coming to visit us next week."

"What!" said Charlene, Edwa, Roscoe, Justin.

"I got a letter a few days ago saying he was coming for a visit the eleventh. Is there anything so remarkable about that?"

"Who was he going to stay with?" asked Justin.

"I said I got the letter."

"He's going to stay with you."

"For pity's sake, yes. What is there——"

"I got the same letter," said Justin, "only he said he was going to stay with us."

"What!" said Martha, Edwa, Roscoe, Bryan.

"Why," said Edwa in slow astonishment, "he did not write us a letter."

"It's a doubtful honor either way," said Bryan.

"But I write to him at least twice a year," said Edwa, who was not much interested in honor.

Two letters a year were more than were written to Gordon by all the others in the room combined: they were silent.

"How very thoughtless of him," she said, and meant at least that.

There was a great *crack* outdoors, and the dark sky flashed bluish-white.

"The fireworks!" said Edwa.

"The children won't want to miss them," said Roscoe.

But the kitchen was empty.

"They must be up on the roof of the apartment house down the street," said Edwa. "Let's go down."

"I'd better stay with baby, hadn't I, honey?" said Charlene to Justin, her hands on his shoulders.

It rose to his lips to say he was going with the others, but he hugged her instead and said, "Sure, honey, I'll wait with you. We can watch from here."

The fireworks were a great success with the children. It was eleven before the families had reassembled themselves at Roscoe's. Bryan had been unable to interest anyone in talking about Gordon's letters; he felt even a little snubbed. He had decided to go over to see Charlene the next afternoon, ostensibly to talk about the letters, really to make friends with her again. But he changed his mind: as everyone was saying their good-nights, she ducked into her car before he could kiss her on both cheeks as he always had done before. He kissed Edwa instead, as he seldom did; she patted him as if he were a child, and sent him home.

The children were all in bed and Roscoe was lying in bed watching Edwa work on her hair.

"On days like this," he said, "I'm thankful that all our family live in Oakland."

"Your head doesn't ache?" she said through her hairpins. It usually ached after family gatherings.

"No, not a bit. Fine young woman, Charlene."

"Mommy!" Mary called out.

"Not asleep!" said Edwa to Roscoe. "What, dear?" she said to Mary at the door of the girls' room; she was still fixing her hair.

"Roxana said that's how it would be at the end of the world, Mommy."

"Well, we'll never see it, honey. Go to sleep."

"She said it might happen any old day now."

"Oh no, it won't. She's wrong."

"She said so. She said she read it in a book."

"She was teasing, honey. Go to sleep."

"How do you know it won't?"

"God wouldn't let it happen."

"Oh."

"Sometimes," said Roscoe when she had returned, "I wish we didn't have to tell the children so many lies."

"What lies? I never tell them lies."

"Oh well, whatever you want to call it. The world may end any day you know. Stars do explode."

"Nonsense," said Edwa, turning out the light, "that's a Mottish idea."

She got into bed and told him good-night, and she was sound asleep before he had finally adjusted his pillow.

2

"Well, my boy," said Gordon, "you seem to lead a very agreeable life."

Martha was just joining them from having put the children to bed. They were sitting about the fireplace, in which there was a small fire that was warming the darkness more than any chill in the air. Bryan disliked the thought of building a fire, but when it was actually burning he could stupefy himself gazing into the flames and afterward the embers dying down.

"We like it," he answered noncommittally.

"The children like it," said Martha positively.

"Indeed, indeed. Well they should. Tell me, Bryan, what are you working on these days? I've only seen that one book of poems you published some years back."

"Four years ago. Only individual verses since then, in magazines, a few in anthologies. I'm working on a translation of Racine at the moment."

"Racine!"

"I've done most of Phèdre and half of Andromaque. It goes rather slowly."

"I've always gathered somehow that Racine was untranslatable."

"Have you? That's a rather old-fashioned notion, like the one that *Lear* won't go on stage."

"It's a very strong impression all the same."

"Have you ever read Racine in French?"

"Yes."

"Oh. Well, do you see any reason why he can't be translated like any other great poet?"

"Yes. It sounds like prose in English."

"You're a scientist," said Bryan with a levity that was yet not far from surliness.

"The thing is," said Martha, who was darning socks, "that Bryan likes challenges. Racine is supposed to be untranslatable; Bryan sets about translating him. He tries his hand at a novel; it turns out to be too short for a book and too long for a magazine. He starts a poetic play full of fine speeches, but he's never been backstage and he won't go because he can't stand little-theater characters; the play is unactable. His stories almost always have some shocking passage or idea in them; therefore they're published, if at all, only in magazines no one ever heard of, with names like *Stormy Petrel* or *K* or *Tangent* or *South Dakota Quarterly Review*."

"It sounds," said Gordon, "as though he were ducking out from under."

"That's our Bryan," said Martha. She got up and kissed him on the back of the neck, but he was staring into the fire.

"Yet his poetry suffers from none of these complaints that I can see."

"Yes, but being a poet is rather like being a bird-watcher; what competition there is comes from other bird-watchers, and they are really doing it for its own sake; and no one else takes it seriously at all. Still it's respectable and everyone knows about it, and most people have even looked at poems a few times."

"Usually in zoos."

"He can be more serious about writing since it's a less serious occupation."

"I understand that perfectly," said Gordon. "I work much better when I'm on something that has no apparent utility than on, say, a problem in electronics."

"You do," said Bryan heavily, "you do, eh?—You," he said at Martha, "have said too much too soon and too fast. Even if what you said were true, as it is not, even so you should not have said it. At least, not like that."

"Why, darling——" she began.

"What was wrong with what she said?" said Gordon.

"What she left out."

"Which was?"

"The world. Would you rather have sherry or port, Gordon? The sherry is better."

"Sherry."

"Sherry for you," he said to her. He stood up with a bitter expression on his mouth, glanced at each of them a moment, and went for the sherry.

"Well," said Gordon, "I hope he doesn't put poison in the wine."

"Come."

"Come what?"

"We don't keep poison in the kitchen."

"Good. Perhaps we oughtn't to be so harsh on him."

"It was very wrong of me to have said all that."

There was a little stillness between them.

"I must make it up to him," said Martha.

"How?"

"How? What a question. I haven't thought about it."

"I ask because my wives were always threatening to make it up to me for something atrocious they'd done."

"Didn't they ever do it?"

"Sometimes they would get me all involved in a project I had no interest in, such as a family picnic with some brothers and sisters of theirs. That's as close as they ever got to it, as I remember."

"You were poor at picking wives, I should say."

"I must exempt Thelma from this condemnation." Bryan entered. "You remember Thelma, Bryan?"

"We met her only once. What about her?"

"I was just extoling one of her many virtues to Martha. She could choose with consummate tact precisely what would please me."

"It's a pity she died. No one else can."

The conversation came to a brief pause, which was filled with the whicker of blades.

"That was unnecessary of me," said Bryan.

"Worse than that," said Martha.

"Well, well," said Gordon. "Perhaps the air is clearer now."

"Tell me," said Bryan, "what sort of person was Thelma? I'd the impression she flowed with kindness rather than love."

"True. If we bore each other any love it was of a very pacific variety. She combined all the virtues of a nurse and a mistress, and I, I flatter myself, the best qualities of a patient and lover."

"But you are never sick," Martha exclaimed.

"Exactly. I was never sick. What better attribute can a patient have? And I was usually not around, which is a primary virtue in any lover."

"You talk of her so coolly," she said, "and here she's been dead only a few months. You really didn't love her, did you?"

"Pacifically. But the dead are so dead."

"I'm sleepy," said Bryan.

"Perhaps," said Martha, "we ought to clear up this misunderstanding about Justin and Charlene before Gordon goes to bed."

"There is no misunderstanding," said Bryan to her. "He knew what he was doing."

"I envy you two the openness of your warfare," said Gordon.

"Surely, Father, we could learn from you some of the subtleties of marital discord."

"Not at all, not at all. I was always, nearly always, courteous to my wives, but I used to murder them on an average of three times a month. That is not subtle."

"No," said Bryan.

"You mean," said Martha sharply, "in fancy."

"Well, there is a distinction," said Gordon, "though not, I am told, in the eyes of God."

"Bryan, you never had such an impulse, did you?" his wife asked.

"My dear, only the laws of the land have kept you from being an angel lo these many years."

"Motts," she said to her darning.

"You make it sound like an ugly little epithet," said Bryan.

"It was so intended."

"Your mother, Bryan, used to say Motts somewhat like that, only with heavier scorn. Maureen was cruder than you," he said, addressing himself to Martha, "but a fine, high-spirited creature of the purest blood."

"I am not unacquainted with her," said Martha coolly.

"Ah, so you are, so you are. I find it difficult to remember that what is so totally past to me may have a living present of its own."

"Try it all the same."

"I will, will indeed. And how is she now?"

"Mother seems contented enough with the man she lives with. Her second husband died a few years ago, you know."

"No, I didn't. Where is she living, Bryan?"

"Up in the Mother Lode country, in a little town named Poulterville."

"Tell me, does she still have, well, a physical life?"

"It was not ectoplasm that threw its arms about me last fall and called me her sweetest mistake."

"That last," said Martha, "was gratuitous of you."

"Oh," said Gordon, "that is exactly what he is. But what I meant by physical was—sexual."

"I am sure, Father——"

"No," said Martha, "she does not."

"It was perhaps indelicate of me to ask," said Gordon with a sigh.

"To ask me, yes," said Bryan.

"Well, well, no harm done."

"What's the matter?" asked Martha. "Past not past enough?"

"Oh it's dead now, but it kicked so when it was alive. She's not poor?"

"Not particularly. Tell me, what did you mean, I am a mistake?"

"Not what our low leer implies, Son."

"Crude for a Mott," said Martha to Bryan, who was chagrined.

"Well, what did she mean and what do you mean?"

"I meant, Maureen is, or was then, one of those who believe that the beautiful sentiment precedes the beautiful itch. With me her passion was handsome indeed, and by reverse logic she deduced that she must have loved me too. You were born before she discovered she didn't. The troubles we had while she was finding it out."

"So. I am the fruit of lust and hate."

"No!" cried Martha.

"Indeed not," said Gordon lightly. "Our desire was very great and very satisfied, and we were fond of each other. But the fondness she felt for me, when she came actually to look at it, seemed a pea beside the melon she had expected. A rather dry, yellowish pea at that."

"She does not speak of you bitterly," said Martha.

"I'm glad of that. A little regret perhaps?"

"Perhaps."

"I wish, Gordon, that you had not told me this in front of Martha."

"Husband and wife should have no secret one from the other," said his father.

"Huh," said Bryan, and left the room without saying good-night.

"You must promise me, Martha, not to use this against him."

"I will not."

"Use it?"

"Promise. I view Bryan in the only way a wife can view a husband tainted with genius—simple and dangerous and not quite explainable. A slightly divine fool."

"That's a very inaccurate description of him. He may be foolish sometimes, but a fool he is not."

"No, no, I mean fool in the old sense."

"A fool in the old sense he is not. From the way you said that, I would guess that you read that about a slightly divine fool in some essay. Somebody like Chesterton, flashy and wrong most of the time."

"I did not!" she cried with great vigor because what he had said was true.

"If I were to use any such word for Bryan, I would say he was artless. And I wouldn't trust his artlessness very far either."

"Artless." She was still rallying.

"Yes. He assumes that everyone is going to like him, which is artless enough. Of course you know him better than I."

"Well, whatever you call it, I don't know what I would do if I couldn't laugh at him once in a while."

"Yet you seem fond of him."

"Yet!" She stopped putting her darning away to glare at him a moment.

"Well, well, my dear. It seems you will stay married a while yet."

"Of which I am thankful and proud."

"But the time will come, my dear—I hope unfaithfulness is not one of your bugbears."

"We move faster nowadays," she said. "But then, I am not so indiscreet as you." And she left him these shards of meaning to piece together if he would. At most, he discovered, they would not construct a whole sense.

By the time Martha had seen that the children were tucked in and had turned out the hall light, Bryan was in bed with his face to the wall.

"Darling," she said affectionately as she took off her stockings.

He rolled over and looked at her.

"I'm terribly sorry I hurt your feelings."

"Echch," he said like a cat whose tail has been stepped on, and rolled back.

"Oh dear, now I've done it again."

She undressed in silence; as she began her nightly toilet she said in a musing tone, "Gordon seems to have an effect on both of us." At which Bryan began a grunt that became a roar, and she said no more.

She got into bed, and patted his arm and kissed the back of his neck; he did not respond. When she turned over to sleep, she pressed her bottom to his; she wriggled it once in a friendly way, and then again. The third time she did it he rolled over and hugged her and bit her ear rather hard; she said nothing, but turned her face to him. He kissed her, and very soon went to sleep, with his arm over her body and her scent in his nostrils, most comfortably.

"My dear," said Gordon as Charlene brought tea in to the three men, "marriage and maternity are turning you into a beautiful woman."

"Thank you," she said, not blushing. "How do you take your tea, Father?"

"Medium strong and, I hope, straight. What kind is it?"

"Oolong with a little Darjeeling."

"Perfect. You could not have pleased me more."

This time she did blush a little.

"Why do you wear that frock?" Gordon continued. "It's false-naïve, for you, my dear."

"Why, it's sort of gay and young. Justin thought it set my figure off well. Didn't you, honey?"

"I like it," Justin said.

Charlene, without asking him, put two spoonfuls of sugar in Bryan's cup of tea, and passed it to him with a knowing smile. He did not reach out for it.

"Charlene," he said mournfully, "it's Roscoe that likes sugar. I take lemon."

"Oh!" she said, with dismay but not much of it. "Really, Bryan, it's the only way I ever get you mixed up with Roscoe."

"It means something," said Bryan, shaking his head. "I don't know what, but it must mean something. A dove was seen to fall lifeless before the statue of Mars yesterday. Signs of an evil age."

"Oh, Bryan baby," she said, hugging his head and winking at Gordon over it, "I'll never do it again, I promise. Forgive me?"

"This once," he said with more lightness in his voice than in his eyes.

"You are too beautiful," said Gordon, "to hug your male relative."

"That for you," she said, snapping her fingers under his nose. "Cream and sugar, honey?"

"Please," said Justin. "I'm going to bring Michael in."

"Oh, honey, not while we're having tea—please not."

"In his playpen, Sharly?"

"Oh, that's all right." She turned to Gordon. "The other day he looked so wise and solemn for a minute, Father, just like you. I'm so glad you're getting to know him now when he's still nothing but pure candy."

"Wise," said Gordon reflectively. "Wise. That's it, Charlene. In another five or six years your figure will be mature and your face will be wiser. What a pity that all the bloom will be rubbed off by then. It's impossible to be pretty and wise at once, and wise is better."

"I would say," said Bryan, "that your present loveliness, Charlene, is its own reward. I do not need to wait five years to love you dearly."

"I would say," said Justin, bearing Michael; he was cut off by a biff on the nose with a pan. "I would say," he recommenced a little truculently, "that she's mine to love now and she'll be mine to love five years from now and I hope she'll be mine to love fifty years from now when she's wrinkled and cranky."

Charlene beamed at his sentiment and smiled at the crudeness of its expression and ran over to hug Michael, who biffed her too. It was a good noisy pan.

"Pure candy, eh, Charlene?" said Bryan as diversionary. Being a poet, he could not easily separate a sentiment from its expression; indeed it went against his grain even to try; besides, this particular sentiment at this particular time annoyed him.

"Well," she said, nursing her bruise, "after all you expect little boys to be rough."

"Certainly," said Justin as he swung Michael by the feet in a great arc. "If they're not rough enough you make them rough. Rough and tough."

He hurled Michael through the air onto the davenport; for a moment the baby's eyes were huge and scared, but then they crinkled and he squealed with pleasure, demanding more.

"Very well, Justin," said Gordon, "you have now displayed yourself as a he-man with mate and male young. That, however——"

"And," said Justin loudly; he was irked at the ringing din of these pellets on his armor, "and more coming."

"Really, my dear?" said Gordon to Charlene.

"Oh, Justin," she said, reddening.

"How soon, Sharly?" said Bryan, though that name for her was Justin's special right.

"It may just be a false alarm," she said. "Seven months."

"No false alarm," said Justin. "Three boys and a girl, that's what we're going to have."

He was putting Michael through some more calisthenics of an inuring sort. His face was stern, his motions were bold, and his hands on the baby were firm and gentle as any healer's—though he would not have agreed to this had he been asked.

"All that," said Gordon, "has nothing to do with Charlene's

beauty. Which, as I said, is the sort that improves with age, acquaintance, and experience."

"Is that so?" said Justin where Oh? would have been enough.

"I think it is."

"I mean, you're only talking about the sort of beauty that hasn't got anything to do with love, just admiration. What really counts is the beauty seen with loving eyes. That hasn't got anything to do with wrinkles and bloom and all that."

"But I see her," said Bryan, "with the eyes of love. And though I love her dearly, I love her none the less for being young and beautiful."

"As long as you put that 'dearly' on," said Justin as he turned to Michael, finished with this conversation.

"I am fortunate in my daughter-in-law. I wonder if my son deserves her."

"Of course he does," said Charlene, who was pouring tea where none was wanted.

"Do you not find this conversation flattering?" asked Gordon.

"Yes. Flattering."

"*Touché*," said Bryan to his father.

"*Touché*."

"You are going to stay a week apiece with all three of us?" said Charlene.

"Why," said Gordon, taken aback a little, "that was my intention."

"You're going to settle down for the rest of your life among your sons."

"Yes," he said, "I had planned to."

"Do you know where you're going to stay?" she asked, and everyone was silent in the pause before Gordon answered.

"No, not yet," he said, and went over to Michael, showing for the first time his age in his gait and posture. "I have not decided yet, nor have any of you." He advanced a great tickling finger at Michael, who bit it. He settled down to winning Michael over. "My dear," he said to Charlene, though in a soft voice for Michael's benefit, "you have done what I had not intended to have done. How could you state so surely what my intentions were?"

"It's a knack," she said. "It hasn't got anything to do with anything. I knew it when you wrote those two letters, to Bryan and us."

"Really. I had not expected that result."

"Yes. I knew that was what you were saying. You're really very shy."

At which there was braying laughter from his two sons.

"He is too," said Charlene sharply to Bryan, in whom she com-
batted, as she often did, such Mottishness as she could least abide.

"He's usually thought of as something of a wolf with women, you
know," said Bryan.

"Oh, that," she said. "Anybody can be a wolf that wants to be."

"A shy wolf," said Bryan.

"If you don't know what that means, you're not much of a poet."

"Oh I know what it means," said Bryan, who wanted her to think
of him as indeed much of a poet. "I'm just wondering if it applies."

"Certainly it does. Take my word for it."

At eight o'clock Michael fell over the side of his crib onto the floor
and howled about it. All three adults came flapping and clucking in,
and the day was begun.

By the time Justin had shaved, breakfasted and left for work,
Michael had forgotten about his mishap, and Charlene was beginning
to agree that he was probably not maimed for life.

As they were sitting over coffee, she said to Gordon, "But he never
did it before."

"I gather as much, my dear," said Gordon. "He begins to cease to
be a baby, to become a kid. But then, it's a gradual process and he's
been a baby long enough."

"Not for me, he hasn't."

"He thinks so."

"How do you know what he thinks?"

"Cuddle him and find out for yourself."

She tried to cuddle him, but he stiffened and yelled. Finally she
released him onto the floor. He immediately ran to the sink-board and
grabbed a paring knife, which Charlene took from him, and then into
the front room where he began banging on the piano.

"Well," she said to Gordon, "even if you're right you oughtn't to
be so happy about it."

"Don't you want him to grow up?"

"Of course!"

"How?"

"Oh heavens, Father, you push me so."

"How?"

"Just the way everybody does, I guess. Not really." She glared at
him.

"As he needs you less, you love him less."

"No!"

He paid no attention to her cry.

"That's the ideal form of a nasty necessity."

"Oh, Father, nasty?"

"Its nastiness is clear enough when the roles are inverted, as they are with me."

"How could you say such a thing?" she said. On her way around the table to hug him it occurred to her how he might say such a thing, and she added, "To me."

"Well," he said into her right clavicle, "I do not deny that there are saints. Let St. Charlene increase the mundane calendar."

"Don't say such things," she said as she returned to her place. "It isn't safe. You don't know what might be listening."

"No, you don't," he replied, repressing a rejoinder concerning *hubris* on Redwood Road.

There was a demolishing interruption from Michael; then dishes to wash and beds to make and lunch to prepare; and after lunch while Michael napped, conversation in the patio sunbathing.

"Would you mind, Father," Charlene said in that tone with which one customarily approaches a tender subject, "telling me something that I have never been able to make out from what Justin has said?"

"I would not, though I do not know what it is."

"It's about Justin's mother," she said, looking at his sun-glasses through her sun-glasses.

"Ah, Diana," he said smiling. "You know her?"

"Hardly at all. She's lived in Omaha ever since I knew Justin. I just went back to visit her with him one summer."

"What did you think of her?"

"Oh, she's a splendid person. So handsome and dignified and very intelligent. I think she thought I was too flighty for Justin."

"Very likely she did."

"I can't say how much I admire her. Still, I'm just as glad it's you that's here, and not her. She is, maybe, just a little cool."

"Oh, just a little."

"I don't want to be unfair to her, and I'm sure she is splendid in her position—it's a fine orphanage, you know, one of the very best in the country, they say, it's all her doing—still, you know."

"Oh, I know indeed."

"I don't mean it that way."

He did not respond.

"What I wondered is . . . You see, Justin sort of resents you, what you and his mother did, he blames you sort of, though he won't say why and she never mentioned it, and I wondered if you'd tell me what went wrong."

"She didn't die soon enough."

"Father!"

She sat up and took off her glasses.

"That is not true and it is not funny. Never say such a thing again."

"You asked me. I told you."

"Why do you make it so hard for people to love you? What do you mean by such a thing?"

The expression of hurt appeared on his face, but she ignored it.

"Explain yourself."

"I meant that she did not die in my heart soon enough."

"Go on."

"She was the only woman whom I ever both loved and hated at the same time. If I had just hated her I could have left her decently, as I did for another reason Bryan's mother. But I could not leave her. Her coldness and air of superiority infuriated me. She seemed to condescend to me. She made love as a favor. So I hurt her as badly as I could, though I thought at the time I was moved by passion: I was unfaithful to her with her sister. I believe I have never done anything more reprehensible. Does that satisfy you?"

"Oh, that last was not kind. But why did you ever love her?"

"She was handsome and very intelligent and not always so cold. The coldness grew with time. And I had just been having more sensuality than was good for me, in Bryan's mother."

"How you must have hurt her."

"We need not talk about it," he said lightly.

"Oh, but we must. Why did you have to do it?"

"We really need not," he repeated, so that she lay back down again.

Presently she said, "Then you married Thelma?"

"Then I married Thelma. She was a saint of sorts too. I had hoped we might reside in Oakland as we were dying. You would have liked her."

"I am sure I would."

"And it is not nothing to administer an orphanage well."

"Of course not. It's a wonderful thing to do."

"Well," he said, arising, "a not entirely unhappy ending. I am too hot."

He looked down at her smooth round golden body for a moment. Partly he was sorry that his own was so pale and gnarled, for in earlier years he would not have restrained his desire for her because she was Justin's wife; but partly at this moment he was glad that it was so old, for he was kept by its age from making her unhappy, as he was sure he would once have done. He took himself into the house and set himself to thinking about electrons and their ways.

"Henry!" Edwa called up the stairs. "Come on down, Henry. Father Mott is here."

Gordon, in the living room, winced.

"Must she refer to me so? I am neither a priest nor a jolly old fellow with goodies in my bulging pockets."

"It's a custom," said Bryan, "like many another brought to us from the teeming middle plains of the nation."

"Let it teem in Nebrasky," said Gordon. "Here English is spoken. Roscoe, this is within your jurisdiction. See to it."

Roscoe, who was of the same height as his father, looked at him as though he were a good half-head taller; he managed this by holding himself very erect, tilting his face back a little, and looking down his bill like an ostrich.

"What would you prefer she call you to the children? Their other grandfather, you know, is often here."

"I don't know. Gordon, Grampa Gordon. Mott is not a name to be rolled on the tongue."

"Henry!" she called again. There was a trampling upstairs. "Come down now."

She joined the men.

"He's always going out in the evenings," she said apologetically. "There doesn't seem to be enough to hold the young people at home these days. But I made him promise," she said, patting Gordon on the arm, "to spend a lot of time with his Father Mott before he leaves. He'll be with you all this evening, I know."

Gordon gave her a look (which was the only point of appearance that Justin shared with him) of pure direct calculating distaste. This he achieved by making his face blank as a sheep's and looking square-on at the object of his distaste.

"I'm sure we will both benefit by it," he said.

She saw that he was displeased with something; but, being conscious of no malice or error in her behavior, she thought he was bilious and was sorry for him.

Henry entered, being large, dark of mane, and marked by acne. He was eighteen. He had had a date.

"Hello," he said to no one in particular.

"Well, Henry," said Gordon, "it is planned that you sit at my feet in a sort of diffused discipleship, and become wiser by a week."

Henry looked up from under his eyebrows at his grandfather, suspicious and buffalo-like. An extraordinary distance separated his eyes, and they glowed with hostility.

"Huh," he said. "It is, is it?"

"He plans to be in law," said Edwa, putting her arm about him. "Harvard Law School."

"What sort of law, Henry?" asked Gordon.

"I don't know," said Henry. "Any kind, I guess."

"Patent attorneys make a lot of money."

"I guess so."

"Oh, I know it."

Henry had nothing more to say.

"Edwa," said Bryan, "may I get the stuff that Martha phoned about? She wanted to give it to Aylmer before suppertime?"

"Is Aylmer sick?" asked Roscoe down to Bryan.

"Same thing that Clyde and Mary had." He turned to Henry. "And don't forget, nephew, there's always real estate."

"Well, well," said Roscoe. "Let the boy make up his own mind."

"Yes, let him," said Gordon as though agreeing to some other proposition.

Bryan and Edwa left for the medicine chest. When he presently returned to the room where Roscoe, Gordon and Henry were still stiffly standing, Bryan heard a phrase that stopped him for a moment: "Law's at the very bottom of what we have, of course." A sort of film, like a chicken's second eyelid, only not physical, covered his eyes; this happened when he was thinking in a special way or when he was hurt or when he was very despondent; it let him know what was happening in the world without having to feel about it.

"Well," said Roscoe to him, "we'll see you a week from Saturday at the latest."

And for a considerable moment (the sheep, the ostrich and the buffalo staring at the chicken eyes) Bryan considered what it was that

law could be at the bottom of. But then they all four shook themselves, and he said, "A week from Saturday?"

"Yes, Henry's farewell dinner."

"You're leaving so soon?" asked Bryan.

"August tenth," said Henry, to whom it seemed none too soon.
"I'm going to spend two or three weeks with some aunts in New York
before I go on to Harvard."

"Two of Edwa's sisters. They are in import," said Roscoe.

"Well," said Bryan, "fine."

"Fine," said Gordon.

"Hrmph," said Roscoe down his beak.

"Yeh," said Henry.

"Well, good-bye," said Bryan. "I'll see you before long."

Gordon followed him, to get a briefcase he had left in Bryan's car.
Bryan had transported him over from Justin's this afternoon for his
week with Roscoe.

"My God," he said to Bryan, "a whole evening unarmed amongst
them."

"A whole week," said Bryan. "There's always *Time*. They take it."

"You abandon me, then?"

"Ah, my dear Father, hope is deciduous."

"I see you for the first time."

"And me without a tie on. Farewell, Father Henry-at-the-feet Mott.
May quiring angels guard thee."

"Unnatural child."

When Gordon went back into the house, he was greeted by Edwa
and the four smaller children. They were all scrubbed and lined up
and awkward for the occasion. Everyone, including Gordon, knew
what to say, and said it.

"Grampa Gordon," said Clyde sturdily, after this Midwestern ceremony was over. "I know how to tie a bowline."

"Oh, Clyde," said Ann, who was impressed less by Gordon than the
other children were, "don't bother him with little-kid stuff."

"Well," said Clyde, who was the most impressed, "I can."

Gordon, who shared Ann's views on bowlines, but after all was a
grandfather, said in a kindly voice that he would like to see Clyde tie
one; as he walked out with Clyde and John he winked and shrugged
at Ann in a knowing way, as though she were another adult.

"Ann," said Mary when they were alone, "why did he wink at
you?"

"Well," said Ann, who was not quite sure, "that's something you'll understand when you grow up."

"You're so grown up."

"Pretty much," said Ann. "Sometimes I feel a lot more grown up than you'd even understand."

"Huh," said Mary. "I suppose that's why you played see-saw with us today?"

Ann thumbed her nose at Mary, and ran out of the room. Nose-thumbing was something for which Mary could tattle on Ann, but, seeing nothing to be gained by it, she decided to go watch the bow-line-tying instead.

Dinner was roast beef, broccoli and mashed potatoes, cole slaw, bread and jam, and a choice of berry or custard pie. It was all very good, and Gordon ate far beyond his capacity; indeed, he was not allowed not to.

"Now, Father Mott," said Edwa as she served the pie, "we have a plan for every day this week. Sunday we're going to take a ride over to Marin County, to the redwood grove."

"Can we all go?" said Clyde, who knew they all could not.

"Count me out," said Henry. "I've got a date."

"Perhaps," said Edwa to Clyde. "Don't worry, dear. Drink your milk. Monday we're going to have a picnic in Tilden Park. A real picnic."

"Can we ride the merry-go-round?" said Ann.

"Of course. We hope Daddy will be able to go with us."

"Grampa Gordon," said John, who was already bored by the calendar of coming events, "are you going to live with us?"

Gordon expected a dead silence after this question, or a sharp reprimand. Instead Edwa spoke in her usual tone.

"I don't think Father Mott knows yet where he's going to settle down, John. He knows that he's welcome to stay with us as long as he wishes, but I think we should let him make up his own mind before we ask him."

She was the first one in Oakland, indeed the first one anywhere, to say these words to Gordon; he found he could tolerate even "Father Mott" from her in such a speech.

She finished the seven days.

"And there's one thing more important than all the rest, Henry's good-bye dinner. You can't disappoint us, Father. You will be here for it, won't you?"

"If it is at all possible," said Gordon. He knew, he resolved, that it would be quite impossible, but he could not find it in his heart to tell her so now.

Roscoe asked him if he wanted some more coffee, and Gordon looked at him in amazement. He had been more conscious of silent, watching Mary than of Roscoe. He was going to say something elaborate to Roscoe about being an absentee host, but the thought of translating it into Roscoe's language oppressed him. Instead, he went into the living room and sat in a very comfortable chair which Edwa said was now sacred to him.

To him there the smaller children came for jokes and advice and to say good-night. Roscoe had a headache and went to his room early. Edwa stayed with Gordon and Henry for a while listening to their logy conversation. She was spurred by it to relate much more entertaining experiences of her own; by ten she too went off to bed. The moment she was gone Henry excused himself and went rushing off into the adolescent night somewhere. Gordon found a copy of *Time* he hadn't read before, and looked at it; but it wasn't annoying enough to keep him awake. By eleven o'clock, against the habit of years, he was in bed and asleep.

3

"Henry," said Bryan, "this is the last time you will think of us as your uncles and aunts, your dad and mom. When the Harvard tenants have moved into your head, we will have acquired first names in your mind and we will seem annoying heirlooms you can't decently chuck out. Is it not sad, Rosalee?"

The pink and blue at Henry's side giggled.

"Bryan," said Roscoe, who liked Rosalee, "will you pass the yams? . . . My dear, this is the best ham I have ever eaten."

"Thank you," said Edwa. "Henry went clear to the city to get the ham and up to Berkeley to get the cake. My little boy," she said, squeezing his forearm beside her, to his annoyance.

"Henry," said Justin, who was feeling more than seven years older than his nephew, "I never went to college."

"My goodness," said Charlene, "he knows you never went to college. Why say it?"

"What I meant was, Henry, I envy you this opportunity I never took."

"Why?" said Martha, who was suddenly seized with the urge to bring him down.

"Why?" said Justin. "Everybody should have a college education."

"Can't you manage your factory without one?" she asked.

"Yes, but think of everything I'm missing."

"I doubt," she said, "whether a Ph.D. itself would enable you to see what you don't already see, Justin."

He did not know what she had done to him, but he knew that she had done something.

"It's just an advantage," he said, "and I'm glad you're getting it, Henry. Michael is going to Harvard if I have to do his homework myself to get him good grades in high school."

"Justin," said Charlene, "reads Great Books, like Aristotle."

"Is there anything wrong with that?" he demanded in a belligerent, if cracked, voice.

No one answered; he shrank into silence, so sitting a bird that not even Martha had the heart to shoot again.

"I did hope Father Mott could be here tonight," said Edwa. "Henry had so little chance to benefit from being with him. Such a rare opportunity," she said, beaming at Henry.

"Oh, Mother," he said in a sort of pastel agony.

"Henry," whispered Rosalee, leaning against him, "be nice to her. She loves you so much."

He growled.

"You were able to be with Father Mott a good deal these past days, weren't you, dear?"

"Yes, Mother," said Henry, who viewed it as a sort of being hobbled in barren pastures.

"I'm sure you benefited greatly from knowing him."

"Yes, Mother," said Henry for Rosalee's sake, for he had not.

"We should all be thankful to have known him," said Charlene.

"Oh, we are still going to know him," said Martha. "For years and years, I have no doubt."

"Father Mott does have the best of health."

"Well, I know," said Justin in a voice so loud that everyone looked at him, "where he's *not* going to live from now on."

There was a short silence, which each of the three women felt she must smooth over for Rosalee's sake.

"Honey," said Charlene, "you mustn't be so aggressive about it. We don't know."

"That's something for another time," said Edwa.

"Sometimes," said Justin, "I don't even feel like he was my father." This was Roscoe's province.

"Justin," he said, "we will not talk about that at the table."

"How could *he* be *my* father?"

"That will be enough, Justin," said Roscoe in a very loud voice.

Henry held his breath. It seemed to Henry that he could not possibly be a true member of this family but that God had put him among these exquisite clowns to test him. The day was coming when his true rank should be revealed.

As soon as the silence had relaxed a little, he spoke.

"Mom, when are we going to have dessert? Rosalee and I have to get going."

"Time to clear the table for dessert," said Edwa. "Everybody's ready?"

"I'll go lie down in the living room," said Bryan, "while you all gorge."

It was lonesome in the living room, but he stayed till they were through.

As Rosalee and Henry were in the hallway preparing to go, she said to him in one of those whispers that are like the sound of a bugle at dawn: "You sure have the craziest family. How do you *stand* them?" Edwa, who heard it, was cut to the quick; but Roscoe, to whose ears also the sound reached, heard it not. The others thought less of Rosalee than they had, and all the adults went into the living room logily.

"The children will be all right, dear?" said Roscoe.

"Ann and John are very good with them today," said Edwa.

"Can we hear Michael if he wakes up?" said Justin.

"I just took a peek at him, honey. He's sound asleep."

"Well," said Bryan, who was sprawled on the couch, "here we are. The last time we were assembled we had Gordon hanging over our heads."

"And now," said Martha, "we have him hanging around our necks."

"Martha!" said Charlene. "That's no way to talk."

"Why, Martha," said Edwa, "you told me you didn't find him such a terrible burden."

"Not for a week, maybe, but what about for the rest of his life?"

"He's mighty damned healthy," said Justin.

"Honey!" said Charlene. "He's your father."

"How do I know? Only my mother knows whether that's true and she never said."

"Justin!" she said. "That's unforgivable of you."

"He'll never live in my house," said Justin.

"Oh no?"

"No."

"The point is," said Bryan languidly, "he'll live with whomever he wants to live with. We have nothing to say about it."

And for putting that unpleasant doubt into words he was rewarded by having everyone turn against him.

"That," said Roscoe, "is scarcely true."

"He certainly can't live with us if we don't want him to," said Charlene.

"Say," said Justin, "whose side are you on anyway?"

"I'm not on your side," she said furiously. "I'm just against Bryan. And furthermore——"

"And furthermore," said Bryan, "your slip shows. Quit talking so much."

"You can't insult me!" she cried. "Justin!"

"Bah," said Justin.

"Are you trying to see," said Martha to Bryan, "just how mad you can get everybody?"

"I am sure," said Edwa, "that Father Mott will decide for himself where he is going to live. I know that he's welcome to live with any of us ('Oh yeh,' said Justin), but perhaps he might be encouraged to go live with Bryan as he ought."

"What!" cried Martha.

"Oh, I see," said Bryan sitting up.

"Great," said Justin. "He lives off the old man anyhow."

"I see, I see," said Bryan.

"You do have plenty of room," said Edwa. "Bryan doesn't work. He could help Martha."

"If you think writing isn't work——"

"Shut up," said Martha. "Now, look here, Edwa, we're not taking him in just like that. I can't stand the old goat any more than anyone else can."

"Whose side are you on?" said Bryan.

"I'm on my own side," she said; "don't bother me."

Justin roared with laughter, and Charlene scowled at him.

"I'm the only one who loves him," she said.

"That's all right," shouted Justin. "I hate him enough for two. Bryan gets Gordon."

Bryan strode over to him.

"For two bits I'd knock your block off."

Justin fished a quarter out of his pocket.

"Here you are, Blowhard. Let's see whose block gets knocked off."

Edwa and Roscoe separated them.

"Come, now," said Roscoe. "When Gordon comes back from his vacation we'll talk to him about it. We won't make any decisions now."

"Oh, the decision is made," said Justin. "Bryan gets him."

"Oh, I do, do I? That for you, brother."

"You live off the old man. You can earn your keep for a change."

"Damn you. Who gave you a factory to manage? Who gave Roscoe a house and a fistful of shares in American Lite? What do you fatheads do with it?"

"Come on," said Martha, "Gordon will make up his own mind. You know that. Calm down."

"Justin," said Charlene, "if you don't quit insulting everybody I'll take Michael and go off to Mother's."

"Edwa," said Roscoe, "it was very ill-chosen of you to say that just then."

"Well, please, let's not disturb the children," said Edwa, who fancied she had heard scufflings on the stairs. She had.

"What did I ever do to get mixed up with a family like this?" said Justin. "Why don't you go to Greenwich Village with the other longhairs?" he said to Bryan.

"By God," said Bryan, "come outside and I'll show you who's the man around here. If you're not chicken, that is."

"Chicken!" said Justin. "Against you? I'd be afraid of hurting you."

Charlene ran out in tears, and presently Michael began wailing. Justin left to follow her.

Martha walked, stiff-legged with fury, up to get Roxana and Aylmer. She found all six children sitting in the girls' room completely silent.

"Come on," she said with as much naturalness as she could summon. "We're going home now."

"Is anything the matter, Mommy?" said Roxana.

"You know there is," said Martha. "Don't ask foolish questions."

Edwa came in and quietly told her children to get ready for bed. With no objections, even ritualistic ones, they did as she bade.

"Aunt Edwa," said Alymer, "we had a very good time."

"The ham was delicious," said Roxana.

"I'm glad you liked it," said Edwa.

"Come on," said Martha crossly, and dragged them out.

"What's the matter?" said Roxana. "Don't you want us to be polite?"

"It's the wrong time," said Martha.

Justin and Charlene with Michael in her arms came out of the guest room and went straight out to their car without a word for anyone, even to Aylmer, who said good-night.

"They weren't kind," said Aylmer.

"It's never the right time to be unkind," said Roxana. "Is it, Mommy?"

"No, no," said Martha, her voice full of both remorse and vexation, "never."

The children bid Roscoe a long and very polite good-night, with Bryan snapping at them to hurry up, and they went home.

Roscoe found Edwa preparing for bed.

"Edwa," he called from the bathroom, "where are the aspirin?"

"They might be on your night-stand."

"Yes. There are only two left."

"Isn't that enough?"

"I doubt it tonight."

"Well, they'll have to be."

"Are the children in bed?"

"Yes," she replied.

"I hope they didn't hear any of that disgraceful ruckus."

"I'm sure they did not. I don't think I'll bring the subject up with them. What do you think?"

"Of course not," he said. "Bryan was unforgivable."

"Well, you can hardly blame him."

She was in bed settling herself.

"Well, he had to know sooner or later," he said.

"Roscoe," she said with a last flurry of feeling, "we're losing our first baby. Do you realize that?"

"Hrmph," he said; he did not think of Henry as his first baby and felt vaguely deficient as a father that he did not.

Bryan dropped his book and looked attentively at Martha.

"That's Gordon coming up the front steps," he said.

She dropped her darning.

"Are you sure?"

"I can tell by his tread."

"Now, darling," she said with alarm in her voice, "you must be firm. But do be polite."

"Oh yes," said Gordon, who had opened the door without having knocked, "oh gracious yes, do be polite."

"Gordon!" exclaimed Martha, standing up.

"Who else?"

"Why, I thought it might have been Justin."

"Justin? Come, my dear Martha, since when has Justin taken to dropping in on you in the evenings?"

"I hoped he had come to apologize for something he said to Bryan."

"Well, Gordon," said Bryan, taking his coat.

"Mommy," came Roxana's voice from upstairs. "Who is it, Mommy?"

"Not asleep yet," said Martha.

"I have a couple of bags that the taxi-driver left down at the foot of the stairs, Bryan." Bryan went for them. "Let me go kiss the children good-night, Martha."

"Very well. I did not realize you liked them that well."

"Nor did I, my dear, until I spent a week at Tahoe in a guest hotel with none but elderly, respectable people."

"Can we come see him, Mommy?" called Aylmer.

"I'm coming right up, children," he said. "I have discovered that I am more attached to my grandchildren than I had thought possible. One is so conscious of the irritations at the time one is with them, but afterwards that heaven of grandfathers, love without responsibility, is all that is left."

He bade them good-night; Bryan put the suitcases in the guest room; Martha discovered that he had had his dinner at a restaurant; and they settled down in front of the empty fireplace.

"And what," said Gordon, bending forward and rubbing his hands as though there had been a blazing fire to warm them before, "what did Justin do that you should imagine he would come to apologize for it?"

"Well," said Bryan, "at Henry's farewell dinner we had a pretty terrific argument. He insulted me."

"Why?"

Martha looked distressed. Bryan gazed at her without expression for a moment before he answered.

"Well," said Bryan, "jealousy, I think. I had made rather a pass at Charlene before dinner."

"Oh," said Martha, looking greatly relieved, "he never knew about it."

"Maybe not with the top of his head," said Bryan, "but I think he knew it someplace else."

"I hope that will teach you to lay off Charlene after this."

"Oh, Martha," he said, "what's the good of a family dinner if I can't even kiss my pretty sister-in-law? Do you want me to read *Time* till dinner is served?"

"What frivolity," said Gordon. "Indeed, I might go so far as to say, how jejune."

"He sounds worse than he is," said Martha. "At least, worse than he is most of the time."

"The scoundrel's fallacy, that charm forgives all."

"Tell me, Gordon," said Bryan, "did you have a pleasant time at Tahoe?"

"What a paltry hypocrite. If you want me to believe such a question, you've got to put a little conviction in it."

"Did you?"

"The weather and the scenery are, as you know, superb. This dispute with Justin the night of the dinner—was my name not brought up during the argument?"

"Yes."

"And with no excess of love, I dare say."

"No excess."

"Did you come to blows, or stop at words?"

"Everyone conspired to keep us from actually fighting. I wish we had though, even if he'd beat me up a little. The satisfaction of landing one in the middle of that soulless face is something I cannot forego forever."

"And Roscoe, what role did he play?"

"Oh my heavens," said Martha, "quit beating about the bush. They were arguing about where you are going to live."

Her face was very strained as she said this.

"Well," said Gordon, "you did prick my little balloon of circumlocution very neatly."

"No circumlocution," she said, "but an elaborate system for making us uneasy."

"That was not my intention."

"Perhaps. It was your accomplishment."

"I don't think," said Gordon, "that I'll go to live with Justin."

"No," said Bryan, "neither does he. He in fact sometimes doubts that you are his father."

"A convenient doubt for one in his frame of mind, but not a probable one."

"He does seem to have more mother than father in him," said Bryan.

"Yes, to his hurt. Well, but Charlene is a most attractive woman. You, I take it, agree."

"I do. The spontaneity of her emotions is rare and winning."

"I had not thought of her that way," said Gordon. "How do you mean it?"

"I'm afraid," said Bryan, "that this is not a propitious time for me to elaborate upon that theme."

"Martha," said Gordon, "what do you think of her charms?"

"Not being the woman under discussion, but being a woman, I do not think my opinion would be unbiased."

"The power of her charm," said Gordon, "does not lessen your much subtler attraction, my dear."

"I have often been told that. I have never believed it."

"Martha," said Bryan, "believes that there is just so much admiration to go around. The more someone else gets, the less for her."

"Well," said Martha, "if there weren't so many Charlenes around, maybe more men would make passes at my subtle attractions."

"Yours," said Gordon, "are not the charms that ripen and then fade, but rather the intellectual powers that only mature with time and endure into the impotence of old age. They partake of eternity."

"Lovely," she said. "But who kisses my enduring intellect?"

"I," said Bryan.

"When I'm old and withered," she said as though he had not spoken, "I suppose I'm to sit around hoarding my few drops of eternity and look down on other women, since all they have is a thousand pleasant memories?"

"Memories," said Gordon, "are the easiest substitute for satisfaction, but they are no satisfaction. I think I can speak with more authority than you about this."

"Well, use it on someone who's more impressed with it than I am. Let's drop me as a subject."

"Sorry," said Gordon. "When I said, Bryan, that I was not going to live with Justin, I was thinking of another reason than his distaste for the idea. I fancy I could have dealt with that."

"The boredom, then?"

"Oh no, boredom can be dealt with too. I am going to continue my work wherever I settle down. There are books and concerts and pic-tures. No, I was thinking that wherever I settle I want to settle for good, and I distrust the permanence of Justin's household."

"Oh, come, Gordon," said Martha, "not everyone divorces as readily as you."

"So it would appear," he replied. "However, it seems to me that if the time ever comes when Justin opposes or escapes from Charlene's rule, she will leave him."

Neither of the others said anything. Bryan because he agreed and Martha because she did not want another argument.

"And I do not want to be left high and dry."

"That leaves you three choices," said Bryan.

"Three?"

"Yes, Roscoe, myself, or living alone."

"Ah, living alone. I thought of that once or twice, but I rapidly put it out of my mind. I even thought of marrying again, but no. I have decided to be old."

"Do you mean that?" asked Martha. "Or are you being ironical as usual?"

"I mean it. The irony is a protection from the pain of admitting it. It is not pleasant to run down, but it is even less pleasant to have to watch yourself doing it."

"Well, even wives get old," she said.

"Yes, but a grandfather is a great deal closer to heaven than a hus-band. I exist only in relation to others, so that in solitude I would blow up like a balloon and pop. I am what the resistance of others makes me. And grandchildren are like the arms of the acclaiming populace bearing the victor home."

"Stirring," said Bryan. "Well, Roscoe has four acclaimers around the house to our two."

"True, but yours are superior in quality."

And just before Martha could say what she was going to say, he forestalled her.

"I believe you know very little about Roscoe's mother."

"Very little," said Bryan. "My mother said once she thought you still loved Roscoe's mother when you married her. That was three or four years after she'd died, wasn't it?"

"Over three years. Her name was Hannah. I have never loved anyone else so much as I loved her. I often wonder whether her memory did not influence my later relations with women. She remained perfect in my mind—she was yielding yet firm like healthy young flesh, beautiful, not quite predictable, and she thought I was a god."

"She died just in time," said Martha, but when she saw the blind pain in his eyes she apologized almost tearfully for her cruelty, and left the room to make tea.

"She is very good at deflating the male ego," said Bryan.

"At least that," said Gordon, and seemed to be going to relapse into silence.

"What were you going to say about Roscoe's mother?"

"Just that the memory of her somehow is made stronger by Roscoe. Something of her lives in him; what, I could not say, nor how."

They were silent until Martha had brought the tea in.

"And furthermore," said Gordon, looking steadily at Martha, "Edwa is a great deal pleasanter to live with than you are."

The confusion of wounded feelings, and gratitude that it was not they whom he was going to live with, and shame which kept her from responding to this thrust, reduced Martha to tears. Bryan looked very uncomfortable.

"Well, we're quits," said Gordon. "I shall go to bed if you don't mind. You may take me to Roscoe's tomorrow."

"I'll make up the bed," said Martha, going out again.

"You are very unkind to those you love," said Bryan to Gordon.

"Always, when I have trouble dominating them. That's the great thing about Roscoe, I have so little trouble keeping him under. Besides he has respect for me, and respect is fear and love combined in proportions that suit my taste excellently."

"Why do you always make the better cause appear the worse?"

"It is usually the correct explanation of motive, I have found, and when it is incorrect, it is incorrect in such a gratifying way."

"Well," said Bryan, standing up, "whenever you want a good conversation you must call on us."

"That's why I came to you this evening," said Gordon. "One of the reasons. And when I want to recall my prime I will call on Charlene. You may tell Martha that she is not the least of the reasons I decided against settling down with you, nor the least of the reasons I almost did."

They went to the spare bedroom, where Martha was putting the finishing touches on the bed.

"May you both sleep well," said Gordon, meaning, You ought to sleep badly.

"Of course," said Bryan, meaning, I doubt if we will.

"It takes a lot to keep Bryan awake," said Martha, trying to mean by a brittle double-irony that a lot had happened.

"Oh?" said Gordon, and suddenly nobody knew what anybody meant any more.

Nobody knew what Martha meant by squeezing Gordon's hand very hard and running from the room, or Gordon by turning his back to Bryan, or Bryan by approaching his father, flapping his right arm twice like a broken wing, and then going after Martha.

In bed Martha said to Bryan, "Oh, darling, why was I so mean to him?"

"Well, don't worry about it. Now I can get back to work. I've lost the better part of six weeks."

"He made me be mean to him."

"No one is harder to forgive than the one who makes you behave badly."

"Is Edwa really easier to live with than I am?"

"No, of course not, my dear."

"Why does he try to be so sentimental with us? I didn't believe a word of that about Roscoe's mother, did you?"

"No, no, of course not."

"The old goat. He's so mean."

"Come, come. I love you dearly."

"You must forgive me for behaving like that," said Martha. "I'm sure he won't."

"I forgive you."

"I forgive you too. Well, I'll try to make it up to him."

Turning over, Bryan said, "Let's go to sleep now."

"I've got to do the wash in the morning," she said, and bottom to bottom, they pretended to go to sleep.

HERBERT GOLD, *who was born in 1924 in Cleveland, Ohio, writes that he was educated by Columbia College, the Army, Cornell, Columbia University Graduate School, and the Sorbonne. Since returning from a Fullbright scholarship in France, he has been night manager of a hotel, editor of an entertainment magazine, city planner, and an instructor in philosophy at Western Reserve University. He has, he says, "usually left his job in order to work at a writing project and gone back to a job, in order to feed his wife, his two innocent children, and himself." His first novel,* Birth of a Hero, *appeared in 1951; his second,* The Prospect Before Us, *will be published in the spring of 1954 by the World Publishing Company; and he is at work on a third.*

THE WITCH

FROM THE YALE REVIEW

He and his wife disagreed about the woman who left garbage outside their door. They knew who she was; they watched from a crack in the milk chute. She came tiptoeing down the hall with a stealth that was more than the price of pleasure, that was joy itself, and she hesitated with her sack of coffee grounds and orange peels, and she listened. They waited.

She had smudged black eyes, like those of silent-movie sirens found starving in hotel rooms, found dying by gas, eyes dark with the moral mascara of defeated beauty. She was a small worn woman with hennaed hair fiercely spaced by ribboned curlers against her skull. Rising daintily on tiptoe, she lifted herself into a tense arc at their door, let the bag fall with a soft *plosh*, and pirouetted off on silent feet. Those rapturous feet scurried past the milk chute from which they watched. Whatever the pleasure she felt, it was one that left her without laughter and even without a profound breathing. Married, the watchers nonetheless remembered—and looked this thought at each other—that no solitary joy can set laughter free. The celibate lives in his prison, the pleasure in one cell, the laughter far away in another, and no signal, not even a tapping, between.

"She runs like a mouse," he said.

"No, she doesn't, Dan," his wife said, "you're wrong about that. That isn't how she goes."

Then, later, perhaps back in her own apartment, she telephoned the janitor, played tricks with her voice, and told him that those filthy people on the second floor dropped refuse on the hall carpet instead of carrying it to the incinerator. Although their Mr. Wartner believed that evil was the natural product of tenancy, blaming the sinners for everything from cobwebs on the ceiling to the failure of the furnace to draw air, they were eloquent enough to convince him that the garbage at the door was not their own.

"See, it was just dumped," Dan Parsons said.

"I don't know who did it, probably some nut," the janitor querulously insisted.

"We *know* you don't know. We're just showing you." This had been the first time, before they had seen her. "Doesn't look like an accident, Mr. Wartner."

"Look, Mr. Wartner," Phyl Parsons said, "it isn't spilled at all—it's just dropped there. Deposited."

"Spitework, eh? These people. Never had any property of their own, never will. I know them. Why, they just slam the front door when they go out and then they come to me and complain. The glass is broke, they say, fix it, there's a draft——"

"We just wanted you to see, Mr. Wartner. Next time it happens, please try to recognize the voice. It must be someone in the building."

"I don't know, personally; you'd think people'd have enough sense to just let a door ride shut. What do they think the Correctulator's there for? They just slam it, bang, and they act like all I got to do all day is——"

One night they found her out through the crack in the milk chute. The solitary devotion of her advance down the hall, the ritual cockings and self-shushings of her caution, the supple perch of her skinny head, the wary head of a bird frozen in flight culminated in a single gesture as she offered up the sack, raised it high, then let it fall untended. Swiftly she was gone. Eggshells and, this time, a soupbone lay in a heap on their mat.

It might have been a simple matter to deal with her at this point.

"Confront her," he said. "Clip her like a chicken. Just pop up and say, 'Look here, Missus What's-your-name——' "

But Phyl was shaking her head. "No, you can't do that, Dan. We never did anything to her."

"Of course we didn't. What's the matter with you?"

"I mean, that's why we can't say anything to her now. We never even talked to her."

"*Talked* to her? I'll give her a conversation, by God, I'll——"

"No, no," his wife insisted. "Didn't you see her? She's crazy."

She had been as silent as the dead, not a flicker of laughter in her face, not a murmur of it to keep her stealth company down the hall toward them or to warm the flight of her feather-thin feet away. He stopped to listen to his wife, frowning, trying to fix in his memory the flow of the old woman's coming. He paused only an instant. He shook his head impatiently.

"Do I need old Wartner to tell me she's crazy? Did I have to see her to know that? Listen, it has nothing to do with it, crazy or not, when she pulls that kind of a stunt——" He stopped because his wife was not listening and because this absence of hers, this dreamy withdrawal from him, signified a disagreement which might once have been trivial but no longer was. A sufficiency unto herself in time of trouble had always frightened him and had at last drawn him to her. "I was talking to you, Phyl," he said. "I was telling you something."

"I know. I just don't want you to take off after her that way. It isn't what she does that bothers me——"

"It's what bothers me, friend." He was reassured by talk. Discussion gets things done, he always said. "It bothers me till my scalp itches, Phyl. It—— Sure, I'll take off after that crank, and when I catch her——"

"But you can't *blame* a woman like that. Wait a minute. Wait. She's just dropped her marbles, cracked, that's all"—his wife suddenly scheming, wheedling him. She had returned to him with reasons and method, and he sensed the method in her hand against him and the reasons in the coolness of it. He was too busy with himself, with the luxury of anger, to worry about her. She put her hands on his. "Dan, she must have had a miserable life."

Have it out, have it out, that's good, he was thinking. This insane thing, their being attacked and unable to meet it together, hurt them both. It was a fact. The loony could do it to them in a moment of crisis, but it was true of them every day. It troubled him.

"Jeez, Phyl, this isn't the time to start understanding the old hag. If you want to hire a psychoanalyst for her, a white-coated scientist, okay, you go find the checking account. Go read a book about it. But me, personally, all I'm interested in is getting her to keep her little dump truck to herself."

"Of course, we ought to find out *why* she's behaving aggressively toward us. I don't know why she should. I'm not sure. We've never even spoken to her——"

"You keep saying that. What does that have to do with it? We don't speak to a lot of people."

"Well, if we could figure out what's in her mind——"

"Look," he said, "let's make a contract. Look, goddammit, she's a crazy old witch, but I didn't do it to her. Garbage! Listen, don't you shake your head and pucker your lips and say to me, 'Poor lady, how neurotic——' "

"Now you wait a minute, Dan. Just think how happy she'd be if she could see you running around here like a chicken. . . . Maybe she's just lonely, no one ever speaks a word to her——"

"Okay, so she's just making conversation. Okay, you take it. That's our agreement. It's yours to settle now; I give it to you, gratis, egg-shells and all."

Sympathy was fine, so was subtlety; they were nice in a wife; but he decided that this argument had penetrated to a difficult place in Phyl, a secret life walled behind the high comprehension which comes of advanced readings in the conditioned reflex, the trauma, the complex, and the fixation. The world had gone wrong for women, he believed; they were trained, honed down, beautifully sensitized, and then confined to marriage, where they had either to forget all their pretty tricks of sympathy or gather them greedily for the distortion of simple situations like this one. Meanwhile, the calculation of her soft mouth was: I've given him his discussion, his man-to-man conference, his cards-on-the-table. Now maybe he'll be satisfied. "The poor old witch," she murmured. "Maybe we can find some tactful way. Shouldn't we try at least? At least think about it?"

"That's right, you be tactful," he said. "Just ask her in a nice way. Talk to her. Borrow her recipe. Go ahead. You handle it your way, but you clean it up if Psych 101 doesn't work." Nevertheless, having seen the woman, he could almost have admitted that his grumbling and even his anger served mostly to communicate a proper male directness. The prospect of confronting her worried him. For the moment he was content, in fact, to let his wife settle this question without his meeting it head-on. It would be the two of them, anyway. After all, the old woman couldn't hurt them. Yet he couldn't keep from asking, "What are you going to do?"

He put this question during several evenings. She answered him with a shrug or a turning away. He leaned on the question despite her stubborn will to let it go, to let it be, to let it please itself and perhaps —*Oh, please!* her look said to him and to the door—satisfy itself and vanish or diminish or pass somehow into forgetfulness. He insisted, and she said: "I don't know. Maybe I'll telephone."

"What's her name? I don't even know her name."

"How come you didn't ask? Aren't you interested?" This was an accusation. She told him, *Miss Clara Hesper.* "I've seen her at the mailbox," she explained.

"Sure I'm interested. Why do you think I asked? Who wouldn't be if he had to shovel Miss Clara Hesper's Cream of Wheat away from the door every night? *And* her coffee grounds. *And* her eggshells. Look, even if I didn't know Miss Clara Hesper's name, that's no reason for saying——"

"Take it easy, Dan. I'm not saying anything. I know you want to get it settled; it's just that . . . I'm going to call her."

He grinned and handed her the telephone directory. "Okay, go ahead, but what'll you tell her? Personally, I'd grab her right here and sound off."

She ran her finger down the page, then shut the book. "Doesn't have a telephone. Must have phoned Wartner from the drugstore. I should have guessed that. Anyway, you can't just talk to her that way, Dan. You can't just destroy a human being. Not the first time you even speak to her." And she said more gently: "I know you wouldn't."

"Jee-zuz," he groaned.

They were silent, facing each other now. His groan spoke for more than annoyance. He found on her face that smooth and anxious dream which was the reward of other wives than his own for having given up work and career in marriage, for having relinquished the gratifications of public power, all the paraphernalia of self-sufficiency in which they had grown up, when use of the world was the value and coyness the hedge against love. He had a name for this distant stillness on her face: *the shameful dream of evasion.* It was the dividend from the faulty investments of her childhood. Only his acceptance of its challenge could lay to rest the ghost still inhabiting his wife

long after the fantasies of childhood should have been mastered and
put to use. He was too busy.

Within her dream—and his name for the dream could not know
this about it—she judged him and tenderly stood between his own
evasions and his rush to bury revery under a debris of encounters, accomplishments, habitual pleasures, and morseled ways of making his
life. She had known from an early age what he still feared to recognize
—that dreams buried alive sometimes walk in the night. Sometimes,
she decided, even walk in the halls.

"Poor lonely old woman. Old witch. You know. I've never seen her
come in or out with anyone——"

"Jeez, Phyl, you'd think she was slipping ten-dollar bills under our
door, our secret benefactor."

She waited, hoping that her silence might call him back from the
regions of his anger. He had already removed himself from the possibility of bringing both love and exasperation to their vital mediation.
It was an energy he saved for the day and for his life apart in work.
Now, in a way that Phyl feared, the old woman had come to give her
Dan a night-anger. For Phyl, this made his abstraction from her intolerable; she had accomplished the feat of not being jealous as long
as her rival was a phantom, a thing outside, but now that they were
spying together on the phantom, and it had come to live with them,
Phyl felt that balance to which she offered herself careening down.
She put her hands on his shoulders and said, over-loud, "I'll write
to her." Dan was not looking into her face, but glared toward the milk
chute where they had crouched. She brought her voice to a whisper,
as if the mechanical shock of contrast could oblige his attention:
"Write to her, that's what I'll do, Dan."

"Leave it outside her door?"—still looking away, his voice distant,
unresonant, and frail.

"No, I'll just stick a note in her box. Look at me, Dan! I won't sign
it or anything. I won't even have to put a stamp on it. I'll just say——"

"Maybe, since you don't trust me, you ought to let Mr. Wartner
speak to her."

"No, no, let me take care of this. Please. Please." She stood up and
showed him her troubled face, the damp forehead and the light hair
undone over it. "Please, Dan, don't worry any more, I promise I'll
write to her."

Shrugging off his wife's fuss, some feeling about the lost old woman
that apparently went deeper than Psych 101, he decided to wait.

Don't make too much of things—that was a motto for good business.

The woman must have received the note the next morning. They had planned a movie for that evening, a comedy at the Granada recommended by all the critics, but instead remained home. He felt ridiculous, angry, stupid, and inadequate, sitting in the darkened kitchen, watching the milk chute and the ray of light from the hall. At least the chairs at a movie were comfortable, and you could make some sense out of sitting in the dark. You were keeping up with things.

"I didn't sign the note. I didn't want to embarrass her more than we had to," his wife said.

"You should have showed it to me. All I'd have to do is knock at her door and say, 'Listen, you, lady——'" His jaw was working. The woman had given him a rare peach—no, his wife and she doing it to-gether—a slowly ripening fruit of anger, and the tang of resistance against it, a lick at the thick fuzz, and the rich flood on the tongue when anger is not overcome. Now the eating was pointed the wrong way. Somehow it had all been turned around, and sitting foolish among kitchen things while the refrigerator clicked on and off, he felt the stifling in the chest which comes of blaming a loved one. He almost hoped that her note would not settle it. He could not see how they had been put against each other by a crazy old woman down the hall. That isn't the way things are supposed to be. It wasn't fair. He said at last: "I think I could have talked to her, Phyl."

"That's enough."

"If that didn't work, we should have just told Wartner, but I think I knew how to talk to her. Phyl, you listening?"

Her fingers clawed into the muscle of his forearm, and she whispered fiercely: "I don't want you to talk with her. I don't want that. I don't want you to be near her."

"What?"—gaping at her. "Why?"

"She's filthy. She's all dirty inside. I don't want it."

In the dark he gave her his best, most likable, most successful smile, and reproached her, saying, "I thought you were just sorry for her."

No answer.

"Listen to me now, Phyl," he said rapidly, taking her hand off his arm but leaning close to her. "Listen, I know it's enough talk already, but it seems that we haven't told the truth, either of us. I mean you. I mean, if this is what you felt about her all the time, then you had no right—you had me——"

Sh!

They heard a graceful cat-slither in the hall. Phyllis was thinking with despair, "No, no, too much talk here and not enough before, Dan . . ." Then they saw her, her face full now, entranced, amazed, the inner half-smile of a ballerina frozen under a faith in technique, her slender hips turned young again by the rhythm of purpose. Closer to the crack, their heads together amid the faint odor from a sour milktop, they watched her stretch at their door, her feet still but her body swaying. In one hand she held a discolored brown paper bag. She began to raise her arm.

He jerked away and pulled open the door. The woman stood with her arm lifted, stiffened in the attitude of terror that we are given to see once or twice in a lifetime on the face of a loved one carried away by a train. Neither of them spoke. He did not move. It was as if she were signaling to him with her lifted hand. With a quick dip, she stepped back, and then she was gone down the hall, leaving an empty place and not a sound except for the click of her latch.

His wife pulled him in. "My God, did you see her face?" she asked. One more chance, she was thinking: Talk now, talk it away.

"That bitch, that bitch." He was trembling. Perhaps what enraged him was the grace with which she moved away, a music and a dance which left him piously agape, a worshiper made stupid by visitation. "You'd think I did something to her. You'd think I interrupted her. Oh, that bitch. You'd think she can glide away like that just as nice as you please——"

"Leave her alone now, Dan. That's enough. It's all right. All right, all right," and she tried to stroke his head. "All right, that's enough, Danny."

"No! I won't let her. She can't just say bye-bye like that. No, she can't get away with it——" He dashed the door open again and fled down the hall.

"Dan! Don't!"—his wife no longer dared to follow.

Before he reached her door, he felt the anger run out of him, but he caught it up and used it as a tool to do what he thought he needed to do, and he heard it announcing its slogans to drown his thought, proclaiming, "It's not enough, no, it's not enough"—and he let himself be moved slowly, stealthily, into the shadow at the dead end of the hall where she lived. He could have been a dancer. He could have been a young priest, excoriating his sins in ritual but not yet fright-

ened of them. He had shut his eyes in the dark; now he opened them
again.

Even deep in his abstraction something had warned him one last
time. Perhaps it was the smell. On the mat and carpet refuse was scattered and spilled as it never had been at his own door. It was piled.
It was running. She must have spent weeks collecting it for his coming. A mouse downed in its winter coat, anxious and speedy, bounced
against the wall past him. There was so much of some sort of liquid
that his shoes sloshed in it. He stood without moving amid this
sacrifice, forcing himself to think only, No, she will never get away
with it.

The door opened. Shriveled and yellow, with the fierce smudged
eyes of decayed beauty, she regarded him and softly said, "Don't you
run away this time, young man. I suspected there was a reason you
wouldn't speak to me. Please tell me, what were you doing in front
of my house?"

When her lips came apart, and the tongue slipped pink and new
between, he knew at once that she was ready to laugh at him.

"You see? You see?" his wife cried out from the long corridor behind him. "It's all your fault now."

JAMES B. HALL *was born in Ohio. He served as
a chief warrant officer during World War II, and
then attended the University of Iowa, where he
received a Ph.D., and the Kenyon School of English.
He taught for two years at Cornell University, and
is currently teaching creative writing at the University of Oregon. He is married, and has three children. His work has appeared in* The Nation, Furioso,
Poetry, Western Review, *and other magazines, as
well as in such anthologies as* New Directions
and the O. Henry Prize Stories.

ESTATE AND TRESPASS: A GOTHIC STORY

FROM EPOCH

Towards evening they rolled out of a freight car and now in the
harness room of an old livery stable the mechanic was repacking a
blue portmanteau: hot water bottles, the piano wire garrote, a razor
for her veins, four sponges, gloves from a surgeon's ash can. These
things fitted nicely into the blue case, lined before they ever came to
this village with oil cloth.

The livery stable had long ago become a garage where railroad men
parked their automobiles while they went out on freight runs to
Cincinnati and Newark. But the harness in the harness room still
hung from pegs under the name plates of all the dead horses: Indian
Boy, Shotgun, and Whitey. Under a single electric light bulb, the
reins, traces, cruppers, and fly nets hung like dusty vines, impenetrable
as actions past. Yet in the corner and above the mechanic there was
another light, for the unblinking eye of a bridle button, an enamelled
clipper ship on an enamelled sea, shone steadily.

The mechanic pressed his hands, finally, on the hot water bottles in
the blue portmanteau, then closed the lid. He also snapped the fas-
teners on the pockets of his green coveralls and from habit wiped his
hands clean on a bit of cotton waste and said, we will go get her now.

From the red-plush back of the sleigh the artist continued to sketch
a last picture in the series he had been engaged upon all the while the
mechanic was fussing over the tools. The artist felt each new sketch

more clearly defined exactly what the mechanic was. Now that the tools were packed, and it was time, the artist nervously ripped one of his last pictures from the sketch pad and handed it down for the mechanic's inspection.

—This one is nearly it, the artist said.

The mechanic looked at the work. As in the previous versions of this series of pictures there was one eye in the middle of the page looking into another eye framed in a picture window. Since the artist had earlier found and had polished the bridle button in the corner, he had included in all his sketches this motif of the clipper ship, stunsails set, on a bright unblinking sea. Also there was the unmistakable chin scar that flashed from beneath the mechanic's beard. The whole composition was buckled together by a snaking zipper, exactly like the fastener up the front of the mechanic's greasy coveralls.

The mechanic picked up a broken awl handle and ripped the picture again (*huh!*) and again (*there!*) and again (*ha!*). Then he threw it into the corner with all the others that had infuriated him. Though the mechanic was too surly to notice, the artist on the sleigh was livid from what he considered at least an affront.

—If it was a picture of me, I would know it. You are a *stinking* little leech, the mechanic said.

After a few minutes the artist hopped down from the arched back of the sleigh. He was like a tubby bird that has lost its left wing. Beside the mechanic he was not as tall as he thought he was. The artist picked up the little suitcase that the mechanic had daubed with black liquid shoe polish and though this one was empty, except for an oil cloth lining, it seemed too heavy for him.

—Leave that-er sketch pad, the mechanic snarled, you are going to have a hard time.

The storm was ten minutes late but as they walked along the road towards her house at the edge of the village the wind began to rise, making scourges out of the dead weeds along the gravel. The road was hollow under their city shoes and, as the artist had predicted, there were no cars this Sunday night. Only the fog now and again held the weeds and grass in the very lowest parts of the roadside ditches. The outrageous howl of the farm dogs focused on the moon whenever it appeared through the midnight rift of clouds as a round unwinking eye.

The mechanic walked ahead, heavily, as though he were in some gigantic garage and needed a tool from the other end of the long building. He grunted and spat into the wind and said he should not have the artist along at all since he was weak and could not even carry an empty suitcase.

—I think we will get caught, the artist said.

This had never occurred to the mechanic, at all. He pulled his billed motorcycle rider's cap lower over his eyes and said that *he* by God would never be caught by any county sheriff. As for Shorty, as he always called the artist, well we would see about that.

Her house no longer had any real shape. They could see faintly, however, the rising, humped, black hill and her curved gravel driveway that writhed up through the pine trees. The mechanic had found this chateau among pine trees when he had been let off by a motorist who turned him out because of the body odor. Because it was so fated he knocked on the kitchen door of this old homestead and asked for something to eat. When he finished eating, there on the back steps, he poisoned her dogs. Then he caught the only afternoon freight train back to Cincinnati. He went at once to the bus terminal and stole the blue portmanteau. Then he went to the artist's "studio" at the edge of the slums, and slept the rest of the morning. When the artist came to his rooms the mechanic awakened. While the mechanic gobbled the last of the potato salad he told the artist about this fine chateau at the edge of the village and how the dogs were just about keeling over now, and that it was necessary to visit the nice lady once again.

The house itself had simply accumulated. The east wing was made of brick, and the windows had not been opened for years. Artificial wreaths for the funerals of the family were still on the white wire tripods in the dampness of the parlor. The west wing of the center section of the house was of iron. That is, the windows and doors and even the ends of the down-spouts were barred. These screens and bars and rods and pike tips had been welded on the job. The lady who had ordered the mechanic's handout, and her companion, lived alone in this lighted, barred, center section. As they said, it was much like being in jail. As it came about, the companion to the lady had driven the Overland-Willis automobile away and was visiting in Xenia, Ohio, until Monday at two p.m. Even so, the wind now rubbed the pine trees together, and there was a hoarse voice *husking, husking* in the dark branches.

The mechanic slipped across her vacant yard, through the wet blowing grass: the lady was safely inside, behind the huge picture window that had been recently punched into the front of this iron middle section of her house . . . a whim, a desperate stab at improvement.

They saw her through the great clear conscience of her picture window. She was stretched out on a chaise longue in the center of the brightly lighted living room. She had not moved a lamp or a book or the accumulated shelf of Bibles in all the years since her dear husband had passed away. Now she was dozing, her wrists hanging near the floor, the palms turned out, veins exposed. Her dress was flowered, a heavy silver brocade. She wore a ruff and the usual rope of pearls around her neck. On her head the Spanish mantilla reared like a tired old cobra, poised and swaying but asleep. Her face seemed very small, an old bird's nest among branches. Around her thin waist the rhinestones and agates were clasped, hooked, and soldered into a wide belt of metal and leather. Her mouth was slightly agape and she breathed delicately out of the polite upper-half of her lungs while all the diamonds smouldered, asserting the old priority of estate and comfort while she took her accumulated ease before the gas-heated fireplace.

The mechanic and the artist pressed their faces to the picture window and their breath made two white halos of mist on the outside of the glass. The artist trembled in his squeaky shoes. The mechanic walked like a boxer to the small hidden side door behind the bushes. He unsnapped a pocket of his coveralls and took out a blue-steel skeleton key. He panted and thought how soft that ruff would be entwined in his calloused hands . . . like a really young woman's. . . .

The artist thought: this is what she wants. It is her wish, she invited this or she would not have such a vulgar window exposing her living room and attracting such ones as we are. It takes two to make a show like this, and he wondered—in that case—why he needed to be here at all since only the lady and the mechanic were the principals.

The mechanic was breathing hard. He snapped his wrist, turned the key sharply. The door yielded, with only the slightest rustle. The mechanic entered heavily. The tubby artist slipped in after him. The artist took off his hat, hung it on the hall rack. It was as though he were making a formal call. The mechanic had already sprung into the living room.

He kneeled silently behind her chair. He opened the blue portmanteau. He deftly raised the lid and took out the steel handles and the vibrating wire loop of the garrote. And still she dozed in the chaise longue.

The artist tiptoed across the room and pulled the silent curtains across the picture window. He turned, then, and composed the room: he changed the radio to a program of soft indecent jazz, and switched off two floor lamps and the chandelier. He sat down in what had always been the companion's straight-backed chair. He leaned forward as though he were about to begin a polite conversation.

The mechanic was tense, bent for a moment over the chaise longue. There was no sound. The mechanic then placed her ruff around his own neck, as though it were an elaborate unpressed silk foulard. He worked quickly and accurately. He inserted a hollow needle into the veins of the wrist, attached the rubber hose and thus siphoned blood into the hot water bottles. As the bottles bulged and filled he motioned the artist to empty them in the bathroom.

The mechanic slipped all the brocaded cloth (and the slack Spanish mantilla) from the small body. He motioned the artist to hang these clothes back in the closet, as though they had not been worn at all. After every errand of this kind the artist returned to his straight-backed chair and crossed his legs. He admired the mechanic, then. He appreciated the power and deftness and the long practice indicated by the way this man handled a razor. Clearly the mechanic knew exactly how to touch an old tendon with steel, how to dismantle an arm, how to make a brutal snapping sound with his wrists. Even the artist was amused to see how small the limbs actually were, very much like little empty bags of feathers, really.

While the mechanic was humming over the torso the artist went to the bookshelves. He opened a cabinet drawer. From inside the compartment he took several books and looked intently at the gold and red bindings: *The Loves of Marquis Gaol;* and something privately printed, *Genealogy of the Hauptmenner Family.* This last book he opened and extracted from between the pages a piece of old vellum. It appeared blank, but he held it over the brightest light, then smiled. He easily made out the line drawing embedded in the heavy sheet. He compared the drawing with the head which was now perched on the edge of the chaise longue glaring malevolently at him. He turned the paper sideways. Surely the face and the body in the vellum was this same lady, but at a younger age, of course. Someone, perhaps her dead husband, had made this clever drawing, this elaborate watermark in the paper. Here she was, caught forever in his secret watermark. The husband—or perhaps his friend—had surprised this lady the night before the marriage, had come across her in the horse stalls, and had thereby caught her in an indecent situation forever. The artist was amused at his discovery and winked at the staring outraged eyes in the head which was perched like a disturbed jay on the edge of the chaise longue.

By then the mechanic was very angry.

—Get the rest of the stuff and stop loafing. I should have brought me a man.

The artist began to repack the blue portmanteau. He placed the head beside the hot water bottles, then packed everything else in place. He stood on the lid to close it, as though he were going on a long journey.

Only after the mechanic gave the word did they begin looting. Behind the portrait of her husband they found the open safe with the bonds and the seven platinum bracelets. They scooped it all into the small black suitcase. By then the mechanic had taken off the old surgeon's gloves and had rubbed everything with the sponges. The mechanic looked at his watch, then carried the blue portmanteau and the smaller black suitcase to the door. Outside the rain came down and washed away every footprint. Sometimes the mechanic had to wait a minute as they walked along the hollow road to the village and to their freight train.

By three a.m. it was nearly light. The artist stood in the box car door admiring all the rain and all the fog which swirled past. On the high trestle the mechanic slipped up quietly behind the artist and kicked him into the wind and fog of the river—as he had planned from the beginning. Then he kicked the blue portmanteau out the door and watched it make nearly a perfect parabola into the water. Then he went back into his warm corner of the box car and rested his head on what was now clearly his very own black suitcase, and slept.

In the railroad yards in Cincinnati he jumped from the box car with the suitcase full of jewelry in his arms. The policeman snapped the handcuffs on him while they talked.

But when they took him back to the livery stable, the court-appointed lawyer kept saying his client, the mechanic, was honest. The mechanic did not say anything, but he nodded when the lawyer denied everything. The lawyer could see very clearly this: that the tubby little man—obviously a stranger to my client—accidentally boarded this mechanic's empty freight car at Midland City. At daybreak this balding artist did indeed confess as he stood in the box car door; upon confession this maniac *jumped* into the river. This innocent bystander (my client) was only taking the suitcase to the police station to report when a policeman in the yards wrongfully put the handcuffs on him while they were talking. The lady (the respected matriarch of our village) was gone but this was plainly *non sequitur* or *post hoc, ergo propter hoc.* Or both. The lawyer was the executor of the estate just as soon as he could get back to his office, which was in the top of the old livery stable.

So the Sheriff, who was dipping snuff into his lower gums, spoke to the people assembled in the old harness room. He wore coveralls and packed a large white-handled revolver. After he agreed with the lawyer, he fished around behind the work bench and pulled out the artist's sketch pad and all the pictures. The Sheriff snuffled like a horse and said, well at least we know the little fat one who had been washed up on the river bank was an artist all right.

From where he was sitting on the high back of the sleigh the mechanic stared at the sketches he had punched through with an awl handle only yesterday morning: he looked with disdain, once more. The full-sail clipper ship and the enamelled sea of the bridle button were sketched in all the backgrounds, but the picture with the snaking zipper through the composition was of the most interest:

—No jury, Sheriff, the lawyer said, will ever say this is a drawing of my client.

The lawyer looked at the Sheriff's own coveralls.

—Many people wear zippers in the front of their coveralls. Besides there is no likeness: if this was a picture of my client I would know it and you would know it. Either you know it, or you don't.

All the others standing in a half circle around the bench and the pile of drawings grinned and said that was right. . . .

After the artist had snagged on the riffles at Milford, the family claimed the body and the artist was buried decently in Bedford, Mass. He was buried beside a nephew who died by drowning at Normandy, though these same relatives and the Graves Registration team thought he had been shot. The family said the artist had been kidnapped, doubtless, and had slipped while trying to escape. He had always looked for new materials to sketch and they had warned him about this many times.

The blue portmanteau split open when it hit the water. After the river receded from flood stage the head—now almost a skull—was left perched on a sand bar, staring through dense overhanging willows.

This head was found once by a fisherman, but he did not want to be questioned again right now by the police so he fished farther down stream for the next two months.

The rubber hose with the needle in the end was caught in the seine of still another fisherman. He now uses the tubing regularly to siphon gasoline from the tanks of automobiles parked for the day along the river bank.

As it turned out the mechanic had no family. He had no address nor even an illegitimate child—at least none who would claim him. The motorist who first let him off at the house under the pines was ill and did not read the newspapers for one month, so missed seeing the picture of the mechanic. But he would have remembered him because of the body odor.

If the artist had been alive he would have been amused at the mechanic after the trial: the mechanic was handcuffed to the Sheriff's deputy. The mechanic and the deputy were on the bus going to the state penitentiary where the mechanic was going to serve 99 years. The bus was hit at night by a gasoline tank truck, at the intersection of two highways. The deputy was pinned in the wreckage. The mechanic tried to pull away, but he had no tools. He was chained to the wrist by steel handcuffs. In the end, most of the mechanic was dumped into a junk yard with the burnt out bus because he was fused with the springs of the upholstery and with the twisted melted tubes of the bus frame.

At the trial, however, the mechanic had refused to admit anything. In fact his lawyer was going to get a new trial at the time the sleeping truck driver and the sleeping bus driver rammed together at the highway intersection. The county attorney, at the trial, showed that the mechanic had been with the artist in the harness room of the livery stable on that night. He also proved to the jury that the artist had planned everything from the beginning. He proved this because the only thing in the lady's house was the hat which the artist had left there on the hall tree.

In the mind of the jury, however, this did not have much bearing. They convicted on a lingering suspicion that the mechanic did not *prevent* the artist from jumping out of that box car and into the river regardless. Hence they recommended 99 years in the state penitentiary. But there would have been a new trial.

And all of this because in the harness room that first morning when the reporter and the coroner and the Sheriff and the lawyer were questioning each other, this happened: the lawyer reached up and turned off the single light bulb overhead. They had not thought it could be so dark. There on the workbench, on the sketch pad, was the artist's very last picture. It was the final picture he had made of the mechanic.

In a moment of great anger and perhaps even rage, the artist had made a caricature. He used the crayons which glowed only in darkness. Captured on the sketch pad was the mechanic: he was represented in a childish Fauntleroy costume, with a lace collar. The face was accurate, beyond the shadow of a doubt, and glowing.

This final work of art, done in rage, showed the mechanic hunched on a low squat motorcycle riding furiously. The artist had added a billed Sunday school cap, very much like one the artist himself had worn as an innocent boy. In the background of the picture was all the old harness, hanging like nets that would never be cleared away. And in the center of this confusion of harness was the bright reoccurring eye, the bridle button, the clipper ship with stunsails set on course through a luminous sea.

RUTH HARNDEN *is a native of Boston. A gradu-*
ate of Radcliffe, she became so interested in the
Celtic origins of English literature that she spent a
year of study at Trinity College in Dublin. She has
worked in publishers' offices and on the floors of
bookstores in Boston, New York, and Los Angeles.
Her first novel appeared in 1945, and her second,
I, a Stranger, in 1950. Since then, she says, "I've been
struggling with the much more difficult short
story." (Miss Harnden, meet Rex Worthington.)
She was a fellow at the Bread Loaf Conference
in 1953.

REBELLION

FROM TOWN & COUNTRY

Last year, at fifteen, she had been a private person, and next year at
seventeen, so far as she knew, she might expect to be so again. Only
this year she seemed to have been thrust into the public domain,
made to feel as conspicuous, and at the same time anonymous, as
though she were ludicrously fat, or suffered from any condition that
was the accepted butt of stale, universal humor brought out again
and again with the zeal of discovery. *Sweet sixteen.*

"What a lovely thought, Dr. Mulcahey, or Mr. Byrne, or Colonel
McGuire," she would have liked to say, looking stonily back into
their archly smiling faces. "Did it just come to you? Or is it a quotation, perhaps?" Or she might simply say, "I feel sour, thank you.
Quite sour!" and turn and walk out of the alien, enormous room
filled with the aged or the aging who had no respect for her whatso-
ever, only a terrible, stripping curiosity.

She was either interested in people—deeply, passionately—or she
barely saw them at all. But now she began to wonder whether she,
too, was doomed to arrive one day at this peculiar, repulsive condition
in which interest had given place to a dull, sly curiosity for something
that had lost all reality.

An only child, too much of her life had been lived in an adult
world. As a result she was mentally precocious, which she knew, and

emotionally somewhat in arrears, which she was only beginning to know. The latter awareness manifested itself in a nameless impatience. She had become very critical, was frequently short-tempered, and was ridden by a continual unrest. It was partly on this account that her parents had chosen this season to ship her off to her uncle and his wife, who had no children of their own and an "interesting life" in the diplomatic service.

"You're a born rebel, Susie," her uncle had begun to say almost from the day she arrived, and it did seem as if her unrest was a kind of imminent rebellion that any minute, or any day, she would find the strength to express properly. In the meantime it came out in small intellectual attacks fairly well within the bounds of good manners.

"What's the matter with having *both* central heating and open fires?" she wanted to know when it was explained to her that many people could afford central heating, that some had even had it installed and then never connected it because they preferred the intimate comfort of fires in every room.

"Why don't they pasteurize their milk?" she demanded when she learned that it was customarily left raw, and that tuberculosis was rife in the country. But the chief object of her attack was the terrible inequality, the lack of democracy. At first it had seemed to her that people here must be wealthier than the same sort of people at home, but her aunt put her straight on that. "Heavens, no!" she said, "it's just the other way around. This is a poor country, and America's one of the richest." It was the servants, Susan explained. "Oh—that!" her aunt said. "But they're so cheap here. We can get four servants for the price of one in the States."

"You mean," Susan pointed out unsparingly, "that a great many people have nothing so that a very few can have everything?"

"Highty tighty," her uncle broke in at that. "A disciple of Marx?"

"No," she said coldly, "but if I lived here I'd probably become one."

"Of course it spoils us dreadfully," her aunt admitted with one of her gestures of delicate, side-stepping surrender that no one could mistake for defeat. She was a small, fastidious woman who managed to look fragile and feminine even in the most robust tweeds. At an age when she should have faded, the soft moist Irish weather had given her skin a renascent bloom. She kept her graying hair short and exquisitely groomed, and had never neglected the care of her hands. Beside her Susan felt a little gross—overgrown and underorganized. She was likely to do clumsy things, drop a teacup or a walking stick, stumble over a rug, although she was normally well co-ordinated. But more devastating than her aunt's person was her bland, humorless sweet temper that could uncurdle the sourest wit, that blunted the edge of argument so effectively that even discussion died stillborn.

"We have to take things as we find them," her uncle had said in a terminating voice. He found them very comfortable indeed and this knowledge only increased Susan's critical impatience. They were old and they had given up. They would rather be comfortable than alive. And being very uncomfortable, she told herself that she would rather be alive. But still she had this uncertainty of her own life; not that it had ended, but that it was unbegun. During that single, suspended week of freedom on the boat it had seemed likely at any moment to begin. She had played Ping-pong and danced a few times with an older man, a Swiss who traveled for Du Pont. He was perhaps thirty and had given her a heady sense of imminent danger. But nothing at all had happened, and in recollection the whole thing gave her the feeling she got from developing a film that turned out to have been light-struck in the camera so that even her anticipation had been meaningless. She told herself in honest hindsight that he had treated her like a nice kid, as though she wore her obstructing innocence like a brand. And if she did—if that were the case—then how could anything happen? And if nothing happened, then how was it lost?

There were only two things in which she was uncritically content because in them she could be wholly involved as nothing else in life any longer seemed willing or able to involve her. She loved to drive a car and to ride a horse, particularly the latter. Occasionally she would ride badly, failing to quite manage the horse, and at these times she would need to take out the car, to drive it with a combination of abandon and precision that almost restored her self-esteem. But it wasn't the same thing, and she knew it with a glancing, secret contempt for the inert manageability of machines. You had no relationship with a machine, and along with the speed and the exhilarating presence of potential danger, which removed her restlessness, it was exactly the *relationship* she craved. The lonelier she felt in this alien place, in the embarrassment of her conspicuous youth, the more she needed it.

Dublin was a good place to have come to if you liked riding. Diplomatically it was not a brilliant post, but for that reason neither was it taxing. After some ten years her aunt and uncle had relaxed into a close resemblance, at least, of the amiable, indolent ways of the county born and bred. Their frequent receptions had preserved a formality—in the dress, in the food and liquor served, and in the conversational interchange or the musical intrusions. These gatherings usually showed, too, a considerable urban variety of guests. But their weekly At Homes had pretty well boiled down to the informal hard-riding set, who might occasionally talk of their gardens but never got any further away than that from the turf. Prosperous farmers or titled gentry, they had identical hard-planned, weather-burned faces and conducted their conversations in an identical manner, the voices booming, the diction blurred. Men and women dressed alike, in the tough, unregarded tweeds that never seemed to reach retirement, and it even appeared to Susan that there was little other difference between them, except that the women were apt to have deeper voices, and their faces were frequently harder.

Through this florid, shouting, unintelligible crowd she would move every Thursday afternoon at the same hours, passing buttered bread or refilling teacups and saying, "No, I don't hunt," for the hundredth time, or "No, I haven't been out yet." "Hunt?" or "Started to hunt yet?" was offered to her over and over, or perhaps simply "Been out yet?" which she learned quite soon could have, in their changeless context, only the one reference.

She had done a little jumping at home, but only over the simplest hurdles. After a trial hour in the field with her uncle it had been decided that she was not, or not yet, up to the banks. Evidently an Irish invention, the banks were towering, beveled mounds of earth. She had no notion of their actual height but would have guessed it at no less than twelve feet. Put at the bank, the horse would leap and then scramble up the angled sides, pause briefly on the leveled top, and then plunge headlong to the ground at the far side. It was the downward leap that appalled her, that sent her frightened, betraying hands to the saddle, and that formed the basis for her uncle's decision.

"You'll go out every morning," he told her, "with one of the grooms." In point of fact their horses were supplied by the nearby army post and the "grooms" were any of the enlisted men whose services were an added diplomatic courtesy on demand. The actual arrangements were made by her aunt on the telephone. Any course might be determined by her husband, but its execution, the applied diplomacy, usually fell to her lot. She had to a high degree that capacity for verbal indirection which results in the most unmistakable directness.

After the first few days the stolid, middle-aged sergeant her aunt had unerringly selected, sight unseen, was unexpectedly hospitalized with a ruptured appendix. On Saturday morning, at the customary hour, a young corporal came up with the horses. He was a thin, tallish boy who looked to be little older than Susan herself. While he adjusted her stirrups, standing at her horse's head, she examined his stark boy's face with the fine pink girlish complexion, the intent, impersonal gray eyes, and it came to her that he knew all about horses and that he knew nothing else. As far as people, as far as Life was concerned, he was way back there at the beginning with herself. Out of the simplicity of this bond and this freedom she began to talk to him as easily as she could talk to no one else in this place, not even thinking how to begin, as she had had to think with the sergeant so that she'd never begun at all.

"First I thought I'd never be able to handle a horse on a snaffle," she told him. "At home we use the curb, too, you know. Or if it's a single rein, then it's the curb. That's what they use in the West. That's what the cowboys use."

"For a fact?" he said, interested, his intent, unconcealing eyes coming up to hers without embarrassment or curiosity even, except for the words she was saying. "Anyone could hold a horse on a curb," he said then, swinging into his own saddle.

"I know it," she said just as naturally. "And I still don't know how I'd handle him on a snaffle if he wanted to run." He laughed at that. "Why would you be wantin' to hold him in that case?" he asked her. "Sure he'd have to stop when he got to the sea." That made her laugh, and presently they were cantering across the sere, stubbled grass of Phoenix Park as if they'd been doing it every morning of their lives.

There was no end to what they found to say without ever leaving the subject of horses and riding. He was teaching her a great deal but she was able to tell him a lot too. "This is the way the cowboys ride," she'd say, sitting to the trot, "taking the jolts on their stomachs. Of course they prefer a single-foot," she might add, "and anyone can sit to that."

"You can train 'em to that sometimes," he'd say, "sending 'em against the bit. But you've a better chance if they're inclined that way."

"But I like to post," she told him. "I *enjoy* it." She was even able to confess to him that she was scared of the banks. "I grabbed the saddle," she said, looking him straight in the eye, daring him to accept this and still go on knowing her.

"You've a good seat," he told her, looking straight back as if there were no disgrace standing between them. "Just leave it to the horse. Give him his head and leave it to him."

"I'd have to stop when I got to the ground?" she asked him, and they laughed together over this for a long time.

There was so much to say that by the end of the week she found herself talking to him when he wasn't there, asking him questions or explaining something to him, or going back over some point that had come up the day before, or that morning.

He never called her "Miss" the way the sergeant did, and still he'd never used her name either. It was just "you" or else he was simply talking as if she were anyone, or a number of people. But she knew that it wasn't like that. If it were he could have used her name. She knew this without knowing that she knew it until the day that he used her name.

They had gone up into the hills that morning for another try at the banks. "We'll take 'em together," he suggested. "Just give the horses the office and relax." But she decided that she'd rather, the first time, he waited for her on the far side, and finally he agreed to do that. It was on the far side, reaching the ground, that her horse stumbled and then fell. It seemed to her, reviewing it afterward, and even dimly at the time, that she'd barely felt the earth with her shoulder before he was off his horse and standing over her saying, "Susie, are you hurt? Are you hurt?" and it wasn't only her name but the sharp pain in his voice that she heard. "You're shakin'," he said, helping her up, holding her against the tension of his arm. "Are you all right?"

"Just dirty, I guess," she said, trying to laugh. He took out his handkerchief and dabbed at her forehead, her cheekbones, but when he got to her mouth he stopped and stuffed the handkerchief back in his pocket. "The thing to do," he said, speaking quickly in an oddly light voice, "is to get straight back on again. You've always got to do that at once or you'll maybe never do it again. Come along now," he said, busying himself with the two sets of reins he'd caught up through his arm, "up and at it again. You did fine—just fine! It was only for the beast stumblin' or you'd be in the saddle now easy as sittin' in the barn." It was like the time on the boat, and it was entirely different, because this time the nothing that had happened had happened to both of them.

It was more than a week before her aunt caught up with the fact that a substitution had been made in her plans. She happened to drive up from town just as Susan had got into the house, so of course she met the corporal coming down the driveway leading the second, riderless horse. "Hullo. Was that Sergeant Blair?" she asked casually, standing in the hall stripping the string gloves from her hands. It was a minute before Susan could think who Sergeant Blair was. "Oh!" she said then, remembering, "Oh, he's in the hospital. His appendix broke. Two weeks ago, I guess it was. Or maybe it was ten days." "Really?" her aunt said, examining herself in the hall mirror. "As long as that?" "It seems much longer," Susan told her innocently, out of the moment's disarmed surprise. "It seems like a month at least that I've been riding with Jimmy."

"Really?" her aunt said again, having turned from the mirror now, and after a minute the irresolution in her face, studying Susan's, resolved itself in a smile. "How nice that you've made a friend," she said. "We must meet him. Would you like to ask him for dinner one night?"

"Oh, no!" Susan said out of the unexamined but certain instinct of an animal sensing an ambushed trap. "We just like to talk about horses," she said quickly, reaching for some protection of this thing that was hers alone in this alien place, this estranging time. "In that case," her aunt said sweetly, "just have him in Thursday," and she put her gloves down on the table, the tough leather palms turned up, and went into the morning room.

She ought to have thought quicker, and further. She ought to have seen past the logic of Thursday when everyone who came talked about horses. But the moment was past and she was caught. She was caught beyond escape in her aunt's logic, and in her graciousness—switching at once to the thing that Susan might prefer.

She waited until the end of their ride on Thursday and then, getting off at the house, handing him her reins, she gave it to him the way it was: not a thing that needed accepting, or could possibly be refused. "Aunt Helen wants you to come for tea. About four they usually come. Any time between four and five. I'll see you then," she told him, and turned and went into the house without waiting to see what it might be that finally found its way to the surface of his intent, uncomplicated face.

It was perhaps four-thirty and everyone had gathered when she saw him at the threshold to the room, his young face looking exposed and raw hanging in uncertainty above the poise of her aunt's head. "I'm sure you know the army people already," her aunt was saying when she got to them, "though I'm afraid they're all aged career men."

"Hullo," Susan said, searching his face for any sign that he, too, had heard how her aunt had taken away with the one word what she had given with the other. There was nothing to be read but a certain wariness when he said, "How do you do?" speaking as distinctly as if the words belonged to a foreign tongue. "Introduce Corporal Faley to the Colonel, darling," her aunt said, "and to Captain Sweeney and to Major Cunningham. And then get him a cup of tea," and she moved away.

"Come on," Susan said, not looking at him any longer, her face set in the stubborn, reckless hope that something might still be saved.

Colonel McGuire opened his mouth and barked something that might have been an acknowledgment of the introduction in this room where introductions were not made, and might as well have been the beginning of the story he launched into at once: some incident from the week before when he'd been out with the Killing Kildares. No one needed to ask the corporal which hunt he rode with, or even if he hunted at all. No one seemed to feel the need to ask him anything at all, and after a minute Susan said, "I'll get you some tea," and moved away from the identical faces which had assumed a further identity now. Without exception they were united at this moment in the bland, incurious conviction that anyone who was at all worth knowing they knew already.

She never did get him the tea although she made three tries going back after another cup when the first one was taken by Mr. Kavenaugh, stopping her in the middle of the room. Everyone all at once was determined to stop her, to engage her in conversation, to deflect her eyes searching the room for his face, from old Lady Closs, who wanted to know if she was going to any of the dances, to Mr. Byrne, who expressed a sudden interest in her political views. She knew she was being wooed, and she knew why. She knew exactly what was going on, and had known from her aunt's first words. But when she was stopped with the third cup, her stubborn frustration went down to helpless defeat. She felt it go as certainly as she might have watched a sentinel leaving his post. But it was no less gone for that.

She was one of them now. No longer anonymous, and briefly comical, she was addressed, consulted, attended. She might have been grown-up; she might have been eighteen. And she began to hear her own voice rising on the competitive tide, her own words running together in expedient haste. It was a kind of intoxication, heady and numbing at once. She had really forgotten Jimmy's presence when her aunt's voice broke the spell at last. She thought Susan ought to know that Corporal Faley was leaving and surely she wanted to see him out.

He was standing alone in the hall, his back to the broad mirror that alone preserved the image of his integrity—the squared competent shoulders, the stark attention of the head. "I'm sorry——" she began, and then she stopped, and it was perhaps after all the only thing she had to say.

"That's all right," he said very quickly, possibly to spare her or perhaps to spare himself further. Into the unaware, youthful dignity of his face had come the beginning of adult confusion. His eyes shifted to some focus beyond her. "I'll . . ." his lean, assured boy's hand that was so certain on a horse's mouth lifted in a faltering gesture, as though it moved toward a cap he wasn't wearing. "I'll bring the horses 'round in the morning," he said in final definition of the status they had assigned him. Without looking at her again he crossed the hall, treading the carpet lightly, and let himself out the front door.

For a minute she stood alone in the hall. Behind her, across the wide house, the shouting unintelligible crowd sounded like one voice now, single as the voice of the pack. Her rebellion flared briefly, a last time. *Why did you let them?* she asked of the door that had closed behind him. If he hadn't fallen into their trap; if he hadn't accepted that identity they gave him; if he hadn't proved their point—her rebellion guttered and died because she had proved their point herself, as well. She belonged to the hunted no longer. She had become a member of the hunt.

DONALD JUSTICE *is from Miami, Florida, and has done graduate work at the Universities of North Carolina, Stanford, and Iowa, where he taught a course in fiction writing. Poems of his have appeared in a variety of magazines, and his first and only other story, "The Lady," was reprinted in a previous* O. Henry Prize Stories *collection. He is twenty-eight years old, and married to Jean Ross.*

VINELAND'S BURNING

FROM WESTERN REVIEW

Billy Campbell lived with his mother in an old vine-eaten house, across the street from a new family by the name of Curry. The Currys had moved in with the depression, and for more than a year the Campbells saw them coming and going every day without a word passing between them. The Campbells were one of the old Vineland families, dying out; all they had in the world was each other, and an orange grove somewhere in Florida. They didn't get out in the world much. Both had weak hearts, and the mother kept to her bed mostly. The rare times she was in spirits, she tied her tennis shoes on around the ankles and climbed a chair out on the front porch trying to train the vines to keep out the light. That usually brought on another spell.

She would go rather white, then, and seem to forget how to breathe. For days on end she lay flat on her back, stretched out. Sometimes then she called out to Billy to bring her a drop of wine. The doctor having forbidden it, Billy always pretended not to hear. "Billy boy, bring me a little of the strawberry," she would cry. "Hurry up now, or I'll come in there and whip you!" Under his breath Billy would murmur, "Mama, I only wish you could, I only wish you could." At times like that he loved her more than anything, but he appreciated the humorous side of it, too. The humorous side was that Billy weighed all of two hundred and fifty pounds and could have picked her up in the one hand, even if she could have got up off her back. He was burning to explain this to somebody, somebody besides his one true cousin, but he made up the lack by telling this cousin every time she came, which wasn't too often.

When he did manage to get downtown, Billy was always trying to overhear what people were saying. He never had much luck. For one thing, he was too big to be forgotten. Unless the crowd was exceptionally large, they would nod to him—some of them would—and then *remember* he was there. However, he picked up something now and then. For instance, about air currents. The volunteer fire chief, who had a loud voice, happened to be saying something about air currents just as Billy was going by one day, something about how the cool ones liked to travel close to the ground, and by the time Billy got home he had already figured out how to apply this to his own problem.

It was summer, and summers had always been hell for him, because of his size. So what he did was to pick the mattress off his bed and start carrying it to different places in the house, in the dark, dropping it down anywhere he pleased on the floor and stretching out, trying to get some sleep.

Mrs. Campbell, who was in between spells for the time being, was up and about a good deal at night herself, wanting a drink of water and one. thing and another. Wherever she turned, there was Billy to be stepped over. "I'm not complaining," she told him. "It's just that you ought to assign yourself a regular place and stick to it."

So Billy began to concentrate on the downstairs, which he ought to have thought of in the first place. In keeping with this notion of his, he was bound to end up in the kitchen, which happened to be an addition to the house set on a lower level than the rest. There, on the hottest nights, in the long still stretches, he fancied he could hear the ice not only shift in the icebox, but actually in the process of melting. That made it cooler; seemed to, anyhow. When he thought of leaving the icebox door open, he saw right away how convenient it was, for reaching in after things. He'd reach in after an orange to suck, when he couldn't sleep.

The nights weren't always still, of course. Something that sounded like owls kept waking him up. The first night or two Billy thought it was real owls that had settled in the trees outside, when really it was only the boys in their cars driving past the Curry house across the street, whooping and imitating things. Mrs. Curry and a friend of hers from the other side of town, the new side, had got the idea from somewhere that you could go *society* by sitting up till all hours. (From the Atlanta *Journal*, people said, the Sunday rotogravure.) As a consequence there was a light on nearly every night in the Curry parlor. It was a crazy idea, and what with the depression on and everyone else being so careful about electric lights, the two husbands couldn't walk a block along Vine Street without somebody shaking his head or giving them the wink. The kids especially thought it was pretty funny. The wilder sort of young people had got in the habit of driving past the Currys' new house, going about ten miles an hour and making all kinds of noises, with the girls giggling and throwing their hands up over their mouths to scream in a polite way. On the way home from the picture show in Valdosta, late at night, was the usual time, and Saturday nights, around ten-thirty or eleven, it got to be like cars leaving a wedding, with horns tooting and everybody having a good time, and somebody was sure to get stuck in the ditch turning around. Inside, Mrs. Curry and her friend only turned their backs to the traffic, acting like they didn't hear a thing.

As for Billy, he never had liked owls, and one night when he couldn't stand it any longer he took the flashlight out to the oaks and flashed the light through every tree pretty thoroughly, without flushing one owl. He shook the branches, but everything was quiet for a change. Fear that the limbs might crack under all his weight was the only thing that kept him from climbing up after them. He might have tried it anyway if a dog hadn't started yapping down the street, but as he was a little afraid of dogs, he gave it up and went in.

Later, the owls did commence. Again he went out with the flashlight and this time picked up some gravel from the road to throw up into the trees. He was no more than taking aim when two cars happened to turn up the street, creeping along. He ducked behind a tree, as well as he could. When the boys in the cars started their hoo-hooing, Billy gave a glance at the trees and then another glance at the cars and then he just stood his ground back of the tree like a statue, the gravel slipping out between his fingers. He was up all night with the worry of the thing, not to mention the heat.

After that the cars really got on his nerves. The later the hour the more like a megaphone the still night would become, to swell every sound. Even when the boys kept quiet, the car would turn out to be the rattly kind, and the tires would scuff up a racket of pebbles against the fenders. On wet nights the tires whispered. He couldn't sleep at all. Soon he was getting up from the floor several times a night to go to the window to watch for the next carload. The lights, too, over at the Currys', which he hadn't paid much attention to before, began to wear on his nerves. He put in a lot of time trying to figure out some logical connection between the lights and the boys in the cars.

Then one night he caught Mrs. Curry in the act of looking out the window just as he was doing, facing him across the ditch. He felt so close to her he almost said hello, which he hadn't ever done; then the next minute a very white, Northern-looking face bobbed up beside hers, and by the time he realized what they were up to he was feeling pretty silly being gawked at in his nightshirt. (Nightshirts were cooler.) He drew the curtains to. In fact, he made the rounds of the downstairs windows drawing the curtains, and upstairs he pulled down the shades and went in to his mother to warn her they were being spied on. She was resting so easy, though, he hadn't the heart to disturb her.

The only person the Campbells saw, really to talk to, was this cousin of theirs. She had a regular day for coming in from the country to visit: not quite every Wednesday. But the Campbells sometimes forgot what day it was, and the cousin would stand out on the front porch maybe five minutes, rattling the old knocker and the door itself and pushing the buzzer that even she knew didn't work. It was no use calling; they wouldn't answer. They thought everybody was a salesman, even on Wednesdays.

Ordinarily she had to go around and let herself in the back way, through the kitchen. She got tired, that summer, of stumbling over Billy's mattress back in the kitchen. Going by, she would give the icebox door a good slam, to let them know who it was. Duty was all she came for: to tie back the window curtains and let in some light, to raise the shades and turn off any lights they'd forgotten. They'd leave them on all day—the rest of their lives as like as not—if she didn't come in now and then to turn them off.

Upstairs the old mother might ask why she hadn't brought her little boy along to play with Billy—and Billy thrice his age. This could turn into the worst moment: she had to hold her breath. "Billy needs *somebody*," Mrs. Campbell would say. And of course there couldn't be any answer to this. She would have some magazines along, fresh from the drugstore, to start reading from, just in case—her thumb ready between any odd pages, it didn't matter which. Quite often Billy would drift in, about then, to hear. It was like reading to the deaf ladies out at the Home—the listening looks would steal over their faces, but what were they hearing, really hearing? Billy and his mama were like that, off in some corner of their own.

When the time would come for her to leave—all too soon for Billy

—he would follow her down the old sagging stairs, repeating the things he'd already told her a hundred times before. But though Billy loved his cousin next to his mother, he never mentioned the secret of Mrs. Curry and the cars to her. As soon as he had let her out the front way and watched her out of sight around the corner, he would bolt the door behind her. Then he would untie the curtains and lower the shades again. He was almost sorry to.

By the middle of the summer Billy was in the habit of setting the alarm clock at odd hours, so as to be reminded to go to the window and see if Mrs. Curry and her friend were still watching him. Of course they tried fooling him, now and then, by turning out the lights. But he knew better. He would sneak out an orange and stand sucking it in front of the icebox door awhile, to cool off, and then he would reset the alarm, doggedly.

The night the fire alarm sounded, Billy thought it was his own clock till he had tried turning it off. At once, down the street, the same old dog started howling, and beyond that another dog, and in a minute all the dogs in Vineland were at it.

Which meant a fire, and Billy had always loved a fire. He pulled his pants on over his nightshirt and, still buttoning, dashed out in his bare feet to the back yard and searched the sky for the glow. Toward town, it was. He was already running. He cleared the ditch in stride and passed the dogs, one after the other, without a thought. Lights were coming on in the houses he passed: each light was a thrill. He wished, suddenly, the whole town would burn—but nobody get hurt.

The fire was at one of the unpainted houses, over on the poor side of town, which was next to the new side. Billy puffed the whole way: it turned out he was the first to arrive except for the close neighbors. He was pretty embarrassed to have to flop down on the scraggly yard grass as soon as he got there, to get his breath. But he had to, in front of everybody: his heart was turning over—like a fish in a bucket.

There in the little yard he was so close to the heat it played like a steady blush on his cheek. He only wished he could be with them, helping save the piano: it was the only thing saved, the only thing worth saving really. But from his sitting position he could only look up in a friendly, apologetic way at the crowd gathering on the dusty sidewalk.

Finally the volunteer firemen—without their hats, most of them—rolled up with their pushcart and trained a couple of hoses on what was left of the house. The house dog commenced to yap at the firemen's legs, and Billy was trying to keep one eye on this dog when all of a sudden one of the leaky hoses started spurting him. The water was cool, though. It cooled him off a little and, anyway, he was just too fagged out to budge.

By the time the firetruck from Valdosta—thirty miles away—came roaring up, nothing was left but the thin little chimney. They had their hats on, Billy noticed. He was storing it all up to tell his mother, when he got home. But people were beginning to leave by then, and Billy felt obliged to trail along after them, even if he hadn't quite caught his breath yet. He would have stayed, but he just didn't want to be left practically alone there.

For days Billy was useless, because of this fire. In a way, he never did get over it, never did quite catch his breath again, never had time to. The next time the alarm sounded, he did try to moderate his pace to a fast walk. But even that could tire him out. Nevertheless, Billy attended every fire he could walk or catch a ride to.

This kept him pretty busy, because all over Vineland houses were burning to the ground.

And everywhere he went, from his own edge of the crowd, Billy heard them talking about it, about how the people in Vineland were burning their houses down for the insurance, but he couldn't believe it. It was even spreading out into the country, they said, and it was true that some barns were beginning to go, but Billy knew that he loved his own house too much ever to think of burning it down, for any amount of money, and he couldn't believe it about them. They could be saying it just to throw him off, seeing him there, and anyhow it came too late. He was sure by then he could tell by the way people looked at him that they thought he was the firebug. Somebody had to be, the way he looked at it. He knew that much.

Mrs. Curry and her friend were the worst about this. He ran into them at fire after fire, and from under her hat Mrs. Curry would look up at him in a peculiar way she had. "Aren't you Billy Campbell?" she said, finally, pretending to be polite. And her friend with her, the Northern-looking one, looked him up and down in the identical way and said, "Not *the* Billy Campbell!" As if they hadn't been spying on him all these weeks. He nodded, though it seemed to him like an admission of guilt. He made one last, despairing effort: he tried smiling at them. But it didn't work. He could tell. When he looked around, he could see the look spreading.

From then on, being the way he was, Billy resigned himself to an inferior station at the fires, half a block or so from wherever the fire happened to be. There was a fire a week, sometimes more, through July and into August. In all, some dozen houses went, and the blacksmith shop, and the Masonic Lodge, and any number of barns out in the country. There were so many fires Billy forgot to watch for the Curry lights, and long before the boys in their cars had tired of their hooting and whistling and imitating things, Billy had stopped caring one way or the other about them. About anything, in fact. Even with his mother, alone with her upstairs in her room with the shades down, he couldn't seem to find the words to tell her how it was.

Some insurance people came to town in August, put up at the old Vine Hotel. Billy picked them out once or twice, strangers among the crowd at the last few fires in the summer, but no more strange to him now than people that had nodded to him all his life. He answered every alarm, night and day, but from his new distance he couldn't even feel the heat: if the wind was wrong, he could almost not smell the smoke, sniffing as hard as he could, and the gay sounds of the crowd and the firemen and the dogs floated more and more indistinctly towards him. The fires—they were like his heart burning inside of him. Sometimes he couldn't even bear to wait for the Valdosta firetruck before turning away for home.

Once when he got home his mother said to him: "Son, it's not good for your heart. It's wearing you out. You know it's not good for your heart, don't you?"

And he had to admit it wasn't. Maybe some night, getting up from the mattress and pulling his pants on over his nightshirt, hearing out in the night the wonderful mad sound of the siren, maybe some night he would keel over, just keel over, and the cousin could come in the next Wednesday to raise the shades and find him stretched out there on the floor. Then everybody would know the truth about him, because the fires would go on and on without him, on and on without him there to be blamed for starting them, and he would be exonerated. He would be smiling his nicest smile, the one he saved for his own family, what was left of it. "What a nice smile!" everybody would say then.

P. H. LOWREY *was born in Verona, Mississippi.*
He grew up there and in Baltimore, attended a
number of schools, including Sewanee and Chicago,
spent the latter part of the war on a destroyer in
the Pacific, wrote for a year at Stanford. He is now
teaching at Vassar and working on short stories and
a novel. He is twenty-nine years old.

TOO YOUNG TO HAVE A GUN

FROM THE SATURDAY EVENING POST

Kirk knew it was his own fault. He wouldn't have needed the gun
if he hadn't got mad and tried to stand up to Butternose McKitridge.
And then it wouldn't have turned into a man's bet, and mama
wouldn't be mad at him.

"You're not going to have any shotgun," mama said, "that's all."
He knew she meant it. She just couldn't understand. He crooked his
arm around the worn BB gun, letting it lie across his thin chest, barrel
up, the way it was in the pictures of hunters and pioneers, and started
back across the pasture toward the house. Even though he knew it
would do no good, he thought he might as well give it one more
try.

His mother was making preserves; the kitchen was hot and smelled
lovely. She looked up when the screen door screeched open and
slammed noisily behind him.

"Don't slam that door," she said.

"Can I have some?" he said. He did not want to come right out
with it.

"Too hot. Maybe later. You feed those dogs?"

"I will," he said. "Mama?"

He pointed the BB gun at the screen door, holding the barrel up
the way his father had taught him, though he knew it wasn't pumped.
"Always do that before you set a gun down," his father said, "even
though you just took the shells out, understand?"

"What?" his mother said. She looked hot, standing there stirring
the preserves. She turned to him, pushing back her iron-gray hair

with one hand. She was a big, strong-limbed woman. "Come on. What?"

"Mama, since I gotta be ready for this bet with old Butternose, can't I buy the little .410? I'll earn it."

He knew he shouldn't have said it, right away. She looked mad; the stirring spoon was cocked out from her hip, and he knew he should have waited until she was sitting quietly on the front porch.

"Kirk, how many times do I have to say no?" she said. "I don't care about the bet. I'm not going to have any twelve-year-old boy running all over this county shooting any shotgun. And you can tell your father that too."

She turned back to the jam, then, and stirred it savagely.

"Yes'm," he said.

"And don't call that poor child 'Butternose.' No wonder he bullies you."

"Aw, mama!" he said. No woman could ever understand. He kicked idly at the sack of dog meal by the stove. "He's fourteen! Anyway, he don't let us call him 'Butternose.' He makes us call him 'Duke.' That's the way he starts to fight you, and daddy says you just got to stand up to him; you heard him say that."

He knew he ought not to go on with it, but he had to make her understand somehow.

"Stop it," she said, and he thought she was going to turn and really give it to him. But then he saw that she was trying hard not to smile, so he knew it was all right.

"You're smilin'," he said.

"Oh, stop it!" she said, but he could see now she was almost laughing. He knew he would have to work fast.

"It isn't funny," she said, trying to look mad. "It's a sin before God."

"You can't stop laughing," he said, grinning. "You think I'm a limb of Satan." That did it. She had to laugh then. He liked the way she laughed suddenly.

"Get on out of here and feed those dogs," she said, still laughing. "And stop lawyerin' around about that gun. You're worse than your father!"

"All right," he said, "but it's a man's bet." He went out fast so she could not say anything more to him.

While he fed Bump and Pompey, crooning to them in the high tone he reserved especially for them, he thought about it. The dogs were in good shape now, lean and hard. He had trained them well, but he was still afraid they were no match for the McKitridge dog, Blue Mike. Blue Mike was a pointer, too, but very tall and big-muscled, even for a McKitridge dog. When he looked at Bump and Pompey and compared them, it scared him a little. He could remember the first time he had ever seen Blue Mike work, and that had been a little frightening too.

He came across a ridge late one afternoon and looked down into the next bottom and saw Old Man McKitridge. For a moment, he did not see the dog. Then he looked far out ahead of Old Man McKitridge, and saw the flat, uncoiling white shape, going away in a perfectly straight line. As he watched, the dog turned and quartered back, still moving in that odd straight line, going very fast. He saw Blue Mike slide diagonally across the field and then drop to a dead point in one corner, standing there like something in marble until Old Man McKitridge came up slowly. It took a long time. After the shot, the dog retrieved fast and was gone again, covering the field in long stretched-out strides, so that he knew it was a big dog before he ever saw it close up.

He opened the chicken-wire door of the dog run when Bump and Pompey finished. Each day now, he let them run after he fed them. He fed them only once a day now, though it was only October. When they finished wolfing the food, he ran them, stopping them occasionally to make them come back and go to heel.

They passed him again, running head to flank, starting on around the house, and he let them get clear around before he called.

"Hyah!" he yelled, and he heard one of them smack into the other and hit the ground, so he knew they had turned. When they came in, he made them follow him to the turtle pen where he kept the snapper.

"Come on, Snapper," he coaxed, prodding at the squat heavy shape of the turtle with a stick. "Come on!" The turtle's malignant eyes followed the prod a moment, and then, without warning, the big snakelike head slammed forward viciously. He prodded again, watching the turtle's open beak carefully. Bump barked and began to lunge at it.

"Git back!" he commanded, kicking at the dog with his bare foot. "You let Snapper get your nose, you won't hunt anything, you fool."

He kicked listlessly at Pompey, too, to keep him back from the turtle. He did not feel like working them today, because he was too worried about Butternose and the gun. He wished he had gone on and fought Butternose, right at first when it happened, even though he knew Butternose would have licked him.

He had gone into town early that morning, to Callicutt's store. Mr. Brannan, the night watchman, was kidding him about the dogs.

"What kind of dogs are they, Kirk?" Mr. Brannan said, smiling out of one corner of his leathery face. "They bird dogs or boy dogs?"

He grinned, because Mr. Brannan always kidded him about the way the dogs trailed him on the bicycle.

"I seen 'em come sniffin' through town here, about thirty minutes behind you, the other day," Mr. Brannan said, "goin' hell for leather. 'Callicutt,' I said, 'I reckon them things would follow that-air train right to Memphis if Kirk took a notion to get on it.' They certainly are good train dogs."

"I like 'em," he said, "they're good dogs."

"I reckon so," Mr. Brannan said. "Didn't I see 'em point that box-car the other day, when you was in it? I know they're good."

He watched Mr. Brannan go on back to the rear of the store, to the dark little counter under the mule collars and farm tools, where the men sat and talked and occasionally slipped the bottle of white whisky up to their lips. He liked it when Mr. Brannan kidded about the dogs.

When he went out the door, Butternose had little Rat Rickert by the neck, holding Rat up against Callicutt's window. Butternose's meaty face, with the peculiar squarish nose glistening and pitted, was close down to Rat's head. He could see Butternose's hand working into the soft flesh of Rat's neck.

"What's my name now, Rat?" Butternose said.

"Duke," Rat said, trying not to show how it hurt. "Duke, Duke, Duke!"

"Don't forget it no more," Butternose said, working his fingers in again.

"O.K., Duke!" Rat gasped, and broke free. He could see the tears held back in Rat's eyes, and he was scared then, because he knew what he was going to do. He wasn't surprised when Butternose grabbed his arm.

"Well, skinnybone," Butternose said, holding his arm tight, "now you tell me my name."

"Fred'rick McKitridge," he said. He could tell from the way Butternose flexed his knee that it was going to be a corn.

"My nickname," Butternose said.

He was about to say "Duke" when the knobby knee came up quick and sharp, just once, into his thigh.

"Butternose!" he said, because the pain of the corn had forced it out of him. "Butternose, Butternose!" He wrenched free and jumped back with his fists up.

He had a minute to get set, because Butternose stood there staring at him. He swung once, and felt his fist hit the shoulder; something jerked his head back and he was swinging as hard as he could, and he felt the red-hot knee again, and then he didn't seem to be hitting anything. When he opened his eyes, Mr. Callicutt had Butternose by the scruff of the neck.

"Same breed as your old man, ain't you, McKitridge?" Mr. Callicutt said, his voice very soft and furry. "Only he don't spoil for trouble till he's drunk." Butternose still looked surprised. "You ain't gonna beat nobody half your size in front of my store."

By that time the men had come out of the store too. Mr. Brannan; Amos Beesinger, who was part Indian, and in whose face you could still see the high cheekbones and flat nose of the race; Sheriff Kent and two farmers. He could not remember how the bet started, because he was still too mad and his jaw had begun to hurt. But he knew Mr. Brannan suggested it. He listened, and he knew he had missed some, but what Mr. Brannan said was clear.

"Now, Kirk here likes to hunt," Mr. Brannan was saying, "and you McKitridges is pot-hunters. Kirk's got him some dogs. I reckon a shootin' match would be right fahr, now I think on it." Mr. Brannan looked over at him carefully. "You ought to agree to that to settle it. Kirk ain't never gonna have flesh to fight you, and you got all them fine dogs, and all."

"Him!" Butternose was saying then. "Him! Hell, he ain't big enough to tote a gun, even! I can beat him with a ol' single shot!"

"I reckon," Mr. Kent, the sheriff, said. "We'd just count the birds in the bag on Christmas Day." The sheriff stroked the white grizzle on his chin, and it sounded like sandpaper. "That suit you, Kirk?"

He was mad then. His leg hurt, and he did not think about it.

"Sure," he said, "I'll match him, Christmas Day." He did not have time to think about how hard it would be.

"He's done offered you a bet, McKitridge," Mr. Callicutt said. That was when he realized; from the stiff, hard way Mr. Callicutt said it, he knew it was a man's bet.

After that, there was nothing he could do. Mr. Brannan offered to buy a pop all around on it, and everybody except Butternose went inside.

"I reckon you done pretty good, Kirk," Mr. Callicutt said, when they got the drinks out.

"I'll bet five on him," Amos Beesinger said. "I'll just take five of that-air little spunky."

"You gonna have to find a McKitridge to take that bet, Amos," the sheriff said. Then the sheriff laughed. "But that won't be hard," he said. "The woods is simply full of them things."

Everybody laughed at that, and he tried to grin too. Then they were arranging for the sheriff to judge the match.

"And you better send Peters out to warden on the other side of town that day, in case they should chancet to go over the limit," Mr. Brannan said.

"Shoot!" the sheriff said. "Peters is liable to hate missin' it so much, he'll resign the warden's job just to come along!"

While they were laughing, he managed to slip out.

He did not tell even his father that day. His father looked at him strangely when he came in that night, but he did not want to tell anybody until he had it arranged. It took him two days to get up nerve to ask Mr. Callicutt about the .410. Standing in Mr. Callicutt's store, he worked the pump, being very careful to do it all right.

"Tell you what," Mr. Callicutt said finally. "That gun ain't sold. I'll give it to you wholesale price."

He thought about that carefully for a while.

"Ten per cent off for cash, of course," Mr. Callicutt said, not looking at him.

"I guess it's still too much," he said.

"Oh?" Mr. Callicutt said. They thought a minute. "You might get a job."

"Yes, sir," he said, "if there was one around."

"Oh," Mr. Callicutt said, "yes."

"Yes, sir," he said. "Well, thank you." He turned, letting his hand run along the counter, starting for the door.

"Wait," Mr. Callicutt said. "I been needin' a boy, afternoons. I'd expect a lot. Can't pay much."

"Would it be enough?" he said.

Mr. Callicutt got out the pad and pencil, and began figuring.

"You'd have a little left over for shells, you work all day Satiddys," Mr. Callicutt said finally.

"Yes, sir," he said, and tried to walk to the door.

When he got outside, he ran. He ran straight to the kitchen and found his mother and told her all at once; how Amos Beesinger was going to bet five, and about Mr. Callicutt, and his mother said no, at once. She began to look queer when he told her, and then she said no.

When his father came in from the farm, they talked about it.

"I'm just not going to allow it," his mother said. "No, sir."

"Now, mama," his father said.

His mother held her head very straight, and he could tell she was mad. Afterward, when she began to cry, he and his father went out and sat on the porch. His father puffed on his pipe for a long time.

"She'll come around," his father said finally.

But she did not come around. She would not budge an inch, so it did not surprise him, really, when his father winked at him the first morning, early in October, and motioned him outside right after breakfast.

"Tell her you're going with me to the farm," his father said.

When they were in the car, his father jerked his head toward the back seat. He looked at the gunny sacks on the floor, and he thought at first it was the .410, but when he unwrapped it, he saw it was his father's big twelve gauge. His father grinned.

"She didn't say anything about the twelve gauge," his father said.

That first day he could remember very well. When they got to the dump, out toward the farm, his father began throwing tin cans up for him. At first he missed, and the gun seemed to kick a lot, but his father just kept sailing the cans out flat and hard.

"That's the way they fly," his father said. "You don't sight 'em. Just swing with them, and when it feels right, pull. You'll get so you know." His father was sweating by that time, grunting when he threw.

By the end of that week, he was hitting a few of them, and the kick did not bother him any more. They went to the dump whenever they could slip away; his father threw the cans and grunted, and he shot. In November Amos Beesinger began to go out with them, so they could put up two cans at once, and before long he was beginning to get both of them. They worked with the dogs, too, trimming them down until their rib cages showed all along the flank, training them, and he talked a good deal to Amos Beesinger and Mr. Brannan about woods shooting and covey flushes and the things you needed to know.

"He just shoots so natural-like, Mr. Frank," Amos said one day as they rode back into town. "It is a purty thing to watch."

"Cans aren't quail," his father said. But Kirk was already feeling fairly sure about it. Amos, particularly, told him a lot; about opening the craw of the first bird, to see what they were eating, and about figuring the way the birds would turn before the flush.

"And quail ain't dumb," Amos told him one day. "Quail talk. They tell each other where they be going. About seventy-eighty foot out, ol' outside birds turn back in toward the center and crost close, so they kin talk and get together again. You wait for 'em, pull just then, you get both birds on one shot." Amos looked at him carefully. "My pappy use' to do that to save shells."

"Do they really talk, Amos?" he said.

"Sompen. Anyways, they crost close."

"I'll remember," he said; "just wait till the season opens."

And he did try to remember everything they told him when the season opened a week later. He spent all his spare time hunting, staying out in the clear, crisp December afternoons until the sun went down. His mother did not suspect anything; she noticed that he came in tired and hungry, but she was used to his being out, and he was careful to be secret. Occasionally his father went with him, but usually he went alone, ranging out over the hills and bottoms and farms which he knew as well as anybody, because he had always traveled over them. One Saturday, Callicutt let him go, and he hunted all day, pausing at the tops of the hills to watch the dogs work the fields of sedge or lespedeza. He was getting doubles on the coveys then. The dogs were working beautifully, and he felt fine about it. That day he got the limit.

"O.K.," his father said, grinning, "we give 'em hell." Then his father thought a minute. "But it's going to be tough."

"Yes, sir," he said, "I know it."

Three days before Christmas the weather turned bad. He kept on hunting, staying out in the damp, sweet-smelling cold until his hands were red and raw in his pockets. Woods shooting still bothered him, but he worried more about the bet and about the McKitridge dog. Maybe that was why, on the day of the match, he was nervous and missed the first two shots.

The first one was a covey, and he thought he was on the birds. He shot twice, and nothing happened. By the time Bump pointed one of the singles from the covey, he was shaking pretty badly. He was very conscious of the line of quiet men behind him and of the fact it was a man's bet, and he missed the bird clean.

He had been nervous about it all morning. He was up before light, and saw it dawn clear and windless. His mother heard him and was up, too, thinking he wanted to open the presents. When they sat around the little tree, after a quick breakfast, he had trouble even thinking about the presents. He could tell his mother knew something was wrong, because his father was quiet, too, even though he and his father had agreed the day before to make it as much like any Christmas as they could. And after the presents there was nothing to do but worry about it until ten o'clock. That part, at least, was easy; he always went with his father to hunt on Christmas Day.

By the time they got to Callicutt's store, all the men were waiting. The sheriff and some of the townsmen, in the sheriff's car. Mr. Brannan; Amos Beesinger, on a tired-looking mule. The McKitridges were there, too, in a mud-splashed pickup. Old Man McKitridge, his face as carved and expressionless as ever, and Butternose and three more of the McKitridge boys. One of the boys was hunkered down in the bed of the pickup with his arm over Blue Mike. Blue Mike just stood there, his big flat head up and alert, looking out balefully at the men, waiting. The way they were all waiting, watching him, scared Kirk. His hands were already shaking a little when they started out, sliding across the muddy hill roads in a long slow line. He turned back once and saw Amos slapping at the tired mule, and Amos waved to him, so he felt a little better. But when they got out at Markham's farm, Markham and his son were waiting too. The men all piled out, quiet and not smiling.

He had trouble getting the shells into the big pump, but he thought he was all right when Pompey pointed the first covey. Then he missed, and by the time he took the shot at the single, his eyes were hot and sandy and he knew he was not on the bird.

The gun seemed to kick a lot on the single. He heard Butternose's gun on the right, two shots, and then one, and Butternose's raucous laugh. And all of a sudden he got mad.

It boiled up in him like getting sick at the stomach; he forgot the line of quiet men behind him, and his father and everything. He yelled at the dogs once and waved his arm hard in the direction he wanted to go, and then he began to walk fast. It was Pompey that pointed then. It was a beauty, and it helped a lot. The dog was quartering a sedge field, moving fast, and came to a log and jumped to it to go on over. But when Pompey's feet hit the top of the log he recoiled suddenly and teetered there, balanced in the clear dead air, ears cocked and head turned down. Kirk could hear the quiet, admiring "Ah-h-h-h" of the men behind him. He got behind the dog quickly; when the birds came up this time, he was not shaking, he was sure, and the first bird collapsed. He took his time on the second shot and saw that one go down too.

"You good dog," he said proudly, when Pompey brought the bird in. "You good ol' dog."

After that he was sure of the shooting. Although he hit the first, he missed the second shot on the next covey, but he did not mind because it was a turning shot into the trees. He got two singles that came from that covey too. Bump and Pompey were hot now; they were not so fast as Blue Mike, but they hunted intelligently and handled the birds well. He was aware of the long white streak that was Blue Mike, far out ahead; he heard Butternose shooting again, and then again, and a third time. But he was busy with his own dogs and the next covey. He got two from that one, and Bump hunted down a single after the covey shot. So it surprised him to hear the sheriff yell for a break and lunch. That meant one o'clock.

It was harder then, standing in the gathered circle of men, while Old Man McKitridge and Mr. Brannan laid out the birds, and the sheriff counted. He tried not to look at the birds, because he was worried again.

"Gentlemen," the sheriff said, "I make it Kirk eight, McKitridge eleven." When the sheriff said, "Eleven," it kept echoing in his mind, *Eleven, eleven, eleven-eleven-eleven.* It was a lot of birds.

Old Man McKitridge squatted close to Butternose, chewing. "My boy got one bird the dogs ain't found," Old Man McKitridge said. His sky-blue eyes stared off into nothingness and his face never changed. No one said anything for a moment.

"I understand it is just birds in the bag," the sheriff said. The sheriff was watching Old Man McKitridge carefully.

"Shuah," Old Man McKitridge said, "that's right, shurf. I was just saying. My boy gonna get plenty more birds."

"I just wanted it clear," the sheriff said.

"That's right," Old Man McKitridge said, still squatting there, not looking at anything. "We ain't worried. Why, that dog ain't even run none yit. He ain't tired."

Kirk knew that was true too. Blue Mike sat at the edge of the circle, erect and still, and he did not look as if he had been running at all. Bump and Pompey were both stretched out, their tongues lolling. When he compared them with Blue Mike, he knew he could count on only one thing. Blue Mike was really Old Man McKitridge's dog; his father thought that Butternose might begin to push the dog too hard and make him run over birds.

He threw away the sandwich he could not eat, when the men stood up again. A wind was blowing from the north now, and dark, spotty clouds had formed, so that they walked under a billowing shade which sometimes swept away, leaving the tawny fields reddened and smelling of earth again. It meant a storm; the birds would be hugging close to cover. They would be hard to find, and time was running out.

By two, the clouds were solid and the wind was strong. He did all he could to coax the dogs; he was pleased that they responded and began to work faster. He got a single, and then one more from a covey in a stand of pin oak where there was no time for a second shot. He heard Butternose shoot twice, and then, later, he could hear him cursing Blue Mike. That helped some; maybe what his father had said was happening now. Maybe Butternose was pushing Mike too fast.

"Forty-five minutes!" the sheriff yelled. "Kirk at ten, McKitridge at thirteen!" The sheriff yelled twice, once to each side. *Three birds,* he kept thinking, *three birds, that means a covey and a single, and now there isn't any time.*

When Bump got the single, he could tell the bird was running. Bump stalked him nervously, trying to hold it, walking stiff-legged as though there were eggs under him. He began to run then; he glanced back once and saw Amos Beesinger right behind him. Amos' thick body was leaning forward a little and his big, flat nose was up, as though he were sniffing. The bird flushed before he got to the dog. He had to throw the heavy gun up and shoot before it got to the trees, and for a moment he thought he had missed. Then he heard Amos' little yip behind him, and he knew the bird was down.

After that he could not remember very well, because it went too fast. He heard Butternose cursing Blue Mike again, violently, and he heard someone yell, "Fifteen minutes!" and he saw Pompey, far out ahead, running hard down a draw, covering ground between birdy spots. Then suddenly Pompey was flattened out to the ground, as though he had come to a full stop in mid-stride. He heard his own voice, yelling, too, then, because it was an absurd point; the dog's head was twisted down and over his right shoulder, and his body was cramped up. The birds were right under him, and it seemed impossible to hold them. He could remember running hard, calling to the dog to hold, and Amos, close up behind him, running, too, calling to him in a strange, quivering voice.

"Ain't no time, Kirk! Get the single and wait! Get 'em when they crost close!"

He ran on, watching the crouched, hewn dog, thinking the covey was bound to break any time. But Pompey had them, and then he was coming slowly, very calm and tired. The birds came up neatly, spread like a fan; he dropped the first one quickly and then he waited, consciously, for what seemed much too long, until the outside birds began to turn in, and he kept on waiting until they were a foot apart, and then he shot.

He never did see the birds go down. He just heard Amos' wild and awful shout close behind him, and felt the big man grab him up and almost throw him down again; he could hear Amos laughing crazily and yelling; something about "I be pretty be-damn!" The men were all laughing and pounding him, but they stopped when Pompey came in the second time, bringing the last bird. The dog was worn down and came in slowly. Kirk forgot the men then, and dropped to his knees to hug the dog, crying now because he was not ashamed any more. From somewhere behind him the sheriff's voice kept going.

"A triple!" the sheriff kept saying. "I am a foolish, fritterin' idiot for shore!"

When the McKitridges came in, everyone got quiet. Butternose was talking loudly, saying something was wrong with it, asking about the time.

"Shut up," Old Man McKitridge said. His voice was sharp and dignified. "You just been whupped fahr, that's all. . . . Shurf, I owe you ten." Old Man McKitridge walked slowly toward the sheriff, tugging for his wallet in the overalls breast pocket.

Then Old Man McKitridge stopped and turned and looked at him so hard he dropped his eyes. It was very quiet; from somewhere he could hear a peckerwood hammering.

"I send my compliments," Old Man McKitridge said quietly. "Ain't many men kin do that. My compliments."

That evening, when he was sitting still in front of the open fire, feeling very tired, he wondered about it. His mother had looked so surprised when he and his father burst in from the car and told her. She had not said much; she just stood there, looking rather white, smiling at him strangely. She had been quiet, too, at supper. He did not know whether she was angry or not.

His father and mother came in then.

"I guess you'd better tell him, mama," his father said. "He's earned it."

His mother looked at the floor. When she spoke, she sounded serious. "Mr. Callicutt brought you a present," she said. "Two presents. They're there on the mantel." She pointed to a long brown package and an envelope that he had not noticed.

He opened the envelope first, because he knew just how the .410 looked and felt, so he did not need to unwrap that. In the envelope were twenty-six one-dollar bills, all new, and a note.

"Any man can do that deserves his pay and his gun both," the penciled note said. It was signed, "Callicutt."

He grinned, and then stopped and looked at his mother, wondering.

"I guess you can keep it," she said, beginning to cry. "It looks like you're old enough to use it."

JAMES A. MAXWELL, *who was born in Cincinnati, Ohio, in 1912 has worked as bank teller, stock-company actor, radio writer, and editor of a sales magazine for an insurance company. Entering the Army as a member of the Counter Intelligence Corps in 1942, he wrote his first short stories while serving in North Africa. They were bought by* The New Yorker: *and since then, as a free-lance writer, his fiction and articles have appeared in* Collier's, Woman's Day, Esquire, *and other magazines. Houghton Mifflin published a collection of his first stories,* I Never Saw an Arab Like Him, *in 1948. He is married to Gene Ludwig.*

FIGHTER

FROM COLLIER'S

Several years will often go by without my thinking of George Schumacher, and then one day, for no apparent reason, something I see —a youngster skipping rope, a man with fear etched into his face like an ugly mutilation, any of a hundred unrelated encounters—will bring him vividly, painfully to mind. Since I have neither seen George nor heard about him for over thirty years, I've often wondered why I remember him so clearly. He was, it's true, the first prize fighter I had ever known, and I was of an age to be impressed with the experience. Also, it was through him that I had my first, if indirect, brush with tragedy.

Probably, however, my memory of George Schumacher is sharp because of the tortured uncertainty of my feelings about him during the time I knew him, and long afterward.

I first saw George one Saturday afternoon in June of 1921, when he and his parents moved into a two-room flat on the third floor of our tenement building in the West End of Cincinnati. They brought their red plush overstuffed chairs, brass bed, heavy oak table and other furniture on a borrowed truck, and George, who did most of the work, handled everything as though it were made of papier-mâché. He was about eighteen and an inch or so below average height, but the symmetry of his body made him seem taller. He had close-cropped blond hair, an open, Teutonic face, a thick neck, powerful, slightly sloping shoulders, impressively muscular arms and legs, and negligible hips and waist. He wore an old pair of blue trousers which, however, were sharply creased, and a gray work shirt, apparently fresh from the laundry.

His mother remained upstairs to arrange the furniture while his father, a huge, fat man with a heavy, untrimmed black mustache, spent most of his time on the truck, fussing ineffectually with the household possessions and shouting meaningless directions at George in a German accent. There was never any indication on George's face that he heard his father.

Our building, which occupied a corner lot, was L-shaped, and within the angle was a fairly large, concrete yard. It was there that I saw George the next morning. When I came out of the back door of our first-floor flat, I was startled to find him dressed in trunks, undershirt and gym shoes, busily skipping rope. Since I had always looked on this as a pastime exclusively for girls, I would have probably laughed had it not been for his skill. The rope circled about him so rapidly that it was almost a blur, and it created an odd rhythm of hisses and slaps as it alternately swished through the air and struck the ground. His feet, scarcely seeming to leave the pavement, provided a counterbeat.

George looked at me, neither annoyed nor pleased at my presence. After a few minutes he stopped, consulted his watch, quickly but carefully folded his rope, and laid it down next to a bathrobe which was lying a few feet away. Then he unfurled the robe, spread it flat on the cement, lay down on it, propped up his hips and legs with his arms, and began "bicycle riding."

"What are you doing that for?" I asked.

"To make my legs strong," he said, as he continued to thrash them in the air. He spoke in the impersonal manner of a man giving directions to a stranger on the street. His tone would probably have discouraged me from further questioning if I hadn't been so curious about his antics.

"Why do you want to make your legs strong?" I asked.

He didn't answer me for several moments, and I thought he had decided to ignore me. "A fighter needs strong legs," he said at last. I couldn't talk for a while. The thought of living in the same house with a prize fighter was only slightly less exciting than being neighbors with a player on the Cincinnati Reds.

He glanced at his watch several times as he continued to work his legs. Finally he completed his allotted time, lowered the up-ended part of his body to the ground, and permitted himself a minute or two of relaxation. Sweat poured from his body and turned the gray robe black around him. He was frowning slightly, because the bright sun struck his face.

"Who do you fight?" I asked.

"Anybody," he said, "so long as they're middleweights."

"Do you win?" I said. "Do you knock guys out?"

"Sometimes I win, sometimes I lose," he said, and he started to get up.

"Will you teach me how to fight?" I asked, suddenly overwhelmed by the memory of countless injustices that could be avenged if I became proficient with my fists.

"Why should I?" he asked. He didn't speak unpleasantly; he asked the question as though he expected a reasonable answer. He was on his feet now, and he made a tidy bundle of his robe and placed it next to the rope. Again he looked at his watch, and then he began to shadowbox, moving easily, with a curious kind of stolid grace.

I stared miserably at him, simultaneously hating him for presenting me with a problem I didn't fully understand, wishing that I had something to offer so that he would teach me how to box as he did, and desperately trying to think of something to say that would break through his detachment. He stopped after a while and looked at me. "Want to help me train?" he asked.

"Sure," I said, with an enthusiasm that was difficult to express because of the tightness of my throat. He asked my name in a business-like manner, and, when I'd answered, he told me his.

"I don't do nothin' for other people free," he said, "and I don't expect them to do things free for me. You could maybe rub oil in my fighting shoes and show me places around here to run and watch the time when I'm exercising; and I have to build a frame for my punching bag. If you want to do stuff like that, I'll give you some lessons and maybe some tickets to my fights. We'll keep track of time. You help me work out for an hour, I'll give you, say ten minutes of lessons. Okay?"

"Sure," I said, thrilled as much by being treated as an adult as I was by the opportunity he gave me.

He went to his bathrobe and pulled a slip of paper out of a pocket. "Here's the training schedule my manager gave me," he said. "When

I get good enough so's I can give up my regular job and fight full time, he'll take over. Now, I only see him when I go to the gym on Saturday and just before fights."

I looked at the handwritten list of exercises and the time opposite each. "You did the first two," I said, feeling more important than I ever had before in my life. "I don't think you did the last one ten minutes."

"I ain't finished yet," he said. He took his watch off and handed it to me. "Don't drop it. I did four minutes. Tell me when it's six minutes more."

I held the heavy timepiece in my cupped palm, the two pieces of damp leather strap curling clammily around my hand, and stared hard at the dial. He resumed his shadowboxing. George, I soon found, followed his schedule as literally as a religious rite.

He had been doing calisthenics for about a half hour when his father's voice boomed, "Hey, box-fighter, stop that dumb kid business and come upstairs. Mama's got breakfast ready."

I looked up and saw Mr. Schumacher on the small porch that adjoined the flat. George was on his bathrobe again, alternately lying flat and rising to a sitting position to touch his toes. As he had done the day before, George completely ignored his father.

The older man looked down at us contemptuously. "*Dummkopf*," he shouted. "Cut out that monkeyshines and come right away upstairs. You think we wait all day for you?"

But the rhythm of George's movements didn't change. I looked back and forth from father to son in embarrassment. "Your father . . ." I finally said.

"I can hear," George muttered between deep breaths. "How much time?"

I looked at the watch and then up at the glowering face of Mr. Schumacher. "Four more minutes," I said unhappily. The belligerent man on the porch frightened me, and I felt that I was partially responsible for his growing anger.

"You going to make like jumping jack all day?" he bellowed. "Kid stuff, all the time, kid stuff." Faces began to appear at various windows to see the cause of the commotion. "You think we wait all day till Mister Box-fighter is ready to eat? Come up right away or I throw your eggs in the garbage." He spat over the porch rail and stomped indoors.

George didn't halt his exercise until I had told him that the proper time had elapsed. Then he methodically dried the sweat from his face and arms with a ragged but clean towel that he had carried in his robe pocket, put on the bathrobe, and picked up his rope. "What time do you eat supper during the week?" he asked.

"About six-thirty," I said.

"Good," he said. "I get home from work a little after five. That gives us an hour to work out. See you tomorrow." I handed him his watch, and he turned and started briskly for the steps.

A new and tremendously exciting period of my life began. The fact that George and I did exactly the same thing every evening did nothing to lessen my enthusiasm, since I felt certain that he would become a world champion, and each session seemed another step toward that goal. Our routine called for a half hour of exercise in the back yard, and then we'd go to Lincoln Park, which was two blocks away, for the road work. Afterward we'd return to the yard, and George would give me my ten minutes—never more or less—of instruction.

It must have been dull, frustrating work for him to teach the basic elements of boxing to a nine-year-old boy who had only average co-ordination and no real desire to endure the discipline of learning. Yet he never attempted to avoid what he considered his obligation, and I was too afraid of upsetting our tenuous relationship to suggest omitting lessons, even though I often grew enraged at his constant demand for perfection. Both of us, I'm certain, were grateful for the brevity of the period.

His teaching was put to almost immediate use. Soon almost every boy in the neighborhood heard about George and wanted to join his circle. I had to fight to maintain my prerogatives. On most evenings, he had an audience of anywhere from eight to twenty boys in the yard, and I can still recall the ecstatic sensation I had when I'd yell, "Time's up! Punching bag next!" and the other boys would look at the watch in my hand with all the envy of gem merchants staring at the Kohinoor diamond.

In retrospect, it's difficult to see why we were so faithful to him. Certainly he did nothing to encourage hero worship. He tolerated the boys, I believe, not because of any sympathy with them but rather because his icy concentration made him almost totally unaware of their presence. He never spoke to any of us except to warn someone not to come too close to the area of activity or to ask me about the time. I suppose that all of us were impressed with a man so obviously dedicated to his craft.

I would probably have learned almost nothing about George if it hadn't been for the evenings I spent in the Schumacher flat. He always accepted my excuses when I said that his fighting shoes needed treatment with saddle soap or that the punching bag required inflation from my bicycle pump, so I frequently saw him in what was, for him, a relaxed atmosphere. Even then he was not especially talkative, but he did tell me a little about himself.

He worked, I found, crating parts in a nearby machine shop, but he looked upon his job as only a stopgap until he could devote his full time to fighting. His plans, however, didn't stop with the ring. He hoped to make enough money with his fists to go into business when he was too old to fight, and, with this end in view, he was taking a high-school correspondence course.

On most evenings Mr. Schumacher left the flat almost immediately after supper and played pinochle until bedtime with some cronies in a nearby pool hall. Sometimes, however, he'd spend the night at home, and on those occasions I usually shortened my visit with George. The older man talked almost constantly in a loud, complaining voice. He found fault with his wife, a pale, drab woman who always worked at a feverish disorganized pace, but he directed most of his vituperation at his son.

Boxing, according to Mr. Schumacher, bred only bums, crooks, and thugs, and the constant blows on the head made a man crazy. He pretended to find evidence of mental regression already apparent in his son's behavior. The fact that Mr. Schumacher expressed the same thoughts in almost exactly the same words each time he launched an attack never diminished his vehemence. Apparently George had been exposed to this incessant gabble for so long that he had developed the kind of selective deafness that protects a man who works in a foundry. In any case, George never bothered to refute any of his father's statements, regardless of how outrageous they became.

But even Mr. Schumacher couldn't charge George with engaging in the usual teen-age frivolities. Whatever interest George had in girls, for example, was completely subjugated to the pursuit of his career. I don't think that he had a single date during the period that I knew him. Only once did he display any enthusiasm for seeing a movie and that was when the pictures of the Dempsey-Carpentier fight were shown at our neighborhood theater one Sunday in early July. "Dempsey's a fighter and Carpentier's a boxer," he said. "I want to see everything they do."

George and I went to the first showing at about two in the afternoon. During the fight scenes, he sat on the edge of his seat and
riveted his attention on the screen with the concentration of a medical student observing a rare operation. During the feature film and
the serial which followed, however, George relaxed and closed his
eyes. At first I thought he had gone to sleep, but then I noticed a
rhythmical clenching and relaxing of his hands. When I looked more
closely, I saw that he had a sponge-rubber ball in each palm and was
using the interlude between fight sequences to strengthen his wrists.
I sat through two complete shows with him, and then I had to go
home to dinner. George, who had come provided with several sandwiches and some candy, stayed until nine that night and saw Dempsey knock out the Frenchman five times.

In late August, I saw my first prize fight. The event took place in
the outdoor arena at Fort Thomas, Kentucky, just across the Ohio
River from Cincinnati, and George was on the card in one of the preliminary bouts. He had given me two tickets as part of my pay, and
I'd persuaded my father to take me.

I fought every moment of that bout with George. I felt pain when
he was hit and fierce exultation when he landed a blow. I was, I'm
certain, much more emotionally involved in the contest than George
was. He went about his work coolly, and when his opponent landed a
solid blow, George showed only puzzled concern, as if he had made
an error in adding up a column of figures. I continued to scream encouragement to George throughout the bout, and, at the end of the
scheduled five rounds, when the referee raised George's hand in a
symbol of victory, I became almost hysterical.

After a fight, George did no training for three days, so I didn't see
him the next afternoon. As soon as I had bolted my dinner that evening, however, I hurried upstairs to the Schumacher flat to offer my
congratulations. I carried with me a clipping from the sports page
of the evening paper.

The Schumachers were still eating when I burst into the kitchen,
which also served as dining room, living room, and George's bedroom. "You really beat up that guy, George," I called happily as I
came through the door. "You got your name in the paper and everything. Just listen. *George Schumacher showed promising form in taking a five-round decision from Babe Lehman.*" I handed the clipping
to George. "You can have it if you want it."

He looked at the words soberly. "That's good, that 'promising,'" he said. "That's good."

Mr. Schumacher flung his fork down hard on the thick, white plate. "Next you hold up a bank and get your name on the *first* page," he bellowed, with a mixture of anger and mockery. "Dumb kid stuff. So now you're big, important man just like the mayor, with your name in the paper. Already your head is soft like a melon, Mister Box-fighter. After fists comes guns. Then we come see you in jail." His round, fat face became flushed as his anger mounted, and his mustache quivered as though it were mounted on a spring.

Mrs. Schumacher looked anxiously at her husband and son. "He's a good boy, Papa," she said, looking at her plate.

"*Dummkopf!*" Mr. Schumacher bellowed. "*Dummkopf!*"

George finally looked up from the paper. "Shut up, Papa," he said in a low, carefully controlled voice.

Mr. Schumacher half rose from his chair. "Who you telling shut up?" he yelled.

George stared at his father, and a curious overtone of pleading crept into his voice. "Don't make me mad, Papa," he said.

For the first time, I saw uncertainty in the older man's face. Slowly he resumed his seat. "Why we don't have coffee, woman?" he demanded loudly of his wife.

George won all three of the fights he had during the next two months. One victory was by a knockout. The sports writers began to devote more space to him, and gradually he became as much a celebrity with the adults in our neighborhood as he was with the boys of my age. A number of men began to visit our training area in the back yard, and even a few giggling girls of George's age joined the group. I basked in the attention I received as George's associate.

In mid-November, George won another fight by a knockout. The next night I was so anxious to see him that I waited on the front steps for him to come home from work. Again I had a clipping with me, and this time there was an entire paragraph about him.

George was more buoyant than I'd ever seen him before. He gave a quick glance at the story I handed to him and then thanked me gravely for my exuberant compliments on his performance in the ring. "That was an important fight for me last night," he said as he returned the clipping to me. "My manager said that now we're getting more money, he wants me to train at the gym every night."

For a moment the significance of his statement didn't strike me. When it did, I found it difficult to speak. "Then what about . . ."

"They got guys over there to time you and take care of equipment and stuff," he said. "I won't need you any more." He spoke as though he were telling a newsboy to discontinue the evening paper.

For a moment the steps seemed to be dissolving under me. My face actually stung, as if he had slapped me. I couldn't look at his eyes, and when I glanced down I saw the big silver watch on his wrist. Suddenly I knew I was going to cry, and a strange mixture of blind fury, despair, and unbearable shame flowed through me in a sickening flood.

He put his hand on my arm, and for the first and only time that I knew him, his voice was intimate and almost gentle. "We had a business arrangement," he said. "Everybody has business arrangements," he said. "Everybody has business arrangements." Then he went up the stairs, two at a time, easily, lightly, as he always did, and the sound of his steps became gradually fainter and fainter until finally it was inaudible.

For some time after that I tried to pretend to myself that I was no longer interested in George's fortunes. Since I was a daily reader of the sports page, this self-deception wasn't easy. I tried to look at only the stories about football and basketball, and at the usual winter predictions about the Reds' chances in the next baseball season, but I always ended by reading all the fight news, too. George's name didn't appear often, but whenever it did, my breath would become short.

He continued to do well. He didn't fight in December, but he won two bouts in January and knocked out his man in March. A small picture of George was in one of the evening papers after this last triumph, and the statement was made that he was being considered as one of the fighters in the "semi-windup"—the second most important match of a charity boxing show at the ball park in late May.

None of this changed the habits or attitudes in the Schumacher home. George continued to hold his job in the machine shop, and Mr. Schumacher, if anything, increased the volume and acrimony of his attacks. Although I no longer visited the Schumacher flat, there was no difficulty in hearing him in our apartment on the first floor. Whenever Mr. Schumacher was especially bad, I found myself, strongly against my will, again an ally of George's.

There was considerable excitement throughout our immediate neighborhood in early May when the papers announced that George had been signed for the predicted position on the charity card. His opponent, Kid Flannigan, according to the stories, had been an outstanding middleweight in and around Cincinnati three or four years before, and since that time had been fighting on the West Coast. The sports writers made much of the fact that he was a thoroughly experienced, competent fighter and concentrated heavily on the middle-aged veteran *vs.* strong-young-novice aspect of the match.

One evening, about a week before the fight, George came home from work and called to me as I was tossing a ball with a friend. Reluctantly, I walked to the entrance of the tenement, where George was waiting for me. "Want to go to the fight?" he asked.

I swallowed hard. "I guess so," I managed to say.

"I got two tickets," he said. He took two narrow strips of green cardboard from his pocket and seemed to weigh them in his hand. "I don't think my father will want to use them," he added dryly. It was the only approach to humor I'd ever heard him make.

"That's Friday night, ain't it?" I asked, to cover my feeling of awkwardness. I, of course, knew not only the date and place of the fight, but also the respective weights, arm lengths, ages, and won-and-lost records of both the fighters.

George nodded. "I'll give you the tickets if you'll work on my shoes Thursday night. I want them nice and easy. This might be a tough one. Nobody's seen this guy fight for a long time, and he don't get in from California till Wednesday."

"Sure," I said, and for the moment all previous humiliation was forgotten. "I'll do them."

Father agreed quickly when I asked him to take me to the fights. The night we went to the ball park was clear and cool, and I wore a heavy sweater underneath my coat. Redland Field looked strangely unfamiliar with the ring and temporary seats set up in right field and the portable electric lights throwing a shadowless glow over the area. We were in the fourth row, and since Father had the foresight to bring a cushion for me to sit on, I had an excellent view of the proceedings.

I grew warm with excitement as the preliminary fights ended and George's match was about to begin, so Father let me remove my jacket. Finally George came down the aisle and climbed through the ropes, and I swelled with pride as the large crowd applauded. There was a similar greeting when George's opponent, Kid Flannigan, entered the ring, but there was an undertone of murmurs, too, at the sight of his balding head and the gray around his temples. He was, I knew, only about thirty-six, but he looked older.

The current of low talk turned into laughter and scattered hoots of derision when the men took off their robes after the usual mid-ring conference with the referee. Flannigan was obviously fat and out of condition. A roll of flesh hung over the top of his trunks, and his skin, under the glare of the ring lights, looked snail-colored and lifeless. "Hey, Flannigan," a man behind me shouted, "how long since you was a 'Kid'?" and another in our row yelled, "Schumacher, you oughtta be ashamed to hit your own grandfather!" There were similar cries from other parts of the stands. I felt like hiding under the seats.

But the first round surprised us all, probably George included. Flannigan's crouching style made him a difficult target to hit, and he still possessed enough skill to block almost all of George's punches. I could see puzzlement in George's eyes as he tried to fathom the other man's defense. Aside from a few light blows at George's stomach, Flannigan concentrated almost entirely on protecting himself. There was nothing to thrill the spectators, but I think everyone was relieved that the expected butchery did not take place. At the end of the round, Flannigan managed to smile at his handlers as he walked toward his corner, but he was gasping for breath as if he'd run a mile at full speed.

The second and third rounds were duplicates of the first, and a number of men in the crowd began a slow, rhythmical clapping. As soon as the fourth round began, however, it was apparent that Flannigan's body could no longer respond to the shrewd generalship that his mind was providing. He tried to block as he had before, but his movements were a split second too slow, and George's punches began to land on the older man's face, starting a flow of blood from his nose and making a cut over his right eye. George went about the business efficiently, calmly, like a man firing a gun at an empty oil drum. A curious quiet came over the ball park.

And yet I don't think that anyone was completely prepared for the knockout when it came. George aimed a right hook to the jaw, but Flannigan partially parried the blow, and the glove landed with no great force high on the side of his head. An expression of excruciating pain came over Flannigan's face, and then he collapsed to the floor. George stared down at him in bewilderment, and the referee had to push George out of the way to begin counting over the prone body. Flannigan's handlers had to lift their inert, blood-smeared fighter through the ropes. There were only a few cheers as George left the ring.

I tried to capture the exultation I had always had when George won other fights, but I couldn't rid myself of a vague, persistent sense of shame. I hated myself for being disloyal to George, and I tried to take pride in the skill he had shown in beating the other man so badly. The queasiness remained, however. Father must have sensed my disquiet, because he asked if I wanted to leave before the main event. I nodded.

Before breakfast the next morning, while I was washing my hands and face at the kitchen sink, Bill Palmer, a friend of mine, flung open the screen door and rushed into the room. "Hey," he cried, "did you know George killed that guy last night?"

My knees suddenly felt weak, and I clung to the edge of the sink with my elbows. "You're nuts," I said.

"Yeah?" he said triumphantly. "Well, it's right on the front page of the *Enquirer*. They took him up to the General Hospital, and that's where he died. How'd George do it, huh? How'd George do it?"

I couldn't think of anything to say, and the water continued to pour on my hands until my mother said, "Turn off the faucet. You're splashing the floor."

Nothing followed its usual course that Saturday. Contrary to his custom, George hadn't gone to work that morning, but I didn't know that until about ten o'clock when a policeman came for him. I was on the street in front of the house when the two men came out. The officer seemed to be talking to him in a friendly fashion, but I couldn't hear what was being said. My companions began to discuss George's going to the penitentiary. I made a hurried, incoherent excuse and went home.

I was sitting on the front steps alone when George returned about noon. As he walked toward me, he passed a number of people who knew him. Most of them obviously wanted to stop and speak to him but could think of no appropriate remarks. George seemed as phlegmatic as ever when he returned their brief greetings.

My relief at seeing him temporarily blotted out any other sensations. "That cop," I said when he came up to me, "I thought you . . ."

George shook his head. "I just had to make a statement. Whenever a man is—whenever something happens, the other guy has to make a statement." His voice was even, but he was flexing his hands, and, for an absurd moment, I thought he was exercising them with rubber balls as he had that day in the theater.

"Is it all right, then?" I asked.

"Let's go back to the yard," he said. "My old man's about due home from work." As he walked through the hall, he continued, "The promoter and Flannigan's manager will maybe catch hell for letting him fight. But that's about all."

We sat down on a cellar door in the yard. Neither of us said anything for several minutes, and I found myself looking with a kind of superstitious awe at George's right hand.

"It ain't like I did it on purpose," George said at last. "I mean, I didn't hit him with an illegal punch or anything. I didn't even hit him hard. It just caught him wrong, high up on the head like that, and started a hemorrhage in his brain."

"Sure," I said, and for the first time since the fight there seemed to be a lessening of the pressure on my chest, "you didn't hit him hard."

"It's just one of the chances a guy takes when he fights," George said, "like anything else. Bricklayers fall off buildings and cabdrivers get in wrecks, don't they? It could happen to anybody." He had, I think, forgotten that I was there. He sounded like a lawyer presenting a logical, unemotional argument before a court. But there was a slightly tentative quality to his voice, too, as if he expected someone to attempt to refute his evidence.

"Look at ballplayers," I said eagerly, "or even guys who just go to the games. Sometimes even they get hit with a foul tip or a wild throw." I wanted George to go on; I wanted everything to be as it had been before the fight.

"It's like that with anything you do," George said, and his tone was stronger now, more certain. "It could of been me instead of the other guy. I was just doing what I was gettin' paid for. I was in there taking a chance, too. He just wasn't lucky."

I began to feel good again. As George continued to talk, the memory of the previous night became dimmer, and Flannigan's death became more and more a remote, unavoidable mishap, like a newspaper account of a man tripping on the stairs.

I don't know how long Mr. Schumacher had been standing in the doorway between the hall and the yard. I happened to look up and see him there, and a queer hollowness seized my stomach. He seemed strangely shrunken in the shadows, and he looked at his son with a kind of fear I had never seen.

George didn't see his father until the older man started to walk slowly, laboriously, toward us. George's body became taut, and a dark red flush started below his collar and spread over his face. His hands began to tremble uncontrollably; he made fists of them and held his arms rigid by his side. After he had glanced up to see who was coming, he shifted his gaze to his feet stretched before him and stared at them.

Mr. Schumacher didn't stop until his knees were almost touching his son's arm. He looked down at George for at least a minute without saying anything. When he did speak, his voice was gravelly. "It was accident, Georgie," he said. "It was accident." Then he turned and walked back the way he had come.

For several moments after Mr. Schumacher had gone, George remained in his frozen position. And then he gave a short brutal laugh. " 'It was accident, Georgie,' " he said mockingly. "That's all I need, that big dumb ox feeling sorry for me." He began working his hands again, and a note of desperation came into his voice. "Instead of yelling his brains out, he's gonna sit across the table every damned night looking at me and making me feel like I got drunk and run over a kid with an automobile." Suddenly he began to pound on his leg with his right fist, harder and harder, as if he were driving a nail into the flesh. "The dirty——!" he said; then his voice broke into a sob. "The dirty son of a——!" His face contorted, and I knew he was going to cry like a child. In panic, I ran across the yard and into the house.

A week went by after that, and I didn't see George although I looked for him through our front window every day about the time he usually came home from work. Then one morning, I gathered my courage and stopped Mr. Schumacher as he came down the steps. "Where's George?" I asked.

Mr. Schumacher at first looked at me in bewilderment as if he didn't recognize me. "He went," he said slowly. "I don't know where. He just went." Then he walked past me.

For a long time after that, I used to look at the sports page every night, but I never saw George's name again except for a single story which reported that he had left town. If he continued to fight, he did so under another name. Somehow, I don't think he did.

About a month after George had gone, Mr. and Mrs. Schumacher also left our building. But this time, professional movers handled their furniture.

FLANNERY O'CONNOR *was brought up in Savannah, Georgia, and attended parochial schools there. She attended Georgia State College for Women and the State University of Iowa. Her first novel,* Wise Blood, *was published by Harcourt, Brace in 1952. "Now," she says, "I live outside Milledgeville, Georgia, and keep a few peafowl."*

THE LIFE YOU SAVE MAY BE YOUR OWN

FROM KENYON REVIEW

The old woman and her daughter were sitting on their porch when Mr. Shiftlet came up their road for the first time. The old woman slid to the edge of her chair and leaned forward, shading her eyes from the piercing sunset with her hand. The daughter could not see far in front of her and continued to play with her fingers. Although the old woman lived in this desolate spot with only her daughter and she had never seen Mr. Shiftlet before, she could tell, even from a distance, that he was a tramp and no one to be afraid of. His left coat sleeve was folded up to show there was only half an arm in it and his gaunt figure listed slightly to the side as if the breeze were pushing him. He had on a black town suit and a brown felt hat that was turned up in the front and down in the back and he carried a tin tool box by a handle. He came on, at an amble, up her road, his face turned toward the sun, which appeared to be balancing itself on the peak of a small mountain.

The old woman didn't change her position until he was almost into her yard; then she rose with one hand fisted on her hip. The daughter, a large girl in a short blue organdy dress, saw him all at once and jumped up and began to stamp and point and make excited speechless sounds.

Mr. Shiftlet stopped just inside the yard and set his box on the ground and tipped his hat at her as if she were not in the least afflicted; then he turned toward the old woman and swung the hat all the way off. He had long black slick hair that hung flat from a part in the middle to beyond the tips of his ears on either side. His face descended in forehead for more than half its length and ended suddenly with his features just balanced over a jutting steel-trap jaw. He seemed to be a young man but he had a look of composed dissatisfaction as if he understood life thoroughly.

"Good evening," the old woman said. She was about the size of a cedar fence post and she had a man's grey hat pulled down low over her head.

The tramp stood looking at her and didn't answer. He turned his back and faced the sunset. He swung both his whole and his short arm up slowly so that they indicated an expanse of sky and his figure formed a crooked cross. The old woman watched him with her arms folded across her chest as if she were the owner of the sun, and the daughter watched, her head thrust forward and her fat helpless hands hanging at the wrists. She had long pink-gold hair and eyes as blue as a peacock's neck.

He held the pose for almost fifty seconds and then he picked up his box and came on to the porch and dropped down on the bottom step. "Lady," he said in a firm nasal voice, "I'd give a fortune to live where I could see me a sun do that every evening."

"Does it every evening," the old woman said, and sat back down. The daughter sat down too and watched him with a cautious sly look as if he were a bird that had come up very close. He leaned to one side, rooting in his pants pocket, and in a second he brought out a package of chewing gun and offered her a piece. She took it and unpeeled it and began to chew without taking her eyes off him. He offered the old woman a piece but she only raised her upper lip to indicate she had no teeth.

Mr. Shiftlet's pale sharp glance had already passed over everything in the yard—the pump near the corner of the house and the big fig tree that three or four chickens were preparing to roost in—and had moved to a shed where he saw the square rusted back of an automobile. "You ladies drive?" he asked.

"That car ain't run in fifteen year," the old woman said. "The day my husband died, it quit running."

"Nothing is like it used to be, lady," he said. "The world is almost rotten."

"That's right," the old woman said. "You from around here?"

"Name Tom T. Shiftlet," he murmured, looking at the tires.

"I'm pleased to meet you," the old woman said. "Name Lucynell Crater and daughter Lucynell Crater. What you doing around here, Mr. Shiftlet?"

He judged the car to be about a 1928 or '29 Ford. "Lady," he said, and turned and gave her his full attention, "lemme tell you something. There's one of these doctors in Atlanta that's taken a knife and cut the human heart—the human heart," he repeated, leaning forward, "out of a man's chest and held it in his hand," and he held his hand out, palm up, as if it were slightly weighted with the human heart, "and studied it like it was a day-old chicken, and, lady," he said, allowing a long significant pause in which his head slid forward and his clay-colored eyes brightened, "he don't know no more about it than you or me."

"That's right," the old woman said.

"Why, if he was to take that knife and cut into every corner of it, he still wouldn't know no more than you or me. What you want to bet?"

"Nothing," the old woman said wisely. "Where you come from, Mr. Shiftlet?"

He didn't answer. He reached into his pocket and brought out a sack of tobacco and a package of cigarette papers and rolled himself a cigarette, expertly with one hand, and attached it in a hanging position to his upper lip. Then he took a box of wooden matches from his pocket and struck one on his shoe. He held the burning match as if he were studying the mystery of flame while it traveled dangerously toward his skin. The daughter began to make loud noises and to point to his hand and shake her finger at him, but when the flame was just before touching him, he leaned down with his hand cupped over it as if he were going to set fire to his nose and lit the cigarette.

He flipped away the dead match and blew a stream of grey into the evening. A sly look came over his face. "Lady," he said, "nowadays, people'll do anything anyways. I can tell you my name is Tom T. Shiftlet and I come from Tarwater, Tennessee, but you never have seen me before: how you know I ain't lying? How you know my name ain't Aaron Sparks, lady, and I come from Singleberry, Georgia, or how you know it's not George Speeds and I come from Lucy, Alabama, or how you know I ain't Thompson Bright from Toolafalls, Mississippi?"

"I don't know nothing about you," the old woman muttered, irked.

"Lady," he said, "people don't care how they lie. Maybe the best I can tell you is, I'm a man, but listen, lady," he said, and paused and made his tone more ominous still, "what is a man?"

The old woman began to gum a seed. "What you carry in that tin box, Mr. Shiftlet?" she asked.

"Tools," he said, put back. "I'm a carpenter."

"Well, if you come out here to work, I'll be able to feed you and give you a place to sleep but I can't pay. I'll tell you that before you begin," she said.

There was no answer at once and no particular expression on his face. He leaned back against the two-by-four that helped support the porch roof. "Lady," he said slowly, "there's some men that some things mean more to them than money." The old woman rocked without comment and the daughter watched the trigger that moved up and down in his neck. He told the old woman then that all most people were interested in was money, but he asked what a man was made for. He asked her if a man was made for money, or what. He asked her what she thought she was made for but she didn't answer, she only sat rocking and wondered if a one-armed man could put a new roof on her garden house. He asked a lot of questions that she didn't answer. He told her that he was twenty-eight years old and had lived a varied life. He had been a gospel singer, a foreman on the railroad, an assistant in an undertaking parlor, and he had come over the radio for three months with Uncle Roy and his Red Creek Wranglers. He said he had fought and bled in the Arm Service of his country and visited every foreign land and that everywhere he had seen people that didn't care if they did a thing one way or another. He said he hadn't been raised thataway.

A fat yellow moon appeared in the branches of the fig tree as if it were going to roost there with the chickens. He said that a man had to escape to the country to see the world whole and that he wished he lived in a desolate place like this where he could see the sun go down every evening like God make it to do.

"Are you married or are you single?" the old woman asked.

There was a long silence. "Lady," he asked finally, "where would you find an innocent woman today? I wouldn't have any of this trash I could just pick up."

The daughter was leaning very far down, hanging her head almost between her knees, watching him through a triangular door she had made in her overturned hair; and she suddenly fell in a heap on the floor and began to whimper. Mr. Shiftlet straightened her out and helped her get back in the chair.

"Is she your baby girl?" he asked.

"My only," the old woman said, "and she's the sweetest girl in the world. I wouldn't give her up for nothing on earth. She's smart too. She can sweep the floor, cook, wash, feed the chickens, and hoe. I wouldn't give her up for a casket of jewels."

"No," he said kindly, "don't ever let any man take her away from you."

"Any man come after her," the old woman said, " 'll have to stay around the place."

Mr. Shiftlet's eye in the darkness was focussed on a part of the automobile bumper that glittered in the distance. "Lady," he said, jerking his short arm up as if he could point with it to her house and yard and pump, "there ain't a broken thing on this plantation that I couldn't fix for you, one-arm jacklet or not. I'm a man," he said with a sullen dignity, "even if I ain't a whole one. I got," he said, tapping his knuckles on the floor to emphasize the immensity of what he was going to say, "a moral intelligence!" and his face pierced out of the darkness into a shaft of doorlight and he stared at her as if he were astonished himself at this impossible truth.

The old woman was not impressed with the phrase. "I told you you could hang around and work for food," she said, "if you don't mind sleeping in that car yonder."

"Why listen, lady," he said with a grin of delight, "the monks of old slept in their coffins!"

"They wasn't as advanced as we are," the old woman said.

The next morning he began on the roof of the garden house while Lucynell, the daughter, sat on a rock and watched him work. He had not been around a week before the change he had made in the place was apparent. He had patched the front and back steps, built a new hog pen, restored a fence, and taught Lucynell, who was completely deaf, and had never said a word in her life, to say the word "bird." The big rosy-faced girl followed him everywhere, saying, "Burrttddt ddbirrrttdt," and clapping her hands. The old woman watched from a distance, secretly pleased. She was ravenous for a son-in-law.

Mr. Shiftlet slept on the hard narrow back seat of the car with his feet out the side window. He had his razor and a can of water on a crate that served him as a bedside table and he put up a piece of mirror against the back glass and kept his coat neatly on a hanger that he hung over one of the windows.

In the evenings he sat on the steps and talked while the old woman and Lucynell rocked violently in their chairs on either side of him. The old woman's three mountains were black against the dark blue sky and were visited off and on by various planets and by the moon after it had left the chickens. Mr. Shiftlet pointed out that the reason he had improved this plantation was because he had taken a personal interest in it. He said he was even going to make the automobile run.

He had raised the hood and studied the mechanism and he said he could tell that the car had been built in the days when cars were really built. You take now, he said, one man puts in one bolt and another man puts in another bolt and another man puts in another bolt so that it's a man for a bolt. That's why you have to pay so much for a car: you're paying all those men. Now if you didn't have to pay but one man, you could get you a cheaper car and one that had had a personal interest taken in it, and it would be a better car. The old woman agreed with him that this was so.

Mr. Shiftlet said that the trouble with the world was that nobody cared, or stopped and took any trouble. He said he never would have been able to teach Lucynell to say a word if he hadn't cared and stopped long enough.

"Teach her to say something else," the old woman said.

"What you want her to say next?" Mr. Shiftlet asked.

The old woman's smile was broad and toothless and suggestive. "Teach her to say, 'sugarpie,' " she said.

Mr. Shiftlet already knew what was on her mind.

The next day he began to tinker with the automobile and that evening he told her that if she would buy a fan belt, he would be able to make the car run.

The old woman said she would give him the money. "You see that girl yonder?" she asked, pointing to Lucynell, who was sitting on the floor a foot away, watching him, her eyes blue even in the dark. "If it was ever a man wanted to take her away, I would say, 'No man on earth is going to take that sweet girl of mine away from me!' but if he was to say, 'Lady, I don't want to take her away, I want her right here,' I would say, 'Mister, I don't blame you none. I wouldn't pass up a chance to live in a permanent place and get the sweetest girl in the world myself. You ain't no fool,' I would say."

"How old is she?" Mr. Shiftlet asked casually.

"Fifteen, sixteen," the old woman said. The girl was nearly thirty but because of her innocence it was impossible to guess.

"It would be a good idea to paint it too," Mr. Shiftlet remarked. "You don't want it to rust out."

"We'll see about that later," the old woman said.

The next day he walked into town and returned with the parts he needed, and a can of gasoline. Late in the afternoon, terrible noises issued from the shed and the old woman rushed out of the house, thinking Lucynell was somewhere having a fit. Lucynell was sitting on a chicken crate, stamping her feet and screaming, "Burrddttt! bddurrddtttt!" but her fuss was drowned out by the car. With a volley of blasts it emerged from the shed, moving in a fierce and stately way. Mr. Shiftlet was in the driver's seat, sitting very erect. He had an expression of serious modesty on his face as if he had just raised the dead.

That night, rocking on the porch, the old woman began her business at once. "You want you an innocent woman, don't you?" she asked sympathetically. "You don't want none of this trash."

"No'm, I don't," Mr. Shiftlet said.

"One that can't talk," she continued, "can't sass you back or use foul language. That's the kind for you to have. Right there," and she pointed to Lucynell sitting cross-legged in her chair, holding both feet in her hands.

"That's right," he admitted. "She wouldn't give me any trouble."

"Saturday," the old woman said, "you and her and me can drive into town and get married."

Mr. Shiftlet eased his position on the steps.

"I can't get married right now," he said. "Everything you want to do takes money and I ain't got any."

"What you need with money?" she asked.

"It takes money," he said. "Some people'll do anything anyhow these days, but the way I think, I wouldn't marry no woman that I couldn't take on a trip like she was somebody. I mean take her to a hotel and treat her. I wouldn't marry the Duchesser Windsor," he said firmly, "unless I could take her to a hotel and give her something good to eat.

"I was raised thataway and there ain't a thing I can do about it. My old mother taught me how to do."

"Lucynell don't even know what a hotel is," the old woman muttered. "Listen here, Mr. Shiftlet," she said, sliding forward in her chair, "you'd be getting a permanent house and a deep well and the most innocent girl in the world. You don't need no money. Lemme

tell you something: there ain't anyplace in the world for a poor disabled friendless drifting man."

The ugly words settled in Mr. Shiftlet's head like a group of buz-
zards in the top of a tree. He didn't answer at once. He rolled himself
a cigarette and lit it and then he said in an even voice, "Lady, a man
is divided into parts, body, and spirit."

The old woman clamped her gums together.

"A body and a spirit," he repeated. "The body, lady, is like a house:
it don't go anywhere; but the spirit, lady, is like a automobile: always
on the move, always. . . ."

"Listen, Mr. Shiftlet," she said, "my well never goes dry and my
house is always warm in the winter and there's no mortgage on a
thing about this place. You can go to the courthouse and see for
yourself. And yonder under that shed is a fine automobile." She laid
the bait carefully. "You can have it painted by Saturday. I'll pay for
the paint."

In the darkness, Mr. Shiftlet's smile stretched like a weary snake
waking up by a fire. "Yes'm," he said softly.

After a second he recalled himself and said, "I'm only saying a
man's spirit means more to him than anything else. I would have to
take my wife off for the weekend without no regards at all for cost. I
got to follow where my spirit says to go."

"I'll give you fifteen dollars for a weekend trip," the old woman
said in a crabbed voice. "That's the best I can do."

"That wouldn't hardly pay for more than the gas and the hotel,"
he said. "It wouldn't feed her."

"Seventeen-fifty," the old woman said. "That's all I got so it isn't
any use you trying to milk me. You can take a lunch."

Mr. Shiftlet was deeply hurt by the word "milk." He didn't doubt
that she had more money sewed up in her mattress but he had already
told her he was not interested in her money. "I'll make that do," he
said, and rose and walked off without treating with her further.

On Saturday the three of them drove into town in the car that the
paint had barely dried on and Mr. Shiftlet and Lucynell were married
in the Ordinary's office while the old woman witnessed. As they came
out of the courthouse, Mr. Shiftlet began twisting his neck in his
collar. He looked morose and bitter as if he had been insulted while
someone held him. "That didn't satisfy me none," he said. "That
was just something a woman in an office did, nothing but paper work
and blood tests. What do they know about my blood? If they was to

take my heart and cut it out," he said, "they wouldn't know a thing about me. It didn't satisfy me at all."

"It satisfied the law," the old woman said sharply.

"The law," Mr. Shiftlet said, and spit. "It's the law that don't satisfy me."

He had painted the car dark green with a yellow band around it just under the windows. The three of them climbed in the front seat and the old woman said, "Don't Lucynell look pretty? Looks like a baby doll." Lucynell was dressed up in a white dress that her mother had uprooted from a trunk and there was a Panama hat on her head with a bunch of red wooden cherries on the brim. Every now and then her placid expression was changed by a sly isolated little thought like a shoot of green in the desert. "You got a prize!" the old woman said.

Mr. Shiftlet didn't even look at her.

They drove back to the house to let the old woman off and pick up the lunch. When they were ready to leave, she stood staring in the window of the car, with her fingers clenched around the glass. Tears began to seep sideways out of her eyes and run along the dirty creases in her face. "I ain't ever been parted with her for two days before," she said.

Mr. Shiftlet started the motor.

"And I wouldn't let no man have her but you because I seen you would do right. Goodbye, Sugarbaby," she said, clutching at the sleeve of the white dress. Lucynell looked straight at her and didn't seem to see her there at all. Mr. Shiftlet eased the car forward so that she had to move her hands.

The early afternoon was clear and open and surrounded by pale blue sky. The hills flattened under the car one after another and the climb and dip and swerve went entirely to Mr. Shiftlet's head so that he forgot his morning bitterness. He had always wanted an automobile but he had never been able to afford one before. He drove very fast because he wanted to make Mobile by nightfall.

Occasionally he stopped his thoughts long enough to look at Lucynell in the seat beside him. She had eaten the lunch as soon as they were out of the yard and now she was pulling the cherries off the hat one by one and throwing them out the window. He became depressed in spite of the car. He had driven about a hundred miles when he decided that she must be hungry again and at the next small town they came to, he stopped in front of an aluminum-painted eating place called The Hot Spot and took her in and ordered her a plate of ham and grits. The ride had made her sleepy and as soon as she got up on the stool, she rested her head on the counter and shut her eyes. There was no one in The Hot Spot but Mr. Shiftlet and the boy behind the counter, a pale youth with a greasy rag hung over his shoulder. Before he could dish up the food, she was snoring gently.

"Give it to her when she wakes up," Mr. Shiftlet said. "I'll pay for it now."

The boy bent over her and stared at the long pink-gold hair and the half-shut sleeping eyes. Then he looked up and stared at Mr. Shiftlet. "She looks like an angel of Gawd," he murmured.

"Hitch-hiker," Mr. Shiftlet explained. "I can't wait. I got to make Tuscaloosa."

The boy bent over again and very carefully touched his finger to a strand of the golden hair and Mr. Shiftlet left.

He was more depressed than ever as he drove on by himself. The late afternoon had grown hot and sultry and the country had flattened out. Deep in the sky a storm was preparing very slowly and without thunder as if it meant to drain every drop of air from the earth before it broke. There were times when Mr. Shiftlet preferred not to be alone. He felt too that a man with a car had a responsibility to others and he kept his eye out for a hitch-hiker. Occasionally he saw a sign that warned: "Drive carefully. The life you save may be your own."

The narrow road dropped off on either side into dry fields and here and there a shack or a filling station stood in a clearing. The sun began to set directly in front of the automobile. It was a reddening ball that through his windshield was slightly flat on the bottom and top. He saw a boy in overalls and a grey hat, standing on the edge of the road and he slowed the car down and stopped in front of him. The boy didn't have his hand raised to thumb the ride, he was only standing there, but he had a small cardboard suitcase and his hat was set on his head in a way to indicate that he had left somewhere for good. "Son," Mr. Shiftlet said, "I see you want a ride."

The boy didn't say he did or he didn't but he opened the door of the car and got in, and Mr. Shiftlet started driving again. The child held the suitcase on his lap and folded his arms on top of it. He turned his head and looked out the window away from Mr. Shiftlet. Mr. Shiftlet felt oppressed. "Son," he said after a minute, "I got the best old mother in the world so I reckon you only got the second best."

The boy gave him a quick dark glance and then turned his face back out the window.

"It's nothing so sweet," Mr. Shiftlet continued, "as a boy's mother. She taught him his first prayers at her knee, she give him love when no other would, she told him what was right and what wasn't, and she seen that he done the right thing. Son," he said, "I never rued a day in my life like the one I rued when I left that old mother of mine."

The boy shifted in his seat but he didn't look at Mr. Shiftlet. He unfolded his arms and put one hand on the door handle.

"My mother was a angel of Gawd," Mr. Shiftlet said in a very strained voice. "He took her from heaven and giver to me and I left her." His eyes were instantly clouded over with a mist of tears.

The boy turned angrily in the seat. "You go to the devil!" he cried. "My old woman is a flea bag and yours is a stinking polecat!" and with that he flung the door open and jumped out with his suitcase into the ditch.

Mr. Shiftlet was so shocked that for about a hundred feet he drove along slowly with the door still open like his mouth. Then he reached over and shut both. A cloud, the exact color of the boy's hat and shaped like a turnip, had descended over the sun, and another, worse looking, crouched behind the car. Mr. Shiftlet felt that the rottenness of the world was about to engulf him. He raised his arm and let it fall again to his breast. "Oh, Lord!" he prayed, "break forth and wash the slime from this earth!"

The turnip continued slowly to descend. After a few minutes there was a guffawing peal of thunder from behind and fantastic raindrops, like tin can tops, crashed over the rear of Mr. Shiftlet's car. Very quickly he pushed in his clutch and stepped on the gas and, with his stump sticking out the window, he raced the galloping shower into Mobile.

MIRIAM RUGEL *was born in Philadelphia in 1911.
She early decided to write, and her first job, at the
age of eleven, was a weekly column on a local
paper. Since then she has been writing and publishing in all fields, and her work has appeared in such
varied magazines as* Epoch *and* Woman's Day. *She
writes concerning "The Flower" that on first
reading it to a manuscript group, "it was unanimously pronounced vulgar, cheap, common,
and 'comic'; it caused a near-riot and the later
disintegration of the group."*

THE FLOWER

FROM HARPER'S MAGAZINE

Every year, around the time of the high holidays, Deborah's mother
tried to save the soul of her father, who was an atheist. She seemed
to believe if she could persuade Deborah's father to go to synagogue
just once a year, on Rosh Hashanah, which is New Year's, or on Yom
Kippur (the Day of Atonement), he would turn into a real Jew, a
religious Jew. She never succeeded, but she never gave up trying,
either.

The year Deborah was thirteen her mother tried, too. It was fall.
They were doing the supper dishes in the little kitchen behind their
Family Shoe Store.

"It is time we wrote in for *shule* tickets, Morris," her mother said.
"Dry every fork twice, Deborah. For you one drying is not enough.
You hear, Morris? This year, two tickets!"

Her father was sitting at the kitchen table, reading a book he had
bought at an auction. Catullus. When he had bid up to fifty cents for
it he hadn't known it was in Latin: now he had to learn enough Latin
to get his fifty cents' worth. When Deborah's mother spoke, he laid
aside a small dictionary and turned his mild eyes to her.

" 'Religion is the fairy tale of morality,' " he said. He looked at
Deborah and her brother Davie. "Santayana," he told them. "To be
moral, I don't need fairy tales."

"Don't quote me," her mother said. "Merely write in for two tickets."

There was silence.

"It's a good thing, I think, to sit in a synagogue once a year and listen to the words of a rabbi," said her mother.

"If you think, then go," answered her father.

"Alone?" asked her mother.

Silence.

"I'm a widow? I married a goy? I'm divorced?"

Silence.

"It's wrong to enjoy a cantor's singing, to pray a little, to sit together in a family like *menchen?*" *Menchen* meant respectable people, substantial people. When her mother said, "Be a *mench!*" she meant be a person of worth, dignity, self-respect. "It hurts," she continued, "to remember once a year you are a Jew?"

Her father looked up so you could see the way his hair, just brushed with silver, grew high in a wave above his full forehead.

"To remember I'm a Jew I don't need a synagogue. The Jew remembers he is a Jew, not by religion only but by blood. Across the centuries and all the countries of the world, the blood remembers. The memory of suffering is a blood memory."

"Thank you for the speech and that's sufficient this evening," said her mother, swinging her eyes toward Deborah and Davie. "Kindly pick up your feet, I will give the linoleum a lick and a promise."

Her father picked up his feet and continued tranquilly. "Several times a week I remember I'm a Jew and several times a week it occurs to me it would be better if there were no Jews and no Gentiles, but only people, together. Who recognize their human dignity and so behave."

Her mother wiped up the whole floor, polished the sink spigot, and arranged the sweet potato vine the way it was right for her. Then they all went into the store where the chairs were comfortable and her mother opened the newspaper to the "Evening Story," which was her favorite relaxation. But she didn't relax.

"Every year," she said, "I think this is the year we will go, together. Every family on the street, every relative, can go. Only my family. By my family each day is like the other and my children are raised as goyim, God forgive me."

"God will forgive you," said her father.

"Me, maybe," her mother answered. "So what good will that be, without you?" She folded the paper. "Every year the families sit so nice together——"

"What is this together?" interrupted her father. "Together! In the real synagogue, the orthodox synagogue, the wife is forbidden to sit with her husband. Upstairs she sits. Separate."

"That's old-fashioned," said her mother. "In a million synagogues today the wife sits downstairs. By right. By the husband!" she sighed. "All day Yom Kippur the families sit, from early in the morning until sundown not a morsel of food, not a sip of water passes their lips, only prayers, and just before evening, just before the Shofar is blown, the children come bringing the mother flowers." She was silent. "This is a beautiful thing to see."

"Why do they bring flowers?" asked Deborah. "For what?"

Her mother looked at Deborah.

"For honor," she answered softly. "For honor to the mothers. All year the mothers pay attention to the children, so once a year it can be vice versa." She was still looking at Deborah and the way she looked reminded Deborah of the way she watched, from the store door, when the ladies passed outside, going to a matinee. "In the afternoon, movies!" she always said. "Imagine." And now she looked the same, only a hundred times more so. And Deborah's father had stopped reading.

"Flowers . . ." he said. "This is religion? With flowers. Tell me. Where is it written that on a certain day at a certain time the children must come with flowers? Show me the reference."

"Who knows reference?" said her mother. "What is done in the synagogue under the rabbi is reference and religion and that's all."

"All? I have read in the Talmud, in the Commentaries, the interpretations, you understand, and nowhere have I met a point of law concerning flowers. For the very good reason that this law does not exist. So this is not religion, not tradition even, but a custom merely. An isolated custom without basis, which I have never seen outside your synagogue——"

"How should you see? Did you trouble to look? All right. We invented. But in the synagogue on Bridge Street, the orthodox synagogue, who invented? They bring flowers. And in the big synagogue, the biggest of all, between the bank and the movie, who invented? There they bring the biggest flowers. And in my mother's synagogue, ever since I was a little girl, I saw and I brought, with the first pennies I earned I ran to bring my mother Yom Kippur flowers. Yes,

and to your mother also I brought—this you didn't know—I brought
and your brother Nathan, he brought, yes, to your own mother in
her own synagogue on Cassell Street we both brought, and religion
or custom, invented or not invented, she was happy. Believe me,
she was happy."

Her father was back in his book.

"*Scripsit* . . ." he said restlessly. "What could it mean, *scripsit?*"
But he did not open his dictionary. "They put on a new man in the
office," he said. "Jim Boyle. An inspector. I invited him for supper
tomorrow, but don't prepare. I will prepare."

"Boyle?" said her mother. "It's Friday, he'll eat fish. I'll make
flounder. Children, to your lessons! Mrs. Marks stops by the window.
Open the door, Morris. And, please, do not begin to whistle when she
does not buy the first pair!"

Deborah went to her lessons, but she thought more about her
mother's face when she had spoken of the flowers. She thought of
the way her mother would sit in the synagogue, alone on the holiday.
Ashamed because there was no family beside her. She thought of
how, on the Day of Atonement, all the mothers would be brought
flowers; all her aunts would be made proud by their children; her
friends, Hannah and Hortense and Anne, would bring flowers and
only her mother would sit. Without honor. And although she admired her father and went to Sunday School only on Purim when the
boxes of candy were passed out, still when she thought of her mother
her heart hurt.

She understood what her father meant when he said he needed no
synagogue to remember he was a Jew. Every day she, too, was reminded because every day on her way to school Larry Hannigan
chased her, throwing a stone or two, and shouting "Jew! Jew! Your
grandfather crucified Jesus!" So she knew. But, shamefully, she was
less disturbed by the name-calling than the name-caller because that
year when she was thirteen she was deeply in love with Larry Hannigan, his red hair and his wild eyes and his brave reckless way in
the classroom.

She knew about being a Jew and she knew about being an atheist.
Sometimes at night when Hannah or Hortense stayed over, late, late,
after they had giggled and gossiped and read Davie's *Casanova* translation in secret, she would be awakened by a hand on her shoulder;
she would hear a frightened whisper: "Listen! Somebody's yelling,
somebody's fighting!"

"Nobody's yelling. Nobody's fighting," she would answer grumpily. "That's only my father arguing with the priest about God."

And even in the dark she could feel her guest's horror at the thought of a priest in their house. But Father Callahan was the closest of all the friends who came here; her father and the priest had argued the Resurrection for three years. And long after Hannah or Hortense slept again she would lie awake and listen, hearing names like Darwin, Thomas Paine, Hardy. But no matter how long she listened or how hard she thought, she could never decide definitely for herself whether she was an atheist or not.

Her mother made no mention of synagogue for more than two weeks. The store was very busy because everyone wanted new shoes for the holiday. Once she and Davie ate sandwiches for two days running. Her mother kept a little jar of boric acid solution ready with which to bathe her eyes, because looking up and down shoe shelves is hard on eyes. And after his day's work in the installment office her father helped in the store, too, and came into the kitchen more and more often between customers to whistle, savagely.

It was almost twelve one night when they locked the door. But as soon as she drew the blind, her mother started.

"Everyone has tickets!" she said. "There's no time left for deciding."

"Who's deciding?" asked her father. "Religion is the veil man draws over his soul to hide the nightmare of his own inadequacy."

"Don't quote me! Without argument, write and send!" Her mother began to throw dollar bills out of the register, hunting the checkbook she always hid too well to find. "Already only the back rows are left. Who wants to sit in the back row?"

"The front row is nearer God? He is deaf, the closer you sit to the Torah the better He hears your prayers?"

"For once forget you are smart! Be dumb. Like me. Or will it be this year like always? Will I sit in my brother's seat free for an hour while he goes out for a breath of fresh air? Will I be again the *schnorrer*, the beggar who begs whether he must or not? All because I have a husband who thinks he is smarter than anyone else but is only more stubborn!"

"Don't yell," said her father calmly. " 'As rain breaks through an unthatched roof, so passion through the unreflecting mind.' Buddha. Do I deny you your religion? Would I take away the cripple's crutch? Therefore should you object if I prefer walking through life on my own legs?"

Her mother sat wearily.

"A husband I picked . . . I could have married the owner of the factory where I met your father. In limousines I could be riding. But he wasn't smart enough for me, that factory owner. And besides every time he walked me home your father followed, two steps behind, whistling! But I could have married that factory owner."

"Or the poet," said her father. "Remember the poet, Sarah? He went to Italy for inspiration, you had to take up a collection to bring him home?"

"He was a fine boy, that poet! Now he's a judge. And him, too, I could have married."

"Beyond a doubt. Your mother was a beautiful girl, her house was crowded with boys. Especially the poet. Only him, too, I followed and in case your mother didn't know I helped him not only back from Italy but on his way, also."

Her mother wouldn't smile.

"Maybe I shouldn't go, anyhow," she said. "I have no dress."

"Get a dress. Tomorrow I'll come home from work early. I invited Komorowski from the office but he follows Thoreau, he eats nuts only. Chopped nuts and raisins."

Next day her father was home by noon. He brought nuts to chop for Mr. Komorowski and he brought a synagogue ticket for her mother.

"The second row!" her mother said, when she saw it. "What's the matter, God is deaf, He can't hear from the cheap seats? I won't buy a dress."

But she went to look at them, anyway. Before she left she told Deborah's father, "Please. Don't insult anybody. If a customer asks off half a dollar, give off. It's the holidays."

As soon as she had gone, Deborah took out the little razor box in which she saved money. She had saved for a long time, ever since she had seen the advertisement: "HOW DO YOU KNOW YOU CAN'T DRAW? Picture Above, Miss Althea Crumwell, $50 Cartoon Sale After Three Lessons." This course was ten dollars and money was serious in Deborah's house. But she didn't care about starting all over. She had made up her mind the night her mother had told of the flowers. She, too, would go shopping the day before Yom Kippur, like her friends Hannah and Hortense. And for once she would sit beside her mother on the holiday and they would be *menchen*, too.

And that night was a fine night for Deborah. Oddly, few customers came. Her father was busy with Mr. Komorowski and all evening her mother talked to her, about how handsome her father had been as a youth, how everyone in the factory had respected him, and how, all day as they worked together, he had sung to her in his beautiful voice, songs nobody else in the world knew, especially their favorite, "Let's Go to America," taught to him by his father in the old country. And she gave Deborah four long strips of the brown wrapping paper, which was expensive but wonderful to draw on because you didn't have to bother with pages.

On Rosh Hashanah her mother looked happy, even if she did have to go to *shule* alone. She wore the new dress, wine-red with steel beads around the hem, a hat exactly the same color, and her ring with the three imitation diamonds. She looked younger, not tired, more like the girl her father had called beautiful, the one with the house crowded with boys, the stranger Deborah could not picture. But she didn't give up, even at the last minute.

"For an hour," she said to Deborah's father, "you wouldn't need a ticket. They would let you in."

"Enjoy yourself," was his answer.

"I am not going to enjoy! I am going to pray for my sins."

"Tell me," her father said. "A woman works shoulder to shoulder with her husband. Fourteen hours a day she works her children should have all the advantages, her house shines, between she cooks and she washes, at night she falls into sleep like a diver from the clifftop, and this woman has sins? In her leisure she takes a lover? She squanders the milk money on horse racing? Dummy," he finished gently, "pray for the politicians. Yourself, enjoy!"

Yom Kippur comes ten days after Rosh Hashanah. That year it was Thursday. On Wednesday Deborah went to a real florist. She bought, not flowers, but a plant. A great golden chrysanthemum. The pot was wrapped in shiny green paper, fluted around the top edges. She hid it in the basement behind the stock of galoshes where her mother would not be going. She watered it so it wouldn't get thirsty. She told no one, not even Davie, so the surprise would be complete.

At sundown, according to custom, they closed the store. They had a large holiday dinner, prepared by her mother between the rush of this last day. They had chicken soup with the matzo meal balls a little lumpened by hurry, challah, roast chicken, kasha, honey-cake. After, her mother sat with closed eyes, limp in the chair, motionless except for rubbing her fingers which were shiny and swollen.

"Children," she said, "the dishes! Tonight I can move no more."

At nine o'clock Davie and her father began to crack walnuts, but Deborah did not break her Yom Kippur fast because this year she wanted to be truly a Jew and taste the flavor of virtue. She did not drink water and she decided that in the morning she would not wash as her ancestors had not washed in all the countless years before her, but had thought only of atonement and of how on this day, in the Book of Life, God counted the sum of their sins and observed the depth of their repentance.

She watered the plant and went to bed, counting her own sins: she had been greedy in the movies, eating more candy than she gave David; she had lied about not wanting breakfast and gone every morning to Hannah's for hot chocolate; she had bragged about school marks without humbleness or modesty.

But most of all she lay picturing the fact of her mother when tomorrow she, Deborah, would walk down the synagogue aisle and silently offer the flower and saying no word take her own place as Jew. She pictured her mother's face. And she fell asleep, feeling hungry and pure.

And in the blackness of middle night, deep in her sleeping, she heard noise. She heard her father's voice and it was strange. She leaped out of bed without knowing she had wakened and she trembled with the knowledge of disaster before she ran into their room.

Her mother lay on the bedroom floor. Her littleness was twisted in the folds of a white nightgown. Over the littleness her father bent, his two hands extended without purpose. Deborah saw he had tried to raise her mother and she ran to help but her mother motioned with the hand at her chest, negatively.

She said, "Don't—move—me." She said, "I hope—this pain—passes."

"Get whisky!" her father ordered. "Get the doctor!"

Davie called the doctor. Deborah ran down the black stairway into the store but her fingers would not unbolt the door. Davie did it. The doctor came with his bag and ran up the steps faster than she and yet everything seemed to her to move very slowly. He kneeled on the floor beside her mother with a long close look and then he moved very surely with his instruments and hypodermic. Deborah held her mother in her arms and she felt the needle's pain. She looked at her mother's lips and their blueness and into her eyes where she saw what she had never seen there before. She had seen love in her mother's eyes and anger and a great willingness for the fight which is living, but she had never before seen fear.

"Now!" said the doctor so bravely. "Now she'll be better." And he stood. And he walked into the hall and motioned to Davie. "Call my home," he told Davie. "Tell my wife not to expect me."

Deborah knew her mother heard. She knew because her mother's eyes, which had been filmed with the fear, now focused into a terrible question. Her mother moved. She turned wholly to Deborah's father and the hand which had been clenched at her chest took his hand. She smiled. She said, "Children——" Then she sighed, her eyes closed, and her head which Deborah had been holding felt heavier for an instant. And Deborah thought her mother was sleeping. The doctor came swiftly back and bent over them both and Deborah heard him say, "It's over." And she heard her father's cry, "Do something!" and the doctor's answer, "There is nothing I can do." And she saw her father stand and draw back his arm and she heard his fist drive into the wall and she watched the wallpaper and the plaster crumble. Then she understood they were saying her mother had died.

She knew nothing after that but her father. Her father began to talk. He talked to her mother all night. He never stopped talking. People came; the doctor drugged him and put him in Deborah's bed. She and Davie sat beside their father all night. And he talked. Sometimes he whispered and sometimes he rose in the bed, shouting. He went back to years Deborah did not know to places she had never seen to things she had known had happened. He lived through a whole life with her mother and she listened and felt her cheeks freeze. And no matter what he said, long after his voice was a thread of hoarseness, he came to one clear wondering question. He asked, "*Sarah, where are you?*" And he said, "*My darling, come back.*"

When the light began to break she left Davie beside him and went to her mother's room. Her mother lay alone. A blanket had been drawn across the slight figure; one corner had slipped and exposed a small foot. It was perfect, the toes, instep, ankle. Beautiful and perfect as though newly made. But it was marble.

She sat on the radiator and felt nothing but coldness. She stared into the face which was strange to her in its stillness and she bent close above it and whispered. She said, "*Sarah, where are you?*"

It was the first time in her life she spoke and her mother did not answer.

She went down to the store and down the store steps to the basement. There were people in the kitchen, crying: they didn't hear her. She crawled back of the galoshes and she brought out the flower. It seemed larger than yesterday, more golden. In the wavy basement light it glowed. She touched the bright petals and they were soft and living. When she felt their aliveness and thought of her mother she believed for the first time her mother was dead.

And she said, "God? Is this all, God?"

She looked around the lightening cellar, into its corners, and up through its narrow window. And she went on in her mind, with labor. She thought, "To live. To work and love. To want things—movies in the afternoon, honor from your children—— And then, before anything is finished—— Is this all?"

She listened. Through the floors of the house she heard her father, sobbing.

And she said out of the numbness and the astonishment inside her, "God? Why didn't you let her get the flower?"

But there wasn't any answer.

She walked up the half-flight of steps through the trapdoor and around to the street. The dawn was no longer gray. The new air was beautiful. She looked, as though she stood on a height, at the stores, the houses, the school across the way, all spiked with radiance. She saw every part of the street with such clearness her eyes ached. She thought of the street in the daytime, the children in the schoolyard, the people criss-crossing. She thought of the pattern this street made and every other street in every other country in the world, the roads, the paths, boats on the sea, trains up a mountain, and she thought, "All this cannot just have happened." She looked at the trolley track before her and she thought of the trolley which rode it and this seemed to her the biggest miracle of all. And she thought, "All this cannot be accident."

She looked at the high sky which became more blue every moment and she said, "God? If You are God, send a sign. Give me a sign!"

But, though she was patient, she saw no sign.

She went back to the house and dressed and crept back into the basement for the flower. She hurried but again, as last night, every movement seemed weighted and endless. She carried the plant across the street and through the schoolyard and down the alley into the woods that belonged to the farmer. There was still this one farmer in the neighborhood.

She walked into the wet greenness where every spring she searched for lilies of the valley and through the clumped trees where the crazy man had once chased her and to the private little knoll where the grass was worn thin with her sitting.

And she said, out of the ball of hardness and fury which was as much a core as the heart is, "God, *why didn't You let her have the flower?*"

And when there was no answer she set down the pot and she kicked it and stamped on it until no bit of the shining paper was left and the curly petals were ground into muddiness and slime.

On the way to the synagogue she stopped at a bakery and bought two rolls, one for each coat pocket. She walked up the synagogue steps into the auditorium and when she sat on a bench-end nobody stopped her. The room was hot and smelled old. On the platform the rabbi was pale in his black robe; the cantor stood facing the Sacred Ark, chanting in tremolo. Over them the six-pointed star hung, ancient and mysterious, reflecting the rays of the Eternal Light. Two men, prayer-shawled, walked up the steps and with tenderness lifted the twin rolls of the Torah and descended to the people.

When the Torah reached the second row she looked for her mother's seat and she saw the bench was crowded. There was already no room left for her mother. And when the people bent humbly forward to kiss the white satin and stiff gold fringes, she tore off a piece of one roll and sat, staring into the face of the rabbi, chewing loudly on the day of fast, chewing and choking against the first tears she had felt for her mother.

JEAN STAFFORD *was born in 1915 in Covina, California, and was educated at the University of California and the University of Heidelberg. She taught for a year at Stephens College, and was secretary for a year and a half on* The Southern Review. *She has held two Guggenheims, in 1945 and 1948, and has received a grant from the National Institute of Arts and Letters. She has published three novels,* Boston Adventure (1944), The Mountain Lion (1947), *and* The Catherine Wheel (1950), *and a book of short stories,* Children Are Bored on Sundays (1953). *At present she is working on a new novel.*

THE SHORN LAMB

FROM THE NEW YORKER

"Oh, there's no whitewashing the incident. The child's hair is a sight, and it will be many moons, I can tell you, before I'll forgive Hugh Talmadge. But listen to me. The worst of it is that this baby of five has gone into a decline like a grown woman—like you or me, dear, at our most hysterical. Sudden fits of tears for no apparent reason and then simply hours of brooding. She won't eat, she probably doesn't sleep. I can't stand it if she's turning mental."

The child, Hannah, sitting hidden on the attic steps, listened as her mother talked on the telephone to Aunt Louise. The door to the bedroom, across the hall, was half open, and through the crack of the door at the foot of the attic steps Hannah saw that in the course of the night her parents had disarrayed the pale-green blanket cover and now, half off the bed, drooping and askew, it looked like a great crumpled new leaf, pulled back here and there to show the rosy blankets underneath. In the bedroom it is spring, thought Hannah, and outdoors it is snowing on the Christmas trees; that is a riddle.

Her mother lay in the center of the big bed, which was as soft and fat as the gelded white Persian cat who dozed at her side, his scornful head erect, as if he were arrested not so much by sleep as by a coma of boredom and disgust. A little earlier, before he struck this pose, he had sniffed and disdained the bowl of cream on his mistress's breakfast tray, and when she had tried to cajole him into drinking it, he had coolly thrashed his tail at her. In the darkness of her enclosure, Hannah yearned, imagining herself in the privileged cat's place beside her mother, watching the mellowing, pillowing, billowing snow as it whorled down to meet the high tips of the pine trees that bordered the frozen formal garden. If she were Nephew, the cat, she would burrow into the silky depths of the bed up to her eyes and rejoice that she was not outside like a winter bird coming to peck at suet and snowy crumbs at the feeding station.

It was ugly and ungenerous here where she was, on the narrow, splintery stairs, and up in the attic a mouse or a rat scampered on lightly clicking claws between the trunks; some hibernating bees buzzed peevishly in their insomnia. Stingy and lonesome like old people, the shut-ins worried their grievances stealthily. And Hannah, spying and eavesdropping (a sin and she knew it), felt the ends of her cropped hair and ran a forefinger over her freshly combed boy's cut —the subject of her mother's conversation. Something like sleep touched her eyeballs, though this was early morning and she had not been awake longer than an hour. But it was tears, not drowsiness, that came. They fell without any help from her; her cheeks did not rise up as they usually did when she cried, to squeeze themselves into puckers like old apples, her mouth did not open in a rent of woe, no part of her body was affected at all except the eyes themselves, from which streamed down these mothering runnels.

"*Why did he do it?*" Her mother's question into the telephone was an impatient scream. "Why do men do half the things they do? Why does Arthur treat you in public as if you were an enlisted man? I swear I'll someday kill your rear admiral for you. Why does Eliot brag to Frances that he's unfaithful? Because they're sadists, every last one of them. I am very anti-man today."

"What is anti-man?" whispered Hannah.

The stools on either side of the fireplace in the den were ottomans, and sometimes Hannah and her mother sat on them in the late afternoon, with a low table between them on which were set a Chinese pot of verbena tisane, two cups, and a plate of candied orange rind. At the thought of her mother's golden hair in the firelight, and the smell of her perfume in the intimate warmth, and the sound of her voice saying, "Isn't this gay, Miss Baby?" the tears came faster, for in her heavy heart Hannah felt certain that now her hair was cut off,

her mother would never want to sit so close to her again. Unable to
see through the narrow opening of the door any longer, she leaned her
face against the wall and felt her full tears moistening the beaver-
board as she listened to her mother's recital of Saturday's catastrophe.

"On the face of it, the facts are innocent enough, Louise. He
took her to town on Saturday to buy her a pair of shoes, having
decided for his own reasons that I have no respect for my children's
feet—the shoes he got are too odious, but that's another story. Then
when he brought her back, here she was, cropped, looking like a rag
doll. He said she'd begged to have it done. Of course she'd done
nothing of the kind. To put the most charitable construction on the
whole affair, I *could* say that when he went into the barbershop to
have his own hair cut, he'd had a seizure of amnesia and thought he
had Andy with him, or Johnny, or Hughie, and decided to kill two
birds with one stone. And then afterward he was afraid of what I'd
say and so cooked up this canard—and more than likely bribed her
to bear him out. The way men will weasel out of their missteps! It
isn't moral. It shocks me."

He did *not* think I was Andy or Johnny or Hughie, Hannah said
to herself. In the barbershop at her father's club there had been no
one but grown men and a fat stuffed skunk that stood in front of the
mirror between two bottles of bay rum, its leathery nose pointed
upward as if it were trying to see the underside of its chin in the
looking glass. Through a steaming towel, her father had muttered,
"Just do as I say, Homer, cut it off," and the barber, a lean man with
a worried look on his red face, flinched, then shrugged his shoulders
and began to snip off Hannah's heavy curls, frowning with disapproval and remarking once under his breath that women, even though
they were five years old, were strictly forbidden on these premises.
On the drive home, her peeled head had felt cold and wet, and she
had not liked the smell that gauzily hovered around her, growing
more cloying as the heater in the car warmed up. At a red light, her
father had turned to her and, patting her on the knee, had said,
"You look as cute as a button, young fellow." He had not seemed
to hear her when she said, "I do not. I'm not a young fellow," nor
had he noticed when she moved over against the door, as far away
from him as she could get, hating him bitterly and hating her naked-
ness. Presently, he'd turned on the radio to a news broadcast and
disputed out loud with the commentator. Hannah, left all alone, had
stared out the window at the wolfish winter. In one snow-flattened

field she saw tall flames arising from a huge wire trash basket, making the rest of the world look even colder and whiter and more unkind. Her father scowled, giving the radio what for, swearing at the slippery roads—carrying on an absent-minded tantrum all by himself. Once, halted by a woman driver whose engine was stalled, he'd said, "Serves her right. She ought to be home at this time of day tending to business." As they turned in their own drive, he said a lie: "That was a fine idea of yours to have your hair cut off." She had never said any such thing; all she had said, when they were having lunch in a brown, cloudy restaurant, was that she would rather go to the barbershop with him than wait at Grandma's. But she had not contradicted him, for he did not countenance contradiction from his children. "I'm an old-fashioned man," he announced every morning to his three sons and his two daughters. "I am the autocrat of this breakfast table." And though he said it with a wink and a chuckle, it was clear that he meant business. Johnny, who was intellectual, had told the other children that an autocrat was a person like Hitler, and he had added sarcastically, "That sure is something to brag about, I must say."

The voice speaking into the phone took on a new tone, and Hannah, noticing this, looked out through the crack again. "What? Oh, please don't change the subject, pet, I really want your help. It isn't a trifle, it's terribly important, I really think it is the *final* effrontery—— All right, then, if you promise that we can come back to it." With her free hand, Hannah's mother lightly stroked the cat, who did not heed, and she lay back among her many pillows, listening to her sister but letting her eyes rove the room as if she were planning changes in its decoration. "Yes, I did hear it but I can't remember where," she said inattentively. Then, smiling in the pleasure of gossip, forgetting herself for a moment, she went on, "Perhaps I heard it from Peggy the night she came to dinner with that frightful new man of hers. That's it—it was from *him* I heard it, and automatically discounted it for no other reason than that I took an instantaneous dislike to him. If he is typical of his department, the C.I.A. must be nothing more nor less than the Gestapo."

Hannah's head began to ache and she rolled it slowly, looking up the steep, ladderlike steps into the shadowy attic. She was bored now that the talk was not of her, and she only half heard her mother's agile voice rising, descending, laughing quickly, pleading, "Oh, no! It's not *possible!*" and she sucked her fingers, one by one. Her tears

had stopped and she missed them as she might have missed something she had lost. Like her hair, like all her golden princess curls
that the barber had gazed at sadly as they lay dead and ruined on the
tiled floor.

Now that Hannah's hair was short, her days were long: it was a million hours between breakfast and lunch, and before, it had been no
time at all, because her mother, still lying in her oceanic bed, had
every morning made Hannah's curls, taking her time, telling anyone
who telephoned that she would call back, that just now she was
busy "playing with this angel's hair."

Today was Wednesday, and Hannah had lived four lifetimes since
Saturday afternoon. Sunday had been endless, even though her
brothers and her sister had been as exciting as ever, with their jokes
and contests and their acrobatics and their game of cops-and-robbers
that had set the servants wild. But even in their mad preoccupation
it had been evident that the sight of Hannah embarrassed. "The
baby looks like a skinned cat," said Andy, and Hughie said, "It was
a dopey thing to do. The poor little old baby looks like a mushroom."
The parents did nothing to stop this talk, for all day long they were
fighting behind the closed door of the den, not even coming out
for meals, their voices growing slower and more sibilant as they
drank more. "I hate them," Johnny had said in the middle of the
long, musty afternoon, when the cops were spent and the robbers
were sick of water-pistol fights. "When they get stinking, I hate
them," said Johnny. "I bet a thousand dollars he had had a couple
when he had them cut the baby's hair." Janie shouted, "Oh, that
baby, baby, baby, baby! Is that goofy baby the only pebble on the
beach? Why do they have to mess up Sunday fighting over her? I'm
going crazy!" And she ran around in a circle like a dog, pulling at her
hair with both hands.

On Monday morning, when Hannah's father took the older children off to Marion Country Day School on his way to the city, she
had nearly cried herself sick, feeling that this Monday the pain of
their desertion was more than she could bear. She would not let go
of Janie's hand, and she cried, "You'll be sorry if you come back
and find I'm dead!" Janie, who was ten and hot-blooded—she took
after Daddy, who had Huguenot blood—had slapped Hannah's hand
and said, "The nerve of some people's children!" Hannah had stood
under the porte-cochere, shivering in her wrapper and slippers, until

the car went out the driveway between the tulip trees; she had waved and called, "Goodbye, dearest Janie and Johnny and Andy and Hughie!" Only Johnny had looked back; he rolled down the window and leaned out and called, "Ta-ta, half pint." They were all too old and busy to pay much attention to her, though often they brought her presents from school—a jawbreaker or a necklace made of paper clips. The four older children were a year apart, starting with John, who was thirteen, and ending with Janie, and when family photographs were taken, they were sometimes lined up according to height; these were called "stair-step portraits," and while Hannah, of course, was included, she was so much smaller than Janie that she spoiled the design, and one time Uncle Harry, looking at a picture taken on Palm Sunday when all five children were sternly holding their palms like spears, had said, pointing to Hannah, "Is that the runt of the litter or is it a toy breed?" Andy, who was Uncle Harry's pet, said, "We just keep it around the house for its hair. It's made of spun gold, you know, and very invaluable." This evidently was something the barber had not known, for he had swept the curls into a dustpan and thrown them into a chute marked, "Waste." She wondered how long they would keep her now that her sole reason for existence was gone.

In the other days, after Daddy and the children left and the maids began their panicky, silent cleaning, flinging open all the windows to chill the house to its heart, Hannah would run upstairs to the big bedroom to sit on the foot of the bosomy bed and wait while her mother drank her third cup of coffee and did the crossword puzzle in the *Tribune*. When she was stuck for a definition, she would put down her pencil and thoughtfully twist the diamond ring on her finger; if it caught the sun, Hannah would close her eyes and try to retain the flashing swords of green and purple, just as she unconsciously tried to seal forever in her memory the smell of the strong Italian coffee coming in a thin black stream out of the silver pot. Hannah remembered one day when her mother said to the cat, "What is that wretched four-letter word that means 'Allowance for waste,' Nephew? We had it just the other day." Finally, when the puzzle was done and Edna had taken away the tray, she stretched out her arms to Hannah, who scrambled into her embrace, and she said, "I suppose you want your tawny tresses curled," and held her at arm's length and gazed at her hair with disbelieving eyes. "Bring us the brush, baby." All the while she brushed, then combed, then made long, old-fashioned sausage curls, turning and molding them on her index finger, she talked lightly and secretly about the dreams she had had and Christmas plans and what went on inside Nephew's head and why it was that she respected but could not bear Andy's violin teacher. She included Hannah, as if she were thirty years old, asking for her opinion or her corroboration of something. "Do you agree with me that Nephew is the very soul of Egypt? Or do you think there are Chinese overtones in his style?" After telling a dream (her dreams were full of voyages: one time she sailed into Oslo in Noah's ark and another time she went on the *Queen Mary* to Southampton in her night clothes without either luggage or a passport), she said, "What on earth do you suppose that means, Hannah? My id doesn't seem to know where it is at." Bewitching, indecipherable, she always dulcified this hour with her smoky, loving voice and her loving fingers that sometimes could not resist meandering over Hannah's head, ruining a curl by cleaving through it as she exclaimed, "Dear Lord, I never saw such stuff as this!" Actually, her own hair was the same vivacious color and the same gentle texture as Hannah's, and sometimes her hands would leave the child's head and go to her own, to stroke it lovingly.

Lately now, for this last month, when the afternoons were snug and short and the lamps were turned on early and the hearth fires smelled of nuts, there had been another hour as well when Hannah and her hair had been the center of attention. Every day at half-past two, she and her mother drove in the toylike English car over to Mr. Robinson Fowler's house, three miles away, on the top of a bald and beautiful hill from which it was possible, on a clear day, to see the beaches of Long Island. In a big, dirty studio, jammed with plaster casts and tin cans full of turpentine and stacked-up canvases and nameless metal odds and ends, Mr. Fowler, a large, quiet man who mumbled when he talked, was painting a life-size portrait of Hannah and her mother. Her mother, wearing a full skirt of scarlet felt and a starched white Gibson-girl shirt and a black ribbon in her hair, sat on a purple Victorian sofa, and Hannah, in a blue velvet jacket trimmed with black frogs and a paler-blue accordion-pleated skirt, stood leaning against her knee. In the picture, these colors were all different, all smudgy and gray, and the point of this, said Mr. Fowler, was to accent the lambencies of the hair. Before they took their pose, all the morning's careful curls were combed out, for Mr.

Fowler wanted to paint Hannah's hair, he murmured in his closed mouth, "In a state of nature." Occasionally, he emerged from behind his easel and came across to them with his shambling, easygoing, friendly gait, to push back a lock of hair that had fallen over Hannah's forehead, and the touch of his fingers, huge as they were, was as light as her mother's.

Hannah liked the heat of the studio, and the smell of the tea perpetually brewing on an electric grill, and the sight of the enormous world of hills and trees and farms and rivers through the enormous windows, and she liked the quiet, which was broken only once or twice in the course of the hour's sitting by an exchange of a casual question and answer between Mr. Fowler and her mother, half the time about her hair. "It must never be cut," said the painter one day. "Not a single strand of it." After the sitting was over and Hannah and her mother had changed back into their regular clothes, Mr. Fowler drew the burlap curtains at the windows and turned on the soft lamps. Then he and her mother sat back in two scuffed leather armchairs drinking whiskey and talking in a leisurely way, as if all the rest of the time in the world were theirs to enjoy in this relaxed geniality. Hannah did not listen to them. With her cup of mild, lemony tea, she sat on a high stool before a blackboard at the opposite end of the room and drew spider webs with a nubbin of pink chalk. Mr. Fowler and her mother never raised their voices or threw things at each other or stormed out of the room, banging doors, and Hannah was sorry when it was time to go home where that kind of thing went on all the time, horrifying the housemaids, who never stayed longer than two months at the most, although the cook, who had a vicious tongue herself, had been with them ever since Johnny could remember.

The picture, when it was finished, was going to hang in the drawing room over an heirloom lowboy, where now there hung a pair of crossed *épées*, used by Hannah's father and his adversary in a jaunty, bloody *Studentenmensur* at Freiburg the year he went abroad to learn German. The lilac scar from the duel was a half moon on his round right cheek.

Now the picture would never be finished, since Hannah's corn-tassel hair was gone, and the sunny hour at the start of the day and the teatime one at the end were gone with it.

Hannah, sitting on the attic stairs, began to cry again as she thought of the closed circle of her days. Even her sister's and her brothers' return from school was not the fun it had been before; her haircut had become a household issue over which all of them squabbled, taking sides belligerently. Janie and Andy maintained it did not matter; all right, they said, what if the baby did look silly? After all, she didn't go to school and nobody saw her. Johnny and Hughie and the cook and the maids said that it did matter, and Johnny, the spokesman for that camp, railed at his father behind his back and called him a dastard. But all the same, no one paid any attention to Hannah; when they spoke of "the baby," they might have been speaking of the car or a piece of furniture; one would never have known that she was in the room for even when they looked directly at her, their eyes seemed to take in something other than Hannah. She felt that she was already shrinking and fading, that all her rights of being seen and listened to and caressed were ebbing away. Chilled and exposed as she was, she was becoming, nonetheless, invisible.

The tears came less fast now, and she heard her mother say, "How can I *help* looking at it closely? I shall eventually have to go to an analyst, as you perfectly well know, if I am to continue this marriage until the children are reasonably grown. But in the meantime, until I get my doctor, who can I talk to but you? I wouldn't talk to you if you weren't my sister, because I don't think you're discreet at all." Sad, in her covert, Hannah saw that her mother was now sitting up straight against the headboard and was smoking a cigarette in long, meditative puffs; the smoke befogged her frowning forehead.

"Forget it, darling," she continued. "I know you are a tomb of silence. Look, do let me spill the beans and get it over with. It will put me into a swivet, I daresay, and I'll have to have a drink in my bath, but the way I feel, after these nights I've had, that's in the cards anyhow. . . . Oh, Christ, Louise, don't preach to me!"

Briefly, she put down the telephone and dragged Nephew to her side. Then she resumed, "Excuse me. I was adjusting my cat. Now, dear, right now, you can forget my 'charitable construction' because, of course, that's rot. At this juncture, neither one of us does anything by accident. I cannot believe that criminals are any more ingenious than wives and husbands when their marriages are turning sour. Do you remember how fiendish the Irelands were?

"Well, the night before the haircutting, we had a row that lasted until four, starting with Rob and going on from him to all the other men I know—he thinks it's bad form (and that's exactly how he puts it) that I still speak fondly of old beaux. He suspects me of the direst things with that poor pansy the decorators sent out to do the carpets on the stairs, and he's got it firmly rooted in his mind that Rob and I are in the middle of a red-hot affair. He doesn't know the meaning of friendship. He's got a sand dune for a soul. He suggested loathsomely that Rob and I were using Hannah as a blind—oh, his implications were too cynical to repeat.

"All this went on and on until I said that I would leave him. You know *that* old blind alley where any feint is useless because when five children are involved, one's hands are tied. Unless one can be proved mad. If only I could be! I would give my eyes to be sent away for a while to some insane asylum like that one Elizabeth loved so.

"It was hideous—the whole battle. We were so squalid with drink. We drink prodigiously these days. The ice ran out and we didn't even take time to go get more, so we drank whiskey and tap water as if we were in a cheap hotel, and I kept thinking, How demeaning this is. But I couldn't stop. This was the worst quarrel we've ever had —by far the most fundamental. The things we said! We could have killed each other. In the morning, not even our hangovers could bring us together. And let me tell you, they were shattering. If I hadn't known it was a hangover, I would have sent for an ambulance without thinking twice. Hugh sidled around like a wounded land crab and swore he had fractured his skull. Fortunately, the children, all except the baby, had been asked to the Fosters' to skate, so at least we didn't have to put up appearances—we do that less and less as it is. But finally we began to pull ourselves together about noon with Bloody Marys, and when he proposed that he take Hannah into town and buy her lunch and some shoes, I almost forgave him everything, I was so delighted to have the house to myself. I would not rise to that bait about my neglecting the welfare of my children's feet. All I could think of was just being alone.

"I should have known. I think I might have sensed what was up if I hadn't been so sick, because as they were about to leave, the baby asked why I hadn't curled her hair and Hugh said, 'You leave that to me today.' Now, looking back on it, I can see that he rolled his eyes in that baleful, planning way of his and licked one corner of his mouth. But even if I had noticed, I still would never have dreamed he would be so vile.

"It goes without saying that we have been at swords' points ever since, and it doesn't help matters to see the child so woebegone, wearing this look of 'What did I do to deserve this?' How can one explain it away as an accident to a child when one perfectly knows that accident is not involved? Her misery makes me feel guilty. I am as shy of her as if I had been an accessory. I can't console her without spilling all the beans about Hugh. Besides, you can't say to a child, 'Darling, you are only a symbol. It was really *my* beautiful hair that was cut off, not yours.' . . .

"Rob *crushed?* Oh, for God's sake, no, not crushed—that's not Rob's style. He's outraged. His reaction, as a matter of fact, annoys me terribly, for he takes the whole thing as a personal affront and says that if Hugh had wanted to make an issue of my afternoons in his studio, he should have challenged him to a duel with the Freiburg swords. His theory, you see, is that Hugh has been smoldering at the thought of these testimonials of his manliness being replaced by the portrait. Rob claims that Hugh hates art—as of course he does—and that it is the artist in him, Rob, not the potential rival, that he is attacking. Needless to say, this gives him a heaven-sent opportunity to berate me for living in the camp of the enemy. He was horrid on Monday. He called me an opportunist and a brood mare. It depresses me that Rob, who is so intuitive about most things, can't see that *I* am the victim, that *my* values have been impugned. Today I hate all men.

"What am I going to do? What can I do? I'm taking her this afternoon to Angelo to see what he can salvage out of the scraps that are left. I'll get her a new doll—one with short hair. That's all I can do now. The picture will never be finished, so the dueling swords will stay where they are. And I will stay where I am—— Oh, there's no end! Why on earth does one have children?"

For a minute or two her mother was silent, leaning back with her eyes closed, listening to Aunt Louise. Hannah no longer envied the cat curled into her mother's arm; she hated his smug white face and she hated her mother's sorrowful smile. Hot and desolate and half suffocated, she wished she were one of the angry bees. If she were a bee, she would fly through the crack of the attic door and sting Nephew and her mother and her father and Janie and Andy and Mr. Fowler. "Zzzzzzz," buzzed the child to herself.

After the telephone conversation was over and her mother had got up and gone to run her bath, Hannah let herself silently out the door into the hall and went downstairs to the kitchen. The cook was dicing onions, weeping. "There's my baby," she said as Hannah came to stand beside her, "my very own baby." She put down her knife and wiped her hands and her eyes on her apron and scooped Hannah up in a bear hug.

"I love you, Mattie," said Hannah.

The cook's teary face looked surprised and she put the child down and said, "Run along now, kiddikins—Mattie's got work to do."

Hannah went into the den and kneeled on the window seat to watch the snow settling deeply on the branches of the trees. "I love you, snow," she said. It fell like sleep.

RICHARD G. STERN *was born in New York in
1928. He has degrees from the University of North
Carolina and from Harvard, and is currently working on his doctorate at the University of Iowa.
He has spent several years abroad. "The Sorrows of
Captain Schreiber" was his first published story,
and a second appeared in* The Kenyon Review.
*He is married to Gay Clark, has two children, and
is working on a novel.*

THE SORROWS OF CAPTAIN SCHREIBER

"An American novel today, mademoiselle?" asked Schreiber, craning
around Goupin to see the paperbound book in the pocket of Verité's
pullover. They were walking home along the Cher.

"So you see, Captain," and she pulled the book out so that he could
see the title.

"*Le loup de mer*," he said. "I've never read him."

"London," said Goupin, also looking. He pronounced the name in
the French manner. "I'd thought he was English."

"You read a great deal here, I've noticed," said Schreiber.

"We are far from Paris, Captain," she said.

"Thank God," added Goupin, looking at his daughter.

"I wonder," she said softly.

"I had only two days in Paris," said Schreiber. After a pause, he
asked, "What sort of books do you prefer, mademoiselle?"

She raised her eyes to him and then beyond to the Cher. "Would
you think philosophy, Captain?"

"Perhaps," he said.

"I shall be getting to that soon, I'm afraid. There are only a few
novels left and then only history and poetry intervene. Perhaps you
have books I might borrow, Captain?"

"Verité!" said Goupin sharply.

"I should be delighted, mademoiselle. I'm only afraid my tastes
wouldn't suit you."

Copyright, 1953, by The Western Review.

"You are right, Captain," she said, and looked down again at the road. "One doesn't broaden one's tastes in a tannery."

"A rather novelistic remark, my dear," said Goupin softly.

His daughter made no response. Her pullover pinched her under the shoulders and she was wondering if this was what made Schreiber stare at her, the bones bulging through the grey wool as haphazardly as potatoes in a sack.

They came to the side path.

"Will you come over this evening, Captain?" asked Goupin, easing his eyes from his daughter's squally hair to Schreiber's soft, blue-tinted face. "We still have two bottles of Calvados in reserve. What better way to celebrate the arrival of spring?"

"That's awfully kind, Goupin," said Schreiber. "May I accept for another time? The corporal is driving me to Bourges after dinner."

"Good things will wait, Captain. Perhaps it would be all right to invite the corporal as well?" He phrased it this way knowing the Americans were strange about Negroes.

"I'm sure he'd be honored," said Schreiber.

They parted with some ceremony, handshaking and bowing, and then Schreiber followed the beech-lined path to his billet while the Goupins continued on up the Cher road.

Verité always watched Schreiber move off down the path to her aunt's house. He was plump and ungraceful and she felt that his movements were a fit mockery of his position as the local representative of the liberating forces. "It's the black corporal who has the soldier's posture," she said to her father, and then blushed, feeling that her father imagined she was really thinking of the other corporal, whom she had nearly forgotten. Without realizing that she said it aloud, she cried, "A German corporal's higher than an American one."

"Perhaps," said her father, "but they do not have the staying power." He found this amusing but he did not wish to smile and cause his daughter embarrassment.

She did not have the energy to laugh or to answer him properly. "To him, I'm everybody's fool," she thought. "What's the difference?" and her eyes fastened on the brown dirt under her feet, the road she had walked so many times that she thought now there would be no other for her, ever, and that the most she could hope for would be to be swallowed by the oblivion of the habit and to leave it all as soon as God willed.

2

Schreiber lived in a two story greystone house built around a cobble-stone courtyard with a garden in the middle of it. There in the garden, watering the blackberry bushes she raised there now instead of sweet pea and syringa, stood a small, square woman with straggly grey hair. When she heard the clacking on the cobblestones, she put down the hose, wiped her hands on her apron and turned around.

"Good evening, Captain Schreiber."

"Good evening, Mme. Cassat," said Schreiber, and inclined his head to her, touching his cap.

Often, before dinner, he sat with her in the garden but tonight, al-though Mme. Cassat made the smoothing gestures which served as invitation to such occasions, Schreiber walked across to the door which led to his room.

"Have you seen my brother, Captain?" she pushed out, smoothing her hair and dress and sleeves.

"Just now, madame," replied Schreiber, half-turning from the door-way.

"I must tell him something about the radishes," she said, and blushed. She picked up the hose and, tightening the spout, concen-trated the stream on the tiny shoots of lawn. "He wouldn't have been allowed in the parlor before the war," she grumbled, listening to him go up the stairs. The reflection warmed over the embarrassment of her improvisation with him and reassured her of her own permanent respectability.

Upstairs, Schreiber had started to type. Mme. Cassat listened to the clicking resentfully and, as her husband came out to the garden, al-most snarled at him, "What's he chipping away at? All his papers and numbers and ugly American. Probably counting our china."

Actually Schreiber was engaged in more abstract calculations. He was doing a study of the villagers' evasion of certain censorship re-strictions based largely on circumlocutions they employed in letters to avoid these restricted topics. He had begun the study as a sub-section of his first administrative report on the village but he had gotten interested in it and decided to pursue it on his own in a scholarly fashion. He had never before done anything so thorough, not even in law school, but he seemed to have an instinct for research and it went very smoothly. Indeed, he found that the techniques of research were almost as pleasurable for him as the contemplation of the effects the completed study would have, the small, significant circles it would excite and the delightful sensation of his own position at the center of them, the authority on this particular fragment of the world. The books piled on his desk, commandeered from the Library of Bourges and from Army Special Studies, pleased him by their bulk and solemn titles. The typewriter too was pleasing to him; its noises reminded him of tiny nails being hammered into meaningful junctions.

In the evenings, he usually typed out the results of whatever meditations he'd had on the walk from his office to his billet. Then he would read a chapter or two from two or three of the books and type notations on memorandum cards. All this went very easily for him. The thoughts came dreamlike and he typed as if the mechanics of his wrists and fingers determined the conclusions themselves. As, on the walk, conversation with the Goupins was no hindrance to his private meditation, so part of his mind was detached from the work as he typed. Often the dull, rusty face of Verité Goupin appeared under the little black hammers of the machine. "Pitiful," he thought, and he hammered a comma into one of the muddy eyes of his vision.

When the dinner bell sounded, he tapped a semicolon and went over to the basin. He rinsed his hands, emptied the water into the slop jar and went downstairs to the dining room.

It was this evening, as Mme. Cassat offered him the usual choice of *fromage à chèvre* or *port salut* at the end of the meal, that the feeling which had often come upon him as he deliberated the choice—the Cassats waiting with ridiculous intensity for his varying answer—became recognizable as the feeling that he was here, now, and for the first time in his life, at home. Before he'd come to France, four months ago in the fall of forty-four, Schreiber's preoccupation had been writing long letters to his wife filled with bitter analyses of the military life and alien manners. Two weeks after he'd been assigned to the village, however, he'd written her that he had time to write only the briefest notes and that she in turn should direct all her letters through the APO to his office. Now he hardly ever thought of the squat, white house in Rye or his wife and he could scarcely remember the color of his daughter's hair.

"Do you think the *chèvre* too soft this evening, Captain?" asked Old Cassat.

"Not particularly, monsieur. It seems quite good."

"One doesn't like it too soft but when it's hard it dribbles all over the floor. It's really only good in Brittany," said Cassat, as if reproaching his wife for keeping him here in Cher. He sucked the last curds from his gums, his dentures rattling with the effort, and took up a knife to take the skin from a fine Italian pear.

"Yes, I've been through," said Schreiber, staring at the yellow membrane spiraling delicatelv from the white meat, and thinking of Verité.

3

Tiberius lived with Mme. Verna Zapenskya just above her bakery two blocks from the Hôtel de Ville on the rue Bulwer-Lytton. It was not his official billet but there were only seven enlisted men in the village and Capt. Schreiber did not worry them with regulations. In return for her favors and domestic provisions, Tiberius gave Mme. Zapenskya the double distinction of living with a non-commissioned officer and a Negro. In addition, her bakery was soon doing a lively trade in American cigarettes, chocolate bars, soap, underwear and other valuable items from the PX in Bourges.

Mme. Zapenskya and her neighbors dreaded the release of her husband from the PW camp in Germany; as the son of a White Russian officer's *valet de chambre*, he was looked upon as inordinately jealous and vindictive. Numerous offers were available to Tiberius to exchange the comforts of the rue Bulwer-Lytton for similar but less precarious ones. He had, however, a fondness for Mme. Zapenskya. She had a huge picture of Franklin D. Roosevelt pinned to the wall next to a mezzotint of the Virgin ("The Lady smiles but the American laughs," she said) and Roosevelt was one of Tiberius' personal idols. He persuaded her to add a somewhat smaller picture of another idol, Jack Johnson, and under this trinity of images he lived quite happily.

Tiberius had studied French at Bucknell and within a month of his arrival in the village, he spoke it better than Capt. Schreiber. In this month he became one of the central forces of the village, a judge of disputes and a councilor of difficulties; he also became Schreiber's most valuable source of information.

One night a week he drove Schreiber in to headquarters at Bourges and on these drives he gave him reports on the village.

Tonight, the most important news was Fougère's decision to close the tannery.

"What do you mean, 'close it'?" asked Schreiber. "It's been there fifty years. Doesn't he like us?"

"Probably that too, Max. In general he's just had enough. In his pockets and of this place. He's going down to his daughter's in the Midi. 'No coal thieves there,' he says." Tiberius drove carefully over the bridge. "I guess you'll have to get that Goupin girl a job in the office."

"What about the others? There're five or six of them."

"They'll find something. Verna needs somebody. Metayer too. They'll find something."

"I'd like to take the girl in. She's a little slow but very nice. The old man invited me over tonight."

"She had a little German beau last year. A corporal, except corporal's a little higher with them." He stretched his arm under Schreiber's fat jaw, so close to it that the stripes on his sleeve looked like scars on Schreiber's neck. "There's the cathedral."

"We've seen it," said Schreiber, looking.

"They've got a lot of thirteen-century glass stored away. You ought to put in a request to get it back in."

"I suppose it could still be shelled."

"Things are pretty well wound-up, Max."

The major at headquarters worked at night and he always tried to keep Schreiber for drinks. Schreiber never accepted but the major managed to delay him at least an hour with fatuous questions and quibblings. Schreiber was always worn out after the sessions and he and Tiberius usually went to a bar outside of town for some Cinzano or Pernod to pick them up.

"They're starting to let the G.I.s out," said Tiberius when Schreiber got back to the jeep. "I drove over to the place and they're swarming over it. M.P.s all over too. Guess we'd better go home."

"He murdered me tonight," said Schreiber. "I could really use one," but they drove back.

In front of his billet Schreiber said, "She'll have to learn English, you know."

"That's not much of a problem. She's probably had it in school. Maybe you could help her a little."

"We'll see," said Schreiber. "She's a pretty decent girl."

The Goupins were talking with the Cassats in the living room when he came in. Verité was in the corner, head bent over a book.

"Have you heard what's happened, Captain?" asked Mme. Cassat, calling to him from the door.

"Fougère closes the tannery in three weeks and Verité has no job. Like that," she cried, clapping her hands together sharply.

"These things happen, madame," said Schreiber, "and they are always difficult—but it so happens that I may be able to help. If mademoiselle would consider working with us, we've been needing someone for a long time. It's only a question of knowing a little English . . ."

"English!" cried Mme. Cassat. "Wonderful! She's studied it for years, haven't you, my dear?"

"That's very kind indeed, Captain," said Goupin. "Very kind."

"I should never speak it," said Verité.

"Nonsense!" cried Mme. Cassat. "Why it's quite simple. I remember it myself and it's forty years since I've said a word," and she said quickly, in English, "Good morning. Goodbye. What hour is it? Jolly good."

"I've never heard you speak English, Germaine," said Old Cassat. "It sounds elegant, doesn't it, Captain?"

"Indeed, monsieur. Mademoiselle shall learn it almost as well if she cares to try. I should be happy to spend some time helping her myself."

This statement produced some seconds' silence.

"That would be very generous, Captain," said Mme. Cassat softly.

"You will find me a difficult student, Captain," said Verité, looking up from her book.

"You learned German fairly well," said her father evenly, and there was another wordless interval.

"We can begin tomorrow evening, mademoiselle. In three weeks we should be able to do a good deal." Schreiber bowed slightly and said, "Good evening."

"We shall see," said Verité, and stared at Schreiber's back moving down the hall.

4

Schreiber told Verité that the north side of the river lay in an exposed position within two kilometers of the freight yards and that they would do better to hold their lessons on the south side.

"Of course he doesn't mind our being blown up before or after the lessons," thought Verité, but, nevertheless, twice a week she walked with him across the bridge below her house and a mile up the river to a clearing in a beech grove. Here they had the lesson.

Goupin went down to his sister's after they left and he could see them walking on the bridge, his daughter a few steps in back of Schreiber and stooping till she was just his height. They never looked at each other.

"I hope he will be as cautious as the German," said Goupin to his sister.

"This type always is, Axel. Anyway, more can come from it. Willy was nice but he could bring only trouble."

"I suppose nothing much can happen to her," said Goupin. "Only better. She will have a job, it will give her some amusement and," he laughed here, "she will learn American."

They stopped talking when Old Cassat came into the garden to talk about prices.

Despite forebodings about her adequacy, Verité learned English very rapidly. Schreiber was industrious and patient. After they left the house, he would ask her the vocabulary he'd assigned at the end of the preceding lesson. When they reached the grove, he corrected, in the last of the daylight, the sentences she had written out. The last hour and a half was devoted to conversation. Here Verité was brilliant. With a limited vocabulary, she could say, after the first lessons, almost anything she wished. She was in a sense more fluent in English than in French; it was as if the feeling of exposure which hindered her in ordinary conversation disappeared in the foreign idiom. Although most of their talk concerned natural objects or typical situations, Verité managed to infuse her talk with more of her own feelings than she had ever before put into words.

"You amaze me, mademoiselle," said Schreiber as they crossed back after the fourth lesson.

Verité, to whom the word "amaze" was new, fathomed its meaning and made it her own.

"It's very fine to amaze someone, Captain. One considered me amazing only for being so not-amazing. I am very disappointing to Poppa." She said *"trompante"* for "disappointing."

"We are nearly always disappointing to our parents," said Schreiber, hesitating over "disappointing" to let her learn it. "And they to us."

"Sometimes," she said.

Goupin, walking up the road, noticed they walked almost flank to flank now and it amused him. He waited for them at the bridge and called in English, "Have you learned much this evening?"

"It comes slowly, Poppa," Verité answered in French.

"Your daughter is modest, Goupin. It goes very well."

"I'm glad," said Goupin. "Come refresh yourself now after your labors, Captain. We have not opened the Calvados yet."

"Delighted," said Schreiber.

At the Goupins' the next hour, Schreiber mentioned that his work was decreasing at the office and, since the weather was so nice, that they might hold their lessons more frequently.

"You take too much trouble, Captain," she said.

"An extraordinary kindness, Captain," said Goupin.

"It is you who do me the kindness, mademoiselle," said Schreiber. The Calvados had warmed and exalted him and, after he had said this, he wondered if it had not sounded awkward. Later, walking home, he decided that it had but that Verité had understood it even beyond its intention and had not disapproved.

5

"What was it like?" asked Schreiber when he met Verité at the bridge the evening the tannery closed.

"Quite sad," she said. "I'd nearly forgotten it was really going to end. Fougère called us in at four and told us we could go home an hour early. He said he supposed he would never see us again. We all wept."

"Europeans have very strong sentiments," said Schreiber.

They walked across the bridge and on the other side Schreiber touched her arm with his fingers.

"I ask myself sometimes if your wife is sad at home," she said.

He dropped his hand and said, "I don't really know. I hear so little. She has much to occupy her time but she may be sad."

"Americans have not such strong sentiments," she said.

"Some," said Schreiber.

"You are here," she said, "and are one of us here."

They walked to the grove and sat down. There were no longer any sentences to correct.

"The permission to hire you came from Bourges today. A week or two and the money will be—we say, 'allocated.'"

"I understand," she said. "I will enjoy working in your office."

"You will really be in Tiberius' office but I come in there often."

She looked expectant and he added, "The work is not difficult."

"Is it interesting?" she asked.

"You file—*classez*—letters. If you read them, it's interesting." She smiled at him.

"Will it go on much longer, do you think?" she asked. They both understood "the war" for "it."

"I don't think so. Perhaps."

They both thought of the war being over and what would happen.

"It could go on a long time," she said. "The Germans are soft alone but very hard together. It could last for years."

Schreiber said he didn't think so.

6

Two days before the war actually ended, the report was broadcast that an armistice had been signed. Verité was in the office at the Hotel de Ville—she had worked there almost two weeks—when Tiberius ran in with the news. Verité ran up to Schreiber's office but he wasn't in. Then, like everyone else in the building, she ran outside.

The streets were filling. Over the village, people ran into each other's houses to announce that the end had come. The bars and cafés and the square in front of the church were filled with people. The priest rang the bells and the people in the fields, hearing, started coming into town.

Tiberius was in the jeep shouting and singing. Eight people piled in with him and they passed around bottles of red wine and American whiskey. They kissed each other, men and women, and waved to people in the streets.

Verité started running home. Halfway there she met the Cassats on the way to town.

"What's happened? Is it all over?" called her aunt.

"Yes, it's all over. The war is over."

"We must go to church," said Old Cassat.

"Yes, Poppa. You're coming too, Verité?" but her niece was running up the path.

"She should come," said Old Cassat.

Nobody was home. Verité waited.

In an hour Schreiber came. He had run most of the way from town and he was gasping and sweating.

"Come," he said.

She took his hand and they walked quickly to the bridge and over to the other side. They said nothing. In the shade of the trees they slowed down. When they came to the clearing, they stretched out on the ground and held each other.

They were there about ten minutes when they heard a terrible noise far down the road on the other side of the river. They sat up and stared and soon they distinguished the rasping horn of the jeep and Tiberius and the others shouting. They watched the jeep drive wildly over the bridge and turn up the path which led to the clearing. They stood up quickly and brushed off their clothes.

"Come on, Max," yelled Tiberius. "Climb aboard. Let the lessons go tonight."

Schreiber said nothing. He walked over to the jeep and pointed towards town. Someone spilled wine on his jacket. "Get back, Corporal," he said. "Get back on the double."

Tiberius looked at him. "Christ, Schreiber, it's all over," he said slowly. He spun the jeep around and drove back. The horn began sounding halfway down the path. They could hear it for two or three minutes.

They had sat down again but now he started to get up. She touched his arm but he shook his head, brushed off his clothes and held out his hands to help her up. She took them and he pulled her up and held her hands till they stopped trembling.

"Later, my dear," he said. "They might come back tonight."

7

People were not overly disappointed that the armistice report turned out to be false because the announcement of it was coupled with an assurance that the real end was imminent. The day after, the bells and cannon were heard from Bourges. In the village there was no celebration. People nodded to each other as if to say, "Well, there it is," and that was all. Those who had celebrated too wildly before kept inside as much as possible.

That night Schreiber met Verité at the bridge as usual but this time they walked down instead of up the river. They walked for three quarters of an hour before they found a place where they could be comfortable.

They talked little, in French, about what would happen. Mostly they waited for it to get dark.

They met every night for almost two weeks, staying out till three or four in the morning.

On the twelfth evening, Verité was at the bridge listening for the footsteps. When she heard the steps which were not Schreiber's, she said, "Now it's over."

It was Mme. Cassat. "He said you'd be here," she said. "He gave me this for you." She took an envelope from her sleeve and handed it to Verité. It was one from his office and stamped with the legend, "Passed By Censor." "He came back for an hour to pack his clothes and papers. The black one calls for them tomorrow but he left tonight. He gave me the letter and told me to give it to you, that you'd be here."

Verité was reading the letter. Mme. Cassat turned away. "These things happen," she muttered, smoothing her sleeves. She was rehearsing what she would say.

The note was in English: "They called me today and I'm going to Germany. I'll be on my way as you read this. I'll get a leave (*congé*) before long. You know what I think about everything. We shall arrange things." It was initialed, "M." She had never called him Max, didn't even know it was his name till she had heard Tiberius use it. It was this that made her cry.

Mme. Cassat turned around and held out her arms. "These things happen, my dear," she said.

8

Schreiber was assigned to Mainz. He drove there in the front seat of an army truck; twenty enlisted men were packed into the back. They arrived at night and cruised around the center of the city looking for a building they could requisition to sleep in. There was almost nothing standing. Only the cathedral. Here and there smoke rose and water flowed in the streets. Nobody was awake. They saw a few people rolled up on the grass, and down by the river there were hundreds more. Women, children, old men and cripples. Across the Rhine they could see American barracks. Two bridges stretched halfway across it; they looked like broken fingers.

They went to sleep on the banks.

The disorder upset Schreiber. He tried to think of Verité, hoping her image would compose him to sleep. Instead he could see only piles and piles of white cards toppling over on hundreds of desks. The vision made him feel sick and he went down to the river. He threw up in the water and then he washed off his face. He got up and saw that an old woman had been watching him. "I was sick," he called to her in French. She looked him over and said something in German. He nodded, smiling to her and then suddenly he felt much better and he thought how good it was that the war was over.

The next day they began working, setting up headquarters, contacting troops, registering the populace, establishing market lines. Schreiber worked harder than he had ever worked in his life. He went to bed every evening as soon as he was off duty. Only when the French command took over the town did he have leisure and then he allowed himself to think about Verité.

He wrote to her, putting the letter sealed into an envelope addressed to Tiberius. In a week he wrote another. His first letter was returned, stamped, to his amazement, "Absent Without Leave. Returned By Censor." Then he wrote directly to her. There was no answer. He wrote again saying that he would be returned to the States in less than six months.

It was nearly two months now since he had seen her or heard from or about her. The mystery revived and sharpened his passion. He began to think of her all day long. He considered taking his discharge in Europe, of never going back to the States, or only after the affair had run the course he'd heard these affairs must run.

Finally, he requested a week's leave and got it. He waited two days for a ride to Strasbourg and there three days for one to Dijon. He was already a day late when he started for Bourges. In Bourges, for eight cigarettes, he hired a taxi to drive him to the village. It was seven in the evening when he saw the Hôtel de Ville. He told the driver to wait there and in an hour to drive up the road to Goupin's. He gave him another cigarette and fifty francs.

He walked as quickly as he could up the path. When he saw the bridge, he started trembling so much he had to stop. He sat down under a beech tree and gripped the bark. He held it so tightly his arms numbed to the elbow. Then he got up and ran to the Goupins'. There were no lights in the house. He opened the door and shouted, "Hey." There was no one there but he shouted twice more. He switched on the light and the first thing he saw was a great heap of books piled up in the corner. He went over and looked at them a second and then kicked at the middle of the pile. The books tumbled against the wall. Six or seven of them remained stacked; he picked up the top one, put it to his lips and then dropped it.

He ran out of the house down the road to the Cassats'.

They were sitting with Goupin in the garden. Mme. Cassat was frightened at the running and called, "Who's there?"

"It's Schreiber," he called, and he ran to her at the edge of the courtyard. He saw Goupin sitting with Cassat in the garden and he called, "Goupin, where's Verité?"

"Come," said Mme. Cassat, and she took him by the sleeve to where the two men sat.

He started to say, "What's wrong?" but he couldn't summon the French for it.

Old Cassat said, "Mlle. Verité is gone, Captain, gone off."

"With the black one," said his wife. "No one knows where. Nearly two months."

Schreiber looked at them all and turned away. At the gate he said in English, "A taxi is waiting for me."

He walked down the side path to the river. He didn't dare look at the bridge.

The taxi would be coming soon, he thought. He wondered if he should wait for it in the bushes and then slip under the tires. "I'm thinking of suicide," he thought. "Over love." In his pain he was almost proud. He said, "*Un peu ridicule.*"

He wondered how deep the river was off the banks. "Not enough," he thought. He started to cry thinking of her but also because he couldn't do anything to himself.

At the road he sat under a tree to wait for the taxi. The ground was wet and his legs were cold. It seemed incredible to him that he was here. When the taxi drove up, he climbed in and said, "Back to Bourges." About halfway there he started to cry. He cried all the way back to the city, not caring what the driver thought nor about anything at all.

AUGUSTA WALKER *received her B.A. and M.A. from the University of Michigan in 1944 and 1945 and then tought English for two years at the Woman's College of the University of North Carolina.* "After that," she says, "I accepted a three-year teaching contract at Lingnam University in Canton, China, and during this period many things happened to China and to me, including the Communist War. I spent two years getting home, most of it in Italy, France and Spain, where I learned the languages and other interesting things, and did some writing. For the past year I have been studying at Columbia University, and expect to go back to teaching. This story is my first publication, but another will be published by* Partisan Review, *and I have a little novel in its final stages."*

THE DAY OF THE CIPHER

FROM THE YALE REVIEW

The landlady did not answer that day when Lorna said, "Good Morning," passing her on the stairs. The landlady was carrying a broom and and a bucket, and she turned her head halfway, but said nothing. Lorna went on down thinking of something else and not being really quite aware that the landlady had said nothing.

She went to the dining room and took her usual place at the table for breakfast. The usual people were there—the schoolteacher, the lady who had a pension, the lady who ran the stenotype and the mimeograph machine—and they were talking about the things they always talked about. They were saying something this morning about an underwear sale at Grosset's, and they did not notice her when she sat down. "Lace-trimmed with elastic in back, and three-piece sets all to match," the lady who ran the stenotype and the mimeograph machine was saying. Quotations of price followed, and Lorna shammed a sort of attention, staring at the little Venetian birdbath of yellow marble with marble birds around it on the lace doily in the center of the table; but she was not really focused on the talk or on the birdbath, not being quite willing to have anything to do with either.

Then she observed that the three ladies seemed to have drawn inward towards each other with their shoulders, as if there were someone there whom they did not want to partake of what they were saying. They had closed off that half of the table; the marble birdbath separated their half from the half they left to her. It was as though they had something secret to say among the three of them. And yet they were not lowering their voices. On the contrary they were talking with a kind of emphasis that the subject of the underwear sale did not seem to justify, and something about them made Lorna feel that they were not really talking about the underwear sale at all, but something else for which this was a kind of code. They were nursing something among them that called for an exaggerated indifference.

She finished her toast and coffee quickly and was glad to go. She would have left all these impressions in the dining room if she had not looked around just as she was closing the door, and at just that moment they were looking around, too. And there on the face of the woman who ran the stenotype and the mimeograph machine was a little smile of derision.

It was a shock to Lorna. She stared at herself in the hall mirror. She turned around carefully but could see nothing wrong with her hair or dress or face. There was nothing special about them either. She looked as she always did. She looked very much like other people in the ordinary way of life. She was not especially pretty or otherwise, not differently dressed, not noticeably more or less of anything than a young working woman normally is.

She put on her coat and went down and out to the street. It was a very cold day, wet and coarse. The season was four o'clock in the morning of the year. It was the hour of the year when people huddle themselves inwards, hoarding the slowed pulse of their subsided powers, reluctant to wake. It was the before-dawn when all the beauty and challenge of cold have gone, and people are weary of resisting it. Withered women propelled themselves past, carrying little bags of groceries. The bus came full of people at the low ebb of their lives, reading their morning papers. There was no seat for Lorna, so she stood and looked at news headlines, and felt the people driving themselves with weariness against the current of nature towards their offices. She got off in front of the city library, and the others struggled on towards the center.

It was warm in the city library. She passed through to the back behind counters and stacks to a darkish hidden place that was hers, where she sat always with piles of new books around her. Her job was to read the beginnings and ends of books and glance comprehensively through the middles in order to see what kind they were. The books then passed to the hands of other persons, who gave them numbers, so that they could then be carried to the proper shelves in the proper departments and each placed among its own sort, so that people who wanted a book of that sort could find it quickly and thus avoid the annoyance and loss of time of having to read anything by mistake.

Lorna's friends envied her because she could keep up on her reading, and, indeed, had to, which is the only possible way of ever being able to. She had always to keep up on the new books and to know who the new authors were and what was said about them on the jackets by other authors. This gave her the advantage of being able to talk about them, to enter any conversation, and feel at home in any company. Her friends envied her a great deal because they had no time to keep up on their reading.

And there was a period when Lorna read on all subjects and felt at home in any company, ready to enter any conversation. But it passed. She no longer liked anybody who kept up on his reading or who did not keep up on it because he lacked the time.

She sat down at her desk and began where she had left off yesterday. But it was different now. She still read the beginnings and ends and looked comprehensively through the middles. But it was different.

Other people came and went. A little man in a grey apron kept trundling by a cartload of books. There was something of the hospital orderly about him, intent and knowing and possessive, wheeling patients to and from the operating room. A thin boy walked mincingly with a limp, carrying slips of paper in his hand or a stack of books against his concave chest. The librarians passed with spectacles and pencils and humped shoulders. Lorna saw all this without looking, from the accumulation of other days. But once she glanced up suddenly to find one of the librarians standing a little distance from her, slightly to the rear, looking at her with concentration. There was a curious little sneer on her face, not quite a smile. And this was of today.

Lorna's reflex was to try to protect herself by not knowing. But when she was sure the librarian had moved away, she turned to look again to see if she could dispel the impression. There was no doubt. There had been a sneer.

She got up and went to the rest room where there was a mirror, and looked at herself carefully again. She could see nothing the matter. Then it was something she had done. The thought made her a little frantic because, not knowing what it was, she could do nothing to correct it.

She went back to her desk and sat down. Now she decided that there was nothing at all except in her imagination, and she began to work again.

But it was no use. Self-investigation had set in, and she kept thinking back over everything that had happened the day before. At last when she considered the librarian's position a little behind her, and the intentness of her look, as though she had been standing there for some time watching, it occurred to Lorna that the librarian had seen what she was doing with the books. This was startling. She had not thought before that what she did with the books was irregular, or in the least observable, or, least of all, anything that could arouse anybody's scorn. And how could this connect with the ladies around the breakfast table at her boardinghouse?

But looking back, she could see that things had been going a little this way for some time, and it was now quite plain that to sit with these same ladies that evening around the dinner table was an affront to nature, even an impossibility. Once not so long ago these ladies had been all right, and she had been glad to have a room with board in a clean house. People said, "It's a nice place, they are a nice class of people." But a boardinghouse for women is only a place of waiting. It is a place of waiting for marriage or for death, and for those who are plainly not for marriage and not yet for death, it is a place of waiting until something happens to them, and now Lorna had served her term. It was over, all the waiting time of being young. Looking back, she remembered a yard full of school children, and long Sunday afternoons of white dresses, and the Friday of the football game when she was fifteen, with a boy, and the school colors on her coat. All this was waiting, and now the term was served.

She thought of sitting at the table with the other three ladies, and after bleak strain saying, "The weather is so tiresome—it gets no better from one day to the next." But it was no use; they would know. If she said a really ordinary little thing, they knew it was not real conversation. She had served her time and she would go.

At lunch hour she took a newspaper and looked for "Rooms to rent." She found an address closer to the library and convenient, and she had three quarters of an hour, enough time to go at once and inquire.

She got off the bus at the number. It was an apartment house, new, and in very good condition, with a wet, cold smell of cement in the stairway, and covered galvanized garbage cans at the doors. She rang, and the door was opened by a man who stood looking at her with a triumphant expression as though he had been expecting her, almost as though he had made a bet with somebody that she would come. Behind him in the hall stood two women and a little girl. One of the women was middle-aged, evidently the wife, and the other was old. Lorna looked at them all wonderingly. She thought that they must have been waiting for somebody and mistook her for that person.

"I am looking for a room," she said.

"Come in," said the man.

He led her into the living room, and the others followed. The apartment was new and things were placed uncomfortably as though the occupants were afraid to settle into it. In the living room a new piano was sitting at an awkward angle, as if left there to be stored. The man pulled a chair into the center of the room and invited her to sit down. He pulled up another and sat down facing her. His eyes were sleazy with suspicion. He was expecting to triumph about something. The two women and the child ranged themselves along the wall. They looked expectant and fearful and as though they intended to enjoy themselves.

"Are you married?" the man asked. Lorna answered no, but he looked her over for some sign that she had not told the truth.

"Are you employed?"

"Yes, I work in the city library."

It was plain that he did not believe her.

"You will be expected to furnish your own sheets," he said.

Lorna thought for a minute.

"And have them laundered," he added. "You must have them laundered out. Also your clothes. You can't use the iron."

The younger woman and the little girl began to giggle nervously. They turned their faces to the wall and tried to smother their titters.

"Do you have a health card?" the man asked.

"A health card? For what?"

"For your health."

Lorna thought again. "I probably have an old vaccination card."

"Please show it to me," he said.

It was evident that if she could not produce it all his suspicions would be confirmed. She opened her purse and began to hunt, but she knew there was no vaccination card there, and her hands trembled. She found her old social security card and held it out, still shaking. She hoped he would not know the difference; he did not seem to be a man who understood things. He turned it over and looked at it. It made him proud to look at it. He examined it carefully, holding it to the light. He did not notice that it was not a vaccination card. The two women and the child looked over expectantly at the card and waited for the outcome. He handed it back to her.

"Where do you live now?" he asked.

She told him, and then added, "Mrs. J. R. Pillar is very well known here. Her husband was a subsuperintendent in the factory before his death." She told him how respectable it was, for professional women only, and everybody spoke highly of it.

"Then why do you have to leave there?" he cried, and now his triumph had arrived. His eyes seized what they had been waiting for. He half arose from his chair and beetled over her. His face was full of the surreptitious joy of having trapped her. The wife and child began to giggle again. The older woman, shriveled, grey, and black, stood at attention, looking up at the man as though awaiting a command from him. Obviously they thought she was someone else. But how could they be expecting any particular person to come asking for their room, and what was this person supposed to have done?

"Why do you have to leave there?" he repeated.

Now she knew there was something to hide, but she stood up proudly, in order to keep him from hanging over her, and said, trying to be indignant, "I don't have to leave there. I'm leaving because I want to change my way of living. I want a different atmosphere."

"And what kind of way of living do you want?" The triumph was flooding now, running into the ready creases of recognition in his face. "You can't bring any men here!"

Now both women smothered their mouths in their hands. Lorna began to move towards the door. The simple explanation was that the family were all insane, and she could not yet be forced to live in a madhouse.

"One minute, please," he shouted, and he strode into the hallway ahead of her to seize the telephone. He called operator and asked the number of the city library. Then he called the city library and asked for the director. Meanwhile he jotted things on a pad.

"I'm calling to ask about a young lady who says she works there," he said, and he began to describe her, looking her up and down. Lorna wandered towards the door and let herself out. The last words she heard were, "Well, she's leaving now—I didn't think she would stay."

Back in her warm cave at the library, she thought the interview had taken place on another planet. She felt as one waking at four in the morning from the bubble of a dream of horrors, knowing that in some helpless way one has created the dream for himself in his own mind and is responsible for it.

But now she remembered the director of the library and wondered what he must have thought of the telephone call, and if anything would come of it. While she worked at the books, she thought, and at last decided to go and see the director and tell him everything. She would start by asking about the call, and explain that it meant nothing—she had only encountered, while inquiring about a room, a man who was a little crazy. The director was intelligent and he might understand something of this. He might even explain it to her.

She thought of everything first. He might think her a neurotic girl fast becoming an old maid. He might even look at her coolly and comment that her work was no longer what it should be. But all this was worth risking for the chance of his saying in a confidential voice, "I know. But it will pass. It is a temporary thing."

At the top of the stairs she met the director coming out of his office. He was carrying his coat, hat, and brief case, and he looked at her as though attracted by some object behind her head.

"Is there something?" he asked. "I am just going away."

"It isn't important," Lorna said. "Another time."

"You could leave a memo with Miss Grey," he said.

"Yes," said Lorna, "I will."

He went down the stairs and she went into the office.

"Yes?" Miss Grey said, looking up.

"I wondered if there was a telephone call a while ago," Lorna said. "A man called to ask about me."

"About you? I don't remember anything."

"Then it doesn't matter," Lorna said. "I may be mistaken."

"Oh, yes, I remember, there was something. Someone called about one of our employees and asked why she was resigning. Yes, of course it must have been you. We told him we didn't know."

"But I wasn't resigning," Lorna said. "Why should he have said that?"

"I don't know," Miss Grey answered. "But people told me you were resigning."

Lorna went out, feeling with her hand for the door because she had forgotten her directions. She went back to her cave.

Evening came. She left the books in order as though to begin the next day where she had left off. She went out, and on the street thought about what little errands she must do before going home. She needed to buy some things. She needed to buy a newspaper and a quarter of a yard of material to fix the collar of a dress. And a package of little pastries because it was her turn to furnish something for the Reading Club. She went to the proper places and bought the things, but only from habit. None of this applied to anything any more, but she did not know how to stop.

On the bus she saw a woman sitting with a little boy on her lap, and the woman had a completed look. It was a look full of anxiety and trouble, but also of completion, for all had come to her, all the waiting and getting ready of being young, all had come to her, and it was not happiness, but it was completion.

On the bus she saw a young man who was searching. For it was evening, and he had nothing for his evening, and so he was hunting with his eyes and with his body. He looked in her face, waiting for her to make a sign, and Lorna looked drearily up at an advertisement. She had watched the little drama between others, in wonder that it always went on the same, that they never tired of it. The woman always stole a look sooner or later, after first holding her profile carefully for him, and it embarrassed Lorna to see how much they wanted their vanity caressed.

She stared drearily at the advertisement, and when she got off the bus, the young man got off, too, and came two steps behind. Then he moved close and walked beside her until they came to the corner where she had to turn, and there she paused because he was standing in her way. She looked up at him and was stupefied by his leer.

"I know who you are," he said. "I know all about you."

After an empty moment of staring, hoping for recognition, Lorna pushed past him and went on her way, stumbling a little. She was shattered now. In a moment she would fall into tired weeping and walk along the street like an old mad woman. One of the packages fell from her arms and bumped against her leg, but she did not notice. She walked on with her face breaking in little spasms. She did not know where to go, but it seemed fantastic to go back to the boardinghouse. Then there were footsteps running behind her. Someone came up and thrust into her arms the package she had dropped. The person spoke in a flow of gentle words, and she looked up, her face gone quiet and normal again. She thought that this was someone she knew from ordinary life, and without thinking, she grasped his coat sleeve. But she had never seen him before. He was young and shaggy and his hands that were thrusting the bundle into her arms were work-hands. He kept talking in a gentle, urging tone. But she realized now that he was talking in some foreign language of which she did not understand a word.

She kept hold of his coat sleeve. They walked along. He took the bundle from her arms again and carried it himself. They seemed not to be going to any particular place. At last they paused in front of a steamed-over glass door; he opened it and they went in. There were some little tables and a smell of new-ground coffee. They sat down, and in a moment a girl came bringing two little cups of coffee, very strong. The young man kept talking. He was explaining something to her and reassuring her. She did not know what, because there was not a word of it that she could understand, nor did she even know what language it was in. It had a calm, curbless movement, and he spoke so low that only she could hear. She knew he was explaining something because he spoke in an explaining tone of voice with helpful gestures of the hands. And she knew he was reassuring her because now and then his voice went tender as though to a small child in the night.

They drank the coffee and she felt much better. Then he took a pencil from his sagging coat pocket and fished for a scrap of paper, and on this he drew some little pictures, still talking. He drew something that looked vaguely like a pineapple and then something like rocks shooting out the top of a volcano. Then he made five swift little lines and the musical clef across them, and two notes, each with pennant attached. At last he stopped talking and looked at her expectantly. He was waiting for her to answer.

She began to answer.

"It seemed to me," she said, "that there was some secret about the world, a secret about why it exists. And people are afraid they will find it out. They are afraid somebody will tell them. Because then all the things they want to do will not belong in anything."

And she went on talking. She took the pencil from him and drew a picture of a steeple with a clock. There was not room in the steeple to put the clock, so she put it at the side. There was not room in the clock for all the numbers, so she put them around it. He watched her with quiet, waiting eyes.

"But I do want to know, I do want to know, it is a waste of time not to know. All this not knowing, it is like spending all your life making a dress."

They sat until they knew they could not stay there any longer, but it was not possible to think of not going on as they were. The young man was working out a plan. He drew a sketch of what seemed to be the main square of the city, for the lines were drawn at the angles of the streets and there was a little scriggle in the middle for the water serpent statue. He looked at her inquiringly, and she nodded. He looked up at the clock over the counter of the café. It said seven-thirty. Then he took her drawing of the clock for the steeple and made hands which pointed to nine-thirty. He looked at her again inquiringly, and she nodded. He marked a little x beside the fountain. So then everything was solved. They would meet in two hours at the city square, and little by little they would say and explain everything in the world. He paid the waitress, and they went out in the cold. He buttoned her coat and arranged the little packages in her arms. They parted with a look of inestimable fidelity, and she hurried away as though her body had become a bird.

She went back to the house where her things were. She did not think much what to do with them. In a drawer she had a loaf of bread and some apples and cheese, and she ate a little while she went around the room getting ready.

But it was strange getting ready. She could not think what she ought to take with her, and she wasted time just standing and trying to divine what she would need. Warm sweaters? Would it be cold there? But this was a bizarre question, and she did not know what it meant. She did not know what was beyond the city square. A change of clothes, some woolen socks, at least a towel and soap. But no, these things were all wrong; he would not know what to make of them. Nothing would do. She did not know what one would need there. And all these little things around her that were so much trouble. All these little things that she had made or bought or been given for Christmas, and that always had to be thought of as though they were alive. She could not take any of them because she did not know what one would need there. But she kept thinking, "I must get ready." There was only an hour left. And it was like one of those dreams in which you cannot find what you must have in order to do what you must do, because you don't know what it is you must do.

She took what was left of the bread and cheese and apples and wrapped them in a package to take to him, in case he had not had a chance to eat anything, for he would be getting ready, too. At the last minute she took her reading lamp with the green shade from the head of the bed, and a photograph of a little nephew from the dresser, because these were the last things she noticed, and it seemed as though one ought to take something.

She went out. The night was colder than the day had been. It was the bitter cold that can come only in the month when one waits the long wait that is always one week more. She hoped he would not be cold. His overcoat had not seemed very heavy. Her eyes watered. She hurried along, for it was almost nine-thirty. There were many people in the street, and they were all hurrying. The city square seemed farther away than she had thought, and when she neared it she saw that nearly everybody was going in that direction.

She was amazed on reaching the square to find a large crowd around the center fountain. She wondered if there was something special going on this evening. But the people were not doing anything. They did not appear to be there together. Some walked quickly back and forth as though they were about to do something, or had something in mind. Others stood in one spot and stamped their feet for warmth. Lorna began to look around eagerly. She knew he would be there. He would not be late. But she did not see him. She thought for a minute that she saw him, but when she approached the man, she could not recognize his face, and he stared back without any sign of knowing her. It was not he. She began to wander around. Now she was in a frenzy of anxiety because she knew what the trouble was. She had forgotten what he looked like. She still retained a clear impression of his personality and voice and even his movements, but she could not remember any special physical thing. At first she walked quickly back and forth as though she were about to do something, and then she thought it might be better to wait and let him find her. So she stood in one spot and stamped her feet.

But now she knew what the real trouble was. He had forgotten, too, what she looked like. He was here hunting and waiting.

She looked for someone who was looking for someone. But it was hard to tell. They all had the appearance of not having finished something important. She looked in their faces, and each young man at first looked a little like him, but none of them turned out to be. They looked back at her with varying degrees of unsureness and of wanting.

Lorna drifted through the flotsam of shoulders and elbows and corners of articles, and now she knew. It was to be like this, it was the way things were now. This was the way they must be from now on always. At first the great desolation was too great, and she thought she would not go on with the world this way. But then, remembering him, she knew that he knew all this about things, and that he was going on anyway, and so she, too, would find out how it was done, because now things had become like this for her, too, and they would be so always.

The night had grown up to a high, late wind, and most of the people were drifting away from the square. Lorna waited until nearly all were gone, and she looked around once more at the few who stood with their backs to the blast and their collars up before she started back. On the return walk the street looked strange. She did not remember having seen it before. But now it was natural that the street was strange. It was the way of things, and she knew.

ROBERT WALLACE, *after graduation from Princeton and active service in the U. S. Navy, has been a writer of fiction and is now a staff writer at Life. He lives in Connecticut.*

THE SECRET WEAPON OF JOE SMITH

FROM HARPER'S MAGAZINE

Joe Smith was a gentle, quiet man, no more aggressive than a glass of stale water. He had begun his career at twenty as a reporter for a New York newspaper and at fifty was still a reporter for the same newspaper, writing brief pale stories about the activities of various subcommittees of the United Nations. When the Security Council was in session and heavyweights such as Russia's Yakov Malik were in town, the newspaper assigned a heavyweight reporter to the UN. When the session was over Joe Smith was sent back to pick up the dull fragments of news that remained.

Still, there were three unusual things about Joe Smith. He had actually managed to save some money during his thirty years as a reporter and owned a big, if decrepit, brownstone house not far from United Nations headquarters in east Manhattan. Many years ago, somehow overcoming his paralyzing shyness, he had proposed to an attractive woman who had married him and then presented him with five children, to whom he was a good, quiet father. The third unusual thing about him was that he was, on a small scale, a landlord. He had rented two rooms and a bath to a man named Pyotr Votichenko, delegate from one of the Peoples' Republics.

Joe Smith's associates on the newspaper were not surprised that he had taken in a Communist lodger. It was, they thought, precisely in character. Smith was no more revolutionary than a saucer of Jello. It was his kindliness, his deep belief (sometimes at large cost) in the fundamental goodness of men, that had led him to do it. He had often said that if each man will make an effort to understand the Communists, all may yet be well.

But his idea did not work in practice. Joe Smith had fondly hoped that he might see something of Pyotr Votichenko on a social basis, but as it turned out he rarely saw him at all, except when they passed each other in the corridors of the UN buildings. In the beginning Smith had several times stopped Votichenko and had asked him to dinner, but Votichenko, without smiling, had simply said, "No!" At Thanksgiving and again at Christmas Smith had gone to Votichenko's apartment, which was separate from the rest of the house and had its own entrance, and had asked him to have cocktails with the family. Votichenko had not merely refused; he had slammed the door in Smith's face.

Whenever Votichenko had occasion to get in touch with Smith, which he did once or twice a month when he wished to complain about the plumbing, the ventilation of the rooms, the noise of Mrs. Smith's radio, or some similar thing, he used the telephone. "Hello?" he would say. "Here is Votichenko. I have observed a rat in the bathroom." This would upset Joe Smith, who had several times called in the exterminators and had several times been informed that there were no rats in the building. But Smith would call the exterminators once more, and receive the same information.

Or the tenant would say, "Here is Votichenko. Your children are creating such a crude disturbance that I cannot sleep," upon which Smith would tell his children, who were quiet, studious persons like himself, that they really must not talk aloud after 9:00 P.M.

"He's a good man," Smith would say. "He's alone in a strange country, uneasy and full of mistaken notions. In time, kindness and honesty will win him over."

But Votichenko was not won over. One evening, after he had been a tenant for almost a year, he visited Smith's part of the house for the first time. It was a very strange incident.

"Why, Mr. Votichenko," Smith said, standing openmouthed in his doorway. "And Patrolman Weiss. Is something wrong?"

Patrolman Weiss, who had worked the beat for many years and knew Smith well, was obviously embarrassed. "I—I'm very sorry," he said. "We've had a complaint. Mr. Votichenko called the station, and the sergeant sent me over."

"Complaint?" said Smith. "I don't understand."

Votichenko stood beside the policeman, saying nothing, his heavy face red, his eyes sullen. He was wearing the same ridiculously small black fedora, the black necktie, and the black suit, a size too small for him, that Smith had always seen him in.

"Well," said the patrolman. "This man, Mr. Votichenko, says someone broke into his room today."

"Really?" Smith said, amazed. "I'm terribly sorry. Was anything stolen?"

"He doesn't say. But he does say he thinks someone in this house did it."

Smith flinched as though Weiss had struck him. "We?" he said. "We broke into his room? That's—why, that's unbelievable."

"Well, it doesn't seem as though you'd do it," said Patrolman Weiss. "It's just that we've had this complaint. All I'm to do is to tell you, and warn you, since he doesn't say anything's been taken. So I've told you, and I've warned you, and I consider that's all there is to that."

"Mr. Votichenko," Smith said. "In Heaven's name, do you really——?"

Votichenko said nothing. He turned and walked away. The policeman stared after him, then looked blankly at Smith. "I don't know," he said. "I swear I don't know. But I've got to pay attention to him, since he is who he is. Good night, Mr. Smith, and forget it."

Smith went back into his living room and sat down.

"I've never——" began his wife. "I've absolutely never——"

"Nor I," Smith said. "But I think I understand."

"Understand?" his wife said. "You always think you understand everything. The man is either crazy or malicious beyond belief. I've never heard of such a thing."

"No," Smith said. "Look at it this way. He's alone here, except for the other delegates from his country, of course, and they don't live with him. He's frightened."

"Of what?" demanded his wife.

"Of what people think. Not our people, his people—here and at home. He has to keep proving that he doesn't like us, he has to build a case for himself."

Her voice rose in exasperation. "Good Heavens!" she cried. "Has to build a case! Do you suppose that includes calling the police?"

"Please," he said. "Don't be upset. He's got—well, a strange mind. Primitive. Calling the police means nothing to him, except that he can use it to show his superiors that he hasn't gotten soft."

"Joseph," she said. "Joseph Smith. Suppose he takes it into his mind that the way to prove he isn't soft is to set fire to the house?"

"Don't be hysterical," he said. "You really must try to understand."

"I don't understand anything except that you've got to get that man out of this house."

"I can't," Joe Smith said. "I mean, I won't. But I'll talk to him."

Next day Smith found Votichenko in one of the UN corridors. He held out his hand but Votichenko instantly brushed it aside. "No!" he said. "I have nothing to say to you."

"I have something to say to you," Smith said. "I'll make it brief. No one will think we're friends if they see us standing here for a minute."

Votichenko glowered but stood still.

"Look," Smith said. "I really do understand. I understand that we can't possibly have any friendly relations, and even that you've got to—that you think you've got to—take certain steps. But I want to warn you. No more police, no more trouble like that. It's too much."

Votichenko looked at the earnest little man beside him and shrugged his shoulders.

"Really," Smith said. "I'm not asking you to like me, or to like my family. I'm not even asking you to give up the rather repulsive attitude you have. But if you go out of your way to make trouble, I'll——"

"You'll what?" Votichenko said.

Smith spoke softly and, he thought, with good dramatic effect. "Look. You can make trouble for me, I admit it. But I can also make trouble for you. A lot of trouble."

"Ha!" Votichenko said. "You are a fascist whelp."

"I'm very serious," Smith said. "Have you ever thought that you could be destroyed? I could destroy you. I could do it"—he paused and appeared to be counting on his fingers—"I could do it with words. Perhaps ten small words."

Votichenko's big face reddened and he made a loud honking sound. Laughter.

"All right," Smith said. "That's all I have to say. But if I were you, I'd remember it."

Within a week it happened again. Smith returned to his office at the end of day to write another of his small, dull stories and found a note in his typewriter. "Pls see me. Joe T."

Joe T. was the managing editor. When Smith came into his office Joe T. cleared his throat uncomfortably and smiled. "This is a stupid thing," he said, "but I felt I had to talk to you about it."

"What's that?"

"This letter. It's from one of the delegates. He accuses you of falsifying your stories, rifling his room, and several other crimes."

"Votichenko," Smith said.

"Yes."

"You don't believe him?"

Joe T. laughed aloud. "Great day," he said. "I've read the stories. The only crime is that they're dull."

"Well——" Smith said.

"But the trouble is, he threatens to make a formal complaint to the Secretary of State. State can't actually do anything about it, of course, but it could embarrass everybody."

"I see. What do you want me to do?"

"Well," Joe T. said, "be nice to him. Butter him up. You understand, it's a ridiculous thing but there's no sense in——"

"Sure," Smith said. "I understand."

"Good."

Three days passed before Smith found Votichenko again. Once more he held out his hand and once more Votichenko brushed it aside.

"You remember what I said to you before?" Smith said. "I have the list of words I mentioned to you. Ten of them. Tonight I am going to use two."

Votichenko laughed.

"You do read, don't you?" Smith said. "The newspapers?"

Votichenko continued to laugh.

Late that afternoon Smith sat at his typewriter and began another story. It had to do with the subcommittee on cultural relations, of which Votichenko was a member.

"Pleasant, warm-hearted Pyotr Votichenko——" he wrote, then stopped. Warm-hearted. He thought. I wonder whether that counts as one word, or two? One, I suppose. "Pleasant, warm-hearted Pyotr Votichenko, delegate from——"

Next evening as Smith sat in his living room the telephone rang. "Hello? Here is Votichenko. I have read your lying, filthy story. I forbid you ever to write my name again."

"Forbid?" Smith said. "Really?"

"I forbid it!"

"Ah," Smith replied. "But that's impossible. I have already written the story for tomorrow. It contains two words that may be of interest to you. Good night." The words, which Smith had arrived at after considerable thought, were "constructive" and "co-operative."

A day later when Votichenko called again, his voice had an edge of terror. "Mr. Smith," he said. "I forbid——"

"Forbid?"

"I implore you——"

"Ah. That's a nice word."

"Please do not write any more."

"But that's impossible. I have already written——"

"No!" Votichenko shouted.

"Yes."

Smith paused.

"Please. There will be no more trouble."

"Ever?"

"Never. Upon my word."

"I don't know," Smith said. "Your word——"

"Please. I beg you."

"Very well. But I must ask you to bear in mind that I still have six more words. I have used only four."

"I will bear it in mind."

"Good night, then."

"Good night."

Smith hung up the telephone, then picked it up once more and called the newspaper office. "Composing room, please."

"Yes?"

"This is Joe Smith. I have a little story on the UN that should be on the slab now. Will you make a change for me?"

"Sure."

"You'll find a reference to a man named Pyotr Votichenko. I called him friendly and pro-Western. Will you kill the adjectives?"

"Right. Did you get sore at him or something?"

"No, I'm not angry at him. Just kill them. Thanks."

He hung up the telephone.

"What's wrong with you?" his wife said. "Why are you sitting there looking so toothy?"

"Nothing," Smith said. "I've taken care of Votichenko. There'll be no more trouble, you'll see. Do you know something?"

"What?"

"If I were—if I had the inclination—I could ruin most of the Communists in the world. The ones outside Russia, anyway. I could arrange to have every steamship loaded with Communists being called home to be shot."

"Have you lost your mind?"

"No. It's just a little idea I have. I don't suppose I'll ever do anything with it."

JESSAMYN WEST *is a native of Indiana, a gradu-*
ate of Whittier College, and a Quaker. Her stories
have appeared in Collier's, Harper's, The Atlantic,
and many other magazines, and a collection of
them was published under the title of The Friendly
Persuasion. *She is also the author of a novel,*
The Witch Diggers.

BREACH OF PROMISE

FROM HARPER'S MAGAZINE

Every afternoon between two and four, depending upon the amount
of business or conversation he had encountered on his route, the mail
carrier came by in his ramshackle, mud-spattered car. He didn't drive
up the lane to the house, a lane a quarter of a mile long and crossing
at one point a brook, which after heavy rains was something more
than a brook, but put the mail in the wobbly tin box, set the flag,
honked three times, and drove on.

Ordinarily I waited for these three honks before I walked down
to the box. But now and then, because I was at that time so eagerly
hoping for a certain letter, I would convince myself, in spite of the
fact that I had been listening intently, that the mail carrier had
passed without my hearing him. Invariably, after I had walked to
the box on these occasions to find I had been mistaken, the mail
carrier would be unusually late. Then, because my work had already
been interrupted and because my eagerness for the letter I awaited
always made me hopeful that the mail carrier would be along in
another minute or two, I didn't return to the house. Instead, I paced
up and down to examine the veining in some curious pebble or to
watch an island of foam, seemingly as imperishable as the pebble,
float by.

At the time, I would be scarcely aware, however, of the objects I
scanned. All of my consciousness would be focused in a fury of attention on the wished for letter: imagining its size, shape, color to the
eye, weight to the hand, the heavy down strokes of the writing, even
the postmark, Yorba Linda, California.

The letter, not the one which I wanted but the one of which I am writing, came on a day when I was in this manner examining pebbles at the brookside. The mail carrier saw me and honked three times but, nervous and irritated after what had seemed my long wait, I continued obstinately to bend over my pebble. He honked again, I picked up the pebble I had been admiring and with it in my hand walked down to the mailbox.

"You got another letter here addressed to that other name," he told me.

He held this letter close to his chest, as if it were a winning card in a crucial game. The mail carrier had never been reconciled to the fact that I received letters addressed in two ways: to my "own" name, and to what he called "that other name," the name I used in my writing. The letter I had hoped for would not be addressed to "that other name," so I didn't care how long he held this square white envelope to his chest.

"It's addressed care of the Seulkes," he said (the Seulkes were the people with whom I was boarding, the house at the end of the lane), "so I reckon it's for you."

He ended on a rising note and looked at me, through spectacles as blurred and spattered as some old windowpane. "It's from Persis Hughes," he said. "You know her?"

"No," I told him, though I knew that a Mr. Hughes owned a large farm, down the road a mile or so and that he had a grown daughter.

"Funny thing," he said. "Persis writing you when she didn't know you."

There was no use telling him that writers get letters from people they don't know, so I agreed with him. "Yes," I said, "it's a funny thing."

"You'd think she'd just walk up the pike if she had anything to say to you and save her three cents."

"Yes," I said again.

He finally handed me the letter from Persis Hughes, but he hadn't finished with talking yet.

"I notice it takes four days for a letter from California to reach you," he said.

"If they don't air-mail it," I agreed.

"You get homesick, back here by yourself?" he asked.

"I'm pretty busy working," I told him, and he didn't notice that I hadn't answered his question.

"Working?" he asked, and I could see that he thought I had found myself a job of some kind in town.

"Writing," I said, and from the way he repeated, "Oh, writing," it was plain writing wasn't his idea of work. But he drove on without any more questions, leaving me standing by the mailbox, Persis Hughes' letter in one hand, my prettily veined pebble in the other. On a sudden impulse I opened the box, placed the smooth little stone in its tin emptiness and tightly closed the lid. I did this without thinking, but I suppose that bitterly, subconsciously, I was thinking, I asked for bread and you gave me a stone, and that I felt some relief in thus being able to objectify my emotions, to symbolize my self-pity.

I didn't open my letter from Persis Hughes until I reached my room. Though if the letter I wanted had come I would have read it six times over before I reached the house. My room at the Seulkes' was a perfect place for reading unwanted mail. It was sad, sad. Strange, unpleasant colors, peculiar furniture, odd smells, and a most distressing, a really horrifying picture.

This picture was of the Seulkes' only son Albert, aged twelve, taken three days before he died of lockjaw. After Albert's death Mrs. Seulke had had his picture enlarged, covered with convex glass, and framed. And now Albert, looking, it seemed, already swollen, feverish, and in pain, watched me the whole time I was in the room.

A marble-topped "center table," a wicker rocker with crocheted back and arm tidies, a wooden chair, one of the dinette set which the Seulkes used in their kitchen, these, together with a large brass bed, made up the furnishings of my room.

I lived on that bed like a castaway on a desert island, like a lone survivor on a raft. It was my desk, chair, filing cabinet, table, sofa, home, world. Neither of the chairs was fit to sit on and the marble-topped table was too encumbered with decorative feet, claws, and legs to permit anyone with feet and legs of his own to get near it. It was on this bed, under Albert's picture, that I read Persis Hughes' letter.

Dear Miss or Madam [the letter began]:

I have heard that you are married but since I do not know for sure about this and do not want to call you Madam if you are really Miss, I address you thus.

I know you are a writer. I have read several of your stories in magazines. Some of them were interesting to me, and I suppose all must have been interesting to somebody because I do not think editors pay money for stories unless they are pretty sure about this.

This is not a "fan" letter though, to say I like your stories, for frankly some of them I do not because they do not seem to me to be about real life, but about some idea you have which you think is "real life." Or maybe you know it isn't but write about it because you think it is better than real life. Or maybe more interesting.

What I want to ask you is this, wouldn't you like to *do* some *good* by your writing? That is not just *write about* goodness. You usually do write about good people, etc., but I don't think this does any real good in the world and it may do harm. People may read about all these good characters of yours and say to themselves, "Well, if the world is such a good place a little badness from me won't do any particular harm."

And wouldn't you like to find out more about real life, too? Not just your own ideas about life which you think will make a good story, but *real* life, the way a woman suffers it?

I know a writer writes for money. So what I have to ask you is, not only wouldn't you like to do some good with your writing and find out more about how things really are than you seem to know (judging by your stories), but also make some money?

I could have invited you for a social call, to have supper with me, then have asked you these things. But I think that would have been sailing under false colors, which I do not care to do. Now that you know that my purpose is mainly not social would you care to have supper with me on Tuesday of next week at six o'clock? I will be honored by your presence. Please reply.

Sincerely,
Persis Hughes

When I finished Persis Hughes' letter it was dark. I had read it a line or two at a time, not caring about it, thinking only of my own letter, the one which had not arrived. I remembered all those letters in stories and novels which never arrive or rather which are, ironically, delayed or lost until their arrival means nothing. I had almost convinced myself that my own letter had been held up in a like way, that all I needed to do was to send a telegram saying, "Your letter delayed, wire contents," to have by bedtime an answering wire and the words I had awaited the past weeks.

Almost, but not quite. By the time Persis Hughes' letter was read I had given up this silly dream. Would I like to know life, "the way a woman suffers it"? This made me smile. Persis Huges was not much over twenty, if what I had heard was true. Still, I knew I would go to see her. For the mail carrier had been right. I was lonely here, heart-sick.

Mr. Seulke drove me down the pike toward the Hughes' on Tuesday evening. I didn't tell him where I was going. Persis Hughes' father was a widower and I did not care to be twitted about him, as I would have been had Mr. Seulke known my destination, for nothing so interested him as what he called "he-ing and she-ing."

Mr. Seulke was very imaginative about such things. The first time I had hired him to drive me I asked him to take me to a small stream for the afternoon and pick me up later. With a sudden downward look Mr. Seulke had asked me, "Who you meeting, sis?"

At first I didn't understand his meaning and answered quite literally that I was going only to walk along the stream because it was beautiful and to note the kinds of trees and bushes which grew by it.

"That's your story, sis," he had said. "You stick to it."

I asked Mr. Seulke to let me out a short distance from the Hughes' farm. "You needn't come after me," I told him. "I have a way home." Persis Hughes, when I accepted her invitation, had told me she and her father would drive me back to the Seulkes'.

I can't write what Mr. Seulke said then, though to him it was no more than a half-humorous gallantry and nothing that any woman in that neighborhood would have taken amiss.

The Hughes' house was a nice place to be walking toward in the dusk. Chrysanthemums, bronze and gold, though grayish in the dark, were staked up along the path which led to the front door, and light, soft and yellow from kerosene lamps, shone out through the windows. Persis Hughes herself answered my knock and asked me in. She seemed neither nervous nor emotional, the two things I had feared. A gusty fall wind was blowing and she shut the door quickly behind me.

"Father's old-fashioned," she said. "He likes supper early, and he eats it early, so there'll be only the two of us to eat now."

She put away my coat and purse and led me into the dining room. It was a real dining room, a room planned only for eating and there was nothing in it which did not have to do with eating or one's comfort while eating or afterward: a big, fumed-oak sideboard, six fumed-oak chairs, a china closet through whose curving glass sides cut glass sparkled. Under each of the two windows was a Boston fern in a wicker fern stand and between these was a narrow couch upholstered in red rep on which one might rest or nap after eating. The table itself was round, covered with a white cloth whose corners touched the floor, and lighted by a hanging kerosene lamp. In one corner of the room the isinglass eye of a small wood stove glowed rosily and its fire made an occasional dry tick, tick.

Persis Hughes seated me opposite her at the table. Between us was a very fine meal: an old hen, baked with dressing, glazed parsnips, baked squash, gravy, a casserole of tomatoes, slaw, a spongecake covered with boiled custard, and besides these a number of jams and relishes.

"Did you cook all this?" I asked Persis.

"Oh, yes," she said. "Who else? There'd be only my father to cook if I didn't."

"Do you like cooking?" I asked.

"Not particularly," she said, "but it has to be done and I like good things to eat. So I cook as quickly and well as I can."

She carved the hen deftly, filling my plate with dark meat, white meat, dressing, gravy. I watched her as she did this. Afterward, but not then, I tried to see Persis Hughes through a man's eyes, which is a mistake, a thing a woman can never do. A woman, summoning all the latent masculinity she possesses, focusing it like a spyglass to peer through, remembering every item of female appearance ever lovingly described by man, will still see awry, unlike a man.

No, this particular spyglass is useless, and at that time it did not occur to me to look through it at Persis Hughes, anyway. I thought only, as I watched her carve, that she was very pretty. Persis Hughes was plumper, perhaps, than she should have been. She was hazel-eyed and had wavy sorrel-colored hair which she piled high on her head in a loose knot.

It was I, who for a time, in spite of what she had said in her letter, tried to keep the evening "social." "How long have you lived here?" "All of my life." "Where did you go to school?" "Local high school and the Cincinnati Conservatory." "Oh, you play?" "Yes." "What instrument?" "Piano, that is I did." "Why did you give it up?" "I can't write music and I don't want to go through life going do-do-do to another man's tune." I suppose I showed my surprise at this.

"Would you want to spend the rest of your life reading aloud what other people wrote?" she asked.

"I don't know," I replied. "Perhaps if I were good at it. One likes to really succeed at something."

She refilled our plates and as she did so she asked, "Did you ever see yourself unexpectedly in a mirror and not know yourself?"

I had of course and I said, "Yes. It's an awful experience, isn't it?"

"Did anyone," she asked, "ever see herself in a mirror, not recognize herself, but think, What a beautiful, stylish woman that is coming down the street?"

This was something I had never thought of. "I suppose not. We're only surprised at our ugliness not at our good looks."

"Then," said Persis, "we all actually look far worse than we have any idea we do."

"I'm afraid so."

"Writing is a kind of mirror isn't it?" she asked.

"A mirror?" I repeated, seeing how this was at once true and not true.

"I mean," she said, "a man might see himself truly for the first time in his life in a story, mightn't he? See how he really was, wicked and ugly perhaps, instead of handsome and good."

"He might, but he'd probably not recognize himself. Just as we'd never recognize ourselves in the mirror on the street except that the awful woman approaching us is wearing our hat, walking in our shoes, carrying our purse."

"That's just it," said Persis eagerly. "*He'd* recognize himself in the same way. He'd read the story and think to himself, Why that's what I said, that's what I wore that day, that's where we went and what we ate. He'd have to recognize himself by these things. Then, seeing himself as someone else saw him he'd see how bad, how foolish he'd been. And he would be filled with remorse."

I began to understand Persis Hughes' letter—a little. "If he *did* recognize himself," I asked, "and he *was* filled with remorse, what would he do then?"

"Change," she said promptly. "Mend his ways. Do what he promised."

She left the table to get more custard for our cake and poured us both coffee. She took no more than two bites of her own dessert, then carried her coffee over to the sofa and sat there bolt upright, sipping it. "Please go ahead and eat," she said. "I'm not hungry."

I did eat. The cake and custard were very good.

"I thought perhaps you would write this story," she said.

"What story?" I asked.

"Dallas'," she said. "Dallas' and mine."

"Who is Dallas?" I asked.

"A man," she said. "The man who promised to marry me."

"I don't know him. I don't know your story."

"You could meet him," she said. "He doesn't live far from here. And I'd tell you everything about us. I've thought over everything so much these past weeks I could talk to you all night and not a word would be untrue. I see and hear it all of the time. But you wouldn't know how that is, probably."

Not know that long, never dissolving panorama of memory? That sound track which runs on and on repeating the very words which are most painful to hear? That film which replays, even against the closed eyes, particularly against the closed eyes, the very scenes one longs to forget?

"What good would it do if I were to write this story? How would it help you or anyone else?"

"Dallas would read it. He reads a great deal. And if he didn't happen to have the magazine it was in, I'd see he got it. Then it would be like the mirror. He would say to himself, 'If that is how I really am, God help me, I will change.' "

"Why do you want him to change?" I asked.

"I want him to do what he promised. I want him to marry me." She saw that my coffee cup was empty and refilled it from the pot she had left to keep warm on the stove.

There were so many objections to her scheme that I didn't know which to point out first. "Even if I wrote it," I said, "this story, you couldn't be sure a magazine would print it."

She wouldn't believe this. "It would be so real, so true," she said, "they would have to. They could see it was nothing anyone had imagined. That it was what a real person had suffered."

"Do you like to read about suffering?" I asked her.

"Yes," she said, "I do. I don't feel so alone then."

"Editors don't think that," I told her. "They think people want to read about happiness."

"Editors!" she said scornfully. "What do they know about people? Happiness, happiness, happiness! It breaks my heart to read about happiness."

"It breaks my heart to write about it sometimes, too," I said.

"Then why do it? I didn't intend to say this, but all those happy stories of yours! They sound silly to me. Besides," she said, changing her tack very swiftly, "this might have a happy ending."

"Even so," I told her, "written in the best way I know, no one might want to print it."

She had a new idea. "It might be even better to have it printed in the *Republican*. That way Dallas would be sure to see it."

The *Republican* was Lane County's weekly paper. "I didn't know the *Republican* ever printed stories," I said.

"It doesn't. But it would if I paid them. Oh, I have the money to do it all right," she said, as if I had questioned her. "My mother left me," she stopped, as if her native hill-country suspicion and shrewdness had just reminded her that she was talking, after all, to a stranger with whom reticence about money matters was advisable, "a considerable sum," she finished. "I will also pay *you*," she said, "in that case, whatever a magazine would. And this way you'd have a sure thing. Not have to take a chance on an editor's liking it."

She put her coffee cup down on the floor with a gesture of finality, as if everything had been settled.

I said there had to be more in a piece of writing than promise of pay, otherwise writers wouldn't be writing at all but doing something that paid regularly the first of every month.

"You could do good, too," she reminded me, "by writing this story. Doesn't that interest you?"

"How?" I asked.

"You will help a man keep his word. And you will help save him from being ruined. For if he doesn't marry me, I will sue him for breach of promise. And if I do I will take from him everything he has. I can do it," she assured me. "I have his letters."

She picked up her cup again trying to find a few more drops in it. I refilled both our cups. Coffee keeps me awake, but I didn't expect to sleep anyway that night.

"I know exactly what the story should be called," she said.

"What?" I asked.

" 'Breach of Promise.' "

"That isn't a very interesting title," I said, "not very pleasant or inviting."

"What do I care about that? Interesting! Pleasant! That title will catch Dallas Hindshaw's eye, because he knows very well what I will do if he doesn't marry me. 'Breach of Promise,' " she repeated. "Yes, that's it."

I said nothing. What is there to say to the naïveté which outlines and names a piece of writing for you as specifically as if the work involved were of the same order as that needed for spading a garden plot or scrubbing a piece of linoleum? Perhaps Persis Hughes saw some of this in my mind. Anyway she said rather sadly, "Doesn't our story interest you?"

I couldn't help smiling. "I don't know your story," I told her, "the story of Persis Hughes and Dallas Hindshaw."

"What do you want me to tell you about Dallas and me?" she asked.

"Whatever you like." I put my empty coffee cup on the table, pushed the table nearer the wall, turned down the wick in the lamp, pulled up a second chair for a footrest, and prepared to listen. "Tell me whatever you like."

Persis lay back against the red sofa's bulging, built-in hump. The wind had died down, but not enough to stop the rustling of some vine against the wall of the house or to end the slight movement of the overhead lamp.

"I remember it all so well . . . the train we met . . . his first words, everything. The only trouble is that our story is so strange, so unusual, it's hard to tell you. It isn't as if it were everyone's story."

But that was exactly what it was, everyone's story . . . my story. "Dallas was already on the Seymour train when I got on." . . . Does it make any difference whether the train runs between Cincinnati and Seymour or San Francisco and Salinas, if *he* is on it? . . . "It was snowing—that made it seem so much more close, private, shut away from everyone else." . . . What difference does the weather make? In rain, in a wind storm, in a time of quiet, not a leaf stirring, if *he* is there everyone else is shut away. . . . "Dallas had such a nice way of eating. I've never enjoyed seeing other people eat, but Dallas' hands went flying around the table, helping me, helping himself, and when he chewed there was no sign of it except a kind of shadow on his cheek. It was a pleasure to watch Dallas eat." . . . Whatever *he* does is a pleasure to watch: things unbearable in anyone else, how pretty they are in him; flip, flip, two aspirin on the back of the tongue, a gulp of water washing them down, and the smooth Adam's apple momentarily jutting out under the skin, the only grace in that, is *his* grace. . . . Ted's grace. "Dallas loved my faults, freckles, stubby eyelashes, anger, he didn't exclude them." *He* loves the whole person, always, unites what is severed and makes what was fractional complete. . . . "Dallas says there is no one else, so why doesn't he marry me? When he wanted to so much? All I need do is wake him up, show him himself in the mirror. Wake him up from this crazy dream he's in."

This crazy dream . . . this crazy dream . . . I put more wood in the stove. They were burning apple wood. The wind came up again and the lamp's arc widened. Back in the house a clock kept striking, quarters, halves, and wholes. After the hour struck there was always a little quaver, a kind of audible tremor as if the effort of that transition had almost overwhelmed the clock's mechanism.

Persis Hughes took down her hair, wound it up again in a tighter knot, took it down and braided it. Her father came to the door, with so big a yawn I could scarcely make out his face.

"Good night, girls," he said. "I'll lay down with my clothes on for a little snooze, call me when you want me." I stopped listening to Persis Hughes and thought my own thoughts and listened again and couldn't tell where my thoughts left off and her words began, so moved back and forth between the two and mixed them up thoroughly.

"That is Dallas' and my story," she concluded, unbraided her hair, sat up, leaned forward so that her face parted her long wavy hair the way a rock parts a waterfall. "Now you know it well enough to write it."

"Too well," I told her, "to write it."

"How can you know it too well?" she asked.

I couldn't say I had lived it.

"It's like the multiplication table. I know it by heart. I wouldn't write that."

"Do it for me," she urged.

"I can't. You can only write about what you don't know, and find out about it in the writing."

"You won't do it then?"

"I can't."

"You won't!"

"Very well, I won't. Besides, it wouldn't help you any."

"All right, then, I will sue him. You like to write about good people but you won't be troubled to do good. I will sue Dallas Hindshaw, and everything he has I will take away from him."

If she could not understand writing, I could not understand suing. We were at a standstill. "Do you love Dallas Hindshaw?"

"Were you asleep?" she asked.

"Then why do you want to ruin him, make public everything that is private and sacred?"

"I am honor bound to do so," she said. "It is a terrible thing to do but I am honor bound to try everything to bring him back."

"Bring him back!" I said. "You will make him hate you."

"If he won't marry me, I hope he will hate me enough to want to kill me. I hope every morning he will wake up thinking how he could kill me, put his hands around my throat and strangle me, or open up my dress and plunge a knife in my heart."

"You are crazy," I said. But I knew she wasn't crazy. She was speaking the truth.

"All right, I am crazy. If Dallas Hindshaw doesn't love me he must hate me. He must *do* something about me."

"You will be suing him for money. It will look to him and everyone else that you care for his money. That you can be paid with money for not having his love."

"Dallas' money is part of him. He worked for it, he invented this machine, peddled it about from house to house. If I have his money I have part of him. But I do not want a part of him. I want Dallas. Write our story."

"No," I said.

"Will you go to see him then? You might change your mind."

"I won't change my mind. And how could I go see him? What excuse have I for calling on a man I've never seen?"

"Women go to see him all the time to buy this machine. It shreds up vegetables, makes them come out finer than shavings. You could go to his house to buy one."

She was suddenly exhausted and sleepy. She fell down onto the sofa as if she were boneless, her head resting on the deepest swelling of the hump so that her hair flowed backward over it, touching the floor.

"Shall I tell him you sent me?" I asked angrily. Had I moved away from the painful emotions of my own life to be caught up in a pain that wasn't even my own? Was I to become that absurd creature, a woman without a husband who knows how husbands should be handled? The childless woman, full of advice to mothers?

"Whatever you want," she said, closed her eyes, and slept. It was three. I put another stick in the fire, blew out the lamp, and settled onto my two hard chairs. In California it was one, the October air warm; those who slept were quiet in their beds and those who were wakeful had company to solace their wakefulness. Had *he* company?

Toward morning Persis Hughes turned on her side and I saw that she was no longer sleeping. I asked her the question which had been in my mind.

"What happened?"

"What happened?" she repeated drowsily.

"Between you and Dallas? Why does he no longer love you?"

Then she was wide awake and furious. "I tell you he does love me."

"But he won't marry you? What happened?"

"Nothing happened," she said, "nothing, nothing, nothing. Don't ask me that again."

I didn't, but I knew better. Something has always happened when we deny it so strenuously. Something we cannot bear to face.

At daybreak I walked home to the Seulkes', undressed, slept till noon under Albert's accusing picture, awakened, ate a package of dried figs, spent the afternoon writing a long letter, put the California address on it, and at dusk destroyed it. Then I washed, dressed, and went downstairs to supper.

When supper was over I said, "Will you drive me over to Dallas Hindshaw's, Mr. Seulke?"

"You planning to spend the night out again, sis?"

"No," I said, "tonight I plan to spend in my own comfortable bed."

Usually I tried to keep Mr. Seulke's conversation in channels of seemliness. But as we drove along that evening I thought, You're sixty years old, Mr. Seulke, and these are matters you've had on your mind since the age of ten, or younger. If you've learned anything, Mr. Seulke, if you've got any knowledge in fifty years of thinking, speak up. If experience is a lamp, turn up the wick, Mr. Seulke, light the way for stumbling feet. Shine your light on Persis and Dallas and Ted and me. Shine it on hate and love and deceit. Shine it on hope deferred, Mr. Seulke, that maketh the heart to sicken. Shine it on a wife away from home, Mr. Seulke, lost and waiting and full of pride.

But Mr. Seulke, the minute he saw non-resistance in me, was interested in nothing but the weather, spoke of nothing but the weather. It was a mild evening, the sky curded with clouds. Occasional long drops of rain like warm fingers (there was no glass on the right-hand side of Mr. Seulke's Tudor) touched our faces.

Mr. Seulke wiped the drops from his brown face. "But it won't rain," he said. "My mother could foretell the weather and I've heired enough of her gift to prophesy wet from dry." Sniffing the air and prophesying, mild as the evening itself, Mr. Seulke drove the Tudor skillfully along the narrow graveled roads toward Dallas Hindshaw's. He pointed out Hindshaw's house from a distance. As we came nearer I saw it was small, a cabin really, with an open porch extending across its front.

"Hindshaw," said Mr. Seulke, "is an interesting fellow and of an inventive turn of mind. He's made considerable, I understand, with this vegetable reamer of his. A pity he's humpbacked."

Rousing from the lull of the weather talk, I said, "Humpbacked? That must be another Hindshaw. The Hindshaw I know isn't hunchbacked."

"Know?" asked Mr. Seulke. "My understanding was you'd never seen him."

"I haven't," I said, thinking of the six hours' talk in which he had seemed to be present, "but I've heard him spoken of considerably."

"Persis Hughes?"

"Yes," I said.

"Hindshaw jilted her," said Mr. Seulke, "and you can take for sour grapes anything she has to say about him."

But this fox had said the grapes he couldn't get were sweet, not sour; that had been the whole burden of Persis' story!

"See for yourself," said Mr. Seulke, pointing, "he's humpbacked," and I saw on the porch steps a figure, even in the growing darkness, plainly misformed.

"I'll wait for you, sis," said Mr. Seulke, and there was nothing for it but to walk up that long, shell-lined path toward the man who sat motionless, watching me approach.

"Mr. Hindshaw?" I asked.

The man on the porch step was smoking a pipe. One hand was buried in the long black and white hair of a small dog which lay beside him, the other was lifted above his head clasping the post he leaned against. He was gazing out across the countryside which his cabin, situated on a little rise, overlooked. He shifted his eyes from the landscape to me but didn't get up.

"I've come to ask," I said diffidently, "if I could buy one of your vegetable reamers."

Mr. Hindshaw then got to his feet. Except for his deformity he would have been a very tall man. As it was, he was taller than I, dark, withdrawn, much thickened and broken about the neck and shoulders.

"I'm sorry," he said. "I don't sell them here any more—only in stores."

That seemed to end the visit. Mr. Hindshaw stood, obviously willing for me to leave; the dog got up, ready to walk to the gate with me; a lean, big-faced gray cat at the other end of the porch folded her feet beneath her in anticipation of the return of solitude. Still I stood there thinking, Why won't you marry her? She'd rescue you from all of this, she'd have lights in the house at this hour, a white cloth on the table, the table set, and two bowls on the back porch, one for the cat, one for the dog. She'd be willing to play a note or two for you on the piano, after you'd eaten, and lie, without talking, her hair hanging over the edge of the sofa while you smoked your pipe. She's ten years younger than you; if she's naïve, you could teach her whatever it is you think she'd be better for knowing. It isn't everyone in the world who'll love you, Mr. Hindshaw, and Persis loves you, desperately. So much, to judge by her talk, she doesn't even know your back isn't straight. You loved her once, promised to marry her, and she hasn't changed. What's come over you, Mr. Hindshaw, why have *you* changed?

With all the craft and skill of a person whose own plans miscarry, I stood there making plans for Mr. Hindshaw, even thinking that he might say, "It was all a mistake," and that I might carry this word to Persis. But Mr. Hindshaw said nothing. His live pipe dying unsmoked in his hand, Mr. Hindshaw waited for me to leave.

"Persis Hughes told me about the reamer."

Mr. Hindshaw turned, knocked out his pipe on the post behind him. "That was kind of her," he said, and once more waited.

"She's very beautiful," I said.

"Yes, she is," agreed Dallas Hindshaw.

"She will sue you," I said, "for breach of promise if you don't marry her." I felt bewitched saying these things, as if I had not the power to choose what I would say, as if I were Persis Hughes herself.

"So Persis tells me," said Mr. Hindshaw.

I hoped he would sick his dog on me, throw his pipe at my head, get rid of me. I could not mention his back, say, Persis loves you, hunchback and all, where will you find another like that? I did say, "Persis loves you just as you are."

Then I ran down the steps and down the path toward Mr. Seulke's car but I heard Dallas Hindshaw say, "I'm afraid you're mistaken."

Mr. Seulke said, "You left in kind of a hurry, sis."

"Yes," I said, "I did."

"Get your reamer?"

"He doesn't sell them at his house any more."

"I could have told you that," said Mr. Seulke, "but I figured you wanted an excuse to talk to the fellow." He turned into the home driveway. "Well," he asked, "what do you make of our jilter?"

I didn't know what to make of the jilter or of Persis or of Albert with his unanswered question, or of the empty mailbox, or of Mr. Seulke, purely a weather man nowadays. I lived on my hard bed, did the writing and notetaking I had come to do and was glad, as winter drew on and the trial of Hughes versus Hindshaw for Breach of Promise was announced, that I was called away. The books I had asked for were available at the State Library: they didn't circulate, I would have to come up to the capital to use them. I'll go tomorrow, I thought, and not come back until the trial is over. The thought of the trial had been a horror to me, like the wreck along the highway, which the eye, knowing it will be sickened, still seeks out. I'll go tomorrow, not come back until the trial is over. And not have my mail forwarded, I thought. Since reason had not worked, I would try magic. If I made the gestures of not caring about my letter, went off without leaving a forwarding address, no longer listened impatiently for the mailman, perhaps it would come.

I lived in a hotel room near the State Library, a room very high and lodged between two jutting wings of the hotel like a matchbox in a crevice of the Apennines. It was a great pleasure to be free of hoping for the letter I had no right to hope for, free of the temptation to attend the trial, and able to work on the old books. I went to the library early and stayed late, writing down much that I needed to know and much that was useless but which I could not resist. My notebooks were filled with long lists, I was happy, almost drugged, as a child becomes repeating a series of words until finally they are without meaning, nothing but a loop of sound binding him to mystery.

The wonderful names in the old newspapers; the names a writer can never achieve, names which only a loving mother can imagine: Alert Miller, Talkington Trueblood, Cashie Wade, Leadona Leahigh, Else Grin, Omer Bland.

The names of fish: Bass, salmon, pike, buffalo, red horse.

Of apples: Imperial Winesap, Baldwin, Romanite, Russet, Northern Spy, all these ripening in October.

The useless facts: A good deer skin fetched 50 cents, raccoon 37½ cents, muskrat 25 cents.

Then, coming in after lunch one day, another list, in a folded newspaper left on my table, caught my eye: "Dearest, dear heart, sweet sorrel, Puss-Precious, my burning bush, long-loved, long-loving. These," the article continued, "are but a few of the terms of endearment culled from the love letters of Dallas Hindshaw and addressed by him to Persis Hughes. These letters have formed the high light of the Breach of Promise suit in which Miss Hughes, daughter of Clayton M. Hughes, prominent Lane County farmer, is attempting to obtain $10,000.00 of Mr. Hindshaw in lieu of marriage, which she says he promised her." My eyes went from one list to the other, from my list, got out of the books in the State Library, to this other list, the words written first in the letters of Dallas Hindshaw, and copied now in a city newspaper. They went from "muskrats, Northern Spies" to "dear heart, dear Tawny, long-loved, long-loving." Was Persis right? Walled up in a crack of the Apennines, did I avoid what she called "life, as a woman suffers it"? Should I stop reading about the past, go back to the Seulkes', go to the trial, go down to the mailbox? Was there a letter waiting for me there? And if there wasn't, write myself? Say, "Dear husband, having no word from you these past weeks I hasten to assure you that I regret my hasty leave-taking, my long silence. It is enough that you love me. You need not also . . ."

But perhaps there *was* a letter waiting. Was it this, instead of the trial which took me back to the Seulkes'? I don't know. There was no letter, anyway, and the trial had ended the day before I got back. Persis, who had asked for ten thousand dollars, had been given five.

"That poor fool, Hindshaw," said Mr. Seulke, on the evening I returned, "he asked to have his money taken away from him." But I was too tired, after my trip and after searching through my mail for the letter which had not arrived, to listen to him, and I went upstairs to my hard bed and wrote nothing myself—letter *or* list—but relived old scenes.

Next afternoon the mailman honked three times and I flew downstairs, but Mr. Seulke was waiting to tell me about the trial.

"That poor fool, Hindshaw!" he began again. "Wouldn't have a lawyer, and set on representing himself! And for all the good he done himself he'd better've given the girl the money in the first place and spared making himself the laughingstock of the county with all those letters of his read out loud."

"Did he say he hadn't promised to marry her?"

"In a way he did," said Mr. Seulke, "but small good it done him, letter after letter saying, 'My sweet pigeon, I can hardly wait till we are married.' Sweet pigeon!" said Mr. Seulke laughing. "Sweet vulture is what he thinks now, I reckon."

"What defense *did* he have?" I asked.

"None," said Mr. Seulke flatly. "He had no defense, only a quirk in his mind. He wouldn't marry Persis Hughes, he said, because she was changed. She wasn't the girl he had asked to marry him in the first place because that girl accepted he was humpbacked, and this girl, the one he was refusing to marry, did not accept it. He called up two dozen witnesses to testify that she never would mention his hump, talked about him as if it didn't exist, and tried to make out, in her own mind, and to others, he was straight-backed. I've got a hump, he said, and the person who don't accept my hump don't accept me."

"Why didn't she?" I asked. Why didn't I? *He* was made that way when I married *him*.

"Why didn't she what?" said Mr. Seulke.

"Accept his hump? Accept the fact his back was crooked?"

"I don't know *why* she didn't," said Mr. Seulke, "but I know when it started. And I know it was the cause of Dallas Hindshaw's refusing to marry her. I was there and I saw it happen."

I remembered my question that night at Persis Hughes' and her, "Nothing, nothing, nothing! Nothing happened."

"What was it?" I asked.

"It was a dance at Zenith and I was as close to them as I am to you. Dallas was a good dancer and a young fellow passing by clapped Dallas on the back and said, 'This frog sure can hop.' He meant it a compliment or at most a joke and Dallas took it so. But Persis slapped the boy not once but a half-dozen times and screamed, 'It's not, it's straight.' Hindshaw grabbed her. 'My back's crooked but my mind's straight,' he said, and that was the beginning. That's what broke them up."

"Did Hindshaw tell this at the trial?"

"Not in so many words, but he said, 'I do not intend to be a half-wed to somebody who sorts me out and marries what suits her, only. I could sue Persis Hughes,' he says, 'with as much justice as she sues me, for she has not kept her promise to my hump. And as I was made shorter than most men,' he says, 'by reason of a horse stepping on me when I was a boy now I will not be still further whittled down by a woman's marrying part of me only and maiming me beyond the first damage.'

"So it went," said Mr. Seulke. "But Hindshaw had no real defense and nobody thought the girl didn't have a legal right to the money. But nobody would've wanted to stand in her shoes to get it."

Mr. Seulke followed me out onto the porch, sniffed a few times, and said, "It's going to snow."

It was already snowing, a first, soft, downward feathering.

"What do you make of it?" asked Mr. Seulke. "You seen and talked to them both."

"I don't know, Mr. Seulke, I don't know what to make of it." I didn't want to make anything of it, its meaning was striking too close.

I stood there on the porch, the big flakes blowing against my face like cold cobwebs. Mr. Seulke stood there, too, not speaking, so presently I went down the lane toward the mailbox. I remembered saying to Persis Hughes, "I understand it all too well, it's like the multiplication table," and remembered Dallas' words, "She didn't keep her promise to my hump." Do you understand that? I asked myself.

I jumped across the brook, cold now as it ran across its pretty stones and specked with falling snow. I hesitated, as I always did, to open the box, then did so quickly. The only letter in the box was one from Persis. In my disappointment I couldn't pick it up for a while, but stood looking at it, and the orange-veined pebble beside it. Finally, I took it out and opened it.

Dear Miss Marsden [it began]:
    Though I know now that this is only your writing name, not your real name, it seems more natural to me because I used it first, so I keep on doing so. I understand that you have left the Seulkes' but trust that this will be forwarded to you.

    I am sorry you did not come to the trial and still sorrier you would not write the story. But it is too late to worry about this now. I did as I said I would and as I think I was duty bound to do, that is, show Dallas Hindshaw that I was willing to do anything to get him to marry me, even sue him.

    I don't regret having done this but I find I don't want his money now and I want you to know it. So will you seal up and mail this envelope which I have enclosed and addressed, after you have read what is in it? You will see I am not keeping the money.

    Since you live quite a ways off I don't expect we'll see each other again and I want to wish you the best of luck in everything, and hope you understand I did what I was honor bound to do.

Sincerely and with good wishes,

Persis Hughes

I read the letter Persis Hughes had enclosed as I had been told to do, replaced it, and sealed the envelope. It was addressed to Dallas Hindshaw. All this trouble, all this sorrow, and who had moved a step forward? I, I told myself, I have moved a step forward. It was the truth. When I put the letter back in the mailbox I took the stone out and at the brook I stooped down and laid it once more beside its brothers at the water's edge, then I walked on up to the house. "Sort him out," and make him pay for refusing the sorting—and give the money back. It made no sense.

Mr. Seulke still stood on the porch, arms folded, watching the weaving patterns of the falling snow. "Well, did you get your letter, sis?" he asked.

I had never spoken to Mr. Seulke of my letter, nor of any letter for that matter, but I felt neither evasive nor glib now.

"No," I said, "it didn't come."

"What do you figure on doing now?" he asked.

"I'm going home," I said.

"Home? I didn't know you had a home, sis."

"I have."

"Home and husband?"

"Home and husband."

"That's more like it, sis."

"It is," I said.

I went upstairs to write and stop my waiting.

STANFORD WHITMORE *was born in Sioux City, Iowa, in 1925, but grew up on Chicago's South Side. For three years as a private first class in the Marines he served as a gunner on medium and dive bombers. He was introduced to literature by a labor organizer aboard ship, and in Japan was converted to Catholicism. After the war he returned to Chicago, worked in the steel mills, left the Church, lost quickly in the Golden Gloves, and went to the University of Illinois at Navy Pier. In 1948 he enrolled at Stanford and got his A.B. in writing under Wallace Stegner in 1950. Stories of his have appeared in* New-Story, Accent, *and the* Pacific Spectator. *He is living in Chicago and finishing a novel.*

LOST SOLDIER

FROM ACCENT

On the morning of the first day Corporal Wolfe had lain near the base of a scrub pine with his mouth in leafmold and snow as artillery fire shredded the trees where his platoon had been. That afternoon he had crawled some eighty feet into a shallow ravine. He had discovered a cut on the back of his left hand.

On the second day he moved out of the ravine and crossed three smooth hills. He heard only scattered small-arms fire in the distance. At night he ate a handful of snow and a fruit bar, checked his Garand, and slept in the lee of a drift.

Now, the third afternoon, the war seemed to have stopped. Since a half-hour past daybreak he had moved in the general direction of south, plotting his course by the infrequent, cold sun and taking care to avoid contrasting himself against the many troughs of snow. He estimated that he had traveled nearly five miles. At any time he might meet an American patrol. Once he heard the chilling whistle of aircraft far away and high, but could neither locate nor identify them. Crouched, running across a clearing with heavy, clubbing strides, crouched again, watching from behind shelter, eyes slitted at sounds, he heard only his openmouthed breathing.

As he rose and went on and moved up the side of the ridge, his confidence increased with each step. The war was almost behind him.

From the crest of the ridge, then, he saw the road. Two hundred yards to his right only a short length of the dry, rutted strip was visible as it flanked the draw between the ridge he stood on and the opposite hill. The road was thin and deserted and unchanged, and he knew it wound southeast to the American lines. He was no longer lost.

At his first short left-footed step down into the shadowed draw, he saw the lone Chinese soldier.

Without panic, mechanically, as he had been taught, faintly surprised at his calmness, Corporal Wolfe pivoted and flung himself full length on the frozen ground and rolled down behind the crest. He waited. He counted to fifty, slowly, listening between each number, his eyes focused on nothing so that he might hear better. Then he cradled the M-1 in his bent arms and crawled along the rise towards the road. He reached a heaved-up shelter of earth and rock. And listened again. After a minute he released the safety and looked over into the draw.

The Chinese was sitting about a hundred yards to the right and below, with his back to Corporal Wolfe. He was alone. It was evident that he had seen and heard nothing. In the brown quilted coating he looked like a rag doll stuck in the snow. No communications equipment was in sight. Every so often the miniature right arm bent and the hand went up to the face. A weapon lay nearby on a pile of something like straw. The doll sat quietly behind the mound of raw earth that commanded the twenty yards of unprotected road.

Only the road looked real. There was something deeply cold and dead about the silence weighing over the entire tapering length of the draw. The depression itself had a diseased quality in its outcroppings of stumps and pockmarks of rough stones, even to each shadow that lay on the snow like a bruise. Except for the brittle, tiny movement of the far-off arm, there was nothing else—nothing real but the wind now, cold and dry, blowing into Wolfe's eyes as he searched.

After a while he pushed down behind cover of a rise and rolled onto his back. The air seemed to have become colder. Lying there absently rubbing his thin, rough jaw, he watched the thick scud of storm clouds fleeing northeast and spreading their shadows over the rippled water standing in the fields. He longed for a canteen cup of coffee.

He decided that the best thing to do was to kill the Chinese. There was the road but the Chinese commanded it. There was the closed end of the draw but to circle it would involve at least a mile of walking along the steep slope. And there was always the chance that more Chinese might be sitting hidden in snow-caves. The only thing to do was to get this single Chinese. The sound of the shot had to be chanced. It had to be good. One shot—one firm slow steady squeeze of the trigger, and the war would be finally behind in the wood and the paddies and the patches of snow.

Like a lizard he moved across the stubbled ground towards the road, his head angled up and to the height of the protective crest ten inches above his vision. When he had carefully estimated the distance he stopped, rechecked his rifle, and looked over the rise.

The Chinese was not more than forty yards away and presented his quilted back as a target.

Wolfe could give and he could take away. There was no one in the world—the feeling was new. He thought about himself. There was not much thinking to the killing before. It was different noises and everybody clumsy, running into things, and when it was over he had been neither proud nor feeling guilty. What had impressed him most was the way in which the faces smeared and melted and were then nothing in the smoke. It was not the same as this.

The Chinese turned his head and Wolfe, after flinching, saw that he was young. Again the arm and hand moved, the short fingers touched and scratched the chin. The hand withdrew and the young Chinese inspected his bent forefinger. There was a peculiar saneness in the action. Alone and sitting like a small boy behind the hump in the snow, he picked at his chin and stared into the gradual gray haze of late afternoon and paid no attention to the submachinegun which lay nearby with its stock of thin metal like the framework of a crutch.

Wolfe looked at the road and then down at the Chinese. One shot was all he could afford against the machinegun. He brought the tip of the front sight up and held it steady just below the right ear of the Chinese. The corporal breathed once, his nostrils flaring, realigned the sight, and saw the head jerk suddenly as the Chinese stiffened and sat upright.

Wolfe slid below the ridge and waited. Voices, faint and fluttering in the wind, came from the road. He listened and shut his eyes. He wanted to throw up and he wanted to cry. He had waited too long. Any moment he would hear the shouts of greeting and then he would have to lie with his eyes in the leaves and pray they would not discover him. He was dead. He had almost made it, and he was dead.

The voices did not seem to grow louder. There was no sound from the Chinese in the draw. Wolfe waited, very slowly wet his lips with his tongue, and edged his vision over a cluster of spiny leaves.

The greasegun still lay within arm's-length of the mound behind which the Chinese sat drawn into such tight watchfulness that he appeared ready to spring six feet into the air at any second. But he did not move. He looked at the road, and Corporal Wolfe looked at the road, and on the road were three American soldiers, none of whom acted as though he was within twenty miles of danger.

They came slowly along the road until they reached the open stretch. They kicked at frozen mud-ribs and walked wide-legged. None of them wore helmets. One had on a brown knit cap; the others wore fur-flapped caps tied together at the top. The three grouped on the road as the one in the knit cap lighted a cigarette into the wind.

Wolfe snapped his front sight back to the Chinese and waited for a movement in the direction of the machinegun. The Chinese raised his hand to his chin and continued watching the road.

Wolfe could not account for it. The range was point-blank and the scouting-party was in a three-yard circle, their carbines slung over their right shoulders, thumbing the slings like suspenders. There wasn't a chance of getting away if the machinegun opened up, and still the Chinese did nothing. And still the three stood together, now and then stamping their boots, taking turns at the cigarette—scouting nothing, Wolfe thought, thinking about nothing except the tobacco taste and dogging it until they could report back that no contact had been made.

For an instant Wolfe saw them cut down by the machinegun while he watched. They went down on all fours on the cold hard ground and then their stomachs and just when the Chinese was congratulating himself Wolfe put a bullet in his ear. He shook the image out of his head, feeling a mixed sense of guilt and anger. Why didn't the Chinese go for them with the machinegun?

So, it occurred to him, he's afraid of giving himself away. Three Americans mean more are coming, and he doesn't want to draw the artillery. He'll sit there and wait like a statue, and when they go back to report no contact, he'll come back over this ridge and head north. With his muzzle unwavering, Wolfe lay quietly and considered.

One of the scouts began to beat his arms against his sides to keep off the cold. The one in the knit cap put his hands on his hips and quite deliberately studied the draw. Nothing happened. The third soldier stood beside the second and they both looked around. The first soldier stopped clapping his arms and packed a snowball. He threw it at a bony tree and missed. All three of them made snowballs and threw at the tree. One puffed white, there was a thin shout, but Wolfe could not tell whose aim had scored. The first soldier moved his head and neck, and together the three scouts turned and walked back along the road, carelessly closing the open space as though there was nothing, not a sign of danger, almost behind the shelter of the base of the hill, and then they were gone.

Wolfe watched the Chinese. The arm bent across the chest and inside the quilted coat; the hand extracted a cigarette. The Chinese held a match to the white stick and smoked. It was getting dark and cold.

There was no telling how far the scouts had to go before reaching their troops—but it was probably less than a mile. Still, judging from the silence, from no sounds of trucks or jeeps or tanks, and feeling the cold pressing onto the fields, Wolfe was sure that the Americans would not advance until morning. The Chinese knew it too, he thought. At some time during the night the rag doll would get up and come back over the ridge. Meanwhile the face stared from behind the mound and the mouth tasted the rich smoke and sucked it in warm and thick, and the cold came down.

The cold came through Wolfe's jacket and boots and made his feet feel like stumps. The cut on his hand started to hurt, and began to throb the more he thought about it. He rubbed his ankles and felt nothing through the heavy leather. He could be eating hot food and in warm clothes in an hour or less. By going just one hundred yards west, behind the cover of the ridge, he would reach the road. But then he would have to cross the open stretch in front of the Chinese. He squinted into the dusk at the machinegun lying within reach of the hand that held the cigarette. Why hadn't it been used on the scouting-party?

It was getting more difficult to see. In a few minutes he would be able to run across the short open space and out of sight almost before the Chinese saw him. The cold brought his teeth together uncontrollably. His hand pulsed at the end of his sleeve. A moving target would be impossible to hit. Still, there was the machinegun. There was the cold and the Chinese and the machinegun.

He fixed the front sight on the neck of the Chinese. He took a breath and held the black point steady. Dimly the small head rested on top of the cold barrel. A pinpoint orange glow lit the flat features.

"Yo!" Wolfe called, and the face turned, full face above the barrel, the cigarette-ash pale green for an instant, and then was the explosion as he fired. The head disappeared.

The Chinese lay on his back in the snow with his right leg bent under the left. His arms were outflung, palms up and half-gripped. He did not move. He lay in the snow as if he had been hurled from a cliff.

Wolfe came down into the draw and went over to the quilted coat and dull gleam of upper teeth. He saw that the cigarette had fallen on end and was still burning. He covered it with a scrape of his boot. Then he slung his M-1 on his shoulder and picked up the submachinegun. It was cold to the touch and surprisingly light. He handled it clumsily and even looked into the bore. There was a magazine clipped behind the trigger. He did not look into the magazine.

Snow sprayed from his legs as he carried the weapon by its thin canvas strap. When he was almost at the road he stopped and stood for a long time without looking back. Then he lifted the gun and detached the magazine.

It was full.

He weighed it in his hand and clicked it back in place. Holding the weapon by its muzzle, he turned to face the draw, coiled, and threw it as far as he could. Through the dusk he saw it lurch against the sky, and fall, and tear a dark gash in the crusted snow. Then he hitched his rifle on his shoulder and walked.

REED WHITTEMORE *was born September 11, 1919. He graduated from Yale in 1941, and from 1941 to 1945 was in the Army and Air Force, ending as a captain in Air Force Supply. After the war he resurrected* Furioso, *which he and a college roommate had begun in 1939, and continued publishing it until the spring of 1953. After a year of graduate work at Princeton he began teaching at Carleton College in 1947, and has been doing that off and on since. A book of poems,* Heroes and Heroines, *was published by Reynal and Hitchcock in 1946, and he has contributed to such magazines as* The New Yorker, Harper's Bazaar, *and* Poetry.

THE STUTZ AND THE TUB

FROM WESTERN REVIEW

They went to a restaurant built on a pier out over the water, which was low (it is always low tide at Savin Rock). They sat in a dark corner from which the sea was not visible but where the smell of the mud-flats was particularly strong, and they waited a very long time to be served a bad meal. They talked about those who fitted their pasts together in that weak pattern they were obliged to make the most of for the evening—about Johnny Clark who was now working for the bank, and Peggy Brown who eloped with a soldier and went off somewhere—New Mexico? Georgia?—in the middle of the night. They sipped their watery coffee and were reminded of an evening when Alec spilt a whole pot of coffee on Mrs. Clark's airedale. They worked the past over and over, and then they went out and walked around the park, with the smell of cheap candy, hot dogs and gunpowder in their heads—past *The Whip*, which he remembered as enormously fast and frightening and which now looked like an obsolete invention for upsetting the stomach, past the motorboats no longer sleek and bright, floating, heavily, in apple-core and orange-peel sewer water, past the *Mystery House*, boarded up, the signs fading, the façade leaning precariously out over the street, and past the stalls of shooting galleries, dart games and *wheels* where without exception the same cheap prizes of ashtrays and grotesque china figures that he remembered from twenty years ago were lined up in rows, as if in all that time either nobody had won a prize or nobody, having won a prize, had accepted it but had gone home, raging mad, to say, "I punctured three balloons with three throws and what did they offer me but a goddam ashtray which said on it 'Souvenir of Savin Rock.'" And the girl, Esther, said to Alec in front of the *Virginia Reel*, "It hasn't changed much, has it?"

She was impossible. All that good breeding in private schools in Pennsylvania, all those dancing lessons at the Lawn Club, all that broadening travel to France and California and the Caribbean and Mexico, and all those parties at Yale and Princeton and maybe for practice Williams—all of that for years and years and she stood in front of the *Virginia Reel* and said, "It hasn't changed much, has it?"

The Stutz was parked in front of the *Virginia Reel*. It had been converted into a kind of gross pick-up and the back end had been sliced off and a box-like affair inserted for carrying, say, bricks. It might have been blue once, like Alec's mother's, but now it was that withered black all really old cars achieve. The channel in the front fender for the spare tire was empty; the front bumper was held up on the right side by a rope; two of the windows, broken, were backed up by boards. Not only had the distinguished lady who formerly mounted the radiator cap vanished, but the radiator cap had vanished too, and steam rose from the rusty aperture.

"Heavens, that can't be a Stutz," Esther said.

"Do you remember our Stutz?"

Of course she remembered. How could she forget?

"That might even be it."

"That? Oh no, Alec, *really*."

But the man in the ticket box of the *Virginia Reel* thought that it might be. "I couldn't help overhearing," he said, and he allowed as how he was the owner of the Stutz and had bought it in New Haven—did Alec live in New Haven and did Alec remember where his mother had sold it? It wasn't, he admitted, the best car he had ever owned but wouldn't Alec like to buy it as a souvenir of the old days?

"Alec, let's get out of here," Esther said.

But Alec went over to the Stutz, with Esther in tow saying this was too silly really; and the man from the *Virginia Reel* came out of the ticket booth to show them what he called the fine points. He was sorry that the car was so dirty and he hoped that they would overlook

the dirt and the dents, the rope on the bumper, the missing radiator
cap and the broken door handles because, if they did, they would
see what a fine piece of machinery it was *basically* though it wasn't,
he would tell them frankly, the most reliable machinery any more
and did Alec want to make an offer?

Alec opened the back door. The rear section had been left almost
intact when the car had been converted into a truck; the box had
been inserted from the back and pushed in until it rested against the
front seat (in the other direction it extended about three feet outside
the car). The carpet on the floor in the rear had never been removed
but it was covered, except at the edges, by the box as well as a thick
layer of dirt.

Esther wanted to know what he was doing. He lifted the box about
three inches on the right side and scraped at the dirt with the first
thing he found in his pockets, his key ring. The dirt was thick and dry
and swirled up in his face; twice he sneezed and had to let the box
down and stand away from the dust cloud, but in two or three minutes he had uncovered it—it was still there, though the charred material on the edges had worn away leaving a much larger hole than he
remembered.

"I never would have believed it," Esther said. "You mean you *remember* burning a hole in a carpet twenty years ago?" She was standing outside the car at a considerable distance from the owner who
said it was really wonderful what people remembered sometimes and
Alec would be surprised how little he would have to pay for the burnt
rug, if he wanted it.

"Now Alec, don't be an idiot," Esther said from her distance; but
Alec opened the front door and slipped in behind the wheel. Everything was right; the deep grooves for the fingers on the under side of
the wheel, the speedometer that went up to one hundred and ten, the
sharp bend, halfway up the shaft, in the gearshift lever and, especially,
the horizontal lines of piano wire embedded in the windshield. In
the garage at home he had sat for hours behind this wheel, going
through all the motions. At first he had had trouble reaching the
accelerator and the clutch even with his mother's pillow behind him,
but by the time he was eleven he could do it. He had sat there shifting and shifting, making motor noises with his lips and steering
through the Connecticut countryside at precisely one hundred and
ten. When his mother drove downtown he had sat beside her and
begged her not to let the other cars—none of which, surely, could go

one hundred and ten—pass her. He was disgusted because all that power indicated by the speedometer was being left untapped, unexplored, unused. Once when she parked, near Malley's Department Store, she left him in the car and left the key in the ignition switch. He started the motor, pushed in the clutch, shifted into first; and when he let out the clutch somehow the car lurched forward more quickly than he had expected. He forgot all about the brake and banged into the car fortunately parked only three or four feet in front of him. When his mother came back she was angry because the car in front had backed into her, but he didn't say anything.

"What would you say if I bought it?" he asked Esther.

"Oh, Alec, not really."

But the man from the *Virginia Reel* knew that Alec would be surprised how low he would go. "Just make an offer, that's all."

Alec asked if it ran at all.

The man said it ran like a dream. Smooth as silk, with that big-car feeling.

"How are the tires?"

"Tires? You want tires too?" The man was prepared to be perfectly frank; the tires were not so good, he couldn't guarantee the tires, but how did Alec like the gearshift knob?

"Alec, really," Esther said. "You've got a car."

The man had an answer for this. "This isn't exactly a car, lady. This is an heirloom." And he admitted that he was prepared to let it go, though it was a steal at the price, for ten dollars.

Alec's mother had packed the eight of them in the Stutz and taken them to Savin Rock for the afternoon, paying all their expenses on the scooters, in the *Tunnel of Love*, in the *Mystery House* and then back, again and again, on the *Scooters*. She had not let them go on the *Thunderbolt* or the *Virginia Reel* because she "had to draw a line somewhere," and when she insisted that they ride on the merry-go-round they were all bored and disgusted until they found out about the rings they could reach for as the merry-go-round went around; and then she had to draw another line. Johnny Clark was lost for fifteen minutes in the *Mystery House*, and when Alec's mother got the management stirred up to look for him he appeared, mumbling about a big hole in the floor with ogres with horns. Johnny Clark also ran head-on into Billy Altman with his scooter and knocked Billy out onto the floor on his head. The party cost more than twenty-five dollars. They went on the scooter six times, and the last time Johnny shouted, "Jesus, another dollar-forty." They were all sick when they got home and Alec's mother declared frequently for fifteen years thereafter that she had learned the absolute limits of her endurance there and then. Alec went to lunch at Johnny's house the next day and Mrs. Clark thanked him ostentatiously for the wonderful birthday party and said, "But you must remember, Alec, that most of us cannot afford that sort of thing." Alec reported this to his mother and the next week she doubled his allowance.

But the man from the *Virginia Reel* thought that ten dollars was as low as he could go, even for such a special customer as Alec. "You think it over," he said. "You can't lose." And he went back in his ticket box.

Alec got out of the car. Esther said she was very glad he had not gone completely out of his mind. They walked slowly down a side street lined with stalls out of which fat men in bright vests and fat women with bright shawls draped over their shoulders leaned and called to them to take three throws for ten cents, to take a chance on winning a beautiful clock for their mantel, to spin the wheel and win a prize every time. They came to the new ferris wheel but Esther said that she did not like high places. They came to the *Rocket*, but Esther did not want to be turned upside down. They came to the *Scooters*; Alec went in while Esther stood outside, but Alec's scooter was in bad repair and wouldn't steer properly, so after bumping into the side and getting miserably caught in a corner he came out and they walked toward the parking lot.

Separate from the other concessions, near the dark area where Savin Rock trolleys let passengers off and the conductors pull down the front pole and let up the rear pole for the trip back to New Haven, was *The Tub*. It was an ordinary washtub about three feet in diameter and half full of water, set back six feet from the rail. Alec bought three rings for fifteen cents and tossed them carefully into the tub. One of them hit a stick (set in a round, floating base) and sent it bobbing up and down, but the ring slipped off into the water. The others weren't even close.

"Really, Alec," Esther said as he bought three more rings. In the back of the tent, on shelves behind the tub, were the ashtrays and clocks and china figures. Alec tossed the three rings rapidly, carelessly; one stayed on a stick.

"There you are," said the fat concessionaire in the bright vest, producing an ashtray on which was written "Souvenir of Savin Rock."

He pointed out that Alec could keep this or try for a better prize, such as a beautiful china figure for his mantel at home, or a genuine Waterbury clock, or even a radio. But Alec said he wanted to keep the ashtray, and he put down fifteen cents more.

"You're not going to do it again?" Esther said.

Alec bought five more rounds of rings, and with each set he tried a different technique. He found that he was most successful when he shot quickly and without looking. It seemed as if the flat, accurate shots were the shots that knocked the sticks over while the flukes caught the sticks, as it were, by surprise. When he had finished the five rounds Esther said he had spent a dollar five, just thrown it into that tub for three of those damned ashtrays. The concessionaire said he could trade in the three ashtrays for a china figure, but Alec decided to keep the ashtrays. He bought five more rounds.

By the time he had spent four-fifty he had twelve ashtrays. Then Esther disappeared for about ten rounds and when she came back she told him in no uncertain terms that there was a trolley in twenty minutes and she would be on it unless he gave up this foolishness.

Alec said he would be through pretty soon.

"Really, Alec," she said. But he bought some more rounds, the trolley came and went, and Esther was still there, standing about six feet from Alec and lighting one cigarette after another.

When he had spent nine-ninety and had sixty-four ashtrays, the concessionaire said he was very happy that Alec liked both *The Tub* and the ashtrays, but that he had no more ashtrays and wouldn't Alec like to trade some of them in for, say, a nice clock for the mantel?

Alec said he would prefer to keep the ashtrays.

"Nine dollars and ninety cents," Esther said, "and sixty-four ashtrays."

"These aren't exactly ashtrays," Alec said. "They're . . ." but he didn't know what they were. He asked the concessionaire to do him a favor and let him have the last three rings he was going to shoot for ten cents rather than fifteen cents. This would make an even ten dollars and, he said, he wanted it to come out that way. Furthermore, would the concessionaire mind very much getting him another ashtray—or two, or three—if he should win one—or two, or three—on his last three shots since, surely, though *The Tub* was out of ashtrays, there were plenty of ashtrays still to be had in Savin Rock.

The concessionaire agreed, though he really thought that perhaps a clock . . .

Alec took the three rings and closed his eyes and turned his back on the tub. With a careless gesture like that of tossing salt over his shoulder he threw the first ring backwards in a high arc towards the tub.

"Made it," said the concessionaire.

Then Alec carefully measured five paces from the rail and made a mark at that point in the dirt. He sat down with his buttocks up to the line, his back still to the tub, and closing his eyes again he tossed the second ring over his shoulder in an arc even higher than the first.

This also caught on a stick.

He measured an additional five paces out from the rail, drew another line, and, with his back to the tub and his eyes closed and his legs spread wide apart, he bent over and flipped the third ring through his legs in the highest arc of all.

"Really, Alec," Esther said, "really!"

The concessionaire said he'd get those ashtrays and be back in a minute.

HERBERT WILNER is a native of Brooklyn, and twenty-eight years old. He was educated at Brooklyn College, Columbia University, and the State University of Iowa, where he is completing work on the Ph.D. He has taught there, and at the University of Kansas, is married, and has one child. He is completing a novel.

WHISTLE AND THE HEROES

FROM FURIOSO

It is only basketball, yet twice a week, in the early night, Marvin Wessel lives the life of a man. He doesn't play before the Garden crowds, and even the time of club ball is far behind, yet Wednesdays and Fridays are the best days of his week. The community center is open on Monday evenings too, but on that night he drives his mother for her injection. It's a sacrifice for Marvin, and they both know it. She might change the day of her appointment, but he never presses that. Next to the nights that he plays basketball, giving it up on Monday is the other big thing in his week.

His mother alludes often to a devil, and when the doctor first explained her son's cleft palate, she always spoke of it as more of Satan in her life. As a boy, he knew what she said had something to do with him, and he understood no more of it than that. But now he no longer thinks of it. He tries to think of little that is in the past: basketball on the two nights and his job satisfy his idea of time.

Whistle—as his friends have always called him—works as a packer in one of the city's largest department stores. Before that, four years ago, he worked for a button company, but his present job is better. The building is huge and he is shifted between departments often enough to overcome the monotony of his work. The frequent changes make it unnecessary to get too friendly with anyone, and this, also, satisfies Whistle. He feels no need for new friends, and his speech makes it difficult to talk to people he doesn't already know. When the work gets too dull, he thinks ahead to his two big nights.

On a Wednesday or Friday, Whistle is always nervous. This happens as early as breakfast. He fries an extra egg and has milk instead of the usual coffee. He is grateful at these times that his mother always sleeps late and he can manage the mornings for himself. On the subway, he pushes back against the jostling with a little more force, although he is careful to avoid argument. If he is close to a window, he peers at his face, which is trapped there against the darkness of the tunnel. He thinks he hardly looks the part he will play that night, and the deception gives him some kind of advantage over the others in the car. At work, when he walks from the packing table for empty cartons, he pushes hard against the balls of his feet. He can feel his calves tighten, and he has to fight the impulse to run a few steps. Even when he packs, the work is not enough to wear away the energy that mounts within him. He is almost pained by the sense of his body, and he is able to isolate parts of it: the weight of an arm, the tension in a leg, the bunching behind a shoulder. This impatience for great movement compels his mind to wander as he packs, and he lapses into a familiar image of himself. They are jumping under the backboard for a loose ball and he suddenly angles in from the corner of the court and finds an opening. He cuts in cleanly and leaps with the power of his run to snatch the ball out of the air and come down without contact some fifteen feet away toward the other corner, already dribbling quickly downcourt. The picture excites him, and he works with more conviction at the carton on his packing table.

At lunch, he runs the short distance to the cafeteria, finding little spaces in the hurrying noon crowds. He runs with his feet widely apart and his legs bent slightly at the knees so that he might veer sharply through any sudden opening. Though he can tell himself he runs to get a window seat, he doesn't care to understand why this seat isn't so important on other days. He eats quickly, again having milk instead of coffee, and spends the rest of the hour smoking cigarettes and staring out the window. He can usually guess which of the girls that pass are models, and he can even decide between those who work in the high-price houses and the cheaper ones. He has heard enough stories to know they are all tramps, and he has seen it himself when he worked in a dress house. But when one walks by who is beautiful, yet clean—like the fragile girl in a perfume ad—he finds the stories and what he knows hard to believe.

In the afternoon his mind wanders again, and the time passes quickly. If he grows too conscious of his straying thoughts, he works at the packing with a renewed vigor. When it gets toward quitting time, he is pleased by the energy that is still in him. At five o'clock he turns in his slips, knowing that he has packed more than he does on the ordinary days. Men in the same department mutter goodbye to him, and he nods his head and smiles in return. Three middle-aged women work there, but they say nothing to him, though they joke with the other men. In the crowded street he runs again to the subway—the feet wide apart, the knees slightly bent.

When he gets home on Wednesdays or Fridays, he takes the stairs to their first floor Bay Ridge flat two at a time. His mother knows the community center opens at seven, and supper is always ready for him. She finds it a nuisance to have her time fixed this way twice a week, and she complains bitterly about it. She often tells him he must stop playing ball, that he is no longer a boy, that were his father alive he would have to toe the line. But she never forces an argument because she has come herself to depend on these two nights. When he hurries out the door with his gym clothes in a travelling bag, she begins to mutter about the devil as she rubs a hand across her chest.

On the gym floor, Whistle moves with a bird's grace. He uses the game as a gull does the wind, tacking toward the basket in what is almost flight. He is slender and not more than five-ten, and though all the fellows he plays with are much younger than he, many of them are taller and stronger. Some of them, still swelling with their late teens, strip to their shorts so that the sweat will shadow the contours of their bodies. But Whistle wears a grey, fleece-lined sweater and track pants.

They play on only one basket, yet Whistle rarely stops moving. If there is a loose ball—no matter how far away—he chases for it. If someone is about to shoot, he is already moving toward the backboard for the rebound. Even when he crouches to jump for a ball that has not yet begun to drop, there is so much tension in his poise that there is no apparent halting of motion between the wait and the leap. Yet with all his running, there is a great economy to Whistle's movement. He possesses a flawless instinct for knowing where to be. Despite the smallness of the court, he never collides with the other five who play. There are many such collisions in this unrefereed game, but Whistle is seldom involved in the tangle. The kids, often desperate with his near perfection, claim that his one shortcoming is a fear of the rough stuff, and they try to provoke him. But Whistle knows this is not a part of his game, and he is able, by the certainty of his movements, to avoid it.

It does not matter to him that he is twenty-eight and most of the boys he plays with are still in their teens. Nor does it matter that there is no great audience and the game is only a pick-up affair. It is enough that he performs well and the sweat is on his body. But more than other things, there is the odd chemical change as he plays. Sometimes he will put a hand to his abdomen, as though to feel it. Things inside of him—hard things he is unaware of during the day, but feels now he should be able to touch—loosen as though parts of his body had begun to dissolve. After a few minutes on the gym floor, he can almost hear himself unwinding, as though there were something between running and health. When he leaps in from the corner of the court to steal a ball from the taller fellows under the backboard, he may—as he begins to dribble away—raise his head slightly and look back toward the players with a curiously defiant stare in his eyes, a thinning of the lines in his already taut face. Aside from this one lapse, he is all but oblivious to place and time. He does not think once while he plays how much better it all is than his work as a packer, or his life at home. He runs with pursed lips and never speaks, but neither is he aware that he has not spoken.

Yet in his mind are impressions of a long time ago. There are many people and various days, but if he were to remember well there would be only one night, there would be the girl and Bernstein. It was eight years ago and a good time in Whistle's life.

It was a winter evening that came with a heavy snow. He would remember that because the girl sat on his lap and he wouldn't help when the car settled on the ice and the fellows got out to push. It was winter, too, because the last he'd ever seen of Bernstein was after the game when the kid had thrown a snowball at the lamppost outside the school, threw it so well that he hit not the post but the lamp fixture, and when it came down it made a splattering thud in the soft snow. Then Bernstein and his gang ran off around the corner, shouting, and Whistle stood there. He looked into the darkness where the lamp had been, looked up at the falling snow, and listened to the echoes of Bernstein's laughter.

It was the winter of the year. Even with the car as crowded as it was, they made vapor funnels with their breathing, and they passed the bottle around often. She swallowed from it along with the other girls, and when she finished and gave the bottle to Whistle, he saw her shoulders shudder and felt her squirm on his lap. She was broad and thin, and her name was Alice. When she turned her face to hand him the bottle, the edge of her profile was rimmed in a soft light. Whistle thought she was very pretty.

It had been Dox's idea that they take the girls to the game. Whistle worked with Dox in the dress house, and Alice worked there too. Dox's date was a model in the place, but Alice worked in the office. Dox insisted she was too thin to be a model, but Whistle thought she was clean and would not be one. He had never spoken to her, and it was Dox who arranged the date. That made Whistle angry, but he could not understand why. For weeks he had wanted her to see him play. At nights, the desire had made him restless with a new excitement.

After work they went to the New Yorker for dinner. Flip and Artie met them there with their girls, and it was almost a party. They had drinks before dinner, but Artie kept insisting about the game, and so none of the fellows had more than two. Whistle wanted to drink more, but he felt himself tighten when Artie mentioned the game, and he held back. The place was crowded besides with soldiers. Some wore battle ribbons, and they stared occasionally at the girls. They made Whistle feel he should not drink there.

But in the car when the bottle Dox had bought went around and she would swallow from it and then turn to hand it to him, Whistle was afraid she would hear the beating in his chest. There was the soft light on her face, and she said, "Here, Whistle," without even a smile. But there was an edge to her voice that startled him. He did not think from seeing her at work that she would drink the way she did, and he believed she was doing it because the other girls were. But she didn't say anything or even change the expression on her face when Dox's girl started to curse, and Whistle felt the blood inside him to the ends of his fingers. He wanted to take a long swallow when she said, "Here, Whistle," but Artie still kept on about the game, so he ran a little of it over his lip and passed it on. She sat well back in his lap and he had a hand on her shoulder. He thought ahead to when he would be running on the gym floor and she would be watching him. Thinking of that relieved the sense of his awkwardness. It would be much easier for him after the game. He could look forward to the party at Dox's basement. He was almost not afraid to think of taking her home by himself afterwards.

But suddenly, even the thought of the game was strangely frightening. She might know nothing about basketball. She might not care at all about how he played. He remembered he had not spoken a full sentence to her since the evening started. That terrified him now. The others were all making noise in the car. When he listened, he could hear Dox's girl laugh loudly. But Alice was quiet. Maybe Dox had spoken to her before the date. Quickly, without thinking, his fingers—as though they were apart from the anguish inside of him—tightened about her shoulder. He waited for her to protest, wanting now to be out of the car, not caring any more about the game. But she didn't speak. She didn't even move. She just sat there on his lap looking out through the opposite window, the light shading the edge of her fine profile. He felt his fingers loosen, almost not touching her.

Then Flip, sitting in front with his girl on his lap, twisted his head toward the corner where Whistle sat in the back. Looking past Alice, Whistle could see Flip's thick neck wrinkle in two ugly folds.

"It's awful quiet back there," Flip said. "They must be having fun. Whistle didn't even get out to push." Dox's girl laughed. Whistle thought hard for something to say, but Alice was quiet too. Then Artie's girl, sitting next to Whistle, spoke.

"Nothing's going on. You take care of your own troubles."

"What did I say?" Flip called back. "I thought I was being nice, looking out like that for Alice."

"I'm fine, thank you," Alice said without moving. Her voice, clear, brittle, sounded in Whistle's ear like the tapping of metal. It came upon him quietly—as though the thought had been in his mind for years—that he was going to love her. They were on the bridge now, and the water below them was shadowed dark with the twilight. Looking out between the massive, bolted girders at the river, at the boats, at the snow, and at the lights that beamed their narrow tracks of yellow across the water, Whistle lost himself for a moment in a surprising calm. It was as though he had done all this—Alice on his lap and his hand on her shoulder—many times before. He thought he would ask her, after the party, when they stood before her door, to go on a boat ride with him when the warmer weather came. When he turned away from the window, he saw that she had raised a hand to her face to touch precisely with a finger near the corner of her eye. The nail was long and polished lightly, in pink.

"There won't be much for us to do at the game, just watching you guys run around," Dox's girl suddenly said.

"Anxious to get to the party?" Dox asked, and Whistle knew that he smiled.

"It'll be better than the game," she said.

"I suppose it will," Dox said.

"You girls can bet on that," Flip said.

"There he goes again," Artie's girl said.

"For Christ's sake, what the hell's eating you?" Flip answered.

"Oh, can it all already, will you," Dox said. It grew quiet and Whistle wondered why Alice hadn't said anything when they spoke about the game. Then Dox looked quickly at his girl.

"You watch Whistle during the game, honey. That'll give you enough to do."

"Why? Is he something special?" She turned a little, as though to look toward Whistle. He bit his lip to stop the childish grin.

"Just the best basketball player you ever saw," Flip said.

"So what?" she laughed.

"This babe's got the giggles," Flip said. "Listen, kid, if girls were basketballs Whistle would have you all damned run down by tomorrow." Flip laughed, and Dox's girl laughed. A small knot of breath caught in Whistle's throat. Then Alice laughed, louder than the others, filling the car with the sound of it, tilting her head back so that her hair fell against his face. She jerked on his lap as she laughed, and then began to cough and laugh at the same time, so that Whistle heard himself mumble, "Take it easy. Take it easy." When she stopped at last, they were all quiet again. Whistle listened to the continous grinding of the snow beneath the tires.

"It's going to be a rough game," Artie said, breaking the silence.

"Oh, quit worrying," Dox said.

"Is this a very special game?" Alice asked. Whistle shrugged, then nodded toward Artie. "He thinks so," he heard himself say.

"They're only kids," Artie said carefully, "but they play high school ball together. They got this boy Bernstein on the team. He's got offers from colleges already."

"Oh, is that the kid who plays for Madison?" Alice asked. Whistle looked up eagerly at her. Her mouth was half-parted in surprise. It was small, pretty. He turned his head away.

"How did you know?" Flip asked.

"He lives on my block. I used to date his brother."

"No shit? I mean, no kidding?" Flip said.

"Bernstein's a nice kid," Alice said evenly. "I've seen him play."

"You watch Whistle tonight," Dox said.

"Are you really that good, Whistle?" Alice asked, turning her face down to him. He could not see her face for the shadows, but he thought surely she must hear the beating of his heart. He wanted to be out of the car and on the gym floor. He wanted that very much. He opened his mouth to say something, not knowing what he would speak. But then Dox began.

"He ought to be that good. Hell, even I might be if I worked at it like him. Hey Artie, you remember when we were kids and it was ass-cold outside. Below zero, remember? We were going to a movie— 'Captain Blood,' wasn't it? Funny how that stuck. You nearly lost an ear on the way. And when we passed the schoolyard, there was Whistle running around in a sweater and steaming like the Fourth of July. He even shoveled the damn snow away from the backboard, remember?"

"I ought to," Artie said. "I had to go to the doctor account of my ear. Jeez, Whistle, you were sure a crazy kid." Whistle smiled broadly. He could not mistake the admiration in Artie's voice.

Flip began to sing a song, and his girl joined in. Then Dox and Artie sang, and Alice hummed. Whistle thought confidently of the game. He had hardly spoken to her, had not really touched her. It would be different afterwards. He would sing with them on the way to Dox's place. The words were almost in his mouth now. He liked the light weight of her on his lap, but he wanted to be in the game already. He thought of it longingly, saw himself often angling in from the corner for that free ball. But it was hard for him to think only of the game. He got it mixed with the metallic ring of her voice which had said, "Here, Whistle. Here, Whistle," when the bottle was going around.

When the car pulled up before the community center, Whistle thought he should help Alice out, but she was on his lap and had to leave first. Inside the building, they all lingered for a while at the steps to the locker room.

"You girls keep together. We'll see you after the game," Flip said. Then, looking at Alice as the fellows started down the stairs, Flip added, "Having fun, kid?"

"Terrific," she said flatly. Whistle, already hurrying down the steps, did not look back. The word, the sound of it, terrified him. He'd been a fool with her. He should've said more in the car. He should've maybe touched her arm now before leaving her. He should've held her hand when they were going through the snow. The steps had been icy too.

"You got a goddamned big mouth, Flip," Dox said, as he pushed open the door to the locker room.

"Say, what the hell is all this?" Flip complained. "I ain't said one word tonight when everybody didn't come jumping on me."

"Well then, shut up!" Dox said.

"Cut it, will you guys, and think about the game a little," Artie said. "It ain't going to be a breeze with that Bernstein kid."

They met the rest of the team in the locker room, and as they dressed Whistle outlined the way they'd play. But even as he spoke, he heard the single sound of her words, and he urged them all to hurry.

When they were finally on the gym floor for the pre-game practice, Whistle moved with a frantic violence, as though his body had become dependent upon it. His teammates sensed the energy of Whistle's motion, and believing he was being driven only by the thought of Bernstein, their own movements became deliberate with tension. The kids and girls and men of the neighborhood who had come to watch chattered quickly in low voices, looking from one end of the court to the other, from Bernstein to Whistle. But Whistle, even up to the moment when the ball was about to go into the air between the two centers, and Bernstein crouched beside him, thought only that she was watching, that her eyes—with the brows arched curiously—were on him. And a second later, when he moved quickly and the ball was in his hands, he thought of nothing when the ball went through the basket, and only vaguely heard the clamor that rose up with the shot he had made, feeling now only the tremendous uncoiling inside him, as though a wall of air had finally burst from his throat. A moment later when he was under and then past the basket and had scored again, his temples beat with the image of his body that had twisted itself between two men, had gone beneath an outstretched hand and angled the ball against the backboard, all in one great second's motion. He had no thought that he had twice within a minute's time outmaneuvered Bernstein.

So lost was he in the sensation of his running that he could not say when Bernstein first moved in on him, to be no more than six inches away, no matter where Whistle turned or how fast he ran, to stay there continuously as long as Whistle or his team had the ball, hawking him that way with his adolescent face, his eyes bulging, his mouth open, but with no sweat on his body. He did not even know at first that it was Bernstein who had begun to cling to him, and did not know until he had spent the deliberate effort of minutes in trying to shake him off—who would not be so shaken—that the stalking figure always inches away was the Bernstein who'd been spoken of so much, who was the high school star, who had the pop-eyes and open mouth and no sweat and who was to be the way of measuring him. It was against this recognition that Whistle made—when he next got his hands on the ball—his first desperate effort to overcome the kid who was taking him. With a violent wrench of his body that feigned movement in a direction he did not go, Whistle got a foot ahead of Bernstein and drove with his advantage toward the basket. He left his feet, raising the ball for the shot, and then saw, too late, the blur of the hand that came over his shoulder without touching him to hit the ball cleanly from his grasp, and Whistle knew without turning it had been Bernstein's hand. He ran wildly to retrieve the ball he had lost, his body colliding strangely against others as he did so. When the foul was called against him, and Bernstein, unperturbed, went to the line and quickly made his throw, Whistle began, for the first time, to think not in the images he always made, but of himself against Bernstein, began to think in advance even of what movements he might make with the other hounding him so. With his mind working feverishly as he ran, Whistle lost possession of his game. When he began himself to sense the loss, his thoughts went past Bernstein, went to Alice, who was watching him from somewhere in the crowd. Then Bernstein, almost from the center of the court, soon after the foul, lofted a long set-shot that he turned his back on even before he could see it drop cleanly through the basket. Panic welled unfamiliarly in Whistle as he ran. He even looked for a second toward the crowd, trying to find Alice where he could not see one face in the blur that was before his eyes.

During the time-out that Artie called, Whistle could hear the words, but did not listen to what the others said to him. He stared across the floor to where Bernstein stood among his teammates, nonchalant, unsweating, listening and talking. Whistle could see now that Bernstein was not even tall, that he was comically thin, with a sunken chest and no spread at all to his shoulders. Bernstein put a finger to his side and scratched slowly, and Whistle—his eyes hot with a peculiar anger—thought he would like to drive his fist through the ribs where Bernstein's fingers picked indifferently. When they began to play again, Bernstein started to move as he had not before. Something close to fright tore at Whistle as he tried to keep up with him, had to try sometimes even to find him. And always, when

Whistle had the ball himself, Bernstein was on him, never touching him, but never more than six inches away, his face thrust out to Whistle's so that Whistle saw wherever he turned, the popped eyes, the open mouth, the dry skin. Whenever he could get close enough to raise his hands for the shot, there was the other hand raised to the same height, blocking or worrying the ball. Whistle swore at himself for his clumsiness, angry with the body that would not move as he wanted it.

At half-time, on the way to the lockers, moving through the crowd, he passed next to Alice, suddenly, unawares, and he lowered his head. He was grateful she had not seen him, that she was talking with Sonny, who kept score for them and did not play. But when he moved on and heard the brittle pitch of her laughter come after him, he felt anew the panic that had been in him since the first moment after work.

In the locker room, Whistle sulked and the others left him to himself. He ran his hands nervously over his knees, and the legs felt strangely insensitive beneath the touch. He began to think then that he was ill, or having a bad night, and then began to believe that, and believed too—as he remembered the two quick baskets he'd made at the beginning of the game—that it might be only a bad stretch. The name Bernstein came to him from all parts of the room, the words "great" and "what a ballplayer" and "what can you do with him," so that Whistle finally blurted out, "I'm on to the sonofabitch now. I'll get him this half." He spoke so hurriedly and with so little expectation from the others, that even they could not understand the words. But they took from the tone what he had meant, and when they ran from the locker room to the gym, they chattered calls of encouragement to each other.

A minute after play had started again, Whistle was in the corner of the court and there was a ball loose in the air under the backboard. He angled in quickly toward the ball, feeling the oppressive weight fall out of him as his feet came off the ground with his leap, his hand outstretched under the ball he was about to seize. And then it was not there and his fingers clutched futilely against the empty space. When he turned his head the thin, no-shouldered, unsweating Bernstein was dribbling quickly downcourt. Whistle felt the air go out of him—as though from a blow—then ran wildly after Bernstein, finally leaving his feet in a desperate lunge for the ball. He came down with a thud against the hard floor, and he could feel his fingers claw against the smooth, unyielding wood. Even in the sudden darkness before his eyes, he knew that he was rolling, felt the joints of his knee and elbow and shoulder grate against the hardness. Then he knew he was on his feet again and trying to run, but Dox had him by the arms, shouting, "Take it easy, Whistle. Take it easy. It's only a game." They called a foul and Whistle watched Bernstein calmly make it good, watched him while he felt his legs trembling and the blood running from his knee. But he would not leave the game and he was glad about the blood, and began looking once more to the sidelines. He ran wildly after that, not even knowing that Bernstein had begun to ease off, and he fouled freely. He could not hear Dox telling him during the time-outs that it was only a game, that he would be in no shape for the party afterwards, that Alice would get sore.

When they were undressing after the game, Whistle did not know by what score they had lost, nor did he try to think of how many points Bernstein scored and how many he made himself. He started to complain about his knee, and Dox said he would drive him home. But Whistle said no and Dox assumed he would go to the party and went with Flip to find the girls. But Whistle got out of the room later and left the building. He stood for a moment on the corner in the snow that was still falling and saw Bernstein throw the snowball and heard the laughter as they ran away. He started to walk home, not knowing now why he had left. He knew he must have played better than any of the others. Certainly better than Flip. The crowd had clapped when he stayed in the game with the bloody knee. It hurt him now. It hurt a lot. He should get home and clean it out. He wondered if the blood might be staining the snow, but he did not look to see.

He did not go to work the next day, or the day after, then finally quit, telling Dox to say he'd torn the ligament in his knee and the doctor had said to lay off. He learned that Sonny had taken Alice to the party. He could not believe and tried not to care when they told him Sonny had made out.

It was hard to be with the fellows afterwards. No one spoke of Alice to him. He did not want them to talk of her, though it made him uncomfortable to have them say nothing. But they all talked to him of Bernstein. He'd gone on to college and—only a freshman— was the leading scorer in the conference. He had scored less against Whistle than he did against some college players. They told Whistle this often, but they could not make him care. He tried never to think again of Bernstein after the game. He tried not to think at all about that night. And sometimes, most often at night, late and in bed, he'd shut his eyes tight when he heard the brittle, metallic, "Here, Whistle. Here, Whistle." He continued to play at the community center, but the club team had broken up and none of the fellows were there. Flip had bought a car and Artie married. They had parties almost every Saturday night in Dox's basement.

When Whistle's mother some months later insisted they move closer to her relatives, she had—against Whistle's indifference—to abandon unused the many arguments she had prepared.

The three hours are over quickly for Whistle, and only while he takes off the sweated suit in the locker room does he begin to feel the punishment of his body. But under the needling spray of the shower, the fatigue leaves him, and he knows only the pleasant splash of the cool water. He thinks of nothing as the shower breaks against the nape of his neck and, clinging, wets the length of his back. He takes no part in the horseplay, but the others are not angry at his aloofness. They think of Whistle as older and funny, but they never accuse him of playing hero.

Always, after the shower, the close night air of the city lingers on his face with a fragrance it does not really own. When a high breeze slants occasionally from the bay through the deep rows of houses, Whistle is glad he does not bring the car on the nights he plays. He walks the half mile to home in a measured, predictable stride, and there is an inexpressible assertion for him in the small weight of the travelling bag he carries. He has a choice of streets, but he walks along the busiest one, though he pays no heed to the night-noises of the city. The exhaust from a bus, the shouting from a window, a distant, muffled knock are provoking sounds, but Whistle is not trapped in their loneliness. He is conscious only of a curious freedom released inside him, of a restored balance in his body. Occasionally a group gathered idly on a corner will begin to suggest things, but only vaguely, and the impressions are already abandoned by the time he crosses the street. Even on other days, it is hard for Whistle to think back in any specific way. The few fellows that haven't married go their own ways, and months pass before Whistle will bother to look up any of them. Even on the Mondays that he drives his mother to the doctor, he prefers to sit in the car and wait for her, looking absently out the window, stirred only by the annoyance of having the night at the gym taken away from him.

When Whistle gets home his mother is already asleep. He takes one of the picture magazines that always lie about the kitchen and goes into his room. Undressed, in bed, by the dim light that hangs from the ceiling, he scans the pages, unmindful really of what he sees. When he puts the magazine away and flicks the light switch, he smokes a cigarette. The taste of it sharpens his ease. In the bright glow of the cigarette's end, there is a hypnotic focus for his sleep. But with the alternating depth of the small hue as he drags, Whistle's mind begins to make pictures. He thinks ahead to the weekend and the possibility of driving to Scranton once more, or maybe this time to Fall River. Since he has bought the car, he toys frequently with these trips, but does not often go.

When he feels the heat of the cigarette on his fingers, he drops it, still lit, into the ash-tray on the night table. His mind lingers on the impressions of shots he has made that night, of rebounds he has grabbed by angling in that way from the corner of the court. He thinks of Scranton again, and then of the next night that he will play. The poise—so fine before in his enervated body—begins now to crack. Whistle feels once more the dangerous soaring of his anticipations as he waits for sleep.

REX WORTHINGTON *is thirty-one years old. He has an A.B. in English from Indiana University and a master's in creative writing (under William E. Wilson) from the same university. He spent three years in the Army, two of them overseas, mostly in Paris and London. "A Kind of Scandal" is his first published story. "Actually," he says, "I should prefer to write novels, but I have not yet been able to get the hang of that difficult trade." (Mr. Worthington, meet Ruth Harnden.) At present he is working in the Indiana University library. He has a wife and a two-year-old son.*

A KIND OF SCANDAL

FROM ACCENT

Well me and Dumdie was playing catch in the alley with an old softball my brother Fred gave me once and when the stuffings came out we got tired and sat down under Henniger's big tree and pretty soon Dumdie thought it would be a good idea to steal some of Mr. Vanderplagg's apples. We didn't really steal them cause they're always green and got worms in them all the time and Mr. Vanderplagg don't want them anyway. Dumdie just liked to say that word so we went and stole a whole bunch and threw them at telephone poles and Dumdie beat me almost every time cause he was older than I was and then he made me stand way back so I couldn't even throw far enough to hit the telephone pole except once when it bounced and Dumdie said I was a sissy and I got mad and went in the house. I told my mother and she said, "That's what you get, I guess you'll never learn," so I went to the toilet and came back in the kitchen and washed my hands and showed my mother before I made a piece of bread with brown sugar on it and when I was eating Dumdie came in our back yard and looked through the screen door. When I got through I went and told my mother and she said, "Well?" and looked at me at the same time so I went in the kitchen and got a glass of water and threw it through the screen door on Dumdie but that made my mother mad and she made me go out and play with Dumdie. Dumdie said we ought to steal some more of Mr. Vanderplagg's apples and I said "No," till Dumdie said he could get one of Mr. Turpin's golf clubs and we could play golf with the apples and I said he couldn't so we went down in Mr. Vanderplagg's back yard. Mr. Vanderplagg's back yard is all sunk and cooler than other back yards cause my father said Barbee Creek ran through there before I was born but it's under the ground now and Mr. Turpin lived in Mr. Vanderplagg's red house around in the back where we was. That's not where Mr. Vanderplagg lives though. He lives in his own house on the corner but they got the same back yard only he don't rent that one except downstairs and my mother said we'd never live in a place like that even if Mr. Vanderplagg is rich like all the Belgians cause they got lizards I mean snails all the time and sometimes they wake up in the morning with mold on their shoes. Dumdie could pick up snails like fishworms but they make me want to throw up so we hunted awhile but you can't find them in the daytime except that snotty stuff they make all over the place and Dumdie started digging in some crumbly bricks and found one and I said I don't want to play with any slimy, dirty rotten, filthy lousy lizards I mean snails only I said lizards that time and I said I was going to go home. So Dumdie squashed it and we went over to Mr. Turpin's door and Dumdie was going to go in but the door was hooked so we looked through the wire and it was pretty dark in there for daytime but we could see Mr. Turpin in bed and that woman he said was his maid was in there with him and Dumdie said how about letting us use one of his golf clubs to knock apples with and Mr. Turpin said we was too little and go away and I said to Mr. Turpin, "My big brother said you can't afford a maid." They looked quiet for a minute and then Mr. Turpin laughed and she said, "Oh, for goodness sake, let them have one," only she didn't say it just like that and Mr. Turpin said he'd give us his old putter so he got out of bed and got it for us. After we said, "Thank you," we stole some more of Mr. Vanderplagg's apples and went up where he's going to build a garage for his apartment people but all he's got done is the foundation and that makes the ground there even higher than the alley and Dumdie said that'd be a good place to knock apples so we knocked them across the alley against Mr. Peterson's garage till Dumdie hit one clean over the garage and he said, "I bet you can't do that," and I said, "I can too," and I don't know, I almost forget, but while I was taking a big swing Dumdie bent down to pick up an apple and before I knew it I hit him in the place you call the temple and he held his head with both hands and said, "Oh, Jim," in a kind of old tired voice like if my mother'd said it and he ran down the steps in Mr. Vanderplagg's back yard and I thought first he was going to tell Mr. Turpin but he went up the steps on the other side and headed for home and I got scared and ran home too. Then when I saw my mother——

"All right, Jim. That's all we wanted to know. That's fine," the big man in the striped suit said. He turned to the lady with fat legs and said, "All right," and she shut her notebook and went out. Then he turned to Jim and said, "And that's just the way it happened, wasn't it Jim. You don't remember any more?"

"No, sir."

"All right. That's fine," he said. He got up and shook hands with Jim's father and grinned with big cheeks at Jim's mother. "Mr. and Mrs. Ryan—you folks have been most helpful."

"Well, we wanted to do everything right," Bill Ryan said.

"That's right. That's fine." Julia Ryan reached down to take Jim's hand and they were going. In the other room the lady had her legs under a little table, and she was running her typewriter and looking at her notebook. She smiled at Jim, who looked at the floor. Then they went down the hall and got in the elevator. Julia leaned back in the corner and grinned because elevators made her feel funny.

Bill Ryan cleared his throat and said, "Why didn't you say, 'Luther'?"

When they got outside, Julia said, "Thank goodness that's over."

It began one Saturday afternoon when Jim came running down the alley and couldn't get the back gate open. Julia, who was weeding the garden, looked up and said, "What's the matter? You have to go to the bathroom again?" For answer Jim began to scream and dance up and down jerkily, like a puppet. "What in the world?" Julia said and went over and unlocked the gate. He squirmed past her and went running up the path. But instead of going in the house he dived under the back porch. When Julia peered into the shadows under the porch, Jim looked like a frightened cat, and she said, "What's the matter?" Jim began screaming again. "Oh, dear," she said, and got down and crawled part way under the porch. "Now what is it? Tell me."

"I hit Dumdie in the head," he bellowed.

"Oh, my. How? Did you hurt him?"

"We was playing golf. And the blood squirted out like anything."

"Oh, merciful God," she whimpered. "Where? Where'd you do it?"

"Vanderplagg's," he got out. Julia backed out from under the porch and struck her head so hard her glasses fell down from one ear. "I didn't do it on purpose," Jim screamed.

"Oh, shut up and stay there," she said, half mad with pain; and she ran down the path and out into the alley. She found the blood sprinkled on the green apples; it led like a string of beads down the steps into Vanderplagg's yard and up the opposite stairs to the sidewalk. When Julia reached the sidewalk, she hiked up her skirts and came swinging up the street revealing her torn petticoat and the tops of her cotton stockings to all the neighbors. There were already several of them out in their yards, bristling in the quickening air like dogs who have smelled something and don't yet know what it is.

What is it?

Why, I saw him.

It's the Hiller boy.

Myra Hiller met Julia at the door, standing so handsome and self-possessed there in her beautiful house coat that Julia stopped and smoothed her hands down over her skirt. But then, seeing the flush on Myra's cheeks and a strand of lavender hair askew, she cried, "Oh, Myra. Merciful God."

"There, there," Myra said. "I don't think he's hurt too bad." Dumdie was in his parents' bedroom, and Myra's daughter Doreathy was holding a wet towel to his head.

"Well, you're all right, aren't you, Dumdie?" Julia said. Dumdie smiled thinly.

"I think he's all right," Myra said. "I've seen him come home worse than this."

Julia took this up and thought that there was a lot of truth in it because everybody knew that Dumdie was a little odd, and he must be something like that drunk, Hootie Randall, who was always falling down and never got hurt and came home one time with his face looking like he'd had a run-in with a pack of wildcats. That made her feel better.

"Oh, now hush, smarty. I've already called for an A-M-B-U-L-A-N-C-E," Myra said.

Julia couldn't take her eyes off Doreathy, who was sitting on the bed in only her slip. With her round little figure revealed, her pert face and reddish hair, she looked just like Clara Bow. Then out of the blue, Julia remembered that Hootie Randall had shot himself. "You going to take him to the H-O-S-P-I-T-A-L?" she said to Myra, who nodded. Julia glanced back at Dumdie, who had closed his eyes and was as white as the pillow he was lying on. "I'll get Bill up," she burst out, causing Dumdie to open his eyes.

"Oh, let the poor man sleep," Myra protested. "I haven't even called Frank home yet."

"Oh, now never mind," Julia cried peevishly, running out the front door, "I know what I'm doing." Bill worked nights and had to have his rest in the daytime, but why was he always asleep when something happened, and as Julia struggled up the back-yard path, she cried, "Bill, Bill," with all the breath that was left in her.

Bill, when he woke, couldn't seem to get it straight, and he kept asking who Dumdie was. When he learned that Jim was under the back porch, he went out and asked him where in the world he'd got hold of a golf club. But Jim began to cry and Bill couldn't make heads or tails of what he was saying. "Merciful God, c'mon," Julia said, grabbing his arm and pulling him down the path toward the garage. They drove straight to the hospital and stayed there till late that night, when Dumdie died.

"Well, everything's under control here," Gladys Houston called out the back door when Bill and Julia were no more than halfway up the path from the garage. When Julia came up on the porch, Gladys saw the look on her face and knew what she was going to say, and, as if she had to have her say first, she began, "The girls are both in bed and Jim's been in bed hours ago. What a fine healthy appetite those children have—I've often told Harry I wish I could have had some children of my own just to watch them eat. As soon as you called from the hospital I sent Harry to the store for some ice cream, and those kids tore into that like they'd never seen it before."

"Why, Gladys, there were a lot of leftovers in the refrigerator."

"Oh, now, Julia, you don't mind, I'm sure. I love your wonderful children and I thought a special treat would keep their minds off what happened." Gladys, seeing that this brought Julia back to Dumdie and that she was going to speak, went on quickly, "What a fine handsome understanding young man you have in Fred. Why, when he came home, it was like having a man in the house and he kept the girls in line and went out and got Jim out from under the back porch—the poor little fellow was sound asleep—and Fred cleaned him up and put him into bed. After I got the girls to bed I sent Fred to the movies and while he was gone I just thought I'd tidy up the kitchen a bit." And she stepped back from the door for the first time to let Julia and Bill in their own house. Gladys settled herself by the kitchen cabinet and waited; Julia got it out at last, "Dumdie died." It sounded like the beginning of a nursery rhyme, Gladys thought, and she said, "Oh, Julia, you have a lot to be thankful for. It could just as easily been your boy as not. Mrs. Jordan and Mrs. Kuntz came over tonight and they saw Jim and that Hiller boy out there this afternoon when they were coming home from their shopping and they said they said then, 'Somebody's liable to get hurt.'"

Julia, turning uncertainly in the middle of her polished kitchen, stopped and fixed her eyes on Gladys. "You mean it's all over town already?"

"Well, now, Julia," Gladys said, "you mustn't think I did it. They came over here after I got the girls to bed, and you can ask Fred, he was right there with me."

"Julia didn't mean anything," Bill put in.

Julia, thinking of the blood on Vanderplagg's steps and splattered along the sidewalk in the bright afternoon sun right up to the Hiller place, cried out, "Oh, how could they help but know! I haven't seen so much blood since that motorcycle policeman got hit on the corner."

Gladys looked upset, as if this was in bad taste; and Bill, who had seen Dumdie only in the hospital with a neat bandage around his head, replied, "Oh, Julia, don't dwell on it so. There wasn't much blood."

"Don't tell me what I didn't see," Julia said, turning on her husband. "If I could sleep on a picket fence like you can, I wouldn't see anything either."

"Now, Julia," Bill protested gently, while Gladys said, "Well, I'd better get home. I've got a man of my own to take care of."

Julia watched her go but then ran to the door and said, "Gladys, I didn't mean anything, really. Don't be angry. But you know how people are."

Gladys turned, a light like triumph on her face, and whispered through the screen door, "Now, honey, I understand, and I don't think there's going to be much talk. It's like Mrs. Kuntz said, everybody knows that Hiller boy wasn't just right and maybe it was an act of God that it was him instead of your boy."

Julia took that to bed with her, and the next morning being Sunday, she insisted that the whole family go to church. But how could it have got round so fast, she wondered, when, getting there late because Jim had had to go to the bathroom at the last minute, the entire congregation turned to watch the Ryans file in. The only bench open was one down near the front on the side. Walking down the aisle Julia thought she was going to faint because Bill didn't seem to know how to act not having been to church, as everybody probably knew, since he got married over twenty years ago, and kept talking to the children in his street voice just as if nothing was wrong.

The Ryans took up the entire bench by themselves; and when the collection plate came round, Julia discovered that she hadn't any change and Bill had forgot his wallet. The plate was handed to Julia at one end of the row and given by Bill to a monitor at the other end without as much as a red cent being dropped in. By the time Julia got home she was so upset she could hardly get dinner; she crabbed at the girls, who began to cry and pick on Jim, telling him that it was all his fault anyway. That set Jim off, causing Bill to descend on his children; and Fred, being sixteen, said, "You people act like you don't have any sense."

Later in the day the newspaper sent a man over, who asked if he could have a picture of Jim. Julia regretted afterward being so rude, but at the time she was hot and tired and nobody but her seemed to realize how awful this thing was, so that she practically drove him down the steps. The next day there it was in a sub-head right under something about scandals in Washington; and all up and down the street Julia could see the neighbors coming out on their porches after the paper boy had passed, as if he were scattering gold. "Oh, I tell you I'm going to go out of my mind if this doesn't stop," she shouted.

Bill did, in fact, tell her that she wasn't acting at all sensible when she said that Jim would have to go to the funeral. "I don't give a damn what anybody thinks," he said. "It's too much to ask of a little boy."

Julia seemed to have been waiting for this; she breathed a long sigh and said meekly, "You don't think it would be the thing to do then?"

"Damnit, no," he said, feeling his strength, "it's enough that you and me go."

As Julia often told Gladys, "Bill always has to know which way the wind's blowing and who killed Cock Robin, but once he gets everything straight, there's nobody like him." She clung tightly to her husband's arm there in the funeral parlor, when he took her straight up the aisle to view the body past all those eyes like rows of marbles; and she was able to shed a few quiet tears which made her feel as if she had taken a weight off her shoulders and left it on Dumdie's casket. Afterward Myra, looking as smart all in black as an actress, asked Julia and Bill to ride to the cemetery with the Hillers. Then later she had them drop by for cake and coffee and asked several times how Jimmy was taking it all. Julia accepted this with a twinge of guilt, and when she got home, she fell on Jim with so many soft words and caresses that at last he became cross and ended up by crying.

That evening Julia and Gladys talked across the back-yard fence: "They say he's going to marry her," Gladys said.

"Do you suppose this business had anything to do with it?" Julia asked.

"Wouldn't be surprised."

"No wedding ring's going to make a lady out of that woman," Julia said. They were looking across the Houstons' back yard down into Vanderplagg's; Mr. Turpin was moving, and that woman was helping him. Looking neither to the right nor the left, they hurried back and forth from Turpin's rooms to his car, resembling ants each time they disappeared into the apartment only to emerge with a fresh burden. "They see us all right," Julia said.

Across the alley Mrs. Peterson had stuck her head out of an upstairs window to watch, and Mr. Peterson and Mr. Henniger, who were in the alley smoking, were watching too.

"I'll bet they feel nice," Gladys said acidly.

Mr. Turpin came out of the apartment with his bag of golf clubs covered over with a dark cloth and moved up the steps to his car.

"There," Julia breathed.

"May God forgive them," Gladys said.

While Turpin went over to Mr. Vanderplagg's house on the corner, his woman got in the car and waited; he came back shortly, got in the car, and they drove away.

"Well, good riddance of bad rubbish," Gladys said.

"I don't know," Julia said, "maybe they were instruments of God, as they say."

"Why, how's that?"

"Well, like you said, maybe it was an act of God, Dumdie not being just right, you know."

"Well now, you mustn't say I said that, Julia. It was Mrs. Kuntz. I always give God his due and no more. Dumdie was just like any other boy, as far as I'm concerned."

"Still," Julia insisted, "Myra was so nice and all. I don't know how I'd have acted if it was Jimmy. Why, I don't dare think about it."

"You mean you don't think Dumdie was the same as your boy?" Gladys asked intently.

"Nooo, I don't exactly mean that. But you know how wild he was at times."

"Well, 'Let the dead bury their dead,' I always say."

"It's not that I mean anything against Myra, you understand," Julia said. "Myra's always been wonderful to me. Like last winter, I met her uptown on the street with Doreathy, and you know they're both so pretty and dress so smart that you can't tell mother from daughter, and Myra said, 'God, it's cold enough to freeze the hairs in your nose,' and put me right at ease."

"I've always liked Myra," Gladys put in.

"And besides," Julia said, warming to her subject, "you couldn't ask for anybody to be nicer about all this, and I think it was because of the way she acted that nobody misunderstood. The neighbors go out of their way to be nice to Jim, and I think by the time he goes back to school next month, this will all blow over."

Standing with his back against the school building, Jim refused to meet their eyes. They had him encircled now, and more were coming all the time. He could see his two sisters out on the playground looking on with pale faces, and he felt bitter anger, not because they didn't help but that they should see him like this. He made a sudden dash for freedom, but they pushed him back. Then Petie Hern arrived and made his way to the inside-front of the circle. Petie looked at Jim and spit through the space between his front teeth. "He don't look so tough to me," he said. They shoved Petie forward, and he fell against Jim and dug his fist into his ribs.

"Fight! Fight!" they screamed.

MAGAZINES CONSULTED*

ACCENT, Box 102, University Station, Urbana, Ill. AMERICAN MAGAZINE, 640 Fifth Ave., N.Y.C. AMERICAN MERCURY, 11 East 36th St., N.Y.C. ANTIOCH REVIEW, 212 Xenia Ave., Yellow Springs, O. ARGOSY, 205 East 42nd St., N.Y.C. ARIZONA QUARTERLY, University of Arizona, Tucson, Ariz. ASTOUNDING SCIENCE FICTION, 575 Madison Ave., N.Y.C. ATLANTIC MONTHLY, 8 Arlington St., Boston, Mass. BETTER LIVING, 230 Park Ave., N.Y.C. BLUE BOOK, 230 Park Ave., N.Y.C. CALIFORNIA QUARTERLY, 7070 Hollywood Blvd., Los Angeles, Cal. CAROLINA QUARTERLY, Box 1117, Chapel Hill, N.C. CATHOLIC WORLD, 411 West 59th St., N.Y.C. COLLIER'S, 640 Fifth Ave., N.Y.C. COMMENTARY, 34 West 33rd St., N.Y.C. COSMOPOLITAN, 57th St. and Eighth Ave., N.Y.C. COUNTRY GENTLEMAN, Independence Square, Philadelphia, Pa. ELLERY QUEEN'S MYSTERY MAGAZINE, 570 Lexington Ave., N.Y.C. EPOCH, 252 Goldwin Smith Hall, Cornell University, Ithaca, N.Y. ESQUIRE, 488 Madison Ave., N.Y.C. EVERYWOMAN'S, 16 East 40th St., N.Y.C. FAMILY CIRCLE, 25 West 45th St., N.Y.C. FANTASY AND SCIENCE FICTION, 2643 Dana St., Berkeley, Cal. FURIOSO, Carleton College, Northfield, Minn. GALAXY SCIENCE FICTION, 421 Hudson St., N.Y.C. GEORGIA REVIEW, University of Georgia, Athens, Ga. GOOD HOUSEKEEPING, 57th St. and Eighth Ave., N.Y.C. HARPER'S BAZAAR, 572 Madison Ave., N.Y.C. HARPER'S MAGAZINE, 49 East 33rd St., N.Y.C. HOPKINS REVIEW, Box 1227, Johns Hopkins University, Baltimore, Md. HUDSON REVIEW, 439 West St., N.Y.C. HUSK, Cornell College, Mount Vernon, Ia. JEWISH HORIZON, 154 Nassau St., N.Y.C. KENYON REVIEW, Kenyon College, Gambier, O. LADIES' HOME JOURNAL, Independence Square, Philadelphia, Pa. MADEMOISELLE, 575 Madison Ave., N.Y.C. MASSES & MAINSTREAM, 832 Broadway, N.Y.C.

*The editors have decided not to consult the various collections of writing now being published in volume form at intervals through the year. *New World Writing, Discovery, Story* (in book form) and others, while desirable publishing ventures, do not seem to fall in the original category of periodicals on which this anthology was founded.

MCCALL'S, 230 Park Ave., N.Y.C. NEW MEXICO QUARTERLY, Box 85, University of New Mexico, Albuquerque, N.M. NEW-STORY, 6 Boulevard Poissonière, Paris, France. NEW YORKER, 25 West 43rd St., N.Y.C. PACIFIC SPECTATOR, Box 1948, Stanford, Cal. PARIS REVIEW, 8 Rue Garancière, Paris, France. PARK EAST, 220 East 42nd St., N.Y.C. PARTISAN REVIEW, 30 West 12th St., N.Y.C. PERSPECTIVE, Washington University Post Office, St. Louis, Mo. PRAIRIE SCHOONER, 12th and R Sts., Lincoln, Neb. QUARTERLY REVIEW OF LITERATURE, Box 287, Bard College, Annandale-on-Hudson, N.Y. QUARTO, 801 Business, Columbia University, N.Y.C. REDBOOK, 230 Park Ave., N.Y.C. SATURDAY EVENING POST, Independence Square, Philadelphia, Pa. SEWANEE REVIEW, University of the South, Sewanee, Tenn. SOUTHWEST REVIEW, Southern Methodist University, Dallas, Tex. THIS WEEK, 420 Lexington Ave., N.Y.C. TODAY, 638 Deming Pl., Chicago, Ill. TODAY'S WOMAN, 67 West 44th St., N.Y.C. TOWN & COUNTRY, 572 Madison Ave., N.Y.C. UNIVERSITY OF KANSAS CITY REVIEW, University of Kansas City, Kansas City, Mo. VIRGINIA QUARTERLY REVIEW, One West Range, Charlottesville, Va. WEIRD TALES, 9 Rockefeller Plaza, N.Y.C. WESTERN REVIEW, State University of Iowa, Iowa City, Ia. WOMAN'S DAY, 19 West 44th St., N.Y.C. WOMAN'S HOME COMPANION, 640 Fifth Ave., N.Y.C. YALE REVIEW, Box 1729, New Haven, Conn.

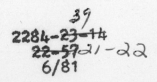

Instructor's Annotated Edition

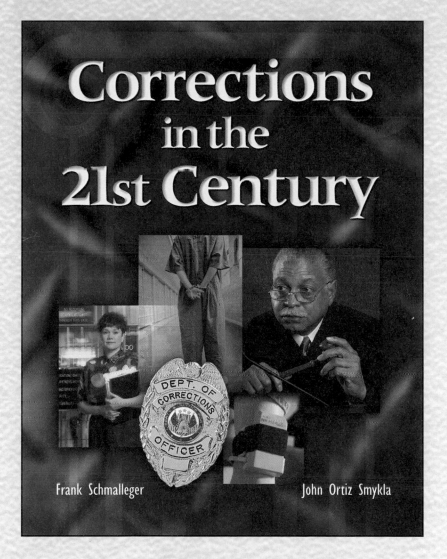

Corrections
in the
21st Century

Frank Schmalleger   John Ortiz Smykla

Frank Schmalleger, Ph.D.
Director
The Justice Research Association

John Ortiz Smykla, Ph.D.
Professor, Department of Criminal Justice
The University of Alabama

Glencoe
McGraw-Hill

New York, New York   Columbus, Ohio   Woodland Hills, California   Peoria, Illinois

FEB 2 8 2002

Glencoe/McGraw-Hill
A Division of The **McGraw·Hill** Companies

Corrections in the 21st Century
Instructor's Annotated Edition

Send all inquiries to:
Glencoe/McGraw-Hill
21600 Oxnard Street
Woodland Hills, CA 91367

ISBN 0-02-802568-7

Printed in the United States of America.

1 2 3 4 5 6 7 8 9 10   027   07 06 05 04 03 02 01 00

CONTENTS

Introducing
Corrections in the 21st Century

> *Knowledgeable, highly skilled, motivated, and professional correctional personnel are essential to fulfill the purpose of corrections effectively.*
>
> —The American Correctional Association, Policy Statement on Correctional Staff Recruitment and Development

Era of Professionalism

A new era in corrections is likely to emerge in the 21st century. Indications now are that it will be the age of professionalism. With it will come a long-awaited passage: the transition of American corrections from the status of a *service occupation* to that of a *true profession.* That transition is already beginning to affect the readers for whom *Corrections in the 21st Century* is written—students in community college and four-year criminal justice programs who are beginning the study of corrections. Many such students will eventually pursue careers in law enforcement or corrections. Some of them are already employed in those areas. Over the course of their careers, they will have to respond more and more to the demands of increasing professionalism.

Corrections in the 21st Century recognizes that the professionalization of corrections is an idea whose time is approaching. It shows students how to maximize the personal benefits of a career in this increasingly important field. Emerging professionalism is evident in all areas of corrections—from probation and parole, through jails and prisons, to juvenile corrections. Enhanced professionalism is of growing concern at all levels, from the individual correctional officer to state and federal administrators charged with running now-massive correctional enterprises.

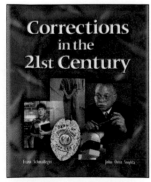

The implications of the changes now underway in corrections are enormous—and more changes are coming. A heightened sense of on-the-job professionalism should soon lead to better funding of correctional programs. The hard-earned expertise of correctional personnel is now being taken seriously by policy makers and legislators working to shape the future of America's correctional system. More immediately, however, higher standards will mean better pay and enhanced job satisfaction for those working in the field.

Changes now afoot will significantly impact correctional personnel in some very basic ways. Twenty-five years ago, when some began their careers in corrections, they were known as *jail guards* in hand-me-down uniforms.

Over the years, correctional officers dedicated their lives to the little-recognized but most dangerous and challenging arm of law enforcement. They elevated their status by hard work and professionalism from that of *jail guards* to *correctional officers*.

Instructional Approach

Corrections in the 21st Century seeks to introduce students to the concepts and practices of modern corrections and to teach them the skills they need to succeed in this field. To meet these goals, *Corrections in the 21st Century* uses a three-pronged instructional approach:

■ A thorough description of correctional *ideology*, including professionalism, policy issues, and society's avowed goals for the correctional enterprise;
■ A comprehensive overview of correctional *practice*, including the everyday operations of correctional agencies, prison facilities, jails, and probation and parole;
■ The development of personal *skills* that students can utilize in any career field.

As the correctional workplace and the world that surrounds it become more complex, correctional personnel will need ever greater abilities. Hence, a central task of *Corrections in the 21st Century* is to assist students in understanding and applying the concepts that will serve them well in any phase of the corrections field. Through chapter materials and practical exercises, *Corrections in the 21st Century* encourages the development of critical thinking skills, as well as an understanding of professional responsibility.

Content Coverage

Corrections in the 21st Century, offers a functional analysis of corrections issues for contemporary corrections. Chapters 1–3 highlight the social history of punishment and the critical development stages of modern corrections. Also established is the professional focus that continues as a thread throughout the text. Chapters 4–6 focus on the correctional system in communities. This part of the text deals with short-term incarceration in local jails, moves to diversion and probation as alternatives to incarceration, and then presents the concept of intermediate sanctions through community corrections. Chapters 7-14 present a picture of the correctional system from both sides of the bars. Environmental conditions, staff and inmate safety, prisoner rights litigation, overcrowding, gender and ethnicity, special needs prisoners, gang control strategies, and growth of supermax prisons are among the many topics treated in this part of the textbook. Chapter 15 presents a unique perspective on the rights of victims of crime and the duties of the correctional system to serve such victims. Finally, Chapter 16 offers a useful introduction to career planning for employment in the corrections field. With an eye to the issues that corrections professionals will face, three Looking to the Future features focus on restorative justice, technology in corrections, and privatization of corrections.

Inside the Student Book

This book was designed to help students learn. It contains 16 chapters, divided into sections. This structure, together with numerous special features, helps students learn and apply the concepts that can help lead them to a career as a corrections professional.

Previewing Chapter Concepts

The chapter opener introduces the key concepts to be learned.

The **opening photograph** sets the stage for the chapter content and provides a visual connection to the chapter.

4 Jails
Way Stations Along the Justice Highway

CHAPTER OBJECTIVES
After completing this chapter you should be able to:
1. List the purposes of jails.
2. Trace briefly the development of jails in history.
3. Explain how first-, second-, and third-generation jails differ in design and in method of inmate management.
4. Outline the characteristics of jail inmates, and explain what special-needs inmates are.
5. Describe how jail vocational and educational programs affect inmate behavior and recidivism.
6. Discuss how religion and a jail chaplain can influence jail inmates and help jail staff.
7. Discuss why jail accreditation is important.
8. Explain why it is important for jail staff to conduct themselves as professionals.

CHAPTER OUTLINE
Purpose of Jails
Jails in History
First Jail in America
American Jails in the Twentieth Century
Architecture and Inmate Management
Characteristics of Jail Inmates, Facilities, and Staff
Jail Inmates
Jail Facilities
Special-Needs Inmates
The Need for Better Data on Jail Populations and Programs
Jail Issues
Privatization
Overcrowding
Ways to Reduce Jail Crowding
Women in Jail
Educational and Vocational Programs
Religious Programs in Jail
Jail Accreditation
Jail Staff as Professionals

88

89

Chapter objectives alert students to the major concepts to learn. Students can turn the objectives into questions, and, as they read the chapter, look for the answers to the questions.

A **chapter outline** introduces the topics that will be discussed. Students can scan the outline to familiarize themselves with the subject matter.

Developing Chapter Concepts

The chapter text explains correctional concepts in a structured, visual format and provides a comprehensive overview of correctional practices.

The **heading structure** shows the relationship among the topics in a section and breaks the material into easily digestible segments of information. Students can scan the headings to locate the information that will help them answer the questions they formed from the chapter objectives.

Concepts are depicted in **visual format** to make them easier to understand.

Jail Issues

Jail administration and staffs face many important issues for the twenty-first century. We will now consider some of these issues and their effects on corrections professionals.

Privatization

Jails can be privatized in whole or in part. Jails can be financed, built, and operated by private groups, or jails can contract out some of their services (e.g., food service, mental health care, and programming).

One of the most hotly debated issues about privatization deals with the limits of governmental delegation of power and liability. Opponents of privatization believe that the administration of justice is a basic function of government and a symbol of state authority and should not be delegated.

Opponents also fear that if we privatize jails, we risk letting private corporations use their political influence to continue programs not in the public interest. For example, would private contractors keep jail occupancy rates high to maintain profit? Might private contractors accept only the best inmates, leaving the most troublesome for public facilities to handle?

Turning a jail over to a private corporation also raises questions about accountability. Who is responsible for monitoring the performance of the private contractor? Who will see that local laws and regulations are followed? As jail incarceration rates continue to rise, the debate over privatizing jails and the competition for new contracts will continue.

Overcrowding

Overcrowding is a problem that all jails, especially large urban jails, have to deal with. The number of persons held in local jails grew 4.5 percent from 1997 to 1998. The increase in the rate of jail incarceration is staggering. Between 1985 and 1998, the rate doubled—from 108 per 100,000 adults to 219. Overcrowding has a number of causes, including mandatory arrests and sentences, overcrowding at state and federal prisons, and an overall increase in the arrest rate as politicians "get tough" on crime. Crowded jails have serious health and safety consequences for staff and inmates, including decreased quality of life; overloaded educational, vocational, and recreational programs; insufficient medical services and supplies; increased discipline problems; spread of disease; and staff and inmate assaults.

Ways to Reduce Jail Crowding

Practices that can reduce crowding include financial and nonfinancial pretrial release, diversion, and new jail construction.

release on bail The release of a person upon that person's financial guarantee to appear in court.

Financial Pretrial Release Financial pretrial release programs are one alternative to the pretrial detention of accused offenders. Releasing a person upon that person's financial guarantee to appear in court is known as **release on bail**. The Eighth Amendment to the United States Constitution reads, "Excessive bail shall not be required, nor excessive fines imposed, nor

108 **CHAPTER 4**

Jails: Way Stations Along the Justice Highway

FIGURE 7–2
Persons Held in State or Federal Prisons

How Many Are in Prison?

9% Federal Prisoners
91% State Prisoners

1,178,978 State Prisoners
123,041 Federal Prisoners
1,302,019 Total

Who Is in Prison?

Gender
6.5% Women
93.5% Men

Race/Ethnicity*
1.1% American Indian/ Alaska Native
48.3% White
48.9% Black
1.7% Asian/Pacific Islander

*Hispanics may be of any race

Age
18.4% 18-24
10.3% 45-54
3.3% 55 or older
29.5% 35-44
38.1% 25-34
0.4% 17 or younger

Why Are They in Prison?

State Prisoners
47% Violent Offenses
21% Drug Offenses
10% Public Order Offenses
22% Property Offenses

Federal Prisoners
60% Drug Offenses
19% Public Order Offenses
12% Violent Offenses
8% Property Offenses
1% Unspecified

Source: Allen J. Beck and Christopher J. Mumola, *Prisoners in 1998* (Washington: Bureau of Justice Statistics, August 1999).

Key terms are also defined in the margin to make it easy for students to learn them.

Key terms are defined when introduced and are printed in boldface to make them easy to find.

Reinforcing Chapter Concepts

In-text examples, graphics, and special features enhance and strengthen students' learning about major concepts and practices in corrections.

Policy implications alert students to the issues facing corrections professionals.

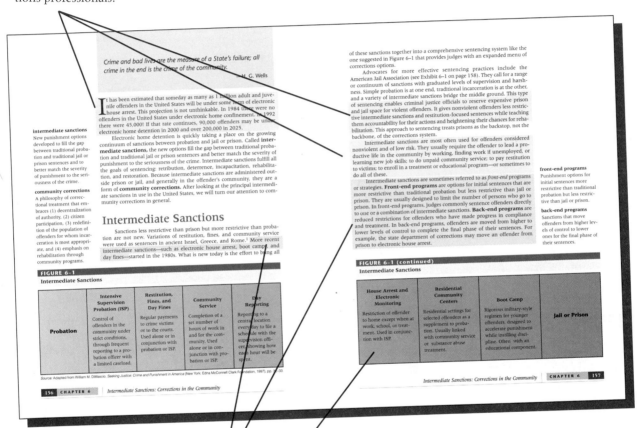

Examples help students understand the concepts being presented.

Graphics reinforce important concepts.

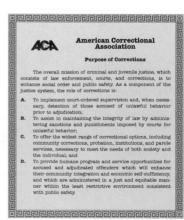

Chapter content focuses on developing **professionalism** among corrections practitioners.

I-8

Special features reinforce effective correctional practices and professional skills.

THE STAFF SPEAKS

I am a psychologist for the New Hampshire Department of Corrections working in a mental health unit at a correctional institution. My job is to lead a treatment program for offenders with moderate to severe Axis 1 (illness-type) mental disorders. Correctional counselors, nurses, or other mental health employees refer inmates to my supervisor, the Chief of Mental Health. If he thinks the inmate may have a serious illness-type mental disorder, he gives the case to me. Then either I or one of my team members carefully reads the inmate's offender record and medical chart, does a thorough interview, and, with the client's written permission, writes for information from mental health professionals who have worked with the client. Usually, the psychiatrist on the team will see the inmate also. If we think the person does have a disorder appropriate for us to treat, we develop a treatment plan and schedule the individual for a treatment team meeting,

attended by a nurse, the correctional counselor, the psychiatrist, my team members, and myself. We talk with the client about goals and interventions. These may include nonaddictive psychotropic medications, psychotherapy (individual and group), case management, and monitoring. When it's appropriate, we refer clients to other programs at the prison, for example, the sexual offender program, or the substance abuse program. As the clients approach release, we do our best to set them up with mental health and other resources in the community, so they will remain in good mental health, and so that a worsening of their mental disorder does not contribute to their re-offending.

Laura Magzis
Psychologist
Mental Health Unit
New Hampshire State Prison for Men

The Staff Speaks presents corrections professionals describing in their own words their work in the corrections profession.

THE OFFENDER SPEAKS

Very few of us do not think about beating the system. After all, the system deprives us of the freedom we cherish. It stands for all that we resent: lack of choice, restricted movement, denial of access to loved ones. We resent the walls, bars, uniforms, being told what to do, what programs we must take.

Moralists argue that we get exactly what we deserve, and many citizens believe that we are treated too well. Few of us can argue that we didn't know what we were getting into when we made the bad choices that landed us in prison. None of us arrived by accident, and if we are honest with ourselves, we'll acknowledge a whole series of destructive behaviors that preceded our committal to a "monastery of the damned."

In view of status and our chances of success upon release, the future doesn't look particularly bright. It's damn depressing to have to accept our collective reality. Hope is found in beating the system, the smart way. The smart way is not the path many of us have continually taken: defiance, conflict with "the man." AA members are familiar with the slogan "I can only change myself, not others." It is always easier to project blame for our inade-

quacies onto others. But until we come to terms with our individual reality; separate the crime from the man, decide that the "I am" is capable of much more than the label implies—we're doomed to failure.

The administration uses education statistics to create the illusion of massive programming. It is up to us to demand the delivery. Enroll in courses. Develop the thirst to learn. Ask for help from peer tutors. An education is the ultimate form of restorative justice. The entire population benefits when just one con becomes literate. Educated cons have reason to lift their heads in self-assurance. We are better able to articulate our needs, better able to negotiate collectively, better able to see a future for ourselves.

Whether "the man" wants to acknowledge it or not, educated prisoners get respect from everybody inside and outside the prison. Adult education and training at every level—whether basic literacy, high school, college or university—are vital. The positive skills we learn in prison can't be taken away from us at the gate.

Joseph E. McCormick

The Offender Speaks presents offenders describing in their own words their experiences and reactions to the correctional system.

Job Ads focus on selected employment offerings from the wide range of opportunities in the field of corrections.

Career Profile highlights the training, educational background, and job responsibilities of current corrections professionals.

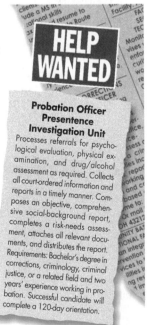

Probation Officer Presentence Investigation Unit
Processes referrals for psychological evaluation, physical examination, and drug/alcohol assessment as required. Collects all court-ordered information and reports in a timely manner. Composes an objective, comprehensive social-background report, completes a risk-needs assessment, attaches all relevant documents, and distributes the report. Requirements: Bachelor's degree in corrections, criminology, criminal justice, or a related field and two years' experience working in probation. Successful candidate will complete a 120-day orientation.

CAREER PROFILE

Quentin X. Escott
Deputy Sheriff
Jefferson County
Birmingham, Alabama

"When I work with an inmate and help him change his life, it's extremely gratifying. But the inmate has to want to change. He has to want help. I can't force it. A lot of prisoners want to know you'll help them and give them a chance. That's all."

Quentin X. Escott has been a deputy sheriff for 1½ years. He is currently assigned to the county jail booking area. His responsibilities include searching incoming prisoners, using the computer imaging system to take inmate photographs and fingerprints, recording personal property, exchanging civilian clothes for jail clothes, and assigning prisoners to housing areas based on their charge classifications.

Deputy Escott has completed almost two years at Lawson State Community College. He is transferring to the University of Alabama at Birmingham, where he will major in criminal justice.

His advice to persons interested in working in a jail? "Treat people like you want to be treated. Yeah, they're prisoners and they broke the law. For that they're in here for punishment. But if I'm going to like my job I have to get along with everybody, prisoners and staff. That means treating everyone with respect and hopefully getting it back in return." For Deputy Escott, the most gratifying part of the job is helping an inmate who really wants help.

Reviewing and Applying Chapter Concepts

End-of-chapter exercises and activities encourage students to apply what they have learned.

Summary by Chapter Objectives sums up the chapter's major themes. The summary is organized by chapter objectives and provides students with general answers to the questions they posed when they began the chapter.

Questions for Review reexamine key points presented in the chapter. These questions test students' knowledge of the chapter concepts and can help them review for exams.

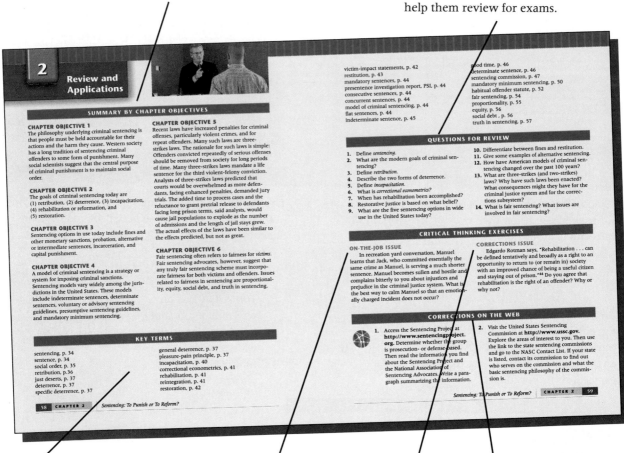

2 Review and Applications

SUMMARY BY CHAPTER OBJECTIVES

CHAPTER OBJECTIVE 1
The philosophy underlying criminal sentencing is that people must be held accountable for their actions and the harm they cause. Western society has a long tradition of sentencing criminal offenders to some form of punishment. Many social scientists suggest that the central purpose of criminal punishment is to maintain social order.

CHAPTER OBJECTIVE 2
The goals of criminal sentencing today are (1) retribution, (2) deterrence, (3) incapacitation, (4) rehabilitation or reformation, and (5) restoration.

CHAPTER OBJECTIVE 3
Sentencing options in use today include fines and other monetary sanctions, probation, alternative or intermediate sentences, incarceration, and capital punishment.

CHAPTER OBJECTIVE 4
A model of criminal sentencing is a strategy or system for imposing criminal sanctions. Sentencing models vary widely among the jurisdictions in the United States. These models include indeterminate sentences, determinate sentences, voluntary or advisory sentencing guidelines, presumptive sentencing guidelines, and mandatory minimum sentencing.

CHAPTER OBJECTIVE 5
Recent laws have increased penalties for criminal offenses, particularly violent crimes, and for repeat offenders. Many such laws are three-strikes laws. The rationale for such laws is simple: Offenders convicted repeatedly of serious offenses should be removed from society for long periods of time. Many three-strikes laws mandate a life sentence for the third violent-felony conviction. Analysts of three-strikes laws predicted that courts would be overwhelmed as more defendants, facing enhanced penalties, demanded jury trials. The added time to process cases and the reluctance to grant pretrial release to defendants facing long prison terms, said analysts, would cause jail populations to explode as the number of admissions and the length of jail stays grew. The actual effects of the laws have been similar to the effects predicted, but not as great.

CHAPTER OBJECTIVE 6
Fair sentencing often refers to fairness for *victims*. Fair sentencing advocates, however, suggest that any truly fair sentencing scheme must incorporate fairness for both victims and offenders. Issues related to fairness in sentencing are proportionality, equity, social debt, and truth in sentencing.

KEY TERMS

sentencing, p. 34
sentence, p. 34
social order, p. 35
retribution, p.36
just deserts, p. 37
deterrence, p. 37
specific deterrence, p. 37

general deterrence, p. 37
pleasure-pain principle, p. 37
incapacitation, p. 40
correctional econometrics, p. 41
rehabilitation, p. 41
reintegration, p. 41
restoration, p. 42

victim-impact statements, p. 42
restitution, p. 43
mandatory sentences, p. 44
presentence investigation report, PSI, p. 44
consecutive sentences, p. 44
concurrent sentences, p. 44
model of criminal sentencing, p. 44
flat sentences, p. 44
indeterminate sentence, p. 45

good time, p. 46
determinate sentence, p. 46
sentencing commission, p. 47
mandatory minimum sentencing, p. 50
habitual offender statute, p. 52
fair sentencing, p. 54
proportionality, p. 55
equity, p. 56
social debt , p. 56
truth in sentencing, p. 57

QUESTIONS FOR REVIEW

1. Define *sentencing*.
2. What are the modern goals of criminal sentencing?
3. Define *retribution*.
4. Describe the two forms of deterrence.
5. Define *incapacitation*.
6. What is *correctional econometrics?*
7. When has rehabilitation been accomplished?
8. Restorative justice is based on what belief?
9. What are the five sentencing options in wide use in the United States today?
10. Differentiate between fines and restitution.
11. Give some examples of alternative sentencing.
12. How have American models of criminal sentencing changed over the past 100 years?
13. What are three-strikes (and two-strikes) laws? Why have such laws been enacted? What consequences might they have for the criminal justice system and for the corrections subsystem?
14. What is fair sentencing? What issues are involved in fair sentencing?

CRITICAL THINKING EXERCISES

ON-THE-JOB ISSUE
In recreation yard conversation, Manuel learns that Jack, who committed essentially the same crime as Manuel, is serving a much shorter sentence. Manuel becomes sullen and hostile and complains bitterly to you about injustices and prejudice in the criminal justice system. What is the best way to calm Manuel so that an emotionally charged incident does not occur?

CORRECTIONS ISSUE
Edgardo Rotman says, "Rehabilitation . . . can be defined tentatively and broadly as a right to an opportunity to return to (or remain in) society with an improved chance of being a useful citizen and staying out of prison."[44] Do you agree that rehabilitation is the right of an offender? Why or why not?

CORRECTIONS ON THE WEB

1. Access the Sentencing Project at **http://www.sentencingproject. org.** Determine whether the group is prosecution- or defense-based. Then read the information you find about the Sentencing Project and the National Association of Sentencing Advocates. Write a paragraph summarizing the information.

2. Visit the United States Sentencing Commission at **http://www.ussc.gov.** Explore the areas of interest to you. Then use the link to the state sentencing commissions and go to the NASC Contact List. If your state is listed, contact its commission to find out who serves on the commission and what the basic sentencing philosophy of the commission is.

Key Terms listing consolidates the corrections vocabulary presented in the chapter. If students can't remember what a term means, the page reference alerts them to the location of its definition in the chapter.

On-the-Job Issues present workplace scenarios that encourage students to apply chapter concepts and develop decision-making skills.

Corrections Issues provide topics of concern in the corrections field that encourage students to develop critical thinking skills.

Corrections on the Web activities encourage students to learn from the vast array of information available on the Internet.

Other Ways for Students to Learn

To help students in learning and applying corrections concepts, the *Corrections in the 21st Century* instructional program provides several study resources in addition to the textbook.

Tutorial With Simulation Applications CD-ROM

A browser-based version of the textbook on CD-ROM includes key terms review, practice tests, and review games. Simulations present real-world situations for students to apply chapter concepts.

Interactive Browser-Based Content Chapter content is delivered in html format with topic search capabilities and links to other chapters.

Application Simulations Chapter concepts and issues are explored and applied through application simulations, which pose real-world situations to which students are asked to respond. Students receive immediate feedback regarding the appropriateness of their choices.

Chapter Review Game A chapter review program in a game format helps you prepare for tests and quizzes.

Glencoe Online If you have Internet access, clicking on this button will start up a browser and connect to the Glencoe *Corrections in the 21st Century* Study Center Web Site.

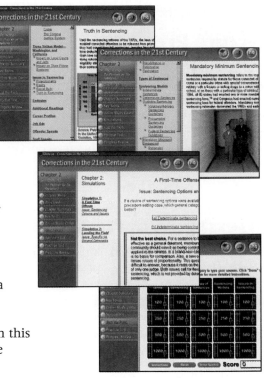

Corrections in the 21st Century Study Center Web Site

This unique study center site contains a wealth of current event material and multiple reinforcement and assessment tools. Visit it at: **http://www.corrections.glencoe.com**. Here is what you will find:

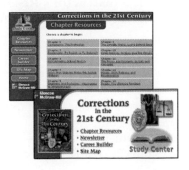

Chapter Resources

- Practice Tests
- Crossword Puzzles
- Concentration Games
- Interactive Exercises

- E-homework
- New Items
- Links to Corrections sites

Newsletter
Career Builder
Site Map

Instructor Resources

Instructor's Presentation and Student Assessment Software CD-ROM

This CD-ROM contains a suite of software products that allow the instructor to conduct an engaging interactive classroom presentation and assess students' understanding of fundamental concepts.

Lecture Presentation Software

A **PowerPoint Lecture Presentation Program** contains over **2000 illustrated lecture screens, graphics,** and **full-color images** that are designed to introduce or reinforce concepts in the classroom.

Integrated into the presentation are **32 topical simulation** modules which apply chapter concepts or dramatize an issue presented in the text.

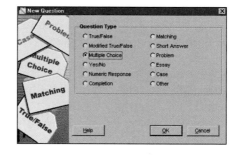

Assessment Software

The *ExamView* **Pro 3.0 Test Generator** allows the instructor to choose from a question bank of 1500 questions and add, delete, or edit questions as desired. Instructors can quickly create printed tests, Internet tests, and computer-based tests. The *ExamView* Pro 3.0 Test Generator offers many unique features, including the QuickTest Wizard, a sophisticated word processor, and numerous test layout and printing options.

Instructor's Resource Manual

The **Instructor's Resource Manual** (IRM) contains a variety of resources for the instructor. Included are the following:

- Sample Course Schedules
- SCANS Correlation Chart
- Chapter Lecture Outlines
- Additional Student Activities
- Answers to End-of-Chapter Exercises
- PowerPoint Notes
- Student Tutorial Notes
- Notes for Using the Video Library

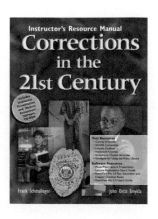

Instructor's Annotated Edition

The **Instructor's Annotated Edition** (IAE) is designed to assist the instructor in creating a dynamic learning atmosphere. **Instructional strategies** for applying concepts, analyzing data, delving into issues, and generating discussion appear as annotations in the text margins.

Professional Issue annotations focus on issues of concern to corrections professionals such as safety, liability, and compensation.

Student Involvement annotations suggest activities to encourage student participation in their learning.

Teaching Tip annotations suggest strategies for developing or reinforcing concepts or for emphasizing an important point.

Cross-Cultural Perspective annotations suggest strategies to build multicultural understanding.

Glencoe *Corrections in the 21st Century* Instructor Web Site

The **Instructor's Web site** contains downloadable resources specifically designed for instructors of *Corrections in the 21st Century.*

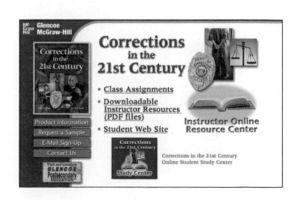

Course Web Site Development

    PageOut™ is a course Web site development tool available to instructors who adopt *Corrections in the 21st Century.* PageOut allows instructors to create their own personal Web site complete with a unique URL to give to their students. Using an Internet browser, instructors follow the course creation templates in the process of building a custom course Web site.

Setup
Creates a custom course site with school, course name, and course description.

Student List
Registers students for the course and manages the classroom roster.

Gradebook
Allows instructors to create and edit assignments and manage course grades.

Web Links
Allows instructors to post annotated Web links to integrate use of the Internet.

Instructor Info
Posts instructor information and notices.

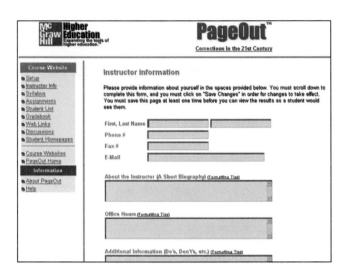

Student Homepages
Allows students to create own Web pages monitored by the instructor.

Syllabus
Displays information about the course.

Assignments
Allows instructors to post assignments.

Discussions
Allows instructors to hold threaded discussions with students.

Glencoe's Criminal Justice Video Library

    The **Glencoe Criminal Justice Video Library** helps make concepts and issues come alive in the classroom. All of the videos are available from Glencoe/McGraw-Hill. Qualified adopters of *Corrections in the 21st Century* are eligible to receive selections free of charge. Local Glencoe/McGraw-Hill representative or regional offices have the details.

Program Components

Components	ISBN
Student Text	0-02-802567-9
Student Text With Simulation Applications CD-ROM	0-02-802574-1
Tutorial With Simulation Applications CD-ROM	0-02-802573-3
Instructor's Presentation and Student Assessment Software	0-02-802572-5
Instructor's Annotated Edition	0-02-802568-7
Instructor's Resource Manual	0-07-821387-8
Glencoe *Corrections in the 21st Century* Study Center Web Site	
Glencoe *Corrections in the 21st Century* Instructor Web Site	
Glencoe Criminal Justice Video Library	
PageOut™ Course Web Site Development Tool	

Please contact your local account manager for more information. Special packages, including state-specific supplements, are available for adopters in California and Texas. In California, call 1-800-423-9534; in Texas, call 1-800-257-5785.

To order or request examination copies call 1-800-334-7344.
For additional information contact your Regional Office.

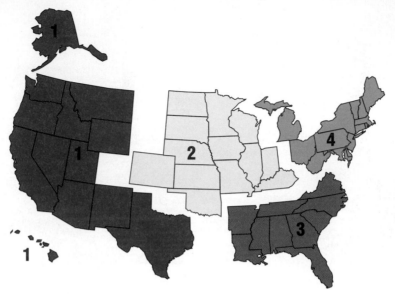

1 **West Region**
Glencoe/McGraw-Hill
21600 Oxnard Street, Suite 500
Woodland Hills, CA 91367
Phone: 800-423-9534
Fax: 818-615-2697
AK, AZ, CA, HI, ID, MT, NM, NV, OR, TX, UT,
WA, WY

2 **Mid-Continent Region**
Glencoe/McGraw-Hill
1415 Elbridge Payne Rd.
Suite 180
Chesterfield, MO 63017-8522
Phone: 636-530-9942
Fax: 636-530-9034
CO, IA, IL, IN, KS, KY, MN, MO, ND, NE, OK,
SD, WI

3 **Southeast Region**
Glencoe/McGraw-Hill
3100 Breckinridge Blvd.
Building 100, Suite 105
Duluth, GA 30096
Phone: 770-717-7007
Fax: 770-717-7422
AL, AR, FL, GA, LA, MS, NC, SC, TN, VA

4 **East Region**
Glencoe/McGraw-Hill
8787 Orion Place
Columbus, OH 43240-4027
Phone: 800-848-1567 Ext. 4990
Fax: 614-430-4999
CT, DC, DE, MA, MD, ME, MI, NH, NJ, NY, OH,
PA, RI, VT, WV

Glencoe
McGraw-Hill

Glencoe/McGraw-Hill
P.O. Box 508
Columbus, OH 43216

*A Division of The **McGraw·Hill** Companies*

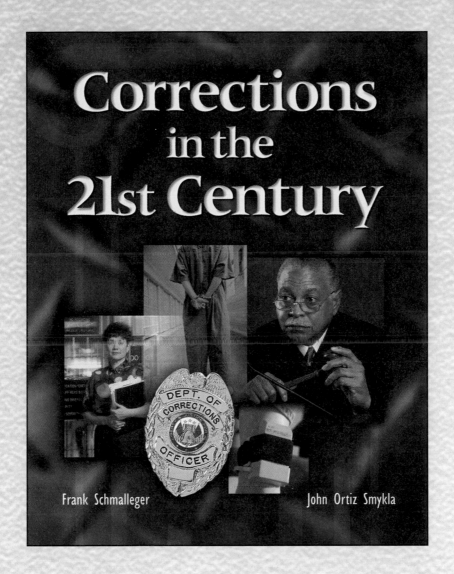

Corrections
in the
21st Century

Frank Schmalleger   John Ortiz Smykla

Frank Schmalleger, Ph.D.
Director
The Justice Research Association

John Ortiz Smykla, Ph.D.
Professor, Department of Criminal Justice
The University of Alabama

Glencoe
McGraw-Hill

New York, New York   Columbus, Ohio   Woodland Hills, California   Peoria, Illinois

Library of Congress Cataloging-in-Publication Data

Schmalleger, Frank.
   Corrections in the 21st century / Frank Schmalleger, John Ortiz Smykla.
     p. cm.
   Includes bibliographical references and index.
   ISBN 0-02-802567-9
    1. Corrections--Vocational guidance--United States. I. Smykla, John Ortiz. II. Title.

   HV9471 .S36 2000
   364.6'023'73--dc21

                                           99-054915

Glencoe/McGraw-Hill
A Division of The **McGraw·Hill** Companies

Corrections in the 21st Century
Student Text

Copyright 2001 by The McGraw-Hill Companies. All rights reserved. Except as permitted under
the United States Copyright Act, no part of this publication may be reproduced or distributed in
any form or by any means, or stored in a database or retrieval system, without prior written
permission of the publisher.

Send all inquiries to:
Glencoe/McGraw-Hill
21600 Oxnard Street
Woodland Hills, CA 91367

ISBN 0-02-802567-9 (student text)
ISBN 0-02-802574-1 (student text with tutorial CD-ROM)

Printed in the United States of America.

1 2 3 4 5 6 7 8 9 10   027   07 06 05 04 03 02 01 00

Brief Contents

Expanded Contents

2

Sentencing: To Punish or To Reform?　32

3 · Punishments: A Brief History   62

4 Jails: Way Stations Along the Justice Highway   88

5 Diversion and Probation: Alternatives to Imprisonment 122

8   The Staff World: Managing the Prison Population   220

9 The Inmate World: Living Behind Bars 246

11 The Prison Environment: Issues and Concerns 308

14 Juvenile Corrections: End of an Era? 400

15 The Victim: Role in the Correctional Process 426

16 Careers: Your Future in Corrections 452

Inside Your Book

This book was designed for you to help you learn. It contains 16 chapters, divided into sections. This structure, together with numerous special features, helps you learn and apply the concepts that can help lead you to a career as a corrections professional.

Previewing Chapter Concepts

The chapter opener introduces the key concepts to be learned.

The **opening photograph** sets the stage for the chapter content and provides a visual connection to the chapter.

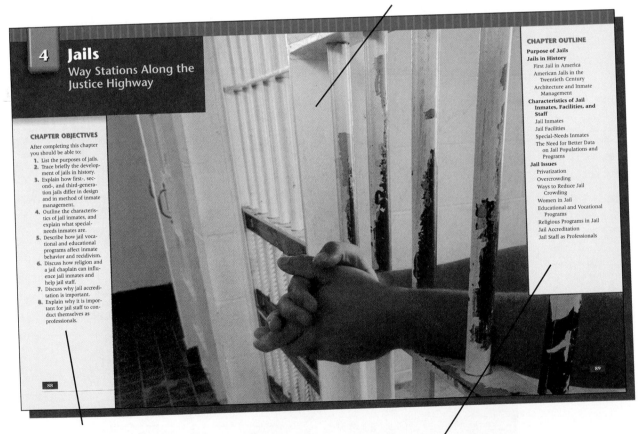

4 Jails
Way Stations Along the Justice Highway

CHAPTER OBJECTIVES

After completing this chapter you should be able to:

1. List the purposes of jails.
2. Trace briefly the development of jails in history.
3. Explain how first-, second-, and third-generation jails differ in design and in method of inmate management.
4. Outline the characteristics of jail inmates, and explain what special-needs inmates are.
5. Describe how jail vocational and educational programs affect inmate behavior and recidivism.
6. Discuss how religion and a jail chaplain can influence jail inmates and help jail staff.
7. Discuss why jail accreditation is important.
8. Explain why it is important for jail staff to conduct themselves as professionals.

CHAPTER OUTLINE

Purpose of Jails
Jails in History
  First Jail in America
  American Jails in the Twentieth Century
  Architecture and Inmate Management
Characteristics of Jail Inmates, Facilities, and Staff
  Jail Inmates
  Jail Facilities
  Special-Needs Inmates
  The Need for Better Data on Jail Populations and Programs
Jail Issues
  Privatization
  Overcrowding
  Ways to Reduce Jail Crowding
  Women in Jail
  Educational and Vocational Programs
  Religious Programs in Jail
  Jail Accreditation
  Jail Staff as Professionals

88

89

Chapter objectives alert you to the major concepts to learn. Turn the objectives into questions, and, as you read the chapter, look for the answers to the questions.

A **chapter outline** introduces the topics that will be discussed. Scan the outline to familiarize yourself with the subject matter.

Developing Chapter Concepts

The chapter text explains correctional concepts in a structured, visual format and provides a comprehensive overview of correctional practices.

The **heading structure** shows the relationship among the topics in a section and breaks the material into easily digestible segments of information. Scan the headings to locate the information that will help you answer the questions you formed from the chapter objectives.

Concepts are depicted in **visual format** to make them easier to understand.

Jail Issues

Jail administration and staffs face many important issues for the twenty-first century. We will now consider some of these issues and their effects on corrections professionals.

Privatization

Jails can be privatized in whole or in part. Jails can be financed, built, and operated by private groups, or jails can contract out some of their services (e.g., food service, mental health care, and programming).

One of the most hotly debated issues about privatization deals with the limits of governmental delegation of power and liability. Opponents of privatization believe that the administration of justice is a basic function of government and a symbol of state authority and should not be delegated.

Opponents also fear that if we privatize jails, we risk letting private corporations use their political influence to continue programs not in the public interest. For example, would private contractors keep jail occupancy rates high to maintain profit? Might private contractors accept only the best inmates, leaving the most troublesome for public facilities to handle? Turning a jail over to a private corporation also raises questions about accountability. Who is responsible for monitoring the performance of the private contractor? Who will see that local laws and regulations are followed? As jail incarceration rates continue to rise, the debate over privatizing jails and the competition for new contracts will continue.

Overcrowding

Overcrowding is a problem that all jails, especially large urban jails, have to deal with. The number of persons held in local jails grew 4.5 percent from 1997 to 1998. The increase in the rate of jail incarceration is staggering. Between 1985 and 1998, the rate doubled—from 108 per 100,000 adults to 219. Overcrowding has a number of causes, including mandatory arrests and sentences, overcrowding at state and federal prisons, and an overall increase in the arrest rate as politicians "get tough" on crime. Crowded jails have serious health and safety consequences for staff and inmates, including decreased quality of life; overloaded educational, vocational, and recreational programs; insufficient medical services and supplies; increased discipline problems; spread of disease; and staff and inmate assaults.

Ways to Reduce Jail Crowding

Practices that can reduce crowding include financial and nonfinancial pretrial release, diversion, and new jail construction.

release on bail The release of a person upon that person's financial guarantee to appear in court.

Financial Pretrial Release Financial pretrial release programs are one alternative to the pretrial detention of accused offenders. Releasing a person upon that person's financial guarantee to appear in court is known as **release on bail**. The Eighth Amendment to the United States Constitution reads, "Excessive bail shall not be required, nor excessive fines imposed, nor

Jails: Way Stations Along the Justice Highway

FIGURE 7–2

Persons Held in State or Federal Prisons

How Many Are in Prison?

9% Federal Prisoners
91% State Prisoners

1,178,978 State Prisoners
123,041 Federal Prisoners
1,302,019 Total

Who Is in Prison?

Gender
6.5% Women
93.5% Men

Race/Ethnicity*
1.1% American Indian/ Alaska Native
48.3% White
48.9% Black
1.7% Asian/Pacific Islander

*Hispanics may be of any race

Age
18.4% 18–24
10.3% 45–54
3.3% 55 or older
29.5% 35–44
38.1% 25–34
0.4% 17 or younger

Why Are They in Prison?

State Prisoners
47% Violent Offenses
21% Drug Offenses
10% Public Order Offenses
22% Property Offenses

Federal Prisoners
60% Drug Offenses
19% Public Order Offenses
12% Violent Offenses
8% Property Offenses
1% Unspecified

Source: Allen J. Beck and Christopher J. Mumola, *Prisoners in 1998* (Washington: Bureau of Justice Statistics, August 1999).

Key terms are also defined in the margin to make it easy for you to learn them.

Key terms are defined when introduced and are printed in boldface to make them easy to find.

Reinforcing Chapter Concepts

In-text examples, graphics, and special features enhance and strengthen your learning about major concepts and practices in corrections.

Policy implications alert you to the issues facing corrections professionals.

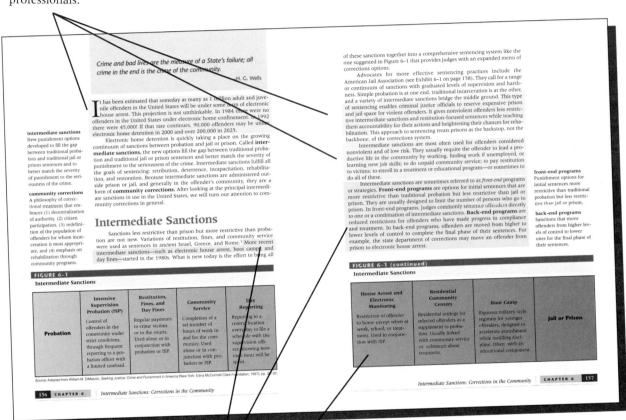

Examples help you understand the concepts being presented.

Graphics reinforce important concepts.

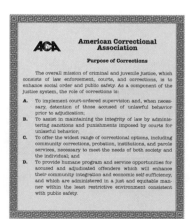

Chapter content focuses on developing professionalism among corrections practitioners.

Special features reinforce effective correctional practices and professional skills.

The Staff Speaks presents corrections professionals describing in their own words their work in the corrections profession.

The Offender Speaks presents offenders describing in their own words their experiences and reactions to the correctional system.

Career Profile highlights the training, educational background, and job responsibilities of current corrections professionals.

Job Ads focus on selected employment offerings from the wide range of opportunities in the field of corrections.

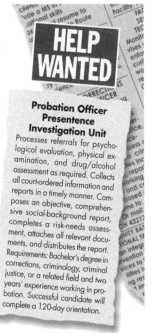

Reviewing and Applying Chapter Concepts

End-of-chapter exercises and activities encourage you to apply what you have learned.

Summary by Chapter Objectives sums up the chapter's major themes. The summary is organized by chapter objectives and provides you with general answers to the questions you posed when you began the chapter.

Questions for Review reexamine key points presented in the chapter. These questions test your knowledge of the chapter concepts and can help you review for exams.

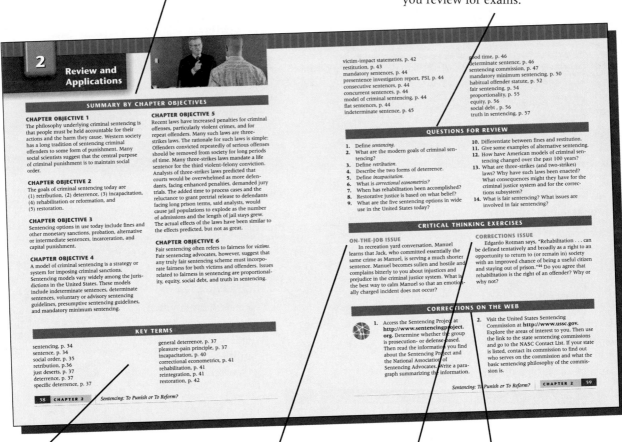

Key Terms listing consolidates the corrections vocabulary presented in the chapter. If you can't remember what a term means, the page reference alerts you to the location of its definition in the chapter.

On-the-Job Issues present workplace scenarios that encourage you to apply chapter concepts and develop decision-making skills.

Corrections Issues provide topics of concern in the corrections field that encourage you to develop critical thinking skills.

Corrections on the Web activities encourage you to learn from the vast array of information available on the Internet.

Other Ways for You to Learn

To assist you in learning and applying corrections concepts, the *Corrections in the 21st Century* instructional program provides several study resources in addition to the textbook.

Tutorial With Simulation Applications CD-ROM

A browser-based version of the textbook on CD-ROM includes key terms review, practice tests, and review games. Simulations present real-world situations for you to apply chapter concepts.

Interactive Browser-Based Content
Chapter content is delivered in html format with topic search capabilities and links to other chapters.

Application Simulations
Chapter concepts and issues are explored and applied through application simulations, which pose real-world situations to which you are asked to respond. You receive immediate feedback regarding the appropriateness of your choices.

Chapter Review Game
A chapter review program in a game format helps you prepare for tests and quizzes.

Glencoe Online
If you have Internet access, clicking on this button will start up a browser and connect to the Glencoe *Corrections in the 21st Century* Study Center Web Site.

Corrections in the 21st Century
Study Center Web Site

This unique study center site contains a wealth of current event material and multiple reinforcement and assessment tools. Visit it at: **http://www.corrections.glencoe.com**. Here is what you will find:

Chapter Resources
- Practice Tests
- Crossword Puzzles
- Concentration Games
- Interactive Exercises
- E-homework
- New Items
- Links to Corrections sites

Student Newsletter
Career Builder
Site Map

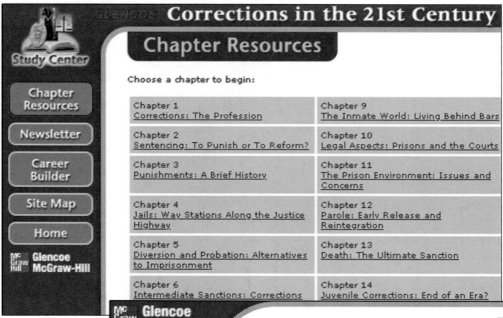

How to Study Corrections

Corrections in the 21st Century is divided into 16 chapters and is organized to provide a logical approach to understanding how the corrections system operates in the United States. Chapter 1 contains important background information for topics presented elsewhere in the book. It presents a brief overview of the criminal justice system, with emphasis on the role of corrections in the system. Chapter 1 also introduces the theme of professionalism that is carried throughout the text.

Chapter 2 discusses the goals of sentencing and describes the types of punishments imposed on convicted offenders. Chapter 3 presents a brief history of punishments for crime and explains how incarceration came to be used as a criminal punishment. Chapters 4, 5, 6, and 7 focus on the institutional and non-institutional ways of punishing criminals. Chapters 8, 9, 10, and 11 describe the people and environments of living behind bars. Chapter 12 focuses on the concerns of early release and reintegration into society. Chapter 13 discusses the issues of the ultimate punishment, the death penalty. Chapter 14 focuses on juvenile corrections; Chapter 15 on victims; and Chapter 16 on careers in corrections.

Corrections, like any other course, builds in stages. Information presented in later chapters often assumes knowledge of information introduced in earlier chapters. You cannot afford to fall behind and then expect to catch up in one massive cramming session.

To get off to a good start, prepare yourself before the course begins by setting learning goals, organizing your time, studying your syllabus, and examining your own learning style.

Set Learning Goals for Yourself

The purpose of setting goals is to understand exactly what you plan to accomplish. Ask yourself what you want out of this course. Is it a specific grade? Perhaps you need an A or a B to keep up your grade average. Perhaps you need a certain body of knowledge from this course to get into a higher level course. Perhaps you need a specific set of skills. You may be taking this course to meet a requirement for your job, to attain a personal career goal, or simply to satisfy your curiosity about the subject. Be forewarned, however: if you set your goals too low, you are likely to achieve only those low goals. For example, if you are not interested in the course but are taking it only because it is required of all majors, you should not be disappointed if you earn less than an A or a B.

Organize Your Time

Now that you have set your goals, you need to organize your time to accomplish them. Time management allows you to meet your goals and still have time for activities. It helps you work smarter, not just harder. As a rule of thumb, for every class hour, allow two study hours. If an exam is coming up, allow more study time. Plan to study when you are most alert. You will retain information longer if you study on a regular basis, rather than during one or two cramming sessions. Either before or after a study session, have some fun! Timely breaks from studying enhance the learning process.

Study Your Syllabus

Usually the course syllabus is available on the first day of class, but sometimes it is available sooner. If you can get a copy early, you will be that much ahead. The syllabus is your map for navigating the course. It should define the goals or objectives of the course, specify the textbook and supporting materials to be used, and explain course requirements, including the method or formula for determining final grades. The syllabus will also include a course schedule indicating when particular topics will be covered, what material needs to be read for each class, and when tests will be given. Other useful information on a course syllabus may include the instructor's name, office location, phone number, and office hours and, perhaps, the types of extra credit or special projects you may complete. Keep the syllabus in your notebook or organizer at all times. Review it at the beginning of each class and study session so you will know what course material will be covered and what you will be expected to know. Write down important due dates and test dates on your calendar.

Eight-Step Study Plan to Maximize Your Learning

This plan is based on research that shows that people learn—and remember—best when they have repeated exposure to the same material. This technique not only helps you learn better but can also reduce anxiety by allowing you to become familiar with material step by step. You will go over material at least six times before you take an exam.

Step 1: Use a Reading Strategy

In most cases, you will be asked to read material before each class. The SQ3R (Survey, Question, Read, Recite, and Review) method can help you get the most out of the material in every chapter of your book. Reading the material before class will acquaint you with the subject matter, arouse your interest in the subject, and help you know what questions to ask in class.

Survey   By surveying an assignment, you are preparing yourself for a more thorough reading of the material.

Read the Chapter Title, the Chapter Objectives, and the Chapter Outline   What topics does the chapter cover? What are the learning objectives? Do you already know something about the subject?

Read the Summary by Chapter Objectives   This will give you an overview of what is covered in the chapter.

Look for Key Terms   Key terms are the words associated with the important concepts covered in the chapter. Key terms are printed in boldface type in the text. Definitions of the key terms appear in the margins near the text in which they are introduced.

Question   Turn the chapter objectives into questions. For example, if the objective is, "Explain prisoner classification and its purposes." turn it into a question by asking yourself, "What is prisoner classification and what are its purposes?" Look for the answers to your questions as you read the chapter. By beginning the study of a chapter with questions, you will be more moti-

SQ3R Reading System

Letter	Meaning	Reading Activity
S	Survey	Survey the assigned reading material. Pay attention to the title, objectives, outline, key terms, and summary.
Q	Question	Find the major heads. Try to make questions out of these heads.
3 R	(1) Read	Read the material, section by section.
	(2) Recite	After reading a section or part, try to briefly summarize aloud what you have read. Make sure your summary answers the question you formed for the section's head.
	(3) Review	After reading the entire assigned material, review your question heads. Make sure you can recall your original question and your answers. If you cannot, go back and reread that section.

vated to read the chapter to find the answers. To make sure your answers are correct, consult the summary at the end of the chapter.

You can also write a question mark in pencil in the margin next to any material you don't understand as you read the chapter. Your goal is to answer all your questions and erase the question marks before you take an exam.

Read Before you begin a thorough reading of the material, make sure that you are rested and alert and that your reading area is well-lighted and ventilated. This will not only make your reading time more efficient but help you understand what you read.

Skim the Material Generally, you will need to read material more than once before you really understand it. Start by skimming, or reading straight through, the material. Do not expect to understand everything at once. You are getting the big picture and becoming familiar with the material.

Read, Highlight, Outline The second time, read more slowly. Take time to study explanations and examples. Highlight key terms, important concepts, numbered lists, or other items that will help you understand the material. Most students use colored highlighting markers for this step. Put question marks in pencil in the margin beside any points or concepts you don't understand.

Outline the chapter in your notebook. By writing the concepts and definitions into your notebook, you are using your tactile sense to reinforce your learning and to remember better what you read. Be sure you state concepts and definitions accurately. You can use brief phrases or take more extensive notes for your outline, depending on the material.

Apply What You Read In criminal justice, as in other courses, you must be able to apply what you read. The critical thinking exercises at the end of each chapter allow you to do this. Complete those exercises when you have finished studying the chapter.

Recite In this step, you do a self-check of what you have learned in reading the chapter. Go back to the questions you formed from the chapter objectives and see if you can answer them. Also, see if you can answer the Questions for Review at the end of each chapter. Try explaining the material to a friend so that he or she understands it. These exercises will reveal your strengths and weaknesses.

Review Now go back and review the entire chapter. Erase any question marks that you have answered. If you still don't understand something, put a Post-it by it or mark it in your text. These items are the questions you can ask in class.

Step 2: Combine Learning Styles in Class

Think of the time you spend in class as your opportunity to learn by listening and participating. You are combining many learning styles in one experience. Knowing your preferred learning styles can increase your effectiveness in school or at work. Look at the chart on page 00 to determine your preferred learning styles.

Attendance: More Than Just Showing Up
Your attitude is a critical element. Attend class *ready to learn*. That means being prepared by having read and reread the assignment, having your questions ready, and having your note-taking materials organized.

Because corrections, like other courses, builds in stages, it is important for you to attend every class. You cannot ask questions if you are not there. And you may miss handouts, explanations, or key points that often are included on a test.

One final note. If you cannot attend a class, call the instructor or a classmate to find out what you have missed. You do not want to show up the next day and find out the instructor is giving a test!

Attention: Active Listening and Learning
During most classes, you spend more time listening than you do reading, writing, or speaking. Learning by listening, however, calls for you to become an active listener and to participate in the class. Here are some active listening strategies for you to implement:

Desire to Listen You must want to be a better listener and realize that listening is an active rather than a passive process.

TYPE OF INTELLIGENCE	CHARACTERISTICS	LEARNER LIKES
Verbal/Linguistic Learner	Learns through words and language, written and spoken. Loves to read and write. Also tends to enjoy talking.	reading; answering questions; writing essays; discussion groups; playing word games
Logical/Mathematical Learner	Looks for patterns when solving problems. Creates a set of standards and follows them when researching in a sequential manner.	problem solving; experiments; working with numbers; asking questions; exploring patterns and relationships
Visual/Spatial Learner	Relies on sense of sight and being able to visualize an object, to create mental images. Learns through pictures, charts, graphs, diagrams, and art.	drawing, building, designing, creating things; jig saw puzzles; daydreaming; watching videos; looking at photos; drawing maps and charts
Kinesthetic/Bodily Learner	Learning is related to physical movement and the brain's motor cortex, which controls bodily motion. Eager to solve problems physically.	hands-on methods; demonstrating skill in crafts; tinkering; displaying physical endurance; performing; challenging self physically
Interpersonal Learner	Likes group work and working cooperatively to solve problems. Learns through person-to-person relationships and communication.	talking to people; joining groups; playing cooperative games; solving problems as part of a group; volunteering help when others need it.
Intrapersonal Learner	Enjoys opportunity to reflect and work independently. Often would rather work on his or her own than in a group.	working alone; pursuing own interests; daydreaming; keeping a journal or diary; independent assignments
Naturalistic Learner	Learns by observing, understanding, and organizing patterns in the natural environment. Has a strong connection to nature.	observing the world around them; spending time outdoors and working with plants, animals, and other parts of the natural environment
Musical/Rhythmic Learner	Recognizes tonal patterns, including various environmental sounds. Has a sensitivity to rhythm and beats.	Singing and humming; listening to music; playing an instruments; moving body when music is playing, making up songs

Be Open and Willing to Learn   Be open to different points of view, different styles of lecturing, and learning new ideas. Don't make up your mind that the instructor is wrong and that you are going to challenge that is said. It is easy to misinterpret the meaning of a message if you are defensive, bored, judgmental, or emotionally upset.

Postpone Judgment   Don't judge your instructor or his or her message based on clothes, reputation, voice, or teaching style. Go to class with an open mind and focus on the message, the course content, and your performance.

Be mindful   Being mentally and physically alert is vital for active listening. Focus your attention, concentrate on the subject, and keep your mind in the present.

Use Empathy and Respect   Focus on understanding the message and viewpoint of the speaker. Look for common views and ways that you are alike rather than different.

Observe   Observe your instructor and watch for obvious verbal and nonverbal clues about what information is important. Repetition, writing information on the board, and handouts gives clues to important information. Watch for words that signal important information.

Predict and Ask Questions   Keep yourself alert by predicting and asking yourself questions. What are the main points of the lecture? Do the examples clarify the concept? What test questions could be asked about this material?

Look as If You Are Listening   Sit up, keep your spine straight, and uncross your legs. Maintain eye contact, and lean slightly forward. Don't lean back, cross your legs, or look bored. Respond with nods, smiles, and open facial expressions. Participate in discussions or when asked questions.

Reduce Distractions   Don't sit next to friends or someone who likes to talk or is distracting. Sit near the front. Carry a bottle of water with you to sip if your energy starts to lag.

Be Quiet   Be quiet while the instructor is speaking. Don't interrupt or talk to classmates. Really listen until the instructor is finished.

Participation   In reading the material before class, you will have made a list of questions. If those questions are not answered in class, then ask your instructor to answer them. If the instruc-

tor makes a point you do not understand, jot it down and ask him or her to explain it as soon as you can.

Note Taking   Why take notes? We forget nearly 60 percent of what we hear within one hour after we hear it. Memory is highly unreliable. This is why taking notes during class is so important.

Note taking involves both listening and writing at the same time. You must learn not to concentrate too much on one and forget the other. Follow these tips for taking good notes.

Listen for and Record Main Ideas You do not need to write down everything your instructor or other students say. By reading your assignment before class, you will know what the main topics are. Listen for those topics when your instructor goes over the material in class, then take notes on what he or she says about them. If the instructor emphasizes the importance of a topic for a test, be sure to make a note of this information as well (for example, "This section really important for exam"). If you think you have missed a point, either ask your instructor to repeat or rephrase it right away, or mark the point with a question mark and ask your instructor about it later.

Use Outline Style and Abbreviations Set up your notes in outline style, and use phrases instead of complete sentences. Use abbreviations of symbols whenever possible (& for and, w for with, and so on). This technique will help you write faster to keep up with the instructor.

Step 3: Review Class Notes

Listening and taking notes are critical steps in learning, but reviewing your notes is equally important. Remember: Repetition reinforces learning. The more times you go over material, the better you learn it.

Fill in the Blanks   As soon as possible after a class, review your notes to fill in any missing information. Make sure you do it the same day. Sometimes you may be able to recall the missing information. If you can't, check your textbook or ask to see another student's notes to obtain what you need. Spell out important abbreviations that you may not recognize later.

Highlight Important Information Marking different types of information helps organize your notes. You want to find what you need when you need it. Try these suggestions for highlighting your notes.

1. Use different colored highlighting pens to mark key terms, important Supreme Court decisions, and other kinds of information. Then, you will know that green, for example, always indicates key terms; blue indicates Supreme Court decisions; and so on. This method will help you find specific information quickly and easily.
2. Write a heading such as "Costs of Incarceration" at the beginning of each key topic. These headings can either correspond to those in the chapter, or you may make up your own headings to help you remember key information.

Step 4: Reread the Text

After reviewing your notes, you are ready to reread the chapter to fix the concepts in your mind.

Read for Details

- Go over the key points and main ideas carefully. Make sure you understand them thoroughly and can explain them to someone in your own words.
- Review the Chapter Objectives (that you have turned into questions) and the Questions for Review. Make sure you can answer all the questions and that you understand your answers.

Mark Your Text

- Highlight any important terms or concepts you may have missed in your previous reading.
- Highlight any figures or tables you feel contain information that is important to remember.
- Erase any question marks in the margin that represent questions you have answered.
- Use Post-it notes to mark anything of which you are still unsure. Ask questions about those points in the next class, talk them over with other students, or make an appointment to meet with your instructor to discuss your questions.

Step 5: Get Help if Necessary

What if you have read the material, taken notes, and asked questions, and you still do not understand the material? You can get further help. As soon as it becomes apparent that you need some help, ask for it. If you wait until the semester is nearly over, it may be too late. Here are several sources of help.

Your Instructors Most instructors are willing to spend extra time with students who need help. Find out what your instructor's office hours are and schedule an appointment to go over the material in more detail. You may need several sessions. Remember to take notes during those sessions.

Study Groups Join a study group in your class, or start your own. What one person does not learn, another does. Study groups take advantage of each member's expertise. You can often learn best by listening and talking to others in such groups. Chances are that, together, you will be able to master the material better than any one of you could alone. This is an example of power in numbers.

Learning Labs Many schools have learning labs that offer individual instruction or tutoring for students who are having trouble with course material. Ask your instructor or classmates for information about the learning labs in your college or university.

Private Tutors You might consider getting help from a private tutor if you can afford the fee. Although this route will cost you more, it may take only a few sessions to help you understand the material and keep up with the class. Check with your instructor about the availability of private tutors.

Step 6: Study Creatively for Tests

If you have read your assignments, attended class, taken notes and reviewed them, answered the Questions for Review, and completed the Critical Thinking Exercises, then you have been studying for tests all along. This kind of preparation means less stress when test time comes around.

Review: Bringing It All Together   You should enter all exam dates on your calendar so that you know well in advance when to prepare for a test. If you plan extra time for study during the week, you will not have to cram the night before the test.

During that week, bring together all your textbook notes, all your handouts, and other study materials. Reread them, paying particular attention to anything you marked that the instructor emphasized or that you had trouble understanding.

In addition to studying the Summary by Chapter Objectives, Key Terms, and Questions for Review at the end of each chapter, it is a good idea to make a summary sheet of your own that lists all the major points and other information that will be covered on the test. If you have quizzes or tests you have already taken, review them as well. Focus on the material you either missed or did not do well on before.

Do not hesitate to ask the instructor for information about the test, in particular:

- The types of test items he or she will use (multiple-choice, true-false, matching, fill-in-the-blanks, short answer, essay)
- What material, if any, will be emphasized, and what material, if any, will not be included
- How much time you will have to take the test

Step 7: Test-Taking Strategies

No matter how well you prepare for a test, you will feel some anxiety just before and even during the exam. This is natural—everybody feels this way. The guidelines in this section will help you manage your anxiety so that you can do your best.

Before the Test: Get Ready   Use this checklist to help you prepare the night before or a few hours before an exam.

- Gather supplies: unless instructed otherwise, at least 2 sharpened pencils with good erasers, a

watch for timing yourself, and other items if you need them (such as a blue book for essay exams).
- If the test is in your first class, get up at least an hour before the exam to make sure you will be fully awake.
- Eat well before the test, but avoid having a heavy meal, which can make you sleepy.
- Arrive early to review your notes and study materials. Remember: luck favors the prepared!

During the Test: Go for It!   Memorize these strategies to help you during the exam.

- Follow the directions. Listen carefully to the instructor's directions and read the printed directions carefully. Ask questions if the directions are unclear.
- Preview the test. Take a few minutes to look over the entire test. This will give you an idea of how much time to allot to each of the components.
- Do the easier sections first. If you get stumped on a question, skip it for now. You can come back to it later. Finish with the harder sections.
- Go back over the test. If you finish ahead of time, double-check your work and look for careless errors. Make sure your writing is legible if you are taking an essay exam or an exam that requires short answers. Make sure that your name and other information the instructor requires are on the test papers.

Step 8: Reviewing Your Results

Never throw away any of your quizzes or tests. Tests give you direct feedback on your progress in the course. Whether the test is a weekly quiz or a mid-term, do not just look at the grade and put the paper in your file or notebook. Use the results of each quiz or test to help you achieve your goals.

Learn From Your Successes   First review the test for those questions you answered correctly. Ask yourself the following questions:

- What are my strongest areas? You will know which topics to spend less time studying for the next exam.

- What types of items did I find easiest to answer (multiple-choice, true-false, etc.)? You might want to start with these types of items on the next exam, giving you more time to work on the harder items.

Learn From Your Mistakes Look over your errors, and ask yourself these questions:
- What types of items did I miss? Is there a pattern (for instance, true-false items, Supreme Court decisions)?
- Did I misunderstand any items? Was it clear to me what each item was asking for?
- Were my mistakes the result of carelessness? Did I read the items incorrectly or miss details? Did I lose track of time? Was I so engrossed in a test section that I forgot to allow myself enough time to get through the entire test at least once?

Look back through the textbook, your notes, class handouts, and other study materials to help you understand how and why you made the mistakes you did. Ask your instructor or classmates to go over your test with you until you know exactly why you missed the items. Evaluating your errors can show you where you need help and what to watch out for in the next test.

Refine Your Action Plan: The Learning Spiral You can think of the eight-step action plan as an upward spiral. Each time you travel a full cycle of the plan, you accumulate more knowledge and experience. You go one turn higher on the spiral.

Use your test feedback and classroom work to help you refine your plan. Perhaps you need to spend more time reading the textbook or reviewing key terms. Perhaps you did not allow enough time for study during the week. Or you might need extra help from your instructor, your classmates, or tutors. Make adjustments in your plan as you tackle the next part of the course.

Acknowledgments

Writing a textbook requires a great deal of help and support. We would like to acknowledge and thank the many individuals on whom we relied. Special thanks go to Dennis Stevens at the University of Massachusetts at Boston for his research on the special features and to Jody Klein-Saffran at the Federal Bureau of Prisons and Gary Bayens at Washburn University for their contributions to Chapters 12 (Parole) and Chapter 14 (Juvenile Corrections), respectively. We also gratefully acknowledge the contributions of the following individuals who helped in the development of textbook.

Tom Austin
Shippensburg University
Shippensburg, PA

Sharon Beck
University of Alabama at
   Birmingham
Birmingham, AL

Robert Bohm
University of Central Florida
Orlando, FL

Shelby Chandler
University of Alabama
Tuscaloosa, AL

Barbara Dahlbach
University of Alabama
Tuscaloosa, AL

E. Dorworth
Montgomery College
Rockville, MD

Lynn Fortney
EBSCO Subscription Services
Birmingham, AL

Donna Hale
Shippensburg University
Shippensburg, PA

Tavis Hardin
North Birmingham Elementary
   School
Birmingham, AL

Stephanie Holloway
University of Alabama
Tuscaloosa, AL

Julius Koefoed
Kirkwood Community College
Cedar Rapids, IA

Noelle Koval
Linda Nolen Learning Center
Alabaster, AL

Walter B. Lewis
St. Louis Community College at
   Meramec
Kirkwood, MO

Jess Maghan
University of Illinois at Chicago
Chicago, IL

Justine McNutt
University of Alabama
Tuscaloosa, AL

Alvin Mitchell
Delgado Community College
New Orleans, LA

Sarah Nordin
Solano Community College
Suisun City, CA

Michael F. Perna
Broome Community College
Binghamton, NY

Scott Plutchak
University of Alabama at
   Birmingham
Birmingham, AL

Sally Reeves
University of Alabama
Tuscaloosa, AL

William Selke
Indiana University
Bloomington, IN

John Sloan
University of Alabama at
   Birmingham
Birmingham, AL

Anthony C. Trevelino
Camden County College
Blackwood, NJ

Shela R. Van Ness
University of Tennessee at
   Chattanooga
Chattanooga, TN

Gennaro F. Vito
University of Louisville
Louisville, KY

Ed Whittle
Florida Metropolitan University
   at Tampa College
Tampa, FL

Robert R. Wiggins
Cedarville College
Cedarville, OH

Finally, we would like to express our appreciation to our publishing team at Glencoe/McGraw-Hill, whose vision, guidance, and support helped bring this project to fruition. Working with them has been an honor.

Frank Schmalleger
John Ortiz Smykla

About the Authors

Frank Schmalleger is director of the Justice Research Association, a private consulting firm and think tank focusing on issues of crime and justice. The Justice Research Association is based in Hilton Head Island, South Carolina.

Dr. Schmalleger holds a bachelor's degree from the University of Notre Dame and both a master's and a doctorate in sociology from The Ohio State University with a special emphasis in criminology. From 1976 to 1994, he taught criminal justice courses at the University of North Carolina at Pembroke, serving for many years as a tenured full professor. For the last 16 of those years, he chaired the Department of Sociology, Social Work, and Criminal Justice. As an adjunct professor with Webster University in St. Louis, Missouri, Schmalleger helped develop a graduate program in security management and loss prevention. He taught courses in that curriculum for more than a decade, focusing primarily on computer and information security. Schmalleger has also taught in the New School for Social Research's on-line graduate program, helping to build the world's first electronic classrooms for criminal justice distance learning.

Frank Schmalleger is the author of numerous articles and many books, including *Criminal Justice Today* (Prentice Hall, 2001); *Criminal Law Today* (Prentice Hall, 1999); *Criminology Today* (Prentice Hall, 1999); *Crime and the Justice System in America: An Encyclopedia* (Greenwood, 1997); *Computers in Criminal Justice* (Wyndham Hall, 1991); *Criminal Justice Ethics* (Greenwood Press, 1991); *Finding Criminal Justice in the Library* (Wyndham Hall, 1991); and *Ethics in Criminal Justice* (Wyndham Hall, 1990). He is founding editor of the journal *The Justice Professional* and serves as imprint advisor for Greenwood Publishing Group's criminal justice reference series.

Schmalleger is also the creator of a number of award-winning Web sites. He is a member of the Advisory Board of APB Online, an innovative web-based criminal justice news service, where he also runs the CJ Professionalism Channel. He is founder and codirector of the Criminal Justice Distance Learning Consortium, a project of the Justice Research Association.

John Ortiz Smykla has been a professor of criminal justice at the University of Alabama since 1977, serving as chair of the department from 1986 to 1996. Using multimedia, he teaches undergraduate and graduate courses in research methods and corrections and has supervised more than 50 master's and doctoral students. He has taught two-way interactive corrections courses across several campuses of the University of Alabama system .

Smykla earned the interdisciplinary social science Ph.D. in criminal justice, sociology, and anthropology from Michigan State University. He holds bachelor's and master's degrees in sociology from California State University in Northridge. A former juvenile probation officer, Smykla conducted research with the Federal Bureau of Prisons in Pleasanton, California.

Dr. Smykla is the author of *Community-Based Corrections: Principles and Practices* (Macmillan, 1981) and *Probation and Parole: Crime Control in the Community* (Macmillan, 1984), co-author of *Executions in the United States, 1608–1995: The Espy File* (University of Michigan, 1995), co-editor of *Intermediate Sanctions: Sentencing in the 1990s* (Anderson, 1995), and editor of *Coed Prison* (Human Sciences Press, 1984). He serves on the editorial boards of a number of journals, including *Women & Criminal Justice*, *American Journal of Criminal Justice*, *Criminal Justice Review*, and *Journal of Crime and Justice*. He has published more than 40 research articles on jails, probation, parole, intermediate sanctions, same-sex and coed prisons, capital punishment, and juvenile corrections. He has delivered more than 50 conference papers in the United States and abroad.

Dr. Smykla is a member of the Academy of Criminal Justice Sciences and the Southern Criminal Justice Association. In 1996, the Southern Criminal Justice Association named him educator of the year. In 1997, he served as chair of the ACJS annual program committee. In 2000, he served as president of the Southern Criminal Justice Association. A supporter of community involvement, Smykla is a volunteer in the burn unit of Children's Hospital, Birmingham. In 1999, the nursing staff nominated him for volunteer of the year.

Dedication

For Malia Hope
—Frank Schmalleger

A mi esposa, Evelyn, con amor siempre
—John Ortiz Smykla

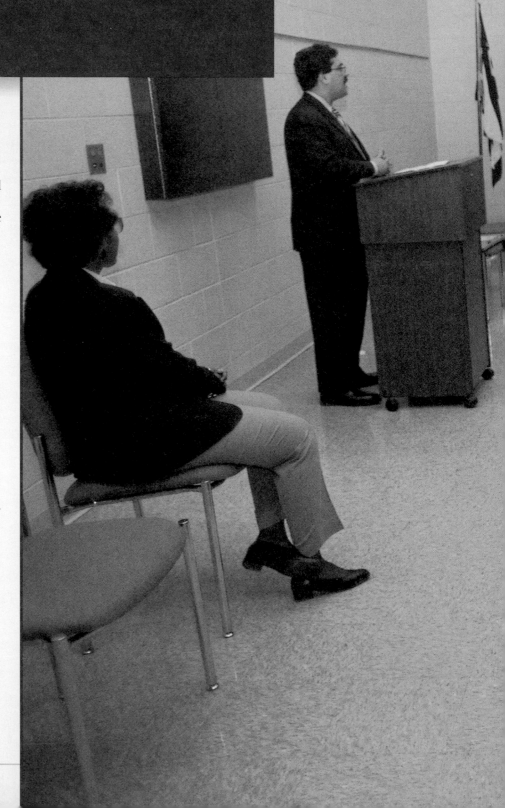

1 Corrections
The Profession

CHAPTER OBJECTIVES

After completing this chapter you should be able to:

1. Explain why correctional populations continue to rise even though the rate of serious crime in the United States has been declining.

2. Understand how rising correctional populations affect the costs of corrections.

3. List the kinds of crimes that cause people to enter correctional programs and institutions.

4. Describe how crime is measured in the United States and explain the differences between the two major crime reporting programs.

5. List and describe the various components of the criminal justice system.

6. List the major components of the corrections subsystem.

7. Describe criminal justice as a *system* and as a *process*.

8. Define the term *corrections*.

9. Explain the importance of professionalism in the corrections field.

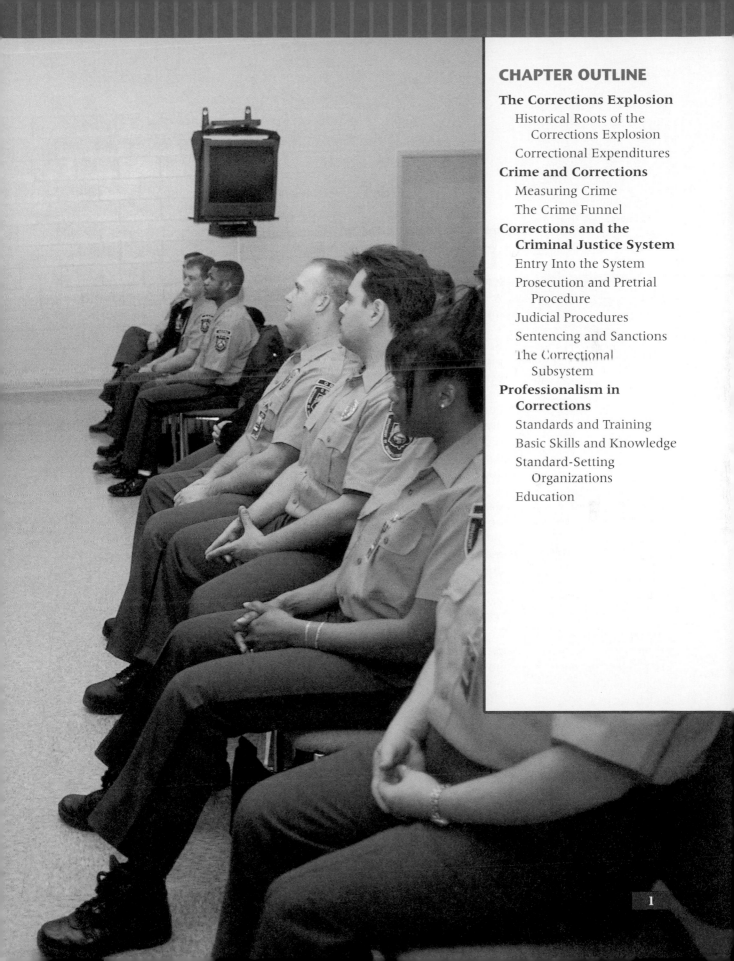

Teaching Tip

Use the introductory story to begin discussing students' preconceived notions about prison— that is, about who is in prison, what goes on there, and who works in the prison.

correctional clients

Prison inmates, probationers, parolees, offenders assigned to alternative sentencing programs, and those held in jails.

Changes in the institutions and the correctional system as a whole require that correctional officers be capable of interacting with offenders and with colleagues in a manner which reflects attitudinal change and a knowledge base different from that generally accepted in the past.

—P. H. Hahn

For decades, Father Patrick Moloney fought against drugs and was a prominent advocate for the homeless on New York City's Lower East Side.[1] These days, however, the Irish-born Catholic priest is known as federal prisoner 28251-0545. He spends his days behind bars and barbed wire at the Federal Correctional Institution at Loretto waiting for his 51-month sentence to expire.

Moloney was convicted of hiding $2 million, part of a $7.4 million Brink's armored car robbery in 1993. Prosecutors claim that the 64-year-old priest has ties to the Irish Republican Army—an allegation they have never been able to prove. Moloney now performs his priestly duties at a prison— one built, ironically, on the site of a former Franciscan seminary in Pennsylvania's Allegheny Mountains. "I spent my whole life fighting drugs—heroin, cocaine, crack, and marijuana," Father Moloney said in a recent interview. "Now I am in a cell with five other men, all of whom are convicted dealers." The priest has maintained his innocence, although all appeals of his conviction and sentence have been denied.

Because of prison regulations, Moloney cannot wear a clerical collar, is officially barred from conducting church services, and is not permitted to hear the confessions of other prisoners. On a typical day, he is assigned to cleaning toilets and shower stalls. Unofficially, however, Moloney conducts masses for some of the inmates at Loretto, leads a few men in group prayers, and counsels inmates in need of a receptive ear. Sometimes inmates ask the priest for special blessings. "When sending out their appeals they ask me to bless the document and pour holy water over it," said Moloney. "I tell them, 'I blessed mine and it didn't do anything for me.' "

Father Moloney's story illustrates the fact that **correctional clients,** as prison inmates, probationers, parolees, and those held in jails are called, are not all the same. Correctional clients are as diverse as the forms of criminal behavior that result in their encounters with the criminal justice system. The characteristics of the correctional population in the United States today are described generally in Figure 1–1.

The Corrections Explosion

Not long ago, Fox Butterfield, a staff writer for the *New York Times*, wrote an editorial in which he noted: "It has become a comforting story: for five straight years, crime has been falling, led by a drop in murder. So why is the number of inmates in prisons and jails around the nation still going up? Last year [1996], it reached almost 1.7 million, up about seven percent a year since 1990."[2]

FIGURE 1–1

Characteristics of the Correctional Population

Correctional Population

In the United States, almost 6.1 million adults (about 2.9% of the resident U.S. adult population) are under some form of correctional supervision

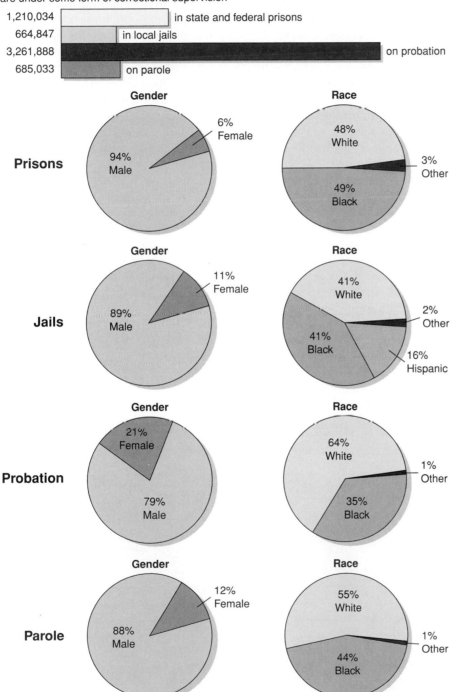

1,210,034   in state and federal prisons
664,847   in local jails
3,261,888   on probation
685,033   on parole

Prisons

Gender — 94% Male, 6% Female

Race — 48% White, 49% Black, 3% Other

Jails

Gender — 89% Male, 11% Female

Race — 41% White, 41% Black, 16% Hispanic, 2% Other

Probation

Gender — 79% Male, 21% Female

Race — 64% White, 35% Black, 1% Other

Parole

Gender — 88% Male, 12% Female

Race — 55% White, 44% Black, 1% Other

Student Involvement
Direct students' attention to Figure 1–1, "Characteristics of the Correctional Population." Ask them to briefly study the data in the figure and to offer generalizations about the data. Ask students if the characteristics depicted in the figure are what they expected.

Professional Issue
Special Treatment The introductory story in this chapter is about Father Moloney, a Catholic priest who is in prison. Ask students if they think correctional personnel might be tempted to give special treatment to a cleric. Ask them if correctional personnel might be tempted to treat any other "special" categories of prisoners differently from most prisoners. If so, which categories, and why? Would such special treatment by a correctional professional be appropriate? Why or why not?

Sources: Allen J. Beck and Christopher J. Mumola, *Prisoners in 1998* (Washington: Bureau of Justice Statistics, August 1999); Thomas P. Bonczar and Lauren E. Glaze, *Probation and Parole in the United States, 1998* (Washington: Bureau of Justice Statistics, August 1999, revised October 13, 1999); Darrell K. Gilliard and Allen J. Beck, *Prison and Jail Inmates at Midyear 1998,* Bureau of Justice Statistics Bulletin (Washington: Office of Justice Programs, March 1999).

Student Involvement

Have students reread the statistics on prison growth in this section. Ask them why the number of prison inmates in the United States continues to increase even as the crime rate appears to be declining. Ask students if they can think of any reasons beyond those presented in the text.

As Butterfield observes, one amazing fact stands out from all the information about corrections. While serious crime in the United States has consistently declined throughout much of the 1990s, the number of people under correctional supervision in this country—not just the number of convicted offenders sent to prison—has continued to climb. Crime rates are approximately 15 percent lower today than they were in 1980. They are at their lowest level in 20 years. But the number of people on probation is up almost 300 percent since 1980, the nation's prison population has increased by more than 400 percent, and the number of persons on parole has increased by almost the same proportion. Figure 1–2 illustrates these trends.

The question is, why? Why the steady increase in correctional populations in the face of declining crime rates? The answer to this question, like the answers to most societal enigmas, is far from simple. Pursuit of the answer is important, however. As Franklin Zimring, director of the Earl Warren Legal Institute at the University of California at Berkeley, points out, "The change in the number of inmates tells us . . . about our feelings about crime and criminals."[3]

The answer has a number of dimensions. First, it is important to recognize that get-tough-on-crime laws, such as the three-strikes (and two-strikes) laws that were enacted in many states in the mid-1990s have fueled rapid increases in prison populations. The conservative attitudes that gave birth to those laws are still with us. Noted criminal justice scholar John P. Conrad summarizes today's mood this way: "There is an unprecedented consensus on the necessity for strengthening criminal justice. This consensus can be summed up in one sentence. Criminals must be locked up and kept off the streets."[4] Conrad goes on to explain: "The vast expansion of corrections today has not come about without good cause. For the citizen on the streets, there is only one reasonable response to the violence he or she fears. Lock them up, and hang the expense."[5]

Student Involvement

Refer students to Figure 1–2, "Trends in Corrections Since 1980," and ask them why they think there has been only a slight growth in the number of offenders on parole.

Sources: FBI, *Crime in the United States, 1998* (Washington: U.S. Government Printing Office, 1999); Thomas P. Bonczar and Lauren E. Glaze, *Probation and Parole in the United States, 1998* (Washington: Bureau of Justice Statistics, 1999); Allen J. Beck and Christopher J. Mumola, *Prisoners in 1998* (Washington, Bureau of Justice Statistics, 1999).

FIGURE 1–2

Trends in Corrections Since 1980

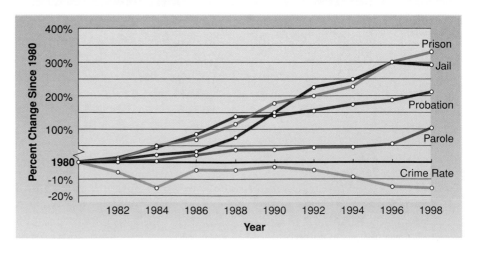

Corrections: The Profession

TABLE 1–1

Number of Prisoners by Offense

Type of Offense	State	Federal
Violent Offenses	494,349	13,021
Property Offenses	230,177	5,964
Drug Offenses	216,254	55,069
Public-Order Offenses	103,344	13,026
	1,044,124	87,080

Source: Adapted from Christopher J. Mumola, *Substance Abuse and Treatment, State and Federal Prisoners, 1997.* (Washington: BJS, January 1999).

Teaching Tip
Refer students to Table 1–1, "Number of Prisoners by Offense," and reiterate the significance that the nation's War on Drugs has had for prison populations. Direct students to compare the totals for Property Offenses and Drug Offenses, especially on the federal level.

A second reason correctional populations are rapidly increasing can be found in the nation's War on Drugs. The War on Drugs has led to the arrest and conviction of a large proportion of the country's populace, resulting in larger correctional populations in nearly every jurisdiction (especially within the federal correctional system). In Table 1–1, compare the total number of individuals incarcerated for drug offenses with, for example, the total incarcerated for property offenses. Drug arrests continue to increase. Although they account for a large proportion of the nation's correctional population, they do not figure into the FBI's calculations of the nation's rate of serious crimes. Hence, the War on Drugs goes a long way toward explaining the growth in correctional populations even while the rate of "serious crime" in the United States appears to be declining.

Third, parole authorities, fearing civil liability and public outcry, have become increasingly reluctant to release inmates, contributing to a further expansion of prison populations. Fourth, as some observers have noted, the corrections boom has created its own growth dynamic.[6] As ever greater numbers of people are placed on probation, the likelihood of probation violations increases. Prison sentences for more violators result in larger prison populations. When inmates are released from prison, they swell the numbers of those on parole, leading to a larger number of parole violations, which in turn fuels further prison growth. Statistics show that the number of criminals being sent to prison for at least the second time has increased steadily, rising to 35 percent of the total number of admissions in 1995, from 18 percent in 1980.[7]

Historical Roots of the Corrections Explosion

Seen historically, the growth of correctional populations may be more the continuation of a long-term trend than the result of recent social conditions. A look at the data shows that correctional populations have continued to grow through widely divergent political eras and economic conditions. Census reports show an almost relentless increase in the rate of imprisonment over the past 150 years. In 1850, for example, only 29 people were imprisoned in this country for every 100,000 persons in the population.[8] By 1890 the rate had risen to 131 per 100,000. The rate grew slowly until 1980, when the rate of imprisonment in the United States stood at 153 per 100,000. At that point, a major shift in the use of imprisonment began. While crime rates rose sharply in the middle to late 1980s, the rate of imprisonment rose far more dramatically. Today the rate of imprisonment in this country is about 500 per 100,000 persons, and it shows no signs of declining.[9] Figure 1–3 illustrates changes in the rate of imprisonment over the past 150 years. Probation statistics—first available in 1935—show an even more amazing rate of growth. Although only 59,530 offenders were placed on probation throughout the United States in 1935, more than 3 million people are on probation today.[10]

Teaching Tip

Refer students to Figure 1–3, "Rate of Imprisonment in the United States, 1850–2000." Point out that the changing nature of society has resulted in the imprisonment of a far greater proportion of the population than ever before. Ask students to identify some of the social changes that have led to such high rates of imprisonment.

FIGURE 1–3

Rate of Imprisonment in the United States, 1850–2000

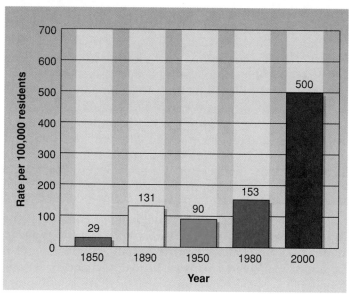

Sources: Margaret Werner Cahalan, *Historical Corrections Statistics in the United States, 1850–1984* (Washington: U.S. Department of Justice, 1986); Allen J. Beck and Christopher J. Mumola, *Prisoners in 1998* (Washington: BJS, 1999).

Correctional Expenditures

Growing correctional populations also mean heightened costs. Budgetary allocations for corrections have grown in step with correctional populations. In 1965, the nation spent $1 billion on correctional services—including funding for juvenile institutions and programs. Thirty years later, in 1996, a staggering $22.8 billion was allocated to state and federal correctional budgets—with many additional dollars going to alternative programs for juveniles.[11] Most of the money spent on corrections today (about 75 percent) funds the day-to-day activities of correctional programs and institutions. Another 10 percent is allocated for the construction of new facilities—mostly prisons and jails.

As the trend continues toward ever greater use of correctional services, state and federal allocations are expected to continue to expand. The federal government alone spent $2.8 billion on correctional activities and services in 1996, $3.2 billion in 1997, and $3.3 billion in 1998. Federal expenditures on corrections are expected to exceed $3.8 billion by 2002,[12] and state correctional budgets are expected to rise proportionately.

The costs of running America's constantly expanding prison systems have begun to impose an enormous burden on government at all levels. Already, California and Florida spend more on incarceration than on higher education.[13]

On the flip side, growing correctional populations and increasing budgets have led to a dramatically expanding correctional workforce, and to enhanced employment opportunities within the field. According to historical reports, persons employed in the corrections field totaled approximately 27,000 in 1950.[14] By 1975 the number had risen to about 75,000. The most current statistics available show that the number of correctional officers alone has grown to more than 180,000.[15] When probation and parole officers, correctional administrators, and other corrections professionals are added, the total stands at nearly 340,000.[16] Figure 1–4 shows some of the employment possibilities in corrections.

New prisons mean jobs and can contribute greatly to the health of local economies. Some economically disadvantaged towns—from Tupper Lake, in the Adirondack Mountains of upstate New York, to Edgefield, South Carolina—are cashing in on the prison boom, having successfully competed to become sites for new prisons. The competition for new prison facilities is reminiscent of the efforts states made some years ago to attract new automobile factories and other industries.

Student Involvement
Have students study newspapers, magazines, and other sources of information about your state to determine what cities and regions in your state have recently experienced new prison construction. Ask students to list the economic impacts such construction might have on local communities.

FIGURE 1–4

Careers in Corrections

Careers	Careers	Careers
academic teacher	field administrator	psychologist
activity therapy administrator	fugitive apprehension officer	recreation coordinator
business manager	human services counselor	social worker
case manager	job placement officer	statistician
chaplain	mental health clinician	substance abuse counselor
correctional officer	parole caseworker	unit leader
classification officer	parole officer	victim advocate
clinical social worker	presentence investigator	vocational instructor
children's services counselor	probation officer	warden/superintendent
chemical dependency manager	program officer	youth services coordinator
dietary officer	programmer/analyst	youth supervisor
drug court coordinator	program specialist	

Crime and Corrections

The crimes that bring people into the American correctional system include felonies, misdemeanors, and minor law violations that are sometimes called *infractions*.

Felonies are serious crimes. Murder, rape, aggravated assault, robbery, burglary, and arson are felonies in all jurisdictions within the United States, although the names for these crimes may differ from state to state. A general way to think about felonies is to remember that a **felony** is a serious crime whose commission can result in confinement in a state or federal correctional institution for more than a year.

In some states a felony conviction can result in the loss of certain civil privileges. A few states make conviction of a felony and the resulting incarceration grounds for uncontested divorce. Others prohibit convicted felony offenders from running for public office or owning a firearm, and some exclude them from professions such as medicine, law, and police work.

Huge differences in the treatment of specific crimes exist between states. Some crimes classified as felonies in one part of the country may be misdemeanors in another. In still other states they may not even be crimes at all! Such is the case with some drug law violations, and with social order offenses such as homosexual acts, prostitution, and gambling.

Misdemeanors, which compose the second major crime category, are relatively minor violations of the criminal law. They include crimes such as petty theft (the theft of items of little worth), simple assault (in which the victim suffers no serious injury, and in which none was intended), breaking and entering, the possession of burglary tools, disorderly conduct, disturbing the peace, filing a false crime report, and writing bad checks (although the amount for which the check is written may determine the classification of this offense). In general, misdemeanors can be thought of as any crime punishable by a year or less in confinement.

Within felony and misdemeanor categories, most states distinguish between degrees, or levels of seriousness. Texas law, for example, establishes five felony classes and three classes of misdemeanor—intended to guide judges in assessing the seriousness of particular criminal acts. The Texas penal code then specifies categories into which given offenses fall.

A third category of crime is the **infraction.** The term, which is not used in all jurisdictions, refers to minor violations of the law that are less serious than misdemeanors. Infractions may include such violations of the law as jaywalking, spitting on the sidewalk, littering, and certain traffic violations, including the failure to wear a seat belt. People committing infractions are typically ticketed—that is, given citations—and released, usually upon a promise to appear later in court. Court appearances may be waived upon payment of a small fine, which is often mailed in.

Measuring Crime

Two important sources of information on crime for correctional professionals are the FBI's Uniform Crime Reports (UCR) and the Bureau of Justice Statistics' National Crime Victimization Survey (NCVS). Corrections professionals closely analyze these data to forecast the numbers and types of correctional clients to expect in the future. The forecasts can be used to project the need for different types of detention and rehabilitation services and facilities.

Uniform Crime Reports   The FBI's Uniform Crime Reports (UCR) are published annually. Individual reports are often referred to by their official title, *Crime in the United States*. The UCR contains information on eight major crimes: murder, forcible rape, robbery, aggravated assault, burglary, larceny-theft, motor vehicle theft, and arson. These major crimes are divided into two subcategories: **violent crime** and **property crime.** Violent crime consists of murder, forcible rape, robbery, and aggravated assault. Burglary, larceny-theft, motor vehicle theft, and arson fall into the property crime category. Table 1–2 summarizes the crimes reported to police in the eight index crime categories.

The data, gathered from police agencies across the country, include only the crimes known to the police. Unreported or undiscovered crimes, which might outnumber those reported to the police, are not included in the UCR.

The sum total of all major crimes provides a national **crime index,** useful in comparing the occurrence of major crimes over time. The UCR also

violent crime
Interpersonal crime that involves the use of force by offenders or results in injury or death to victims. In the FBI's Uniform Crime Reports, violent crimes are murder, forcible rape, robbery, and aggravated assault.

property crime
Burglary, larceny, automobile theft, and arson as reported in the FBI's Uniform Crime Reports.

crime index   An annual statistical tally of major crimes known to law enforcement agencies in the United States.

TABLE 1–2

Major Crimes Known to the Police, 1998

Offense	Number	Rate per 100,000	Clearance Rate
Violent Crimes			
Murder	16,914	6.3	69%
Forcible rape	93,103	34.4	50%
Aggravated assault	974,402	360.5	59%
Robbery	446,625	165.2	28%
Total Personal Crimes	1,531,044	566.4	49%
Property Crimes			
Burglary	2,329,950	862.0	14%
Larceny-theft	7,373,886	2,728.1	19%
Motor vehicle theft	1,240,754	459.0	14%
Arson[1]	78,094	39.0	16%
Total Property Crimes	10,944,590	4,049.1	17%
U.S. Total	12,475,634	4,615.5	21%

1. Only fires determined through investigation to have been willfully or maliciously set are classified as arsons.

Source: Adapted from FBI, *Crime in the United States, 1998* (Washington: U.S. Government Printing Office, 1999).

Teaching Tip
Refer students to Table 1–2, "Major Crimes Known to the Police, 1998." Point out the eight major crimes chosen by the FBI to represent the nation's overall rate of crime. Ask whether others might be included to give a more realistic picture of crime in the United States. Explain to students that such choices make an impact on what we think of as "crime."

reports a **crime rate** each year. The rate of crime is calculated by dividing the total number of major crimes by the population of the United States. The result is expressed as the number of crimes per 100,000 people. Crime rate comparisons provide a more realistic portrayal of changes in crime over time—and of the likelihood of victimization—than do simple comparisons of crime index totals.

The FBI reported that a total of 12.5 million major crimes occurred throughout the United States in 1998. The 1998 crime rate of 4,615.5 offenses per 100,000 United States inhabitants was the lowest since 1984. Regionally, the crime rate was 5,223 offenses per 100,000 inhabitants in the South; 4,879 in the West; 4,379 in the Midwest; and 3,474 in the Northeast. The violent crime rate in 1998 was 566 per 100,000, while the rate of property crimes was 4,049 offenses per 100,000.

If we look at Table 1–2, we see that 16,914 murders were recorded in 1998. The murder rate was 6.3 offenses per 100,000 inhabitants. According to supplemental data in the UCR, 76 percent of murder victims in 1998 were male and 88 percent were persons 18 years old or older. Of victims whose race was known, 50 percent were white and 48 percent were black. Eighty-nine percent of murderers were male, and 89 percent were 18 or older. Of murderers whose race was known, 49 percent were black, and 49 percent were white.

The UCR includes supplemental data for each index crime. Such data, along with the crime index totals, offers corrections personnel a glimpse of the background, makeup, and motivation of the offenders who may eventually become clients of the correctional system.

The UCR also includes data on the numbers of arrests in the United States for all types of crimes. Offenses not included in the crime index are called Part II offenses. Law enforcement agencies made an estimated 14.5 million arrests in 1998 for all offenses except traffic violations. The highest arrest count for a specific crime category was 1.6 million arrests for drug abuse violations. Larceny-theft and simple assaults each registered 1.3 million arrests. Arrests for driving under the influence numbered 1.4 million. In 1998 the nationwide rate of arrest was 5,534 per 100,000 people.

Most crimes reported to the police are not solved. Crimes that are solved are said to be *cleared.* For the UCR, a known offense is considered *cleared* or *solved* when a law enforcement agency has charged at least one person with the offense or when a suspect has been identified and located but circumstances have prevented charging the suspect.

The *clearance rate* is the number of offenses cleared, divided by the number of offenses known by police. Law enforcement agencies nationwide recorded a 21 percent crime index clearance rate in 1998. The clearance rate for violent crimes was 49 percent; for property crimes, 17 percent. Among crime index offenses, the clearance rate was highest for murder (69 percent), and lowest for burglary and motor vehicle theft (14 percent each). For many consensual crimes, such as prostitution, gambling, and drug abuse, rates of arrest are lower still. Table 1–2 shows the clearance rates for the index crimes reported in 1998. The clearance rates for individual index crimes help corrections professionals know the types and numbers of clients to expect in the correctional system.

National Incident-Based Reporting System (NIBRS) The FBI is implementing a new crime reporting program called the National Incident-Based Reporting System, or NIBRS. Under the new system, many details will be gathered about each criminal incident. Included among them will be information on place of occurrence, weapon used, type and value of property damaged or stolen, personal characteristics of the offender and the victim, the nature of any relationship between the two, disposition of the complaint, and so on. The new reporting system gathers data on 22 general offenses: arson, assault, bribery, burglary, counterfeiting, vandalism, narcotic offenses, embezzlement, extortion, fraud, gambling, homicide, kidnapping, larceny, motor vehicle theft, pornography, prostitution, robbery, forcible sex offenses, nonforcible sex offenses, receiving stolen property, and weapons violations. Data will also be gathered on bad checks, vagrancy, disorderly conduct, driving under the influence, drunkenness, nonviolent family offenses, liquor law violations, "peeping Tom" activity, runaway, trespass, and a general category of all other criminal law violations.

The FBI began accepting crime data in NIBRS format in January 1989. Although NIBRS was intended to replace the old system by 1999, delays have been frequent. It will be a few more years before all police departments report their crime data to the FBI in NIBRS format.

National Crime Victimization Survey (NCVS) The nation's second crime measuring tool is the National Crime Victimization Survey (NCVS).[17] The NCVS was begun by the Bureau of Justice Statistics (BJS) in 1973. It provides a detailed picture of crime incidents, victims, and trends. The survey collects detailed information on the frequency and nature of the crimes of rape, sexual assault, personal robbery, aggravated and simple assault, household burglary, theft, and motor vehicle theft. It does not measure homicide or commercial crimes (such as burglaries of stores).

Racial minorities are overrepresented among all segments of the correctional population in comparison with the ethnic makeup of America. What is the cause of this lopsided ethnic representation?

Corrections: The Profession **CHAPTER 1** 11

To gather data for the NCVS, U.S. Census Bureau personnel each year interview all household members at least 12 years old in a national representative sample of approximately 49,000 households. The total sample contains about 101,000 persons. The NCVS collects information on crimes suffered by individuals and households, whether or not those crimes were reported to law enforcement agencies. It estimates the proportion reported for each type of crime covered by the survey, and it summarizes the reasons that victims give for reporting or not reporting. For many types of offenses, the NCVS shows more crimes being committed than does the UCR. There are, however, some crimes—homicides and assaults—in which the police count more crimes than does the NCVS. Table 1–3 shows total victimizations reported by the NCVS for 1998. Compare the totals for similar categories in Table 1–3 and Table 1–2. This comparison will help you understand the importance of knowing the source and the manner of compilation of the data you use to make corrections decisions.

The NCVS provides information about victims (age, sex, race, ethnicity, marital status, income, and educational level), offenders (sex, race, approximate age, and victim-offender relationship), and crimes (time, place, weapons, injuries, and economic consequences). Questions also cover the

Teaching Tip
Describe the NCVS as a survey-based system for gathering data on crime. Then refer students to Table 1–3, "Criminal Victimizations, 1998," and ask them to briefly study the data in the table. Ask them to speculate about how gathering data directly from victims has both advantages and disadvantages over the UCR's method of using only crimes reported to police.

TABLE 1–3

Criminal Victimizations, 1998

Type of Crime	Number of Victimizations
All Crimes	31,307,000
Personal crimes[1]	8,412,000
Crimes of violence	8,116,000
Completed violence	2,564,000
Attempted/threatened violence	5,553,000
Rape/sexual assault	333,000
Robbery	886,000
Completed/property taken	610,000
Attempted to take property	277,000
Assault	6,897,000
Personal theft[2]	298,000
Property crimes	22,895,000
Household burglary	4,054,000
Motor vehicle theft	1,138,000
Theft	17,703,000

1. The NCVS is based on interviews with victims and therefore cannot measure murder.

2. Includes pocket picking, purse snatching, and attempted purse snatching not shown separately.

Source: Adapted from Callie M. Rennison, *Criminal Victimization, 1998* (Washington: U.S. Department of Justice, July 1999).

experiences of victims with the criminal justice system, self-protective measures used by victims, and possible substance abuse by offenders. NCVS data are published annually under the title *Criminal Victimization in the United States*.

According to the most recent NCVS,[18] U.S. residents age 12 or older experienced approximately 31.3 million crimes in 1998. Seventy-three percent of those crimes, or 22.9 million, were property crimes; 26 percent (8.1 million) were crimes of violence; and 1 percent were crimes of personal theft. NCVS findings show that in 1998, Americans age 12 or older experienced fewer violent and property crimes than in any other year since 1973, when the NCVS began.

The Crime Funnel

Not all crimes are reported, and not everyone who commits a reported crime is arrested, so relatively few offenders enter the criminal justice system. Of those who do, some are not prosecuted (perhaps because the evidence against them is insufficient), others plead guilty to lesser crimes, and others are found not guilty. Some who are convicted are diverted from further processing by the system or may be fined or ordered to counseling. Hence, the proportion of criminal offenders who eventually enter the correctional system is small, as Figure 1–5 shows.[19]

Teaching Tip
Create a blank two-column chart on the board or on a transparency. Label one column "UCR," the other "NCVS." Have students offer entries for the two columns that show the source, scope, and content of the two measures of crime. Ask students which measure is more meaningful to corrections professionals.

Student Involvement
Refer students to Figure 1–5, "The Crime Funnel." Ask them to explain why so few criminal offenders are formally handled by the criminal justice system—and why fewer still become correctional clients.

FIGURE 1–5

The Crime Funnel

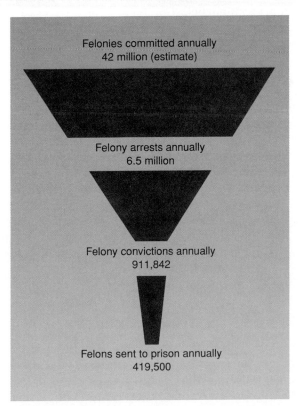

Felonies committed annually
42 million (estimate)

Felony arrests annually
6.5 million

Felony convictions annually
911,842

Felons sent to prison annually
419,500

Sources: Statistics compiled from Bureau of Justice Statistics data. Felonies include violent crimes, attempted personal victimizations, selected property crimes (such as burglary and motor vehicle theft), and various drug offenses. The estimated number of felonies committed annually is calculated from NCVS data, FBI data on drug and other felonies, and general knowledge about unreported crimes. Also see Bureau of Justice Statistics, *Felony Sentences in the United States, 1994* (Washington: BJS, 1997).

criminal justice The process of achieving justice through the application of the criminal law and through the workings of the criminal justice system. Also, the study of the field of criminal justice.

criminal justice system The collection of all the agencies that perform criminal justice functions, whether operations or administration or technical support. The basic divisions of the criminal justice system are police, courts, and corrections.

Corrections and the Criminal Justice System

Corrections is generally considered the final stage in the criminal justice process. Some aspects of corrections, however, come into play early in the process. We have been talking about the criminal justice *process*. Keep in mind, however, that although the term **criminal justice** can be used to refer to the justice *process*, it can also be used to describe our *system* of justice. Criminal justice agencies, taken as a whole, are said to compose the **criminal justice system.** As you already probably know, the components of the criminal justice system are (1) police, (2) courts, and (3) corrections. Each component, because it contains a variety of organizations and agencies, can be termed a subsystem. The subsystem of corrections, for example, includes prisons, agencies of probation and parole, jails, and a variety of alternative programs. Since the activities of criminal justice agencies routinely involve other system components, the word *system* encompasses not only the agencies of justice, but also the interrelationships among those agencies.

The *process* of criminal justice involves the activities of the agencies that make up the criminal justice system. The process of criminal justice begins when a crime is discovered or reported.

Court decisions based on the due process guarantees of the U.S. Constitution require that specific steps be taken in the justice process. Although the exact nature of those steps varies among jurisdictions, the description that follows portrays the most common sequence of events in response to serious criminal behavior. Figure 1–6 on pages 16–17, a diagram of the American criminal justice system, indicates the relationship among the stages in the criminal justice process.

Entry Into the System

The criminal justice system does not respond to most crime because, as previously discussed, much crime is not discovered or is not reported to the police.[20] Law enforcement agencies learn about crimes from the reports of citizens, through discovery by a police officer in the field, or through investigative and intelligence work. Once a law enforcement agency knows of a crime, the agency must identify and arrest a suspect before the case can proceed. Sometimes a suspect is found at the scene; sometimes, however, identifying a suspect requires an extensive investigation. Often no one is identified or apprehended—the crime goes unsolved. If an offender is arrested, booked, and jailed to await an initial appearance, the intake, custody, confinement, and supervision aspects of corrections first come into play at this stage of the criminal justice process.

Prosecution and Pretrial Procedure

After an arrest, law enforcement agencies present information about the case and about the accused to the prosecutor, who decides whether to file formal charges with the court. If no charges are filed, the accused must be released. The prosecutor can also drop charges after filing them. Such a

THE OFFENDER SPEAKS

Very few of us do not think about beating the system. After all, the system deprives us of the freedom we cherish. It stands for all that we resent: lack of choice, restricted movement, denial of access to loved ones. We resent the walls, bars, uniforms, being told what to do, what programs we must take.

Moralists argue that we get exactly what we deserve, and many citizens believe that we are treated too well. Few of us can argue that we didn't know what we were getting into when we made the bad choices that landed us in prison. None of us arrived by accident, and if we are honest with ourselves, we'll acknowledge a whole series of destructive behaviors that preceded our committal to a "monastery of the damned."

In view of status and our chances of success upon release, the future doesn't look particularly bright. It's damn depressing to have to accept our collective reality. Hope is found in beating the system, the smart way. The smart way is not the path many of us have continually taken: defiance, conflict with "the man." AA members are familiar with the slogan "I can only change myself, not others." It is always easier to project blame for our inade-quacies onto others. But until we come to terms with our individual reality; separate the crime from the man, decide that the "I am" is capable of much more than the label implies—we're doomed to failure.

The administration uses education statistics to create the illusion of massive programming. It is up to us to demand the delivery. Enroll in courses. Develop the thirst to learn. Ask for help from peer tutors. An education is the ultimate form of restorative justice. The entire population benefits when just one con becomes literate. Educated cons have reason to lift their heads in self-assurance. We are better able to articulate our needs, better able to negotiate collectively, better able to see a future for ourselves.

Whether "the man" wants to acknowledge it or not, educated prisoners get respect from everybody inside and outside the prison. Adult education and training at every level—whether basic literacy, high school, college or university—are vital. The positive skills we learn in prison can't be taken away from us at the gate.

Joseph E. McCormick

---

choice is called *nolle prosequi,* and when it happens, a case is said to be "nolled" or "nollied."

A suspect charged with a crime must be taken before a judge or magistrate without unnecessary delay. At the initial appearance, the judge or magistrate informs the accused of the charges and decides whether there is probable cause to detain the accused. Often, defense counsel is also assigned then. If the offense charged is not very serious, the determination of guilt and the assessment of a penalty may also occur at this stage.

Teaching Tip
Use Figure 1–6, "Overview of the Criminal Justice System," to take students on a tour of the criminal justice system. Pay special attention to the corrections subsystem as it is represented in the chart, describing each component.

Corrections: The Profession **CHAPTER 1** 15

FIGURE 1–6

The Criminal Justice System

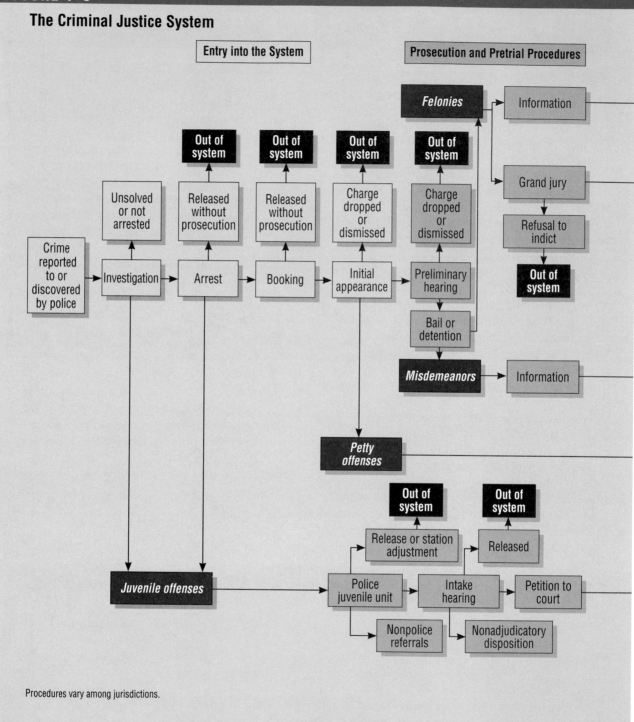

Entry into the System

Prosecution and Pretrial Procedures

Procedures vary among jurisdictions.

Corrections: The Profession

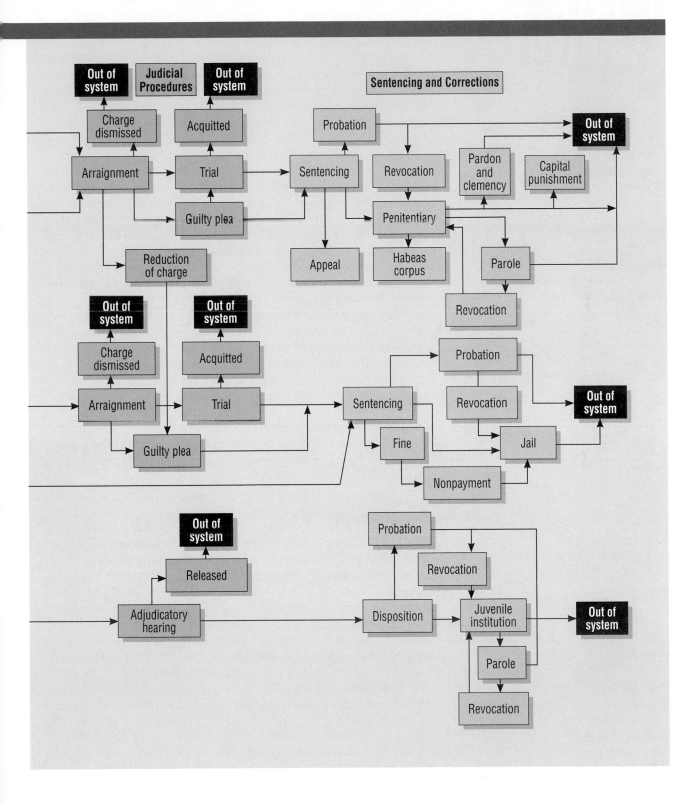

In some jurisdictions, a pretrial-release decision is made at the initial appearance, but this decision may occur at other hearings or at another time during the process. Pretrial release on bail was traditionally intended to ensure appearance at trial. However, many jurisdictions today permit pretrial detention of defendants accused of serious offenses and deemed dangerous, to prevent them from committing crimes in the pretrial period. The court may decide to release the accused on his or her own recognizance, into the custody of a third party, on the promise of satisfying certain conditions, or after the posting of a financial bond.

In many jurisdictions, the initial appearance may be followed by a preliminary hearing. The main function of this hearing is to determine whether there is probable cause to believe that the accused committed a crime within the jurisdiction of the court. If the judge or magistrate does not find probable cause, the case is dismissed. However, if the judge finds probable cause for such a belief, or if the accused waives the right to a preliminary hearing, the case may be bound over to a grand jury.

A grand jury hears evidence against the accused, presented by the prosecutor, and decides if there is sufficient evidence to cause the accused to be brought to trial. If the grand jury finds sufficient evidence, it submits an indictment to the court.

Not all jurisdictions make use of grand juries. Some require, instead, that the prosecutor submit an information (a formal written accusation) to the court. In most jurisdictions, misdemeanor cases and some felony cases proceed by the issuance of an information. Some jurisdictions require indictments in felony cases. However, the accused may choose to waive a grand jury indictment and, instead, accept service of an information for the crime.

Judicial Procedures

adjudication The process by which a court arrives at a final decision in a case.

Adjudication is the process by which a court arrives at a decision in a case. The adjudication process, however, involves a number of steps. The first is arraignment. Once an indictment or information is filed with the trial court, the accused is scheduled for arraignment. If the accused has been detained without bail, corrections personnel take him or her to the arraignment. At the arraignment, the accused is informed of the charges, advised of the rights of criminal defendants, and asked to enter a plea to the charges.

nolo contendere A plea of "no contest." A no-contest plea may be used where a defendant does not wish to contest conviction. Because the plea does not admit guilt, however, it cannot provide the basis for later civil suits.

If the accused pleads guilty or pleads ***nolo contendere*** (accepts a penalty without admitting guilt), the judge may accept or reject the plea. If the plea is accepted, no trial is held and the offender is sentenced at this proceeding or at a later date. The plea may be rejected if, for example, the judge believes that the accused has been coerced. If this occurs, the case may proceed to trial. Sometimes, as the result of negotiations between the prosecutor and the defendant, the defendant enters a guilty plea in expectation of reduced charges or a light sentence. *Nolo contendere* pleas are often entered by those who fear a later civil action, and who therefore do not want to admit guilt.

If the accused pleads not guilty or not guilty by reason of insanity, a date is set for trial. A person accused of a serious crime is guaranteed a trial by jury. However, the accused may ask for a bench trial, in which the judge, rather than a jury, serves as the finder of fact. In both instances, the prosecution and defense present evidence by questioning witnesses, and the judge decides issues of law. The trial results in acquittal or conviction of the original charges or of lesser included offenses.

Sentencing and Sanctions

After a guilty verdict or guilty plea, sentence is imposed. In most cases the judge decides on the sentence, but in some states, the sentence is decided by the jury, particularly for capital offenses, such as murder.

To arrive at an appropriate sentence, a court may hold a sentencing hearing to consider evidence of aggravating or mitigating circumstances. In assessing the circumstances surrounding a criminal act, courts often rely on presentence investigations by probation agencies or other designated authorities. Courts may also consider victim impact statements.

The sentencing choices available to judges and juries frequently include one or more of the following:

- The death penalty
- Incarceration in a prison, a jail, or another confinement facility
- Community service
- Probation—in which the convicted person is not confined but is subject to certain conditions and restrictions
- Fines—primarily as penalties for minor offenses
- Restitution—which requires the offender to provide financial compensation to the victim

Teaching Tip
Review the list of commonly available sentencing choices shown in the text. Describe each as a correctional option available to judges at sentencing, but explain that such options are generally limited by law and by the nature of the crime committed.

In many states, laws mandate that persons convicted of certain types of offenses serve a prison term. Most states permit the judge to set the sentence length within certain limits, but some states have determinate sentencing laws (discussed in Chapter 2). Such laws specify the sentence that must be served, and these sentences cannot be altered by a parole board.

After the trial, a defendant may request appellate review of the conviction or the sentence. In many criminal cases, appeals of a conviction are a matter of right; all states with the death penalty provide for automatic appeal of cases involving a death sentence. However, under some circumstances in some jurisdictions, appeals are in the discretion of the appellate court, which may grant or deny a defendant's petition for a **writ of *certiorari*.** Prisoners may also appeal their sentences through civil rights petitions and writs of *habeas corpus,* in which they claim unlawful detention.

writ of *certiorari* A writ issued by an appellate court to obtain from a lower court the record of its proceedings in a particular case.

The Correctional Subsystem

After conviction and sentencing, most offenders enter the correctional subsystem. Before we proceed with our discussion, it is best to define the term *corrections*. As with most words, a variety of definitions can be found.

In 1967, for example, the President's Commission on Law Enforcement and Administration of Justice wrote that *corrections* means "America's prisons,

institutional corrections That aspect of the correctional enterprise that "involves the incarceration and rehabilitation of adults and juveniles convicted of offenses against the law, and the confinement of persons suspected of a crime awaiting trial and adjudication."

noninstitutional corrections (also *community corrections*) That aspect of the correctional enterprise that includes "pardon, probation, and parole activities, correctional administration not directly connectable to institutions, and miscellaneous [activities] not directly related to institutional care."

Teaching Tip
Explain the difference between institutional corrections and community corrections, noting that they are sometimes considered alternatives to one another.

Teaching Tip
Draw student attention to the definition of *corrections* in the text. Ask what it means to say that corrections is essentially a management activity.

corrections All the various aspects of the pretrial and postconviction management of individuals accused or convicted of crimes.

jails, juvenile training schools, and probation and parole machinery. . . . " It is "that part of the criminal justice system," said the Commission, "that the public sees least of and knows least about."[21]

A few years later, in 1975, the National Advisory Commission on Criminal Justice Standards and Goals said in its lengthy volume on corrections, "Corrections is defined here as the community's official reactions to the convicted offender, whether adult or juvenile."[22] The Commission noted that "this is a broad definition and it suffers . . . from several shortcomings."

We can distinguish between institutional corrections and noninstitutional corrections. A 1997 report by the Bureau of Justice Statistics (BJS) says that **institutional corrections** "involves the confinement and rehabilitation of adults and juveniles convicted of offenses against the law and the confinement of persons suspected of a crime awaiting trial and adjudication."[23] BJS goes on to say that "correctional institutions are prisons, reformatories, jails, houses of correction, penitentiaries, correctional farms, workhouses, reception centers, diagnostic centers, industrial schools, training schools, detention centers, and a variety of other types of institutions for the confinement and correction of convicted adults or juveniles who are adjudicated delinquent or in need of supervision. [The term] also includes facilities for the detention of adults and juveniles accused of a crime and awaiting trial or hearing." According to BJS, **noninstitutional corrections,** which is sometimes called *community corrections,* includes "pardon, probation, and parole activities, correctional administration not directly connectable to institutions, and miscellaneous [activities] not directly related to institutional care."

As all these definitions show, in its broadest sense, the term *corrections* encompasses each of the following components, as well as the process of interaction among them:

- The *purpose* and *goals* of the correctional enterprise
- Jails, prisons, correctional institutions, and other *facilities*
- Probation, parole, and alternative and diversionary *programs*
- Federal, state, local, and international correctional offices and *agencies*
- Counseling, educational, health care, nutrition, and many other *services*
- Correctional *clients*
- Corrections *volunteers*
- Corrections *professionals*
- Fiscal appropriations and *funding*
- Various aspects of criminal and civil *law*
- Formal and informal *procedures*
- Effective and responsible *management*
- Community *expectations* regarding correctional practices
- The machinery of *capital punishment*

When we use the word *corrections,* we include all of these elements. Fourteen elements, however, make for an unwieldy definition. Hence, for purposes of discussion, we will say that **corrections** refers to all the various aspects of the pretrial and postconviction management of individuals accused or convicted of crimes. Central to this perspective is the recognition

EXHIBIT 1–1

Teaching Tip
Have students read the ACA policy on the purpose of corrections. Ask them how each of the roles presented reflects society's correctional goals.

ACA American Correctional Association

Purpose of Corrections

The overall mission of criminal and juvenile justice, which consists of law enforcement, courts, and corrections, is to enhance social order and public safety. As a component of the justice system, the role of corrections is:

A. To implement court-ordered supervision and, when necessary, detention of those accused of unlawful behavior prior to adjudication;

B. To assist in maintaining the integrity of law by administering sanctions and punishments imposed by courts for unlawful behavior;

C. To offer the widest range of correctional options, including community corrections, probation, institutions, and parole services, necessary to meet the needs of both society and the individual; and

D. To provide humane program and service opportunities for accused and adjudicated offenders which will enhance their community integration and economic self-sufficiency, and which are administered in a just and equitable manner within the least restrictive environment consistent with public safety.

that corrections—although it involves a variety of programs, services, facilities, and personnel—is essentially a management activity. Rather than stress the role of institutions or agencies, this definition emphasizes the human dimension of correctional activity—especially the efforts of the corrections professionals who undertake the day-to-day tasks. Like any other managed activity, corrections has goals and purposes. Exhibit 1–1 details the purpose of corrections as identified by the American Correctional Association (ACA).

The Societal Goals of Corrections The ACA statement about the purpose of corrections is addressed primarily to corrections professionals. It recognizes, however, that *the* fundamental purpose of corrections "is to enhance social order and public safety." In any society, social order and public safety depend on effective social control. Some forms of social control take the form of customs, norms, and what sociologists refer to as *mores*.

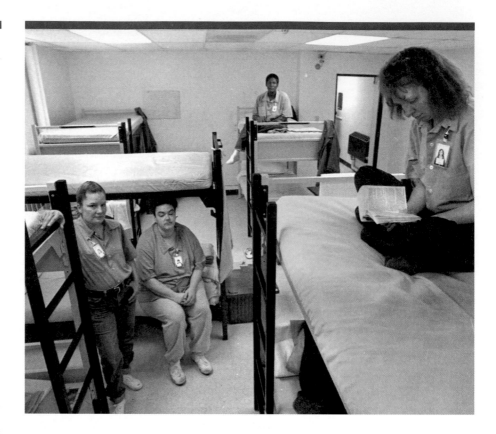

The percentage of women under correctional supervision, although still relatively small, has doubled over the past 10 years. How does this increase in female offenders affect institutional corrections?

Mores are behavioral standards that embody a group's values and the violation of which is a serious wrong. They generally forbid such activities as murder, rape, and robbery. **Folkways,** in contrast, are time-honored ways of doing things. Although folkways carry the force of tradition, their violation is unlikely to threaten the survival of the group.

Societal expectations, whatever form they take, are sometimes enacted into law. The **criminal law,** also called **penal law,** is the body of rules and regulations that define public offenses, or wrongs committed against the state or society, and specify punishments for those offenses. Social control, social order, and public safety are the ultimate goals of criminal law.

The correctional subsystem is crucial in enforcing the dictates of the law because the rewards and punishments it carries out play a significant role in society's control of its members.

Professionalism in Corrections

What is a professional? It isn't easy to say, but we seem to know when we encounter one. Professionals can exist in any field—even a field without clear-cut standards of professionalism, or one in which other professionals are rare. Professionalism and professional attitudes are important in just about any field because they win the respect and admiration of others, and because they make one a trusted participant in almost any endeavor. We

need not limit this discussion to individuals, however. It is possible for a field of endeavor to be recognized as a profession. The legal profession, the medical profession, the nursing profession, and many other fields are now recognized as occupations in which people hold themselves to high standards. Not every participant in these fields is without faults, of course, but the public generally recognizes that, taken as a whole, those who call themselves doctors, for example, can be expected to act professionally and responsibly.

Only a few decades ago, some writers bemoaned the fact that the field of corrections had not achieved professional status. Luckily, much has changed over the past few decades. By 1987, Bob Barrington, who was then the executive director of the International Association of Correctional Officers, was able to proclaim, in a discussion about prisons, that "correctional facilities . . . run smoothly and efficiently for one basic reason: the professional and forward-thinking attitudes and actions of the correctional officers employed."[24]

Barrington noted the dawning of an age of professionalism in corrections. Professionalism, he noted, is rapidly becoming the foundation on which the practice of modern corrections rests. As Barrington wrote, today's correctional officers can say: "I am a corrections professional, and corrections is a profession in its own right."[25] Corrections professionals, added Barrington, ought to be proud to proclaim, "My profession is corrections!"

Some writers on American criminal justice have said that the hallmark of a true profession is "a shared set of principles and customs that transcend self-interest and speak to the essential nature of the particular calling or trade."[26] This definition recognizes the selfless nature of professional work. Hence, "professionals have a sense of commitment to their professions that is usually not present among those in occupational groups."[27] Work within a profession is viewed more as a 'calling' than as a mere way of earning a living. "Professionals have a love for their work that is above that of employment merely to receive a paycheck."[28]

Although it is important to keep formal definitions in mind, for our purposes we will define a **profession** as an occupational group granted high social status by virtue of the personal integrity of its members. We can summarize the *attitude* of a true professional by noting that it is characterized by:

- A spirit of public service and interest in the public good.
- The fair application of reason and the use of intellect to solve problems.
- Self-regulation through a set of internal guidelines by which professionals hold *themselves* accountable for their actions.
- Continual self-appraisal and self-examination.
- An inner sense of professionalism (i.e., honor, self-discipline, commitment, personal integrity, and self-direction).
- A commitment to lifelong learning and lifelong betterment within the profession.

Most professional occupations have developed practices that foster professionalism among their members.

Programmer/Analyst
Plans, develops, and implements computerized database systems, using own knowledge and guidelines established by department of corrections. Prepares system specifications to meet user requirements. Creates test data and programs, ensures uniformity of data definitions, and maintains standards for data dictionaries. Required qualifications include graduation from an accredited institution with a bachelor's or master's degree in civil engineering, computer operations, programming, computer science, business, business administration, engineering, mathematics, statistics, or statistical analysis.

profession An occupational group granted high social status by virtue of the personal integrity of its members.

Student Involvement
Ask students to review the list of characteristics of a professional attitude. Ask which aspects of a professional attitude can be applied to them. Which of these qualities do they feel they are likely to take with them into the work world?

Corrections: The Profession

Standards and Training

Through training, new members of a profession learn the core values and ideals, the basic knowledge, and the accepted practices central to the profession. Setting training standards ensures that the education is uniform. Standards also mandate the teaching of specialized knowledge. Standards supplement training by:

- Setting minimum requirements for entry into the profession.
- Detailing expectations for those involved in the everyday life of correctional work.
- Establishing basic requirements for facilities, programs, and practices.

From the point of view of corrections professionals, training is a matter of personal responsibility. A lifelong commitment to a career ensures that those who think of themselves as professionals will seek the training needed to enhance their job performance.

Historically, professional corrections organizations and their leaders have recognized the importance of training. It was not until the late 1970s, however, that the American Correctional Association (ACA) Commission on Accreditation established the first training standards. The commission:

THE STAFF SPEAKS

I had been a warden for several months when I discovered that it was extremely difficult to obtain basic training for in-service corrections officers. The problem essentially revolved around the cost associated with sending officers to the existing academy, some six hours away, and the overtime required to replace them for four weeks. Our solution was to develop a regional basic training academy at Mercyhurst College in Erie, Pennsylvania. Since the inception of this academy, we have made the training available to students who are not currently employed by any correctional agency. This collaborative effort between the county, the college, and our state oversight agency will produce officers who are not only well trained, but are also invested, both financially and mentally, in the corrections field. These individuals tend to see employment in a prison or jail as not just a job, but a career. I strongly encourage other correctional systems to develop a similar program or to make similar arrangements in order to enhance both custodial service and community involvement in their correctional enterprise. It's a win-win situation all the way around.

Warden Art Amann
Director of Corrections
Erie, PA

- Specified standards for given positions within corrections.
- Identified essential training topics.
- Set specific numbers of hours for preservice (120) and annual inservice training (40).
- Specified basic administrative policy support requirements for training programs.[29]

Following ACA's lead, virtually every state now requires at least 120 hours of preservice training for correctional officers working in institutional settings; many states require more. Probation and parole officers are required to undergo similar training in most jurisdictions, and correctional officers working in jails are similarly trained.

Basic Skills and Knowledge

In 1990, the Professional Education Council of the American Correctional Association developed a model entry test for correctional officers. The test was intended to increase professionalism in the field and to provide a standard criminal justice curriculum.[30]

The council suggested that the test could act "as a quality control measure for such education, much as does the bar exam for attorneys." The standard entry test was designed to "reveal the applicant's understanding of the structure, purpose, and method of the police, prosecution, courts, institutions, probation, parole, community service, and extramural programs." It was also designed to "test for knowledge of various kinds of corrections programs, the role of punitive sanctions and incapacitation, and perspective on past experience and current trends."

More recently, in 1997, Mark S. Fleisher of Illinois State University identified four core traits essential to effective work in corrections.[31] The traits are:

- **Accountability** "Correctional work demands precision, timeliness, accountability and strong ethics." Students may drift into patterns of irresponsibility during their college years. Once they become correctional officers, however, they need to take their work seriously.
- **Strong Writing Skills** Because correctional officers must complete a huge amount of paperwork, they need to be able to write well. They should also be familiar with the "vocabulary of corrections."
- **Effective Presentational Skills** "A correctional career requires strong verbal skills, and an ability to organize presentations." Effective verbal skills help officers interact with their peers, inmates, and superiors.
- **A Logical Mind and the Ability to Solve Problems** Such skills are essential to success in corrections because problems arise daily. Being able to solve them is a sign of an effective officer.

In sum, we can say that a **corrections professional** is a dedicated person of high moral character and personal integrity, who is employed in the field of corrections, and takes professionalism to heart. He or she understands

Tutorial CD-ROM

Refer students to the Tutorial With Simulation Applications CD-ROM. The tutorial is a comprehensive interactive study tool that reinforces and reviews the concepts in Chapter 1. Also included are two simulations that apply concepts presented in Chapter 1.

Teaching Tip

Review the four core traits that, according to Mark S. Fleisher of Illinois State University, are essential to effective work in corrections. Focus on each element, showing how it is important in day-to-day work in corrections.

corrections professional

A dedicated person of high moral character and personal integrity who is employed in the field of corrections and takes professionalism to heart.

Melanie Estes
Day Youth Counselor
United Methodist Family
Services
Richmond, VA

"Working with troubled juveniles is challenging and reward-
ing, especially with abandoned and abused children. I'm not kid-
ding anyone when I say that it is hard to maintain a healthy
balance between friend and caretaker. But one of the greatest
experiences I ever had is to help helpless children."

Melanie Estes has been with the agency for one year and is currently one of two senior counselors. She completed a four-year degree
in Criminal Justice in 1997 and is planning to attend graduate school
in social work at Virginia Commonwealth University.

As a youth counselor, Melanie assists in developing, implementing, evaluating, and modifying individual and group treatment plans.
She ensures that daily routine and expectations are followed in the
residential home. It is also her responsibility to plan, oversee, and
evaluate daily and weekly schedules of agency program activities. She
is the liaison between the agency and the residents' social workers,
probation officers, parents, and any others that may be involved in the
youths' treatment. She keeps all parties informed of residents'
progress.

As a staff member, Melanie's foremost duty is to act as a change
agent for clients in the program. She believes that it is important that
staffers learn that their interactions and interventions with one
another are as crucial to the habilitative process as their interactions
and interventions with youth. As a team member, she is asked to evaluate her coworkers' performance and to provide support, feedback,
and training for other team members. Once a month, she is the chair-
person and recorder for the weekly team meeting.

---

the importance of standards, training, and education, and the need to be proficient in the skills required for success in the correctional enterprise. The corrections professional recognizes that professionalism leads to the betterment
of society, to enhanced social order, and to a higher quality of life for all.

Standard-Setting Organizations

A number of standard-setting organizations and agencies in the field of
corrections have developed models of professionalism. Among them are the
American Correctional Association (ACA), the American Probation and Parole
Association (APPA), the American Jail Association (AJA), and the federal Bureau of Prisons (BOP). Although the first three of these groups are **professional
associations,** BOP is the agency that runs the federal prison system.

Standard-setting organizations like these offer detailed sets of written
principles for correctional occupations and corrections administration. The
ACA, the APPA, and the AJS, for example, all have developed standards to
guide training and to clarify what is expected of those working in correc-

professional associa-
tions Organized groups
of like-minded individuals
who work to enhance the
professional status of
members of their occupa-
tional group.

EXHIBIT 1–2

Federal Bureau of Prisons (BOP)

Mission Statement

It is the mission of the Federal Bureau of Prisons to protect society by confining offenders in the controlled environments of prison and community-based facilities that are safe, humane, and appropriately secure, and that provide work and other self-improvement opportunities to assist offenders in becoming law-abiding citizens.

Source: Federal Bureau of Prisons, July 1998.

tions. Moreover, many professional associations have developed codes of ethics, outlining what is moral and proper conduct. Some of these codes will appear in later chapters.

Correctional associations also offer training, hold meetings and seminars, create and maintain job banks, and produce literature relevant to corrections. They sometimes lobby legislative bodies in an attempt to influence the development of new laws that affect corrections.

The BOP is especially significant as a standard-setting organization because its standards have wide influence. BOP standards govern the day-to-day activities of BOP personnel and institutions. They are also often studied closely by state departments of corrections, which frequently adapt the standards for their own use. Exhibit 1–2 is the Bureau's mission statement.

We will also present ACA policies in future chapters. The ACA policies, like BOP standards, are important because they guide the development of training and because they influence the work environment of many agencies and institutions.

Teaching Tip
Emphasize the importance of professional organizations in the corrections field. Point out that professional associations offer training and help set standards. Explain how they also raise the level of correctional professionalism.

Education

Besides basic job skills and job-specific training, education is another component of true professionalism. Training, by itself, can never make one a true professional, because complex decision-making skills are essential for success in any occupation involving intense interpersonal interaction—and they can be acquired only through general education. Education builds critical-thinking skills, it allows the application of theory and ethical principles to a multitude of situations that are constantly in flux, and it provides insights into on-the-job difficulties.

Correctional education that goes beyond skills training is available primarily from two-year and four-year colleges that offer corrections curricula and programs of study. The day will come when at least a two-year degree will be required for entry into the corrections profession.

Teaching Tip
Refer to Chapter 1 of the *Instructor's Resource Manual* (IRM) for additional activities and for answers to the end-of-chapter exercises.

SUMMARY BY CHAPTER OBJECTIVES

CHAPTER OBJECTIVE 1

Although crime rates are at their lowest level in more than 20 years, correctional populations have been increasing because of get-tough-on-crime attitudes, the nation's War on Drugs, and the increasing reluctance of parole authorities, fearing civil liability and public outcry, to release inmates.

CHAPTER OBJECTIVE 2

Growing correctional populations mean increasing costs. Budgetary allocations for corrections have grown in step with correctional populations. Growth in correctional populations and in spending has also led to a dramatically expanding correctional workforce, and to enhanced employment opportunities within the field.

CHAPTER OBJECTIVE 3

The crimes that bring people into the American correctional system include felonies, which are relatively serious criminal offenses; misdemeanors, which are less serious crimes; and infractions, which are minor law violations.

CHAPTER OBJECTIVE 4

Two important sources of crime statistics are the FBI's Uniform Crime Reports (UCR), published annually under the title *Crime in the United States*, and the National Crime Victimization Survey (NCVS), published by the Bureau of Justice Statistics under the title *Criminal Victimization in the United States*. The UCR reports information on eight major crimes: murder, forcible rape, robbery, aggravated assault, burglary, larceny, automobile theft, and arson. The NCVS provides a detailed picture of crime incidents, victims, and trends. While UCR data are based upon crime reports made to the police, NCVS data are derived from annual nationwide surveys of American households.

CHAPTER OBJECTIVE 5

Criminal justice agencies are said to make up the criminal justice system. The main components of the criminal justice system are (1) police, (2) courts, and (3) corrections. Each can be considered a subsystem of the criminal justice system.

CHAPTER OBJECTIVE 6

The major components of the corrections subsystem are jails, probation, parole, and prisons. Jails and prisons are examples of institutional corrections, while probation and parole are forms of non-institutional corrections.

CHAPTER OBJECTIVE 7

The term *criminal justice* can be used to refer to our *system* of justice, or it can refer to the activities that take place during the justice *process*. Criminal justice agencies, taken together, make up the criminal justice system. Since the activities of criminal justice agencies routinely involve other agencies, the word *system* encompasses not only the agencies of justice, but also the relationships among those agencies. The justice process, on the other hand, refers to the events that unfold as a suspect is processed by the criminal justice system.

CHAPTER OBJECTIVE 8

Corrections refers to all aspects of the pretrial and postconviction management of individuals accused or convicted of crimes.

CHAPTER OBJECTIVE 9

Professionalism in corrections is important because it can win the respect and admiration of others outside of the field. Moreover, professionals are regarded as trusted participants in any field of endeavor.

correctional clients, p. 2
felony, p. 8
misdemeanor, p. 8
infraction, p. 8
violent crime, p. 9
property crime, p. 9
crime index, p. 9
crime rate, p. 10

criminal justice, p. 14
criminal justice system, p. 14
adjudication, p. 18
nolo contendere, p. 18
writ of *certiorari*, p. 19
institutional corrections, p. 20
noninstitutional corrections,
   p. 20

corrections, p. 20
mores, p. 22
folkways, p. 22
criminal law, p. 22
penal law, p. 22
profession, p. 23
corrections professional, p. 25
professional associations, p. 26

QUESTIONS FOR REVIEW

1. Compare crime rates with correctional populations over time. What differences stand out? How might you explain them?

2. What three major categories of crime are discussed in this chapter? Explain the differences between them. Why is it important for corrections professionals to understand these differences?

3. Compare and contrast the Uniform Crime Reports and the National Crime Victimization Survey. What are the major differences? What are the similarities? What is the significance of these sources of information to the field of corrections?

4. What are the major components of the criminal justice system? Why did we say that the term *criminal justice* can be used to refer either to our system of justice or to the activities that take place during the justice *process?*

5. According to the ACA, what are the four fundamental purposes of corrections?

6. Explain how the UCR calculates its yearly crime rate.

7. According to the UCR, when is a crime considered *cleared* or *solved?*

8. What is the major difference between the original UCR system and the new system—NIBRS?

9. List four components of the corrections subsystem.

10. What is the function of a preliminary hearing?

11. Name and describe the first step in the adjudication process.

12. List at least five sentencing choices available to a judge or jury.

13. Based on the ACA statement defining corrections, what is the *fundamental* purpose of corrections?

14. Define criminal law.

15. List five characteristics of a true professional.

CRITICAL THINKING EXERCISES

ON-THE-JOB ISSUE

Today is the first day of your job as a correctional officer. A severe statewide shortage of officers required you to begin work immediately. You are scheduled to attend the training academy in three months. You are ushered into a meeting with the warden. He welcomes you to his facility and gives you a brief pep talk. He asks if you have any concerns. You tell him, "Well, I feel a little uneasy. I haven't gone through the academy yet." "Don't worry," he says, "all our new recruits get on-the-job experience before a slot in the acad-

emy opens up. You'll do fine!" He shakes your hand and leads you to the door.

After you leave the warden's office, you are given a set of keys and a can of mace. The shift supervisor, a sergeant, gives you a brief tour of the prison. Then he tells you that as you learn your job, you will spend most of your time with another officer; though pairing up will not always be possible.

The officer you are assigned to accompany is named Harold Gates. At first, you follow Officer Gates across the compound, getting more familiar with the layout of the facility. Then you spend an uneventful afternoon working with Officer Gates in the yard.

At 4:30, Officer Gates instructs you to make sure that all inmates have left the classroom building in preparation for a "count." As you enter the building, you encounter a group of six inmates heading toward the door. Before you can move to the side, one of the inmates walks to within an inch of you and stares at you. The others crowd in behind him. You can't move. You are pinned to the door by the men.

The man directly in front of you is huge—over six feet tall and about 280 pounds. His legs look like tree trunks, and his arms are held away from his body by their sheer bulk. You're staring at a chest that could easily pass as a brick wall. With a snarl he growls, "What do you want?"

1. How will you respond? Would you feel more confident responding to a situation like this if you had had some training?

2. If you tell the inmates that it's time for a count, and to move along, what will you do next? Will you ask anyone for guidance in similar future situations, or just chalk the encounter up as a learning experience? Who might you talk to about it?

3. Suppose you were a manager or supervisor at this facility. How would you handle the training of new recruits?

CORRECTIONS ISSUES

1. Dianne Carter, President of the National Academy of Corrections, once said, "Too often in corrections, only worker skills are targeted for training, and the organization misses a significant opportunity to communicate its vision and mission."[32] Do you agree or disagree with this statement? Why?

2. Harold Williamson, a writer in the corrections field has noted, "Higher levels of professionalization require greater amounts of training and usually involve increased specialization when compared to lesser professionalized activity. Higher levels of professionalization also involve the learning of more abstract knowledge and information."[33] Do you agree? Why or why not?

CORRECTIONS ON THE WEB

Access the Web sites of the following professional corrections organizations. For each one, determine the organization's mission, membership, services offered, and benefits of membership. Then, using the information you have gathered, decide whether you, as a correctional professional, should be a member of the organization, and whether the agency with which you are associated should be a member. Explain the reasons for your answers.

American Correctional Association
http://www.corrections.com/aca

American Jail Association
http://www.corrections.com/aja

American Probation and Parole Association
http://www.csg.org/appa

International Association of Correctional Officers
http://www.acsp.uic.edu/iaco/about.htm

National Sheriffs' Association (includes jailers)
http://www.sheriffs.org

ADDITIONAL READINGS

DiMascio, William M., *Seeking Justice: Crime and Punishment in America.* New York: The Edna McConnell Clark Foundation, 1997.

Gilbert, M. J., "Correctional Training Standards: A Basis for Improving Quality and Professionalism," in Ann Dargis (ed.), *State of Corrections: Proceedings of ACA Annual Conference, 1989.* Lanham, MD: ACA, 1990, pp. 44–58.

Haas, Kenneth C., and Geoffrey P. Alpert. *The Dilemmas of Corrections: Contemporary Readings,* 2d ed. Prospect Heights, IL: Waveland Press, 1991.

Josi, Don A. and Dale K. Sechrest, *The Changing Career of the Professional Officer: Policy Implications for the 21st Century.* Boston: Butterworth-Heineman, 1998.

ENDNOTES

1. Details for this story come from Selwyn Raab, "A Shadow Priest Who Ministers to His Fellow Convicts," *New York Times* News Service, August 17, 1997.
2. Fox Butterfield, "Crime Keeps on Falling, but Prisons Keep on Filling," *New York Times* News Service, September 28, 1997.
3. Quoted ibid.
4. John P. Conrad, "The Pessimistic Reflections of a Chronic Optimist," *Federal Probation*, Vol. 55, No. 2, 1991, p. 4.
5. Ibid., p. 8.
6. See, for example, Jory Farr, "A Growth Enterprise." http://www.press-enterprise.com/focus/prison/html/a growth industry.html
7. Bureau of Justice Statistics, *Correctional Populations in the United States* (Washington: U.S. Department of Justice, May 1997).
8. Margaret Werner Cahalan, *Historical Corrections Statistics in the United States, 1850–1984* (Washington: U.S. Department of Justice, 1986).
9. Allen J. Beck and Christopher J. Mumola, *Prisoners in 1998* (Washington: BJS, 1999).
10. Thomas P. Bonczar and Lauren E. Glaze, *Probation and Parole in the United States, 1998* (Washington: BJS, 1999).
11. Kathleen Maguire and Ann L. Pastore (eds.), *Sourcebook of Criminal Justice Statistics*. Online, available: http://www.albany.edu/sourcebook, posted October 15, 1997.
12. Ibid., Table 1.11.
13. Butterfield.
14. Cahalan.
15. Greg Wees, "Fewer Correctional Officer Positions Created in 1996," *Corrections Compendium*, August 1996, pp. 12–14.
16. Statistics courtesy of David M. Wakefield at the American Correctional Association, fax transmission, June 12, 1998. Preliminary data for the table "Personnel in Adult and Juvenile Corrections" in ACA, *Vital Statistics in Corrections* (forthcoming).
17. Some of the material in this section is adapted from Bureau of Justice Statistics, *The Nation's Two Crime Measures* (Washington: U.S. Department of Justice, November 1995).
18. Callie Marie Rennison, "Criminal Victimization 1998: Changes 1997–98, With Trends 1973–98." (Washington: BJS, 1999).
19. The figure may be somewhat misleading, however, because an offender who commits a number of crimes may be prosecuted for only one.
20. Much of the following material is adapted from Bureau of Justice Statistics, *Report to the Nation on Crime and Justice*, 2d ed. (Washington: BJS, 1988), pp. 56–58.
21. President's Commission on Law Enforcement and Administration of Justice, *The Challenge of Crime in a Free Society* (Washington: U.S. Government Printing Office, 1967), p. 159.
22. National Advisory Commission on Criminal Justice Standards and Goals, *Corrections* (Washington: U.S. Government Printing Office, 1975), p. 2.
23. Bureau of Justice Statistics, *Correctional Populations in the United States, 1995* (Washington: U.S. Government Printing Office, 1997).
24. Bob Barrington, "Corrections: Defining the Profession and the Roles of Staff," *Corrections Today*, August 1987, pp. 116–120.
25. Ibid., paraphrased.
26. Arlin Adams, *The Legal Profession: A Critical Evaluation*, 93 Dick. L. Rev. 643 (1989).
27. Harold E. Williamson, *The Corrections Profession* (Newbury Park, CA: Sage, 1990), p. 79.
28. Adams.
29. Ibid., p. 20.
30. P. P. Lejins, "ACA Education Council Proposes Correctional Officer Entry Tests," *Corrections Today*, Vol. 52, No. 1 (February 1990), pp. 56, 58, 60.
31. Mark S. Fleisher, "Teaching Correctional Management to Criminal Justice Majors," *Journal of Criminal Justice Education*, Vol. 8, No. 1, Spring 1997, pp. 59–73.
32. Dianne Carter, "The Status of Education and Training in Corrections," *Federal Probation*, Vol. 55, No. 2 (June 1991), pp. 17–23.
33. Williamson.

2 Sentencing
To Punish or To Reform?

CHAPTER OBJECTIVES

After completing this chapter you should be able to:

1. Describe sentencing philosophy and identify the central purpose of criminal punishment.
2. Name the five goals of criminal sentencing.
3. List and explain the sentencing options in general use today.
4. Explain what a model of criminal sentencing is and identify models in use today.
5. Describe three-strikes laws and their impact on the correctional system.
6. Identify and explain some major issues related to fair sentencing.

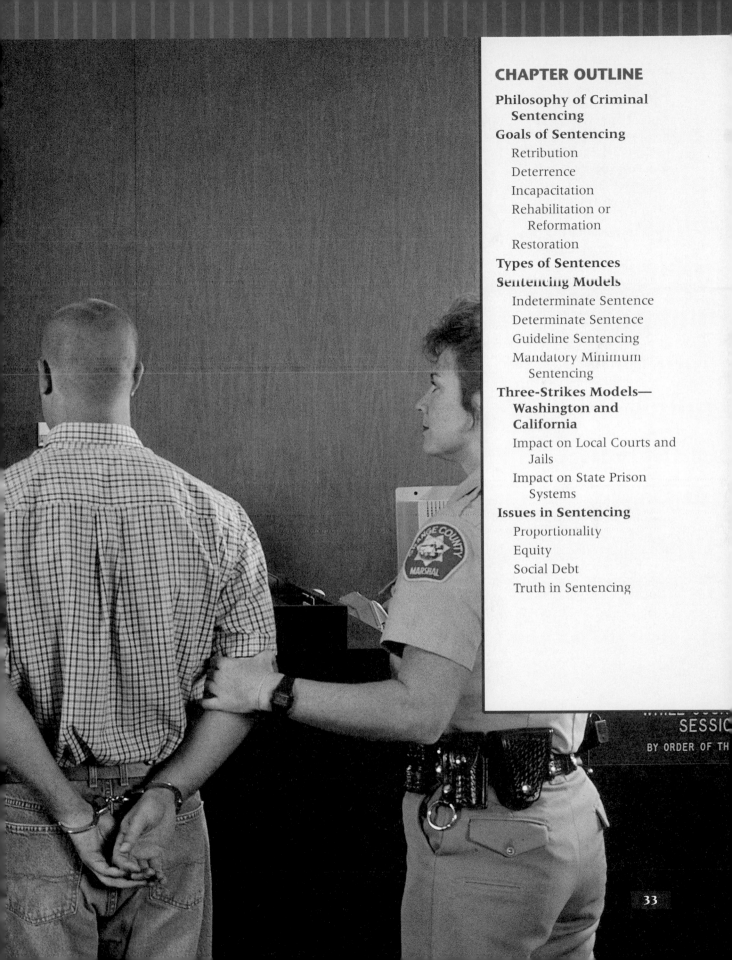

CHAPTER OUTLINE

Philosophy of Criminal Sentencing

Goals of Sentencing

   Retribution

   Deterrence

   Incapacitation

   Rehabilitation or Reformation

   Restoration

Types of Sentences

Sentencing Models

   Indeterminate Sentence

   Determinate Sentence

   Guideline Sentencing

   Mandatory Minimum Sentencing

Three-Strikes Models— Washington and California

   Impact on Local Courts and Jails

   Impact on State Prison Systems

Issues in Sentencing

   Proportionality

   Equity

   Social Debt

   Truth in Sentencing

SESSIC

BY ORDER OF TH

33

Teaching Tip

Distinguish between the action of *sentencing* (a judicial process resulting in the imposition of sanctions on a convicted offender) and a *sentence* (the penalty so imposed). Remind students that a judge can sentence an offender.

sentencing The imposition of a criminal sanction by a sentencing authority, such as a judge.

sentence The penalty a court imposes on a person convicted of a crime.

> *We will not punish a man because he hath offended, but that he may offend no more; nor does punishment ever look to the past, but to the future; for it is not the result of passion, but that the same thing be guarded against in time to come.*
>
> —Seneca (3 B.C.–A.D. 65)

On Halloween day 1997, 19-year-old British *au pair* Louise Woodward was sentenced to life in prison for second-degree murder.[1] One day earlier, a Massachusetts jury had found Woodward guilty of killing 8-month-old Matthew Eappen, a child in her care. Medical testimony at Woodward's trial convinced the jury that the boy died from injuries he had received while being severely shaken. According to medical experts, the boy's head had also been slammed against a wall. The child died five days later in a local hospital. Prosecutors argued that Woodward had fatally injured the boy during a fit of rage induced by his constant crying. Under Massachusetts law, Woodward, who denied hurting the boy, would have been eligible for parole in 15 years.

In an astonishing turnabout, Woodward was released a week later by state superior court judge Hiller B. Zobel, who overturned her murder conviction, reducing it to involuntary manslaughter. Woodward was sentenced to the time she had already served—279 days in jail. The judge ruled that Woodward's second-degree murder conviction had been a "miscarriage of justice," and concluded that "it is time to bring the judicial part of this extraordinary matter to a compassionate conclusion." The Woodward case, while relatively unusual, demonstrates judicial power in the determination of sentences.

Most criminal convictions, however, are not overturned. On the day before Woodward was convicted, the South Carolina Supreme Court upheld an 8-year prison sentence for Cornelia Whitner. Whitner had pleaded guilty in 1992 to child neglect after giving birth to a baby with measurable amounts of cocaine in its blood. Finding that a viable fetus is a "person" covered by the state's child-abuse laws, the state supreme court upheld the criminal prosecution of pregnant women who use drugs.[2] Ms. Whitner's attorneys planned to appeal the decision to the U.S. Supreme Court. "If women who use drugs during pregnancy can be prosecuted for child abuse," they asked, "what about women who drink or smoke while pregnant, or fail to get prenatal care?"

Although these cases are significantly different in many ways, both highlight the role of sentencing in the justice process. **Sentencing** is a court's imposition of a penalty on a convicted offender. A **sentence** is the penalty imposed.

This chapter concerns itself with the nature, history, purpose, and philosophy of criminal sentencing. One of the most crucial issues surrounding sentencing is whether to punish or to reform. The punish or reform debate has a long history and continues to concern many people today. We turn now to an examination of the history of sentencing philosophy.

Philosophy of Criminal Sentencing

One of the most crucial issues in sentencing is whether to punish or to reform. The punish-or-reform debate has a long history and continues to concern many people today. Western society has a long tradition of punishing criminal offenders. Historically, offenders were banished, exiled, killed, or physically abused. Corporal, or physical, punishments became common during the Middle Ages, replacing executions as the preferred penalty. Physical punishments such as flogging and mutilation, though severe in themselves, prevented rampant use of the death penalty. Eventually, as we shall see in later chapters, imprisonment and a variety of other sentencing alternatives replaced corporal punishments as criminal sanctions.

Even so, the sentencing of offenders is still intimately associated with historical notions of punishment. Crimes are frequently seen as *deserving* of punishment. We often hear it said that the criminal must "pay his or her debt to society," or that "criminals deserve to be punished." John Conrad puts it another way: "The punishment of the criminal is the collective reaction of the community to the wrong that has been done."[3] Conrad goes on to say, "It is the offender's lot to be punished."

Philosophers have long debated *why* a wrongful act should be punished. Many social scientists suggest that criminal punishment maintains and defends the **social order.** By threatening potential law violators and by making the lives of violators uncomfortable, they say, punishments reduce the likelihood of future or continued criminal behavior.

Still, one might ask, instead of punishing offenders, why not offer them psychological treatment, or educate them so that they are less prone to future law violation? The answer to this question is far from clear. Although criminal sentencing today has a variety of goals, and educational and treatment programs are more common now in corrections, punishment still takes center stage in society's view. Some writers, like Conrad, have suggested that society will always *need* to punish criminals because punishment is a natural response to those who break social taboos.[4] Others disagree, arguing that an enlightened society will choose instead to reform law breakers through humanitarian means.

Goals of Sentencing

In late 1997, Chautauqua County, New York, District Attorney Jim Subjack announced that he would pursue charges of reckless endangerment against 20-year-old Nushawn Williams. Williams, a convicted drug dealer, was accused of infecting as many as 103 teenage girls and young women with the AIDS virus in a series of drugs-for-sex encounters.[5] Subjack said that Williams had sex with the women while knowing he was HIV positive, keeping a journal of his many "conquests." The prosecutor charged Williams with reckless endangerment for each sexual encounter, and with first-degree assault for each partner who subsequently became infected. He was also charged with statutory rape for allegedly having sex with a 13-year-old

Teaching Tip
Discuss historical punishments such as banishment, flogging, mutilation, branding, and death. Point out that sentencing today is still closely associated with notions of punishment and that a sentence is often seen as appropriate or not because of the degree of punishment that it imposes.

social order   The smooth functioning of social institutions, the existence of positive and productive relations between individual members of society, and the orderly functioning of society as a whole.

Student Involvement
This chapter raises the question, "Instead of punishing offenders, why not offer them psychological treatment, or educate them so that they are less prone to future law violation?" Ask your class to respond.

retribution A sentencing goal that involves revenge against a criminal perpetrator.

girl, who later tested positive for the virus. "It takes an individual with no regard for human life to do something like this," Subjack said.

The Williams case demonstrates a crucial component of contemporary sentencing philosophy: that people must be held accountable for their actions, and for the harm they cause. From this perspective, the purpose of the criminal justice system is to identify persons who have acted in intentionally harmful ways and (where a law is in place) to hold them accountable for their actions by imposing sanctions. Seen this way, our justice system is primarily an instrument of retribution.

Sentencing also has a variety of other purposes. As shown in Table 2–1, the modern goals of sentencing are: (1) retribution, (2) deterrence, (3) incapacitation, (4) rehabilitation or reformation, and (5) restoration.

Retribution

One of the earliest goals of criminal sentencing was **retribution,** the payment of a debt to society and, thus, atonement for a person's offense.

TABLE 2–1

Goals of Criminal Sentencing

Goal	Rationale
Retribution	Punishment is appropriate for wrongdoing. Punishment serves a purpose for both society and the wrongdoer. Wrongdoers should be punished.
Incapacitation	Some wrongdoers cannot be changed and need to be segregated from society. Society has the responsibility to protect law-abiding citizens from those whose behavior cannot be controlled.
Deterrence	Punishment will prevent future wrongdoing by the offender and by others. Punishment must outweigh the benefits gained by wrongdoing.
Rehabilitation or Reformation	Society needs to help offenders learn how to behave appropriately. Without learning acceptable behavior patterns, offenders will not be able to behave appropriately.
Restoration	Crime is primarily an offense against human relationships, and secondarily a violation of a law. All those who suffered because of a crime should be restored to their previous sense of well-being.

Historically, retribution was couched in terms of "getting even," and it has sometimes been explained as "an eye for an eye, and a tooth for a tooth." *Retribution* literally means "paying back" the offender for what he or she has done. It is often equated with vengeance or revenge. Retribution, in a very fundamental way, expresses society's disapproval of criminal behavior and implies the payment of a debt to society.

Retribution remains one of the central goals of sentencing today—although it is now often expressed as **just deserts.** Just-deserts advocates claim that criminal acts are *deserving* of punishment and that justice is served by the imposition of appropriate punishments on criminal-law violators. As one contemporary author explains it, "Many of us have turned to retribution not only as the object of punishment, but as a basis for making sentences fair and equitable."[6] Even so, it is not always easy to determine just how much punishment is enough.

Deterrence

A second goal of criminal sentencing is **deterrence.** Deterrence is the discouragement or prevention of crimes similar to the one for which an offender is being sentenced. Two forms of deterrence can be identified: specific and general.

Specific deterrence is the deterrence of the individual being punished from committing additional crimes. Long ago, specific deterrence was achieved through corporal punishments that maimed offenders in ways that precluded similar crimes in the future. Spies had their eyes gouged out and their tongues removed, rapists were castrated, thieves had their fingers or hands cut off, and so on. Even today, in some countries that follow a strict Islamic code, the hands of habitual thieves are cut off as a form of corporal punishment.

General deterrence occurs when the punishment of an individual serves as an example to others who might be thinking of committing a crime—thereby dissuading them from their planned course of action. The **pleasure-pain principle** is central to modern discussions of general deterrence. The pleasure-pain principle assumes that the threat of loss to anyone convicted of a crime should outweigh the potential pleasure to be gained by committing the crime.

For punishment to be effective as a deterrent, it must be relatively certain, swiftly applied, and sufficiently severe. *Certainty, swiftness,* and *severity* of punishment are not always easy to achieve. The crime funnel, described in Chapter 1, demonstrates that most offenses do not end in arrest and most arrests do not end in incarceration. Although it may not be easy for all offenders to get away with crime, the likelihood that any individual offender will be arrested, successfully prosecuted, and then punished is far smaller than deterrence advocates would like it to be. When an arrest does occur, an offender is typically released on bail, and because of an overcrowded court system, the trial, if any, may be a year or so later. Moreover, although the severity of punishments has increased in recent years, modern punishments are rarely as severe as those of earlier centuries. Arguments over just how much punishment is enough to deter further violations of the criminal law rarely lead to any clear conclusion.

just deserts The punishment deserved. A just-deserts perspective on criminal sentencing holds that criminal acts are *deserving* of punishment and that justice is best served by the imposition of appropriate punishments on criminal-law violators.

deterrence The discouragement or prevention of crimes similar to the one for which an offender is being sentenced; a goal of criminal sentencing.

specific deterrence The deterrence of the individual being punished from committing additional crimes.

general deterrence The use of the example of individual punishment to dissuade others from committing crimes.

pleasure-pain principle The idea that actions are motivated primarily by a person's desire to seek pleasure and avoid pain.

Teaching Tip
Point out the differences between *general* and *specific deterrence.* Ask whether certainty, swiftness, and severity of punishment contribute more to general deterrence or to specific deterrence.

Well, here I am, about 2½ years into my life sentence in prison. The worst part so far for me has been the loneliness. It really gets to me sometimes. I'm close to 3000 miles away from my family, and I'm locked away from the people I hold dear and love. I really don't have anyone right now. I think my family is still digesting the fact that I'm in prison. I don't hear from them very often. They've never been ones to write, and I guess I really haven't, either.

I don't have a lot of human contact because I'm locked up in a single cell with a steel door. When the door shuts, I'm left to myself. I do get out about an hour a day, which includes 20 minutes for each meal. I also get out to exercise three times a week for 1½ hours. Other than that, it's cell time.

With all the time I have alone in my cell, my brain works overtime. I think about my life over and over again. I think about the good times and the bad times. It all comes out when you're left to yourself. Your mind goes in so many directions. I think about all the people I've hurt over the years, whether physically, emotionally, or financially. I'm just now feeling the pain that I caused so many years ago to so many people. My mind makes me remember the things that I don't want to remember. Then I have to deal with them internally.

I think about my crime every day of my life. I took a human life. What makes a man do that? I don't really know. All I can remember is the anger I felt and the hurt feelings. I can remember my heart hurting so bad that I couldn't function normally anymore. I cried all the time and I couldn't eat or sleep. At first it was all jealousy and then it was anger and pain. I guess it all came to a head that night. I had never felt that much rage before in my life. When it was over, I was holding a lifeless body in my arms. I couldn't speak or move. All I could feel was my soul leaving my body. It was an emptiness that I hope I never feel again. It was like I too had died that night.

So many what-ifs go through my mind these days. What if I wasn't an alcoholic? What if I hadn't lost my temper? What if I'd had the will to turn and walk away? So many what-ifs.

I often think about what effect all this has had on my friends and family. I remember the day I was sentenced like it was yesterday. It was one of the hardest times of my life. I knew ahead of time what I was getting, but it didn't make it any easier. The tears, the stares, the looks, and the glares were all directed in court from people who were once my friends. It was the final stop on the road of heartbreak and misery. I was sentenced to life so I couldn't hurt anyone else ever again (or at least I thought so). I called home that afternoon to let my family know that it was all over and that I was going down for life. My father told me that my Mom had tried to kill herself by putting a .38 in her mouth. By a miracle of God, my Dad had called home at that very moment and talked her out of it. He made it home in time to save her life. She was so depressed about me, plus she was addicted to painkillers because she had so many back operations. I wanted so much to comfort her, but I couldn't. I didn't know how. I didn't know how to get in touch with my feelings. I guess my pain and suffering tried to reach out for another victim, but luckily God intervened that time.

I think all the pain that I ever caused people comes back to me twofold. I experience all the pain that I caused and then some.

I remember the time I saw my father cry. It was a day I'll never forget. It was a day or two after I was arrested and a week before I was extradited to Arizona when he came to visit me in the county jail in Pennsylvania. I was so nervous knowing that he was coming that day. We hadn't talked in years. He didn't like me much at all because I had disappointed him so many times over the years. I couldn't blame him. I was a failure in his eyes as well as mine. I walked down the hallway to where my father was sitting. I sat down in a chair and looked at him through the glass that separated us. He looked so broken and so sad. We picked up the phones and started to talk. The tears just started to run down his face. I had a lump in my throat so that I couldn't swallow. My heart was bleeding inside and the pain was unbearable to see a rock of a man crumble before me because of what I had done. I wanted to end my life right there. My father didn't deserve what I was putting him through. He tried so hard to be a good father. He was strict but fair. I know it wasn't easy for him. I was his stepson. All through my childhood, he never treated me like less than his own son. We were just two very different people, and I rebelled against him every chance I could. As I looked into my father's eyes, I wished that he could hug me and I could cry too. I wanted to release all of this pain. We talked for a while and then he left. I knew I might never see him again.

I never wanted to cause my family pain again. I never want to cause a tear. I can't change what I've done with my life, but I sure can change myself. I can be a person that people can be proud to know. For the first time in my life, I'm drug- and alcohol-free. It's all new

to me, and it's a great feeling. I can't remember a time I wasn't high since I was 15 years old.

I guess I should thank God for letting me live for 31 years. I tried to destroy myself so many times with drugs, alcohol, and suicide attempts. I lived on the edge of life most of my life, and occasionally I fell off. In a way, prison has saved my life. I would have died at a young age from drugs or alcohol, or maybe the suicide attempts would have worked sooner or later. I guess in a sense I'm lucky. I know it's a strange way to look at things, but that's the way I see it. I'm just thankful I was able to overcome all the demons in my life. I'm a better person now. I'm responsible, caring, and able to be kind. I guess that's all part of growing up and that's what I've done the past few years. I still have a long way to go, but it's a start.

I guess my mind did work overtime on this story. It's sad, but a true part of my life. I tried to clear these things from my mind, but I couldn't. The mind never forgets. It's always there. Sometimes it just reminds you of an event or an experience, just to keep you humble, and when you sleep, it's there to haunt you through your dreams.

The mind is so awesome. I want to share my knowledge and all my thoughts and feelings with someone. It's time. I don't want to be lonely anymore. I'm going to place an ad in the newspaper for a pen pal. I need to get on with the rest of my life. I want to find the woman of my dreams, my best friend. I now know I'm a human being.

George Killian, #82256
ASPC-Eyman Complex
Meadows Unit
Florence, Arizona

Incapacitation

incapacitation The use of imprisonment or other means to reduce an offender's capability to commit future offenses; a goal of criminal sentencing.

Many believe that the huge increase in the number of correctional clients has helped lower the crime rate by incapacitating more criminals. Many of these criminals are behind bars, and others are on supervised regimens of probation and parole. **Incapacitation** restrains offenders from committing additional crimes by isolating them from free society. A 1997 report by the National Center for Policy Analysis, for example, observed that a "major reason for [the] reduction in crime is that crime has become more costly to the perpetrators. The likelihood of going to prison for committing any type of major crime has increased substantially."[7] The center reported that over the previous four years:

- The murder rate dropped 23 percent as the probability of going to prison for murder rose 17 percent.
- Rape decreased 12 percent as the probability of imprisonment increased 9 percent.
- Robbery decreased 21 percent as the probability of imprisonment increased 14 percent.
- Aggravated assault decreased 11 percent as the probability of imprisonment increased 5 percent.
- Burglary decreased 15 percent as the probability of imprisonment increased 14 percent.

Student Involvement
Discuss the belief of many people that increasing expected punishments will reduce the incidence of crime. Ask what the basis for such an argument might be. Is such a belief valid?

The report claims that "the best overall measure of the potential cost to a criminal of committing crimes is *expected punishment*." Expected punishment, said the report, "is the number of days in prison a criminal can expect to serve for committing a crime." The center calculated expected punishment by multiplying the median sentence imposed for each crime by the probabilities of being apprehended, prosecuted, convicted, and sentenced.

As a goal of sentencing, incapacitation restrains offenders from committing more crimes by isolating them from society. Does this threat of isolation from society encourage law-abiding behavior?

Sentencing: To Punish or To Reform?

Crime rates are declining, said the report, because expected prison stays are significantly longer today than two decades ago for every category of serious crime.

According to the center, "between 1980 and 1995, expected punishment more than doubled for murder and nearly tripled for rape. It increased by about three-fourths for burglary and larceny/theft and increased 60 percent for motor vehicle theft."

A number of studies have claimed to show that incapacitating offenders through incarceration is cost-effective. Such studies conclude that imprisoning certain types of offenders (especially career or habitual offenders) results in savings by eliminating the social costs of the crimes offenders would be likely to commit if they were not imprisoned. Those social costs include monetary loss, medical costs of physical injury, and time lost from work.

One of the most frequently cited studies attempting to quantify the net costs of incarceration was done by Edwin W. Zedlewski.[8] Zedlewski used a Rand Corporation survey of inmates in three states (Michigan, Texas, and California) to estimate the number of crimes each inmate would commit if not imprisoned. In the survey, the average respondent reported committing anywhere from 187 to 287 crimes annually just before being incarcerated. To calculate the cost associated with each crime, Zedlewski divided the total criminal justice expenditures in the United States by the total number of crimes committed in the United States. From this he concluded that the average crime "cost" $2,300. Multiplying $2,300 by the 187 crimes estimated to be committed annually by a felon, Zedlewski calculated that society saves $430,100 per year for each felon who is incarcerated. Figuring that incarceration costs society about $25,000 per prisoner per year, he concluded that prisons produce a cost-benefit return to society of 17 to 1 ($17 saved for every $1 spent)—leading him to strongly support increased incarceration.

Three years after Zedlewski's work, well-known criminologist John DiIulio performed a cost-benefit analysis, using a survey of Wisconsin prisoners. The study, called "Crime and Punishment in Wisconsin," led to the conclusion that prisons saved taxpayers in Wisconsin approximately $2 for every dollar they cost.[9]

Studies such as those by Zedlewski and DiIulio are part of the growing field of correctional econometrics. **Correctional econometrics** is the study of the cost-effectiveness of various correctional programs and related reductions in the incidence of crime.[10]

Rehabilitation or Reformation

The goal of **rehabilitation** or reformation is to change criminal lifestyles into law-abiding ones. Rehabilitation has been accomplished when an offender's criminal patterns of thought and behavior have been replaced by allegiance to society's values. Rehabilitation focuses on medical and psychological treatments and on social skills training, all designed to "correct" the problems that led the individual to crime.

A subgoal of rehabilitation is **reintegration** of the offender with the community. Reintegrating the offender with the community means making the offender a productive member of society—one who contributes to the

Teaching Tip
Point out that *correctional econometrics* is based on cost-benefit analysis, that is, a comparison of the costs and benefits of a particular action for the purpose of assessing its desirability. Ask students if they think this principle can validly be applied to corrections. Ask them to explain their answers.

correctional econometrics The study of the cost-effectiveness of various correctional programs and related reductions in the incidence of crime.

rehabilitation The changing of criminal lifestyles into law-abiding ones by "correcting" the behavior of offenders through treatment, education, and training; a sentencing goal.

reintegration The process of making the offender a productive member of the community.

general well-being of the whole. *Social integration* might be another way to express this goal.

During the 1970s, rehabilitation came under harsh criticism, even though it had been the primary rationale for punishing offenders since the early 1900s. Some states abandoned rehabilitation altogether or de-emphasized it in favor of the goals of retribution and incapacitation. In other states, attempts at rehabilitation continued. Today some governments and private organizations are returning to a belief in rehabilitation, emphasizing treatment and education. According to Edgardo Rotman, "In order to neutralize the desocializing potential of prisons, a civilized society is forced into rehabilitative undertakings. These become an essential ingredient of its correctional system taken as a whole. A correctional system" with no "interest in treatment," says Rotman, "means . . . de-humanization and regression."[11]

Restoration

restoration The process of returning to their previous condition all those involved in or affected by crime—including victims, offenders, and society; a recent goal of criminal sentencing.

victim-impact statement A description of the harm and suffering that a crime has caused victims and survivors.

In recent years, a new goal of criminal sentencing, known as **restoration,** has developed. Restorative justice is based on the belief that criminal sentencing should involve restoration and justice for all involved in or affected by crime. Hence, while advocates of restorative justice believe that the victim should be restored by the justice process, they also suggest that the offender and society should participate in the restoration process.

A restorative justice perspective allows judges and juries to consider **victim-impact statements** in their sentencing decisions. These are descriptions of the harm and suffering that a crime has caused victims and their survivors. Also among the programs being introduced on behalf of victims and their survivors are victim assistance and victim-compensation programs.

Other efforts at restoration place equal emphasis on victims' rights and needs and on the successful reintegration of offenders into the community. Restorative justice seeks to restore the health of the community, repair the harm done, meet victims' needs, and require the offender to contribute to those repairs. Thus, the criminal act is condemned, offenders are held accountable, offenders and victims are involved as participants, and repentant offenders are encouraged to earn their way back into the good graces of society.

Student Involvement
Discuss restoration as a sentencing goal. Do students think it is possible to "restore" the victim and to have the offender and society in general be part of the restoration process?

Teaching Tip
Remind students that a law must define a behavior as a crime for there to be a punishment associated with engaging in that behavior.

Types of Sentences

Legislatures establish the types of sentences that can be imposed. The U.S. Congress and the 50 state legislatures each decide what is against the law and define crimes and their punishments in the jurisdictions in which they have control. Sentencing options in wide use today include the following:

- fines and other monetary sanctions
- probation
- alternative or intermediate sanctions such as day fines, community service, electronic monitoring, and day reporting centers
- incarceration
- death penalty

As punishment for unlawful behavior, fines have a long history. By the fifth century B.C., Greece, for example, had developed an extensive system of fines for a wide variety of offenses.[12] Under our modern system of justice, fines are usually imposed as punishment for misdemeanors and infractions. When imposed on felony offenders, fines are frequently combined with another punishment, such as probation or incarceration.

Fines are only one type of monetary sanction in use today. Others include the court-ordered payment of the costs of trial, victim restitution, various fees, forfeitures, donations, and confiscations. **Restitution** consists of payments made by a criminal offender to his or her victim as compensation for the harm caused by the offense. While fines are usually paid to the government, restitution may be paid directly to the victim (or paid to the court and turned over to the victim). Some innovative courts have ordered offenders to donate specified amounts to specified charities in lieu of a fine.[13] Restitution is an example of a restorative-justice sentencing option.

With a sentence of probation, the convicted offender continues to live in the community, but must comply with court-imposed restrictions on his or her movements. Alternative or intermediate sentencing options usually combine probation with some other punishment, such as community service or house arrest with electronic monitoring. A sentence of incarceration, or total confinement away from the community, is used when the community needs to be protected from further criminal activity by an offender. The death penalty, or capital punishment, is the ultimate sentence. Figure 2–1 displays recent trends in three sentencing options compared with parole.

The sentence is generally imposed by the judge. Sentencing responsibility can also be exercised by the jury, or a group of judges, or it may be man-

restitution Payments made by a criminal offender to his or her victim (or to the court, which then turns them over to the victim) as compensation for the harm caused by the offense.

Student Involvement
Refer students to Figure 2–1. Why do they think the figures for probation are so high?

FIGURE 2–1

Adults on Probation, in Jail or in Prison, or on Parole

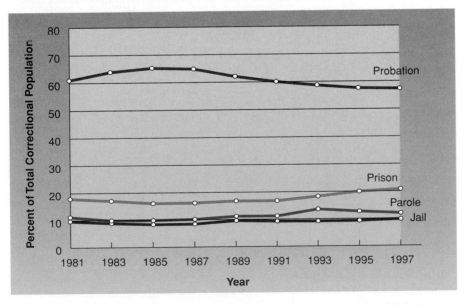

Source: Adapted from Kathleen Maguire and Ann L. Pastore (eds.), *Sourcebook of Criminal Justice Statistics 1997* (Washington: Bureau of Justice Statistics, October 1998), p. 464.

mandatory sentences
Those that are required by law under certain circumstances—such as conviction of a specified crime or of a series of offenses of a specified type.

presentence investigation report (PSI)
A report, prepared by the probation department of a court, that provides a social and personal history as well as an evaluation of a defendant as an aid to the court in determining a sentence.

consecutive sentences
Sentences served one after the other.

concurrent sentences
Sentences served together.

model of criminal sentencing   A strategy or system for imposing criminal sanctions.

flat sentences   Those that specify a given amount of time to be served in custody and allow little or no variation from the time specified.

Teaching Tip
Refer students to Table 2–2. Use the descriptions of the sentencing models to review and reinforce for students the differences among the types of sentences.

dated by statute. **Mandatory sentences** are those that are required by law under certain circumstances—such as conviction of a specified crime or of a series of offenses of a specified type. Mandatory sentences may add prison time to sentences for offenders who carried weapons during the commission of their crimes, who used or possessed illegal drugs, or who perpetrated crimes against elderly victims. Such sentences allow judges no leeway in sentencing.

Even when there is no mandatory sentence, judges cannot impose just any sentence. They are still limited by statutory provisions. They also are guided by prevailing sentencing goals. A judge usually considers a **presentence investigation report**, sometimes called a **PSI**. This report, prepared by the probation department attached to a court, is a social and personal history as well as an evaluation of the offender. Finally, judges' sentencing decisions are influenced by their own personal convictions and characteristics.

Once the sentence is chosen, the judge must decide how it will be served, especially if more than one sentence is being imposed. Sentences can be consecutive or concurrent. **Consecutive sentences** are served one after the other. When a person is convicted of multiple offenses, a judge might impose, for example, a sentence of 10 years for one offense and 20 years for another. If the sentences are to run consecutively, the offender will begin serving the second sentence only after the first one expires. **Concurrent sentences** are served together. If the sentences in the example are to run concurrently, the 10-year sentence will expire when the offender has served one-half of the 20-year sentence. The offender will then need to serve the remainder of the 20-year sentence before being released.

Sentencing Models

A **model of criminal sentencing** is a strategy or system for imposing criminal sanctions. Sentencing models vary widely (Table 2–2). Over the past 100 years, a shift has occurred from what might be called a judicial model of sentencing to an administrative model. Judges generally have far less discretion in sentencing decisions today than they previously did. The majority of sentences imposed in American courts today follow legislative and administrative guidelines.

Sentencing in nineteenth century-America involved mostly fines, probation, and "flat" prison sentences. **Flat sentences** specify a given amount of time to be served in custody and allow little or no variation from the time specified. A typical flat sentence might be stated as "five years in prison." Flat sentences generally meant that an offender had to complete the sentence imposed and could not earn an early release.

Indeterminate Sentence

By the close of the nineteenth century, sentencing reform in the United States began replacing the flat sentence with indeterminate sentences.[14] At the time, the criminal justice system was coping with a rapidly expanding and increasingly diverse prison population, the increased efficiency of the police and courts, and other factors. Overcrowded prisons and the warehousing of inmates resulted.[15]

TABLE 2–2

Sentencing Models

■ **Determinate Sentencing**

Sentencing to a fixed term of incarceration that may be reduced by good time. Usually, explicit standards specify the amount of punishment and a set release date, with no review by a parole board or other administrative agency. Postincarceration supervision may be part of the sentence.

■ **Indeterminate Sentencing**

Sentencing in which an administrative agency, generally a parole board, has the authority to release an incarcerated offender and to determine whether an offender's parole will be revoked for violation of the conditions of release. In one form of indeterminate sentencing, the judge specifies only the maximum sentence length (a fixed term); the associated minimum is automatically implied but is not within the judge's discretion. In the more traditional form of indeterminate sentencing, the judge specifies maximum and minimum durations within limits set by statute. The judge has discretion over the minimum and maximum sentences.

■ **Presumptive Guidelines Sentencing**

Sentencing that meets all the following conditions: (1) The appropriate sentence for an offender in a specific case is presumed to fall within a range authorized by guidelines adopted by a legislatively created sentencing body, usually a sentencing commission; (2) judges are expected to sentence within the range or provide written justification for departure; and (3) the guidelines provide for review of the departure, usually by appeal to a higher court. Presumptive guidelines may employ determinate or indeterminate sentencing structures.

■ **Voluntary/Advisory Guidelines Sentencing**

Recommended sentencing policies that are not required by law. They serve as a guide and are based on past sentencing practices. The legislature has not mandated their use. Voluntary/advisory guidelines may use determinate or indeterminate sentencing structures.

■ **Mandatory Minimum Sentencing**

A minimum sentence that is specified by statute for all offenders convicted of a particular crime or a particular crime with special circumstances (e.g., robbery with a firearm or selling drugs to a minor within 1000 feet of a school). Mandatory minimums can be used in both determinate and indeterminate sentencing structures. Within an indeterminate sentencing structure, the mandatory minimum requires the inmate to serve a fixed amount of time in prison before being eligible for release with the approval of a parole board. Under a determinate sentence, the offender is required to serve a fixed amount of time in prison before being eligible for release.

In an **indeterminate sentence**, the judge specifies a maximum length and a minimum length, within limits set by statute, and a parole board determines the actual time of release. The parole board's determination depends on the board's judgment of whether the prisoner has been reformed, has been cured, or has simply served enough time. An example of an indeterminate sentence is "five to ten years in prison." A second form of indeterminate sentencing requires the judge to specify only the maximum sentence length, with the associated minimum set by statute. Some states, for example, require an offender to serve as little as one-quarter of the sentence before becoming eligible for parole.

indeterminate sentence

A sentence in which a judge specifies a maximum length and a minimum length, and an administrative agency, generally a parole board, determines the actual time of release.

good time The number
of days or months prison
authorities deduct from a
sentence for good behav-
ior and for other reasons.

Professional Issue
Good-Time Credits Pose the
following scenario: You are
a corrections officer. The
state legislature recently
repealed the law granting
good-time credits.
Prisoners sentenced prior
to the repeal will continue
to earn credits; those sentenced since the repeal will
not. How might this situation affect you?

determinate sentence
(also called *fixed sentence*)
A sentence to a fixed term
of incarceration, which
can be reduced by good
time. Under determinate
sentencing, for example,
all offenders convicted of
the same degree of bur-
glary are sentenced to the
same length of time
behind bars.

With an indeterminate sentence, discretion is distributed, not only among the prosecutor, defense counsel, and judge, but also to prison officials and the parole board, which have considerable influence over an offender's length of stay. Prison officials have discretion over the amount of **good time** an inmate earns, which can affect parole eligibility, the discharge date, or both. The parole board decides the actual release date for most inmates. The result is a system of sentencing in which few people understand or can predict who will be imprisoned and for how long.

Under indeterminate sentencing, punishments are made to fit the criminal rather than the crime. Proponents of indeterminate sentences assume that crime is a product of individual deviation from the norm and that rehabilitation can be achieved within a prison system designed to punish and not treat inmates. They also assume that prison personnel have the knowledge to impose treatment or to predict recidivism accurately enough to justify discretion over when an inmate should be released. The use of indeterminate sentences has prompted numerous accusations of disparity in sentencing as well as protests from inmate groups, penologists, and other critics of the penal system. These protests spurred a movement for sentencing reform.

Determinate Sentence

A **determinate sentence** (also known as a *fixed sentence*) specifies a fixed period of incarceration, which can be reduced for "good time" served. The term is generally used to refer to the sentencing reforms of the late 1970s. Determinate sentences are generally based on the incapacitation and deterrence goals of sentencing. The theory behind determinate sentencing is that criminals will be off the streets for longer periods of time. The other advantage, supporters say, is that prisoners know when they will be released. In most determinate sentencing models, parole is limited or is replaced by the use of good-time credits. With good time, inmates are able to reduce their sentences by earning credits. The amount of the reduction depends on the number of credits earned. Good time credits can be earned by demonstrating good behavior and not being "written up" for violating prison rules. It can also be earned by participating in educational programs, community service projects, or medical experiments. The procedure for earning credits and the number that can be earned vary from state to state. Prison administrators generally favor determinate sentencing and good time credits because they aid in controlling prison populations.

Guideline Sentencing

As we have seen, the sentences that judges impose are regulated by law. As part of the movement to eliminate sentencing disparities, some states, as well as the federal government, have enacted sentencing guidelines for judges to follow. The guidelines fall into two categories.

Voluntary/Advisory Sentencing Guidelines Among the earliest guided-sentencing innovations in the United States was the experiment with voluntary guidelines, also called advisory guidelines. These are recommended sentencing policies that are not required by law. Usually they are based on past sentencing practices and serve as a guide to judges. Voluntary or advisory guidelines have had disappointing results, often because they are not enforced and are sometimes ignored. In some instances, insufficient time has been allowed for the guidelines to take hold. More important, the guidelines are voluntary; judges can simply ignore them. A review of all the major studies conducted on voluntary and advisory guidelines reveals low compliance by judges and, hence, little reduction in disparity.[16]

Presumptive Sentencing Guidelines   By the early 1980s, states had begun to experiment with the use of presumptive sentencing guidelines. (See Table 2–3 for a summary of sentencing practices by state.) These models differ from determinate sentences and voluntary or advisory guidelines in three respects. First, the guidelines are developed, not by the legislature, but by a **sentencing commission** that often represents diverse interests, including private citizens as well as all segments of the criminal justice system. Second, the guidelines are explicit and highly structured, relying on a quantitative scoring instrument. Third, the guidelines are not voluntary or advisory. Judges must adhere to the sentencing system or provide a written rationale for departure.

The forces stimulating presumptive sentencing guidelines were the same as those that had driven the moves to determinate sentencing and voluntary or advisory guidelines: issues of fairness and prison crowding. These concerns provided the impetus for states to adopt guidelines, replace indeterminate sentencing with determinate sentencing, and abolish or reduce discretionary parole release.

The first four states to adopt presumptive sentencing guidelines were Minnesota (1980), Pennsylvania (1982), Washington (1983), and Florida (1983). The Minnesota model, in particular, with its focus on controlling prison population growth, has often been cited as an example of the successful control of disparity and rising corrections costs through sentencing guidelines. Like those of most other states, the Minnesota model uses a sentencing matrix of offense severity and offender's prior criminal history to indicate the sentence is appropriate in any given case. The matrix provides ranges for specified offenses within which judges can impose sentence.

Federal Sentencing Guidelines   In the early 1980s, the U.S. Congress focused its attention on disparity in sentencing.[17] Congress concluded that the sentencing discretion of federal trial judges needed boundaries. The resulting legislation, termed the Sentencing Reform Act of 1984,[18] created the U.S. Sentencing Commission. The nine-member commission, first organized in October 1985, is a permanent body charged with formulating and amending national sentencing guidelines. The commission's guidelines apply to all federal criminal offenses committed on or after November 1, 1987. Congress has mandated that federal trial judges must follow the guidelines in their sentencing decisions.

The commission may submit guideline amendments to Congress each year between the beginning of the regular congressional session and May 1. Suggested amendments automatically take effect 180 days after submission unless Congress rejects them.

Student Involvement

Refer students to Table 2–3. Have them find the categories marked for your state. Ask students what your state's sentencing practices indicate about the state's primary goal in sentencing.

sentencing commission

A group assigned to create a schedule of sentences that reflect the gravity of the offenses committed and the prior record of the criminal offender. The commission often includes private citizens as well as representatives of the criminal justice system, including law enforcement, courts, and corrections.

Teaching Tip

Describe the role of sentencing commissions in the preparation of sentencing guidelines. Tell how the role of commissions differs from legislative creation of guidelines.

Teaching Tip

Describe the role accorded to the U.S. Sentencing Commission under the Sentencing Reform Act of 1984. Mention the purposes the guidelines were to serve, according to the law.

TABLE 2–3

Sentencing Practices by State, 1996

State	Determinate Sentencing	Indeterminate Sentencing	Guideline Sentencing by Type	Mandatory Minimum Sentencing
Alabama		◆		◆
Alaska		◆		◆
Arizona	◆			◆
Arkansas		◆	Voluntary/Advisory	◆
California	◆			◆
Colorado		◆		◆
Connecticut		◆		◆
Delaware	◆		Presumptive	◆
District of Columbia		◆		◆
Florida	◆		Presumptive	◆
Georgia		◆		◆
Hawaii		◆		◆
Idaho		◆		◆
Illinois	◆			◆
Indiana		◆		◆
Iowa		◆		◆
Kansas		◆	Presumptive	◆
Kentucky		◆		◆
Louisiana		◆	Voluntary/Advisory	◆
Maine	◆			◆
Maryland		◆	Voluntary/Advisory	◆
Massachusetts		◆	Under Study	◆
Michigan		◆	Under Study	◆
Minnesota	◆		Presumptive	◆
Mississippi	◆			◆
Missouri		◆	Voluntary	◆
Montana		◆	Under Study	◆

TABLE 2–3 (continued)

Sentencing Practices by State, 1996

State	Determinate Sentencing	Indeterminate Sentencing	Guideline Sentencing by Type	Mandatory Minimum Sentencing
Nebraska		◆		◆
Nevada		◆		◆
New Hampshire		◆		◆
New Jersey		◆		◆
New Mexico	◆			◆
New York		◆		◆
North Carolina	◆		Presumptive	◆
North Dakota		◆		◆
Ohio	◆		Presumptive	◆
Oklahoma		◆	Voluntary/Advisory	◆
Oregon	◆		Presumptive	◆
Pennsylvania		◆	Presumptive	◆
Rhode Island		◆		◆
South Carolina		◆		◆
South Dakota		◆		◆
Tennessee[1]		◆	Presumptive	◆
Texas		◆		◆
Utah		◆	Voluntary/Advisory	◆
Vermont		◆		◆
Virginia	◆		Voluntary/Advisory	◆
Washington	◆		Presumptive	◆
West Virginia		◆		◆
Wisconsin[1]		◆		◆
Wyoming		◆		◆
TOTAL	14	37	17	51

1. Tennessee and Wisconsin continue to have sentencing guidelines; the sentencing commissions were abolished in 1996.

Source: Prepared by National Council on Crime and Delinquency. Published in Bureau of Justice Assistance, *1996 National Survey of State Sentencing Structures* (Washington: U.S. Department of Justice, September 1998) NCJ169270.

Research Associate

The Criminal Sentencing Commission seeks a Research Associate who will perform a wide variety of studies focusing on criminal sentencing decisions and their impacts. This position will work with Commission project teams to develop sentencing models, identify risk factors of recidivism, analyze impacts of proposed policy changes, and on other justice system topics. Requirements: proficiency in social science research methods and ability to communicate complex information to lay audiences. An advanced degree in a social science discipline is desirable. Experience with statistical software is required.

---

mandatory minimum sentencing The imposition of sentences required by statute on those convicted of a particular crime or a particular crime with special circumstances, such as robbery with a firearm or selling drugs to a minor within 1000 feet of a school, or on those with a particular type of criminal history.

Teaching Tip

Point out that a qualifying felony is one defined as serious or violent under a state's law.

Federal sentencing guidelines take into account the defendant's criminal history, the nature of the criminal conduct, and the particular circumstances surrounding the offense. Ordinarily, a judge must choose a sentence within a range set forth in the guidelines. Deviations from that range must be explained in writing.

In addition to creating the Sentencing Commission, the Sentencing Reform Act abolished parole for federal offenders sentenced under the guidelines. The sentence imposed is essentially the sentence served. Under the law, inmates may earn up to 54 days of credit (time off their sentences) each year for good behavior.

Mandatory Minimum Sentencing

Mandatory minimum sentencing refers to the imposition of sentences required by statute for those convicted of a particular crime or a particular crime with special circumstances, such as robbery with a firearm or selling drugs to a minor within 1000 feet of a school, or on those with a particular type of criminal history. By 1994, all 50 states had enacted one or more mandatory minimum sentencing laws,[19] and Congress had enacted numerous mandatory sentencing laws for federal offenders. Mandatory minimum sentencing rationales dominated the 1980s and early 1990s.

Recently, many states have adopted *sentence enhancements*, usually the mandating of longer prison terms for violent offenders with records of serious crimes. Mandatory sentence enhancements aim to deter known and potentially violent offenders and to incapacitate convicted criminals through long-term incarceration.[20] These sentence enhancements have come to be known as *three-strikes laws* (and, in some jurisdictions, two-strikes laws).

Three-strikes laws vary in breadth. Some stipulate that both the prior convictions and the current offense must be violent felonies; others require only that the prior felonies be violent. Some three-strikes laws count only prior adult convictions; others permit consideration of juvenile adjudications for violent crimes. Under California's three-strikes law, an offender who is convicted of a qualifying felony and has two prior qualifying felony convictions must serve a minimum of 25 years. The law also doubles prison terms for offenders convicted of a second violent felony.[21]

Rationales Mandatory sentences have two goals—deterrence and incapacitation. The primary purposes of modest mandatory prison terms (e.g., three years for armed robbery) are specific deterrence, for already-punished offenders, and general deterrence, for prospective offenders. If the law increases the imprisonment rate, it also serves the goal of incapacitation, leaving fewer offenders free to victimize the population at large. The intent of three-strikes (and even two-strikes) laws is to incapacitate selected violent offenders for very long terms—25 years or even life. Mandatory sentencing laws have become highly politicized. By passing mandatory sentencing laws, legislators can convey that they deem certain crimes especially grave and that people who commit these crimes deserve, and can expect, harsh sanc-

Mandatory sentencing laws are often passed in reaction to public outcries against especially violent or well-publicized criminal acts. Does mandatory sentencing fulfill the goals of deterrence and incapacitation?

tions. Such laws typically are a rapid and visible response to public outcries following heinous or well-publicized crimes.

Impact   Mandatory sentencing has had significant consequences that deserve close attention. Among them are its impact on crime and the operations of the criminal justice system. The possibility that the consequences will be different for different groups of people also bears examination.

Crime   Evaluations of mandatory minimum sentencing have focused on two types of crimes—those committed with handguns and those related to drugs (the offenses most commonly subject to mandatory minimum penalties in state and federal courts). An evaluation of the Massachusetts law that imposed mandatory jail terms for possession of an unlicensed handgun concluded that the law was an effective deterrent of gun crime, at least in the short term.[22]

However, studies of similar laws in Michigan[23] and Florida[24] found no evidence that crimes committed with firearms had been prevented. An evaluation of mandatory sentence enhancements for gun use in six large cities (Detroit, Jacksonville, Tampa, Miami, Philadelphia, and Pittsburgh) indicated that the laws deterred homicide but not other violent crimes.[25] An assessment of New York's Rockefeller drug laws was unable to support their claimed efficacy in deterring drug crime in New York City.[26]

The Criminal Justice System   The criminal courts rely on a high rate of guilty pleas to speed case processing and thus avoid logjams. Officials can offer inducements to defendants to obtain these pleas. At least in the short term, mandatory sentencing laws may disrupt established plea-bargaining patterns by preventing a prosecutor from offering a short prison term (less than the new minimum) in exchange for a guilty plea. However, unless policy makers enact the same mandatory sentences for several related crimes, prosecutors can usually shift strategies and bargain on charges rather than on sentences.

Student Involvement
Explain that mandatory sentencing rationales have led to the creation of two- and three-strikes laws. Ask students what the impact of these laws has been on crime rates and the operations of the criminal justice system.

Michael Tonry, a criminal justice scholar, has summarized the findings of research on the impact of mandatory sentencing laws on the criminal justice system.[27] He concluded that mandatory sentencing laws:

- Do not achieve certainty and predictability because officials circumvent them if they believe the results are unduly harsh.
- Are redundant in requiring imprisonment for serious cases because the offenders in such cases are generally sentenced to prison anyway.
- Are arbitrary in the sentences they require for minor cases.
- May occasionally result in an unduly harsh punishment for a marginal offender.[28]

Most two- and three-strikes laws leave judges no discretion to deviate from the sentences dictated by legislatures. Another central feature of such laws is the extraordinary length of the prison terms they require. Offenders serving life sentences in California and North Carolina under such legislation, for example, become eligible for parole only after serving 25 years, those in New Mexico after 30 years, and those in Colorado after 40 years. Three-strikes laws in some states mandate life without the possibility of parole. Two- and three-strikes laws came about in response to public concerns about crime and the growing belief that many serious offenders were being released from prison too soon.[29] Proponents view such legislation as the best way to deal with the persistent, serious violent offender—the proverbial three-time loser.

Two- and three-strikes laws are a form of **habitual offender statute.** Although habitual offender laws have been on the books in a number of jurisdictions since the 1940s or earlier, the older laws were often geared to specific types of prior offenses, such as crimes of violence, sex offenses, or crimes perpetrated with guns. Moreover, most early habitual offender laws allowed enhanced sentences, but did not make them mandatory as do two- and three-strikes legislation.[30]

Three-Strikes Models— Washington and California

Between 1993 and 1995, 24 states and the federal government enacted new habitual offender laws that fell into the three-strikes category.[31] Washington state was the first of those to do so.[32] California soon followed with a considerably broader version of the three-strikes law. As those laws were being implemented, the impact they would have on the criminal justice systems of those states was debated. Proponents predicted the laws would curb crime and protect society by warehousing the worst offenders for a long time. Opponents argued that defendants facing lengthy mandatory sentences would be more likely to demand trials, slowing the processing of cases, and that more offenders would serve long terms of incarceration, ballooning prison populations, already at crisis levels in many states.[33]

Although they were enacted within months of each other, amid the same "three strikes and you're out" rallying cry, and they include many of the same offenses as strikes, the Washington and California laws differ in

habitual offender statute   A law that (1) allows a person's criminal history to be considered at sentencing or (2) allows a person convicted of a given offense, and previously convicted of another specified offense, to receive a more severe penalty than that for the current offense alone.

three important ways. First, in Washington all three strikes must be for felonies specifically listed in the legislation. Under the California law, only the first two convictions must be from the state's list of "strikeable" offenses; any subsequent felony can count as the third strike. Second, the California law contains a two-strikes provision, by which a person convicted of any felony after one prior conviction for a strikeable offense is to be sentenced to twice the term he or she would otherwise receive. There is no two-strikes provision in the Washington law. Third, the sanctions for a third strike differ. The Washington statute requires a life term in prison without the possibility of parole for a person convicted for the third time of any of the "most serious offenses" listed in the law. In California a "third-striker" has at least the possibility of being released after 25 years.[34]

Impact on Local Courts and Jails

When three-strikes laws were first passed in Washington and California, some analysts projected a much greater impact on local criminal justice systems in California, because the California law had a much broader scope.[35] They predicted that California courts would be overwhelmed as defendants facing enhanced penalties demanded jury trials. The added time to process cases through trials and the reluctance of courts to grant pretrial release to defendants facing long prison terms, they said, would cause jail populations to explode as the number of jail admissions and the length of jail stays grew.[36]

Early evidence from California supported these predictions. A review of 12,600 two- and three-strikes cases from Los Angeles, for example, showed that two-strikes cases took 16 percent longer to process, and three-strikes cases 41 percent longer, than nonstrike cases.[37] In addition, strikes cases were three times as likely to go to trial as nonstrike felonies, and four times as likely as the same types of cases before the law took effect. This effect led to a 25 percent increase in jury trials, as well as an 11 percentage-point rise in the proportion of the jail population awaiting trial, from 59 percent before the law was enacted to 70 percent. Furthermore, a survey of sheriff's departments showed that the pretrial detainee population in the state had grown from 51 percent of the average daily population before the three-strikes law to 61 percent by January 1, 1995.[38]

According to more recent data, however, at least some California counties are learning to handle the changes brought about by the law. A survey of eight California counties with populations of more than 1 million identified several that were successfully disposing of two- and three-strikes cases early in the process.[39] In addition, data from the Los Angeles County Sheriff's Department suggest that the pace of strikes cases coming into that system may be slowing.[40]

Impact on State Prison Systems

The impact of the Washington and California laws on state corrections departments has not been as severe as projected. Planners in Washington

Drug Court Coordinator

Duties include (1) coordinating a variety of specialized and complex clerical tasks related to court operations, (2) assisting litigants and attorneys using the court system, (3) informing them of court procedures and policies, and (4) answering questions and correspondence about court procedure and status of cases. Required qualifications: associate's degree or paralegal certification from a professional training program, along with two years of increasingly responsible experience demonstrating the knowledge, skill, and ability to perform the duties listed above.

Tutorial CD-ROM

Refer students to the Tutorial With Simulation Applications CD-ROM. The tutorial is a comprehensive interactive study tool that reinforces and reviews the concepts in Chapter 2. Also included are two simulations that apply concepts presented in Chapter 2.

I am a Director and Regional Administrator for the state prison system, and I supervise nursing students in a locked ward with criminally insane clients. In addition, I'm a researcher for the National Commission on Correctional Health Care. The Commission surveys prisons, jails, juvenile facilities, and immigration facilities all over the United States. I have directed teams in 29 states, in facilities ranging from 38 to 1000 beds. Part of my job in prison is to consult and transport clients to other countries, which have in the past included Spain, Portugal, Canada, Panama, and Venezuela.

I love this field and encourage students who want a challenge and a career that is interesting to give corrections, especially work with the criminally insane, a look. Every day and every interaction with our clients is different. No two days are alike, and no two situations are similar.

Dr. Roger Childers
Supervisor, Psychiatric Unit for Criminally
*   Insane*
Bryce Hospital
Tuscaloosa, Alabama

Student Involvement
Ask selected students to research the 1996 California Supreme Court case of *People v. Superior Court (Romero)*. Have them report to the class, telling what the court decided and what impact that decision is likely to have on mandatory sentencing in California.

fair sentencing
Sentencing practices that incorporate fairness for both victims and offenders. Fairness is said to be achieved by implementing principles of proportionality, equity, social debt, and truth in sentencing.

had expected that 40 to 75 persons would be sentenced under three-strikes provisions each year. The actual numbers, however, have been much lower. During the first three years the law was in effect, only 85 offenders—not the 120-225 projected—were admitted to the state prison system under the three-strikes law.[41]

A similar overestimate was made of the impact the California law would have on prisons there. As of January 1, 1997, a total of 26,074 offenders had been admitted to the California Department of Corrections (CDC) for two- or three-strikes sentences.[42] Of this number, nearly 90 percent were sentenced under the two-strikes provision. Although the sheer number of cases affected by the law is significantly higher than for any other state, the numbers are not as great as originally projected.

Issues in Sentencing

Many sentencing reforms have been an attempt to reduce disparity in sentencing and make the process more fair. The term **fair sentencing** or *fairness in sentencing* has become popular in recent years. Although fair sentencing today often refers to fairness for *victims*, many suggest that any truly

Joseph L. Hackett
Correctional Case
Analyst
Neuse Correctional
Institution
Wayne County, NC

"I think 90 percent of them [offenders] came from a dysfunctional family and encountered drug abuse or alcohol abuse. Yes, they made the decisions to do the crimes they committed, but if we, as a great society and a great state, can provide support and education to some of these individuals, we can make a difference, which could lead some of them to productive lives. It really gives me great pleasure to be part of that enterprise."

Joseph L. Hackett is a correctional case analyst with Neuse Correctional Institution in Wayne County, North Carolina. He joined the department as a correctional officer in 1993, three months before earning his associate's degree from a local community college. Over the next three years, he worked third shift at a medium-custody penitentiary and attended college to complete his four-year degree. After graduation, he had many job interviews throughout the North Carolina Department of Corrections and, finally, after the ninth one, was offered his current position.

Joseph now conducts mental health screenings and makes custody classification recommendations for inmates at a state intake center. Part of his job is to investigate the backgrounds of inmates before he makes recommendations. On a typical workday, Joseph might contact a law enforcement agency, the district attorney's office, and several parole agencies to learn about an inmate. "My job? I love it. I never thought I'd be happy about coming to work. I liked being a CO, but sometimes there was a little too much danger lurking around the yard."

---

fair sentencing scheme must incorporate fairness for both victims and offenders. Issues related to fairness in sentencing are:

- proportionality
- equity
- social debt
- truth in sentencing

Proportionality

Proportionality is the sentencing principle that the severity of punishment should match the seriousness of the crime for which the sentence is imposed. To most people today, the death penalty would seem grossly disproportional to the offense of larceny—even if the offender had a history of such violations. (This, however, has not always been the case. Larceny *was* punishable by death in medieval England.) On the other hand, probation would seem disproportional to the crime of murder—although it is occasionally imposed in homicide cases.

Teaching Tip
Discuss proportionality, equity, social debt, and truth in sentencing. Explain the differences among them.

proportionality The sentencing principle that the severity of punishment should match the seriousness of the crime for which the sentence is imposed.

Equity

equity The sentencing principle that similar crimes and similar criminals should be treated alike.

Equity is the sentencing principle that similar crimes and similar criminals should be treated alike. The alternative to equity is disparity, in which similar crimes are associated with different punishments in different jurisdictions or in which offenders with similar criminal histories receive widely differing sentences. Disparity can also result from judicial discretion when judges hold widely different sentencing philosophies. In a jurisdiction with wide leeway for judges to determine sentences, one judge might treat offenders very harshly while another is lenient. Under such circumstances, now largely eliminated by sentencing reform, one burglar, for example, might receive a sentence of 30 years in prison upon conviction while his partner in crime is put on probation simply because he appears before a more lenient judge.

Social Debt

social debt The sentencing principle that the severity of punishment should take into account the offender's prior criminal behavior.

Social debt is the sentencing principle that the severity of punishment should take into account the offender's prior criminal behavior. As we have seen, a number of laws designed to recognize social debt have recently been passed. Among them are three-strikes and two-strikes laws. Although there is considerable variation in such laws between states, the primary characteristic of these laws is that they "call for enhanced penalties for offenders with one or more prior felony convictions."[43] They require a repeat offender to serve several years in prison in addition to the penalty imposed for the current offense.

FIGURE 2–2

Time Served in State Prisons Compared With Court Sentences

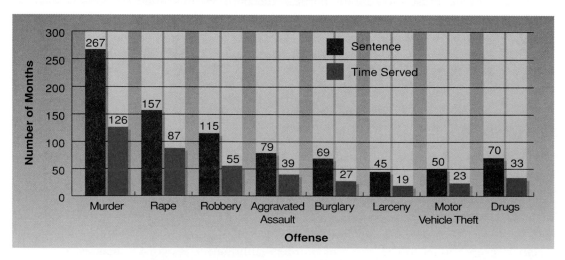

Source: Patrick A. Langan and Jodi M. Brown, *Felony Sentences in the United States, 1994* (Washington: Bureau of Justice Statistics, 1997).

Sentencing: To Punish or To Reform?

Truth in Sentencing

Until the sentencing reforms of the 1970s, the laws of many states enabled convicted offenders to be released from prison long before they had served their full sentences. Inmates frequently had good time deducted from their sentences, or time off for good behavior. *Gain time* could be earned for going to school, learning a trade, or doing volunteer work. Moreover, many states mandated routine parole eligibility after inmates had served one-quarter, or even one-fifth, of their sentences.

Recent truth-in-sentencing laws have changed such practices by requiring offenders to complete sentences very close to the ones they are given. **Truth in sentencing** requires an offender to serve a substantial portion of the sentence and reduces the discrepancy between the sentence imposed and actual time spent in prison. The results of a recent study, comparing actual time served in prison with sentences imposed, can be seen in Figure 2–2 on page 56. The Violent Crime Control and Law Enforcement Act of 1994 includes a truth-in-sentencing provision. To qualify for federal aid under the act, a state must amend its laws so that an imprisoned offender serves at least 85 percent of his or her sentence before being released. Parole eligibility and good-time credits are generally restricted or eliminated in truth-in-sentencing laws.

As you can see, the purposes of sentencing are diverse, and the issues surrounding it are many and complex.

Student Involvement
Direct students to research the truth-in-sentencing requirement in your state. Then ask them to speculate about the effect that requirement might have on prison populations in your state. Also refer students to Figure 2–2 and ask them why actual *time served* is often far less than the *sentence imposed.*

truth in sentencing
The sentencing principle that requires an offender to serve a substantial portion of the sentence and reduces the discrepancy between the sentence imposed and actual time spent in prison.

Teaching Tip
Refer to Chapter 2 of the *Instructor's Resource Manual* for additional activities and for answers to the end-of-chapter exercises.

SUMMARY BY CHAPTER OBJECTIVES

CHAPTER OBJECTIVE 1

The philosophy underlying criminal sentencing is that people must be held accountable for their actions and the harm they cause. Western society has a long tradition of sentencing criminal offenders to some form of punishment. Many social scientists suggest that the central purpose of criminal punishment is to maintain social order.

CHAPTER OBJECTIVE 2

The goals of criminal sentencing today are (1) retribution, (2) deterrence, (3) incapacitation, (4) rehabilitation or reformation, and (5) restoration.

CHAPTER OBJECTIVE 3

Sentencing options in use today include fines and other monetary sanctions, probation, alternative or intermediate sentences, incarceration, and capital punishment.

CHAPTER OBJECTIVE 4

A model of criminal sentencing is a strategy or system for imposing criminal sanctions. Sentencing models vary widely among the juris-dictions in the United States. These models include indeterminate sentences, determinate sentences, voluntary or advisory sentencing guidelines, presumptive sentencing guidelines, and mandatory minimum sentencing.

CHAPTER OBJECTIVE 5

Recent laws have increased penalties for criminal offenses, particularly violent crimes, and for repeat offenders. Many such laws are three-strikes laws. The rationale for such laws is simple: Offenders convicted repeatedly of serious offenses should be removed from society for long periods of time. Many three-strikes laws mandate a life sentence for the third violent-felony conviction. Analysts of three-strikes laws predicted that courts would be overwhelmed as more defen-dants, facing enhanced penalties, demanded jury trials. The added time to process cases and the reluctance to grant pretrial release to defendants facing long prison terms, said analysts, would cause jail populations to explode as the number of admissions and the length of jail stays grew. The actual effects of the laws have been similar to the effects predicted, but not as great.

CHAPTER OBJECTIVE 6

Fair sentencing often refers to fairness for *victims*. Fair sentencing advocates, however, suggest that any truly fair sentencing scheme must incorpo-rate fairness for both victims and offenders. Issues related to fairness in sentencing are proportional-ity, equity, social debt, and truth in sentencing.

KEY TERMS

sentencing, p. 34
sentence, p. 34
social order, p. 35
retribution, p.36
just deserts, p. 37
deterrence, p. 37
specific deterrence, p. 37

general deterrence, p. 37
pleasure-pain principle, p. 37
incapacitation, p. 40
correctional econometrics, p. 41
rehabilitation, p. 41
reintegration, p. 41
restoration, p. 42

QUESTIONS FOR REVIEW

1. Define *sentencing*.
2. What are the modern goals of criminal sentencing?
3. Define *retribution*.
4. Describe the two forms of deterrence.
5. Define *incapacitation*.
6. What is *correctional econometrics?*
7. When has rehabilitation been accomplished?
8. Restorative justice is based on what belief?
9. What are the five sentencing options in wide use in the United States today?
10. Differentiate between fines and restitution.
11. Give some examples of alternative sentencing.
12. How have American models of criminal sentencing changed over the past 100 years?
13. What are three-strikes (and two-strikes) laws? Why have such laws been enacted? What consequences might they have for the criminal justice system and for the corrections subsystem?
14. What is fair sentencing? What issues are involved in fair sentencing?

CRITICAL THINKING EXERCISES

ON-THE-JOB ISSUE

In recreation yard conversation, Manuel learns that Jack, who committed essentially the same crime as Manuel, is serving a much shorter sentence. Manuel becomes sullen and hostile and complains bitterly to you about injustices and prejudice in the criminal justice system. What is the best way to calm Manuel so that an emotionally charged incident does not occur?

CORRECTIONS ISSUE

Edgardo Rotman says, "Rehabilitation . . . can be defined tentatively and broadly as a right to an opportunity to return to (or remain in) society with an improved chance of being a useful citizen and staying out of prison."[44] Do you agree that rehabilitation is the right of an offender? Why or why not?

CORRECTIONS ON THE WEB

1. Access the Sentencing Project at **http://www.sentencingproject. org.** Determine whether the group is prosecution- or defense-based. Then read the information you find about the Sentencing Project and the National Association of Sentencing Advocates. Write a paragraph summarizing the information.

2. Visit the United States Sentencing Commission at **http://www.ussc.gov.** Explore the areas of interest to you. Then use the link to the state sentencing commissions and go to the NASC Contact List. If your state is listed, contact its commission to find out who serves on the commission and what the basic sentencing philosophy of the commission is.

ADDITIONAL READINGS

Bazemore, Gordon, and Mark Umbreit. *Balanced and Restorative Justice: Program Summary.* Washington: U.S. Department of Justice, Office of Juvenile Justice and Delinquency Prevention, 1994.

Briggs, John, Christopher Harrison, and Angus McInnes. *Crime and Punishment in England: An Introductory History.* New York: St. Martin's Press, 1996.

Galaway, Burt, and Joe Hudson (eds.). *Criminal Justice, Restitution, and Reconciliation.* Monsey, NY: Criminal Justice Press, 1990.

Greenwood, P. W., et al. *Three Strikes and You're Out: Estimated Benefits and Costs of California's New Mandatory Sentencing Law.* Santa Monica, CA: RAND, 1994).

Hudson, Joe, and Burt Galaway (eds.). *Victims, Offenders, and Alternative Sanctions.* Lexington, MA: Lexington Books, 1980.

Rotman, Edgardo. *Beyond Punishment: A New View of the Rehabilitation of Criminal Offenders.* Westport, CT: Greenwood Press, 1990.

Umbreit, Mark. *Victim Meets Offender: The Impact of Restorative Justice and Mediation.* Monsey, NY: Criminal Justice Press, 1994.

ENDNOTES

1. *"Au Pair* Faces Life in Prison," *USA Today* Online, http://www.usatoday.com, posted October 30, 1997.

2. The South Carolina case was unusual because courts in at least 30 other states have refused to treat a viable fetus as a person under child abuse laws (although they may for other legal purposes). State supreme courts in Florida, Kentucky, Nevada, Ohio, and Wisconsin have issued rulings contrary to that in the South Carolina case.

3. John P. Conrad, "The Pessimistic Reflections of a Chronic Optimist," *Federal Probation,* Vol. 55, No. 2, 1991, p. 7.

4. Sigmund Freud, *Totem and Taboo,* trans. and ed. by James Strachey (New York: W. W. Norton, 1990).

5. Jackie Cooperman, "AIDS Scare Triples in Scope," ABCNEWS.com, Oct. 28, 1997.

6. Conrad, p. 7.

7. Morgan O. Reynolds, *The Reynolds Report: Crime and Punishment in the U.S., NCPA Policy Report No. 209* (Dallas: National Center for Policy Analysis, 1997). Online, available: http://www.public-policy.org/~ncpa/studies/s209/s209.html.

8. Edwin Zedlewski, *Making Confinement Decisions,* Research in Brief (Washington: National Institute of Justice, 1987).

9. John J. DiIulio, "Crime and Punishment in Wisconsin," *Wisconsin Policy Research Institute Report,* Vol. 3, No. 7, 1990, pp. 1–56. See also William Barr, *The Case for More Incarceration* (Washington: U.S. Department of Justice, Office of Policy Development, 1992).

10. See, for example, Zedlewski.

11. Edgardo Rotman, *Beyond Punishment: A New View on the Rehabilitation of Criminal Offenders* (Westport, CT: Greenwood Press, 1990), p. 11.

12. Graeme Newman, *The Punishment Response* (Philadelphia: Lippincott, 1978), p. 104.

13. See, for example, Andrew R. Klein, *Alternative Sentencing: A Practitioner's Guide* (Cincinnati: Anderson, 1988).

14. Much of what follows is derived from Bureau of Justice Assistance *National Assessment of Structured Sentencing* (Washington: Bureau of Justice Assistance, 1996), NCJ153853.

15. S. A. Shane-DuBow, A. P. Brown, and E. Olsen, *Sentencing Reform in the U.S.: History, Content and Effect* (Washington: U.S. Department of Justice, 1985).

16. J. Cohen and M. H. Tonry, "Sentencing Reforms and Their Impacts," in A. Blumstein, et al. (eds.), *Research on Sentencing: The Search for Reform* (Washington: National Academy Press, 1983), pp. 305–459.

17. The materials in this section are derived from the Web site of the Federal Sentencing Commission, http://www.ussc.gov.

18. Title II of the Comprehensive Crime Control Act of 1984; 18 U.S.C. § 3551–3626 and 28 U.S.C. § 991–998.

19. M. Tonry, *Sentencing Matters* (Oxford, England: Oxford University Press, 1995).

20. U.S. Department of Justice, *Mandatory Sentencing* (Washington: Office of Justice Programs, 1997).

21. In mid-1996 the California Supreme Court ruled the state's three-strikes law an undue intrusion on judges' sentencing discretion, and gave judges greater leeway in deciding when the law applies. In 1998, however, the same court held that cases falling "within the spirit of the law" must be sentenced as the law requires. In 1999,

California's three-strikes law was upheld by the U.S. Supreme Court in the case of *Riggs v. California* (No. 98-5021).

22. G. L. Pierce and W. J. Bowers, "The Bartley-Fox Gun Law's Short-Term Impact on Crime in Boston," *Annals of the American Academy of Political and Social Science,* Vol. 455 (1981), pp. 120–132.

23. C. Loftin, M. Heumann, and D. McDowall, "Mandatory Sentencing and Firearms Violence: Evaluating an Alternative to Gun Control," *Law and Society Review,* Vol. 17 (1983), pp. 287–318.

24. C. Loftin and D. McDowall, "The Deterrent Effects of the Florida Felony Firearm Law," *Journal of Criminal Law and Criminology,* Vol. 75 (1984), pp. 250–259.

25. D. McDowall, C. Loftin, and B. Wierseman, "A Comparative Study of the Preventive Effects of Mandatory Sentencing Laws for Gun Crimes," *Journal of Criminal Law and Criminology,* Vol. 83, No. 2 (Summer 1992), pp. 378–394.

26. Joint Committee on New York Drug Law Evaluation, *The Nation's Toughest Drug Law: Evaluating the New York Experience,* a project of the Association of the Bar of the City of New York, the City of New York, and the Drug Abuse Council, Inc. (Washington: U.S. Government Printing Office, 1978).

27. M. Tonry, *Sentencing Reform Impacts* (Washington: U.S. Department of Justice, National Institute of Justice, 1987).

28. Ibid.

29. Much of what follows is taken from John Clark, James Austin, and D. Alan Henry, *Three Strikes and You're Out: A Review of State Legislation* (Washington: National Institute of Justice, 1997), NCJ165369.

30. Bureau of Justice Assistance, *National Assessment of Structured Sentencing* (Washington: U.S. Department of Justice, February 1996).

31. Donna Lyons, " 'Three Strikes' Legislation Update" (paper presented at the National Conference of State Legislatures, December 1995).

32. Several states have had such laws on the books for many years. For example, South Dakota has had three-strikes-type legislation since 1877.

33. James Austin, " 'Three Strikes and You're Out': The Likely Consequences on the Courts, Prisons, and Crime in California and Washington State," *St. Louis University Public Law Review,* Vol. 14, No. 1 (1994).

34. The Washington law does permit the governor to grant a pardon or clemency, but it also recommends that no person sentenced under this law to life in prison without parole be granted clemency until he or she has reached 60 years of age and is judged no longer a threat to society.

35. Austin.

36. Ibid.

37. Countywide Criminal Justice Coordination Committee, *Impact of the "Three Strikes Law" on the Criminal Justice System in Los Angeles County,* (Los Angeles: November 15, 1995). The number of inmates the jail system can house is limited by a federal court order and the sheriff's budget. Therefore, the use of early-release mechanisms for lower-risk offenders has been accelerated to make room for the growing number of two- and three-strikes cases. This policy has not increased the size of the jail population, but it has changed its composition.

38. California Sheriff's Association, *Three Strikes Jail Population Report* (Sacramento, CA: CSA, 1995).

39. Center for Urban Analysis, Santa Clara County Office of the County Executive, *Comparing Administration of the "Three-Strikes Law" in the County of Los Angeles With Other Large California Counties* (Santa Clara, CA: May 1996).

40. Los Angeles County Sheriff's Department, *"Three Strikes" Law—Impact on Jail: Summary Analysis* (Los Angeles: August 31, 1996).

41. John Clark et al., *Three Strikes and You're Out: A Review of State Legislation* (Washington: National Institute of Justice, 1997).

42. Ibid.

43. Edith E. Flynn et al., "Three-Strikes Legislation: Prevalence and Definitions," in National Institute of Justice, *Task Force Reports From the American Society of Criminology* (Washington: NIJ, 1997).

44. Edgardo Rotman, *Beyond Punishment: A New View on the Rehabilitation of Criminal Offenders* (Westport, CT: Greenwood Press, 1990), p. 3.

3 Punishments

A Brief History

CHAPTER OBJECTIVES

After completing this chapter you should be able to:

1. Describe the types of punishment prevalent in ancient times.
2. List and describe the major criminal punishments used throughout history.
3. Explain the ideas that led to the use of incarceration as a criminal punishment—and as an alternative to earlier punishments.
4. Explain the role of correctional reformers in changing the nature of criminal punishment.

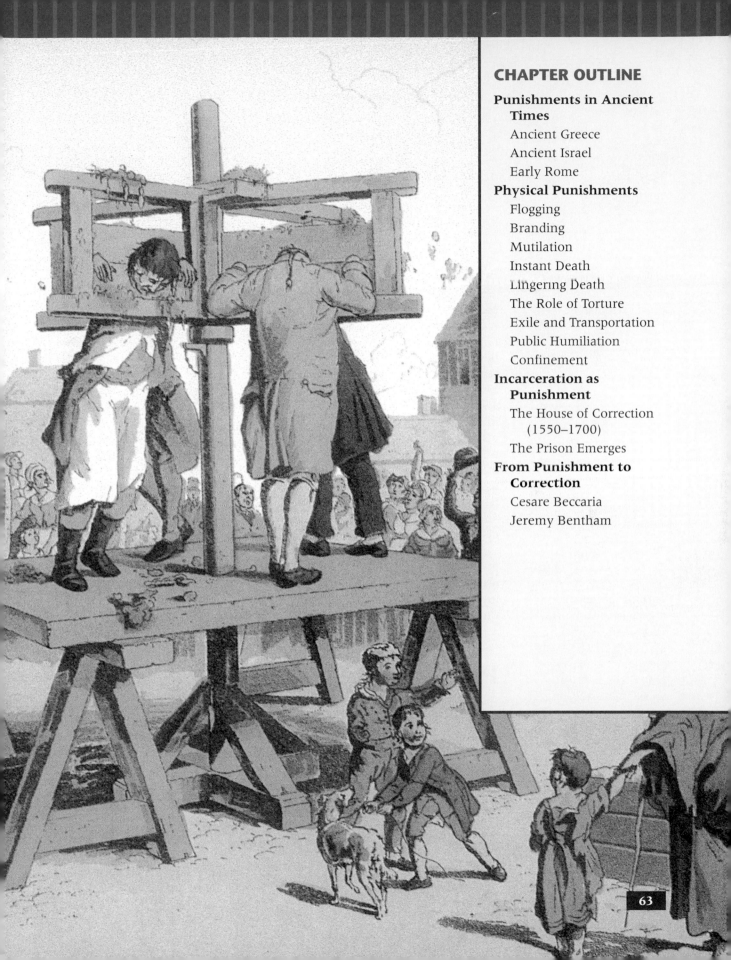

> *No man shall be forced by Torture to confesse any Crime against himselfe nor any other unlesse it be in some Capitall case, where he is first fullie convicted by cleare and suffitient evidence to be guilty. After which if the cause be of that nature, That it is very apparent there be other conspiratours, or confederates with him, Then he may be tortured, yet not with such Tortures as be Barbarous and inhumane.*
>
> —Massachusetts Body of Liberties of 1641, Section 45

corporal punishments
Physical punishments, or those involving the body.

Before the advent of prisons, **corporal punishments** were often imposed for serious crimes. Some, although not regularly administered, were especially gruesome. In 1757 Robert-François Damiens was sentenced to be publicly quartered in Paris for attempting to kill King Louis XV. As the executioners took their places, it was announced that "the flesh will be torn from his breasts, arms, thighs and calves with red-hot pincers, his right hand, holding the knife with which he committed said [homicide], burnt with sulphur, and, on those places where the flesh will be torn away, poured molten lead, boiling oil, burning resin, wax and sulphur melted together and then his body drawn and quartered by four horses and his limbs and body consumed by fire, reduced to ashes and his ashes thrown to the winds."[1] As it turned out, however, Damiens was a very muscular man. He remained conscious throughout the tortures, although a report tells us that he "uttered horrible cries." When it came time for him to be quartered, the four horses were unable to pull him apart—even after repeated attempts. Finally, six horses were used and, when they were still unable to disjoint the prisoner, his muscles had to be "cut through with knives."

Gruesome as this story may be, it illustrates the relative newness of our present system of corrections, which depends largely on the use of fines, probation, imprisonment, and parole. Corrections has evolved over time into the system we know today. This chapter traces the historical and cultural roots of our present system.

Punishments in Ancient Times

Before the large-scale building of prisons began in seventeenth-century Europe, a variety of punishments, based on the law and justice concepts of certain cultural groups, sought to punish wrongdoers and maintain civil order. We will briefly highlight some of these developments and the traditions that have influenced modern correctional practices.

Ancient Greece

In the cultural history of punishments, the Greek city-states provide the earliest evidence that public punishment is part of the Western tradition—and that its roots are in ideas of law and justice. Of all the city-states,

Teaching Tip
Describe how our contemporary correctional system grew out of earlier forms of criminal punishment, which were largely physical (corporal). Use examples from the text about early Greek and Hebrew societies. Ask students whether corporal punishments might still be appropriate today for certain kinds of crimes. If so, which ones?

Punishments: A Brief History

Athens is the best documented. This documentation ranges from the writings of orators and philosophers to plays and poetry. These writings tell us that many early crimes were punished by execution, banishment, or exile. Greek poets described stoning to death, throwing from high cliffs, stake-binding (similar to crucifixion), and ritual cursing as punishments inflicted on convicted criminals. In many cases, the bodies of executed criminals were regarded as dishonored and could not be buried. Their bodies were left to scavengers and the elements—and served as a warning to anyone contemplating similar crimes.

Other punishments in ancient Athens included "confiscation of property, fines, and the destruction of the condemned offenders' houses."[2] Public denunciation, shaming *(atimia)*, imprisonment, and public display of the offender were also used. Criminal punishments in ancient Greece sometimes included civil penalties, such as loss of the ability to transfer property, to vote, and to marry.

Ancient Israel

The chief record of ancient Hebrew history is the Bible. It describes the law and civilization of the ancient Hebrews, including their criminal law and penology. Punishments used by the Hebrews and mentioned in the Old Testament included cursing, banishment, beating, beheading, blinding, branding and burning, crushing, confiscation of property, crucifixion, cutting asunder, exile, drowning, exposure to wild beasts, fining, flaying, hanging, imprisonment, mutilation, plucking of the hair, casting down from a high place, sawing asunder, scourging with thorns, slavery, slaying by spear or sword, use of the stocks, stoning, strangulation, stripes, and suffocation.[3] Michel Foucault, the French historian, says that the purpose of physical punishments was primarily revenge. "It was as if the punishment was thought to equal, if not to exceed, in savagery the crime itself," he writes.[4]

Early Rome

The Twelve Tables, the first written laws of Rome, were issued in 451 B.C. Conviction of some offenses required payment of compensation, but the most frequent penalty was death. Among the forms of capital punishment were burning (for arson), throwing from a cliff (for perjury), clubbing to death (for writing insulting songs about a citizen), hanging (for stealing others' crops), and decapitation. Not mentioned in the Twelve Tables were several other forms of capital punishment in vogue in ancient Rome. For killing a close relative, the offender was subjected to the *culleus*. That is, the offender was confined in a sack with an ape, a dog, and a serpent, and the sack was thrown into the sea. Vestal virgins who had violated their vows of chastity were buried alive. As an alternative to execution, offenders might choose exile. Offenders who went into exile lost their citizenship, freedom, and immovable property. If they returned to Rome, they could be killed by any citizen.[5]

Physical Punishments

The practice of corporal punishment carried over into the Christian era. Physical punishments were imposed for a wide variety of offenses during the Middle Ages. Physical punishments also flourished in the American colonies. "It is common knowledge that the whole baggage of corporal punishments, as they existed in England, were brought to this country, and flourished, especially in New England where the precepts of Calvinism adorned them with pious sanctions."[6] The Puritans, for example, sometimes burned witches and unruly slaves; made wide use of the stocks, the pillory, and the ducking stool; branded criminal offenders; and forced women convicted of adultery to wear "scarlet letters."

As justice historian Pieter Spierenburg notes, many physical punishments during the Middle Ages and in "early modern Europe" were *theatrical punishments*.[7] That is, they were corporal punishments carried out in public. "Punishments that were both physical and public can be divided into five degrees of severity:" (1) whipping or flogging, (2) burning of the skin, (3) mutilation, or "more serious encroachments on bodily integrity," (4) a merciful instant death, and (5) a torturous and prolonged death.[8]

Flogging

Flogging (or whipping) has been the most common physical punishment through the ages.[9] The Mosaic code, for example, authorized flogging, and Roman law specified flogging as a punishment for certain forms of theft. Flogging was common in England during the Middle Ages as chastisement

Student Involvement
Historian Pieter Spierenburg describes criminal punishments during the Middle Ages in Europe as largely theatrical. Ask students to explain what that means. Ask them to write down what they consider the pros and cons of theatrical punishments.

for a wide variety of crimes. In England, women were flogged in private, while men were whipped publicly.[10]

The construction of flogging whips varied greatly, from simple leather straps or willow branches to heavy, complicated instruments designed to inflict a maximum of pain. A traditional form of whip was the cat-o'-nine-tails, consisting of nine knotted cords fastened to a wooden handle. The "cat" got its name from the marks it left on the body, which were like the scratches of a cat. One especially cruel form of the whip, the Russian knout, was made of leather strips fitted with fishhooks. When a prisoner was whipped, the hooks would dig into the body, ripping away the proverbial "pound of flesh" with each stroke. A thorough whipping with the knout could result in death from blood loss.

Flogging was also widely used in the American colonies to enforce discipline, punish offenders, and make an example of "ne'er-do-wells" (shiftless and irresponsible individuals). As a mechanism for gaining compliance with prison rules, flogging survived into the twentieth century. As late as 1959, Harry Elmer Barnes and Negley K. Teeters were able to write, "Floggings have been prison practice down to our own times, and deaths have occurred due to over-severe whippings in southern prison camps and chain-gangs. Tying prisoners up by their hands and allowing them to hang

Teaching Tip
Point out that flogging was once a widely used punishment, and describe the various types of flogging that were employed.

Student Involvement
Ask students how flogging might compare with modern imprisonment in its ability to deter offenders and reduce recidivism. Might flogging again play a role in American corrections sometime in the future? How?

CAREER PROFILE

*Zaira Tena
Correctional Officer
New Mexico Women's
Correctional Facility
Grants, New Mexico*

"I like my job. I like working with people. What I learned and what I'd tell someone is, Be very professional, firm, fair, and consistent at all times, and be able to work under a lot of pressure."

Zaira Tena is employed by Corrections Corporation of America (CCA) as a correctional officer at the New Mexico Women's Correctional Facility in Grants, New Mexico. She started working there 16 months ago. This is Zaira's first job in corrections. Zaira was attracted to CCA and a career in corrections because of the benefits that CCA offered her.

Zaira attended Laramie County Community College in Laramie, Wyoming, before joining CCA. The company provided additional training in interpersonal communication, special-needs inmates, crisis intervention, infectious diseases, suicide prevention, first aid, CPR, and firearms, giving her the skills she needs to ensure the health, welfare, and safety of prison employees and inmates. Since Zaira especially enjoys recreation, she also coordinates the institution's recreation activities.

Zaira's enthusiasm for her own career and professional development shows in her advice (quoted above) to persons thinking about a career in corrections. Wisely, Zaira is taking her own advice. She plans to stay in corrections and hopes one day soon to become assistant shift commander at the Grants women's facility.

Criminal Liability Point out that the stated purpose of branding was to warn people meeting an offender that they were dealing with a criminal. Do we "brand" or label criminals in contemporary society? Discuss how modern technology electronically "brands" offenders by listing them in crime databases. Also mention the release (on CD-ROMs and on Web sites) of sex offender data. Such data can be searched for information about convicted sex offenders. Some states also have laws requiring certain convicted sex offenders to register with law enforcement authorities. Do students think this branding or labeling of criminals is appropriate?

Cross-Cultural Perspective

In norms, values, and beliefs, contemporary culture is quite different from medieval European culture. Discuss those differences. Ask students why mutilation was an acceptable criminal punishment in Western culture during the Middle Ages, and why it would not be acceptable today. Mention that some countries that follow a strict Islamic code still cut off the hands of thieves. Ask how such a practice might continue to survive.

suspended with their toes barely touching the floor or ground has been a common method of enforcing discipline."[11]

Branding

Branding, a type of mutilation, was practiced by Roman society. It was used in England until 1829. Criminals were branded with a mark or letter signifying their crimes. Brands, which were often placed on the forehead or another part of the face, served to warn others of an offender's criminal history. The last documented incident of facial branding of English criminals was in 1699.[12] After that year offenders were branded on the hand, since it was feared that more obvious marks would reduce employment possibilities. Branding was abolished in England during the last half of the eighteenth century. The French branded criminals with the royal emblem on the shoulder. They later switched to burning onto the shoulder a letter signifying the crime of which the offender had been convicted.

Branding was also practiced in the early American colonies. The East Jersey Codes of 1668 and 1675, for example, ordered that burglars be branded on the hand with the letter *T* (for *thief*). After a second offense, the letter *R* (for *rogue*) was burned into the forehead. Maryland branded blasphemers with the letter *B* on the forehead. Women, in deference to their beauty, had to wear letters on their clothing, rather than being branded.

Mutilation

Mutilation was another type of corporal punishment used in ancient and medieval societies. Archaeological evidence shows that the pharaohs of ancient Egypt, and their representatives, often ordered mutilation.[13] In ancient Rome offenders who were mutilated suffered a kind of poetic justice according to the law of retaliation, or *lex talionis. Lex talionis,* as a punishment philosophy, resembles the biblical principle of "an eye for an eye and a tooth for a tooth."

Medieval justice frequently insisted that a punishment should fit the crime. Hence, "thieves and counterfeiters had their hands cut off, liars and perjurers had their tongues torn out, spies had their eyes gouged out, sex criminals had their genitals removed, and so forth."[14] Blasphemers sometimes had their tongues pierced or cut out and their upper lips cut away.[15]

Mutilation had a deterrent effect because the permanently scarred and disfigured offenders served as warnings to others of what might happen to criminals. Sometimes, however, mutilation served merely as a prelude to execution. The right hand of a murderer, for example, was sometimes cut off before he was hanged.[16]

Instant Death

According to Spierenburg, beheading, hanging, and garroting (strangulation by a tightened iron collar) were the most common means of merciful or instant death.[17] Instant death was frequently reserved for members of the nobility who had received capital sentences (usually from the King) or

A 1786 German woodcut depicts a public execution by burning. What purpose did such public dispensing of justice serve for government authorities?

for previously honorable men and women who ran afoul of the law. Decapitation, especially when done by the sword, was regarded as the most honorable form of capital punishment—since a sword was a symbol that was both noble and aristocratic. Hanging, says Spierenburg, "was the standard nonhonorable form of the death penalty." For women, however, hanging was considered indecent. Garroting tended to replace hanging as a capital punishment for women.

Lingering Death

The worst fate a criminal offender—especially one convicted of heinous crimes—might meet in medieval Europe was a slow or lingering death, often preceded by torture. Some offenders were burned alive, while others were "broken on the wheel." Breaking on the wheel was a procedure that broke all of the major bones in the body. A person who had been broken on the wheel and was still alive was often killed by an executioner's blow to the heart.

Offenders who were to be hanged sometimes had their arms and legs broken first, while others were whipped or burned. Burning alive, a practice used in France until the eighteenth century, was undoubtedly one of the period's cruelest forms of capital punishment.

Tutorial CD-ROM

Refer students to the Tutorial With Simulation Applications CD-ROM. The tutorial is a comprehensive interactive study tool that reinforces and reviews the concepts in Chapter 3. Also included are two simulations that apply concepts presented in Chapter 3.

Student Involvement

Describe how torture was used during the Middle Ages to force convicted felons to reveal the names of coconspirators (or other facts about a crime), and how torture was used to gain confessions from heretics. The justifications given for such uses of torture were that "guilty knowledge" was state property and that the souls of heretics needed saving. Ask students to analyze such justifications to see how they fit with today's worldviews.

The Role of Torture

A variety of other corporal punishments were employed, some of which involved torture. Although pain was central to punishments intended to exact revenge, pain was also used to extract confessions and get information. "Torture," said one source, "is the twisting (torsion) from its subjects of guilty secrets."[18] The use of torture in medieval England was based on a theory that knowledge of one's own guilt, or of the guilt of others, was an offense in itself. Moreover, the theory went, such knowledge was a kind of property that rightly belonged to the state. Hence, forcing an offender to relinquish such "property," by any means necessary, was a right of the government.

Tortures of all kinds were also used during the Middle Ages in an effort to gain confessions from heretics. Heresy was considered a crime against the church and against God. At the time, there was no separation between church and state in many Western societies, and church courts were free to impose punishment as they saw fit. Believers were sure that the heretic's soul was condemned to eternal damnation and that confession would lead to salvation. As a result, torture flourished as a technique for saving souls. Some saw the suffering induced by corporal punishments as spiritually cleansing. Others compared it to the suffering of Christ on the cross. They argued that physical pain and suffering might free the soul from the clutches of crime and evil.

A common medieval torture was to be put on the rack—a machine that slowly stretched a prisoner until his or her joints separated. On other prisoners, red-hot pincers called *hooks* were used to pull the flesh away, or thumbscrews were used as their name implies. Some prisoners underwent *cording,* in which the thumbs were tied tightly together behind the back by a rope that passed through a support in the ceiling. Weights were then tied to the ankles, and the prisoner was hoisted into the air by his thumbs. Stones were also used to crush confessions out of prisoners, who were first covered with boards and then forced to suffer as one stone after another was placed on top of them.

Exile and Transportation

In a number of early societies, exile, or banishment, sometimes took the place of corporal and capital punishment. The ancient Greeks permitted offenders to voluntarily leave the Greek state and travel to Rome, where they might gain citizenship. Early Roman law also established the punishment of exile. Exile was regarded as akin to a death sentence, since the banished person could no longer depend on his former community for support and protection. He or she could generally be killed with impunity on attempting to reenter the area.

Exile was practiced in some European communities into the 1800s. One historical study, for example, revealed that between 1650 and 1750, 97 percent of the noncapital sentences handed down in Amsterdam included banishment.[19] Sentences of banishment drove petty offenders out of a municipality and kept known offenders out of town. But banished criminals

resurfaced quickly in neighboring towns, and many communities in Europe confronted a floating population of criminals—especially petty thieves.

Though it was rarely practical to banish offenders from an entire province or nation, England practiced for more than 200 years a form of criminal exile known as *transportation*. An English law authorizing the transportation of convicts to newly discovered lands was passed in 1597. The law was intended primarily to provide galley slaves for a burgeoning English merchant fleet. Soon, however, public support grew for the transportation system as a way of ridding England of felons. As a result, large numbers of convicts were sent to America and other English colonies. One writer[20] estimates that by the beginning of the American Revolution, 50,000 prisoners had been sent to the New World. Most of them "were sold as indentured servants in the southern colonies, where their market value was greater than in New England."

After the American Revolution, convicted felons began piling up in English jails with no place to go. Legislation was soon passed authorizing prisoners to be housed aboard floating prison ships called *hulks*. Many of these vessels were abandoned merchant ships or broken-down warships. Hulks were anchored in rivers and harbors throughout England. They were unsanitary, rat-infested, and unventilated, and the keepers flogged the inmates to force them to work. Disease ran rampant in the hulks, sometimes wiping out all the prisoners on a ship, and the crew and nearby citizens as well. This "temporary" solution lasted about 80 years.

The system of hulks eventually proved impractical, and England soon began shifting its convict population to Australia, which had been discovered by Captain Cook in 1770. Convict transportation to Australia began in earnest in 1787,[21] with English convicts being transported to New South Wales, Norfolk Island, and Van Diemen's Land—now known as Tasmania. The journey was long and demanding, and conditions on prison ships were

Teaching Tip

Explain how transportation, a frequent criminal punishment in some European countries during the 1600s and 1700s, built on the earlier practices of banishment and exile. Ask students whether they believe that new forms of transportation might emerge in the future—and, if so, what those forms might be (e.g., transportation to the moon, to undersea colonies, to other planets, and so forth).

In the late eighteenth century, the English government began turning broken-down war vessels and abandoned transport ships into hulks to house prisoners. What event caused the overcrowding in prisons that made these hulks necessary?

often ghastly. Many convicts did not survive the trip. Those who did were put to work at heavy labor when they reached their destinations, helping to develop the growing region.

Soon convicts who had served their sentences began to receive land grants. In 1791 the governor of New South Wales initiated a program to give released convicts up to 30 acres of land each, along with enough tools, seeds, and rations to last 18 months.

English transportation of criminals began to wane in 1853, when Parliament abolished transportation for prisoners with sentences of less than 14 years. Opposition to transportation was especially strong among the free settlers who had begun to populate Australia and nearby regions. In 1867 the practice of transportation officially ended, although England continued to send inmates from India to its penal colony in the Andaman Islands until World War II.

Other countries also had favorite places of exile for convicted prisoners. Beginning in 1791, French authorities sent prisoners in large numbers to Madagascar, New Caledonia, the Marquesas Islands, and French Guiana. Off the coast of French Guiana, Devil's Island, named for the horrors associated with imprisonment there, continued to function as a prison until 1951. Spanish and Portuguese prisoners went to Africa; Russian exiles were sent to Siberia, a desolate region in central and eastern Russia.

Public Humiliation

Many corporal punishments were carried out in public, primarily to deter other potential lawbreakers. Some forms of punishment, however, depended on public ridicule for their effect. They included the stocks and the pillory.

Stocks held a prisoner in a sitting position, with feet and hands locked in a frame. A prisoner in the pillory was made to stand with the head and hands locked in place. Both devices exposed the prisoner to public scorn.

Student Involvement
Explain how public humiliation resulted from the use of such punishments as the stocks and the pillory. Ask students whether shaming might play a useful role in modern punishments. If so, ask what forms public humiliation or shaming might take.

While confined in place, prisoners were frequently pelted with eggs and rotten fruit. Sometimes they were whipped or branded. Those confined to the pillory occasionally had their ears nailed to the wood, and had to rip them free when released. England abolished the pillory in 1834, but according to at least one source, the pillory was still in use in Delaware in 1905.[22]

Confinement

Confinement by chaining or jailing has been a punishment since ancient times. Sometimes confinement served functions other than punishment for crimes. In early Greece, for example, prisons were used to punish convicted offenders, to coerce the payment of debts, to hold those awaiting other punishments, and to detain foreigners who might otherwise flee before their cases could be heard.[23] Until the 1600s, and the development of prisons as primary places of punishment, prisons were used to detain people before trial; to hold prisoners awaiting other punishments, such as death or corporal punishment; to force payment of debts and fines; and to hold and punish slaves.

Early European prisons were rarely called prisons. They went by such names as *dungeon, tower,* and *gaol* (from which we get the modern term *jail*). Some places used as prisons had been built for other purposes. The Tower of London, for example, was originally a fortified palace that had been used as an arsenal. The French Bastille began as a fortified city gate leading into Paris. Judicial proceedings were not necessary before imprisonment, nor was a formal sentence. Anyone thrown into a dungeon at the behest of authorities was likely to stay there until granted clemency or until death.

Found guilty of the offense of impiety in Athens in 399 B.C., instead of imprisonment, Socrates chose the penalty of drinking poison, a form of execution in ancient Athens. What was the goal of most early penalties for crimes?

Incarceration as Punishment

According to Pieter Spierenburg, a Dutch justice historian, a new form of punishment that emerged around the year 1500 was *penal bondage,* which included all forms of incarceration.[24] "Courts came to use it almost as frequently as physical sanctions. Instead of being flogged or hanged, some offenders were incarcerated in workhouses or forced to perform labor in some other setting." According to Spierenburg, the word *bondage* means "any punishment that puts severe restrictions on the condemned person's freedom of action and movement, including but not limited to imprisonment."

Among the forms of penal bondage imposed on criminals, vagrants, debtors, social misfits, and others were forced labor on public works projects and forced conscription into military campaigns. Later, houses of correction subjected inmates to strict routines.

One early form of incarceration developed in France. For at least 200 years, prisoners were regularly assigned to French warships as galley slaves. The naval importance of galleys steadily declined, but French naval officials continued to have custody of convicted offenders. By the mid-1700s, they had begun to put convicts to work in the shipyards of Toulon, Brest, and Rochefort. At night these prisoners were sheltered in arsenals, where they slept chained to their beds. As Spierenburg notes, "the arsenals were in fact labor camps where convicts had to remain within an enclosed space, so the penalty was more akin to imprisonment than to public works."

The public-works penalty, sometimes called *penal servitude,* became especially popular in Germany and Switzerland in the 1600s and 1700s. According to Spierenburg, "convicts dug ore in mines, repaired ramparts, built roads or houses, or went from door to door collecting human waste."[25]

The House of Correction (1550–1700)

Midway between corporal punishments and modern imprisonment stands the workhouse or the house of correction. The development of workhouses was originally a humanitarian move intended to cope with the unsettling social conditions of the late sixteenth and early seventeenth centuries in England. The feudal system had offered mutual protection for landowning nobles and for serfs, who were tied to the land. By 1550 that system was breaking down in Europe. Hordes of former serfs roamed the countryside, unable to earn a living. Many flocked to the cities, where they hoped to find work in the newly developing industries. This change from an agrarian economy to an industrial one displaced many persons, resulted in growing poverty, and increased the numbers of beggars and vagrants.

Vagrancy became a crime, and soon anyone unable to prove some means of support was imprisoned in a workhouse. The first workhouse in England was called Bridewell because it was at St. Bridget's Well, near the town of Blackfriars. Soon, the word **bridewell** entered the language as a term for a workhouse, and the English Parliament ordered workhouses to be created throughout England. Parliament intended that those housed in workhouses should be taught habits of industry and frugality, and that they should learn a trade.

Student Involvement
Point out that the first bridewell was built in 1557 to house London's "riffraff." It was such a success that Parliament ordered each county to build such an institution. Comparable institutions soon appeared all over Europe. These institutions held many types of "offenders," including debtors, the homeless, insane persons, and criminals. Ask students if they think governments' motives in opening workhouses were humanitarian.

bridewell   A workhouse. The word came from the name of the first workhouse in England.

Bridewells were penal institutions for social outcasts—ranging from vagrants to petty criminals—who were forced to work under strict discipline. What social conditions prompted governments to establish such houses of correction?

At first, prisoners in workhouses were paid for the work they did. Work included spinning, weaving, clothmaking, the milling of grains, and baking. Soon, however, as the numbers of prisoners grew, the workhouse system deteriorated. As workhouses spread through Europe, they became catchall institutions that held the idle, the unemployed, the poor, debtors, the insane, and even unruly individuals whose families could not cope with them. According to one writer, imprisonment in a workhouse could serve "as a tool of private discipline... The family drew up a petition explaining why the individual should be imprisoned, and the authorities decided whether or not to consent. Usually, private offenders were confined because of conduct considered immoral."[26]

Hence, workhouses served as informal repositories for people the community regarded as "inconvenient," irresponsible, or deviant—even if their behavior did not violate the criminal law. In the midst of this large population of misfits and unwanted persons, however, could be found a core group of criminal offenders. In 1706 the British Parliament passed legislation "permitting judges to sentence felons to the house of correction for up to two years."[27]

By the end of the seventeenth century, houses of correction had become mere holding cells with little reformative purpose. Nonetheless, because workhouses relied primarily on incarceration rather than corporal punishments, they provided a model for prison reformers bent on more humanitarian correctional practices.

The Prison Emerges

Teaching Tip
Discuss the two elements that fueled the development of prisons as we know them today: (1) a philosophical shift away from corporal punishments, combined with (2) the passage of laws preventing the imprisonment of anyone except criminal offenders. Ask students whether they agree that only criminals and not civil defendants should be sent to prison. What would it mean to the correctional system in our country if courts started imprisoning defendants who were found liable in civil suits? For what kinds of violations of civil law (if any) do students believe imprisonment might be appropriate?

Two main elements fueled the development of prisons as we know them today. The first element was a philosophical shift away from punishment of the body, toward punishment of the soul or human spirit. By the late 1700s in Europe and America, a powerful movement was underway to replace traditional corporal punishments with deprivation of personal liberty as the main thrust of criminal sentencing. Michel Foucault explains the shift this way: "The punishment-body relation [was no longer] the same as it was in the torture during public executions. The body now serves as an instrument or intermediary: if one intervenes upon it to imprison it, or to make it work, it is in order to deprive the individual of a liberty that is regarded both as a right and as property. The body, according to this penalty, is caught up in a system of constraints and privations, obligations and prohibitions. Physical pain, the pain of the body itself, is no longer the constituent element of the penalty."[28]

The transition from corporal punishments to denial of liberties found its clearest expression in the work of the Philadelphia Society for Alleviating the Miseries of Public Prisons. The society, established by the Pennsylvania Quakers in 1787, had as its purpose the renovation of existing prisons and jails and the establishment of the prison as the basic form of criminal punishment. Thanks largely to the widely publicized works of the society, Pennsylvania became in April 1794 the first state to permanently abolish the death penalty for all crimes except first-degree murder, and it adopted a system of fines and imprisonment in place of corporal punishments.[29] The new Pennsylvania criminal code was important because it "marked the first permanent American break with contemporary juristic savagery, was the forerunner of the reform codes of other American states, and was the essential basis of Pennsylvania criminal jurisprudence until the next systematic revision in 1860."[30]

The second element fueling the development of modern prisons was the passage of laws preventing the imprisonment of anyone except criminals. Civil commitments to prison ended, and a huge class of social misfits were removed from prisons and dealt with elsewhere. Primary among this group were debtors, who historically had been cast into jails as a result of civil rulings against them. John Howard's study of English jails found 2,437 debtors among the 4,084 prisoners he encountered.[31] Many others were vagrants who had committed no "intentional" crime.

According to Pieter Spierenburg, the Dutch were the first Europeans to segregate serious criminals from vagrants and minor delinquents, and Dutch courts were the first European courts to begin substituting imprisonment for corporal punishments.[32] The workhouse in Amsterdam, which opened in 1654, "represented the first criminal prison in Europe," says Spierenburg. By the start of the 1700s, Dutch "courts frequently imposed sentences of imprisonment. During the third quarter of the seventeenth century, the Amsterdam court did so in one-fifth of its criminal cases; a century later, it did so in three-fifths. By the 1670s the court of Groningen-City imposed imprisonment in two-fifths of criminal cases." Even so, the imprisonment of debtors persisted in Holland for another hundred years, and Dutch prisons of the period held both criminal and civil "convicts."

I am a psychologist for the New Hampshire Department of Corrections working in a mental health unit at a correctional institution. My job is to lead a treatment program for offenders with moderate to severe Axis 1 (illness-type) mental disorders. Correctional counselors, nurses, or other mental health employees refer inmates to my supervisor, the Chief of Mental Health. If he thinks the inmate may have a serious illness-type mental disorder, he gives the case to me. Then either I or one of my team members carefully reads the inmate's offender record and medical chart, does a thorough interview, and, with the client's written permission, writes for information from mental health professionals who have worked with the client. Usually, the psychiatrist on the team will see the inmate also. If we think the person does have a disorder appropriate for us to treat, we develop a treatment plan and schedule the individual for a treatment team meeting, attended by a nurse, the correctional counselor, the psychiatrist, my team members, and myself. We talk with the client about goals and interventions. These may include nonaddictive psychotropic medications, psychotherapy (individual and group), case management, and monitoring. When it's appropriate, we refer clients to other programs at the prison, for example, the sexual offender program, or the substance abuse program. As the clients approach release, we do our best to set them up with mental health and other resources in the community, so they will remain in good mental health, and so that a worsening of their mental disorder does not contribute to their re-offending.

Laura Magzis
Psychologist
Mental Health Unit
New Hampshire State Prison for Men

These ideas, that "doing time" was often the most appropriate punishment for criminal activity and that incarceration should be imposed only on criminal offenders, soon combined with a burgeoning emphasis on reformation as the primary goal of criminal sentencing. Reformation, argued many prison advocates of the time, could best be achieved by enforced solitude.

In 1776 the British philanthropist Jonas Hanway published a book entitled *Solitude in Imprisonment*. Hanway's work appears to have had a significant influence on prison advocates. Hanway argued that the interruption of transportation provided a much-needed opportunity to reexamine prevailing policies for dealing with prisoners. He suggested that reformation should be the primary goal of criminal sentencing and said that it was plainly not being met by sentencing practices then in existence. Solitary confinement, said Hanway, would force the prisoner to face his conscience—leading to reformation. Hanway wrote, "The walls of his prison will preach peace to his soul, and he will confess the goodness of his Maker, and the wisdom of the laws of his country."[33]

From Punishment to Correction

Prisons, as institutions in which convicted offenders spend time as punishment for crimes, are relatively modern. They came about largely as a result of growing intellectualism in Europe and America and as a reaction to the barbarities of corporal punishment.

Teaching Tip
Discuss the Enlightenment as a time of faith in science and reason as well as a period of social reform. Ask students how this reliance on science and reason influenced criminal punishments of the times.

The period of Western social thought that began in the seventeenth century and lasted until the dawn of the nineteenth century is known as the Age of Enlightenment. "The phrase was frequently employed by writers of the period itself, convinced that they were emerging from centuries of darkness and ignorance into a new age enlightened by reason, science, and a respect for humanity."[34] The Enlightenment, also known as the Age of Reason, was more than a set of fixed ideas. Enlightenment thought implied an attitude, a method of knowing based on observation, experience, and reason.

One of the earliest representatives of the Enlightenment was the French social philosopher and jurist Charles de Montesquieu (1689–1755). His masterwork, *The Spirit of Laws,* was published in 1748. Montesquieu wrote that governmental powers should be separated and balanced in order to guarantee individual rights and freedom. Montesquieu also strongly believed in the rights of individuals. His ideas influenced leaders of both the American Revolution and the French Revolution.[35] Another celebrated philosopher of the Enlightenment was the French writer Voltaire. He satirized both the government and the religious establishment of France. Voltaire twice served time in the Bastille and chose exile in England over prison for additional offenses. Voltaire deeply admired the English atmosphere of political and religious freedom.

The Enlightenment influenced the justice systems of Western nations. It strongly influenced the directions the correctional enterprise would take over the next two hundred years. Much of its influence was due to a number of important thinkers who adopted the principles of the Enlightenment. We now turn our attention to those individuals.

Cesare Beccaria

Cesare Beccaria (1738–1794) was born in Italy, the eldest son of an aristocratic family. By the time he reached his mid-twenties, Beccaria had formed, with his close friends Pietro and Alessandro Verri, an intellectual circle called the Academy of Fists.[36] The academy took as its purpose the reform of the criminal justice system. Through the Verri brothers, Beccaria became acquainted with the work of French and British political writers such as Montesquieu, Thomas Hobbes (1588–1679), Denis Diderot (1713–1784), Claude-Adrien Helvetius (1715–1771), and David Hume (1711–1776).

In 1764 Beccaria published an essay titled *On Crimes and Punishments.* Although the work was brief, it was, perhaps, the most exciting essay on law of the eighteenth century. In the essay, Beccaria outlined a utilitarian approach to punishment, suggesting that some punishments can never be justified because they are more evil than any "good" they might produce. The use of torture to obtain confessions falls into that category, said Beccaria. Beccaria also protested punishment of the insane, a common practice of the times, saying it could do no good because insane people cannot accurately assess the consequences of their actions. Beccaria said that *ex post facto* laws, or laws passed after the fact, imposed punishment unfairly, since a person could not calculate the risk of acting before the law was passed. He also argued against the use of secret accusations, the discretionary power of judges, the inconsistency and inequality of sentencing, the use of personal connections to obtain sentencing reductions, and the imposition of capital punishment for minor offenses.

Beccaria proposed that punishment could be justified only if it was imposed to defend the social contract—the tacit allegiance that individuals owe their society, and the obligations of government to individuals. It is the social contract, said Beccaria, that gives society the right to punish its members.

Beccaria also argued that punishment should be swift, since swift punishment offers the greatest deterrence. When punishment quickly follows a crime, said Beccaria, the ideas of crime and punishment are more closely associated in a person's mind. He also suggested that the link between crime and punishment would be stronger if the punishment somehow related to the crime.

Finally, said Beccaria, punishments should not be unnecessarily severe. The severity of punishment, he argued, should be proportional to the degree of social damage caused by the crime. Treason, Beccaria said, is the worst crime, since it most harms the social contract. Below treason, Beccaria listed crimes in order of declining severity, including violence against a person or his property, public disruption, and crimes against property. Crimes against property, he said, should be punished by fines.

When his essay was translated into French and English, Beccaria became famous throughout much of Europe. Philosophers of the time hailed his ideas, and several European rulers vowed to follow his lead in the reform of their justice systems.

Cesare Beccaria (1738–1794), an Italian jurist and criminologist, was one of the first to argue against capital punishment and inhumane treatment of prisoners. What writing by Beccaria influenced the criminal justice systems of Western Europe?

Jeremy Bentham

The English philosopher and jurist Jeremy Bentham (1748–1832) was born in London. As a young child, he was considered a prodigy, having been found, at the age of 2, sitting at his father's desk reading a multivolume history of England.[37] He began to study Latin at the age of 3. When Bentham was 12, his father, a wealthy attorney, sent him to Queen's College, Oxford, hoping that he would enter the field of law.

After hearing lectures by the leading legal scholar of the day, Sir William Blackstone (1723–1780), young Bentham became disillusioned with the law. Instead of practicing law, he decided to criticize it, and spent the rest of his life analyzing the legal practices of the day, writing about them, and suggesting improvements.

Bentham advocated **utilitarianism**, the principle that the highest objective of public policy is the greatest happiness for the largest number of people. Utilitarianism provided the starting point for Bentham's social analysis, in which he tried to measure the usefulness of existing institutions, practices, and beliefs against a common standard. Bentham believed that human behavior is determined largely by the amount of pleasure or pain associated with a given activity. Hence, he suggested, the purpose of law should be to make socially undesirable activities painful enough to keep people from engaging in them. In this way, said Bentham, "good" can be achieved.

Bentham's idea, that people are motivated by pleasure and pain and that the proper amount of punishment can deter crime, became known as **hedonistic calculus**. Bentham's hedonistic calculus made four assumptions:

1. People by nature choose pleasure and avoid pain.
2. Each individual, either consciously or intuitively, calculates the degree of pleasure or pain to be derived from a given course of action.
3. Lawmakers can determine the degree of punishment necessary to deter criminal behavior.
4. Such punishment can be effectively and rationally built into a system of criminal sentencing.

Bentham is also known as the inventor of the panopticon (from a Greek word meaning "all-seeing")—a type of prison he proposed building in England as early as 1787. The panopticon was intended to be a means for putting utilitarian ideas to work in the field of penology.

Key to the proposed panopticon was its unique architecture, which consisted of a circular tiered design with a glass roof and with a window on the outside wall of each cell.[38] The design made it easy for prison staff, in a tower in the center of the structure, to observe each cell (and its occupants). Within the wheel-like structure, walls separated the cells to prevent any communication between prisoners. Speaking tubes linked cells with the observation platform so that officers could listen to inmates.

The panopticon, also called an *inspection house,* was intended to be a progressive and humanitarian penitentiary. Bentham thought of it as a social experiment. The design was touted as consistent with the ideals of utilitarianism because only a few officers would be subject to the risks and unpleasantness of the inspection role, while many prisoners would benefit from this enlightened means of institutional management.

After years of personally promoting the concept, Bentham saw his idea for an innovative penitentiary die. The panopticon was never built in England, and in 1820 government officials formally disavowed it. The concept may have fallen victim to the growing emphasis on transportation, which delayed all prison construction in England. Another significant factor in the demise of the panopticon ideal, however, was Bentham's insistence that panopticons be built near cities to deter crime among the general popu-

utilitarianism The principle that the highest objective of public policy is the greatest happiness for the largest number of people.

hedonistic calculus The idea that people are motivated by pleasure and pain and that the proper amount of punishment can deter crime.

Student Involvement
Ask students if they agree with the four assumptions in Bentham's hedonistic calculus. Be sure that they defend their answers.

Teaching Tip
Point out that four circular cell houses built at Stateville, Illinois, between 1916 and 1924 incorporated elements of the panopticon design.

Punishments: A Brief History

Jeremy Bentham (1748–1832), an English philosopher and social reformer, spent his life and trying to reform the law. His innovative plan for a prison, called the panopticon, consisted of a huge structure covered by a glass roof. A central tower allowed guards to see into the cells, which were arranged in a circle. Although the British government did not use Bentham's plan, several U.S. prisons did, including one in Stateville, Illinois. What is the name given to Bentham's principle that the highest object of public policy is the greatest happiness for the greatest number of people?

Teaching Tip
Refer to Chapter 3 of the *Instructor's Resource Manual* for additional activities and for answers to the end-of-chapter exercises.

lation. Although a number of sites were chosen for construction, nearby residents always protested plans to build any sort of prison in their neighborhoods. Despite Bentham's failure ever to construct a facility completely true to his panopticon plan, he will always be remembered for his idea that order and reform could be achieved in a prison through architectural design.

Review and Applications

CHAPTER OBJECTIVE 1

Corporal, or physical, punishments were the most common response to crime for centuries before criminals began to be incarcerated.

CHAPTER OBJECTIVE 2

Criminal punishments of the past generally consisted of flogging, branding, mutilation, exile, transportation, and public humiliation.

CHAPTER OBJECTIVE 3

Many reformist thinkers based their ideas on Enlightenment principles, including the use of rea-

son and deductive logic to solve problems. They laid the groundwork for the use of imprisonment as an alternative to traditional punishments.

CHAPTER OBJECTIVE 4

Beginning in the mid-1700s, a number of correctional reformers fought the use of corporal punishments and sought to introduce more humane forms of criminal punishment. Among those reformers were Cesare Beccaria and Jeremy Bentham.

KEY TERMS

corporal punishments, p. 64
bridewell, p. 74

utilitarianism, p. 80
hedonistic calculus, p. 80

QUESTIONS FOR REVIEW

1. What are corporal punishments? What has been the purpose of corporal punishments throughout history?
2. Which ancient civilization provided the earliest evidence that physical punishment is part of Western society tradition?
3. What were the Twelve Tables?
4. List and describe at least four corporal punishments used in the past for criminal offenders.
5. What were *theatrical punishments?*
6. What role did torture play in the application of corporal punishments? How was the use of torture justified?
7. What purpose did the branding of criminals serve?

8. What two important thinkers discussed in this chapter adapted principles born of the Enlightenment, and applied them to the field of law and corrections? Describe the contributions each made to the field.
9. What was the original intent of a 1597 English law authorizing transportation of criminals to the New World?
10. What factors led to the abolition of transportation to Australia?
11. Describe the house-of-correction movement. How did it develop? What kinds of "offenders" were housed in such institutions?
12. What two elements contributed to the development of modern prisons?

CRITICAL THINKING EXERCISES

ON-THE-JOB ISSUE

You're a parole officer for the state corrections system. You are so burdened with paperwork that you rarely get out of the office to see any of your 200 clients—even though you are supposed to make regular home visits.

While you are shuffling papers one day, one of your clients, Bob Boynton, knocks at your door. It is time for him to make his monthly report. You tell him to have a seat, and you ask him the usual questions: "Have you been in trouble with the law since I saw you last?" "Are you still working?" "Are you paying your bills on time?"

Before you finish the interview, Boynton says, "You know, I'm never going to get anywhere this way. I need a better education. The time I spent in prison was wasted. They didn't teach me anything. I need to learn a skill so that I can make more money. If I can't earn better money I won't be able to pay my bills—and I'm afraid that I'll be tempted to get into the drug business again. I don't want to do that!"

You tell Boynton that there are a number of training schools in the area that can teach him a skill. Some of the computer classes offered at the local community college, you've heard, can lead to jobs paying decent wages. But, Boynton says, "I don't have a high school diploma. I can't get into the college. I'll never learn computers. I'm just too old. Besides, I need to work with my hands."

You go through the list of schools and training centers in the area, but Boynton raises an objection to each one. You sense that Boynton is trying to transfer responsibility for his success or failure to you. What should you do to get him to take responsibility for himself, yet provide support and guidance for his efforts?

CORRECTIONS ISSUE

In 1994 Michael Fay, an American teenager convicted of spray-painting parked cars, was flogged in Singapore. The flogging (called "caning" because it was done with a bamboo rod) caused an international outcry from opponents of corporal punishment. In this country, however, it also led to a rebirth of interest in physical punishments—especially for teenagers and vandals.

The last official flogging of a criminal offender in the United States took place in Delaware on June 16, 1952, when a burglar was tied to a whipping post in the state's central prison and was given 20 lashes. Since then, no sentencing authority in this country has imposed whipping as a criminal punishment, and most jurisdictions have removed all corporal punishments from their statutes. Amnesty International, however, reports that whipping is still in use in parts of the world for certain kinds of prisoners.

After the Fay flogging, lawmakers in eight states introduced legislation to institute whipping or paddling as a criminal sanction. Mississippi legislators proposed paddling graffitists and petty thieves, Tennessee lawmakers considered punishing vandals and burglars by public caning on courthouse steps, the New Mexico Senate Judiciary Committee examined the feasibility of caning graffiti vandals, and Louisiana looked into the possibility of ordering parents (or a correctional officer if the parents refused) to spank their children in judicial chambers. So far, none of the proposals have become law.

1. Would a return to corporal punishments, in the form of whipping or paddling, be justified for some offenders? Why or why not?
2. Might paddling be appropriate for some juvenile offenders? Why or why not?
3. Do you think that any state legislatures will eventually pass legislation to paddle or whip criminal offenders? Why or why not?

CORRECTIONS ON THE WEB

Visit the Web site of the British Home Office, and read about the history of prisons in Britain (**http://www. homeoffice.gov.uk/prishist.htm**).

Learn how British prisons developed during the 1800s and 1900s. Be sure to read about the Gladstone and Mountbatten Reports, the May Inquiry, and the development of the Borstal system.

ADDITIONAL READINGS

Barnes, Harry Elmer, and Negley K. Teeters. *New Horizons in Criminology*, 3d ed. Englewood Cliffs, NJ: Prentice Hall, 1959.

Beccaria, Cesare. *On Crimes and Punishments*. 1764. Reprint, Indianapolis: Hackett Publishing, 1986.

Howard, John. *The State of Prisons*. New York: Everyman's Library, 1929.

Ives, George. *A History of Penal Methods*. London: Stanley Paul, 1914.

Morris, Norval, and David J. Rothman. *The Oxford History of the Prison*. New York: Oxford University Press, 1995.

Newman, Graeme R. *Just and Painful: A Case for the Corporal Punishment of Criminals*. New York: Macmillan, 1983.

Newman, Graeme. *The Punishment Response*. Philadelphia: Lippincott, 1978.

Phillipson, Coleman. *Three Criminal Law Reformers: Beccaria, Bentham, Romilly*. London: Patterson Smith, 1970.

Scott, George Ryley. *The History of Corporal Punishment: A Survey of Flagellation in Its Historical, Anthropological, and Sociological Aspects*. Detroit: Gale Research, 1974.

Solzhenitsyn, Aleksandr. *The Gulag Archipelago, 1918–1956: An Experiment in Literary Investigation*. 3 vols. Translated by Thomas P. Whitney. Vol. 3 translated by H. Willetts. New York: Harper & Row, 1974–1978.

Von Hentig, Hans. *Punishment: Its Origin, Purpose, and Psychology*. London: Patterson Smith, 1937.

Wines, Frederick Howard. *Punishment and Reformation*. New York: AMS Press, 1919.

ENDNOTES

1. *Gazette d' Amsterdam*, April 1, 1757, cited by Michel Foucault, *Discipline & Punish: The Birth of the Prison*, trans. Alan Sheridan (New York: Vintage Books, 1995).

2. Edward M. Peters, "Prison Before the Prison: The Ancient and Medieval Worlds," in Norval Morris and David J. Rothman (eds.), *The Oxford History of the Prison* (New York: Oxford University Press, 1995), p. 6.

3. James Hastings, et al. *Dictionary of the Bible* (New York: Charles Scribner and Sons, 1905), Vol. I, pp. 523 ff., cited in Arthur Evans Wood and John Barker Waite, *Crime and Its Treatment: Social and Legal Aspects of Criminology* (New York: American Book Company, 1941), p. 462.

4. Foucault, p. 8.

5. See Peters, pp. 14–15.

6. Wood and Waite, p. 462.

7. Pieter Spierenburg, "The Body and the State: Early Modern Europe," in Norval Morris and David J. Rothman (eds.), *The Oxford History of the Prison* (New York: Oxford University Press, 1995), pp. 52–53.

8. Ibid., p. 53.

9. Harry Elmer Barnes and Negley K. Teeters, *New Horizons in Criminology*, 3d ed. (Englewood Cliffs, NJ: Prentice Hall, 1959), p. 290.

10. Some of the information in this section comes from Harry Elmer Barnes, *Story of Punishment*, and George Ives, *A History of Penal Methods* (London: Stanley Paul, 1914).

11. Barnes and Teeters, p. 349.

12. Ives, p. 53.

13. Henry Burns, Jr., *Corrections: Organization and Administration* (St. Paul, MN: West, 1975), p. 86.

14. Barnes and Teeters, p. 292.

15. Ives, p. 56.

16. John Howard, *The State of the Prisons* (London: J. M. Dent, 1929).

17. Spierenburg, p. 53.

18. Burns, p. 87.
19. Spierenburg, p. 62.
20. See Abbott Emerson Smith, *Colonists in Bondage* (Chapel Hill: University of North Carolina Press, 1947).
21. For a good account of the practice, see Robert Hughes, *The Fatal Shore: The Epic of Australia's Founding* (Vintage Books, 1988).
22. Barnes and Teeters, p. 293.
23. Peters, p. 7.
24. Spierenburg, pp. 49–77.
25. Ibid., p. 67.
26. Spierenburg, p. 72.
27. Randall McGowen, "The Well-Ordered Prison," in Norval Morris and David J. Rothman (eds.), *The Oxford History of the Prison* (New York: Oxford University Press, 1995), p. 83.
28. Foucault, p. 11.
29. See Wood and Waite, p. 463.
30. Harry Elmer Barnes, *The Repression of Crime* (New York: Doran, 1926), p. 101.
31. John Howard, *The State of the Prisons* (London: J. M. Dent and Sons, Ltd., 1929).
32. Spierenburg, pp. 49-77.
33. McGowen, p. 86.
34. "Enlightenment, Age of," *Microsoft Encarta '96, CD-ROM* (Redmond, WA: Microsoft, 1995).
35. Ibid.
36. Some of the information in this section comes from *The Internet Encyclopedia of Philosophy*, June 26, 1999: http://www.utm.edu/research/iep/.
37. Some of the information in this section comes from the Bentham Project at University College, London, June 25, 1999: http://www.ucl.ac.uk/Bentham-Project/jb.htm.
38. For further information, see Frank E. Hagan, "Panopticon," in Marilyn D. McShane and Frank P. Williams III (eds.), *Encyclopedia of American Prisons* (New York: Garland, 1996), pp. 341–342.

Restorative Justice

What Is Restorative Justice?

In restorative justice, crime is seen as something done against victims and the community, not just against the state. Restorative justice is concerned with repairing the harm to the victim and the community. The harm is repaired through negotiation, mediation, and empowerment, rather than through retribution, deterrence, and punishment.

The efforts of the criminal justice system as a whole, and corrections in particular, are beginning to broaden from an exclusive focus on the offender to a concern for the victim and the community harmed by an offense. When criminal justice agencies seek *restorative justice*—or as some agencies refer to it, *community justice* or *reparative justice*—they hope to repair some of the harm to the victim, through service and support. An important part of restorative justice is having offenders actively address the harm they have caused. The system accomplishes that both by holding offenders directly accountable and by helping them become productive, law-abiding members of their community.[1]

Methods of Restorative Justice

States and localities that wish to implement the restorative justice philosophy rely on broad-based citizen involvement to develop appropriate strategies. Restorative justice is based on the premise that since crime occurs in the context of the community, the community should be involved in addressing it. In a restorative- or community-justice model, you might find any of the following:

- victim-offender mediation
- victim-offender reconciliation
- victim-impact (or empathy) panels
- restorative-justice panels
- community reparative boards
- community-based courts
- family-group conferences
- circle sentencing
- court diversion programs
- peer mediation

Restorative-justice programs try to personalize crime by showing offenders the human consequences of their behavior. Such programs also give victims (who are often ignored by the criminal justice system) the opportunity to release their feelings and speak frankly to offenders. Proponents of restorative justice believe that bringing victim and offender together through such processes as mediation can contribute to a healing process that would not otherwise occur for victims and survivors. The question from a restorative-justice perspective is, "Who has been harmed, what losses did they suffer, and—to the extent that it is possible—how can we make them whole again?"

Restorative Justice and Corrections

Correctional agencies are uniquely situated to hold offenders accountable to their victims and to the community. As a result, more and more correctional agencies are initiating victim-offender programs and are renewing their emphasis on traditional practices, such as restitution, that exemplify the restorative ideal of holding offenders accountable. Correctional agencies now provide a variety of victim services as well as programs to make offenders more aware of and responsible for the consequences of their crimes. Many agencies regularly incorporate victim-impact information into presentence investigation reports, collect and disburse restitution, notify victims of parole hearings, and allow them to participate in those hearings.

Much more needs to be done to involve victims and the community in the correctional process. A recent Department of Justice plan to improve the treatment of crime victims recommended specific steps.[2]

- Every state department of corrections and every parole authority should establish an advisory committee of victims and service providers to guide and support victim related policies, programs, and services.
- Correctional agencies should designate staff to provide information, assistance, and referrals to victims of crime.
- Mission statements of correctional agencies should recognize victims as an important constituency and should address victims' rights and services.
- A correctional agency should notify victims of any change in the offender's status that would allow the offender access to the community or to the victims.
- A correctional agency should place a high priority on ensuring victims' safety from intimidation, threats, or harm by offenders.
- Information about offender status and victims' rights should be accessible in several languages through toll-free numbers and printed materials.
- Correctional agencies should collect and distribute restitution payments as ordered by the court, and wage-earning opportunities should be increased for inmates, wards, and parolees who owe restitution.
- Victims' input should be sought for all decisions affecting the release of adult and juvenile offenders.
- Victim-impact awareness should be a basic component of the education and treatment programs of correctional agencies.
- Protected, supported, mediated dialogue between victim and offender should be available upon the victim's request.

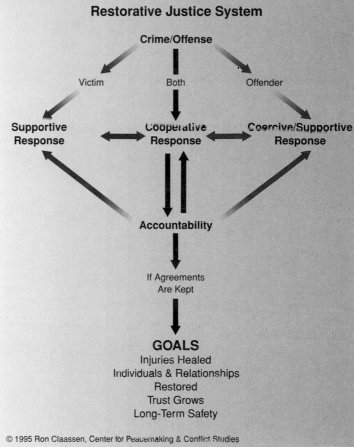

Restorative Justice System

Restorative Justice System

Crime/Offense

Victim — Both — Offender

Supportive Response ↔ Cooperative Response ↔ Coercive/Supportive Response

Accountability

If Agreements Are Kept

GOALS
Injuries Healed
Individuals & Relationships Restored
Trust Grows
Long-Term Safety

© 1995 Ron Claassen, Center for Peacemaking & Conflict Studies

- A crime victim should be notified of any violation of the conditions of the offender's probation or parole and should be allowed to comment before or during the violation hearing.
- Uniform practices should be developed and implemented for notification of a sex offender's release.

1. Marty Price, "Crime and Punishment: Can Mediation Produce Restorative Justice for Victims and Offenders?" Online: http://www.vorp.com/articles/crime.html, access: February 9, 1999.
2. Office of Justice Programs, *New Directions from the Field: Victims' Rights and Services for the 21st Century* (Washington: U.S. Department of Justice, 1998).

4 Jails
Way Stations Along the Justice Highway

CHAPTER OBJECTIVES

After completing this chapter you should be able to:

1. List the purposes of jails.
2. Trace briefly the development of jails in history.
3. Explain how first-, second-, and third-generation jails differ in design and in method of inmate management.
4. Outline the characteristics of jail inmates, and explain what special-needs inmates are.
5. Describe how jail vocational and educational programs affect inmate behavior and recidivism.
6. Discuss how religion and a jail chaplain can influence jail inmates and help jail staff.
7. Discuss why jail accreditation is important.
8. Explain why it is important for jail staff to conduct themselves as professionals.

It is with the unfortunate, above all, that humane conduct is necessary.

—*Fyodor Dostoyevski*

Student Involvement
Ask students for their reactions to R. J. Hawkins's journal entry. What attitude does the entry reflect?

IPSAS CD-ROM
The Instructor's Presentation and Student Assessment Software CD-ROM contains the following:

■ A PowerPoint presentation for Chapter 4. The presentation includes over 100 illustrated lecture screens for introducing or reinforcing chapter content and two topical simulations for applying concepts presented in the chapter.

■ The ExamView Pro Test Generator and a 100-item question bank for Chapter 4.

When R. J. Hawkins was 26 years old, he served a six-month sentence in the Story County Jail in Iowa. He had been convicted of an aggravated misdemeanor (proprietorship of a property where drugs were sold), a class C felony (possession with intent to deliver cocaine), and a class D felony (failure to affix a drug tax stamp). He kept a daily log of his time in jail. He sent it to a friend, who published it on the World Wide Web. Here's his first day's entry:

Well, here I am. Story County Jail, Nevada, Iowa. It could be worse I suppose, but right now I think this is pretty bad. I now call home a 10' x 20' cell that I share with 5 other people. On one wall there are 2 sets of bunk beds which stretch from the front of the cell to the back. Each berth is approximately 36" x 9". Two bunks, a shelf unit, and the toilet on the opposite wall. The two bunk beds are at the front of the cell followed by the shelf unit, which is permanently fastened to the wall, and then the toilet. The bunks at the front of the cell have a nice view of the day room. The day room is a large room with two tables, a phone and a TV. The TV is the center of attention and is on from lock-out to lock-down. During lock-out, my "house" door is open to the day room. We share the day room with another cell that is set up exactly the same as ours. So, during the day, twelve of us cohabitate and share the day room. Wake-up is at 6:00 AM. Breakfast is served at 6:30 AM. Lunch is served at 11:30 AM, and dinner is served at 5:00 PM. Between those times we have absolutely nothing to do. People watch TV, play cards, read books, or sleep. Actually, sleep is the big hobby, especially between lunch and dinner. Every once in a while a guard will walk the hall outside the day room. This or a heated disagreement helps break the monotony of the droning television and constant bitching of the inmates.

Like I said, I've been here one day now and already I know my biggest enemy is going to be boredom. This is county, not the pen, so I don't have to worry about being beaten, bullied, or buggered. Things are audio and video monitored at all times so there is a general feeling of safety. I'm in with short-timers. These are men who are awaiting trial or serving time for drunk driving or other minor alcohol or drug offenses. Average stay is 7–30 days. I, on the other hand, have 180 days to serve. I'm going to be seeing people coming and going and sometimes coming back again.

Right now I'm trying to adjust to my new surroundings, the only experience I have ever had with jail is vicariously through television. In terms, where I am at is no Mayberry, but it's closer to Mayberry than Shawshank, thank God. And for me, for the life of me, I never would have thought I'd end up here, however, I know where I went wrong and why and later I'll get into it. For now, though, I am going to concern myself with the current situation of adjusting to my environment. I know this is just a morsel but more is to come. As I am told, "Just a day at a time."[1]

Hawkins's first-day journal entry includes many topics this chapter will address—the design and purpose of jails, inmate characteristics, and jail programs.

Purpose of Jails

Jails are locally operated correctional facilities that confine persons before or after conviction. On June 30, 1998, local jail authorities held or supervised 664,847 offenders, an increase of almost 4.5 percent from midyear 1997.[2]

Inmates sentenced to jail usually receive a sentence of a year or less, but jails also serve other purposes in the correctional system.

Jails are used to:

- Receive persons awaiting arraignment and hold them pending trial, conviction, or sentencing.
- Readmit probation and parole violators and bail-bond absconders.
- Detain juveniles until custody is transferred to juvenile authorities.
- Hold mentally ill persons until they are moved to appropriate health facilities.
- Hold individuals for the military.
- Provide protective custody.
- Confine persons found in contempt.
- Hold witnesses for the courts.
- Hold inmates about to be released after completing a prison sentence.
- Transfer inmates to federal, state, or other authorities.
- House inmates for federal, state, or other authorities because of crowding of their facilities.
- Operate some community-based programs as alternatives to incarceration.
- Hold inmates sentenced to short terms (generally under one year) of incarceration.

For all their important roles and responsibilities, however, jails have been a disgrace to every generation.[3] Many of the nation's 3,304 locally operated jails are old, overcrowded, poorly funded, scantily staffed by underpaid and poorly trained employees, and given low priority in local budgets. Yet, a strong groundswell of progress is rising for the nation's jails. Tomorrow's jail professionals have tremendous opportunities to continue

EXHIBIT 4–1

American Jail Association

Mission Statement

To band together all those concerned with or interested in the custody and care of persons awaiting trial, serving sentences, or otherwise locally confined; to improve the conditions and systems under which such persons are detained.

To advance professionalism through training, information exchange, technical assistance, publications, and conferences.

To provide leadership in the development of professional standards, pertinent legislation, management practices, programs, and services.

To present and advance the interests, needs, concerns, and proficiency of the profession as deemed appropriate by the membership and their representatives.

Student Involvement

Have students review the American Jail Association's mission statement. Do they think the four goals are appropriate and attainable?

that momentum. Progress is being made because of new emphases on jail education, staff selection and training, professional associations, standards, technology, accountability, and laws, among other reasons. Groups like the American Jail Association (AJA) are advancing jail professionalism through training, information exchange, technical assistance, publications, and conferences. Members of the AJA include sheriffs, jail administrators, judges, attorneys, educators, correctional staff, jail inspection officials, health care providers, and clergy. The AJA mission statement is shown in Exhibit 4–1. This chapter will explore the problems of the past and present and discuss direction for the twenty-first century.

Jails in History

It is believed that King Henry II of England ordered the first jail built, in 1166. The purpose of that jail was to detain offenders until they could be brought before a court, tried, and sentenced. From that beginning, jails spread through Europe but changed in scope and size over time.

With the development of workhouses and poorhouses in the fifteenth and sixteenth centuries in England, sheriffs took on the added responsibility of supervising vagrants, the poor, and the mentally ill. In practice, however, these institutions were indistinguishable from jails. Their squalid, unhealthy conditions and the sheriffs' practice of demanding money from persons under their charge caught the attention of eighteenth-century Enlightenment reformers. One such reformer was the English sheriff John

Teaching Tip

Point out that John Howard was a sheriff. Ask students if they think jail reform today needs the support of sheriffs.

Howard. In 1779, England's Parliament passed the four jail reforms that Howard proposed: secure and sanitary structures, jail inspections, elimination of fees, and an emphasis on reforming prisoners. To this day, the John Howard Association and *Howard Journal* carry Howard's ideas forward.

First Jail in America

The first jail in America was the Walnut Street Jail in Philadelphia, built in 1776. The jail housed offenders without regard to sex, age, or offense. Conditions at the jail quickly deteriorated. According to some, the jail became a "promiscuous scene of unrestricted intercourse, universal riot, and debauchery."[4] The Philadelphia Quakers had wanted the Walnut Street Jail to be a place where inmates reformed themselves through reflection and remorse. In 1790 the Philadelphia Society for Alleviating the Miseries of Public Prisons and the General Assembly of Pennsylvania designated the Walnut Street Jail a penitentiary. Implementing Quaker beliefs, the penitentiary emphasized prisoner reform through reflection and penitence, and rehabilitation through good conduct. Sixteen solitary cells were added to the facility. Workshops were built; alcohol and prostitution were prohibited; prisoners were segregated by sex, age, and offense; diets were monitored; guardians were appointed to care for minors; religious, health care, and educational services were provided. Debtors, however, were housed separate from the general inmate population and had no such privileges. Their prison conditions were pitiful, and many debtors starved.[5]

In 1798 a fire destroyed the workshops. The destruction brought about disillusionment and idleness. Rising costs crippled the jail's budget. Disciplinary problems rose with overcrowding, and escapes and violence increased. The number of inmates who were destitute vagrants or debtors soared, as did the incidence of disease. There were political conflicts between the religious Quakers and the non-Quaker prison board members. Prisoners

Unlike the workhouses, prisons, and jails previously in existence, the Walnut Street Jail, started in Philadelphia in 1776, was used exclusively to house convicted felons. Which religious group's principles influenced correctional institutions in Pennsylvania?

rioted on March 27, 1820. On October 5, 1835, the Walnut Street Jail closed. State prisoners were transferred to the new Eastern State Penitentiary in Philadelphia, the first institution of its kind in the world. County inmates and those awaiting trial were transferred to a new county jail.

By the close of the nineteenth century, most cities across the United States had jails to hold persons awaiting trial and to punish convicted felons. The sheriff became the person in charge of the jail. As crime increased and urban centers expanded, jails grew in importance, as did the sheriffs' control over jails.

American Jails in the Twentieth Century

On any given day, America's jails serve a variety of functions. They detain persons awaiting arraignment or trial. They confine offenders serving short sentences for less serious offenses. Jails also serve as surrogate mental hospitals. They frequently detain persons with drug or alcohol dependency. They are the first stop on the social services highway for the homeless, street people, and some with extremely poor physical health, especially those with HIV, AIDS, and tuberculosis (TB).

Historians refer to America's jails as the "poorhouse of the twentieth century," the dumping grounds for society's problems.[6] Jails in twentieth-century America evolved into institutions of social control, not only for persons who committed criminal acts, but also for those who made up the underclass in American society. Such persons have been called society's rabble.

John Irwin (in 1986) called the purpose of jails **rabble management,** that is, control of persons whose noncriminal behavior is offensive to their communities.[7] The central purpose of jail was to detain the most disconnected and disreputable persons, who were arrested more because they were offensive than because they had committed crimes. They were individuals of whom all were aware, yet whom society ignored: public nuisances, derelicts, junkies, drunks, vagrants, the mentally ill, and street people. Moreover, since jails housed such persons, there was no incentive to improve jail conditions. The purpose of America's twentieth-century jails must, therefore, be understood in relation to the composition of the jail population. Jails not only confine persons before and after conviction, but also hold those who do not fit into the mainstream of American society.

Architecture and Inmate Management

In an attempt to better manage and control inmate behavior, jails have progressed through three phases of architectural design. Each design is based on a particular philosophy of inmate management and control.

First-Generation Jails First-generation jails were built in a linear design that dates back to the eighteenth century. In a typical **first-generation jail,** inmates live in multiple-occupancy cells or dormitories. The cells line corridors that are arranged like spokes. Inmate supervision is sporadic or intermittent; staff must patrol the corridors to observe inmates in their cells. Contact between jailers and inmates is slight unless there is an incident to which jailers must react. See Figure 4–1.

rabble management
The control of persons whose noncriminal behavior is offensive to the community (for example, public nuisances, derelicts, junkies, drunks, vagrants, the mentally ill, and street people). According to John Irwin, rabble management is the purpose of jails.

first-generation jail
A jail with multiple-occupancy cells or dormitories that line corridors arranged in spokes. Inmate supervision is sporadic or intermittent; staff must patrol the corridors to observe inmates in their cells. This linear design dates back to the eighteenth century.

FIGURE 4–1

First-Generation Jail—Intermittent Surveillance

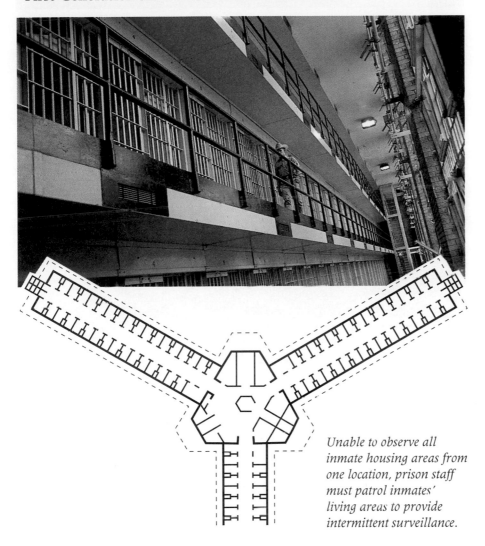

Unable to observe all inmate housing areas from one location, prison staff must patrol inmates' living areas to provide intermittent surveillance.

Teaching Tip
Refer students to Figure 4–1, "First-Generation Jail." Point out that this linear design resembles a hospital in which staff must walk from room to room along a corridor. Ask students what disadvantage such a design has. (Behavior problems, injuries, and illness can occur between staff visits.)

The design of a linear jail reflects the assumption that inmates are violent and destructive and will assault staff, destroy jail property, and try to escape. The facility is designed to prevent these behaviors. Heavy metal bars separate staff from inmates. Reinforced metal beds, sinks, and toilets are bolted to the ground or wall. Reinforced concrete and razor wire surround the facility.

Second-Generation Jails Second-generation jails emerged in the 1960s to replace old, run-down linear jails. They used a different philosophical approach to construction and inmate management. In a **second-generation jail,** staff remain in a secure control booth overlooking inmate housing

second-generation jail
A jail where staff remain in a secure control booth surrounded by inmate housing areas called pods. Bars are replaced with reinforced glass. Although visual surveillance increases, verbal interaction with inmates is reduced. This design emerged in the 1960s.

FIGURE 4–2

Second-Generation Jail—Remote Surveillance

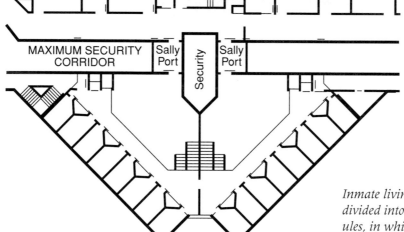

Inmate living areas are divided into pods, or modules, in which cells are clustered around dayrooms that are under continuous observation by staff in a central control room.

areas called pods (see Figure 4–2). Bars are replaced by reinforced glass. Although visual surveillance increases, surveillance is remote, and verbal interaction with inmates is even less frequent. Property destruction is minimized because steel and cement continue to define the living areas. Outside, fences and razor wire continue to discourage escapes as well as unauthorized entry.

Third-Generation Jails Third-generation jails emerged in the 1970s. Their design combines continual observation with staff-inmate interaction. In a **third-generation jail,** inmates are separated into small groups and housed in pods. The pods are staffed 24 hours a day by specially trained officers (see Figure 4–3). Pods are self-contained to reduce inmate movement. They are designed to enhance officers' interaction with and observation of inmates. Soft furnishings are used to reduce inmate stress from crowding, excessive noise, lack of privacy, and isolation from the outside world. Bars and metal doors are absent, reducing noise and the dehumanization common in first- and second-generation jails.

third-generation jail, sometimes called **direct-supervision jail** A jail where inmates are housed in small groups in pods staffed 24 hours a day by specially trained officers. Officers interact with inmates to help change behavior. Bars and metal doors are absent, reducing noise and dehumanization. This approach to jail construction and inmate management emerged in the 1970s.

FIGURE 4–3

Third-Generation Jail—Direct Supervision

Teaching Tip
Refer students to Figure 4–3, "Third-Generation Jail." Ask students to point out the biggest difference between third-generation jails and second- and first-generation jails. (In third-generation jails, officers are stationed *inside* the housing unit.)

Cells are grouped in housing units, or pods. Each pod has a central dayroom. Prison staff are stationed inside *the housing unit to encourage direct interaction between inmates and staff.*

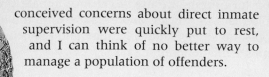
I n 1993 I received my transfer to the direct-supervision Oxbow Jail Facility. I sensed the painful uneasiness over the anticipated challenges of direct inmate supervision.

It is nearing three years since that transition, and—I must admit—these have been the most rewarding three years I have experienced. All of my pre-conceived concerns about direct inmate supervision were quickly put to rest, and I can think of no better way to manage a population of offenders.

Sergeant Rocky Finocchio
Oxbow Jail Division
Salt Lake City, Utah

Third-generation jails, sometimes called direct-supervision jails, maximize staff interaction with inmates by having staff inside each inmate housing unit. Staff movement and interaction encourage officers to view the pods as space they control and in which they exercise leadership. By supervising activities directly, the staff can help change inmate behavior patterns, rather than simply react to them.

Researchers tell us that pods and direct supervision provide a safer and more positive environment for inmates and staff than do first- and second-generation jails.[8] Today, more than 100 facilities in 24 states use direct supervision.

Characteristics of Jail Inmates, Facilities, and Staff

Who is in jail? Why are they there? What do we know about the operation and administration of jail facilities? To these and related questions we now turn our attention.

Jail Inmates

At midyear 1998, local jail authorities held or supervised 664,847 offenders—an increase of 4.5 percent from midyear 1997. Almost 11 percent of these offenders (72,385) were supervised outside jail facilities (see Figure 4–4). Of those offenders supervised outside jail facilities, almost 50 percent were involved in community service or weekender programs. The remaining 89 percent (592,462) were held in local jails.

FIGURE 4–4

Persons Under Jail Supervision

How Many Are Under Jail Supervision?

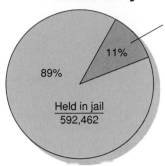

11%

89%

Held in jail
592,462

Supervised outside a jail facility 72,385

Electronic monitoring 10,827
Home detention without electronic monitoring 370
Day reporting 3,089
Community service 17,518
Weekender programs 17,249
Other pretrial supervision 6,048
Workcrews, workgangs and other work alternatives 7,089
Drug, alcohol, mental health and other treatment programs 5,702
Other 4,493

Who Is Under Jail Supervision?

Why Are They Under Jail Supervision?

Status

43%
Convicted

57%
Unconvicted

252,600 Convicted
331,800 Unconvicted

Gender

11%
Female

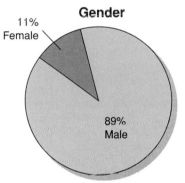

89%
Male

520,581 Males
63,791 Females

Offense

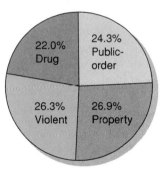

22.0%
Drug

24.3%
Public-order

26.3%
Violent

26.9%
Property

Race/Ethnicity

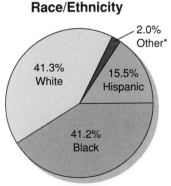

2.0%
Other*

41.3%
White

15.5%
Hispanic

41.2%
Black

244,900 White
244,000 Black
91,000 Hispanic
11,800 Other*

Age

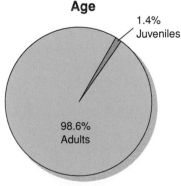

1.4%
Juveniles

98.6%
Adults

584,372 Adults
8,090 Juveniles
6,542 Held as adults
1,548 Held as juveniles

*Asians, Pacific Islanders, American Indians, Alaska Natives

Teaching Tip
Refer students to Figure 4–4. Then ask them the following questions:
1. What fraction of the inmates in the nation's jails are unconvicted? (More than half are unconvicted.)
2. What is the ratio of males to females in jail? (about 8 to 1)

Source: Darrell K. Gilliard and Allen J. Beck, *Prison and Jail Inmates at Midyear 1998,* Bureau of Justice Statistics Bulletin (Washington: Office of Justice Programs, March 1999). Caroline Wolf Harlow, *Profile of Jail Inmates, 1996* (Washington: Bureau of Justice Statistics, April 1998).

**Cross-Cultural
Perspective**
Inmates' lifestyles prior to
jail vary considerably, and
it is important for correctional officers to under-
stand this. Organize the
students into small groups,
each group representing
one of the four types of
special needs discussed in
this chapter. Instruct each
group to write a list of
stereotypes correctional
officers should avoid in
dealing with them and
their special needs. If there
are correctional officers in
the class, invite them to
write a list of behaviors
they fear from special-
needs inmates. Ask stu-
dents what strategies can
be used to build a bridge
between the two sides.

Since 1970, when the first national jail statistics were collected, the number of inmates held in locally operated jails has almost quadrupled. During the 1970s the growth was very modest—13 percent—but during the 1980s it was more than 120 percent—more than 220,000 inmates. Since 1990 the nation's jail population has increased by an average of 4.9 percent a year.

Gender and Jail Populations   Near the close of the twentieth century, we have seen a slow rise in the proportion of adult female jail inmates. In 1985 there were 19,077 adult female jail inmates—7.4 percent of the jail population. By midyear 1998 that figure had risen to 63,791—11 percent of the jail population. Since 1990 the average annual rate of growth has been 7 percent for the female jail population but only 4.5 percent for the male population.

Ethnicity and Jail Populations   From 1990 through midyear 1998, the majority of local jail inmates were black or Hispanic. At midyear 1998 whites made up 41.3 percent of the jail population; blacks, 41.2 percent; Hispanics, 15.5 percent; and other races (Asians, Pacific Islanders, American Indians, and Alaska Natives), 2 percent (see Figure 4–4). Relative to percentages of the U.S. population, the proportion of blacks in local jails at midyear 1998 was 6 times that of whites, nearly 2½ times that of Hispanics, and almost 7½ times that of persons of other races.

Juveniles and Jail Populations   Over the past 25 years, there has been a dramatic reversal in the theory and practice of punishing juveniles. In 1974, for example, juvenile offenders were deemed to have special needs. The Juvenile Justice and Delinquency Prevention Act provided federal money to states and cities that agreed not to hold juveniles in jails where they might have regular contact with adults. By 1996, however, in the face of pressure for more punishment of juvenile offenders, new legislation allowed cities and states to detain juvenile offenders for up to 12 hours in an adult jail before a court appearance and made it easier to house juveniles in separate wings of adult jails. That shift in philosophy and policy has increased the number of juveniles held in adult jails. At midyear 1993, 4,300 juveniles, or 0.9 percent of the jail population, were held in jail. By midyear 1998 that number and percentage had increased to 8,090 and 1.4 percent, respectively. At midyear 1998, 81 percent (6,542) of these young inmates had been convicted or were being held for trial as adults. The remaining 1,548 (19 percent) were held as juveniles (see Figure 4–4).

The Bureau of Justice Statistics has compiled a profile of inmates in local jails. That profile is shown in Table 4–1. Note that at the time of arrest:

■ More than half of the inmates were under supervision by the courts or corrections.
■ Almost one-third were on probation and almost one-eighth were on parole.
■ Seven of every ten had prior sentences.
■ Almost two-thirds used drugs regularly.
■ More than one-third were disabled.

Teaching Tip
Refer students to the profile of jail inmates in Table
4–1. Ask them what spe-
cial duties and responsibilities this profile might
suggest for correctional
officers.

TABLE 4–1

Profile of Jail Inmates

Categories	Percentage of jail inmates 1996	Categories	Percentage of jail inmates 1996
Criminal Justice Status		**Reported Disability,** *continued*	
At Arrest		Difficulty seeing newsprint	9.2%
None	46.4%	Learning disability	9.1%
Status[1]	53.6%	Difficulty hearing	6.1%
On probation	31.7%	Speech disability	3.7%
On parole	13.7%	**Physical Or Sexual Abuse**	
On bail/bond	12.7%	**Of Females**	
On other pretrial release	4.4%	Ever	47.5%
Criminal History		Before age 18	36.6%
None	27.3%	Age 18 or after	26.7%
Priors[1]	72.7%	Physically abused	37.2%
Probation	63.0%	Sexually abused	37.1%
Jail/prison	58.4%	Raped	32.2%
Prior Drug Use		**Employment Status**	
Never	17.6%	Employed	64.3%
Ever[1]	82.4%	Full-time	49.3%
Regularly	64.2%	Part-time	10.4%
In month before the offense[2]	55.0%	Occasionally	4.6%
At time of the offense[2]	35.6%	Not employed	35.8%
Under The Influence Of		**Person(s) Lived With Most**	
Alcohol At Time Of The		**Of The Time**	
Offense[2]		Both parents	39.7%
No	59.5%	Mother only	43.3%
Yes	40.5%	Father only	4.9%
Substance Abuse Treatment		Grandparents	7.0%
Never	57.7%	Other	5.2%
Ever[1]	42.3%	**Perceived Safety Of**	
Since admission	10.3%	**Jail Compared To That**	
Reported Disability		**Of The Streets**	
Any disability	36.5%	Jail safer	20.9%
Physical, mental, or other		Streets safer	43.3%
health	20.7%	About the same	35.8%

1. Detail may add to more than total; inmates may fit more than one category.

2. Based on convicted jail inmates only.

Source: Caroline Wolf Harlow, *Profile of Jail Inmates, 1996* (Washington: Bureau of Justice Statistics, April 1998).

- One-third of the women had been physically or sexually abused or raped.
- One-third were unemployed at the time of arrest.
- Two-thirds grew up in homes without both parents.
- Four of every ten believed that the streets were safer than jails.

Another way to look at the nation's jail population is to consider the rate of incarceration. Jail populations give us a count of the total number incarcerated (e.g., 664,847 held in local jails at midyear 1998). Because of differences in total population, however, such counts do not allow accurate comparison of jurisdictions. Rates of jail incarceration, expressed as the number of jail inmates per 100,000 residents aged 18 and older, allow a more meaningful and useful analysis of trends in incarceration. With rate data, we can compare changes over time. Figure 4–5 shows changes in the

Teaching Tip
Refer students to Figure 4–5, "Jail Incarceration Rate, 1985–1998." Clarify the difference between jail counts and jail incarceration rates. Explain that the incarceration rate is more meaningful for comparison. It takes into consideration changes in the size of the general population, not just changes in the number of people incarcerated.

Tutorial CD-ROM
Refer students to the Tutorial With Simulation Applications CD-ROM. The tutorial is a comprehensive interactive study tool that reinforces and reviews the concepts in Chapter 4. Also included are two simulations that apply concepts presented in Chapter 4.

FIGURE 4–5

Jail Incarceration Rate, 1985–1998

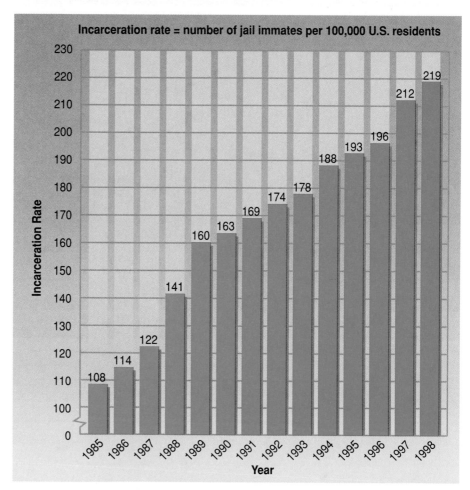

Incarceration rate = number of jail immates per 100,000 U.S. residents

Source: Adapted from Darrell K. Gilliard and Allen J. Beck, *Prison and Jail Inmates at Midyear 1998*, Bureau of Justice Statistics Bulletin (Washington: Office of Justice Programs, March 1999).

Jails: Way Stations Along the Justice Highway

jail incarceration rate from 1985 through 1998. Note that the incarceration rate almost doubled, from 108 jail inmates per 100,000 adults in 1985 to 219 jail inmates per 100,000 adults in 1998.

Jail Facilities

The capacity to house jail inmates has kept pace with the jail population. Between July 1, 1994, and June 30, 1998, the occupied percentage of capacity has remained below 100 percent. As of midyear 1998, 97 percent of local jail capacity was occupied, down from a peak of 108 percent, reached in 1989. The jurisdictions with the largest average daily jail populations reported the highest rates of occupancy. In 1998, the nation's 25 largest jail jurisdictions accounted for 27 percent of all inmates. These jurisdictions were in 12 states—7 in California, 5 in Florida, 4 in Texas, and 1 each in New York, Illinois, Arizona, Louisiana, Pennsylvania, Tennessee, Georgia, Maryland, and Wisconsin.[9] (See Table 4–2 on page 104.)

Special-Needs Inmates

Increasingly, jails are dealing with large percentages of special-needs inmates. **Special-needs inmates** require special treatment or care because they suffer from mental illness, chemical dependency (drug or alcohol), or communicable disease (especially HIV/AIDS and TB). Such jail inmates present substantial operational and administrative problems for jail staff. It is often difficult for the staff to know what they are observing or—once they recognize an inmate's special needs—how to address the situation.

Statewide research on jail management in New Mexico indicated that special-needs inmates require extra attention from jail staff.[10] They must be watched closely for possible suicide. Almost nine out of ten disrupt normal jail activities. Seven out of ten require an excess of scarce medical resources. Four out of ten engage in acts of violence. Almost three out of ten are abused by other inmates. The characteristics of special-needs inmates, the treatment programs offered, and the policies for dealing with those inmates depend on the type of special need.

Substance Abuse Inmates Drug arrests have been a primary factor in increasing the jail population. In fact, the majority of jail inmates—in some jails 70 to 80 percent—have a substance abuse problem at the time of incarceration.[11] Some are arrested for offenses connected with drugs and alcohol (drug sales, DWI, etc.). Others are under the influence of drugs or alcohol when they are arrested for other offenses. Many used drugs or alcohol within the 24 hours preceding their arrests. The National Institute of Justice (NIJ) indicates that 55 percent of convicted jail inmates used illegal drugs the month before the offense, and about 1 in 4 used a major drug (cocaine, crack, heroin) in that month. Thirty-six percent said they were using drugs at the time of their offense (with about 1 in 4 using a major drug), and 41 percent said they had been drinking alcohol. Almost 25 percent of convicted jail inmates drank quantities that, combined with their weight and metabolism, amounted to blood alcohol concentration of 10 gr/ml or higher, the definition of alcoholic impairment in many states.[12] Only a small fraction of

Student Involvement
Refer to Table 4–2, "The 25 Largest Local Jail Jurisdictions, Midyear 1998." Ask students to think about the challenges of dealing with such large populations of inmates who are incarcerated for relatively short periods. What issues might local jail personnel face in such jurisdictions?

special-needs inmates
Prisoners who require special treatment or care because they suffer from mental illness, chemical dependency (drug or alcohol abuse), or communicable disease (especially HIV/AIDS and TB).

Student Involvement
Encourage a group of students to research the programs available for special-needs jail inmates in your area. Have the group report its findings to the class.

TABLE 4–2

The 25 Largest Local Jail Jurisdictions, Midyear 1998

Jurisdiction	Number of Inmates Held	Average Daily Population[1]	Rated Capacity[2]	Percentage of Capacity Occupied Midyear[3]
Los Angeles County, CA	21,268	21,136	21,366	100%
New York City, NY	17,680	17,524	22,584	78%
Cook County, IL	9,321	9,297	9,776	95%
Dade County, FL	7,036	7,836	6,005	117%
Harris County, TX	7,587	7,781	8,657	88%
Dallas County, TX	6,941	7,000	8,182	85%
Maricopa County, AZ	7,019	6,910	6,252	112%
Orleans Parish, LA	6,670	6,398	7,174	93%
Philadelphia County, PA	5,990	5,753	6,179	97%
San Diego County, CA	6,040	5,745	5,815	104%
Shelby County, TN	5,808	5,627	6,583	88%
Orange County, CA	5,546	5,374	3,821	145%
San Bernardino County, CA	5,713	5,103	5,000	114%
Santa Clara County, CA	4,658	4,722	3,774	123%
Broward County, FL	4,640	4,289	3,756	124%
Fulton County, GA	3,827	4,276	2,987	128%
Alameda County, CA	4,164	3,823	4,590	91%
Baltimore City, MD	3,881	3,791	2,966	131%
Orange County, FL	3,865	3,547	3,234	120%
Tarrant County, TX	3,572	3,529	4,739	75%
Sacramento County, CA	3,654	3,507	3,871	94%
Bexar County, TX	3,368	3,398	3,670	92%
Hillsborough County, FL	3,101	3,062	2,909	107%
Milwaukee County, WI	2,850	2,918	2,466	116%
Duval County, FL	2,899	2,755	3,000	97%

Note: Jurisdictions are ordered by their average daily population in 1998.

1. For the year ending June 30. The average daily population is the sum of the number of inmates in jail each day for a year, divided by the number of days in the year.
2. Rated capacity is the number of beds or inmates assigned by a rating official to all the facilities within a jurisdiction.
3. The number of inmates, divided by the rated capacity and multiplied by 100.

Source: Darrell K. Gilliard and Allen J. Beck, *Prison and Jail Inmates at Midyear 1998* (Washington: Bureau of Justice Statistics, March 1999).

the jail inmates who need substance abuse treatment actually receive it. The absence of drug treatment programs is particularly common in small jails.

Drug treatment programs for jail inmates are important, not only because evidence suggests that rehabilitation is more likely for those offenders who complete drug treatment programs, but also because reducing drug-seeking behavior aids in managing the jail facility. A recent NIJ-sponsored research study found that the greatest benefit of drug treatment programs in jails was that they provided a "behavioral management tool" that controlled inmates' behavior and helped lower the incidence of inmate violence.[13]

The study evaluated five drug treatment programs in California and New York. At all five sites, substance abuse inmates in drug treatment programs had lower rates of serious physical violence and other behavioral problems (e.g., insubordination and possession of nondrug contraband) than those not in the programs. As for recidivism, 17 percent of the inmates in drug treatment and 23 percent of the control group were convicted again at least once during a one-year follow-up. Since offenders seldom voluntarily seek substance abuse treatment, jail is an opportunity to introduce treatment and encourage effective aftercare upon release.

HIV-Positive Inmates   In a 1995–96 survey of local jail inmates, 2.2 percent of tested inmates who responded were HIV positive.[14] Among jail inmates who said they had been tested for HIV/AIDS, those held for drug offenses were the most likely to be HIV-positive (3.3 percent).

Professional Issue

Training Programs Arrests for illegal drug use have been a major factor in increasing jail populations. This increase has created an interest in drug treatment programs in local jails. Generally, school districts or substance abuse agencies run the programs. Some programs offer cross-training of jail custody staff and treatment staff. Ask students if they think that jail custody staff should be included in planning and training for drug treatment programs. Do they think that more training of jail custody staff could increase staff support for the programs?

THE OFFENDER SPEAKS

I didn't want to participate in any programs, but that was the only way I could get out of 33rd Street [the main facility] into one of the buildings that have open spaces, only two guys to a cell, and good visitation rights. So I wouldn't have taken MRT [Moral Reconation Therapy, a substance abuse treatment program] if I didn't have to, but I'm glad I did. I learned about myself: I used to blame drugs as the source of my problems, but I learned it's my own attitudes and behavior that are responsible. Once you learn that, other things fall into place. Drug classes I had taken before never did this for me. In the life skills classes, I learned how to write a résumé and how to present myself at a job interview—by sitting up straight and so on. But you have to obey the rules in the program facilities if you want to stay. I've seen guys get busted back to 33rd Street because of shouting matches between inmates, for example. A few come back here again, and then they're careful to behave, because the other facility stinks. There's a loud noise that keeps you from sleeping, it's cold, and there's no carpeting, so they like it here much better.

An inmate in the Orange County (Florida) Jail

Cost-effective management of inmates with HIV or AIDS has at least five essential elements:

1. Early detection and diagnosis through medical and mental health screening of each new jail inmate upon admission.
2. Medical management and treatment by health specialists, including regular reevaluation and assessment.
3. Inmate classification and housing to discourage intravenous drug use and homosexual intercourse or to provide private rooms for terminally ill inmates.
4. Education and training of staff and inmates in the cause of AIDS, the stages of the disease, transmission methods, preventive measures, available treatment and therapies, testing issues and policies, confidentiality issues and policies, classification and program assignment policies, and supervision issues, including transportation and inmate movement.
5. Adequate funds to provide increasingly costly treatment to inmates with HIV or AIDS.

Tomorrow's jail professionals will need a network of medical experts—university medical school faculty, state health department staff, federal health officials, and local health care providers—to consult. Such consultation will give corrections professionals reliable information and familiarize the noncorrectional medical community with the problems facing jails.

Mentally Ill Inmates Every day, our nation's 3,304 local jails face another challenge—dealing with offenders who are mentally ill and require close monitoring, medication, and other services. The percentage of jail inmates with mental disorders significantly outweighs the percentage in the general population.[15] Yet 2 out of 10 jails have no access to mental health

*Because of funding defi-
ciencies and the relatively
short period of jail confinement, treatment options for
mentally ill persons are
often inadequate. What
other special needs inmates
do local jails sometimes
supervise?*

services and 8 out of 10 jail officers receive little or no training in mental health issues.

The NIJ recently sponsored a survey and visits to selected sites to identify successful policies and practices for meeting the needs of jail inmates with mental disorders. Practices included screening, evaluation, and classification of booked detainees; case management services at intake, consisting of crisis intervention services and short-term treatment programs; discharge planning with treatment referrals; mechanisms for dealing with the courts in regard to offenders with mental disorders; and pre- and postbooking programs to divert offenders with mental disorders from jail by working with the courts, the families, and the police.[16]

Because understanding of mental illness is limited, it is unrealistic to expect jail staff to cure these illnesses. The best one can hope for is to help mentally ill detainees achieve some stability in their lives and begin to live independently in the community. Doing so is also likely to lessen a detainee's criminal behavior— mostly thefts, assaults, and involvement with illicit drugs.

Inmates With Tuberculosis   Jails are at great risk for the spread of tuberculosis (TB).[17] This is due to the very close living quarters, overcrowding, poor sanitation, and the large number of inmates with a high risk of having TB, such as HIV-positive detainees, intravenous drug users, and immigrants. When a person who has TB coughs, sneezes, or laughs, tiny droplets of fluid containing TB bacteria are released into the air, which are then inhaled by others. Therefore, a jail inmate who has TB is most likely to spread the disease to those with whom he or she has the most contact.

Experts concerned about TB in jails have indicated that the most important issues for jail professionals are to understand the causes and control of TB, to implement an appropriate and cost-effective screening program, and to develop a close working relationship with local health authorities.

Jailer
The Bureau of Corrections is hiring officers for a new Adult Detention Complex. Duties include the following: Receive and safely keep all persons duly committed to the county jail. File and preserve all papers by which persons are committed. Detain persons enumerated in the state laws. Serve as Bail Commissioner. Fingerprint and photograph prisoners. Record in writing any occurrence in the jail during tour of duty. Operate electronic/video security system. Input data and operate computer terminals. May be required to perform some minor medical functions.

The Need for Better Data on Jail Populations and Programs

The challenge for jail professionals in the twenty-first century will be to manage a growing inmate population with multiple problems. Ken Kerle, managing editor of the American Jail Association, tells us it's time to replace jail ignorance with jail knowledge.[18] Better data can help us decide what works and what doesn't. Then we can improve our programs to better serve our offenders. As taxpayers, we should insist that our jail managers set realistic goals for their jails, their employees, and the inmates, and that they collect performance data toward those goals. Most states do not publish monthly reports on the number of inmates in each jail and those inmates' destinations. All of us should be able to find out easily how our jail system stacks up against other jails in cost, performance, and compliance with standards.

Student Involvement
Increasingly, jails are seen as alternatives to inadequate community-based mental health services. Providing appropriate treatment for inmates with mental disorders is a task for which most jails are ill-equipped. Yet, the Constitution requires that jails protect and, at least minimally, care for such prisoners. Ask students if they think it is fair to make jails responsible for such care. Have them explain why or why not.

Jail Issues

Jail administration and staffs face many important issues for the twenty-first century. We will now consider some of these issues and their effects on corrections professionals.

Professional Issue

Privatization If a private jail exists in your area, invite the jail administrator to speak to the class about jail privatization issues.

Privatization

Jails can be privatized in whole or in part. Jails can be financed, built, and operated by private groups, or jails can contract out some of their services (e.g., food service, mental health care, and programming).

One of the most hotly debated issues about privatization deals with the limits of governmental delegation of power and liability. Opponents of privatization believe that the administration of justice is a basic function of government and a symbol of state authority and should not be delegated.

Student Involvement

Ask two students to play the roles of sheriffs—one who favors privatizing jails and one who doesn't. Have them debate the issue. Each may have one or two advisers to turn to for information during the debate.

Opponents also fear that if we privatize jails, we risk letting private corporations use their political influence to continue programs not in the public interest. For example, would private contractors keep jail occupancy rates high to maintain profit? Might private contractors accept only the best inmates, leaving the most troublesome for public facilities to handle?

Turning a jail over to a private corporation also raises questions about accountability. Who is responsible for monitoring the performance of the private contractor? Who will see that local laws and regulations are followed? As jail incarceration rates continue to rise, the debate over privatizing jails and the competition for new contracts will continue.

Overcrowding

Teaching Tip

Help students understand that jail crowding is affected more by shifts in public attitudes and policy than by the amount of crime. Ask them which factor—mandatory arrests and sentences, overcrowding at state and federal prisons, or "get tough" policies on crime—most affects jail crowding.

Overcrowding is a problem that all jails, especially large urban jails, have to deal with. The number of persons held in local jails grew 4.5 percent from 1997 to 1998. The increase in the rate of jail incarceration is staggering. Between 1985 and 1998, the rate doubled—from 108 per 100,000 adults to 219. Overcrowding has a number of causes, including mandatory arrests and sentences, overcrowding at state and federal prisons, and an overall increase in the arrest rate as politicians "get tough" on crime. Crowded jails have serious health and safety consequences for staff and inmates, including decreased quality of life; overloaded educational, vocational, and recreational programs; insufficient medical services and supplies; increased discipline problems; spread of disease; and staff and inmate assaults.

Ways to Reduce Jail Crowding

Teaching Tip

Ask students which pretrial programs, if any, might coerce defendants to admit wrongdoing and agree to court-ordered sanctions before trial in order to avoid jail detention and possibly to avoid trial altogether.

Practices that can reduce crowding include financial and nonfinancial pretrial release, diversion, and new jail construction.

Financial Pretrial Release Financial pretrial release programs are one alternative to the pretrial detention of accused offenders. Releasing a person upon that person's financial guarantee to appear in court is known as **release on bail.** The Eighth Amendment to the United States Constitution reads, "Excessive bail shall not be required, nor excessive fines imposed, nor

release on bail The release of a person upon that person's financial guarantee to appear in court.

Quentin X. Escott
Deputy Sheriff
Jefferson County
Birmingham, Alabama

"When I work with an inmate and help him change his life, it's extremely gratifying. But the inmate has to want to change. He has to want help. I can't force it. A lot of prisoners want to know you'll help them and give them a chance. That's all."

Quentin X. Escott has been a deputy sheriff for 1½ years. He is currently assigned to the county jail booking area. His responsibilities include searching incoming prisoners, using the computer imaging system to take inmate photographs and fingerprints, recording personal property, exchanging civilian clothes for jail clothes, and assigning prisoners to housing areas based on their charge classifications.

Deputy Escott has completed almost two years at Lawson State Community College. He is transferring to the University of Alabama at Birmingham, where he will major in criminal justice.

His advice to persons interested in working in a jail? "Treat people like you want to be treated. Yeah, they're prisoners and they broke the law. For that they're in here for punishment. But if I'm going to like my job I have to get along with everybody, prisoners and staff. That means treating everyone with respect and hopefully getting it back in return." For Deputy Escott, the most gratifying part of the job is helping an inmate who really wants help.

---

cruel and unusual punishments inflicted." The Constitution does not guarantee defendants an automatic right to bail, only protection from excessive bail. The defendant may post the full amount of the bail, secure the amount privately through a bail bondsman, or deposit a percentage (usually 10 percent) with the court.

Nonfinancial Pretrial Release An alternative form of pretrial release requires only the defendant's promise to appear in court as required. This release without a cash guarantee is called **release on own recognizance (ROR)**. Generally, information about defendants is gathered and verified to determine the appropriateness of nonfinancial pretrial release.

Another type of nonfinancial pretrial release is a **citation.** Similar to traffic tickets, citations are issued by police in some jurisdictions for misdemeanors such as disorderly conduct. A citation binds the defendant to appear in court on a future date. It places no conditions on the released person's behavior and requires no payment to guarantee the court appearance.

In the 1960s and 1970s, a new form of nonfinancial pretrial release emerged. Called **supervised pretrial release,** it imposes more restrictive conditions on defendants. The conditions often include participating in therapeutic or rehabilitative programs, reporting to a pretrial officer, checking in regularly, and so forth. During the same period, a third-party release option developed. A third party—such as the defendant's lawyer, family, or

release on own recognizance (ROR) Pretrial release on the defendant's promise to appear for trial. It requires no cash guarantee.

citation A type of nonfinancial pretrial release similar to a traffic ticket. It binds the defendant to appear in court on a future date.

supervised pretrial release Nonfinancial pretrial release with more restrictive conditions (for example, participating in therapeutic or rehabilitative programs, reporting to a pretrial officer, and checking in regularly).

conditional release
Pretrial release under minimal or moderately restrictive conditions with little monitoring of compliance. It includes ROR, supervised pretrial release, and third-party release.

diversion   Referring defendants to non-criminal-justice agencies for services instead of processing them through the courts.

employer, or a social service agency—assumes responsibility for the defendant's appearance in court. Programs such as ROR, supervised pretrial release, and third-party release are all forms of **conditional release.** They impose minimal or moderately restrictive conditions with little monitoring of compliance. In a number of jurisdictions across the United States today, electronic monitoring is also being used as part of conditional release.

Diversion   Another way jail crowding can be reduced is through the expanded use of **diversion.** Diversion means referring defendants to non-criminal-justice agencies for services instead of processing them through the criminal justice system. For example, persons with substance abuse problems can be diverted to treatment centers, thus relieving jail crowding. Jail inmates with mental disorders can be referred to mental health clinics, where they receive both treatment and custodial supervision. After accepting diversion, a defendant is required to cooperate and participate in treatment, whether or not he or she feels it is necessary. Failure to show progress may lead to reinstatement of charges.

New Construction   Finally, new construction is another way to reduce jail crowding. Proponents of new construction argue that jail incarceration is here to stay. Because the public supports jails, we have a responsibility to build them. Opponents argue that if we continue to add new beds to the nation's jails, we will fill up all the space we create. In other words, some believe that availability drives up occupancy. They also claim that most nonviolent pretrial detainees and convicted offenders do not need to be in jail and that it wastes resources to house them there.

Women in Jail

In mid-1998, there were 63,791 female jail inmates. That was 11 percent of the entire jail population. Two-thirds of the women in jail are mothers with children under age 18. Before incarceration 40 percent used drugs daily. Forty percent had had members of their immediate families sentenced to prison. One out of three grew up in a home where one or both parents abused drugs, alcohol, or both. And one out of three had been physically or sexually abused before she was 18 years old. This profile raises troubling concerns about the children of jailed mothers. See Table 4–1.

When mothers go to jail, children become silent victims. The children may already be victims if their mothers used drugs during pregnancy. Young children, not yet capable of understanding why their mother is gone, where she has gone, and if or when she will return, may develop depression and feelings of abandonment. Even children who are fortunate enough to be placed with emotionally supportive caregivers must cope with seeing their mother only through a glass barrier and hearing her voice only over the phone. Studies have shown that children of incarcerated mothers have more behavioral problems at home and in school and are four times as likely to become juvenile delinquents as children from similar socioeconomic backgrounds with parents at home.

Recognizing that children should not be made to suffer for the poor choices of their parents, jails have established a number of successful par-

Teaching Tip
To help students understand the problems of women in jail, contact your local jail and ask if one or two female offenders (mothers, if possible) can visit your class. If they can't leave the jail, can your class visit the jail and meet with selected inmates? Ask the women what it's like for them to be in jail, and how it affects their children and the rest of their families.

Community-run parenting programs, such as this MATCH program at the North Carolina Correctional Center in Raleigh, teach parenting and life skills to jailed mothers and their children. Such programs feature inmate participation, community involvement, parent-child contacts, support groups, and strict security policies. Why is community involvement in such programs vital?

enting programs. Through such programs, jail administrators have the opportunity to become leaders in preserving families and reducing crime.

Educational and Vocational Programs

Many jail inmates have poor reading skills. National studies show that more than 40 percent of all jail inmates have less than a ninth-grade education.[19] They also have substance abuse problems and few job skills. They frequently cannot find jobs after they are released or can find only low-paid or temporary work. Partly as a result, they often return to a life of crime.

Too many jails simply warehouse inmates and care little about education or job skills. Yes, it does cost taxpayers money to provide educational services to jail inmates—the same people who already have financially and psychologically burdened society through their crimes. Education does not guarantee that an offender will remain free of crime upon release. But consider the alternative: More than 40 percent of defendants on pretrial release have one or more prior convictions. The cost of keeping one inmate in jail for one year ranges from $20,000 to $40,000. And studies also show that inmates who earn their GEDs while incarcerated are far less likely to return to crime. Educational and vocational programs help offenders help themselves, they boost self-esteem, and they encourage legitimate occupations upon release. Overall, it costs less to educate offenders and teach them job skills than to do nothing to change their attitudes, abilities, and outlooks. Ignoring an offender's educational and vocational deficiencies leaves the offender with fewer marketable skills or qualifications when released, increasing the chance of a return to crime.

Recently, the Orange County, Florida, Jail—one of the largest in the nation, with 3,300 beds—began an innovative strategy.[20] The entire jail—the operation, budget, and architecture—now revolves around its educa-

Student Involvement
Organize students into small groups. Ask each group to list technical skills in demand in your area that could be taught quickly to jail inmates in organized vocational programs. Share each group's list with the class. Then ask students to find out if any such training is available at area technical schools.

tional and vocational programs. The jail offers inmates a wide range of structured educational and vocational programs designed to fit inmates' short stays. The jail provides job readiness and placement services. It offers inmates valuable incentives to participate in programs and to avoid misconduct. And it uses the design and philosophy of third-generation jails, discussed earlier in this chapter, to manage inmates in a way that contains costs, promotes inmate responsibility, and allows open areas that can be used as classrooms. According to the National Institute of Justice, "Each of these features is part of a comprehensive corrections strategy that enables programming to flourish at the same time that it saves the county money, keeps inmates occupied and out of trouble, and (it is hoped) reduces recidivism."[21]

The principal steps in the Orange County Jail's educational and vocational programs are presented in Figure 4–6. The jail provides unusually intensive educational and vocational opportunities to most of its inmates. Five features are very important to the success of the programs: incentives for participation, direct supervision, active support by corrections officers, cooperation from schools, and programs tailored to short jail stays.

Religious Programs in Jail

Cross-Cultural Perspective
Inmates have different religious beliefs. Ask students to imagine themselves as jail inmates. What accommodations would they ask the jail administration to make for each of their religions? If any student is currently employed in jail administration, invite him or her to respond as his or her facility might respond to the inmates' religious requests. Invite a jail chaplain to class to join the discussion.

Very little is written about the use and effects of religion in jail. Too often the topic is looked at skeptically by outsiders, who believe that inmates "find God" as a convenient reason for release or forgiveness but really don't mean it. We do not enter that debate. What we present is a view grounded in the experiences of those who minister to jail inmates.

There are at least five benefits of jail chaplaincy. First, most jail chaplains believe that the cycle of crime can only be broken one life at a time. Jail inmates must experience an inner conversion before they change their behavior. Jail chaplains can assist in that conversion. Second, jail chaplains can help jail staff with their emotional and family problems. An on-site chaplain can help staff deal with problems daily, as they develop. Third, jail chaplains are in a unique position to mediate and moderate tensions and conflicts between inmates and staff before they get serious. Pleading for nonviolence is a chaplain's strong tool. Inmates usually see a jail chaplain as neutral—not as "one of them." The chaplain has the unique opportunity to speak his or her mind and be seen as someone who cares enough to confront and comfort. Fourth, ministering to the disadvantaged is legitimate in the eye of the public and helps the community remember those they would just as soon forget (recall the concept of inmates as "rabble," discussed earlier in this chapter). Involving the public as jail volunteers is an added benefit. And fifth, jail chaplains can help inmates confront the truth about themselves and reverse the "everything is relative" attitude that offenders develop to justify their crimes.

In the following excerpt, a chaplain shares some thoughts about his two years on the job:[22]

> A chaplain occupies a unique place in an inmate's thinking. She or he is not seen as "one of them;" we are not associated so much with the institution or judicial system. That gives us unique

FIGURE 4–6

Orange County, Florida, Jail Educational and Vocational Programs

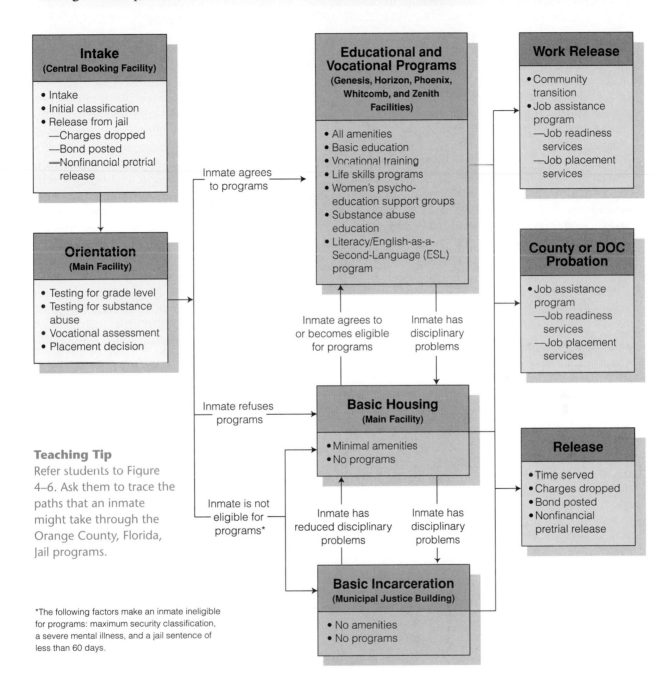

Teaching Tip
Refer students to Figure 4–6. Ask them to trace the paths that an inmate might take through the Orange County, Florida, Jail programs.

*The following factors make an inmate ineligible for programs: maximum security classification, a severe mental illness, and a jail sentence of less than 60 days.

Source: National Institute of Justice, *The Orange County, Florida, Jail Educational and Vocational Programs* (Washington: U.S. Department of Justice, 1997).

opportunities to speak openly and be viewed not as someone who has a sinister hidden agenda, but as someone who cares enough to confront.

Jail Accreditation

Jail accreditation is the formal approval of a jail by the American Correctional Association (ACA) and the Commission on Accreditation. The ACA and the commission have developed standards for the services, programs, and operations they consider essential to good jail management. The standards cover administrative and fiscal concerns, staff training and development, the physical plant, safety and emergency procedures, sanitation, food service, and rules and discipline. Standards are divided into two categories. To be accredited, a jail must have 100 percent compliance with mandatory standards and 90 percent compliance with nonmandatory standards. As of 1995, approximately 125 jails had received some form of national accreditation.

Accreditation is valid for three years. Then the jail may apply for reaccreditation and receive another on-site audit by ACA staff and an accreditation hearing.

Very few jails followed established standards or policies before the 1960s. Several reasons for this have been suggested, including the traditional independence of sheriffs, who operate the jails in most jurisdictions, and the tendency of most sheriffs to focus on law enforcement rather than on corrections.

Although jails were slow to respond to the standards movement, their response has picked up in recent years. There are several reasons jails have been slow to adopt national standards or seek national accreditation. First, accreditation is expensive and time-consuming. Many jails do not have the resources to commit to it. This is especially true of small jails that are already overburdened. Approximately 2,000 U.S. jails are designed to hold less than 50 inmates. Second, jails hold relatively few long-term inmates. Few inmates are in a jail long enough to file a successful legal action regarding poor conditions in the jail. Knowing this, some jail administrators may not be willing to undergo the expense and burden of seeking accreditation. Third, some states have their own standards that jails must meet.

There are at least four reasons for jails to have national accreditation:

1. Accreditation by the ACA and the Commission on Accreditation indicates that a jail adheres to strict standards to protect the health and safety of staff and inmates.
2. Being accredited may help a jail defend against lawsuits over conditions of incarceration.
3. In preparing for the accreditation review, the sheriff's office may evaluate all operations, procedures, and policies, leading to better management practices.
4. With accreditation come professional recognition and status, greater appreciation by the community, and a sense of pride in the achievement and in the hard work that went into it.

The Arlington County, Virginia, Jail is a case in point. The sheriff aspired to accreditation for the jail and instilled that goal in all staff. The jail staff spent eight months assembling the documentation needed to comply with specific standards. The staff also conducted a self-evaluation, looking closely at their policies, procedures, and operational practices. After the self-evaluation, the Arlington County Jail enlisted two professionals from nearby accredited jails to conduct a mock audit. The input of the mock auditors helped the jail further refine its documentation and prepare for the site visit of the national accrediting team.

When the national accrediting team arrived, its members toured the jail, interviewed approximately 25 staff members and 30 inmates, and read all the documentation the staff had prepared. The jail had 100 percent compliance with the mandatory standards and 98.6 percent compliance with the nonmandatory standards. The jail's scores were extremely high, reflecting the effort and time of the staff in meeting the standards, as well as the excellence of the jail's policies and procedures and of the accreditation files the staff had prepared.

Today, the Arlington County Jail displays its national award in the lobby of the jail. The staff takes pride in telling everyone that the jail has been accredited. Here is how some of the staff responded to the question "What does accreditation mean to you individually and as a member of this office?"[23]

Deputy Charles Monroe, currently assigned to the Intake Housing Unit: "Being accredited means to me that the sheriff's office is always striving to meet and go beyond state and national standards and guidelines. By going beyond and meeting these guidelines, it creates a professional attitude among staff members and creates a cleaner and safer environment for staff. It shows that the sheriff's office takes pride in being one of a few offices which meets accreditation standards. It also shows the dedication of the sheriff's office to providing Arlington County residents with the best service it can."

Deputy Jeffrey Tolen, currently assigned to the general population housing unit for women and a member of our emergency response team: "Coming from the old jail system, I feel that being accredited holds me to a higher standard. Having had an opportunity to see the accreditation process, I understand that my department has met standards that not every department can meet."

Deputy Charles Silcox, currently assigned to oversee the community work program: "As with any job, it is a good feeling to know that you are recognized for something that not everyone else in your field has been able to achieve. It's like setting a standard for others to follow."

Deputy Sheriff 1

Employees receive full salary and benefits while attending the Reiger Academy, where, upon successful completion, they will receive certification in corrections. Employees will perform a variety of duties in corrections, inmate transportation, service of legal process, or courtroom/courthouse security. Initial assignment will be in our state-of-the-art direct-supervision detention facility. The County Sheriff's Office is accredited by the American Correctional Association's Commission on Accreditation for Corrections. Qualifications: H.S. graduate or equivalent; age 21 at time of appointment; U.S. citizenship at time of application; valid driver's license.

Professional Issue

Accreditation Ask students how they might feel working in a jail that was accredited rather than one that was not. In essence, what are the benefits of accreditation to the staff of a jail?

Jail Staff as Professionals

Professional Issue

Education Emphasize that expecting jail staff to conduct themselves as professionals can help avoid lawsuits, low morale, agency stagnation, and dead-end careers. Find out the educational requirements to be a jail officer in your area. Ask students, assuming no change in those requirements, what could be done at little or no cost to heighten the image of jail officers as professionals.

Teaching Tip

Refer students to Exhibit 4–2. Ask them if they think that the code of ethics is too strict, not strict enough, or just right. Have them explain their answers.

As this chapter has shown, jail staff assume enormous responsibility, and we expect them to conduct themselves as professionals. Before 1970, training and education for jail officers were virtually nonexistent, for several reasons. Jail officers often aspired to be law enforcement officers or some other occupation, or they were using jail work as their last stop on the road to retirement. Many people also believed that education and training for jail staff were unnecessary because the work was unsophisticated and could be learned on the job.

Since 1970, however, the image of jail staff has changed. Thanks to organizations like the American Jail Association and the American Correctional Association; national, state, and local commissions on jail issues; and studies by practitioners, consultants, and academic researchers, jail work is now recognized not only as difficult but also as a career path that is different from law enforcement and requires different attitudes and skills. Jail staff perform work that is vital, complex, and potentially hazardous, even under the best of circumstances.

To conduct themselves as professionals, jail staff must have strong communication skills, knowledge of the psychology of behavior, multicultural sophistication, ethnic and racial tolerance, human management expertise, endurance, and fitness. Even more important, they must, for their own mental well-being, be able to understand and tolerate the stress of a potentially explosive environment. The American Jail Association's Code of Ethics for Jail Officers is shown in Exhibit 4–2.

The trend toward better educated and trained jail staff is evident across the United States. There are tougher entrance requirements. Applicants must have a higher level of education, increased basic training, more experience, other related skills, and the appropriate personality. Jail staff also learn to conduct themselves as professionals.

Many departments require applicants to have completed a correctional officer training and education program. There are a number of advantages to the policy. First, a department can hire certified correctional officers without paying for training. Second, the department can ask training program staff about applicants' abilities, reliability, and other relevant issues. And third, new jail officers will have the needed skills and an essential understanding of the job.

Teaching Tip

Refer to Chapter 4 of the *Instructor's Resource Manual* for additional activities and for answers to the end-of-chapter exercises.

EXHIBIT 4–2

American Jail Association

Code of Ethics for Jail Officers

As an officer employed in a detention/correctional capacity, I swear (or affirm) to be a good citizen and a credit to my community, state, and nation at all times. I will abstain from questionable behavior which might bring disrepute to the agency for which I work, my family, my community, and my associates. My lifestyle will be above and beyond reproach and I will constantly strive to set an example of a professional who performs his/her duties according to the laws of our country, state, and community and the policies, procedures, written and verbal orders, and regulations of the agency for which I work.

On the job I promise to:

KEEP The institution secure so as to safeguard my community and the lives of the staff, inmates, and visitors on the premises.

WORK With each individual firmly and fairly without regard to rank, status, or condition.

MAINTAIN A positive demeanor when confronted with stressful situations of scorn, ridicule, danger, and/or chaos.

REPORT Either in writing or by word of mouth to the proper authorities those things which should be reported, and keep silent about matters which are to remain confidential according to the laws and rules of the agency and government.

MANAGE And supervise the inmates in an evenhanded and courteous manner.

REFRAIN At all times from becoming personally involved in the lives of the inmates and their families.

TREAT All visitors to the jail with politeness and respect and do my utmost to ensure that they observe the jail regulations.

TAKE Advantage of all education and training opportunities designed to assist me to become a more competent officer.

COMMUNICATE With people in or outside of the jail, whether by phone, written word, or word of mouth, in such a way so as not to reflect in a negative manner upon my agency.

CONTRIBUTE To a jail environment which will keep the inmate involved in activities designed to improve his/her attitude and character.

SUPPORT All activities of a professional nature through membership and participation that will continue to elevate the status of those who operate our nation's jails. Do my best through word and deed to present an image to the public at large of a jail professional, committed to progress for an improved and enlightened criminal justice system.

Adopted by the American Jail Association Board of Directors on November 10, 1991. Revised May 19, 1993.

SUMMARY BY CHAPTER OBJECTIVES

CHAPTER OBJECTIVE 1

Jails serve a number of purposes besides incarcerating persons who have sentences of a year or less. They hold persons awaiting trial, probation and parole violators, adults and juveniles awaiting transfer, and prison inmates about to be released. Sometimes they operate community-based programs.

CHAPTER OBJECTIVE 2

Jails emerged in Europe in the twelfth century to detain offenders for trial. In the fifteenth and sixteenth centuries, the poor and unemployed were detained alongside criminals. The first jail in America was the Walnut Street Jail. Quakers planned it based on the principles of religious reflection and penance. It fell short of reaching its goals and closed in 1835.

CHAPTER OBJECTIVE 3

American jails have progressed through three phases of architecture and inmate management: first-generation jails (linear design and indirect supervision), second-generation jails (pod design and indirect supervision), and third-generation jails (pod design and direct supervision).

CHAPTER OBJECTIVE 4

At midyear 1998, jails held 664,847 offenders, an increase of 4.5 percent from midyear 1997. An estimated 252,600 (43 percent) are convicted offenders. Women represent 11 percent of the jail population; nonwhites, almost 60 percent; and juveniles, 1.4 percent. Special-needs inmates are persons suffering from mental illness, chemical dependency (drug and alcohol abuse), or disease (especially HIV/AIDS or TB).

CHAPTER OBJECTIVE 5

Jail vocational and educational programs are important techniques for managing inmates and reducing recidivism. They keep inmates occupied, they boost self-esteem, and they help inmates find jobs after release.

CHAPTER OBJECTIVE 6

Religion and jail chaplaincy can influence jail inmates in five ways. First, they can help inmates with the inner conversion needed to break the cycle of crime. Second, a jail chaplain can help staff deal with day-to-day problems. Third, a jail chaplain can mediate and moderate tensions and conflicts between inmates and staff. Fourth, jail chaplaincy can involve the public as jail volunteers and remind people that inmates exist. And fifth, chaplains can help inmates confront the truth about themselves.

CHAPTER OBJECTIVE 7

Jail accreditation is important for four reasons. First, accreditation indicates that a jail adheres to strict standards. Second, accreditation may help a jail defend against lawsuits over conditions of incarceration. Third, through accreditation, the sheriff's office may evaluate all operations, procedures, and policies, leading to better management practices. And fourth, accreditation means professional recognition and status, greater appreciation by the community, and a sense of pride.

CHAPTER OBJECTIVE 8

It is important for jail staff to conduct themselves as professionals because jail work is difficult and carries enormous responsibility. It requires a special attitude, communication skills, knowledge of the psychology of behavior, multicultural sophistication, endurance, and fitness. Together, college education and jail training prepare jail staff to work as professionals.

jails, p. 91
rabble management, p. 94
first-generation jail, p. 94
second-generation jail, p. 95
third-generation jail, p. 97
direct-supervision jails, p. 97
special-needs inmates, p. 103

release on bail, p. 108
release on own recognizance (ROR), p. 109
citation, p. 109
supervised pretrial release, p. 109
conditional release, p. 110
diversion, p. 110
jail accreditation, p. 114

QUESTIONS FOR REVIEW

1. What are the main purposes of jails?
2. When and where was the first jail built? What was the purpose of this jail?
3. Who was John Howard?
4. What was the first jail in America, and when was it built?
5. Explain what John Irwin meant by *rabble management.*
6. Describe how first-, second-, and third-generation jails differ.
7. As of 1998, which ethnic groups make up the majority of jail populations in the United States?
8. What are special-needs inmates? What problems do they pose for jail personnel?

9. List some arguments against jail privatization.
10. Outline some strategies to reduce jail crowding.
11. Why is it important to promote positive relationships between incarcerated mothers and their children?
12. Why are educational and vocational programs for inmates important for jail management?
13. How can religion and jail chaplaincy be positive forces in the jail environment?
14. What are the advantages and disadvantages of jail accreditation?
15. List some characteristics of a professional jail employee.

CRITICAL THINKING EXERCISES

ON-THE-JOB ISSUE
You are the administrator of a new county jail with the architecture and philosophy of direct supervision. The new jail replaced the old jail, built in 1912. Some of the senior staff have begun complaining to you about direct supervision. They say they don't like to interact with inmates. They talk about "the good old days" when inmates were "on the other side" of the reinforced glass and steel bars. There's even been a letter to the editor in the local newspaper complaining that the new jail doesn't "look like a jail."

1. What could you tell the senior staff about third-generation philosophy and architecture that might ease their concerns?

2. What strategies might you use to educate the public about the benefits of direct supervision?

CORRECTIONS ISSUES
1. When deciding whether to grant pretrial release, a judge looks at the offense, the evidence, and the defendant's family ties, employment, financial resources, character, mental condition, length of residence in the community, and criminal record. To which of these do you think the judge should give the greatest weight? Why?

2. A major advantage of financial and non-financial pretrial release programs is that they keep the jail population down. That means

less money is spent on jails. Without pretrial release, the number of persons in jail would be higher, and more money would be needed for new jails—money that local communities do not have. When pretrial release programs are properly developed and implemented, defendants appear in court as promised. One criticism of pretrial release programs is that some may coerce defendants, before trial, to participate in therapy, education, or vocational training. Critics argue that such coercion is wrong for defendants who are later acquitted. They also argue that defendants who are convicted are often ordered to repeat the same therapy, education, or vocational training. Do you favor or oppose pretrial release? Explain.

3. The accreditation process can take up to 18 months. When achieved, accreditation lasts three years. Facilities are encouraged to reapply early to prevent a break in accreditation. The process of self-evaluation is almost continuous. Do you think a three-year period of accreditation is too short, too long, or just right? Explain.

4. Correctional facilities seek accreditation to ensure compliance with national standards, to demonstrate to legislators acceptable performance, and to comply with court orders. Which of these reasons do you think should be given the most importance, and why?

CORRECTIONS ON THE WEB

1. Carefully read the mission statement on the Niagara County Sheriff's Department Web page (**http://www.ncsd.com**). What emphasis does the mission statement give to jail operations? If possible, look at the Web pages of other jail facilities and review their mission statements. What do you think the ideal mission statement should say about jail operations?

2. Visit the Web site of the American Correctional Association at **http://www. corrections.com/aca/.** Click on Accreditation to go to the Standards and Accreditation Online Resource Center. Choose among the topics to learn more about the accreditation process.

ADDITIONAL READINGS

Irwin, John. *The Jail: Managing the Underclass in American Society.* Berkeley: University of California Press, 1986.

Kerle, Kenneth E. *American Jails: Looking to the Future.* Boston: Butterworth Heinemann, 1998.

Welsh, Wayne N. *Counties in Court: Jail Overcrowding and Court-Ordered Reform.* Philadelphia: Temple University Press, 1995.

Zupan, Linda L. *Jails: Reform and the New Generation Philosophy.* Cincinnati: Anderson, 1991.

ENDNOTES

1. R. J. Hawkins, "My Own Private Iowa," available: http://www.captivated.com/hawkins/bottom.html.
2. Darrell K. Gilliard and Allen J. Beck, *Prison and Jail Inmates at Midyear 1998* (Washington: Bureau of Justice Statistics, March 1999).
3. National Advisory Commission on Criminal Justice Standards and Goals, *Corrections* (Washington: U.S. Government Printing Office, 1973) p. 273.
4. Marilyn D. McShane and Frank P. Williams III (eds.), *Encyclopedia of American Prisons* (New York: Garland, 1996), p. 494.
5. Ibid., p. 496.
6. Ronald L. Goldfarb, *Jails: The Ultimate Ghetto* (Garden City, NY: Doubleday, 1975), p. 29.
7. John Irwin, *The Jail: Managing the Underclass in American Society* (Berkeley: University of California Press, 1986).
8. Linda Zupan, *Jails: Reform and the New Generation Philosophy* (Cincinnati: Anderson, 1991).
9. Gilliard and Beck, pp. 7–8.
10. G. Larry Mays and Daniel L. Judiscak, "Special Needs Inmates in New Mexico Jails," *American Jails*, Vol. 10, No. 2 (1996), pp. 32–41.
11. Sally Chandler Halford, "Drug Offender Treatment," *American Jails*, Vol. 10, No. 3, July/Aug. 1996, p. 4.
12. Caroline Wolf Harlow, *Profile of Jail Inmates 1996* (Washington: Bureau of Justice Statistics, April 1998), pp. 8–9.
13. Sandra Tunis, et al., *Evaluation of Drug Treatment in Local Corrections* (Washington: U.S. Department of Justice, 1997).
14. Laura Maruschak, *HIV in Prisons and Jails, 1995* (Washington: U. S. Department of Justice, 1997).
15. L. A. Teplin, "Psychiatric and Substance Abuse Disorders Among Male Urban Jail Detainees," *American Journal of Public Health*, Vol. 84, No. 2 (1994), pp. 290–293.
16. Henry J. Steadman and Bonita M. Veysey, *Providing Services for Jail Inmates with Mental Disorders* (Washington: National Institute of Justice, Office of Justice Programs, January 1997).
17. Mason R. Goodman, "An Overview of Tuberculosis in Jails in the United States for Health Care and Administrative Corrections Professionals," *American Jails*, Vol. 10, No. 4 (1996), pp. 45–50.
18. Ken Kerle, "Statistics and Jails," *American Jails*, Vol. 10, No. 6 (1997), p. 5.
19. Harlow, p. 3.
20. National Institute of Justice, *The Orange County, Florida, Jail Educational and Vocational Programs* (Washington: U.S. Department of Justice, 1997).
21. Ibid., p. 3.
22. Sheldon Crapo, "Breaking the Cycle of Crime . . . One Life at a Time," *American Jails*, Vol. 11, No. 1 (March/April 1997), p. 24.
23. Michael Pinson, "Accreditation Is Worth the Effort," *Corrections Today*, Vol. 58, No. 7 (December 1996), p. 73. Reprinted with permission.

5 Diversion and Probation

Alternatives to Imprisonment

CHAPTER OBJECTIVES

After completing this chapter you should be able to:

1. Define *diversion* and know its objectives.
2. Explain the rationales for diversion.
3. Give examples of stages at which diversion occurs in the criminal justice process.
4. Discuss diversion policy issues.
5. Define *probation* and know its goals.
6. Explain the reasons for using probation.
7. Describe some of the characteristics of adults on probation.
8. Explain the different ways that probation is administered.
9. Describe the investigation and supervision functions of probation officers.
10. Describe the measures used to evaluate probation.
11. Discuss the issues facing probation in the 21st century.

Student Involvement
Ask students if they agree or disagree with the statement by the National Advisory Commission on Criminal Justice Standards and Goals. Be sure they explain their reasons.

If all law violations were processed officially as the arrest-conviction-imprisonment model calls for, the system obviously would collapse from its voluminous caseloads and from community opposition.

—National Advisory Commission on Criminal Justice Standards and Goals

Teaching Tip
Write on the board, "The face of probation is changing." Then ask students what they think about putting private corporations on probation. Do they think that probation is an appropriate punishment for corporate crime? Why or why not?

Teaching Tip
Refer to Figure 5–1. Have students trace the decision points for each of the processes.

On December 31, 1998, 3.4 million people were on probation in the United States—1 out of every 60 adults. The number of people on probation is equivalent to the population of Oklahoma.

The typical probationer is a Southern white male who has never married and has either completed high school or earned a GED. He was convicted of a felony and has at least one prior sentence, to probation or confinement. He has five or more probation conditions, including payment of monetary restitution to his victim. At least 40 percent of probationers are ordered to undergo substance abuse treatment.

However, the face of probation is changing. Under the authority of federal sentencing guidelines, federal judges are increasingly ordering probation for *corporations* found guilty of violations of federal law. In 1993, 48 U.S. companies were on probation. By 1996, the number had increased to 96.

As a condition of probation, judges order monitoring of a corporation's activities. They assign a monitor to each corporation put on probation. The role of the independent monitor is to investigate any acts, conditions, or problems brought to the attention of the court or the monitor. The monitor conducts an investigation and then files a report with the judge.

Despite federal judges' increasing use of probation for corporations, probation is imposed most often by local judges on individuals convicted of criminal offenses. This chapter introduces you to two areas of corrections that most offenders first experience—diversion and probation. Diversion

FIGURE 5–1

Case Flow Model for Diversion and Probation

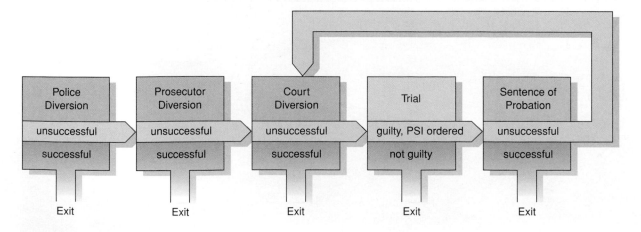

occurs *before* trial. Probation occurs *after* a person has been convicted. Figure 5–1 shows how these two processes can occur in the criminal justice system. Because offenders can be diverted one or more times before they are tried, convicted, and sentenced to probation, we will discuss diversion first.

Diversion

Diversion has been defined as "the halting or suspension, before conviction, of formal criminal proceedings against a person, [often] conditioned on some form of counter performance by the defendant,"[1] and this is the definition we will use. **Counter performance** is the defendant's participation, in exchange for diversion, in a treatment, counseling, or educational program aimed at changing his or her behavior. The candidate for diversion is a person who has been or could be arrested for an alleged offense and who is or could become the defendant in a criminal prosecution. Suspending the prosecution of a case is the hallmark of the diversion process.

In the criminal justice system, diversion is used in two ways. First, it can keep an offender out of the system and avoid formal prosecution and labeling. This is called **true diversion.** For example, a person accused of public drunkenness could be required to attend an alcohol abuse program in lieu of arrest and prosecution. The referral agency, generally the police, may stipulate that if the person successfully completes the alcohol abuse program, no further action will be taken. If the person does not successfully complete the alcohol abuse program, the police might file the initial charge.

The second way of using diversion is to keep an offender from going further into the system. This is called **minimization of penetration.** For example, a man charged with battering his girlfriend could be asked by the prosecutor to attend a batterer's treatment program in lieu of trial, conviction, and sentence. If the accused batterer completes the treatment program, the charge is dropped. If he does not complete the program, the prosecutor may prosecute him for the crime.

Most diversion programs share three objectives:

1. Prevent future criminal activity by diverting certain defendants from criminal justice processing into community supervision and service. This goal is based on the belief that diversion programs are more effective ways to control criminal behavior than taking offenders to court and getting them convicted and sentenced.
2. Save prosecution and judicial resources for serious crimes by offering alternatives to the usual prosecution process for less serious ones. Defendants eligible for diversion are given the opportunity to avoid arrest or prosecution and to obtain medical services, counseling, and educational and vocational training.
3. Provide, where appropriate, a vehicle for restitution to communities and victims of crime.

Rationales for Diversion

Diversion has four rationales. First, the experience and the stigma of being formally arrested, tried, and convicted can actually encourage more

diversion Formal efforts to use alternatives to processing through the justice system; also, "the halting or suspension, before conviction, of formal criminal proceedings against a person, conditioned on some form of counter performance by the defendant."

counter performance The defendant's participation, in exchange for diversion, in a treatment, counseling, or educational program aimed at changing his or her behavior.

true diversion A form of diversion that keeps an offender out of the system and avoids formal prosecution and labeling.

minimization of penetration A form of diversion that keeps an offender from going further into the system.

Student Involvement
Have students use the three objectives of diversion to devise a diversion policy for selected offenses at their college.

Teaching Tip

Explain that the difference between *true diversion* and *minimization of penetration* is that, in true diversion, the police do not make a formal arrest. The police keep the offender out of the criminal justice system altogether. For example, instead of arresting someone who is publicly drunk, the police may take the person to a community shelter.

Teaching Tip

Review the four rationales for diversion. Then offer the example of a young female college student caught shoplifting textbooks for her classes. Ask if this is a case worthy of diversion. If students think diversion is appropriate, have them suggest counter performance measures. (Some possibilities include having her work in the bookstore after hours, giving her last year's bookstore loss estimates and directing her to write a paper on shoplifting, and offering her a part-time job.)

Teaching Tip

Refer to Figure 5–2. Ask students to comment on the conditions of the pretrial release into a diversion program. Are the conditions harsh, not harsh enough, or just right? Why?

criminal behavior. For example, having a criminal record might restrict a person's educational, vocational, and social opportunities, making the person more apt to turn to crime to survive. In addition, as a result of time spent in jail or prison, an offender may be more likely to associate with other offenders.

A second rationale for using diversion is that it is less expensive than formally processing an offender through the criminal justice system. The expense of arrest, trial, conviction, and sentence is easily justified for serious crimes. In most cities and counties across the United States today, however, the police are overworked, the courts are overloaded, the jails and prisons are overcrowded, and probation and parole officers have caseloads that are unmanageable. Diversion is a way to reduce or at least contain these burdens, reserving formal criminal justice processing for the cases that need it the most.

A third rationale for diversion is that the public may think formal processing through the criminal justice system is inappropriate for crimes without perceived victims. These offenses involve a willing and private exchange of illegal goods or services. Examples include prostitution, certain forms of sexual behavior, gambling, and drug sales. Such offenses are called victimless crimes because the participants do not feel they are being harmed. Prosecution is justified on the grounds that these offenses harm society as a whole by threatening the moral fabric of the community. Since formal prosecution of these offenses is costly, however, offenders are often diverted to health clinics and treatment programs.

A final rationale for using diversion is to give the typical diversion client a better chance in life. Our nation's jails, lockups, prisons, and probation and parole caseloads are filled with people who are economically disadvantaged, belong to minority groups, and are young, undereducated, and chronically unemployed or underemployed. Diversion offers such persons help with some of the challenges they face, without adding to their difficulties the stigma of formal arrest, trial, and conviction.

How Does Diversion Occur?

Diversion may occur at any point in the criminal justice process after a criminal complaint has been filed or police have observed a crime. The police, a prosecutor, or a judge may use it. The accused participates voluntarily and has access to defense counsel before deciding whether to participate.

The overall goal of diversion is to reduce recidivism through rehabilitation. Most diversion programs use an assessment process to determine a defendant's needs. Then an intervention plan for that defendant is developed. The diversion program then contracts with the defendant, agreeing on the requirements of the plan and the criminal justice consequences of succeeding or failing in the plan. Figure 5–2 shows the conditions of pretrial diversion used by the Treatment Alternatives to Street Crime (TASC) program in Alabama. Similar conditions are used by diversion programs in many other states. In some states, the diversion process is established by law; in other states, local agreements with prosecutors are the basis for the process.

Diversion programs offer a variety of remedial responses to defendants' problems. Such responses can include drug and alcohol treatment, mental

FIGURE 5–2

Pretrial Release Bond Agreement

STATE OF ALABAMA

vs

___Brett Gould___

- STATE OF ALABAMA
- JEFFERSON COUNTY
- ___District___ COURT
- BOND $ ___$5,000.00___
- CASE NO. ___DC99-6342___917

CONDITIONS OF RELEASE

1. Defendant must appear to answer and must submit to the orders and process of the court having jurisdiction of this case as directed.

2. Defendant must refrain from committing any criminal offense.

3. Defendant must refrain from any contact with prosecutor's witness(s) /the complainant's victim(s). Specifically: ___Karen Koch___.

4. Defendant must continue to reside at ___2055 2nd Ave., Birmingham___ with ___son___, and may not leave the state of Alabama or change residence without written permission of the Court having jurisdiction of this case.

5. Defendant must obtain and/or maintain full-time employment or schooling. Written verification of employment attendance or attempts to secure employment/enrollment will be presented to the TASC case manager.

6. Defendant must report to the TASC Office within 72 hours after release, at 401 Beacon Parkway West, for an evaluation by a case manager.

7. Defendant must submit to random urinalysis for drug screening. Defendant must pay the $20 fee for each month. If drug abuse is indicated, appropriate treatment will be required.

8. Defendant must attend AA/NA/CA meetings ___3___ times per week and provide case manager with written verification of that attendance.

9. Defendant must abide by a curfew requiring presence in house of residence between hours of ___6___ p.m. and ___7___ a.m.

10. Defendant must seek and accept drug and/or alcohol treatment within ___7___ days of release date.

11. Defendant must appear in this court on the next scheduled court date, ___March 20, 2000___.

Done this ___13th___ day of ___March___, 20 ___00___

Carl Stephan
Judge

INSTRUCTION TO DEFENDANT

You have agreed to appear in court whenever ordered. Your responsibility to the above conditions is to remain until either the case is ended or you are released. If you do not appear whenever ordered, you may be required to pay the bond amount.

Brett Gould
DEFENDANT

Terry Williams
WITNESSED

unconditional diversion
The termination of criminal processing at any point before adjudication with no threat of later prosecution. It generally means that treatment, counseling, and other services are offered voluntarily.

conditional diversion
Diversion in which charges are dismissed if the defendant satisfactorily completes treatment, counseling, or other programs ordered by the justice system.

health services, employment counseling, and education and training. They may involve agencies in or outside the criminal justice system. The variety of responses often reflects a community's unique criminal justice population.

Diversion is also used for persons who are classified as mentally ill or incompetent and either are not equipped to stand trial or need a form of incarceration and treatment other than imprisonment. Such persons may be referred to an agency for voluntary treatment or civil commitment to an institution in lieu of prosecution and a prison sentence.

Diversion Policy Issues

Diversion has its supporters and critics. Supporters believe diversion is the first opportunity to give offenders individualized assistance before they get too far down the path of crime. In such cases, diversion resolves problems that lead to offending behavior. Critics argue that diversion tends to force people to give up some of their freedom without being tried and convicted. They argue that it violates the safeguard of due process. Other critics believe that diversion is "nonpunishment" and might actually produce more crime. To these and other issues about diversion we now turn our attention.

Legal and Ethical Issues There is agreement that a diversion program should protect a defendant's rights. Protections include requiring an informed waiver of the right to a speedy trial, the right to a trial by jury, the right to confront one's accusers, and the privilege against self-incrimination, and informed consent to the conditions of a diversion program. For supporters, the risk of violating rights is outweighed by the chance diversion gives defendants to avoid the stigma of a criminal record and by the possibility of resolving problems that might result in future criminal behavior.

Unconditional diversion is the termination of criminal processing at any point before adjudication with no threat of later prosecution. It affords the best protection for a defendant's legal rights because dismissal of charges does not require any counter performance. In effect, the defendant has everything to gain and nothing to lose. In unconditional diversion, treatment, counseling, and other services are offered voluntarily. In addition, the use of any services is voluntary. Many corrections leaders regard voluntary treatment as more likely than coerced treatment to have beneficial effects.

Conditional diversion means that charges are dismissed if the defendant satisfactorily completes treatment, counseling, or other programs ordered by the justice system. Conditional diversion at or after arraignment, with judicial participation, affords greater protection against prosecutorial overreach and more assurance of informed voluntary decisions by the defendant than diversion by the police or the prosecutor. In diversion programs run by the police and prosecutor, some persons diverted might not have been prosecuted at all or would have been exonerated (cleared of blame). Conditional diversion does not, however, avoid the prospect of more severe penalties for divertees who fail the program.

Law Enforcement Issues Does diversion weaken law enforcement? Does diversion invite more widespread violation of laws by allowing offenders to avoid conviction? There is no particular evidence one way or the

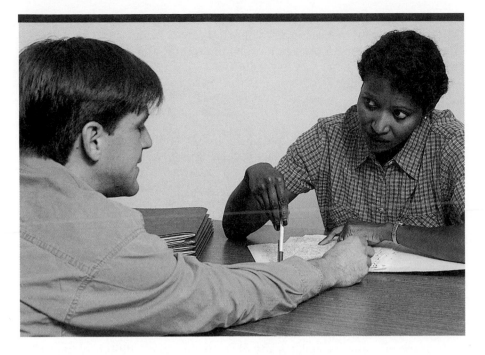

other. Certainly, if unconditional diversion were practiced extensively, there might be increases in violations. However, if such diversion is limited to the first charge, or the second, there is a ceiling on such increases. Conditional diversion requiring supervision and counter performance does not seem more likely to encourage crime than the dispositions it most often replaces—fines, suspended sentences, and probation.

Economic Issues How cost-effective is diversion? What is the least costly method of diversion that will yield acceptable results? What are the tradeoffs in using different kinds of diversion programs? How does diversion compare in cost and effectiveness with traditional prosecution and sentencing practices?

Some argue that in the long run, diversion can protect the community better than traditional processing. Treatment starts promptly after the criminal events. The social handicap of a criminal record is avoided. Exposure to criminal influences is minimized. And diversion is presumably less conducive to recidivism than traditional processing.

Evidence to support these assertions is anything but conclusive. Most diversion programs have shown good results, but efforts to compare them with what would have happened without diversion have been unsuccessful. However, it seems safe to say the community protection that diversion affords is at least comparable to the traditional measures that would most likely be used if prosecution were not suspended. The economic question, then, is, Which approach costs less?

The costs of both diversion and its alternatives include the costs of arriving at a decision; the costs of implementing decisions; and the costs of undesired consequences of decisions, such as reinstatement of prosecution, new charges, or revocation of probation or parole because of a new charge or violation.

Diversion and Probation: Alternatives to Imprisonment

Diversion is not always the appropriate response to criminal behavior. When diversion is not used or when it fails to bring about the desired changes in an offender's behavior, probation is often the next step in the corrections process.

Probation

Probation has long been one of the most popular and most frequently used forms of punishment (see Figure 5–3). It is a way to keep the offender at home in the community, avoid incarceration, and carry out sanctions imposed by the court or the probation agency. **Probation** is the conditional release of a convicted offender into the community, under the supervision of a probation officer. It is conditional because it can be revoked if certain conditions are not met. The judge or the probation department usually imposes a set of restrictions on the offender's freedom. Almost all probationers have at least one special condition on their release.[2] Among them are paying fines or restitution; submitting to electronic monitoring, house arrest, or drug tests; obeying a curfew; and keeping a log of daily activities. More than 80 percent of probationers have three or more conditions on their sentences. The most common condition (84%) is the payment of fees, fines, or court costs. If the probationer violates any of the technical conditions of her or his probation, or commits a new crime, the judge may order that the entire sentence be served in prison.

Under probation, the offender lives at home but is monitored in some way, such as meeting with a probation officer a specified number of times

Student Involvement
Point out that almost all probationers have at least one condition attached to their probation. Ask students if they think probation without any such conditions is ever appropriate, and why. Then refer students to Figure 5–3 and ask them to compare the trends depicted in the graph.

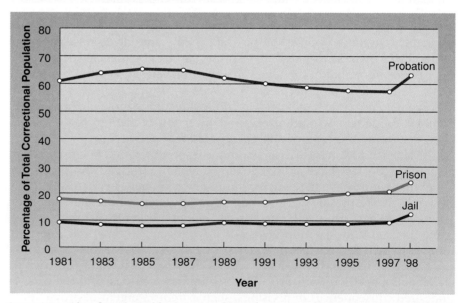

FIGURE 5–3

Adults on Probation, in Jail, or in Prison

Source: Adapted from *Sourcebook of Criminal Justice Statistics, 1997*, Bureau of Justice Statistics (October 1998), p. 464 and Bureau of Justice Statistics, *Probation and Parole in the United States, 1998* (Washington: U.S. Department of Justice, August 1999).

Diversion and Probation: Alternatives to Imprisonment

per month. According to a 1998 report by the Bureau of Justice Statistics, more than three-quarters of probationers maintain regular contact with a probation agency.[3] The rest are not required to have regular contact or cannot be located.

Reasons for and Goals of Probation

Probation is used for at least four reasons. First, probation permits the offender to remain in the community for reintegration purposes. Offender reintegration is more likely to occur if social and family ties are not broken by incarceration.

Second, probation avoids prison institutionalization and the stigma of incarceration. Prison institutionalization is the process of learning the norms and culture of institutional living. It is an artificial environment and not helpful to teaching prisoners how to adjust to the free world. Probationers never experience prison institutionalization, nor do they have to worry about the negative labeling effects of being treated like a prisoner, which decreases even further a prisoner's ability to function as a law-abiding citizen when released.

The third reason to have probation is that it is less expensive than incarceration, more humanitarian, and at least as effective in reducing future criminal activity as is incarceration.

The final reason in favor of probation is that it is fair and appropriate sentencing for offenders whose crime does not merit incarceration. Furthermore, probation is the base from which more severe punishments can be built. Not all crimes deserve incarceration, nor do all crimes deserve probation. Probation is preferred when the offender poses no threat to community safety, when community correctional resources are available, and when probation does not unduly deprecate the seriousness of the offense. The probation risk-needs assessment and statutory sentencing guidelines help identify which offenders deserve community or institutional punishment.

The goals of probation reflect society's values. In the 1960s, when society showed a strong interest in social welfare and offender rehabilitation, probation work reflected that emphasis. Today, probation emphasizes offender control. Most probation programs share five objectives:

1. Protect the community by preparing the presentence investigation (PSI) report to assist judges in sentencing and supervising offenders. The PSI indicates the degree of risk an offender poses to the community. It also identifies the offender's special needs. Offenders posing a threat to the community are then given secure placement, usually incarceration. Offenders who do not pose a threat to the community are given probation supervision. We will return to the PSI later in this chapter.
2. Carry out sanctions imposed by the court. Probation officers accomplish this by educating offenders about the orders of the court, supervising offenders, and removing them from the community when they violate the conditions of their probation.
3. Conduct a risk-needs assessment to identify the level of supervision and the services probationers need.

Cross-Cultural Perspective
The extensive use of probation as a form of punishment is an American institution. Ask students how the cultural attitudes of Americans may have influenced this development.

Teaching Tip
Emphasize that today's probation practices stress offender control. Ask students to offer reasons for that emphasis on control, rather than rehabilitation.

Tutorial CD-ROM
Refer students to the Tutorial With Simulation Applications CD-ROM. The tutorial is a comprehensive interactive study tool that reinforces and reviews the concepts in Chapter 5. Also included are two simulations that apply concepts presented in Chapter 5.

EXHIBIT 5–1

American Correctional Association

Policy on Probation

Probation is a frequently used and cost-effective sanction of the court for enhancing social order and public safety. Probation may be used as a sanction by itself or, where necessary and appropriate, be combined with other sanctions such as fines, restitution, community service, residential care, or confinement. Agencies responsible for probation should:

A. Prepare disposition assessments to assist the court in arriving at appropriate sanctions. The least restrictive disposition consistent with public safety should be recommended;

B. Establish a case management system for allocating supervisory resources through a standardized classification process;

C. Provide supervision to probationers and, with their input, develop a realistic plan to ensure compliance with orders of the court;

D. Monitor and evaluate, on an ongoing basis, the probationer's adherence to the plan of supervision and, when necessary, modify the plan of supervision according to the changing needs of the offender and the best interests of society;

E. Provide access to a wide range of services to meet identifiable needs, all of which are directed toward promoting law-abiding behavior;

F. Assure any intervention in an offender's life will not exceed the minimal amount needed to assure compliance with the orders of the court;

G. Initiate appropriate court proceedings, when necessary, if the probationer fails to comply with orders of the court, supervision plan, or other requirements, so the court may consider other alternatives for the protection and well-being of the community;

H. Oppose use of the probation sanction for status offenders, neglected or dependent children, or any other individuals who are neither accused nor charged with delinquent or criminal behavior;

I. Establish an educational program for sharing information about probation with the public and other agencies; and

J. Evaluate program efficiency, effectiveness, and overall system accountability consistent with recognized correctional standards.

4. Support crime victims by collecting information about the impact the criminal offense had on the victim. This information, reported in a **victim-impact statement,** is presented to the court. The judge considers it when sentencing the offender. The information is particularly valuable for sentences that include restitution.

5. Coordinate and promote the use of community resources. Probation officers refer offenders to community agencies and programs that serve the offenders' needs. Such programs include drug and alcohol treatment, job training, vocational education, anger management, and life skills training.

Not all probation agencies achieve these objectives in the same way. A probation department's orientation is a function of many things, including department philosophy, leadership, the community served, and the offenders supervised. Some departments lean more toward treating the offender; others lean more toward offender control. Probably the majority of probation departments do both, depending on the need and the situation. The American Correctional Association Policy on Probation is found in Exhibit 5–1.

History of Probation

Probation in America developed during the nineteenth century. Its origins, though, stem from English practices.

English Origins Beginning in the thirteenth century, **benefit of clergy** was used to give lesser sentences to clergymen and women from capital punishment and other severe sentences. To receive benefit of clergy, the accused were required to prove their literacy by reading in court the text of the Fifty-first Psalm. Soon the benefit of clergy was extended to anyone who could read (mostly the upper social classes). When the illiterate memorized the "neck verse," as it came to be called, and pretended to read it in court, use of the benefit declined. The practice was abolished by statute in 1827. It never really took hold in the American colonies.

Judicial reprieve became widespread in England in the nineteenth century. At first, judicial reprieve was a temporary suspension of sentence to allow a defendant to appeal to the king for a pardon. However, it developed into a *suspended sentence*, whereby punishment was never imposed. The suspended sentence was adopted in the United States, as early as 1830 in Boston. It became widespread in U.S. courts until the Supreme Court found it unconstitutional in 1916.[4] In that decision, which applied to federal courts only, the Court ruled that judges did not have the power to suspend sentences. The Court stated that Congress could authorize by law the temporary or indefinite suspension of sentences. That opinion gave rise to federal and state statutes authorizing probation.

Probation Begins in America It was in the Boston courtroom of Municipal Court Judge Peter Oxenbridge Thatcher, in 1830, that the groundwork for probation was laid. Searching for a new way to exercise leniency and to humanize the criminal law—sentencing goals that still dominate corrections—Judge Thatcher made the first recorded use of release on recognizance in America, in sentencing Jerusa Chase.

victim-impact statement A report to the court about the effects the offense had on the victim and/or survivors. The judge considers it when sentencing the offender.

Teaching Tip
Remind students that government and religion were intertwined throughout Europe during the Middle Ages. This connection helps explain why benefit of clergy was used in English courts. The practice never took hold in the United States because of the separation of church and state.

benefit of clergy
Practiced in England from the thirteenth century through the early nineteenth century, the release of clergymen and women from capital punishment when they proved their literacy by reading in court the text of the Fifty-first Psalm.

judicial reprieve
A nineteenth-century English forerunner of probation; a temporary suspension, or delay, of sentence. The suspended sentence was adopted in the United States and was used frequently until the Supreme Court found it unconstitutional in 1916.

THE STAFF SPEAKS

When I started as a probation officer in West Virginia, Martinson's "Nothing Works" study supported the philosophy that since rehabilitation and probation failed, the real answer to crime control was to "lock 'em up" for long periods of time. Nothing-works philosophy translated to the "truth in sentencing" perspective and widespread spending in the construction of new federal, state, and local prisons and jails. Probation and rehabilitation advocates were afraid that if they challenged the new philosophy, they would find themselves unemployed. In the 1970s, I helped develop the West Virginia Association of Probation Officers to improve the professionalism of probation in West Virginia. One of our aims was to consolidate probation under the West Virginia Supreme Court instead of having it under the Department of Welfare, the Department of Corrections, and the local courts. Today, probation comes under the West Virginia Supreme Court. Nationally, the American Probation and Parole Association has enhanced probation and community-based programs that have proved to be successful.

Juvenile programs administered by our department include mediation and arbitration for juveniles in which volunteers help resolve conflicts between juvenile offenders, their families, victims, and others. Alternative Learning Center programs provide education for violent juvenile offenders in off-school settings. Volunteers in Probation programs provide a mentor for every juvenile placed on probation. Adult programs include community probation officers for supervision and treatment and the supervision of community service work by offenders. I can honestly say that after 27 years as a probation officer, I am more energized than I have ever been, thanks to our success in the community. And, I know that the 21st century will confirm that probation and its community-based programs are an effective way to reduce crime, rehabilitate offenders, and bring peace to many households and communities.

James R. Lee
Chief Probation Officer
First Judicial Circuit
Wellsburg, WV

Teaching Tip

Remind students that release on own recognizance—the release of an arrested person on his or her pledge to reappear for trial at a later date—is granted to those who are presumed likely to reappear.

The indictment against Jerusa Chase was found at the January term of the court. . . . She pleaded guilty to the same and would have been pronounced at that time, but upon the application of her friends, and with the consent of the attorney of the Commonwealth, she was permitted, upon her recognizance for her appearance in this Court whenever she should be called for, to go at large.[5]

That release had many of the characteristics of present-day probation: suspension of sentence, freedom to stay in the community, conditions on that freedom, and the possibility of revocation of freedom for violation of the conditions.

In 1841—when John Augustus, a Boston shoemaker, became interested in the operation of the courts—the practice of probation began to emerge. Augustus was particularly sensitive to the problems of persons charged with alcohol-related offenses. By posting bail in selected cases, he had the offenders released to his care and supervision. Augustus carefully screened the offenders he sought to help. Here is an entry from his journal:

> In the month of August, 1841, I was in court one morning . . . in which [a] man was charged with being a common drunkard. The case was clearly made out, but before sentence was passed, I conversed with him for a few moments, and found that he was not yet past all hope of reformation. . . . He told me that if he could be saved from the House of Corrections, he never again would taste intoxicating liquors; there was such an earnestness in that one, and a look of firm resolve, that I determined to aid him; I bailed him, by permission of the Court. He was ordered to appear for sentence in three weeks; at the expiration of this period of probation, I accompanied him into the courtroom. . . . The Judge expressed himself much pleased with the account we gave of the man, and instead of the usual penalty—imprisonment in the House of Correction—he fined him one cent and costs, amounting in all to $3.76, which was immediately paid. The man continued industrious and sober, and without doubt has been by this treatment, saved from a drunkard's grave.[6]

So began the work of the nation's first probation officer, an unpaid volunteer.

By the time of his death in 1859, John Augustus had won probation for almost 2,000 adults and several thousand children. Several aspects of his probation system are still common. Augustus investigated the age, character, and work habits of each offender. He identified persons he thought redeemable. He made probation recommendations to the court. He developed conditions of probation. And he supervised offenders during their probation, which lasted, on the average, about 30 days. Until 1878, probation continued to be the work of volunteers—individuals and agencies.

Early Probation Statutes   In 1878 the Massachusetts legislature passed the first statute authorizing probation. The law applied only to Suffolk County (Boston). It required the mayor of Boston to appoint a probation officer from the police department or citizenry. In 1880 a new law authorized probation as an option in all cities and towns in Massachusetts. But because the law remained voluntary and the probation concept was still new, few cities and towns exercised the power. In 1891 the power to appoint probation officers was transferred from the mayor to the court, in response to criticism that the mayor's appointments were influenced by political considerations. The second state to pass a probation statute was Vermont, in 1898.

Probation Officer Presentence Investigation Unit
Processes referrals for psychological evaluation, physical examination, and drug/alcohol assessment as required. Collects all court-ordered information and reports in a timely manner. Composes an objective, comprehensive social-background report, completes a risk-needs assessment, attaches all relevant documents, and distributes the report. Requirements: Bachelor's degree in corrections, criminology, criminal justice, or a related field and two years' experience working in probation. Successful candidate will complete a 120-day orientation.

Teaching Tip
Emphasize the strategies of John Augustus that form the core of modern-day probation: advocacy for offenders, selection criteria (offense, age, character, work habits, probability of change), recommendation to the court, conditions of probation, and supervision.

Kurt Robak
Probation Officer
State of Minnesota

"This is the first job I have had that on Sunday nights I don't mind going to work Monday mornings."

Kurt Robak has been a probation and parole officer for Kandiyohi County Community Corrections in Minnesota for five years. He supervises juvenile and adult offenders on probation and parole. His duties include enforcing court orders, conducting presentence investigations and bail studies, referring offenders for psychological evaluation and treatment, conducting random urinalysis, visiting offenders at home or work, monitoring offenders' restitution and fine payments, and reporting to the court on offenders' progress and compliance with court orders. Previously, he worked as a halfway house case manager for adult male felons and as a juvenile detention officer.

Kurt earned his bachelor's degree in corrections from Mankato State University. When he was a student, classes in probation and parole influenced him the most. He decided to work in corrections because he believed there would be something different to do each day. In his present job, his work schedule is flexible, leading, he says, to less job stress and more time with his family.

For Kurt, the best part about being a probation and parole officer is twofold: referring offenders to community agencies that help them with their problems—for example, domestic violence and alcohol and drug abuse—and holding them accountable for their behavior. He advises students who are thinking about making corrections a career to volunteer in a corrections agency while they're still in school and to do an internship as part of their studies. He believes that those experiences are effective on a résumé and also provide valuable preparation for paid work in the field. Furthermore, he recommends that after graduation students keep up with changes in their state's criminal code because criminal laws are always changing.

As more and more states passed laws authorizing probation, probation became a national institution. On March 4, 1925, probation in the federal courts was signed into law by President Coolidge.[7] The early laws had little in common. Some allowed probation for adults only. Others allowed it for juveniles only. (In fact, the spread of probation was accelerated by the juvenile court movement.) Some laws restricted the crimes for which probation could be granted. Still others provided for the hiring of probation officers, but neglected to provide for paying them. Training for probation officers was brief or nonexistent. Appointments were often based on politics rather than merit, and salaries were typically even lower than those of unskilled laborers. By 1925, probation was available for juveniles in every state; by 1956, it was available for adults in every state.

Characteristics of Adults on Probation

On December 31, 1998, 3,417,613 adults were on federal, state, or local probation, an increase of 120,845 over 1997.[8] One out of every 60 persons age 18 or older is on probation. The average length of probation is 40 months. Figure 5–4 presents selected characteristics of adults on probation in 1998. For example, women made up 21 percent of the probation population. That is almost twice the percentage of women in jail (11%) and more than three times the percentage of women in prison (6.5%). Blacks represented more than a third of probationers, while Hispanics, who may be of any race, made up 15 percent of probationers. Other interesting findings about probationers are that more than half were sentenced for felony convictions, and 17 percent received sentences that included incarceration as well as probation. Such an arrangement is sometimes called a *split sentence.* As Figure 5–4 shows, almost two-thirds of probationers in 1998 successfully completed their probation.

Probationers who violate the conditions of their probation, or who are arrested for new offenses, may face disciplinary hearings. Such a disciplinary hearing, called a revocation hearing, may result in the issuance of an arrest warrant (if the probationer does not appear at the hearing), a sentence of incarceration, or reinstatement of probation with or without conditions.

Probationers who were unemployed were more likely to have had a disciplinary hearing (23%) than those who were employed (16%). Probationers who had a prior sentence were also more likely to have had a disciplinary hearing than those with no prior sentence (23% compared with

Student Involvement
Refer students to Figure 5–4. Ask them to study the data presented and then write a generalization about one of the pie graphs presented, for example, "Most adults on probation are male."

FIGURE 5–4

Selected Characteristics of Adults on Probation, 1998

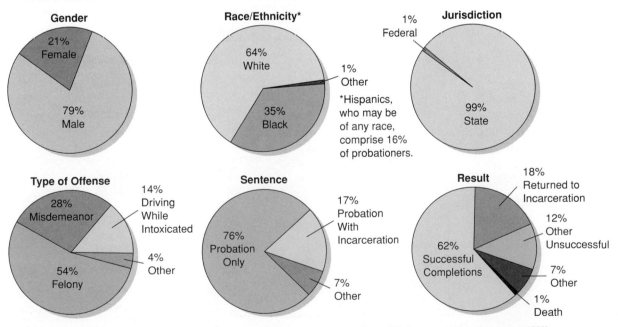

Gender
- 21% Female
- 79% Male

Race/Ethnicity*
- 64% White
- 35% Black
- 1% Other

*Hispanics, who may be of any race, comprise 16% of probationers.

Jurisdiction
- 1% Federal
- 99% State

Type of Offense
- 28% Misdemeanor
- 14% Driving While Intoxicated
- 4% Other
- 54% Felony

Sentence
- 76% Probation Only
- 17% Probation With Incarceration
- 7% Other

Result
- 62% Successful Completions
- 18% Returned to Incarceration
- 12% Other Unsuccessful
- 7% Other
- 1% Death

Source: Bureau of Justice Statistics, *Probation and Parole in the United States, 1998* (Washington: U.S. Department of Justice, August 1999).

Student Involvement
Organize students into small groups. Ask them to write probation conditions for a 22-year-old woman convicted of her third shoplifting offense, this time for stealing $350 worth of merchandise from a clothing store. As students read the conditions aloud, write them on the board. Ask students whether they think there's a relationship between the number of conditions and likelihood of violation. That is, as more conditions are imposed, is there a greater chance that the offender will break some, thus increasing the chances of having a disciplinary hearing?

15%). Of those probationers who had experienced a disciplinary hearing, the most frequent reason was absconding (hiding or leaving the jurisdiction) or failing to contact the probation officer (41%). The next most common reasons were arrest or conviction for a new offense (38%), failure to pay fines or restitution (38%), and failure to complete an alcohol or drug treatment program (22%).[9]

Who Administers Probation?

As probation spread throughout the United States in the late nineteenth and early twentieth centuries, its organization and administration depended on local and state customs and politics. Currently, probation in the 50 states is administered by more than 2,000 separate agencies,[10] reflecting the decentralized and fragmented character of contemporary corrections. The agencies have a lot of common ground, but because they developed in different contexts, they also have a lot of differences in goals, policies, funding, staffing, salaries, and operation.

Probation is commonly considered a part of the correctional system, although it is technically a function of the court system. Figure 5–5 gives a state-by-state breakdown of how probation is administered. The map shows that in most states (31) the responsibility for adult probation rests with the state department of corrections. This means that one statewide agency administers a central probation system for adult offenders and provides ser-

Teaching Tip
Refer to Figure 5–5 to determine how your state administers adult probation. Also note how states that adjoin yours administer probation. Are they the same as yours or different? Could differences in how adjoining states administer probation ever be a problem for probation officers?

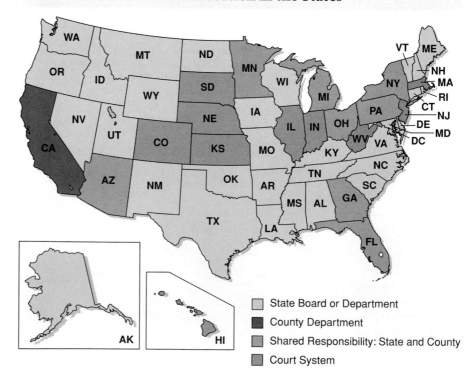

FIGURE 5–5

Administration of Adult Probation in the States

- State Board or Department
- County Department
- Shared Responsibility: State and County
- Court System

vices throughout the state. The second most common way of administering adult probation is through the court system. In ten states and the District of Columbia the responsibility for adult probation lies with the state judiciary. In eight states, the responsibility is shared by the state and the counties. In one state, counties provide adult probation services.

What Probation Officers Do

Probation officers are more extensively involved with offenders and their cases—often starting at arrest—than any other criminal justice professionals. On January 1, 1998, there were 21,878 probation officers employed in the United States. There were more female employees (53%) than male employees.[11] Probation officers interact with many criminal justice agencies and influence many decisions affecting offenders. They do this in two major roles: case investigation and client supervision.

Case Investigation Investigation includes the preparation of a **presentence investigation report (PSI),** which the judge uses in sentencing an offender. The PSI is a report on the charge, conviction, and sentence recommendation, the offender's background and personal attributes, and statements from victims. It has two main purposes. First, it provides information to help the judge choose an appropriate sentence. That information concerns the offender's personal and social circumstances, motivations, and characteristics. The information is crucial because the judge's knowledge of the defendant is limited to what is presented at trial and what is contained in the presentence report. The judge uses the PSI to fashion a punishment that serves the purposes of offender rehabilitation and community protection. Research shows that judges follow the recommendation in the PSI 70 to 90 percent of the time.[12]

The second purpose of the PSI is to outline a treatment plan for the offender. During the investigation, besides determining the degree of risk the offender poses to the community, the probation officer identifies treatment needs so that the offender can receive appropriate services (counseling, treatment, education, community service, restitution, employment, and some form of supervision) during probation or in jail or prison.

In most cases, the court orders the PSI after conviction but before sentencing. The defendant reports to the probation department if released on bond pending sentencing. Otherwise, the probation officer visits the defendant in jail.

In addition to the PSI ordered by the court, the defendant or defense counsel may hire a private agency to prepare a PSI. A privately prepared PSI is sometimes called a **client-specific plan (CSP).** CSPs accomplish three things. First, they are an alternative source of information to judges. Second, they generally favor the defendant, encouraging greater use of treatment, counseling, education, community service, restitution, employment, and supervision. They may, however, call for the offender to pay a greater share of the cost of treatment. Third, they balance the PSIs prepared by government agencies.

presentence investigation report (PSI) A report on an offender's background and personal attributes. The purposes of the PSI are to help the court choose the most appropriate sentence and to outline a treatment plan.

Professional Issue

Presentence Investigation In a number of probation departments, intake officers conduct the PSI while field officers provide supervision. Intake officers have a license to investigate, can include hearsay information, and receive few guidelines on what to include or exclude. Thus the report is often related to the skill of the investigator. Ask students to suggest strategies to reduce the likelihood that an unskilled intake officer might produce a flawed PSI.

client-specific plan (CSP) A privately prepared presentence investigation report that supplements the PSI prepared by the probation department.

The PSI starts with an interview between the probation officer (PO) and the defendant. The interview follows a structured format for obtaining information on the offense and the offender. The PO is expected to verify, clarify, and explore any information to be presented in the PSI. The PO may also talk with the victim. The PO is also expected to estimate the offender's degree of risk to the community. The estimate is based on the offender's lifestyle, prior criminal involvement, and experience with the criminal justice system. The PO summarizes the information gathered and, in most jurisdictions, makes a sentence recommendation. If the sentence recommended is incarceration, in most jurisdictions the length must be within guidelines set by statute (see Chapter 2). However, if the sentence recommended is probation or some other intermediate sanction (see Chapter 6), few jurisdictions have guidelines for sentence length. Only recently have states (for example, Delaware, North Carolina, and Pennsylvania) begun to design sentencing guidelines for nonprison sentences like probation. Copies of the PSI are filed with the court and made available to the judge, the prosecutor, and the defense attorney. Figure 5–6 is an example of a short-form federal PSI.

The quality of a PSI depends on the ability of the person who prepared it. In 1997, about 3,500 federal adult probation officers wrote 52,174 PSIs; on the state level, about 12,000 adult probation officers wrote 674,838 PSIs.[13] Judges give varying weight to different facts in the PSI when making the sentencing decision.

Today software packages can generate PSIs after probation officers enter data from official records and interviews.[14] The software programs can also calculate risk assessment scores. A PO can edit the report before submitting it to the court. Other computer programs help POs track fine and probation payments, alert them when their clients are behind on payments, and help them track whether probationers have satisfied the conditions of their sentences.

Case investigation is one of a probation officer's major roles. What questions would you ask a crime victim as part of the investigation?

Teaching Tip

Have students review the information in the PSI depicted in Figure 5–6. Ask them to pay particular attention to the probation officer's sentencing recommendation.

Diversion and Probation: Alternatives to Imprisonment

FIGURE 5–6

Sample Presentence Investigation Report

IN THE UNITED STATES DISTRICT COURT
FOR THE NORTHERN DISTRICT OF ALABAMA

UNITED STATES OF AMERICA	)	
	)	PRESENTENCE INVESTIGATION
v.	)	REPORT
	)	
EDDIE PALMER	)	Docket No. CR-98-H-248-S

Prepared For: Honorable Casandra Phillips
                   U. S. District Judge

Prepared By: Noelle Koval
                   U. S. Probation Officer
                   Birmingham, AL
                   (205)555-0923

Offense: Count One: Possession With Intent to Distribute a Schedule II Controlled Substance (Cocaine Base), not less than 10 Years and not more than Life and/or $4,000,000 Fine. With Enhancement, Mandatory Life and/or $8,000,000 Fine.

Release Status: Released on $25,000 unsecured bond on 8/26/98. Remanded to custody on 12/14/98.

Identifying Data:

Date of Birth:	1/9/67
Age:	31
Race:	B
Sex:	M

Charge(s) and Conviction(s)

Eddie Palmer was indicted on two counts by the September 1995 Grand Jury for the Northern District of Alabama. Count One charged that on June 12, 1998, the defendant unlawfully possessed with intent to distribute approximately 500 grams of a mixture or substance containing a detectable amount of cocaine, Schedule II controlled substances, in violation of 21 USC § 841(a)(1). Count Two charged that on June 12, 1998, the defendant carried a firearm during the commission of a drug trafficking crime in violation of 18 USC § 924(c)(1). The October 1998 Grand Jury returned a superseding indictment in which the defendant was charged in two counts. Count One charges that

FIGURE 5–6 (continued)

Sample Presentence Investigation Report

on June 12, 1998, the defendant intentionally possessed with intent to distribute approximately 100 grams of a mixture or substance containing a detectable amount of cocaine base and approximately 240 grams of a mixture or substance containing a detectable amount of cocaine, Schedule II controlled substances, in violation of 21 USC § 841(a)(1). Count II charges that on June 12, 1998, the defendant carried a firearm during the commission of a drug trafficking crime in violation of 18 USC § 924(c)(1). On December 14, 1998, Palmer pled guilty to Count One, and Count Two was dismissed on motion of the government. Sentencing was continued generally to a later date.

Pretrial Adjustment

Mr. Palmer was released on a $25,000 unsecured bond on 8/26/98 with special conditions. One drug urinalysis was taken which was negative. Mr. Palmer ceased reporting in person on 10/6/98. He stated that people were looking for him and he was afraid to go out. The defendant had given information on a public corruption case. He was allowed to telephone report. On 12/14/98 Palmer was taken into custody following his plea of guilty pursuant to 18 USC § 3143.

Substance Abuse

Mr. Palmer relates that he started using marijuana around the age of 19. He quit using it for one year while he was in the TASC program. He then started back and quit when he got indicted on this case. He was smoking approximately two marijuana cigarettes per day. He first experimented with cocaine at the age of 20. He used cocaine a few times at the age of 22. Although he states that he did not use it again, test reports from TASC indicate that he had a positive for cocaine in June 1997 and again in July 1997. He went to TASC as a special condition of state probation from 1/3/97 to 2/14/98. He was considered to be making minimal effort to comply with TASC and was terminated after he completed his probation term. He also attended UAB Drug Free but was terminated on 9/13/97 for failure to comply. Additionally, Mr. Palmer previously reported to the state probation office that he had used LSD about ten times in 1987.

Education and Vocational Skills

Mr. Palmer attended El Camino Community College, Torrance, California, from 2/7/89 to 6/15/90. His scholastic standing was average. He was in the Vocational School and took courses in Cosmetology.

Employment Record

Mr. Palmer states that he opened SimplyClean Auto Salon, Inc., in 1993. He is the owner and has a monthly gross income of from $1,200 to $2,000 per month. This company washes, details, and repairs automobiles. Mr. Palmer lists his home address as the address of the company.

Mr. Palmer reports that when he initially moved to Alabama from L.A., he worked as a hairdresser out of his mother's home and was paid in cash. While in L.A., he worked for Simply Raw Beauty Salon in 1990 for approximately six months as a cosmetologist. He states that he worked for the

– 2 –

FIGURE 5–6 (continued)

Sample Presentence Investigation Report

L.A. County Art Museum, Beverly Hills, California, as a laborer earning minimum wage from April through July 1988. The Art Museum could find no record of Mr. Palmer ever working for them. Mr. Palmer states that he often did odd jobs and fixed hair to earn an income.

Mr. Palmer joined the U.S. Army on 9/30/86. He was discharged under honorable conditions on 1/13/88 as a Private, 2nd Class. The discharge was for misconduct which included frequent incidents of a discreditable nature with civil or military authorities.

Financial Condition: Ability to Pay

The following information was verified through a credit report, the Tax Assessor's office, reviewing some household bills, and DEA, who verified values of automobiles and other equipment and is proceeding on forfeiture.

Assets:

    Unencumbered Assets

1985 FJ1100 Yamaha motorcycle, fair market value:	$ 1,500.00

    Equity in Other Assets

Residence	21,000.00
1988 Honda Accord	2,000.00
Total Assets:	$24,500.00

Unsecured Debt:

Attorney Fees	$10,000.00
Medical Center East	4,000.00
Total Unsecured Debt:	$14,000.00

NET WORTH: $10,500.00

Monthly Cash Flow:

    Income:

Net Profit From Business	$ 1,200.00
Spouse's Salary	400.00
Total Income:	$ 1,600.00

– 3 –

FIGURE 5-6 (continued)

Sample Presentence Investigation Report

Necessary Monthly Living Expenses:

Mortgage	$ 634.00
Electricity	80.00
Gas	50.00
Water	14.00
Telephone	150.00
Groceries and Supplies	200.00
Life Insurance	50.00
Transportation	50.00
Medical	300.00
Clothing	200.00
Child Support	400.00
Monthly Installment Payments	250.00
Total Expenses:	$ 2,378.00
Monthly Cash Flow:	$ -778.00

The above information represents the defendant's version of income and expenses. The mortgage payment and utilities were verified. Other expenses and income were not verified although verification was requested. The defendant claims to have filed income tax returns and stated that the information was with his attorney, Warren Skinner. Mr. Skinner was contacted about financial information but was not forthcoming. In fact, he prohibited the family from talking with me after the defendant pled guilty. Therefore, information may not be complete and is possibly inaccurate based on this lack of cooperation.

The bottom line is that it is very difficult to give an accurate reflection of the defendant's financial status. Based on his purported income from illegal activity, it is quite likely that there are other assets available to him. This cannot be stated as fact because it is frankly unknown.

Respectfully submitted,

Noelle Koval

Noelle Koval
U.S. Probation Officer

Approved:

Frank Medina 12/23/98
Frank Medina   DATE
Supervising U.S. Probation Officer

– 4 –

FIGURE 5-6 (continued)

Sample Presentence Investigation Report

SENTENCING RECOMMENDATION

UNITED STATES DISTRICT COURT
FOR THE NORTHERN DISTRICT OF ALABAMA

UNITED STATES V. EDDIE PALMER   DOCKET NO. CR-98-H-248-S

TOTAL OFFENSE LEVEL: 29
CRIMINAL HISTORY CATEGORY: III

	Statutory Provision	Guideline Provisions	Recommended Sentence
CUSTODY:	Mandatory Life	Mandatory Life	Life
PROBATION:	N/A	N/A	N/A
SUPERVISED RELEASE:	Not Less Than 10 Years	10 Years	10 Years
FINE:	$8,000,000	$15,000 to $8,000,000	$15,000
RESTITUTION:	N/A	N/A	N/A
SPECIAL ASSESSMENT:	$50	$50	$50

Justification

The sentence of life is mandatory. Supervised release must be ten years. A $15,000 fine is recommended because it is incumbent upon the defendant to demonstrate that he does not have the financial ability to pay a fine. He and his attorney have not cooperated in providing information, and it appears that he does have the ability to pay the minimum fine based on his purported monthly income from trafficking in illegal drugs.

Voluntary Surrender

The defendant is in custody.

Respectfully submitted,

Noelle Koval

Noelle Koval
U.S. Probation Officer

– 5 –

FIGURE 5–7

Extent of Supervision by Assessed Risk Level

High Risk Supervision	Close Risk Supervision	Intermediate Risk Supervision	Reduced Risk Supervision
2 face-to-face contacts each day	1 face-to-face contact each day	1 face-to-face contact each week	1 face-to-face contact each month
2 drug tests each week	2 drug tests each week	1 drug test each week	no drug tests

supervision The second major role of probation officers, consisting of intervention, surveillance, and enforcement.

Professional Issue

Caseload vs. Workload The American Probation and Parole Association (APPA) recommends that a probation officer's responsibilities be based on a workload model, not a caseload model. Currently, most probation officers have caseloads of so many cases per officer. The workload model is based on case management principles of differentiation among cases.

recidivism The repetition of criminal behavior; generally defined as re-arrest. The primary outcome measure for probation, as it is for all corrections programs.

Supervision The second major role of probation officers is client supervision. Probation **supervision** has three main elements: intervention, surveillance, and enforcement. *Intervention* means providing offenders access to a wide variety of services, such as counseling, employment, and education. *Surveillance* means monitoring the activities of probationers through office meetings, home and work visits, drug and alcohol testing, and contact with family, friends, and employers. *Enforcement* means making probationers accountable for their behavior and making sure they understand the consequences of violating the conditions of probation. The average PO in the United States supervises approximately 175 offenders. In California, POs have caseloads of 900, and as many as 60 percent of probationers are tracked solely by computer, having no contact with a PO. In Atlanta, some POs supervise as many as 650 men and women. Such large caseloads do not allow probation officers time for adequate intervention, surveillance, or enforcement.

Even in average caseloads, not all offenders are supervised. Rather, probation officers use a variety of risk classification instruments to determine the level of supervision a probationer needs. A typical risk assessment might use four levels: high risk, close risk, intermediate risk, and reduced risk. The nature and amount of supervision are matched to the risk level. Figure 5–7 shows typical supervision plans matched to risk level.

Does Probation Work?

The most common question asked about probation is, Does it work? In other words, Do persons granted probation refrain from further crime? **Recidivism**—generally defined as re-arrest—continues to be the primary outcome measure for probation, as it is for all corrections programs. Summaries of probation effectiveness usually report the recidivism rates of felons as if felons represented the total adult probation population, instead of 55 percent of it.[15] Failure to distinguish between felons and misdemeanants explains the differing opinions about whether probation "works."

Recidivism rates vary greatly from place to place, depending on the seriousness of offenses, average length of probation, and the amount and quality of intervention, surveillance, and enforcement. A summary of 17 studies of adult felony probationers found that felony re-arrest rates ranged from 12 to 65 percent.

The American Probation and Parole Association (APPA), representing U.S. probation officers nationwide, argues that recidivism rates measure just

Diversion and Probation: Alternatives to Imprisonment

At probation automated monitoring kiosks, probationers check in by handprint or ID card to answer questions about their progress. These machines are used in some areas to supervise low-risk offenders who do not require face-to-face contact with a probation officer. What advantages and disadvantages do you see in this approach?

one probation task while ignoring others. The APPA has urged its member agencies to collect data on other outcomes, such as the following:

- amount of restitution collected
- number of offenders employed
- amounts of fines and fees collected
- hours of community service performed
- number of treatment sessions attended
- percentage of financial obligations collected
- rate of enrollment in school
- number of days of employment
- educational attainment
- number of days drug-free

Teaching Tip
Have students rank in order of importance the ten alternative measures of probation success.

Advocates of measures other than recidivism tell us that probation should be measured by what offenders do while they are in probation programs, not by what they do after they leave.

Probation in the 21st Century

The American public understands that not all criminals can be locked up. Doubts are being raised about allocating a significant proportion of tax dollars to prisons. Pouring billions of dollars into operating costs and new prison construction ($24.5 billion in 1996) and seeing no reduction in crime will slowly move the public to reassess attitudes toward punishment.

Research also shows that citizens are less punishment-oriented than many political leaders believe. For example, in surveys conducted in Pennsylvania, Delaware, and Alabama, the Public Agenda Foundation of New York City found that "when the public is made aware of the possible range of punishments, and given information about how and with whom they are used, they support alternatives to incarceration—including punishments administered in the community—for offenders considered nonviolent and low risk."[16]

Policymakers are urging probation departments to implement credible and effective community-based sentencing options. But how can such options be made credible and effective? We conclude this chapter with five suggestions.

Implement High-Quality Programs and Enforce Them   Over the past few decades, many jurisdictions have added new kinds of probation sanctions, such as house arrest, electronic monitoring, boot camp, and intensive supervision. These sanctions are designed to be tougher than regular probation but less severe and less expensive than prison. To work, the new conditions must be backed up by mechanisms to ensure compliance.

Invest Adequate Resources in Treatment and Surveillance   When probationers receive *both* surveillance (e.g., unannounced contact and random drug tests) and treatment, recidivism can decline by one-third.[17] However, treatment and surveillance cost money. Adequate funding will be available only if the public believes that new supervision conditions are punitive as well as effective in reducing crime.

Demonstrate That Probation Is Tough on Crime   Policymakers say they send large numbers of persons to prison because the public wants to be tough on crime. But there is a groundswell of evidence that tough punishment may no longer equate with prison.[18] Some offenders see probation as more punitive and restrictive than prison. For example, researchers in Texas and Oregon gave offenders the choice of serving a prison term or serving probation with mandatory drug testing, community service, employment, counseling, and frequent visits with a probation officer. In Oregon, 25 percent of those eligible for probation chose prison. In Texas, many offenders described common prison terms as less punitive than even three to five years on probation. Prison was more attractive than the pressures of close supervision. The public must be convinced that probation sanctions can be just as punitive as prison. And the choice of probation or prison should be for the judge to make, not the offender.

Target Drug Offenders   Drug offenders are prime candidates for tough probation programs. Research has revealed the different risks and needs of traffickers, addicts, and low-level users.[19] The new knowledge is resulting in different laws and punishment strategies for different kinds of drug offenders. Many Americans prefer prison sentences for drug traffickers but are willing to accept something other than prison for other drug offenders.

technical violation
A failure to fulfill the conditions of probation—attending counseling, paying restitution, contacting the probation officer—rather than the commission of a new offense.

Make Probation Research a Priority   With over 3.4 million adults under probation supervision today, probation research should be a priority. It would be useful for probation research to assess the value of revoking probation for persons who commit technical violations. A **technical violation** is a failure to fulfill the conditions of probation—attending counseling, pay-

Diversion and Probation: Alternatives to Imprisonment

My first PO was a man who had years of experience. He was cynical. He took his job too seriously. I cooperated and soon he trusted me. His requirements were few. I was rarely asked to report at his office, and he would call to let me know he was coming to my home for a visit.

After several months, I was assigned a female PO. I was required to give urine samples under her observation. That bothered me, because I had no history of substance abuse. The purpose of these samples seems to have been to humiliate me. I wondered why the feds wanted to be in the business of humiliating people!

Being on supervised release was no big deal, as long as I sent in my monthly reports and got permission to travel outside the district (which meant ten miles to the north and twelve miles to the west). At my request, my second PO processed the forms for my release from supervision one year ahead of schedule. My cooperation paid off.

I don't know if federal probation reduces crime. But I do think that probation should be used more often, instead of incarceration, with community service. I think most prison sentences are too long and disruptive to families. I also think that all efforts should be made to support an offender's attempts to straighten out his or her life. The entire "justice" system needs to become caring and compassionate, putting more people into treatment and job programs than into prison.

Did probation disrupt my life? Yes. But I committed a crime and accepted probation willingly. Still, I think that it was wasteful, since once the feds realized that I had paid my fine off early, had no drug problems, kept a stable work record, and was cooperative, they might have saved us all some money by letting me off even sooner than they did.

Anonymous female,
previously on federal probation

ing restitution, contacting the probation officer—rather than the commission of a new offense.

Technical violations are a serious matter. Judges need assurance that probationers will be held accountable for their behavior, and the public needs assurance that probation sanctions are punitive. More research is needed, however, on the relationship of technical violations to criminal behavior. For example, what types of conditions are imposed? How do those conditions manage offenders, encourage rehabilitation, and protect the community? What are the trends in the number of technical violators and the effect on jails and prisons? What innovative programs, policies, and statutes have emerged in other jurisdictions to deal with technical violators?

Teaching Tip
Refer to Chapter 5 of the *Instructor's Resource Manual* for additional activities and for answers to the end-of-chapter exercises.

5

Review and Applications

SUMMARY BY CHAPTER OBJECTIVE

CHAPTER OBJECTIVE 1
Diversion is the official halting or suspension, before conviction, of formal criminal proceedings against a person, often conditioned on some form of counter performance, such as participation in a treatment, counseling, or educational program. Diversion is intended to (1) prevent future criminal activity by diverting certain defendants from criminal justice processing into community supervision and service, (2) save prosecution and judicial resources for serious crimes by offering alternatives to the usual prosecution process for less serious ones, and (3) provide, where appropriate, a vehicle for restitution to communities and victims of crime.

CHAPTER OBJECTIVE 2
There are four rationales for diversion:
(1) Formal processing can encourage more criminal behavior. (2) Diversion is cheaper than formally processing an offender through the criminal justice system. (3) Formal processing may seem inappropriate for crimes without perceived victims. (4) Formal arrest, trial, and conviction add to the burdens of certain disadvantaged groups.

CHAPTER OBJECTIVE 3
Diversion may occur at any stage in the criminal justice process after a criminal complaint has been filed or police have observed a crime. Common diversion programs involve offenses related to drugs or alcohol.

CHAPTER OBJECTIVE 4
Issues concerning diversion include (1) the legal and ethical issues of protecting a defendant's rights; (2) the law enforcement question whether diversion encourages violation of the law; and (3) the economic question of diversion's cost-effectiveness.

CHAPTER OBJECTIVE 5
Probation is the conditional release of a convicted offender into the community, under the supervision of a probation officer. Most probation programs are designed to (1) protect the community by assisting judges in sentencing and supervising offenders, (2) carry out sanctions imposed by the court, (3) help offenders change, (4) support crime victims, and (5) coordinate and promote the use of community resources.

CHAPTER OBJECTIVE 6
Probation is used for four reasons: (1) It permits offenders to be reintegrated into the community. (2) It avoids institutionalization and the stigma of incarceration. (3) It is less expensive than incarceration and more humanitarian. (4) It is appropriate for offenders whose crimes do not necessarily merit incarceration.

CHAPTER OBJECTIVE 7
On December 31, 1998, federal, state, and local probation agencies supervised 3.4 million adult U.S. residents, with felony convictions accounting for more than half (54%). Twenty-one percent of all probationers were women, and 64 percent of probationers were white. Seventy-six percent of adults received sentences of probation only.

CHAPTER OBJECTIVE 8
In 31 states, adult probation services are administered by the state department of corrections. In 10 states and the District of Columbia, the responsibility for adult probation lies with the state judiciary. In 8 states, the responsibility is shared by the state and the counties. In 1 state, counties provide adult probation services.

CHAPTER OBJECTIVE 9
Probation investigation and supervision are the two major roles of probation officers. Investigation

Diversion and Probation: Alternatives to Imprisonment

includes the preparation of a presentence investigation report (PSI), which the judge uses in sentencing an offender. Supervision includes the functions of intervention, surveillance, and enforcement.

CHAPTER OBJECTIVE 10

Recidivism rates are low for adults on probation for misdemeanors. However, recidivism rates are high for felony probationers, particularly in jurisdictions that use probation extensively, offer probation for serious offenses, and provide minimal supervision because of high caseloads. Corrections professionals urge evaluators to collect data on outcomes other than recidivism, such as amount of restitution collected, number of offenders employed, amounts of fines and fees collected, hours of community service, number of treatment sessions, percentage of financial obligations collected, rate of enrollment in school, number of days employed, educational attainment, and number of days drug-free.

CHAPTER OBJECTIVE 11

A number of issues face probation in the twenty-first century. One is the challenge of implementing credible and effective community-based sentencing options. Our suggestions for meeting that challenge are as follows: (1) Implement high-quality programs and enforce them. (2) Invest adequate resources in treatment and surveillance. (3) Demonstrate that probation is tough on crime. (4) Target drug offenders. (5) Make probation research a priority.

KEY TERMS

diversion, p. 125
counter performance, p. 125
true diversion, p. 125
minimization of penetration, p. 125
unconditional diversion, p. 128
conditional diversion, p. 128
probation, p. 130
victim-impact statement, p. 133

benefit of clergy, p. 133
judicial reprieve, p. 133
presentence investigation report (PSI), p. 139
client-specific plan (CSP), p. 139
supervision, p. 146
recidivism, p. 146
technical violation, p. 148

QUESTIONS FOR REVIEW

1. What is *diversion*?
2. Describe the different types of diversion and the stages at which they occur.
3. What are three objectives of diversion?
4. What are the four rationales for diversion?
5. At what stage of the criminal justice process does diversion occur?
6. Discuss three diversion policy issues.
7. What is *probation*?
8. Trace the English origins of probation.
9. How did probation originate in the United States?
10. When did federal probation begin?
11. What were some of the characteristics of adults on probation in 1998?

12. What are the four ways adult probation is administered? Which is the most common?
13. What are the two most important roles of probation officers for adults?
14. What is the presentence investigation? What is its purpose?
15. List the elements of probation supervision.
16. What do we know about probation recidivism for misdemeanants? For felons?
17. What measures are there of probation effectiveness, besides recidivism?
18. What issues face adult probation in the United States in the twenty-first century?

ON-THE-JOB ISSUES

1. The new diversion program in your county was developed to help first-time misdemeanor drug offenders avoid incarceration and seek help in controlling their dependency. Your job as the new diversion officer is to set the conditions of the diversion program and then monitor and enforce compliance. One of your first clients fails the required weekly drug test. Should you immediately remove that person from the program?

2. While you are conducting an interview for a PSI, the defendant reveals details of the offense that did not come out during the trial. The defendant also implicates others, who have not been charged with the crime. What should you do?

3. At a recent staff meeting, the chief probation officer reports that the department's recidivism rate exceeded the national average by five percent. The chief asks what can be done about it. You speak up and say, "Look at other measures." The chief asks you to explain.

CORRECTIONS ISSUES

1. Critics of PSIs claim that the information in them is not always verified or reliable. Actually, much of the information in a PSI is hearsay. Although defendants or victims may object to the contents of a PSI or the way it characterizes their behavior, they have no right to have the PSI reflect their views. As a probation officer, how would you respond to these criticisms?

2. Recidivism is one current measure of probation effectiveness. Others include the amount of restitution collected, the number of offenders employed, the amounts of fines and fees collected, the number of hours of community service performed, the number of treatment sessions completed, the percentage of financial obligations collected, the rate of school enrollment, the level of educational attainment, the number of days employed, and the number of days drug-free.

   a. In comparison with other measures, how important to you, as a taxpayer, is recidivism as a measure of program success?

   b. Do you believe probation officers can really keep offenders from committing new crimes or violating the conditions of their probation?

   c. If you were a probation officer today, by which outcome measures would you want to be judged? Why?

   d. If recidivism is used as a measure of probation's effectiveness, how should it be defined?

CORRECTIONS ON THE WEB

1. Most probation agencies—whether administered by the state, a county, the state and a county, or the court system—have Web pages. Using the information in Figure 5–5, try to find the Web page of one probation agency for each of the four methods of administration. What difference, if any, does the type of administration make in philosophy, mission, goals, structure, resources, and so forth? Look at the Web page of the Los Angeles County Probation Department (**http://www.co.la.ca. us/probation**) as an example to get started.

2. In 1994 the Consolidated Edison Company (Con Ed) of New York entered a guilty plea in federal court to charges that it had covered up the release of 200 pounds of asbestos by a steam pipe explosion in New York City on August 19, 1989. Con Ed was sentenced to a $2 million fine plus three years' probation. As a condition of probation, Judge Martin required Con Ed to submit to an ongoing review. Access **http://www.essential.org/ monitor/hyper/mm1097.04.html**. Read the reports and determine whether Con Ed has fulfilled the judge's requirements.

ADDITIONAL READINGS

Abadinsky, Howard. *Probation and Parole: Theory and Practice*. Englewood Cliffs, NJ: Prentice-Hall, 1994.

Boswell, Gwyneth. *Contemporary Probation Practice*. Aldershot, England: Avebury, 1993.

Carter, Robert M., Daniel Glaser, and Leslie T. Wilkins (eds.). *Probation, Parole, and Community Corrections*. New York: Wiley, 1984.

Ellsworth, Thomas (ed.). *Contemporary Community Corrections*. Prospect Heights, IL: Waveland Press, 1992.

Petersilia, Joan. *Granting Felons Probation: Public Risks and Alternatives*. Santa Monica, CA: Rand Corp., 1985.

ENDNOTES

1. B. J. George, "Screening, Diversion and Mediation in the United States," *New York Law School Law Review*, Vol. 29 (1984), pp. 1–38.

2. Thomas P. Bonczar, *Characteristics of Adults on Probation, 1995* (Washington: U.S. Department of Justice, Bureau of Justice Statistics, 1997). Online, available: http://www.ojp.usdoj.gov/bjs/pub/ascii/cap95.txt.

3. Bureau of Justice Statistics, *Nation's Probation and Parole Population Reached New High Last Year* (Washington: BJS, August 16, 1998).

4. *Ex parte United States*, 242 U.S. 27 (1916).

5. John Augustus, *A Report of the Labors of John Augustus, For the Last Ten Years, In Aid of the Unfortunate* (Boston: Wright and Hasty, 1852); reprinted as *John Augustus, First Probation Officer* (New York: National Probation Association, 1939), p. 26.

6. Ibid., pp. 4–5.

7. Sanford Bates, "The Establishment and Early Years of the Federal Probation System," *Federal Probation*, Vol. 14 (1950), pp. 16–21; Joel R. Moore, "Early Reminiscences," *Federal Probation*, Vol. 14 (1950), pp. 21–29; and Richard A. Chappell, "The Federal Probation System Today," *Federal Probation*, Vol. 14 (1950), pp. 30–40.

8. All the data in this section are from Bonczar, and Bureau of Justice Statistics, *Probation and Parole in the United States, 1998* (Washington: U.S. Dept. of Justice, Bureau of Justice Statistics, August 1999).

9. Bonczar, pp. 9–10.

10. Howard Abadinsky, *Probation and Parole: Theory and Practice* (Englewood Cliffs, NJ: Prentice-Hall, 1987), p. 21.

11. Camille Graham Camp and George M. Camp, "Categories of Probation and Parole Employees on 1/1/98," in *The Corrections Yearbook, 1998* (Middle-town, CT: Criminal Justice Institute, 1998), pp. 199–200.

12. Comptroller General of the United States, *State and Local Probation: Systems in Crisis* (Washington: U.S. Government Printing Office, 1976).

13. Camp and Camp, p. 179.

14. Jon'a Meyer, "Tradition and Technology: Computers in Criminal Justice," in Laura J. Moriarty and David L. Carter (eds.), *Criminal Justice Technology in the 21st Century* (Springfield, IL: Charles C. Thomas, 1999), pp. 3–16.

15. Bureau of Justice Statistics.

16. William H. DiMascio, *Seeking Justice: Crime and Punishment in America* (New York: Edna McConnell Clark Foundation, 1997), p. 43.

17. Paul Gendreau, "The Principles of Effective Intervention With Offenders," in Alan Harland (ed.), *Choosing Correctional Options That Work: Defining the Demand and Evaluating the Supply* (Thousand Oaks, CA: Sage, 1996).

18. See, for example, Joan Petersilia and Susan Turner, *Evaluating Intensive Supervision Probation/Parole: Results of a Nationwide Experiment* (Washington: National Institute of Justice, 1993); Ben Crouch, "Is Incarceration Really Worse? Analysis of Offenders' Preferences for Prison Over Probation," *Justice Quarterly*, Vol. 10 (1993), pp. 67–88; Joan Petersilia and Elizabeth Piper Deschenes, "Perceptions of Punishment: Inmates and Staff Rank the Severity of Prison Versus Intermediate Sanctions," *The Prison Journal*, Vol. 74 (1994), pp. 304–328.

19. Stanley W. Hodge and Victor E. Kappler, "Can We Continue to Lock Up the Nonviolent Drug Offender?" in Charles B. Fields, *Controversial Issues in Corrections* (Boston: Allyn & Bacon, 1999), pp. 137–151.

6 Intermediate Sanctions
Corrections in the Community

CHAPTER OBJECTIVES

After completing this chapter you should be able to:

1. Define *intermediate sanctions* and know the purposes of intermediate sanctions.
2. Define *net-widening*.
3. Describe how intensive-supervision probation (ISP) works.
4. Explain how day fines differ from traditional fines.
5. Describe what a sentence to community service entails.
6. Explain what day reporting centers (DRCs) are.
7. Describe how house arrest with electronic monitoring works.
8. Explain what residential community centers are.
9. Identify the major features of boot camps.
10. Distinguish between a program-centered approach and a policy-centered approach to planning intermediate sanctions.
11. Define *community corrections*.
12. Explain what community corrections acts are.

154

intermediate sanctions
New punishment options developed to fill the gap between traditional probation and traditional jail or prison sentences and to better match the severity of punishment to the seriousness of the crime.

community corrections
A philosophy of correctional treatment that embraces (1) decentralization of authority, (2) citizen participation, (3) redefinition of the population of offenders for whom incarceration is most appropriate, and (4) emphasis on rehabilitation through community programs.

Crime and bad lives are the measure of a State's failure; all crime in the end is the crime of the community.

—H. G. Wells

It has been estimated that someday as many as 1 million adult and juvenile offenders in the United States will be under some form of electronic house arrest. This projection is not unthinkable. In 1984 there were no offenders in the United States under electronic home confinement. In 1992 there were 45,000! If that rate continues, 90,000 offenders may be under electronic home detention in 2000 and over 200,000 in 2025.

Electronic home detention is quickly taking a place on the growing continuum of sanctions between probation and jail or prison. Called **intermediate sanctions,** the new options fill the gap between traditional probation and traditional jail or prison sentences and better match the severity of punishment to the seriousness of the crime. Intermediate sanctions fulfill all the goals of sentencing: retribution, deterrence, incapacitation, rehabilitation, and restoration. Because intermediate sanctions are administered outside prison or jail, and generally in the offender's community, they are a form of **community corrections.** After looking at the principal intermediate sanctions in use in the United States, we will turn our attention to community corrections in general.

Intermediate Sanctions

Sanctions less restrictive than prison but more restrictive than probation are not new. Variations of restitution, fines, and community service were used as sentences in ancient Israel, Greece, and Rome.[1] More recent intermediate sanctions—such as electronic house arrest, boot camps, and day fines—started in the 1980s. What is new today is the effort to bring all

---

FIGURE 6–1

Intermediate Sanctions

	Intensive Supervision Probation (ISP)	Restitution, Fines, and Day Fines	Community Service	Day Reporting
Probation	Control of offenders in the community under strict conditions, through frequent reporting to a probation officer with a limited caseload.	Regular payments to crime victims or to the courts. Used alone or in conjunction with probation or ISP.	Completion of a set number of hours of work in and for the community. Used alone or in conjunction with probation or ISP.	Reporting to a central location every day to file a schedule with the supervision officer, showing how each hour will be spent.

Source: Adapted from William M. DiMascio, *Seeking Justice: Crime and Punishment in America* (New York: Edna McConnell Clark Foundation, 1997), pp. 32–33.

of these sanctions together into a comprehensive sentencing system like the one suggested in Figure 6–1 that provides judges with an expanded menu of corrections options.

Advocates for more effective sentencing practices include the American Jail Association (see Exhibit 6–1 on page 158). They call for a range or continuum of sanctions with graduated levels of supervision and harshness. Simple probation is at one end, traditional incarceration is at the other, and a variety of intermediate sanctions bridge the middle ground. This type of sentencing enables criminal justice officials to reserve expensive prison and jail space for violent offenders. It gives nonviolent offenders less restrictive intermediate sanctions and restitution-focused sentences while teaching them accountability for their actions and heightening their chances for rehabilitation. This approach to sentencing treats prisons as the backstop, not the backbone, of the corrections system.

Intermediate sanctions are most often used for offenders considered nonviolent and of low risk. They usually require the offender to lead a productive life in the community by working, finding work if unemployed, or learning new job skills; to do unpaid community service; to pay restitution to victims; to enroll in a treatment or educational program—or sometimes to do all of these.

Intermediate sanctions are sometimes referred to as *front-end* programs or strategies. **Front-end programs** are options for initial sentences that are more restrictive than traditional probation but less restrictive than jail or prison. They are usually designed to limit the number of persons who go to prison. In front-end programs, judges commonly sentence offenders directly to one or a combination of intermediate sanctions. **Back-end programs** are reduced restrictions for offenders who have made progress in compliance and treatment. In back-end programs, offenders are moved from higher to lower levels of control to complete the final phase of their sentences. For example, the state department of corrections may move an offender from prison to electronic house arrest.

Student Involvement
Direct students' attention to Exhibit 6–1 on page 158. Ask students to read the AJA resolution and speculate how criminal justice practitioners might determine whether offenders pose a threat to themselves or society.

Student Involvement
Ask students which type of program (back-end or front-end) would be more effective with misdemeanants. With felons? Be sure that students defend their opinions.

front-end programs
Punishment options for initial sentences more restrictive than traditional probation but less restrictive than jail or prison.

back-end programs
Sanctions that move offenders from higher levels of control to lower ones for the final phase of their sentences.

FIGURE 6–1 (continued)
Intermediate Sanctions

House Arrest and Electronic Monitoring	Residential Community Centers	Boot Camp	Jail or Prison
Restriction of offender to home except when at work, school, or treatment. Used in conjunction with ISP.	Residential settings for selected offenders as a supplement to probation. Usually linked with community service or substance abuse treatment.	Rigorous military-style regimen for younger offenders, designed to accelerate punishment while instilling discipline. Often with an educational component.	

Intermediate Sanctions: Corrections in the Community

EXHIBIT 6–1

American Jail Association Resolution

Intermediate Punishments

WHEREAS, the American Jail Association (AJA) recognizes the detrimental impact that crowding places on local jails; and

WHEREAS, many of those who are incarcerated in jails do not pose a known danger to themselves or to society;

THEREFORE BE IT RESOLVED THAT AJA supports the expansion of intermediate punishments in states and localities throughout America for offenders who do not pose a known danger to public safety. AJA believes that intermediate punishments address real concerns of constituents.

net-widening Increasing the number of offenders sentenced to a greater level of restriction. It results in the sentencing of offenders to more restrictive sanctions than their offenses and characteristics warrant.

Teaching Tip
Use the following to explain *net-widening.* A jurisdiction, facing prison crowding, sets up a new intensive-supervision probation program. The target group is nonviolent offenders who would go to prison if the program were not available. Suppose persons who would formerly have been placed on regular probation are now placed on intensive-supervision probation. Those offenders are not the ones for whom the program was established.

Front-end programs tend to draw more heavily from offenders who would otherwise receive less restrictive sentences than from those who would otherwise go to jail or prison. In that way, they contribute to **net-widening**. Net-widening means increasing the number of offenders sentenced to a greater level of restriction. As a result, many offenders may receive more restrictive sentences than their offenses and characteristics warrant. Community service, for instance, might be added to probation. Net-widening happens because judges have more alternatives to confinement for offenders that, in earlier times, they would have put on simple probation. The seductiveness of intermediate sanctions, especially those that provide discipline and structure for disruptive individuals, creates a real threat that large numbers of persons will receive intermediate sanctions, whether or not those sanctions are suitable.

Value of Intermediate Sanctions

From 1985 through 1998, the number of persons confined in state and federal prisons and local jails skyrocketed 164 percent, from 744,208 in 1985 to 1,966,506 in 1998. This unprecedented growth in the nation's prisons and jails has placed a heavy economic burden on taxpayers. That burden includes the cost of building, maintaining, and operating prisons and jails, as well as the loss of offenders' contributions and the cost of caring for the destabilized families left behind. In addition, overcrowded jails and prisons are hard to manage and staff, and they invite disorder.

During the same period, new intermediate-sanction programs expanded rapidly across the United States, and the number of persons sentenced to them increased. The result has been an explosion in the number of persons under correctional supervision. Many intermediate sanctions were started with the goal of reducing the prison population. Though there has been no decline in the number of persons sentenced to prison since these new intermediate sanctions appeared, proponents argue that without the new programs, the number would be even larger. Other supporters say that by increasing the surveillance, punishment, and treatment of offenders under community supervision, intermediate sanctions achieve other correctional goals.

Intermediate sanctions are valuable for a number of reasons. First, they provide a means for offenders who are not dangerous to repay their victims and their communities. Second, intermediate sanctions promote rehabilitation—which most citizens want, but most prisons and jails find difficult to provide—and the reintegration of the offender into the community. And third, once the programs are in place, they can do these things at a comparatively low cost. Compare the lower costs of intermediate sanctions with jail and prison in Table 6–1.

Intermediate sanctions should not be haphazardly planned or implemented. High-quality intermediate sanctions must be thoughtfully conceived, effectively targeted, well planned, and well staffed. Intermediate sanctions bring the added difficulty of controlling an offender's behavior in the less restrictive setting of the free community. That is why one of the popular approaches to counseling in intermediate sanctions programs is behavior modification.

TABLE 6–1

Average Annual Cost of Correctional Options

Correctional Options	Cost per Year per Participant
Prison	$20,261
Boot Camp	20,025
Jail	19,903
Halfway House	16,790
Electronic Monitoring	3,402
Intensive Supervision	3,270
Day Reporting	2,781
Community Service	2,759
Parole	1,690
Probation	1,153
House Arrest	402

Source: Adapted from *Seeking Justice: Crime and Punishment in America* (New York: Edna McConnell-Clark Foundation, 1997), p. 34 and Camille Graham Camp and George M. Camp, *The Corrections Yearbook, 1998* (Middletown, CT: Criminal Justice Institute, 1998), pp. 90–91, 248–249.

Varieties of Intermediate Sanctions

The specific varieties of intermediate sanctions discussed in the following subsections include intensive-supervision probation, day fines, community service orders, day reporting centers, house arrest and electronic monitoring, residential community centers, and boot camps.

intensive-supervision probation (ISP) Control of offenders in the community, under strict conditions, by means of frequent reporting to a probation officer, whose caseload is generally limited to 30 offenders.

Intensive-Supervision Probation Intensive-supervision probation (ISP) is probation with frequent contact between offender and probation officer, strict enforcement of conditions, random drug and alcohol testing, and other requirements. As a technique for increasing control over offenders in the community, ISP has gained wide popularity. It allows offenders to live at home, but under more severe and more punitive restrictions than those of conventional probation. Requirements of ISP usually include performing community service, attending school or treatment programs, working or looking for employment, meeting with a probation officer (or team of officers) as often as five times a week, and submitting to curfews, employment checks, and tests for drug and alcohol use. Because of the frequency of contact, subjection to unannounced drug tests, and rigorous enforcement of restitution, community service, and other conditions, ISP is thought more appropriate for higher-risk offenders.

ISP was initially the most popular intermediate sanction. It has the longest history and has been the most extensively evaluated. Intensive-supervision programs exist in every state. They may be state or county programs and may be administered by parole, probation, or prison departments. As a result, it not easy to estimate the number of ISP programs in the United States.

Student Involvement

Create two columns. Label one "Probation" and the other "ISP." Then ask students to list the corresponding conditions to which offenders in each program might be subject.

In general, evaluators of ISP have concluded that offenders sentenced to ISP commit new crimes at about the same rate as comparable offenders receiving different sentences. Also, technical violation and revocation rates are typically higher for ISP participants because more frequent contact makes misconduct more likely to be discovered. Early proponents of ISP argued that ISP would reduce recidivism rates, rehabilitate offenders, and save money and prison resources. However, most evaluations suggest that the combination of net-widening, high revocation rates, and costs of processing revocations makes savings unlikely.[2]

There is one tantalizing positive finding about ISP: it increases participants' involvement in counseling and treatment programs. There is evi-

Intensive-supervision probation officers conduct random drug tests on offenders at home and at work. What other controls are used to monitor offenders on ISP?

dence that re-arrests are reduced when offenders receive treatment in addition to the increased surveillance and control of ISP programs. The literature demonstrates that participation in drug treatment, whether voluntary or compelled, can reduce both drug use and crime by drug-using offenders. Data indicate that in many cities, one-half to three-fourths of arrested felons are drug abusers; ISP holds promise as a device for getting addicted offenders into treatment and keeping them there.[3]

THE OFFENDER SPEAKS

I was so grateful my sentence was probation because I got three kids. Electronic monitoring meant I could stay home with them. It meant that they wouldn't be put into a foster home or something like that. It meant I could be sure they won't wind up like me. But when I need money, I can't just leave to get it. I can't leave to visit a friend or my mama. Can't visit my man, and he can't come here cause he's off limits for me. He's a violation like my brother. I hate that, but the alternatives are jail time and kids without their mama. It gets bad sometimes because I want to go out and have a good time. I got needs. But that ain't going to happen yet. I take in other kids to watch—washing and ironing, too. Chump money! But I was given a chance and for that I'm grateful. But those feds think they own me. My PO is cool, but he thinks he owns my life, too. Owns my time. Lost my man because of him. But I get to do what's right for my kids and me, and once this is over—I ain't gettin' a parking ticket! I hate being tied down. Hate the drug testing all the time. Hate the questions. But at night—I've got my kids and they got me.

Anonymous

Evaluation of the Florida Community Control Program (FCCP) by the National Council on Crime and Delinquency concluded that ISP graduates commit new crimes at a lower rate than a comparable group of offenders released from prison and that each FCCP participant saved the state $2750.[4]

To reap the benefits of ISP, what must be done is straightforward. Because recidivism rates for new crimes are no higher for ISP participants than for comparable imprisoned offenders, ISP is a cost-effective alternative to prison for offenders who do not present unacceptable risks to public safety. Cost savings are likely to depend, however, on using ISP only for offenders who would have received appreciable prison time. And technical violations require a range of responses, not a rush to incarcerate the violator. Incarcerating all violators cancels out the initial savings of ISP.

Day Fines A **fine** is a financial sanction requiring a convicted person to pay a specified sum of money. The fine is one of the oldest forms of punishment. It is, in practice, the criminal justice tool for punishing minor misdemeanors, traffic offenses, and ordinance violations. To be effective, fines should be proportionate to the seriousness of an offense and should have roughly similar economic impacts on persons with differing financial resources who are convicted of the same offense. In the United States, fines are rarely regarded as a tough criminal sanction. They are not taken seriously, for at least four reasons. First, judicial, legislative, and prosecutorial attitudes restrict their use to traffic offenses, minor misdemeanors, and ordi-

Teaching Tip
Draw student attention to counseling as a condition of ISP and the finding that treatment, combined with ISP surveillance and control, is related to a reduction in re-arrests.

fine A financial penalty used as a criminal sanction.

Teaching Tip
Review the four reasons fines are seldom taken seriously in the United States. Then invite student opinions on which one of the four reasons limits the effectiveness of fines the most, and why.

day fine A financial penalty scaled both to the defendant's ability to pay and to the seriousness of the crime.

Cross-Cultural Perspective
Reinforce that some northern and western European countries have made fines the sentence of choice in a high proportion of criminal cases, including serious crimes. Ask students to speculate what cultural differences might explain the difference in attitudes toward fines as sanctions.

Professional Issue
Planning Review the list of criminal justice professionals generally involved in setting up a day fine program. Ask students to explain why each of the individuals listed would have a stake in planning the program.

nance violations. Second, a judge seldom has enough reliable information on an offender's personal wealth to impose a just fine. Third, mechanisms for collecting fines are often ineffective. Far too often the responsibility for collecting fines has been left to probation officers, who were already overburdened and had no interest in fine collection. As a result, fines were seldom paid. Fourth, many believe that fines work hardship on the poor, while affluent offenders feel no sting.

In contrast, many northern and western European countries have made fines the sanction of choice in a high proportion of criminal cases, including many involving serious crimes. In the Netherlands, a fine is legally presumed to be the preferred sentence for every crime, either alone or in conjunction with another penalty. Judges there are required to provide a statement of reasons in every case in which a fine is *not* imposed. In Germany, since the mid-1980s, a large percentage (sometimes over 80 percent) of all adult criminals sentenced have been ordered to pay fines. In some years, almost 75 percent of those convicted of crimes of violence were ordered to pay fines. In Sweden, fines constitute about 90 percent of all sentences. In England, fines are included in about 50 percent of cases of those individuals convicted of indictable offenses (roughly equivalent to U.S. felonies).[5]

A **day fine** is a financial penalty based on the seriousness of the crime and the defendant's ability to pay. It is called a day fine because it is based on the offender's daily income.

Day fines, also called *structured fines*, have been common in some northern and western European countries for many years. They were introduced in Sweden in the 1920s and were quickly incorporated into the penal codes of other Scandinavian counties. West Germany adopted day fines as a sentencing option in the early 1970s. Today these countries have made day fines the preferred punishment for most criminal cases, including those involving serious crimes. In Germany, for example, day fines are the only punishment for three-quarters of all offenders convicted of property crimes and two-thirds of offenders convicted of assaults.[6]

Day fines have been tried experimentally in some areas of the United States, including New York, Arizona, Connecticut, Iowa, and Oregon. Figure 6–2 is a sample notification of a structured fine program. The notice may be mailed to a defendant along with the summons or handed to the defendant when he or she appears in court.

To be effective, a day fine program must have the support of a cross-section of criminal justice professionals in a jurisdiction, as well as others who have a stake in the operation of the criminal justice system. According to a Bureau of Justice Assistance report[7] on day fines, the following officials should be involved in planning a county day fine program:

- the presiding judges of the general- and limited-jurisdiction courts
- a prosecutor
- a public defender
- a representative of the private defense bar
- a court administrator
- the director of a pretrial services agency
- the chief probation officer or the director of a community corrections agency

FIGURE 6–2

Sample Notification of a Structured Fine Program

A PRELIMINARY COMPLAINT
HAS BEEN FILED CHARGING YOU WITH
AN INDICTABLE OFFENSE

IF CONVICTED, THE COURT <u>MAY</u> IMPOSE ONE OR MORE OF THE
FOLLOWING SANCTIONS:
1. JAIL OR PRISON
2. PROBATION
3. A FINE

If a fine is imposed, the Court may <u>structure</u> the level of the fine
partly according to the seriousness of the offense and partly in
relation to your means or ability to pay the fine. This method of
computing the amount of a "structured fine" is an effort by the Court
and the Polk County Attorney's Office to <u>equalize</u> the impact of
criminal sanctions and to <u>reduce</u> the number of persons who are
sentenced to prison, jail, or formal probation.

In order for the County Attorney's Office to consider recommending
a structured fine to the Court at the time of sentencing, you or your
attorney must schedule an interview with a Structured Fines Officer
at 555-1234, IMMEDIATELY. If you intend to secure an attorney to
represent you on this charge, please make these arrangements prior
to calling the Structured Fines Program.

Your ability to pay a structured fine, as well as the length of time
needed to pay the fine, is based on the information you provide in
the attached AFFIDAVIT OF FINANCIAL CONDITION. It is
required that you and/or your attorney complete this form prior to
meeting with a Structured Fines Officer. It is also required that you
take to your meeting with the Structured Fines Officer verification of
your income in the form of paycheck stubs, income tax returns, etc.

POLK COUNTY ATTORNEY'S OFFICE
STRUCTURED FINES PROGRAM
POLK COUNTY COURTHOUSE, ROOM B-40
DES MOINES, IOWA 50309
555-1234

Appointments with a Structured Fines Officer are available
Monday through Friday, from 1:30 p.m. - 4:30 p.m.

- the sheriff or another jail administrator
- representatives of county government

The planning process for introducing day fines will be unique for each jurisdiction, depending on its organizational structure, traditions, personalities, and local legal culture. Every jurisdiction, however, will have to address similar issues: current sentencing patterns, current fine collection operations and their effectiveness, goals and priorities for the day fine program, and potential legal challenges to the program.

Once a system for imposing day fines has been put in place, the next step is to develop a structured process for setting fines. This structured process is the feature that distinguishes day fines from traditional fines. The process usually has two parts: (1) a unit scale that ranks offenses by seriousness and severity and (2) a valuation scale for determining the dollar amount per unit for a given offender.

The first step in setting a day fine is to determine the number of fine units to be imposed. A portion of the unit scale used in a Staten Island, New York, day fine experiment is shown in Figure 6–3. The number of units ranges from a low of 5 to a high of 120, for the most serious misdemeanors handled by the court. For example, the presumptive number of units for the offense of assault with minor injury and aggravating factors is 70; the range is from 59 to 81 units. The presumptive number is the starting point. Negotiation and consideration of individual circumstances may raise or lower the number. There is no magic in the unit scale established. What is important is to establish a scale broad enough to cover the full range of offenses handled by the courts that will use structured fines.

Once the unit scale is established, the second step is to create a valuation table. The purpose of the valuation table is to establish the dollar amount of each fine. A portion of the valuation table used in the Staten Island experiment is shown in Figure 6–4. Net daily incomes run down the left side, and numbers of dependents run across the top. Net daily income is the offender's income (after-tax wages, welfare allowance, unemployment compensation, etc.) divided by the number of days in a payment period. Staten Island planners also adjusted the net daily income downward to account for subsistence needs, family responsibilities, and incomes below the poverty line.

Suppose a defendant convicted of assault, with minor injury and aggravating factors, has a net daily income of $15 and supports 4 persons, including herself. Find the row for her net daily income. Move across the row to the column for the number of dependents. The figure there is the value of one structured fine unit for that defendant. Multiply the number of fine units to be imposed (70) by the value of a single fine unit (3.38). The product, $236.60, is the amount of the day fine to be imposed.

The National Institute of Justice sponsored an evaluation of the Staten Island experiment. That evaluation showed that judges used day fines for many offenses for which they had formerly used fixed fine amounts—including some property crimes, drug possession, and assault.[8] Most judges cooperated with the new, voluntary scheme throughout the year-long experiment. Research showed that the average fine increased by 25 percent, from $206 before the experiment to $258 during the year day fines were

Student Involvement
Refer students to Figures 6–3 and 6–4. Ask volunteers to use those charts to devise day fine calculation problems for the rest of the class to solve.

Tutorial CD-ROM
Refer students to the Tutorial With Simulation Applications CD-ROM. The tutorial is a comprehensive interactive study tool that reinforces and reviews the concepts in Chapter 6. Also included are two simulations that apply concepts presented in Chapter 6.

FIGURE 6–3

Example of Day Fine Unit Scale

Staten Island Day Fine Unit Scale
(Selected Offense Categories)

Penal Law Charge*	Type of Offense**	Number of Day Fine Units Discount – PRESUMPTIVE - Premium
120.00 AM	Assault 3: Range of 20-95 DF	
	A. Substantial Injury	81 - **95** - 109
	Stranger-to-stranger; or where victim is known to assailant, he/she is weaker, vulnerable	
	B. Minor Injury	59 - **70** - 81
	Stranger-to-stranger; or where victim is known to assailant, he/she is weaker, vulnerable; or altercations involving use of a weapon	
	C. Substantial Injury	38 - **45** - 52
	Altercations among acquaintances; brawls	
	D. Minor Injury	17 - **20** - 23
110/120.00 BM	Attempted Assault 3: Range of 15-45 DF	
	A. Substantial Injury	38 - **45** - 52
	Stranger-to-stranger; or where victim is known to assailant, he/she is weaker, vulnerable	
	B. Minor Injury	30 - **35** - 40
	Stranger-to-stranger; or where victim is known to assailant, he/she is weaker, vulnerable; or altercations involving use of a weapon	
	C. Substantial Injury	17 - **20** - 23
	Altercations among acquaintances; brawls	
	D. Minor Injury	13 - **15** - 17
	Altercations among acquaintances; brawls	

*AM = Class A Misdemeanor; BM = Class B Misdemeanor
**DF = Day Fines

Source: Bureau of Justice Assistance, *How to Use Structured Fines (Day Fines) as an Intermediate Sanction* (Washington: Bureau of Justice Assistance, 1996), p. 59.

used. If day fines had not been held low by state law, the average day fine would have been $440. The news on collections was also good. Eighty-five percent of the defendants in the day fine program paid their fines in full, compared with 71 percent in a control program using routine collection

FIGURE 6–4

Example of Day Fine Valuation Table

**Staten Island, New York, Valuation Table
Dollar Value of One Day Fine Unit, by Net Daily Income
and Number of Dependents**

Net Daily Income($)	Number of Dependents (Including Self)							
	1	2	3	4	5	6	7	8
3		1.05	0.83	0.68	0.53	0.45	0.37	0.30
4	1.70	1.40	1.10	0.90	0.70	0.60	0.50	0.40
5	2.13	1.75	1.38	1.13	0.88	0.75	0.62	0.50
6	2.55	2.10	1.65	1.35	1.05	0.90	0.75	0.60
7	2.98	2.45	1.93	1.58	1.23	1.05	0.87	0.70
8	3.40	2.80	2.20	1.80	1.40	1.20	1.00	0.80
9	3.83	3.15	2.48	2.03	1.58	1.35	1.12	0.90
10	4.25	3.50	2.75	2.25	1.75	1.50	1.25	1.00
11	4.68	3.85	3.03	2.47	1.93	1.65	1.37	1.10
12	5.10	4.20	3.30	2.70	2.10	1.80	1.50	1.20
13	5.53	4.55	3.58	2.93	2.28	1.95	1.62	1.30
14	7.85	4.90	3.85	3.15	2.45	2.10	1.75	1.40
15	8.42	5.25	4.13	3.38	2.63	2.25	1.87	1.50

Source: Bureau of Justice Assistance, *How to Use Structured Fines (Day Fines) as an Intermediate Sanction* (Washington: Bureau of Justice Assistance, 1996), p. 64.

processes. Furthermore, when full payment was not made, partial payment was much more likely in the day fine cases than in cases from before the experiment or in the control group. Thus, the higher fines levied in the day fine cases did not make collection more difficult, and the new enforcement procedures independently improved collection rates.

There has been little research on the effectiveness of fines in reducing recidivism rates. However, since the use of fines could reduce the costs of courts and corrections, and since day fines address problems of inequality, fines are a promising intermediate sanction. At present, most Western justice systems, except the United States, rely heavily on financial penalties. In the next century, U.S. jurisdictions are likely to continue their experiments with monetary penalties and to assign them even greater importance.

community service
A sentence to serve a specified number of hours working in unpaid positions with nonprofit or tax-supported agencies.

Community Service   **Community service** is a sentence to serve a specified number of hours working in unpaid positions with nonprofit or tax-supported agencies.[9] Community service is punishment that takes away an offender's time and energy. Community service is sometimes called a "fine of time." Requiring offenders to compensate victims with their time or money

Intermediate Sanctions: Corrections in the Community

was customary in ancient civilizations. The desire for compensation in time or money was probably at least as common then as the urge to retaliate.

Community service as a criminal sanction began in the United States in 1966 in Alameda County, California. Municipal judges there devised a community service sentencing program for indigent women who violated traffic and parking laws. Too poor to pay fines, these women were likely to be sentenced to jail. But putting them behind bars imposed a hardship on their families. Community service orders (CSOs) increased sentencing options, punished the offenders, lightened the suffering of innocent families, avoided the cost of imprisonment, and provided valuable services to the community. As Alameda judges gained experience with the new sentencing option, they broadened the program to include male offenders, juveniles, and persons convicted of crimes more serious than traffic or parking violations.

The Alameda County community service program received international attention. England and Wales developed pilot projects in the 1970s, using community service as a midlevel sanction between probation and prison and as an alternative to prison sentences up to six months. By 1975, community service had become a central feature of English sentencing. The approach swept throughout Europe, Australia, New Zealand, and Canada.

However, what had begun as an American innovation atrophied in the United States.[10] Today in the United States, community service is seldom used as a separate sentence. Instead, it may be one of many conditions of a probation sentence. Nor is it viewed as an alternative to imprisonment in the United States, as it is in other countries. Generally speaking, in the United States, public officials do not consider any sanction other than imprisonment punitive enough. Substituting community service for short prison sentences is not accepted. This is unfortunate because community service is a burdensome penalty that meets with widespread public approval,[11] is inexpensive to administer, and produces public value. Also, it can largely be scaled to the seriousness of the crime.

Community service can be an intermediate sanction by itself or with other penalties and requirements, including substance abuse treatment, restitution, or probation.[12] Offenders sentenced to community service are usually assigned to work for government or private nonprofit agencies. They paint churches; maintain parks; clean roadways, public parks, and county fairgrounds; remove snow around public buildings; perform land and river reclamation; and renovate schools and nursing homes. Offenders who are doctors may be ordered to give medical service to persons who might otherwise lack medical attention. Traffic offenders may be ordered to serve in hospital emergency rooms to learn about the injuries they risk for themselves and others. Drug offenders who are prominent sports figures may be ordered to lecture in high schools on the dangers of drugs. The service options are limited only by the imagination of the sentencing judge and the availability of personnel to ensure that the offender fulfills the terms of the sentence. To become and remain a tough criminal sanction, community service must have credible and efficient enforcement mechanisms.

By the late 1980s, some form of community service sanction was in use in all 50 states. The Bureau of Justice Statistics estimates conservatively that 6 percent of all felons in the United States are sentenced to perform community service, often in conjunction with other sanctions.[13] The state of

Cross-Cultural Perspective

In the context of the popularity of community service in other countries (even though it started in the United States), discuss with students the cultural reasons for the way the United States lags behind Europe in sentencing innovations. Do students think these barriers can be overcome? How?

Teaching Tip

Ask students if they know anyone who has been sentenced to community service. How did that person react to the sentence? Was the sentence completed satisfactorily?

Community service as a criminal sanction is valuable to the community, the victim, and the offender. How does each benefit?

Washington has made the most extensive use of community service. At least one-third of its convicted felons receive sentences that include community service. Washington state sentencing guidelines permit substitution of community service for incarceration at a rate of 8 hours of work for 1 day of incarceration, with a limit of 30 days. Most jurisdictions recognize 240 hours as the upper limit for community service. Washington State is breaking new ground in sentencing reform with the idea of *interchangeable sentences* for nonviolent or not very violent crimes against strangers. The actual sentence depends on the offender and the purposes to be served. For those with little or no income, community service may substitute for a fine. Before offenders are sentenced to community service in Washington, they complete a community service order questionnaire (see Figure 6–5 on page 169). The questionnaire helps the state Department of Corrections match the offender's abilities and limitations with community service work. A community corrections officer then makes sure the offender performs the required community service.

For offenders who do not present unacceptable risks of future violent crimes, a punitive intermediate sanction like community service—which costs much less than prison, promises comparable recidivism rates, and presents negligible risks of violence by those who would otherwise be confined—has much to commend it.

FIGURE 6-5

Sample Community Service Order Questionnaire

STATE OF WASHINGTON
DEPARTMENT OF CORRECTIONS

COMMUNITY SERVICE WORKER QUESTIONNAIRE
AND RELEASE OF INFORMATION

_____   _____
Name   DOC Number

By action of the Superior Court, or an administrative Department of Corrections action, you have been ordered to perform community service work. This work must be performed within an approved unit of government or non-profit agency. To help us find the best assignment for you, and ensure reasonable accommodation for any sensory, physical or mental limitations or disabilities that you may have, please supply the following information. You are not obligated to disclose conditions that do not relate to your ability to perform community service.

1. List your job skills.

2. Do you have a preference for a certain agency or a particular type of work that you would like to perform?
   If yes, describe:

3. List the hours and days you are available for work.
   Monday _____   Wednesday_____   Friday _____   Sunday _____
   Tuesday _____   Thursday _____   Saturday _____

4. What means of transportation do you have to get to and from the work site?

5. Do you wear contacts or glasses?   Yes   No   N/A   (circle one)

6. Are you pregnant?   Yes   No   N/A   (circle one)

7. Are you currently taking any prescription medications that have side effects that may affect your ability to perform community service work (i.e., drowsiness, slurred speech, etc.)?   Yes   No   (circle one)
   If "Yes," describe side effects:

8. Note whether you have been diagnosed as having any of the following problems:

	Yes	No		Yes	No		Yes	No
Severe Allergy Reactions			Heart Problems			Epilepsy		
Breathing Disorders			Hearing Loss			Uncorrected Vision Problems		
Balance Problems			Diabetes			Other		

If "Yes," please describe:

9. Is there any activity or motion that is difficult for you to do (i.e., crawling, climbing, bending, lifting, etc.)?
   Yes   No   (circle one)   If "Yes," please describe:

10. Do you have any other sensory, physical and/or mental limitations or disabilities that may affect your ability to do community service?   Yes   No   (circle one)   If "Yes," please describe:

11. You are required to provide to your Community Corrections Officer, a clearance from your health care provider, documenting any sensory/physical/mental limitations or disabilities which impact your ability to perform community service hours. This documentation is required within 30 days of today's date, and will be at your expense. Release of information is on the reverse side.

Distributions: ORIGINAL-Community Service Worker, COPY-Worksite, Community Service Coordinator, File

DOC 05-103 (REV 10/97) OCO   COMMUNITY SERVICE PROGRAM

Day Reporting Centers   A **day reporting center (DRC)** is a community correctional center where an offender reports each day to file a daily schedule with a supervision officer. The schedule shows how each hour will be spent—at work or looking for work, in class, at a support group meeting, etc.[14] Aiming primarily to provide treatment and reduce prison crowding, DRCs typically offer numerous services to address offenders' problems, and they strictly supervise offenders who otherwise would be confined.

Day reporting centers first developed in Great Britain in 1972. British officials noted that many offenders were imprisoned, not because they posed a risk to the public, but because they lacked basic skills to survive lawfully. Frequently, such offenders were dependent on drugs and alcohol. In 1985, officials in Connecticut's Department of Corrections learned about British day reporting centers and believed that such centers might alleviate the state's prison crowding problem. A National Institute of Justice survey conducted in mid-1994 identified 114 DRCs in 22 states.[15] Most opened after 1990. Many of the programs are concentrated in just a few states, including Connecticut, Texas, Wisconsin, Oregon, and Kansas.

DRCs commonly require offenders to obey a curfew, perform community service, and undergo drug testing twice a week. Participants check in at the center in person once a day and telephone periodically. They are responsible for following a full-time schedule that includes a combination of work, school, and substance abuse or mental health treatment. Programs range in duration from 40 days to 9 months, and program content differs. Most programs require hour-by-hour schedules of participants' activities. Some are highly intensive, with 10 or more supervision contacts per day, and a few include 24-hour electronic monitoring.[16] Some centers refer clients to service agencies; others provide services directly. Some focus on monitoring; others emphasize support. The 1994 survey showed generally high failure rates, averaging 50 percent. Unfortunately, no substantial evaluations have yet been published.

As DRCs move into the twenty-first century, a number of policy issues will influence their development and implementation. Those issues are (1) ensuring offenders' access to services, (2) responding to violations of DRC regulations in ways that will not add to jail and prison crowding, and (3) conducting evaluation of DRC programs.

House Arrest and Electronic Monitoring   **House arrest** is an intermediate sanction that requires an offender to remain in his or her home except for approved absences, such as work, school, or treatment programs. **Electronic monitoring (EM)** is the tracking of an offender's location by means of electronic signals from a small transmitter on the offender's wrist or ankle to a monitoring unit. When used together, the two are sometimes referred to as *electronic house arrest*.

Electronic monitoring units may be active or passive. An active unit sends a continuous signal. The receiving computer notes any break in the signal and alerts the officer monitoring the offender. For example, the offender wears a bracelet fitted to the wrist or ankle. The bracelet has a wire running through it. If the wire is broken or the offender moves outside the signal range, the receiving computer notes a break in the signal. Passive units respond only to inquiries. Most commonly, the offender receives an

Megan Hill
Case Manager
Day Reporting Center
Boston, Massachusetts

"Probably the best part about my job is working with individuals who are truly dedicated to their recovery and reintegration back into society. The feeling you get from seeing a client start with all the frustrations of job rejections and discrimination to seeing them attain their first legal job and actually enjoy it is pretty satisfying. I am actually helping people put their lives back together."

While an undergraduate at Northeastern University, Megan Hill participated in several co-op programs, including six months at a day reporting center in Boston. Shortly after her co-op ended, the day reporting center advertised for a case manager and hired Megan for the job. Megan credits Northeastern's co-op program with giving her the qualifications to be hired full-time before earning her degree and with providing her the opportunity to explore different aspects of the criminal justice field.

Each day, Megan's responsibilities include approving day reporting clients' daily itineraries, monitoring clients' call-in times, and visiting her clients at home and work. Daily contact, she says, helps her know her clients better, understand what they're going through, and know how to assist them. She also believes it's important to respect clients. "The more respect you give your clients, the more respect and honesty you get in return."

Megan's advice to persons interested in working in corrections is to do an internship or a co-op to find out if they like the work. For Megan Hill, the most important thing is to be happy with your job and to feel that you're making a difference.

---

automated telephone call from the probation office and is told to place the bracelet on an identification unit attached to the telephone. Another method of passive EM is voice verification by means of digitized voice templates. For offenders with alcohol and drug problems, breath testing may be used. The offender blows into the unit, which records drugs or alcohol in the offender's breath. The instrument is often accompanied by a video display that gives visual proof that the subject performing the alcohol or drug test is actually the offender.

Electronic monitoring sometimes, but not necessarily, backs up house arrest. House arrest can stand alone as a sanction or can be coupled with fines and other obligations. The term of the sentence can range from several days to several years.

In theory, electronic house arrest satisfies three correctional goals. First, it incapacitates the offender by restricting him or her to a single location. Second, it is punitive because it forces the offender to stay home when not at work, school, counseling, or community service. And third, it con-

Teaching Tip

Help students understand the difference between house arrest and electronic monitoring (EM) by explaining that EM is a tool that monitors an offender's presence at home.

Teaching Tip
Point out that electronic house arrest satisfies the correctional goals of incapacitation, retribution, and rehabilitation by restricting offenders to a single location, providing constant surveillance, and maintaining family and community ties.

Professional Issue
Privacy Critics of electronic monitoring argue that it intrudes on the privacy of the offender and his or her family. Ask students if they agree with this criticism and why or why not.

Student Involvement
Tell students that they are a local policy-making group writing a proposal to establish and fund an electronic house arrest program. How will they proceed? Write all suggestions on the board, and by consensus, eliminate suggestions until a plan emerges.

residential community center (RCC) A medium-security correctional setting that resident offenders are permitted to leave regularly—unaccompanied by staff—for work, for educational or vocational programs, or for treatment in the community.

tributes to rehabilitation by allowing the offender to remain with his or her family and continue employment, education, or vocational training.

The growing popularity of electronic house arrest is due in large part to prison and jail overcrowding, increasing demands to supervise more offenders, and concerns over the ability of standard probation to protect the community. Electronic house arrest is seen as a cost-effective, humane intervention that allows offenders to maintain or establish ties to the community, which are important to rehabilitation, and to avoid the negative influences of incarceration. Yet, it is also more punitive than standard probation, which provides little supervision to offenders.

Advocates of electronic house arrest point to a number of advantages: the equipment has evolved to a point where it is fairly reliable. It usually pays for itself, since the offender often pays to use the system; it often generates profits for the supervising agency. It's tougher than routine probation. And since offenders can remain at home and keep working, it is more humane. The American Probation and Parole Association supports electronic house arrest.

Critics say that the requirement to have a telephone and pay for the monitoring equipment keeps electronic house arrest out of reach for many offenders who would benefit from it. In addition, electronic house arrest does not guarantee that crimes will not occur in the house. Vice crimes, domestic violence, and assaults—to name a few—occur during electronic house arrest. And electronic monitors intrude on the privacy of the family and increase family stress.

Despite these concerns, electronic house arrest has grown enormously throughout the United States since electronic surveillance technology was introduced in 1969. Not only is the number of offenders on electronic house arrest increasing, but also the offenders are becoming more diverse. Initially, electronic house arrest targeted only the traditional clients of house arrest: low-risk probationers, such as those convicted of driving while intoxicated. More recently, however, it has expanded to include persons awaiting trial or sentencing, offenders released from institutional and community corrections facilities, and juvenile offenders. Furthermore, whereas electronic house arrest initially gained acceptance as a response to property crimes, it is used more and more with selected offenders whose crimes are not very violent. New technology also makes it possible to track an offender's movements throughout the world. Using a network of 24 satellites called Global Positioning System (GPS) orbiting 12,000 miles above earth's surface, a monitoring system called SMART (Satellite Monitoring and Remote Tracking System) can track an offender's bracelet and notify police, victims, and others when the offender enters a prohibited area.

Residential Community Centers A residential community center (RCC) is a medium-security correctional setting that resident offenders are permitted to leave regularly—unaccompanied by staff—for work, for educational or vocational programs, or for treatment in the community. Initially such centers were called *halfway houses* and were for offenders who either were about to be released from an institution or were in the first stages of return to the community. However, as the number of halfway houses grew,

Tippecanoe County Community Corrections, through its Home Detention Program, provides punitive sentencing alternatives for Class B, C, and D felons, Class A misdemeanants, and nonviolent habitual offenders in lieu of DOC commitment to state prison. These offenders, who are classified as high-risk probationers, are those assessed as nonviolent who could benefit from up to 24-hour supervision complemented by a personalized treatment plan designed around employment, education, family, and substance abuse needs. The offenders also pay fees to be in the program. These fees are used to offset operating costs.

Tippecanoe County Community Corrections currently has 7 surveillance officers to monitor between 200 and 250 clients sentenced to home detention. The surveillance officers use both electronic monitoring and daily visits to the client's residence and place of employment.

Electronic monitoring is accomplished by utilizing Suretrac monitoring equipment. The equipment consists of an ankle unit (PIU) and a receiving unit (PRU). The PRU is placed in the client's residence when the client enters the Home Detention Program. The PIU is attached to the client's ankle. The equipment is used to monitor the client whenever he or she leaves or enters the residence. Each client is entered into a main computer and given time frames when authorized to be away from home for employment or appointments (probation, court, counseling, doctor, etc.). The Suretrac equipment uses the client's existing telephone line to communicate with the main computer

as well as with the surveillance officer. Whenever a client leaves or enters the range of the monitoring equipment, the PRU will automatically call the main computer. The main computer will then check the client's curfew, and if there is a violation, it will then call the surveillance officer, using an alphanumeric pager, and state whether the client has entered or left the residence. The equipment will also automatically page the surveillance officer if the client tampers with the PIU, if the power is cut off to the PRU, if the telephone line is disconnected, or if any other problem occurs. With this system, the surveillance officer can react quickly to a given situation.

Visits to the clients' residences take place daily. The purpose of these visits is (1) to determine whether the clients are at home when they are supposed to be; (2) to ensure the clients are not using alcohol or drugs (breathalyzers and random monthly drug screens are performed); (3) to check on the clients' employment status (verify time cards, work hours, etc.); and (4) to check on the clients' well-being and family situation and just to see how they are doing while on home detention.

Clients who violate home detention rules are dealt with immediately. Clients may lose all privileges, may be given road crew hours to complete, or may be sent back to jail to complete their sentences.

David Kuebler
Executive Director
Tippecanoe County, Indiana,
Community Corrections

and new client groups (divertees, pretrial releasees, and probationers) were added, the umbrella term *residential community center* was adopted.

Halfway houses, prerelease and work release centers, and restitution centers are examples of RCCs. Some RCCs specialize in a type of client or treatment—for example, in drug and alcohol abuse, violent and sex offenders, women, abused women, or prerelease federal prisoners. The type of population served varies from community to community and from RCC to RCC. According to the latest figures from the National Institute of Corrections, there are more than 1200 RCCs in the United States,[17] and there is substantial diversity among them.[18] Some are public, and some private. There are RCCs at all levels of government. The largest number of programs (about 40 percent) are operated by private nonprofit agencies. The next largest group (about 35 percent) are run by state government. Then come those run by county government (almost 20 percent), for-profit corporations (less than 10 percent), and other agencies (less than 5 percent). RCCs range from fewer than 10 beds to more than 200 beds. More than half are small, with fewer than 50 beds; almost 30 percent are classified as medium in size, with 50 to 100 beds; and 20 percent are large, with over 100 beds. More than half of RCCs serve only men, 40 percent serve both men and women, and fewer than 10 percent serve only women. According to the American Correctional Association, in 1997 there were more than 35,000 RCC residents.[19]

The objectives of RCCs are community protection and offender reintegration. Community protection is achieved by screening offenders, setting curfews, administering drug or polygraph tests, confirming that when residents leave the center they go directly to work, school or treatment, and by providing a medium-security correctional setting. Reintegration is achieved by giving residents opportunities to learn and use legitimate skills, thereby reducing their reliance on criminal behavior. Staff determine the obstacles to each resident's reintegration, plan a program to overcome those obstacles, and provide a supportive environment to help the resident test, use, and refine the skills needed.

The benefits of RCCs are many. RCCs benefit offenders by providing them with the basic necessities of food, clothing, and shelter while they find housing and employment. RCCs also offer residents emotional support to deal with the pressures of readjustment and help them obtain community services. Benefits to the community include a moderately secure correctional setting in which residents' behavior is monitored and controlled, as well as an expectation that opportunities for offenders to get on their feet will reduce post-release adjustment problems and criminal behavior. For the criminal justice system, an RCC offers a low-cost housing alternative to incarceration for nonviolent offenders. An RCC can control offenders in the community at less cost than building and operating more secure facilities. It may also serve as an enhancement to probation and an option for dealing with probation and parole violators.

There has not been much research on the effectiveness of RCCs. An early General Accounting Office (GAO) report proposed that extensive planning and coordination of information were greatly needed for halfway houses to reach their objectives.[20]

Recently, researchers have concluded that, "Adopting more realistic outcome measures may make it possible to bridge the wide gap between public expectations for the justice system and what most practitioners recognize as the system's actual capability to control crime. By documenting what corrections programs can accomplish, we can move toward integrating programs like work release [as part of a residential community center program] into a more balanced corrections strategy. Such a strategy would successfully return low-risk inmates to the community, thereby making room to incarcerate the truly violent offenders."[21]

Boot Camps   In 1983, in an effort to alleviate prison crowding and reduce recidivism, the departments of corrections in Oklahoma and Georgia opened the first adult prison programs modeled after military boot camps. Since then, boot camp, or *shock incarceration*, has become an increasingly popular intermediate sanction.

Boot camp is a short institutional term of confinement, usually followed by probation, that includes a physical regimen designed to develop self-discipline, respect for authority, responsibility, and a sense of accomplishment. According to the National Institute of Justice, four characteristics distinguish boot camps from other correctional programs: (1) military drill and ceremony, (2) a rigorous daily schedule of hard labor and physical training, (3) separation of boot camp participants from the general prison population, and (4) the idea that boot camps are an alternative to long-term confinement.[22]

Although all boot camps involve a short period of imprisonment in a military atmosphere, the specific components of boot camp programs vary widely. Boot camps differ in whether their activities include work, community services, education, and counseling and whether they provide aftercare support and monitoring for community reintegration. There is some consistency, however, in their goals: reducing prison crowding and changing offenders' behavior and thus their future involvement in crime.

Most boot camps target young, first-time offenders who have been convicted of such nonviolent crimes as drug possession, burglary, or theft and seem more open to changing their attitudes and behavior than older offenders. Most participants are males who do not have extensive criminal histories and are physically and psychologically able to complete the strict military exercise requirements. Disabled offenders or those with nondisabling medical conditions that limit their physical performance (for example, being overweight) are typically excluded.

States differ in their age requirements for boot camp eligibility. For example, in California, participants must be 40 or younger; in Illinois, 17 to 29; in Kansas, 18 to 25; in Maryland, under 32; in New York, 30 or younger; in Oklahoma, under 25; and in Tennessee, 17 to 29.

Several researchers have examined boot camp programs for women.[23] In some programs, women were integrated with male inmates. Others were completely separate female programs. The researchers found that when boot camps combined men and women, few women were in the camps, and those women faced serious problems. They were supervised more intensely

boot camp A short institutional term of confinement, usually followed by probation, that includes a physical regimen designed to develop self-discipline, respect for authority, responsibility, and a sense of accomplishment.

Teaching Tip
Distinguish correctional boot camps from other correctional programs by noting the four characteristics of boot camps: (1) military drill and ceremony; (2) a rigorous daily schedule; (3) separation of participants from the general prison population; and (4) the idea that boot camps are an alternative to long-term confinement.

Professional Issue
Offenders With Disabilities
Boot camp programs typically exclude offenders with disabilities. Do students think that disabled offenders might have a legal claim, under the Americans With Disabilities Act, against a corrections agency for denying them access to a boot camp program that would shorten their terms of confinement? Why or why not?

Professional Issue
Equality Ask students if they think that women offenders should have equal opportunities to enter boot camp programs, and why or why not.

than the men and their activities were restricted to protect them from abuse, harassment, and sexual relations with male drill instructors. Combined programs did not take into consideration women inmates' physical stamina, nor did they offer therapeutic programs for the problems that many of these women faced, such as how to survive sexual assault or battering, make a successful transition into the community, or obtain job skills. Combined programs also failed to take into consideration the importance of children to women in boot camps.

Women in separate programs fared better. The separate camps were more likely to offer therapeutic programs suited to women's needs. Visitation policies were less restrictive, and the women had more opportunities to see their children while in boot camp. The researchers concluded that women should not be combined with men in boot camps designed for men. If boot camps are developed for women, they should be compatible with the needs and characteristics of women offenders.

On January 1, 1998, 84 boot camps involving more than 12,000 adult inmates were in operation by state departments of corrections, jails, and probation and parole agencies.[24] The Violent Crime Control and Law Enforcement Act of 1994 allocated $25 million for the development of boot camp programs, virtually ensuring their continued growth.

Critics have raised questions about using boot camps as a correctional tool. They note that correctional boot camp programs are built on a model of military basic training that the military itself has found lacking and in some cases has revised.[25] Critics also argue that the military model was designed to produce a cohesive fighting unit. That is not a goal of corrections. One analyst wrote, "If an offender can't read [or] write and is drug-involved,

The military-style training and drill of boot camps is sometimes supplemented with substance abuse education and vocational training. What aftercare programs might contribute to the effectiveness of boot camp strategies?

Student Involvement
Title a table "Boot Camp." Under the heading, create two columns, with the labels "Pro" and "Con." Invite students to suggest entries in each column. Ask why each is pro or con.

Intermediate Sanctions: Corrections in the Community

sending him to a 90-day boot camp that does not address his job or literacy needs will only have a short-term effect, if any, on his behavior."[26]

There is reason for both optimism and skepticism about boot camps. Although boot camps are promoted as a means of reducing recidivism rates, there is no evidence that they significantly reduce recidivism or promote socially desirable activities. When behavior during the first year back in the community is examined, there is no evidence that boot camp participants perform any better than those who stayed longer in prison. Some researchers have reported that boot camp graduates have higher self-esteem, have better attitudes toward family, are less likely to see themselves as victims of circumstances, and are more likely to feel in control of their future. However, the research does not always compare boot camp graduates with other groups. Research into what boot camp participants say they'll do is less conclusive than research into what they've actually done.

Also disappointing is that the recidivism rates of boot camp graduates are very similar to those of other parolees.[27] In front-end boot camp programs, one-third to one-half of the participants fail to complete the program and are sent to prison as a result. In most programs, close surveillance of graduates after release leads to technical-violation and revocation rates that are higher than those of comparable offenders in less intensive programs.

Boot camps are also promoted as a means of reducing prison crowding and corrections costs. Here the news is not all bad. Back-end programs, to which imprisoned offenders are transferred by corrections officials, do save money and prison space. Although they too often experience high failure, technical violation, and revocation rates, those rates are no higher than for offenders who have been kept in prison longer. If enough offenders complete boot camp and are released early from prison, the programs can reduce prison crowding. However, many boot camp programs select participants from those who would otherwise be sentenced to probation. Those programs widen the net, including more offenders in prison and requiring additional beds. A number of researchers have found that most boot camps have not reduced prison crowding, because the programs are designed for offenders who would otherwise be on probation, not those who would otherwise have received prison terms.[28] Crowding can be reduced only if boot camp participants are selected from inmates already incarcerated and only if their participation substantially reduces their overall sentence lengths.

Policy-Centered Approach to Developing Intermediate Sanctions

A policy is a statement of intent. It expresses *why* we are engaging in a particular set of activities. It also tells *how* we are to carry out these activities. Policy can be very general, very specific, or in between.

In recent decades sanction options have proliferated, increasing the choices available to judges at sentencing and to governmental agencies moving offenders from higher levels of control to lower ones. As we take stock of the contributions and limitations of the movement toward intermediate

Drill Instructor
The Polk County Sheriff's Office operates a boot camp program for male and female offenders ages 14 to 19. Our program provides an aftercare component directly supervised by the same DIs who monitored the offenders during the in-residence phase of the program. We are looking for DIs who can participate in and lead the physical training as well as provide positive role models. Requirements: Graduation from a two-year associate's program in a human services field and one year of experience as an assistant drill instructor; skill in motivating trainees in a military boot camp environment.

Student Involvement
Solicit a group of volunteers to research the boot camp programs in your state, if any exist. Students can call the state department of corrections and obtain an update on the programs. The student group should report to the class. Another option is for the class to visit a boot camp or for you to invite the program director to visit the class.

sanctions, it is important to think about intermediate sanctions, not as punishments developed in isolation from one another, but rather as parts of a system of policy-driven responses to criminal behavior.

Unfortunately, most intermediate sanctions are discrete local programs, devised and implemented without the participation of the decision makers who will use them. In this **program-centered approach**, planning for an intermediate-sanction program (e.g., electronic house arrest) is usually undertaken by a single agency, which develops and funds the program. The program staff then tries to inform judges, prosecutors, defense counsel, and other corrections agencies about the program, its potential benefits, and the target population for which it is best suited.

The program-centered approach has serious limitations and often results in disappointment. It makes nationwide comparison and evaluation difficult because there is no coordination between the programs of different jurisdictions. Programs that are established this way are seldom evaluated, because most local agencies lack the resources and the understanding of evaluation research. The program-centered approach often leads to many new programs that pursue multiple goals, sometimes even conflicting ones. When that happens, ambiguous and inconsistent operating policies develop. Finally, the program-centered approach tells us very little about how intermediate sanctions affect a jurisdiction's overall sentencing and imprisonment practices, very important information for most intermediate-sanction programs.

The **policy-centered approach** to intermediate sanctions, however, emphasizes the *policy* that spells out the sentencing scheme and the place of each sentencing option as much as the sanctions and programs themselves. This approach draws together stakeholders from inside and outside the corrections agency that will implement the proposed sanction. The planning group often includes decision makers from all three branches of government

program-centered approach A method of planning intermediate sanctions in which planning for a program is usually undertaken by a single agency, which develops and funds the program.

policy-centered approach A method of thinking about and planning for intermediate sanctions that draws together key stakeholders from inside and outside the corrections agency that will implement the sanction.

In Anoka County, Minnesota, a policy team of key stakeholders inside and outside the corrections agency developed a day reporting center for high-risk probationers as one of six intermediate sanctions designed to save jail space for serious offenders. What are the advantages of using a policy-centered approach to devise intermediate sanctions?

Intermediate Sanctions: Corrections in the Community

(judicial, executive, and legislative) and all three subsystems of criminal justice (police, courts, and corrections). The group examines the overall context within which the proposed new sanction will be used and analyzes data on offenses and offenders to form sound policy. Public hearings may also be held. The policy that emerges is a statement of intent. It expresses why the group has decided to provide a particular set of sanctions and explains how those sanctions should be implemented.

Community Corrections

So far in this chapter we have been discussing intermediate sanctions as strategies to control crime. Now we turn our attention from the *strategies* to the *goal* they are designed to achieve. That goal is community corrections. There is no consensus in the field of criminal justice on the definition of community corrections. Sometimes the term refers to noninstitutional programs. Sometimes it refers to programs administered by local government rather than the state. Other times, it indicates citizen involvement.

We define community corrections as a philosophy of correctional treatment that embraces (1) decentralization of authority from state to local levels, (2) citizen participation in program planning, design, implementation, and evaluation, (3) redefinition of the population of offenders for whom incarceration is most appropriate, and (4) emphasis on rehabilitation through community programs.

Community corrections recognizes the importance of partnership with the community in responding to crime. In short, our communities not only have a *right* to safe streets and homes, but also bear *responsibility* for making them safe. All the major components of the criminal justice system have alliances today with the community. Examples include the following:

- *Community policing* A law enforcement strategy to get residents involved in making their neighborhoods safer by focusing on crime prevention, nonemergency services, public accountability, and decentralized decision making that includes the public.
- *Community-based prosecution* A prosecution strategy that uses a combination of criminal and civil tactics and the legal expertise, resources, and clout of the prosecuting attorney's office to find innovative solutions to a neighborhood's specific problems.
- *Community-based defender services* A defender strategy that provides continuity in representation of indigent defendants and helps defendants with personal and family problems that can lead to legal troubles.
- *Community courts* A judicial strategy of hearing a criminal case in the community that is most affected by the case and including that community in case disposition.

Community Corrections Acts

This spirit of correctional collaboration and community partnership has led 28 states to pass **community corrections acts (CCAs)** (see Figure 6–6 on page 180). CCAs are state laws that give economic grants to local com-

Student Involvement

Refer students to Figure 6–6. If your state has a CCA, ask a small group of students to obtain a copy of it from the state legislature, a law school, a public library, or the district attorney's office. Ask students to comment on definitions, offense criteria, and sanctions. What do students think about the way the purposes and goals are stated in your state's legislation? Are they understandable? Are there some purposes and goals that students think should be excluded or others they think should be included?

Teaching Tip

Here, according to *The Prison Journal* (M. Kay Harris, "Key Differences Among Community Corrections Acts in the United States: An Overview," *The Prison Journal*, Vol. 76 (1995), pp. 192–238) are the four most frequently cited: to increase the range or number of sanctions, to increase or maintain public safety, to promote efficiency and economy and to reduce or stabilize prison or jail populations. Ask students which one they believe is the most important in defining community corrections. Obtain a consensus on the most important one or ones, and then ask students how they would measure whether the goal was actually met.

FIGURE 6–6

States With Community Corrections Legislation

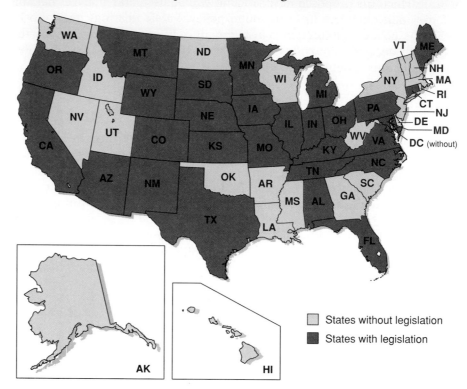

Source: William M. DiMascio, *Seeking Justice: Crime and Punishment in America* (New York: Edna McConnell Clark Foundation, 1997), p. 38. Data on map is as of January 1996.

munities to establish community corrections goals and policies and to develop and operate community corrections programs. Most CCAs transfer some state functions to local communities, decentralizing services and engaging communities in the process of reintegrating offenders. Along with the transfer of correctional responsibility from the state to the community, CCAs provide financial incentives for counties, private citizens' groups, and private agencies to participate. The financial incentives help communities manage more of their own correctional cases rather than ask the state to manage them. With the money, local communities design, implement, and evaluate a complete range of local sentencing options. (The intermediate sanctions discussed earlier in this chapter, for example, can be funded through a CCA.) Locally designed sanctions have a better chance of succeeding because they are based in the community where offenders' families, friends, and other social supports are. Although CCAs authorize and allow funding for a range of sanctions, including intermediate sanctions, they do more than that. CCAs implement community corrections philosophy by providing statewide structures that specify government and citizen roles and responsibilities in the planning, development, implementation, and funding of community sanctions.

Intermediate Sanctions: Corrections in the Community

In 1973, Minnesota became the first state to adopt a CCA. Minnesota officials wanted to reduce fragmentation in criminal justice service delivery, to control costs, and to redefine the population of offenders for whom state incarceration was most appropriate. Communities throughout Minnesota were willing to assume greater correctional responsibility for less serious offenders, as long as the communities were also given state subsidies and significant control over planning and service delivery. The huge success of Minnesota's CCA can be seen in Minnesota's incarceration rate, one of the lowest in the United States today. While the crime rate is not much different from those of other states, the incarceration rate is only 117 persons for every 100,000 residents. The U.S. average on December 31, 1998, was 461 per 100,000 residents. The majority of Minnesota's offenders are handled under the CCA.

There are tremendous differences in the CCAs in the United States. The most common goal, held in 14 states, is expansion of sanction choices. Twelve states cite the promotion of state and community partnerships as the goal. Some CCAs focus on nonviolent offenders; others merely include them. Some CCAs help communities move offenders out of local jails and into correctional programs that are less expensive and offer reasonable community protection. Simply having correctional programs in a community does not mean that a community corrections program exists. Consistent goals and consistent approaches to achieving those goals are the backbone of successful community corrections. Community corrections legislation can help accomplish that consistency.

Teaching Tip
Refer to Chapter 6 of the *Instructor's Resource Manual* for additional activities and for answers to the end-of-chapter exercises.

6 Review and Applications

CHAPTER OBJECTIVE 1

Intermediate sanctions is the term given to the range of new sentencing options developed to fill the gap between traditional probation and traditional jail or prison sentences, better match the severity of punishment to the seriousness of the crime, reduce institutional crowding, and control correctional costs. Punishments typically identified as intermediate sanctions include intensive-supervision probation (ISP), fines, community service, day reporting centers, house arrest, residential community centers, and boot camp.

CHAPTER OBJECTIVE 2

Net-widening means increasing the number of offenders sentenced to a greater level of restriction. As a result, many offenders receive more restrictive sentences than their offenses and characteristics warrant.

CHAPTER OBJECTIVE 3

Intensive-supervision probation (ISP) is control of offenders in the community through strict enforcement of conditions and frequent reporting to a probation officer with a reduced caseload. ISP programs exist in all 50 states. They may be state or county programs and may be administered by parole, probation, or prison departments.

CHAPTER OBJECTIVE 4

A day fine is a financial punishment scaled to the seriousness of the offense and the offender's ability to pay. A traditional fine is based on a fixed amount, without regard to the offender's ability to pay.

CHAPTER OBJECTIVE 5

Community service is a sentence to serve a specified number of hours working in unpaid positions with nonprofit or tax-supported agencies. Research suggests that for offenders who do not present unacceptable risks of future violent crimes, community service costs much less than prison, has comparable recidivism rates, and presents negligible risks of violence by those who would otherwise be confined.

CHAPTER OBJECTIVE 6

A day reporting center (DRC) is a community correctional center where an offender reports each day to file a daily schedule with a supervision officer, showing how each hour will be spent. DRCs aim to provide strict surveillance over offenders and, depending on their resources, provide treatment services, refer offenders to community social service agencies, or arrange to have community agencies offer services on site.

CHAPTER OBJECTIVE 7

House arrest is a sanction that requires an offender to remain in his or her home except for approved absences such as work, school, or treatment programs. Electronic monitoring sometimes helps enforce the offender's compliance with house arrest.

CHAPTER OBJECTIVE 8

Residential community centers are medium security correctional settings that resident offenders are permitted to leave regularly—unaccompanied by staff—for work, for educational or vocational programs, or for treatment in the community.

CHAPTER OBJECTIVE 9

Boot camp is a short institutional term, usually followed by probation, that includes a physical regimen designed to develop self-discipline, respect for authority, responsibility, and a sense of accomplishment.

CHAPTER OBJECTIVE 10

In a program-centered approach, the planning of an intermediate-sanction program (e.g., electronic house arrest) is usually undertaken by a single agency, which develops and funds the program in isolation from other programs. A policy-centered approach, on the other hand, draws together diverse stakeholders to think about and plan for an intermediate sanction.

CHAPTER OBJECTIVE 11

Community corrections is a philosophy of correctional treatment that embraces decentralization of authority from state to local levels; citizen participation in program planning, design, implementation, and evaluation; redefinition of the population of offenders for whom incarceration is most appropriate; and emphasis on rehabilitation through community programs.

CHAPTER OBJECTIVE 12

Community corrections acts (CCAs) are state laws that give economic grants to local communities to establish community corrections goals and policies and to develop and operate community corrections programs. CCAs decentralize services and engage communities in the process of reintegrating offenders by transferring correctional responsibility from the state to the community and by providing financial incentives for communities to manage more of their own correctional cases rather than ask the state to manage them.

KEY TERMS

intermediate sanctions, p. 156
community corrections, p. 156
front-end programs, p. 157
back-end programs, p. 157
net-widening, p. 158
intensive-supervision probation (ISP), p. 160
fine, p. 161
day fine, p. 162
community service, p. 166

day reporting center (DRC), p. 170
house arrest, p. 170
electronic monitoring (EM), p. 170
residential community center (RCC) p. 172
boot camp, p. 175
program-centered approach, p. 178
policy-centered approach, p. 178
community corrections acts (CCAs), p. 179

QUESTIONS FOR REVIEW

1. What are intermediate sanctions?
2. What are the purposes of intermediate sanctions?
3. Define *front-end programs, back-end programs,* and *net-widening.* How do these three terms relate to intermediate sanctions?
4. What is ISP? How is it more punitive than standard probation?
5. What are four reasons fines are not taken seriously as punishment in the United States? Might enforced collection change that perception?
6. Distinguish between *fixed fines* and *day fines*.
7. Describe community service. Where, when, and why were community service orders first used in the United States?

8. What is a *day reporting center* (DRC), and how widespread is the use of DRCs in the United States?
9. What is electronic house arrest? What correctional goals does it satisfy?
10. What are boot camps? How are they different from other correctional programs? What features vary among boot camps?
11. What problems do boot camps pose for women offenders?
12. Describe the differences between a program-centered approach and a policy-centered approach to the development and implementation of intermediate sanctions.
13. What is community corrections?
14. What are community corrections acts?

CRITICAL THINKING EXERCISES

ON-THE-JOB ISSUE

Your state legislature recently passed a bill authorizing day fines as an intermediate sanction. Part of the bill requires each probation department to send one or more probation officers to a workshop to prepare for implementing the bill. The chief probation officer designates you. Before the workshop, you are given two questions: (1) Why are day fines a good idea? (2) What would you do with offenders who don't pay? You are to write a response to bring to the workshop.

CORRECTIONS ISSUES

1. Summarizing the results of a national survey of judges' attitudes toward fines, researchers noted that "at present, judges do not regard the fine alone as a meaningful alternative to incarceration or probation."[29] What could you tell such judges to convince them that day fines, or structured fines, are a viable sentencing option?

2. Supporters of the policy-centered approach to devising intermediate sanctions cite three advantages: (1) It avoids wasting scarce resources on the wrong category of offender, (2) it draws the support of judges, prosecutors, and defense counsel outside the sponsoring agency, and (3) it helps develop consensus on specific goals for a program. Do you agree that these are advantages of the approach? Explain.

CORRECTIONS ON THE WEB

 The National Institute of Corrections (NIC) provides training, technical assistance, information services, and assistance in policy and program development to federal, state, and local corrections agencies. NIC's Web page at **http://www.nicic.org** provides full-text articles on community corrections issues. Click on Publications and then on Community Corrections. Choose an article that interests you. Prepare a one-page report to present in class.

ADDITIONAL READINGS

Ellsworth, Thomas (ed.). *Contemporary Community Corrections,* 2d ed. Prospect Heights, IL: Waveland Press, 1997.

Morris, Norval, and Michael Tonry. *Between Prison and Probation: Intermediate Punishments in a Rational Sentencing System.* New York: Oxford University Press, 1990.

Smykla, John Ortiz, and William L. Selke (eds.). *Intermediate Sanctions: Sentencing in the 1990s.* Cincinnati: Anderson, 1995.

Tonry, Michael. "Parochialism in U.S. Sentencing Policy." *Crime and Delinquency,* Vol. 45, No. 1, January 1999, pp. 48–65.

ENDNOTES

1. Herbert A. Johnson, *History of Criminal Justice* (Cincinnati: Anderson, 1988).

2. Joan Petersilia, Arthur J. Lurigio, and James M. Byrne, "Introduction," in James M. Byrne, Arthur J. Lurigio, and Joan Petersilia (eds.), *Smart Sentencing: The Emergence of Intermediate Sanctions* (Newbury Park, CA: Sage, 1992), pp. ix-x.; see also Elizabeth Deschenes, Susan Turner, and Joan Petersilia, *Intensive Community Supervision in Minnesota: A Dual Experiment in Prison Diversion and Enhanced Supervised Release* (Washington: National Institute of Justice, 1995).

3. Doris Layton MacKenzie and J. W. Shaw, "Inmate Adjustment and Change During Shock Incarceration: The Impact of Correctional Boot Camp Programs," *Justice Quarterly,* Vol. 7 (1990), pp. 125–150; Joan Petersilia and Susan Turner, "Intensive Probation and Parole," in Michael

Tonry (ed.), *Crime and Justice: A Review of Research, Volume 17* (Chicago: University of Chicago Press, 1993), pp. 281–335.

4. William M. DiMascio, *Seeking Justice: Crime and Punishment in America* (New York: Edna McConnell Clark Foundation, 1997), p. 36.

5. Sally Hillsman and Judith Greene, "The Use of Fines as an Intermediate Sanction," in Byrne, Lurigio, and Petersilia; Peter P. Tak, "Sentencing in the Netherlands," *Acta Criminologica*, Vol. 7, 1994, pp. 7–17; Norval Morris and Michael Tonry, *Between Prison and Probation: Intermediate Punishments in a Rational Sentencing System* (New York: Oxford University Press, 1990).

6. Bureau of Justice Assistance, *How to Use Structured Fines (Day Fines) as an Intermediate Sanction* (Washington: Department of Justice, November 1996).

7. Ibid.

8. Ibid.

9. Morris and Tonry, p. 152.

10. Michael Tonry, "Parochialism in U.S. Sentencing Policy," *Crime and Delinquency*, Vol. 45, No. 1 (1999), p. 58.

11. DiMascio, pp. 43–45.

12. Warren Young, *Community Service Orders* (London: Heinemann, 1979); Gill McIvor, *Sentenced to Serve: The Operation and Impact of Community Service by Offenders* (Aldershot, England: Avebury, 1992); Peter J. O. Tak, "Netherlands Successfully Implements Community Service Orders," *Overcrowded Times*, Vol. 6 (1995), pp. 16–17.

13. DiMascio, p. 37.

14. Dale G. Parent, "Day Reporting Centers: An Evolving Intermediate Sanction," *Federal Probation*, Vol. 60, No. 4 (December 1996), pp. 51–54 and George Mair, "Day Centres in England and Wales," *Overcrowded Times*, Vol. 4 (1993), pp. 5–7.

15. Dale G. Parent, Jim Byrne, Vered Tsarfaty, and Julie Esselman, *Day Reporting Centers* (Washington: National Institute of Justice, 1995).

16. Dale Parent, "Day Reporting Centers: An Emerging Intermediate Sanction," *Overcrowded Times*, Vol. 2 (1991), pp. 6, 8; Jack McDevitt and Robyn Miliano, "Day Reporting Centers: An Innovative Concept in Intermediate Sanctions," in Byrne, Lurigio, and Petersilia.

17. National Institute of Corrections, *1989 Directory of Residential Community Corrections Facilities in the United States* (Longmont, CA: National Institute of Corrections, 1989).

18. Kay Knapp, Peggy Burke, and Mimi Carter, *Residential Community Corrections Facilities: Current Practice and Policy Issues* (Longmont, CA: National Institute of Corrections, August 1992).

19. American Correctional Association, *1997 Directory of Juvenile and Adult Correctional Departments, Institutions, Agencies and Paroling Authorities* (Lanham, MD: American Correctional Association, 1997).

20. General Accounting Office, *Federal Guidance Needed if Halfway Houses Are to Be a Viable Alternative to Prison* (Washington: U.S. Government Printing Office, 1975).

21. Ibid, p. 12.

22. Doris L. MacKenzie and Eugene E. Hebert (eds.), *Correctional Boot Camps: A Tough Intermediate Sanction* (Washington: National Institute of Justice, 1996).

23. Doris Layton MacKenzie, et al., "Boot Camps as an Alternative for Women," in Mackenzie and Hebert, ibid.

24. Camille Graham Camp and George M. Camp, *The Corrections Yearbook 1998* (Middletown, CT: Criminal Justice Institute, 1998), pp. 118–121, 194, 250.

25. Merry Morash and Lila Rucker, "Critical Look at the Ideal of Boot Camp as Correctional Reform," *Crime and Delinquency*, Vol. 36 (1990), pp. 204–222.

26. DiMascio, p. 41.

27. Dale Parent, "Boot Camps Failing to Achieve Goals," *Overcrowded Times*, Vol. 5 (1994), pp. 8–11; Doris Layton MacKenzie, "Boot Camps: A National Assessment," *Overcrowded Times*, Vol. 5 (1994), pp. 14–18; and Philip A. Ethridge and Jonathan R. Sorensen, "An Analysis of Attitudinal Change and Community Adjustment Among Probationers in a County Boot Camp," *Journal of Contemporary Criminal Justice*, Vol. 13, No. 2 (May 1992), pp. 139–154.

28. W. J. Dickey, *Evaluating Boot Camp Prisons* (Washington: National Institute of Justice, 1994); Peter Katel and Melinda Liu, "The Bust in Boot Camps," *Newsweek*, February 21, 1994, p. 26; Dale Parent, "Boot Camps Failing to Achieve Goals."

29. George F. Cole, Barry Mahoney, Marlene Thornton, and Roger A. Hanson, *The Practice and Attitudes of Trial Court Judges Regarding Fines as a Criminal Sanction* (Washington: National Institute of Justice, 1987).

Technology in Corrections

Communication

Information is crucial to a well-run correctional system. Knowing what is happening gives correctional administrators the power not only to react to problems promptly, but also to anticipate and prevent them. In recent decades, communication technology has undergone significant changes. Correctional officers can now keep in touch by e-mail and can share information in electronic databases and on Web pages on the Internet.

Videoconferencing is another way to share thoughts and ideas in the correctional community. Meetings and lectures that once required expensive travel can now be "attended" from the comfort of one's office or from a local teleconference site. In addition, satellite TV and video technology have enhanced distance learning for both officers and inmates. Correctional facilities are also starting to use videoconferencing for arraignments, interrogations, and visitation. Friends and family can now save on travel and avoid standing in line by scheduling videoconferences with inmates.

Telemedicine allows medical personnel in prisons to consult with physicians to determine treatment for inmates.

Telemedicine, one of the newest and most exciting advances in medicine, could provide prisoners with adequate, cost-effective health care in the future. Taking a prisoner to a specialist outside the prison poses a danger to correctional officers and the community by giving the prisoner an opportunity to escape or to have contact with other persons in a less controlled environment. Telemedicine allows physicians to consult with on-site medical personnel through videoconferencing and compatible medical devices, such as medical microcameras. It can improve health care in correctional settings, and the substantial savings on in-prison consultations and on trips to local providers can offset the costs of introducing this technology.

Offender and Officer Tracking

Automated kiosks are on the way to replacing routine visits to parole officers. Offenders are instructed to report to a kiosk at a specified location. There they are electronically interviewed, and in some cases tested for alcohol by means of a breath analysis attachment. Using the kiosks, offenders can also e-mail their parole officers to schedule personal meetings. The system identifies the offender by reading a magnetic card and using a biometric fingerprint scanner. Besides fingerprint scanners, other biometric devices are making their way onto the market. One such device is called IriScan. The device scans the eye and identifies the person from the unique patterns in the iris.

Electronic monitoring technology is steadily improving and is likely to be used far more in the future. Fairly new in the field of corrections is the global positioning system (GPS). Already used in airplanes and automobiles, GPS is now also used for monitoring parolees. The GPS tracking unit worn by a parolee allows computers to pinpoint the parolee's location at any time to the precise street address. In the field of inmate monitoring, there is also some discussion about implanting chips in offenders' bodies that would alert officials to undesirable behavior. In some cases, when criminal activity was detected, the chip might even give an electric shock that would temporarily shut down the offender's central nervous system.

Administrators are also relying on new telecommunications technology to help track inmates and former inmates. Speaker ID technology identifies a speaker even if he or she has a cold, just awoke from a deep sleep, or has a poor telephone connection. Systems using Speaker ID can be used to keep track of who calls inmates in prison and to monitor criminal activity such as escape plans, gang activity, and smuggling of contraband. Speaker ID can also be used for low-risk offenders granted early parole as an alternative to incarceration. The system can make random calls and positively identify the speaker from his or her response. The offenders never know when or how they will receive calls. When no one answers the phone or the speaker is not identified, the system alerts authorities to a possible violation.

To increase the efficiency of inmate monitoring and cut administrative costs, a smart card, a plastic card embedded with a computer chip, can be used to store all types of information about the inmate, from medical care to meals eaten.

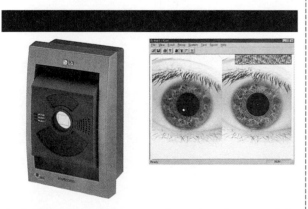

An IriScan device can capture the unique features of the human iris with a camera lens from a distance of 10 to 12 inches, and absolute identification can be accomplished in less than 2 seconds.

Surveillance technology allows correctional staff to view several areas of a prison at the same time.

Electronic monitoring isn't just for inmates. Correctional officers can also wear personal alarm and location units that allow a computer to track their locations and respond to distress signals by sending the closest officers to the site of the emergency.

Detection Technology

To maintain prison security, researchers have developed new detection technologies. One is ground-penetrating radar (GPR), which can be used to locate underground escape tunnels. Another is heartbeat monitoring, which can detect the heartbeat of an inmate trying to escape in a laundry or trash truck leaving the prison. Devices that use X rays to scan the body for concealed weapons and noninvasive skin tests for drugs are also part of the wave of the future.

Implementation

Despite the growth of this technology, there are still obstacles to be overcome. Corrections personnel can be resistant to drastic changes. Another reason for hesitancy to adopt new technology is the cost. Ethical concerns about the rights of offenders might be another barrier to implementing new technology. There is no question, however, that new systems and devices will play an increasing part in the work of correctional agencies.

7 Prisons Today
Change Stations or Warehouses?

CHAPTER OBJECTIVES

After completing this chapter you should be able to:

1. Explain the differences between the Pennsylvania and Auburn prison systems.
2. Outline the nine eras of prison development.
3. Explain prisoner classification and its purposes.
4. Report on the availability of programs for prisoners.
5. Describe the characteristics of today's prisoners.
6. Compare state and federal prison organization and administration.

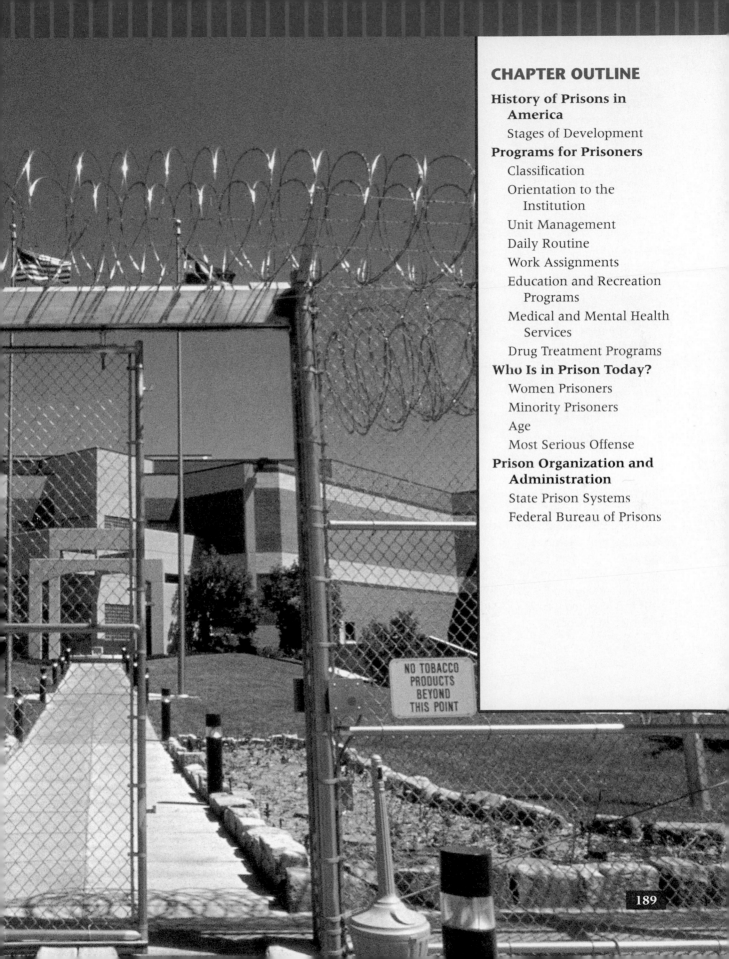

NO TOBACCO PRODUCTS BEYOND THIS POINT

Men copied the realities of their hearts when they built prisons.

—Richard Wright, *The Outsider*, 1953

It's 6 o'clock on Monday morning, still dark outside, when the alarm goes off and Delbert Morris struggles out of bed. He's in and out of the shower in a minute and then nearly cuts himself shaving, he's in such a hurry. He promised a couple of the other guys on the company softball team that he'd meet them for breakfast, but he's already running behind and can't afford to be late for work. It'll have to be just coffee and a quick doughnut on the run.

Just after Delbert punches in at 7, Denise Loftus, the Section 3 supervisor, calls him and the other members of his work team together to go over the day's production schedule. Northern Telecom just put in a rush order for a thousand coaxial cables. The team will have to work with Section 5 if they're going to make the Friday shipping date.

After the meeting, Delbert sets up the work team's hand tools and production boards while some of his crew rush off with the bill of materials to get the parts they need for the job. As soon as they get back, the whole team will start assembling the cables. They want to get started by 7:30.

By 8 the shop is humming, and it stays that way until noon, when everyone breaks for lunch. After lunch, an industrial engineer from the company's main plant stops by to ask the work team what they think about the design for a new IBM cable the company is bidding on. Roberto Kelly, the team's quality control specialist, recommends a change that will allow the cable to fit the team's hand tools more easily. The engineer agrees and alters the design. That's one of the things that Delbert likes about the company—they listen.

Delbert knows he'll be tired when the final whistle blows at 3, but he figures that comes with the job—that and taxes. With taxes, rent, and child support payments, there isn't much left for the car he's been saving for. He gets paroled next month and will need a car for commuting to the Myrtle Beach plant.

At the end of the day, Delbert shows the new man on the team how to do his final inspection and product count, while the other men clean up their work area. After they punch out, they wait in line to go through the metal detector before leaving the shop and walking across the prison yard to their cells.

Delbert (a fictitious name for a real inmate) and the other inmate-workers who assemble wire harnesses for Escod Industries are part of an innovative joint venture inside the Evans Correctional Institution in South Carolina, a maximum-to-medium-security prison holding more than 1,000 prisoners.[1] When prison work programs are mentioned, most people still think of one product and one customer—license plates for state governments. However, a small but growing number of private companies like Escod are paying inmates to produce a wide variety of products and services while in prison.

Joint ventures between a private company and a prison, like the partnership in South Carolina that employs Delbert, are not yet common. In the past decade, however, company executives in an increasing number of states have formed joint ventures with prison officials eager to branch out from their traditional state-use prison industries to produce goods and services for the private sector. Later in this chapter, we'll learn more about prison industries. We'll begin the chapter with a look at the history of American prisons. Then we'll discuss programs for prisoners, the composition of the prison population, and the way America's prisons are organized and administered.

History of Prisons in America

The development of prisons was distinctively American. It reflected and fueled a shift from the assumption that offenders were inherently criminal to a belief that they were simply not properly trained to resist temptation and corruption. The two prison systems that emerged in the United States—the Pennsylvania system and the Auburn system—were copied throughout the world.

The Pennsylvania and Auburn prison systems emerged in the United States at the turn of the nineteenth century. Pennsylvania Quakers advocated a method of punishment more humane than the public corporal punishment used at the time. The Quakers shifted the emphasis from punishing the body to reforming the mind and soul. Together with an elite group of eighteenth-century Philadelphians, they ushered in the first **penitentiary**, a place for reform of offenders through repentance and rehabilitation. They believed prisoners needed to be isolated from each other in silence to repent, to accept God's guidance, and to avoid having a harmful influence on each other. Known as the **Pennsylvania system** or the separate system, this method was first used at the Walnut Street Jail, which the Quakers reorganized in 1789 as the country's first institution for punishment. The construction of the

penitentiary A place for reform of offenders through repentance and rehabilitation. The earliest form of large-scale incarceration, it punished criminals by isolating them so that they could reflect on their misdeeds, repent, and reform.

Pennsylvania system The first style of prison discipline, begun at the Walnut Street Jail to punish offenders with confinement instead of corporal punishment. Conceived by the American Quakers in 1790, it emphasized solitary confinement in silence.

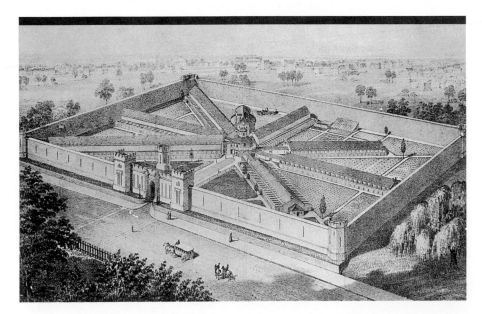

The Eastern State Penitentiary, completed in 1829, was designed for solitary confinement, with instruction in labor, morals, and religion. What name was given to this separate system of prisoner management?

Eastern State Penitentiary in 1829 was also based on these principles. The prison was designed for solitary confinement at labor, with instruction in labor, morals, and religion. For the first time in American history, rehabilitation and deterrence emerged as goals of corrections.

The solitary confinement of the Pennsylvania system was expensive, and it reportedly drove prisoners insane and further hardened criminal tendencies. Reformers responded with what has been termed the **Auburn system:** regimentation, silence unless conversation was required in workshops, congregate working and eating, separation of prisoners into small individual cells at night, harsh discipline, shaved heads, black and white striped uniforms, and industrial workshops that contracted with private businesses to help pay for the institution. The first prison to use this system opened in Auburn, New York, in 1819. The Auburn system, congregate by day and separate by night, eventually gave way to congregate cells at night and removal of the restrictions against talking.

Prison reform in the United States caught the attention of prison officials around the world. The Pennsylvania system of isolation and silence became popular in Europe. In the United States, the two competing philosophies of prison life clashed, and the debate over which system was superior raged on for decades. Supporters of the Pennsylvania system argued that their system made it easier to control prisoners and prevented prisoners from learning bad habits from each other. Supporters of the Auburn system claimed that prisoners' spirits needed to be broken before true reform could begin and that their system of harsh discipline and congregate but silent labor accomplished that. Auburn supporters also argued that their prison system was cheaper to build and the use of contract labor would keep costs down.

A system that was congregate by day (and eventually by night as well) seemed more compatible with the political and economic tone of the time. The Pennsylvania system represented a traditional approach to production: handcraft labor in solitary cells. In contrast, the Auburn system reflected the emerging Industrial Revolution, using power machinery, factory production, and division of labor. The attractiveness of the Auburn system's perceived economic benefits, as well as belief in the rehabilitative value of hard work, settled the debate. Thus, the congregate system became the preferred model of incarceration in the United States. In 1913, Eastern State Penitentiary, the epitome of the Pennsylvania system, changed to the Auburn system, ending the great debate. Congregate prisons have been the mode ever since. Today, however, new voices are calling for a return to long-term solitary confinement.

Stages of Development

Prisons in America have progressed through nine stages of development (see Figure 7–1 on pages 196–7). Many of these changes were influenced by cultural movements in society. As you review the historical stages, think about how the goals of imprisonment changed in each era.

Penitentiary Era (1790–1825) The first of nine eras in prison history was the penitentiary era. It included the emergence of the Pennsylvania and

---

Auburn system The congregate style of prison discipline that began with the opening of the prison at Auburn, New York, in 1819. This system allowed inmates to work silently together during the day. At night, however, prisoners were isolated in small sleeping cells. With time, even sleeping cells became congregate.

Teaching Tip
Create two columns. Label one "Pennsylvania System," the other "Auburn System." After reading the section describing the two systems, have students offer characteristics of the systems to be placed in the appropriate columns.

Teaching Tip
Refer students to Figure 7–1. Point out that the goal of corrections has alternated between rehabilitation, retribution, and incapacitation for the past 200 years. Explain that the changes in the goal of corrections reflect broader changes in social attitudes toward crime and offenders.

Prisons Today: Change Stations or Warehouses?

Auburn prisons, the demise of the Pennsylvania system of separate and silent, and the building of 30 state prisons on the Auburn pattern of congregate by day and separate by night, which eventually became congregate both day and night.

Mass Prison Era (1825–1876) The second era was the mass prison era. During that period, the idea of prison as a place for punishment flourished across the United States. As a result, 35 more Auburn-system prisons were built, including Sing Sing, in New York state, in 1825 and San Quentin, in California, in 1852.

Reformatory Era (1876–1890) The third era was the reformatory era. Influenced by the Progressive Era beliefs that education and science were vehicles to control crime, the first reformatory for young men opened at Elmira, New York, in 1876. The reformatory, whose prisoners had indeterminate sentences, used a grading system that led to early release on parole, and offered academic education, vocational training, individual rehabilitation, and military instruction and discipline. During this era, 20 reformatories opened for men, as well as the first prison for women, Mount Pleasant in Ossining, New York, and the first reformatory for women, the Indiana Reformatory for Women and Girls in Indianapolis.

Industrial Era (1890–1935) Fourth was the industrial era. During this time, inmates worked in prison industries. The first prisons used the **public-accounts system**. The warden at the Walnut Street Jail determined the product, purchased materials and equipment, and oversaw the manufacture, marketing, and sale of the prison-made items. At Auburn, prison industries expanded to include copper, weaving, tailor, blacksmith, and shoemaking shops. However, as more states adopted the Auburn model, the **contract system** replaced the public accounts system. Under the contract system, the prison advertised for bids for the employment of prisoners, whose labor was sold to the highest bidder. The desire to increase profits for the prison and the private contractor often led to exploitation of the prisoners.

During the industrial era, prisons progressed from the public-accounts and contract systems of the Pennsylvania and Auburn prisons, respectively, to *state-use*, *convict lease*, and *public-works* systems. The system used in a state depended on the region the state was in and the period in which the transition was made. At the turn of the twentieth century, many prisons adopted the state-use system. Under the **state-use system**, prisoners manufactured products for use by state governments and their agencies, departments, and institutions. The **convict lease system** was prevalent in the post–Civil War South. Many Southern prisons had been destroyed during the war. Southern states found it easier to relinquish supervision of their prisoners to a lessee. The lessee either employed prisoners within a state institution or transported them anywhere in the state. Railway, lumber, and coal mining companies leased the greatest numbers of inmates. Lessees housed, fed, clothed, and disciplined inmates. The inmates' labor provided revenue to state treasuries. As the Western states developed, a **public-works system** emerged. This system used inmates to build public buildings, roads, and parks.

public-accounts system
The earliest form of prison industry, in which the warden was responsible for purchasing materials and equipment and for the manufacture, marketing, and sale of prison-made items.

contract system A system of prison industry in which the prison advertised for bids for the employment of prisoners, whose labor was sold to the highest bidder.

state-use system A system of prison industry that employs prisoners to manufacture products consumed by state governments and their agencies, departments, and institutions.

convict lease system
A system of prison industry in which a prison temporarily relinquished supervision of its prisoners to a lessee. The lessee either employed the prisoners within the institution or transported them anywhere in the state.

public-works system
A system of prison industry in which prisoners were employed in the construction of public buildings, roads, and parks.

FIGURE 7–1

Stages of Prison History in the United States

Stage	Penitentiary Era	Mass Prison Era	Reformatory Era	Industrial Era
Years	1790–1825	1825–1876	1876–1890	1890–1935
Goal	Rehabilitation and deterrence	Incapacitation and deterrence	Rehabilitation	Incapacitation
Characteristics	Separate and silent Congregate and silent	Congregate labor and living spaces without silence Contract prison labor	Indeterminate sentencing Parole	Public-accounts industries Contract labor State-use labor Convict lease Public-works labor
Examples of Institutions	Walnut Street Penitentiary Philadelphia, PA Eastern State Penitentiary Cherry Hill, PA Auburn Prison, Auburn, NY	Sing Sing Prison Ossining, NY San Quentin State Prison, San Quentin, CA	Elmira, NY Indiana Reformatory for Women and Girls, Indianapolis	Most major prisons

Student Involvement

Organize students into five groups. Assign each group one of the five prison industry systems. Then have them argue for and against the systems, from the perspectives of inmate, warden, taxpayer, legislator, and private business person. Ask students to speculate why labor organizations saw prison industries as unfair competition.

In time, national labor organizations saw prison industries as unfair competition and lobbied Congress to regulate prison industry. In 1929, the Hawes-Cooper Act banned the interstate shipment of prison-made goods. The Ashurst-Sumners Act of 1935 prohibited carriers from accepting prison-made goods for transportation. Ashurst-Sumners also mandated the labeling of prison-made goods. In 1940, Congress passed the Sumners-Ashurst Act, forbidding the interstate transportation of prison-made goods for private use regardless of whether a state banned importation of prison goods (products manufactured for the federal government or other state governments were exempt). Thus, much of the private market was closed to goods made by inmates.

Punitive Era (1935–1945) The closing of prison industries ushered in the punitive era, with its emphasis on strict punishment and custody. The

FIGURE 7–1 (continued)

Stages of Prison History in the United States

Punitive Era	Treatment Era	Community-Based Era	Warehousing Era	Just-Deserts Era
1935–1945	1945–1967	1967–1980	1980–1995	1995–Present
Retribution	Rehabilitation	Reintegration	Incapacitation	Retribution
Strict punishment and custody	Medical model Emerging prisoner unrest	Intermediate sanctions: halfway houses, work release centers, group homes, fines, restitution, community service	Sentencing guidelines End of discretionary parole release Serious crowding More prison riots	Just deserts Determinate sentencing Truth in sentencing Three-strikes laws Serious crowding
U.S. Penitentiary Alcatraz, CA	Patuxent Institution Jessup, MD	Major prison riots (Attica, NY; Santa Fe, NM)	Most major prisons	Rapidly spreading through the United States

holding of prisoners in the Big House, in complete idleness, monotony, and frustration, characterized this era. The "escape-proof" federal prison on the island of Alcatraz in San Francisco Bay opened on the eve of this era.

Treatment Era (1945–1967) The sixth era, treatment, emerged in response to prison riots across the United States. After World War II, the prison population exploded. Overcrowding, idleness, poor food, and other deprivations led prisoners to take matters into their own hands. Prison riots erupted in California, Colorado, Georgia, Illinois, Louisiana, Massachusetts, Michigan, Minnesota, New Jersey, New Mexico, Ohio, Oregon, Pennsylvania, Utah, and Washington. The riots aroused public support for prisoner rehabilitation. Reform through classification, therapy, and increased use of the indeterminate sentence was the focus of the **medical model**, in which criminal behavior was regarded as a disease to be treated.

Teaching Tip
Explain that the new interest in prisoner treatment and rehabilitation stemmed from the failure of "get tough" prisons. Remind students that the medical model assumed that criminal behavior was a disease to be treated with appropriate medication and other therapy.

medical model A philosophy of prisoner reform in which criminal behavior is regarded as a disease to be treated with appropriate therapy.

Prisons Today: Change Stations or Warehouses? CHAPTER 7 195

Maryland's Patuxent Institution, with legions of mental health experts, promised to predict dangerousness accurately and to release only those prisoners who were no longer a threat to the community. However, Patuxent failed to keep that promise. Scholars and advocacy groups were also finding fault with the medical model. In addition, the social and political unrest of the 1960s had found its way into the nation's prisons. A race riot broke out at San Quentin in 1967, and protests, riots, and killings occurred in other prisons. Corrections experts believed that a new approach was needed—one in which offenders were supervised in the community rather than imprisoned in fortresslike institutions.

Community-Based Era (1967–1980)

What emerged in the seventh era was community-based corrections. President Johnson's 1967 crime commission came to the conclusion that the community was a source of offenders' problems. Therefore, they thought it best to rehabilitate offenders by using community resources. Halfway houses, community corrections centers, intensive-supervision probation, work release centers, and the like quickly spread across the United States. However, observers discovered that the approach did not lower the crime rate, reduce the prison population, or make the community safer. The stage was set for more prison riots. In 1969, there were 39 riots in the nation's prisons. In 1970, there were 59 more. After four days of rioting in September 1971, 43 people were dead at Attica prison in New York, the largest number ever killed in a United States prison riot. With the goals of community corrections unmet, the community-based era gave way to the warehousing era.

Warehousing Era (1980–1995)

During the warehousing era, indeterminate sentencing gave way to determinate sentencing in all states. Parole release was abolished in a number of states and the federal government, and the pendulum swung from rehabilitation to incapacitation. Within 15 years, the number of persons under correctional supervision jumped from 1.8 million to almost 6 million. Prisons were over capacity, and controlling prisoners in such an environment was difficult. For staff and inmates alike, the nation's prisons were dangerous places to be. Extreme crowding resulted in violent disturbances, which further hardened the attitudes of correctional policy makers and caused them to crack down even more.

Just-Deserts Era (1995–Present)

The philosophy of just deserts, popular in the 18th century, returned. Under that philosophy, offenders are punished because they deserve it, and the sanction used depends on the seriousness of the offense. Just deserts is not concerned with inmate rehabilitation, treatment, or reform. It separates treatment from punishment. Prisons today provide opportunities for inmates to improve themselves, but participation is not mandatory, nor is it a condition of release, as it was for most of this century. Change is facilitated, not coerced. Determinate sentencing, capital punishment, truth in sentencing, and three-strikes laws have grown in popularity. As we move into the twenty-first century, "supermax" and no-frills prisons are becoming the trend.

Programs for Prisoners

Among the most important elements of an inmate's institutional experience, whether in federal or state prison, are the programs and services available. The American Correctional Association's policy on conditions of confinement advocates strong programs that meet offenders' needs (see Exhibit 7–1). The programs described in this section are classification, orientation, unit management, a daily routine, work assignments, education and recreation, medical and mental health services, and drug and alcohol treatment.

EXHIBIT 7–1

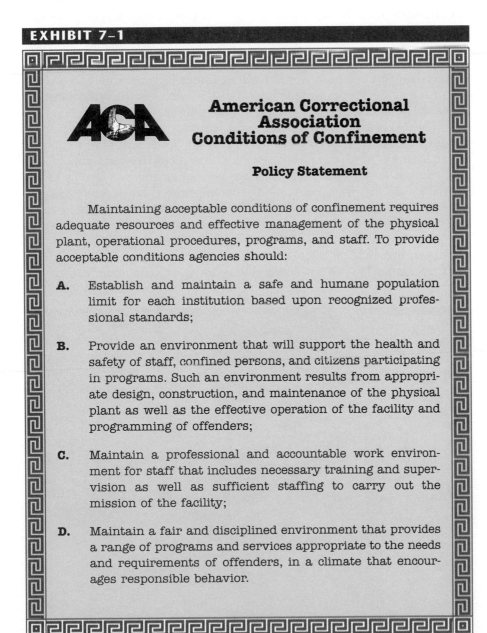

American Correctional Association Conditions of Confinement

Policy Statement

Maintaining acceptable conditions of confinement requires adequate resources and effective management of the physical plant, operational procedures, programs, and staff. To provide acceptable conditions agencies should:

A. Establish and maintain a safe and humane population limit for each institution based upon recognized professional standards;

B. Provide an environment that will support the health and safety of staff, confined persons, and citizens participating in programs. Such an environment results from appropriate design, construction, and maintenance of the physical plant as well as the effective operation of the facility and programming of offenders;

C. Maintain a professional and accountable work environment for staff that includes necessary training and supervision as well as sufficient staffing to carry out the mission of the facility;

D. Maintain a fair and disciplined environment that provides a range of programs and services appropriate to the needs and requirements of offenders, in a climate that encourages responsible behavior.

Student Involvement
Direct students to read the ACA policy on conditions of confinement. Ask them if they agree with the policy. What would they change? What would they add? What would they delete?

Classification

Prisoner classification is the process of subdividing the inmate population into meaningful categories to match offender needs with correctional resources. It is based on the premise that there are wide differences among prisoners. Its purpose is to assign inmates to appropriate prison housing and to help staff understand, treat, predict, and manage prisoner behavior. One hundred years ago, the Elmira Reformatory in Elmira, New York, classified offenders as "specimens" and labeled them "Mathematical Dullards," "Those Deficient in Self-Control," and "Stupid."[2] Today the classifications are more sophisticated. Still, the belief is that "somewhere between the extremes of 'all offenders are alike' and 'each offender is unique' lies a system (or systems) of categorization along pertinent dimensions that will prove to be of value in reaching correctional goals."[3] That is why not all persons who have killed others are in high-security prisons or on death row. Persons convicted of manslaughter generally are not placed under high security and are not sentenced to die. Proper prisoner classification considers the type of institution and the level of security that an offender needs.

The two broad goals of classification are: (1) to assign prisoners to institutions that match their security and program needs and (2) to enhance prison security. In reaching those goals, a clear, objective classification system offers at least four advantages over less systematic assignment.[4] First, separating inmates by risk level and program needs puts extremely aggressive inmates in high security while those who require less security or are at risk of being victimized are kept in low security. Within those levels of security, prisoners' needs can also be considered. Does the facility offer drug and alcohol treatment? Sex offender treatment? Anger management training? GED preparation? Such classification offers prisoners a chance for counseling,

Classification of incoming inmates is based on many factors, including medical and health-care needs, custody needs and institutional risk, work skills, and educational needs. Classification serves the custody goals of a prison but tends to label prisoners. Is such labeling appropriate?

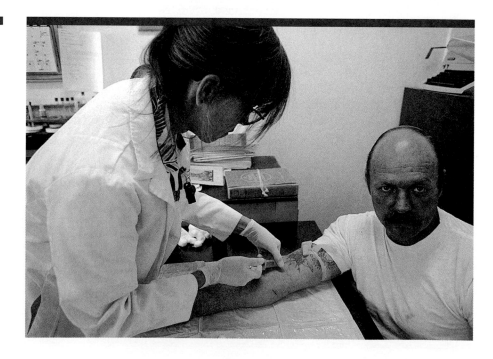

Prisons Today: Change Stations or Warehouses?

education, or vocational training, and it may keep aggressive inmates from assaulting passive inmates.

The second advantage of a good classification system is that it minimizes misclassification, thus promoting a safe environment for inmates and staff. For example, when prisons are over capacity, as they are today, staff feel pressure to classify inmates quickly. This results in misclassification. A good classification system will include safeguards against misclassification. For example, when there is not enough space in maximum-security facilities, the system will direct staff to house only the lowest-risk high-security inmates in medium-security facilities and never to house high-risk inmates in minimum-security units.

The third advantage a good classification system has for enhancing prison security is that it more accurately places inmates and more effectively deploys staff. Without good classification, the tendency is to place inmates in more secure, more expensive prisons than necessary. Good classification controls the inmate population, assigns inmates to appropriate security levels, and allows better deployment of staff. That results in better use of all resources.

The final way a clear classification system enhances prison security is by reducing tension in prison. For example, misclassification can jeopardize a prison's security and increase violence and escapes. Whether high-risk offenders are housed in low-risk prisons not capable of controlling their behavior or low-risk prisoners are housed in high-risk prisons not capable of protecting them, tension, violence, and the number of escapes mount. Good classification helps to reduce these problems. A review of the major developments and trends in prisoner classification over a recent 20-year period found significant improvement in classification technology (for example, computer software to help collect, store, and manage the data) and more sophisticated assessment of risk and of such needs as medical and mental health treatment and education.[5]

Factors commonly used in inmate classification include offense severity, history of escape or violence, expected length of incarceration, and types of prior commitments to correctional facilities. In a number of jurisdictions, including the federal Bureau of Prisons (BOP), additional public safety considerations require increased security measures to ensure the protection of society from certain offenders. These include sex offenders and offenders convicted of the most brutal crimes.

Orientation to the Institution

State and federal prison systems use a standard approach to managing offenders after they are committed to the correctional institution by the court. For the first week or two at an institution, inmates participate in an admission and orientation program. It provides an introduction to all aspects of the institution and includes screening by staff from the case management, medical, and mental health units. Inmates receive copies of the institution's rules and regulations, including the inmate discipline policy, and they are introduced to the programs, services, policies, and procedures of the facility.

Corrections Officer
Medium-security adult correctional facility is seeking qualified individuals for several positions. Shift work. Degree or 2 years' experience in corrections, criminal justice, probation, parole, or law enforcement required. Must be at least 21 years old, possess a valid driver's license, and pass a criminal background check. Duties include monitoring client activities, report writing, filing. Computer skills and prior experience working with offender population desirable. Pay based on experience and education.

Student Involvement
To illustrate the importance of giving inmates a proper orientation, point out that inmates will spend 24 regimented hours a day for years in the institution, and ask students to tell what their first days and weeks on campus were like. Did a structured college orientation system help in that transition? If so, how? If any students did not go through orientation, did they find college life more confusing than those who did? What does this tell them about the importance of a proper orientation to prison?

Prisons Today: Change Stations or Warehouses?

Unit Management

After orientation, each inmate is assigned living quarters. The institution's security level and the inmate's custody status determine whether the inmate will be housed in a single or double cell, a dormitory, or some other multiple-occupant room. In the federal system and in a number of states, prisons use a **unit management system**. A unit is a self-contained inmate living area that includes office space for unit staff, so staff and inmates are accessible to each other. The unit team—typically composed of the unit manager, one or more case managers, two or more correctional counselors, and a unit secretary—is directly responsible for the inmates living in that unit.

After the initial orientation, each inmate meets with the unit team to formulate a program plan, which may include drug treatment, education, and vocational training as well as institution maintenance jobs or other work assignments. The unit team reviews the inmate's progress and makes changes in the program plan as needed. Unit management emphasizes candid, open communication between staff and inmates. Direct and frequent communication helps staff know inmates, understand their needs, and respond appropriately to those needs. In prison systems without unit management, program planning and staff and inmate interaction are not encouraged.

Daily Routine

A typical prison day begins with breakfast at 6:30 A.M. For inmates with prison jobs, work begins about 7:30. By this time, inmates are expected to have cleaned their personal living areas and made their beds. After work and the evening meal, inmates may participate in organized or individual recreation, watch television, or engage in personal hobbies. In most prisons, inmates must remain in their quarters after the 10 P.M. count. The weekend and holiday routines are somewhat more relaxed for all inmates.

Prisons regularly count inmates to ensure that all are where they are supposed to be. How often inmates are counted varies considerably. In some prisons, formal inmate counts are taken five times a day, including a morning count at 6, an afternoon count at 4, and three counts between 10 P.M. and morning. Informal counts may be conducted in program areas at various times during the day, to ensure that inmates are in the proper place. Emergency counts may be held at any time. On weekends and holidays, when routines are more relaxed, counts are still made.

Work Assignments

Work is a very important part of institutional management and offender programs. Meaningful work programs are the most powerful tool prison administrators have in managing crowding and idleness, which can lead to disorder and violence.

Many states operate prison industries to employ and train inmates. Prison administrators believe the training-oriented work helps inmates return to society as useful, productive citizens. The prison industries provide a variety of goods and services for the prisons, thereby reducing the costs of

PRIDE Enterprises of Florida is a unique business. Its mission is to train inmate workers and create job opportunities, which will be strengthened by the establishment of a variety of industries under the Prison Industry Enhancement (PIE) program. PRIDE is chartering a process to ensure the integrity of the present PRIDE operation, while at the same time providing a structure to expand PIE industries. In 1998, PRIDE trained a total of 4,870 inmate workers, surpassing the previous year's total. With 4,321,548 hours worked, this nontraditional workforce is helping to increase productivity and keep jobs in America that might otherwise go offshore. Inmate workers represent a skilled and dependable workforce in today's tight labor market and a ready human resource for private-sector partners. PRIDE alone, with sales of $81.2 million in fiscal 1998, contributed $1.5 million to the state of Florida, including $300,000 for victim restitution and $900,00 for on-the-job training and post-release job placement. An additional $1.9 million was paid in inmate compensation. Under the PIE program, PRIDE paid an additional $74,600 to help offset the myriad costs of crime and incarceration. Now in its eighteenth year of operation, PRIDE is also encouraged by the current national focus on the potential of inmate workers to become an asset to America's economy.

Pamela J. Davis
President and CEO
PRIDE Enterprises of Florida

prison operation, and offer high-quality products and services to businesses and individuals at substantial savings. Some U.S. corporations have entered partnerships with prisons to use inmate labor to manufacture products or to deliver information services. Inmates generally must undergo training after qualifying to participate in the employment program. Once employed, they must meet performance standards, just as they would if employed on the outside. In many instances, success in working while in prison leads to continued employment with the company after release.

Prison-based industries today include agriculture (29 states), manufacturing (49 states), public works (34 states), prison construction (14 states), and prison maintenance (all states).[6] Private companies generally take one of three approaches when partnering with prisons. The first is the **manpower model**, in which the prison's role is similar to that of a temporary personnel service. The company leases rather than employs the prison workforce. The second approach is the **employer model**. In this approach, the prison provides the company space in which to operate and a labor pool of inmates from which to hire. The company supervises employees and makes all decisions related to personnel, products, wages, and market sales. This is the most common model. The third approach is the **customer**

manpower model
An approach to private business partnerships with prisons in which the prison's role is similar to that of a temporary personnel service.

employer model The most common approach to private business partnerships with prisons. The prison provides a company space in which to operate and a labor pool from which to hire. The company supervises its inmate employees and makes all decisions.

Joint ventures between private companies and correctional agencies to operate prison industries offer opportunities for offenders to become gainfully employed and learn salable skills. Left: Female inmates at a correctional facility in Connecticut assemble electronic components. Right: An inmate at a correctional facility in Texas assembles parts for a computer firm. What valuable work habits does joint venture prison employment develop?

customer model An approach to private business partnerships with prisons. In this model, a company contracts with a correctional institution to provide a finished product at an agreed-upon price. The correctional institution owns and operates the business that employs the inmate workforce.

model, in which a company contracts with a correctional institution to provide a finished product at an agreed-upon price. In the customer model, the correctional institution owns and operates the business that employs the inmate workforce. For example, the Hennepin County Adult Correctional Facility in Minnesota operates a job shop employing 50 inmates. The shop provides a variety of light assembly, sorting, packaging, and warranty repair services for dozens of private firms in the Minneapolis–St. Paul area.

The benefits of prison industries are many. For companies, inmates represent a readily available and dependable source of entry-level labor, a cost-effective alternative to foreign work forces. Corrections administrators report that joint ventures provide meaningful, productive employment that helps reduce inmate idleness, a common cause of prison disruptions. Prison employment can also motivate positive inmate behavior and good work habits. Inmates benefit by developing valuable work habits, which may reduce the chances of returning to a life of crime. Many others benefit from inmate employment. Deductions from inmates' wages offset the cost of the inmates' incarceration, increase federal and state tax revenues, fund victim compensation, and support inmates' families.

In the federal prison system, Federal Prison Industries, Inc., employs approximately 15 percent (18,000) of the inmate population. Better known by its trade name, UNICOR, it is a self-supporting corporation owned by the federal government and overseen by a governing board appointed by the President. Its mission is to employ and train inmates by operating factories. In 1998, its gross sales were $534.3 million, and its net profit was $2.4 million.[7] UNICOR products include electronic cable assemblies, executive and systems furniture (it ranks ninth in the United States), metal pallet racks, stainless steel food service equipment, mattresses, towels, utility bags, and brooms. UNICOR also provides services, such as data entry, sign making, and printing. To ensure that UNICOR does not compete unfairly with the private sector, product guidelines require a public announcement and a hearing process for any new product it proposes.

Student Involvement
Have a group of interested students research the prison-based industries in your state. As part of their report to the class, students may wish to display some prison-made products.

Inmates employed by UNICOR start out earning 23 cents per hour. The maximum wage is $1.15 per hour. Although wages are low in most prison industry programs, most inmates who work in them are more interested in doing something meaningful that keeps them busy and makes serving time seem to go faster. In many cases, prisoners also learn job skills and have a better chance of staying crime-free after release.

Education and Recreation Programs

The majority of prisoners cannot read or write well enough to function in society. In fact, the illiteracy rate among prisoners is 3½ times that in the U.S. adult population. Only 38 percent of the 1.3 million state and federal prisoners have completed high school, GED, or above.[8] That's a prisoner illiteracy rate of 62 percent! In comparison, 82 percent of the U.S. adult population have completed high school, GED, or above, and only 18 percent cannot read or write at the high school level.[9] States vary considerably in the education and recreation programs they provide for prisoners. For inmates without a high school diploma, some states provide adult basic education or GED classes. Some states offer academic and life skills programs. Other states form alliances with colleges to provide college-level educational opportunities for inmates.

Each federal prison has an education department which is responsible for providing literacy programs and other education programs for prisoners. Generally, at minimum-security federal institutions, only literacy programs are offered. At higher-security facilities, a broader range of programs is usually provided. Literacy is the only mandatory education program in the fed-

Many state correctional systems channel prison labor into industrial and commercial programs. One such program is the Prison Blues® brand of jeans, tee shirts, work shirts, and yard coats manufactured by Inside Oregon Enterprises, a division of the Oregon Department of Corrections. What benefits to inmates do such work programs provide?

Professional Issue
Inmate Work Experience
Corrections professionals often face opposition from community and labor groups when they advocate meaningful prisoner work experiences. Invite some students to role-play a panel of corrections officials asking a committee of skeptical legislators to approve legislation permitting a computer company to train inmates in the design, manufacture, and marketing of computer game software. The software would draw on prisoners' knowledge of crime for interactive detective, crime, mystery, and adventure games.

Student Involvement
Remind students that the majority of prisoners cannot read or write well enough to function in society. Ask students how such functional illiteracy can lead to criminal behavior as well as impede rehabilitation.

Teaching Tip

Point out that prison recreation programs have two functions: (1) Prisoners meet with others who share their interests and abilities and form positive social contacts; (2) prisoners learn social skills such as cooperation and teamwork.

eral prison system. It is required by statute for all federal prisoners who are functionally illiterate. Non-English-speaking inmates are required to participate in an English-as-a-second-language program until they are able to function at the eighth-grade level. Inmates who do not have a GED or a high school diploma are required by BOP policy to enroll in an adult literacy program for 120 days.

Occupational training is also provided in a wide variety of areas but is often limited to a few inmates. In addition to the occupational training that inmates receive by working in prison industries, some inmates receive training in building construction, heating and air-conditioning, auto mechanics, computer-assisted drafting, electronics, food preparation, and business education.

Although the number of inmates who can participate in occupational training is limited, all inmates are entitled to some form of recreation. Recreation and organized sports can make doing time more bearable and, as a result, make the jobs of correctional officers easier. They can also be used as an incentive for good behavior, and by reducing tension, they can cut the number of prison assaults. Physical and mental health experts tell us that recreation programs can be a vehicle for teaching ways to promote health and prevent disease. Inmates who play hard are more likely to stay fit, possibly reducing health costs. Nutrition experts know that eating healthful food, having a regular exercise program, and stopping smoking are central to maintaining good health in prison. They also reduce the cost of prison medical care.

Medical and Mental Health Services

Prisons vary in the way they provide medical and mental health services. In Oregon, for example, prison medical and mental health professionals are state employees. Georgia, on the other hand, contracts for services with local medical and mental health care providers. Interest in contracting for individual services is growing.

Ordinarily, inmates who are sick are required to make an appointment and get an appointment slip. If an illness occurs after hours, prison staff evaluate the situation and decide whether to seek emergency care. In most prisons, medication is dispensed at a specific location during specified periods. Staff watch while inmates take their medication, to guard against the hoarding of medication for sale or for a possible suicide attempt and to make sure prisoners are taking the medication they need.

Inmates with special health care needs (such as aging and HIV/AIDS) are treated differently in different jurisdictions. Some states segregate HIV-positive prisoners. The federal system provides treatment for HIV-positive inmates through outpatient clinics, inpatient hospitals, and prison hospice programs, emphasizing education, not segregation.

Typical mental health services include initial testing and evaluation, crisis intervention counseling, individual and group therapy, drug and alcohol dependency counseling and awareness, psychological and psychiatric counseling, employment counseling, life skills and community adjustment

THE OFFENDER SPEAKS

I was on my unit doing nothing—gambling and talking slick and hustling inside the institution—the same things I did on the outside, and I got tired of it. So when my friend enrolled in the Life Skills Program, which teaches reading, math, anger management, ways to reduce violence, and life skills like credit and banking, job search, and legal and family responsibilities, I decided to enroll. It broke the monotony of prison—gave me structure. The *Cage Your Rage* book and videos and acting out prison scenes—for example, someone knocking over your cup of coffee—helped me deal with my anger. I used to get angry if someone on the basketball court called a foul. The program taught me a different perspective: considering the consequences of my actions.

A released program graduate
Life Skills Program
Delaware Department of Correction

---

counseling, parent training, and suicide prevention. Inmates judged criminally insane and those suffering from severe mental illness are sometimes cared for in specialized facilities.

Providing inmates adequate health care is of concern to the courts and professional associations. In 1976, the U.S. Supreme Court ruled in *Estelle v. Gamble*[10] that inmates have a constitutional right to reasonable, adequate health services for serious medical needs. However, the Court also made clear that such a right did not mean that prisoners have unqualified access to health care. Lower courts have held that the Constitution does not require the medical care provided prisoners to be perfect, the best obtainable, or even very good.[11] According to an excellent review of legal health care standards and the legal remedies available to prisoners, the courts support the **principle of least eligibility**: that prison conditions—including the delivery of health care—must be a step below those of the working class and people on welfare. As a result, prisoners are denied access to medical specialists, second opinions, prompt delivery of medical services, technologically advanced diagnostic techniques, the latest medications, and up-to-date medical procedures. In addition, prisoners do not have the right to sue physicians for malpractice, or if they do, the damages are lower than those awarded to persons outside prison. Still, health care professionals and inmate advocates—such as the American Medical Association and the American Correctional Health Services Association—insist on alleviating the pain and suffering of all persons, regardless of their status. They believe that no distinction should be made between inmates and free citizens.

Student Involvement
Invite students to explain the principle of least eligibility. Then ask them to contrast that principle with the AMA and ACHSA's position that the quality of medical care should not hinge on whether the patient is a prisoner or a free citizen.

principle of least eligibility The requirement that prison conditions—including the delivery of health care—must be a step below those of the working class and people on welfare.

Drug Treatment Programs

In most prisons today, the percentage of prisoners who are drug offenders is increasing significantly. Officials estimate that 70 to 85 percent of prison inmates need some sort of substance abuse treatment.[12] Drug and alcohol treatment should be particularly important in prison because it is generally accepted that it reduces recidivism. Drug treatment is not guaranteed, and when offered, it is not always of high quality. Most state institutions do not have the staff or the resources to provide treatment to every inmate who needs it. In 1996, only 13 percent of state inmates and 10 percent of federal inmates were in treatment. It is estimated that of the 60 percent of prisoners serving sentences for drug offenses, about one-third have moderate to severe substance abuse problems that urgently need care. Furthermore, as the number of inmates in need of treatment has risen, the proportion receiving treatment has declined.[13]

Recently the BOP evaluated its drug abuse treatment program. The inmates in the evaluation had been released into the community for 6 to 12 months after completing a three-stage treatment program. In the first stage, inmates participated in a residential drug abuse treatment program for 9 or 12 months. Inmates continued the treatment up to 12 more months after they returned to the general prison population. Treatment continued with community drug treatment providers in a community residential center during a transition from prison to parole. The offenders who had completed the program were found less likely to be re-arrested or to be caught using drugs again than were similar offenders who had not participated in the program.[14] Because previous research had indicated that the first 6 to 12 months after release are often a critical period for an offender, the results of this evaluation suggest that drug treatment can improve the lives of offenders and reduce recidivism.

Who Is in Prison Today?

On January 1, 1999, 1,302,019 adults were in the custody of state and federal prison authorities—123,041 in federal prisons, 1,178,978 in state prisons.[15] This is an increase of 4.8 percent from one year earlier, less than the average annual increase of 6.9 percent for every year since 1990. At the start of 1999, approximately 461 persons per 100,000 U.S. residents were incarcerated in a state or federal prison. California had the most inmates (161,904); North Dakota had the fewest (915). See Table 7–1.

States with almost identical populations and crime rates have widely different rates of incarceration. For example, in 1998, Alabama had a population of 4.3 million residents, a crime rate of 4,889 offenses per 100,000 population,[16] and an incarceration rate of 519 per 100,000. Minnesota had 4.3 million residents, a crime rate of 4,413 offenses per 100,000 population, and an incarceration rate of only 117 per 100,000 population. With similar population and crime rates, Alabama's incarceration rate was four times Minnesota's! The difference in rates reflects differences in the way the states use prison. It shows that a state's prison population is not related to the size of its total population or to its crime rate. Rather, a large prison population is a result of a conscious choice to use prison to punish offenders.

Prisons Today: Change Stations or Warehouses?

TABLE 7–1

Prison Statistics Among the States and the Federal Government in 1998

	Number of Inmates		Incarceration Rate per 100,000 State Residents		Number of Female Prisoners	
Ten Highest	California	161,904	Louisiana	736	California	11,694
	Texas	144,510	Texas	724	Texas	10,343
	Federal	123,041	Oklahoma	622	Federal	9,186
	New York	72,638	Mississippi	574	New York	3,631
	Florida	67,224	South Carolina	550	Florida	3,526
	Ohio	48,450	Nevada	542	Ohio	2,912
	Michigan	45,879	Alabama	519	Illinois	2,646
	Illinois	43,051	Arizona	507	Georgia	2,474
	Georgia	39,252	Georgia	502	Louisiana	2,126
	Pennsylvania	36,377	California	483	Oklahoma	2,091
Ten Lowest	North Dakota	915	Minnesota	117	Vermont	45
	Vermont	1,426	Maine	125	Maine	63
	Wyoming	1,571	North Dakota	128	North Dakota	69
	Maine	1,612	New Hampshire	182	New Hampshire	116
	New Hampshire	2,169	Vermont	188	Wyoming	131
	South Dakota	2,435	West Virginia	192	South Dakota	202
	Montana	2,734	Utah	205	West Virginia	211
	West Virginia	3,445	Nebraska	215	Rhode Island	235
	Rhode Island	3,478	Rhode Island	220	Montana	248
	Nebraska	3,676	Washington	247	Nebraska	254

Source: Adapted from Allen J. Beck and Christopher J. Mumola, *Prisoners in 1998* (Washington: Bureau of Justice Statistics, August 1999).

Women Prisoners

Over the past decade, the number of women in prison has tripled while the number of men has doubled. On January 1, 1999, women prisoners constituted 6.5 percent (84,427) of the U.S. prison population. (See Figure 7–2.) The rate of incarceration for women was 57 per 100,000 female residents, compared with 885 males per 100,000 male residents. See Table 7–1 for the states with the highest and lowest female prison populations.

Minority Prisoners

The percentage of state and federal prisoners that belong to minority groups has been increasing. From 1990 to 1997, the percentage of black, Hispanic (of any race), American Indian, Alaska Native, and Asian/Pacific Islander inmates increased from 50 percent to 52 percent. If recent incarceration rates remain unchanged, it is estimated that 1 person out of every 20 will serve time in prison during his or her lifetime. The lifetime chances are

Student Involvement
Refer students to Table 7–1. If your state is listed, ask students to note where it stands in comparison with other states. If your state is not represented, invite interested students to research your state's prison population and report the results to the class.

FIGURE 7–2

Persons Held in State or Federal Prisons

How Many Are in Prison?

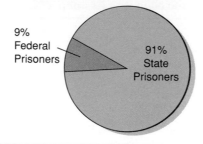
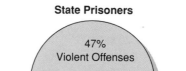

9% Federal Prisoners

91% State Prisoners

1,178,978 State Prisoners
123,041 Federal Prisoners
1,302,019 Total

Who Is in Prison?

Gender

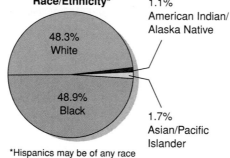

6.5% Women

93.5% Men

Race/Ethnicity*

48.3% White

48.9% Black

1.1% American Indian/ Alaska Native

1.7% Asian/Pacific Islander

*Hispanics may be of any race

Age

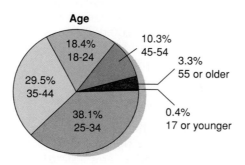

18.4% 18-24

10.3% 45-54

3.3% 55 or older

29.5% 35-44

38.1% 25-34

0.4% 17 or younger

Why Are They in Prison?

State Prisoners

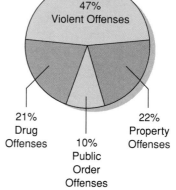

47% Violent Offenses

21% Drug Offenses

10% Public Order Offenses

22% Property Offenses

Federal Prisoners

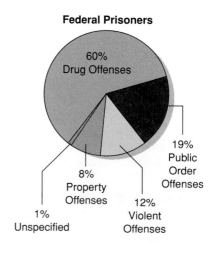

60% Drug Offenses

19% Public Order Offenses

8% Property Offenses

12% Violent Offenses

1% Unspecified

Source: Allen J. Beck and Christopher J. Mumola, *Prisoners in 1998* (Washington: Bureau of Justice Statistics, August 1999).

Prisons Today: Change Stations or Warehouses?

higher for men (9%) than for women (1%) and higher for blacks (16%) and Hispanics (9%) than for whites (2%). Newborn black males in the United States have a chance greater than 1 in 4 of going to prison during their lifetimes, while Hispanic males have a 1-in-6 chance, and white males have a 1-in-23 chance.[17]

Age

The nation's population is aging, and this is reflected in the prison population. Middle-aged inmates make up a growing portion of the prison population. In 1991, 65.2 percent of the nation's prisoners were between 18 and 34 years old, and 23 percent were between 35 and 44. In 1998, 18-to-34-year-olds had decreased to 56.5 percent while 35-to-44-year-olds had increased to 29.5 percent. The percentage of inmates 55 and older remained about 3 percent. (See Figure 7–2).

Most Serious Offense

Another characteristic to compare is the most serious offense of which a prisoner was convicted. Most state inmates (47%) are in prison for violent offenses; most federal inmates (60%), for drug offenses. Figure 7–2 shows the breakdown for other offenses.

Prison Organization and Administration

All 50 states and the BOP operate prisons. In addition, four local jurisdictions in the United States operate prison systems: Cook County (Chicago), Illinois; Philadelphia; New York City; and Washington, D.C. In 1995, the last year for which data are available, there were 1196 state and federal prisons.[18] Of those, 1008 housed only males, 104 housed only females, and 84 housed both.

Jurisdictions use a variety of capacity measures to reflect both the space available to house inmates and the ability to staff and operate an institution. Some use **rated capacity**, the number of beds or inmates a rating official has assigned to an institution. Some use **operational capacity**, the number of inmates that a facility's staff, existing programs, and services can accommodate. Others use **design capacity**, the number of inmates that planners or architects intended for the facility. For instance, an architect might design a prison for 1100 inmates. Administrators might add more staff, programs, and services to be able to confine 1300 in the same space. The design capacity was 1100, but the operational and rated capacities are 1300. The institution is operating 18 percent above design capacity.

rated capacity A measure of prison capacity. It is the number of beds or inmates a rating official has assigned to a prison.

operational capacity A measure of prison capacity. It is the number of inmates that a facility's staff, existing programs, and services can accommodate.

design capacity A measure of prison capacity. It is the number of inmates that planners or architects intended for the facility.

State Prison Systems

The administration of state prisons today is a function of the executive branch of government. The governor appoints the director of corrections,

maximum-security prison A prison designed, organized, and staffed to confine the most dangerous offenders for long periods. It has a highly secure perimeter, barred cells, and a high staff-to-inmate ratio. It imposes strict controls on the movement of inmates and visitors, and it offers few programs, amenities, or privileges.

minimum-security prison A prison that confines the least dangerous offenders for both short and long periods. It allows as much freedom of movement and as many privileges and amenities as are consistent with the goals of the facility, while still following procedures to avoid escape, violence, and disturbance. It may have dormitory housing, and the staff-to-inmate ratio is relatively low.

open institution A minimum-security facility that has no fences or walls surrounding it.

who in turn appoints the wardens of the state prisons. A change in governors often means a change in state prison leadership and administration. The organizational structure of the Ohio Department of Rehabilitation and Corrections, which is similar to the structure of corrections departments in other states, is shown in Figure 7–3.

The organization of most state prison systems, like Ohio's, is around a central authority, based in the state capital. Local communities, private contractors, or the state itself may provide prison services (from treatment and education to maintenance and repair). This method of organizational structure and delivery of services across wide geographical areas is often criticized for its fragmentation; duplication of structure, effort, and services; lack of coordination; and ambiguous goals. Still, for legal control and for maintaining an equitable distribution of resources, a centralized model has been maintained, while in other areas of corrections (for example, community corrections and probation) services are often decentralized.

There is no correct way to organize corrections. Any arrangement that helps corrections reach its goals is appropriate. The organizational styles found across the United States developed over time and are the result of political interaction and accommodation among government agencies and interest groups. Today, prisons borrow consumer-oriented management techniques from private businesses. They periodically survey staff and inmates to identify problems and avoid confrontations. Technological improvements allow prison administrators access to more information for decision making, and management training is more popular.

State prison organizations vary in size.[19] The smallest is North Dakota's, with slightly more than 200 employees and an annual budget of $732.4 million for all adult corrections (including probation, intermediate sanctions, prison, and parole). The largest is California's, with almost 35,000 employees and an annual operating budget of $3.6 billion.

Prisons are classified by the level of security they provide. A **maximum-security prison** is designed, organized, and staffed to confine the most violent and dangerous offenders for long periods. It imposes strict controls on the movement of inmates and their visitors, and custody and security are constant concerns. The prison has a highly secure perimeter with watchtowers and high walls. Inmates live in single- or multiple-occupancy barred cells. The staff-to-inmate ratio is high, routines are highly regimented, and prisoner counts are frequent. Programs, amenities, and privileges are few. More than half of the 298 maximum security prisons in the United States held 1,000 inmates or more apiece in 1995.

A **minimum-security prison** confines the least dangerous offenders for both short and long periods. It allows as much freedom of movement and as many privileges and amenities as are consistent with the goals of the facility, while still following procedures to avoid escape, violence, and disturbance. The staff-to-inmate ratio is low, and inmates live in dormitory housing or private rooms. Some leave the institution for programming in the community. About 80 percent of the 440 minimum-security prisons in the United States held fewer than 500 prisoners each in 1995. Prison farms and camps are minimum-security institutions. They are sometimes referred to as **open institutions** because they have no fences or walls surrounding them.

FIGURE 7–3

Ohio Department of Rehabilitation and Corrections

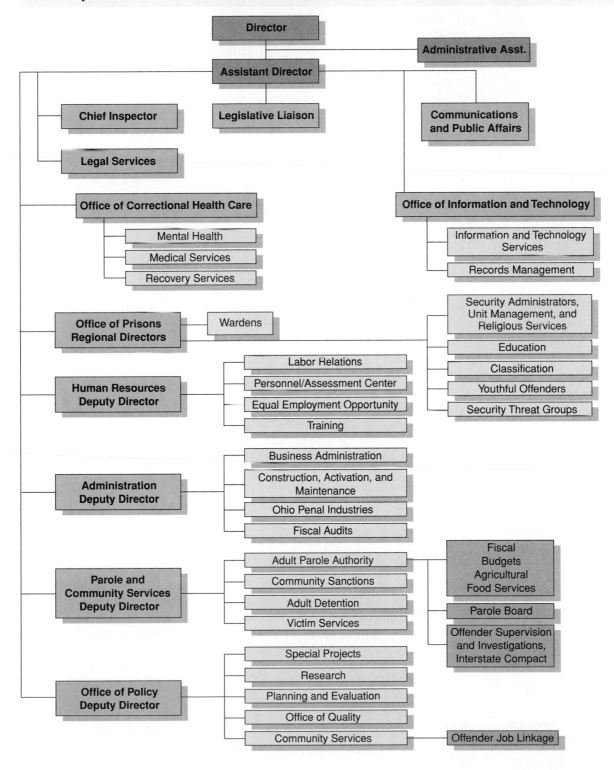

medium-security prison A prison that confines offenders considered less dangerous than those in maximum security, for both short and long periods. It is also designed, organized, and staffed to prevent violence, escape, and disturbance but places fewer controls on inmates' and visitors' freedom of movement than a maximum-security facility. It, too, has barred cells and a fortified perimeter. The staff-to-inmate ratio is generally lower than in a maximum-security facility, and the level of amenities and privileges is slightly higher.

Inmates in a **medium-security prison** are considered less dangerous than those in maximum security and may serve short or long sentences. Medium-security prisons impose fewer controls on inmates' and visitors' freedom of movement than maximum-security facilities. Outwardly, medium-security prisons often resemble maximum-security institutions, and they, too, have barred cells. The staff-to-inmate ratio is higher than minimum-security facilities. Medium-security prisons place more emphasis on treatment and work programs than maximum-security prisons, and the level of amenities and privileges is slightly higher. In 1995, 25 percent of the men's prisons were maximum-security. The rest was split between medium- and minimum-security. There are fewer maximum-security and more minimum-security prisons for women: 19 percent maximum-security, 35 percent medium-security, and 46 percent minimum-security.

Prisons are expensive. Besides the cost of building a prison, there are also annual operating costs. In the same way it took money to build the classroom you're in, it takes money each year to operate it (pay for electricity, heat, air conditioning, supplies, building maintenance and upgrading, teachers' salaries, etc.). In 1996, the states spent $22 billion for adult prisons—to build, staff, and maintain the facilities and to house the prisoners. The federal BOP spent an additional $2.5 billion.[20] Approximately $20.7 billion, or 96 percent of state prison expenditures in 1996, went for salaries, wages, benefits, and other operating expenses. Average inmate cost in 1996 was $20,100.

Federal Bureau of Prisons

Teaching Tip
Refer students to Figure 7-4, the organization of the BOP. After students have briefly studied the figure, ask them to review the mission statement of the BOP in Exhibit 1–2 on page 27. Do students think that the organization of the BOP makes it possible to implement its mission statement?

The BOP is an entirely separate system from state and local prison systems. The mission of the BOP is "to protect society by confining offenders in the controlled environments of prison and community-based facilities that are safe, humane, and appropriately secure, and that provide work and other self-improvement opportunities to assist offenders in becoming law-abiding citizens."[21] The central office in Washington, D.C., 6 regional offices, 2 training centers, and 93 correctional institutions carry out the BOP mission. The BOP also houses the National Institute of Corrections (NIC) which advises and assists state and local correctional agencies throughout the country, primarily through technical assistance, training, and information services. The Attorney General appoints the director of the BOP. Kathleen Hawk Sawyer, the first woman to hold the position of director, was appointed in 1992. The BOP organizational chart is shown in Figure 7–4.

The BOP employs more than 30,900 people nationwide. Its budget for 1999 was $3.3 billion. The largest portion, $1.48 billion, was for institution security and administration, including the costs of facility maintenance, motor pool operations, powerhouse operations, institution security, and other administrative functions for all BOP facilities. The second-highest cost was $1.18 billion for inmate care and programs. This included all food, medical supplies, clothing, welfare services, release clothing, transportation, staff salaries, and the costs of academic courses, social and occupational education courses, religious programs, psychological services, and drug abuse treatment.

FIGURE 7–4

Organization of Federal Bureau of Prisons

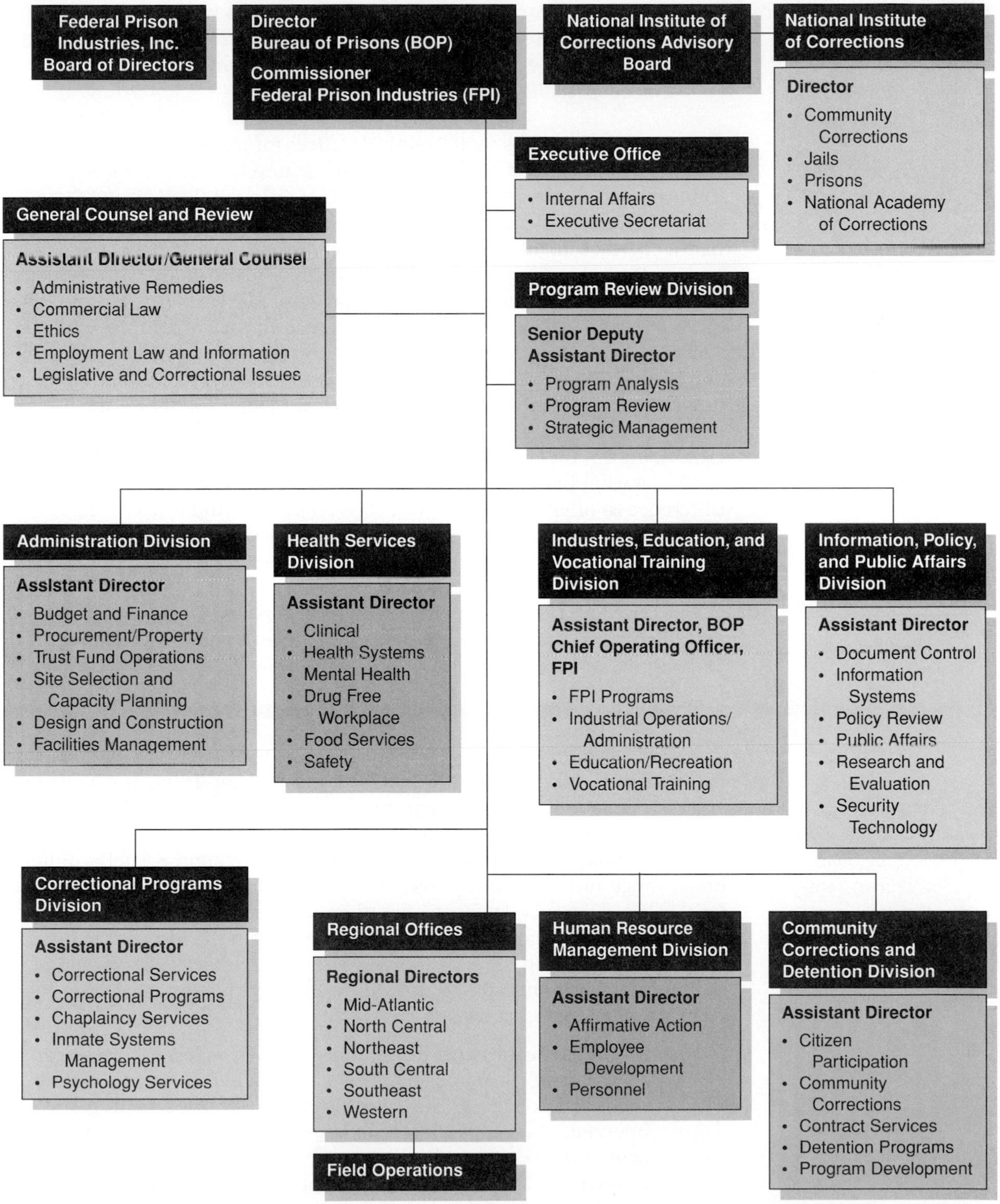

Federal Prison Industries, Inc. Board of Directors

Director Bureau of Prisons (BOP)

Commissioner Federal Prison Industries (FPI)

National Institute of Corrections Advisory Board

National Institute of Corrections

Director
- Community Corrections
- Jails
- Prisons
- National Academy of Corrections

Executive Office
- Internal Affairs
- Executive Secretariat

General Counsel and Review

Assistant Director/General Counsel
- Administrative Remedies
- Commercial Law
- Ethics
- Employment Law and Information
- Legislative and Correctional Issues

Program Review Division

Senior Deputy Assistant Director
- Program Analysis
- Program Review
- Strategic Management

Administration Division

Assistant Director
- Budget and Finance
- Procurement/Property
- Trust Fund Operations
- Site Selection and Capacity Planning
- Design and Construction
- Facilities Management

Health Services Division

Assistant Director
- Clinical
- Health Systems
- Mental Health
- Drug Free Workplace
- Food Services
- Safety

Industries, Education, and Vocational Training Division

Assistant Director, BOP Chief Operating Officer, FPI
- FPI Programs
- Industrial Operations/ Administration
- Education/Recreation
- Vocational Training

Information, Policy, and Public Affairs Division

Assistant Director
- Document Control
- Information Systems
- Policy Review
- Public Affairs
- Research and Evaluation
- Security Technology

Correctional Programs Division

Assistant Director
- Correctional Services
- Correctional Programs
- Chaplaincy Services
- Inmate Systems Management
- Psychology Services

Regional Offices

Regional Directors
- Mid-Atlantic
- North Central
- Northeast
- South Central
- Southeast
- Western

Field Operations

Human Resource Management Division

Assistant Director
- Affirmative Action
- Employee Development
- Personnel

Community Corrections and Detention Division

Assistant Director
- Citizen Participation
- Community Corrections
- Contract Services
- Detention Programs
- Program Development

Rachel Beverly
Staff Training Officer
Arizona Department of
Corrections

"You have to be very inquisitive. You have to know a lot about people. You have to be a good communicator. You especially have to be a good listener and develop training programs that adapt to the evolving challenges in the field."

Rachel Beverly is Staff Training Officer for the Arizona Department of Corrections. She plans the statewide corrections staff training curriculum and coordinates staff training at the Arizona State Prison in Yuma. She joined the department in 1996. Previously, she had worked as an adult probation officer and a jail case manager.

Rachel received her bachelor's degree in criminal justice from California State University at San Bernardino. She feels that a number of undergraduate courses helped her succeed in the corrections field. Constitutional law gave her an appreciation for the ethical issues in corrections. Procedural law gave her an understanding of offenders' due process safeguards. And criminological theory led her to understand that the causes of criminal behavior are complex. She says that criminological theory was "a real challenge."

Rachel believes that careers in corrections can really make a difference in offenders' lives. As a corrections training officer, she believes that her work has additional influences, because she has the opportunity to develop a curriculum that influences the way staff throughout the state interact with inmates.

In the future, Rachel hopes to move forward in corrections administration, possibly doing corrections research and influencing correctional policy.

Professional issue

Employment in the BOP If a BOP facility, regional office, or training center is nearby, invite a representative to talk with your students about careers with the BOP.

Institutions and Security Level At the start of 1999, the BOP held 123,041 inmates (of whom approximately 14,500 were held in privately managed prisons or facilities under contract with the BOP). The BOP operates institutions of several different security levels to appropriately confine a broad range of federal offenders. The classification of facilities by security level is based on such factors as the presence of gun towers, security barriers, or detection devices; the types of housing within the institution; internal security features; and the staff-to-inmate ratio. Each facility is placed in one of five groups—minimum-security, low-security, medium-security, high-security, and administrative.

- Minimum-security institutions, also known as federal prison camps (FPCs), have dormitory housing, a relatively low staff-to-inmate ratio, and no fences. These institutions are work- and program-oriented. Many are adjacent to larger institutions or on military bases, where inmates help serve the labor needs of the institution or the base. There are 12 FPCs. Approximately 28 percent (30,391) of BOP inmates are in minimum-security facilities.

- Low-security federal correctional institutions (FCIs) have double-fenced perimeters, mostly dormitory housing, and strong work and program components. The staff-to-inmate ratio in these institutions is higher than in minimum-security facilities.
- Medium-security FCIs have fortified perimeters (often double fences with electronic detection systems), cell housing, and a wide variety of work and treatment programs. They have an even higher staff-to-inmate ratio than low-security FCIs, providing even greater internal controls. There are 47 low- and medium-security FCIs.
- High-security institutions, known as U.S. penitentiaries (USPs), have highly secure perimeters (featuring walls or reinforced fences), multiple- and single-occupancy cell housing, close staff supervision, and strict movement controls. There are 8 USPs.
- Administrative institutions have special missions, such as detention of noncitizens or pretrial offenders, treatment of inmates with serious or chronic medical problems, or containment of extremely dangerous or escape-prone inmates. There are 26 administrative institutions, holding inmates of all security categories. Figure 7–5 shows the locations of all BOP facilities.

As it moves into the twenty-first century, the BOP is planning 11 new facilities, including 5 low- and medium-security FCIs, 4 camps, 1 penitentiary, and 1 metropolitan detention center, to accommodate the expected growth in the federal inmate population.

FIGURE 7–5

Institutions of the Federal Bureau of Prisons

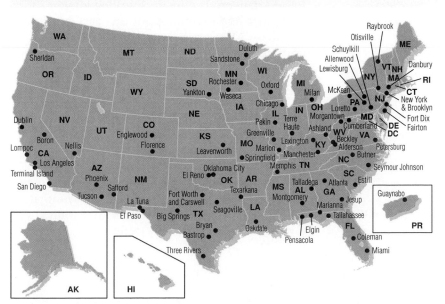

Source: U.S. Department of Justice, Federal Bureau of Prisons, *State of the Bureau: Accomplishments and Goals, Year-End, 1998* (Washington: U.S. Department of Justice, 1999), p. 23. Some locations have more than one institution.

Kathleen Hawk Sawyer, Director, Bureau of Prisons

Prisons Today: Change Stations or Warehouses?

7

Review and Applications

SUMMARY BY CHAPTER OBJECTIVES

CHAPTER OBJECTIVE 1

The Pennsylvania and Auburn prison systems emerged in the United States at the turn of the nineteenth century. The Pennsylvania system isolated prisoners from each other to avoid harmful influences and to allow prisoners to repent. The Auburn system allowed inmates to work together during the day under strict silence. At night, however, prisoners were isolated in small sleeping cells. With time, even sleeping cells became congregate.

CHAPTER OBJECTIVE 2

There have been nine eras in U.S. prison history:
- The Penitentiary Era (1790–1825)
- The Mass Prison Era (1825–1876)
- The Reformatory Era (1876–1890)
- The Industrial Era (1890–1935)
- The Punitive Era (1935–1945)
- The Treatment Era (1945–1967)
- The Community-Based Era (1967–1980)
- The Warehousing Era (1980–1995)
- The Just-Deserts Era (1995–Present)

CHAPTER OBJECTIVE 3

Offenders sentenced to prison are first classified into groups based on offense severity, expected length of incarceration, security risk, and program needs. The purpose is to assign inmates to appropriate prison housing and to help staff understand, treat, predict, and manage prisoner behavior.

CHAPTER OBJECTIVE 4

Programs for prisoners vary among state and federal systems. Prison systems generally offer education and recreation, medical and mental health services, drug abuse treatment, classification, orientation, unit management, daily routines, and work assignments.

CHAPTER OBJECTIVE 5

On January 1, 1999, 1,178,978 persons were in state prisons; 123,041 were in federal prisons. Of these state and federal inmates, 93.5 percent were male, 48.3 percent were white, and 48.9 percent were black.

CHAPTER OBJECTIVE 6

All 50 states, the Federal Bureau of Prisons (BOP), and four local jurisdictions operate prison systems. State prison administration, a function of the executive branch of government, is most often organized around a central authority, operating from the state capital. There are three levels of prison security: maximum, for the most dangerous offenders serving long sentences; medium, for less dangerous offenders serving long or short sentences; and minimum, for the least dangerous offenders. Most prisons are either medium- or minimum-security. The BOP operates 93 federal prisons. The BOP operates minimum-security prisons known as federal prison camps, low- and medium-security facilities known as federal correctional institutions, high-security institutions known as U.S. penitentiaries, and administrative institutions with special missions, such as detention of illegal immigrants, treatment of persons with chronic medical problems, and containment of extremely dangerous or escape-prone inmates. The majority of federal prisoners are confined in low- and medium-security facilities.

| *Prisons Today: Change Stations or Warehouses?*

QUESTIONS FOR REVIEW

1. Distinguish between the Pennsylvania and Auburn prison systems.
2. How and why did the penitentiary era begin?
3. What was the mass prison era?
4. Why did reformatories develop?
5. What were the characteristics of the first reformatories?
6. Why did industrial prisons develop?
7. Distinguish among the five models used to employ prisoners during the industrial era.
8. What caused the decline in prison industry?
9. What caused the punitive era to evolve?
10. Why did the treatment era begin?
11. What is the medical model?
12. What caused the end of the treatment era?
13. What was the reasoning behind the community-based approach?
14. Describe the warehousing era.
15. What is meant by *just deserts?*
16. What is classification, and what are the advantages of a clear, objective classification system?
17. What is unit management?
18. How are prisons partnering with private companies?
19. What purpose does recreation play in prison?
20. What is the principle of least eligibility? How does it affect prisoners?
21. Are drug treatment programs necessary in prisons? Why or why not?
22. Describe state and federal prison organization and administration.
23. Distinguish among maximum-, medium-, and minimum-security prisons.
24. What is the role of the federal Bureau of Prisons?

CRITICAL THINKING EXERCISES

ON-THE-JOB ISSUES

1. According to the Department of Corrections of the state of Washington, the operational capacity of its prisons is 12,966 prisoners.[22] (Recall that *operational capacity* means the number of inmates a facility's staff, programs, and services can accommodate.) If Washington currently incarcerates 14,454 prisoners, what percentage of operational capacity is the inmate population?

2. The state prison where you work as prison industry supervisor contracted with a pharmaceutical company to open an AIDS testing lab and employ 30 prisoners as laboratory technicians. Prisoners will be paid a maximum of one dollar an hour. The local newspaper is running a series of articles on prison industry and wants to interview you. What will you tell them about the advantages of prison industry?

CORRECTIONS ISSUES

1. Charles Dickens, the English novelist, visited Eastern State Penitentiary in 1842. After witnessing solitary confinement, he wrote that "very few men are capable of estimating the immense amount of torture and agony which this dreadful punishment, prolonged for years, inflicts upon the sufferers."[23] He added, "I hold this slow and daily tampering with the mysteries of the brain to be immeasurably worse than any torture of the body; and because its ghastly signs and tokens are not so palpable to the eye and sense of touch as scars upon the flesh . . . , I denounce it as secret punishment." Do you think Dickens's writing may have influenced reformers to seek other systems of punishment?

2. For 200 years prisons have tried to change inmates' negative behaviors. Recently, the BOP has said that prison is not the ideal setting to do that, nor is such change realistic in prison, considering prisoners' resistance and the failure of previous attempts. What realistic goals of prisons would you devise? What measures of outcome would you propose to tell if prisons are meeting those goals?

CORRECTIONS ON THE WEB

1. Go to the Justice Information Center at **www.ncjrs.org** or the Bureau of Justice Statistics at **www.ojp.usdoj.gov/bjs**. Review the documents to obtain sources of prisoner data from your state (for example, number and percentage of offenders in jail; numbers and percentages of women, minorities, and so on). Use the data to construct a pie-chart profile of the current prison population in your state.

2. Access the Web site of a state department of corrections. For example, the North Carolina Department of Correction has a site at **www.doc.state.nc.us/**. Review the topics available at the site. Possible topics include prisoners, programs, industries, employment, and administration. Select several topics related to the chapter content, and review the information provided. Then write a summary of what you learn.

ADDITIONAL READINGS

Branham, Lynn. *The Use of Incarceration in the United States: A Look at the Present and the Future*. Washington: American Bar Association, 1992.

Clements, Carl B. *Offender Needs Assessments*. College Park, MD: American Correctional Association, 1986.

McShane, Marilyn D., and Frank P. Williams III. *The Management of Correctional Institutions*. New York: Garland, 1993.

Sexton, George E. *Work in American Prisons: Joint Ventures with the Private Sector*. Washington: National Institute of Justice, 1995.

Sullivan, Larry E. *The Prison Reform Movement: Forlorn Hope*. Boston: Twayne, 1990.

Zimring, Franklin E., and Gordon Hawkins. *The Scale of Imprisonment*. Chicago: University of Chicago Press, 1991.

ENDNOTES

1. George E. Sexton, *Work in American Prisons: Joint Ventures with the Private Sector* (Washington: National Institute of Justice, 1995), pp. 2–3. Online, available: http://www. ncjrs.org/txtfiles/workampr.txt.

2. Carl B. Clements, "The Future of Offender Classification: Some Cautions and Prospects," *Criminal Justice and Behavior*, Vol. 8 (1981), pp. 15–16.

3. Carl B. Clements, "Offender Classification: Two Decades of Progress," *Criminal Justice and Behavior*, Vol. 23 (1996), p. 123.

4. James Austin, "Managing Facilities: Objective Offender Classification Is Key to Proper Housing Decisions," *Corrections Today*, Vol. 56, No. 4 (1994), pp. 94–97.

5. Carl B. Clements, "Offender Classification."

6. American Correctional Association, *Correctional Industries Information: Correctional Industries Survey Final Report* (Lanham, MD: American Correctional Association, 1992).

7. Cited in *Hoover's Online* at http://www.hoovers.com/capsules/43053.html on September 29, 1999.

8. Bureau of Justice Statistics, *National Corrections Reporting Programs* (Washington: U.S. Department of Justice, 1994), p. 12.

9. Bureau of the Census, *Statistical Abstract of the United States*, 1997 (Washington: U.S. Department of Commerce, 1997), p. 159.

10. *Estelle* v. *Gamble* 429 U.S. 97 (1976).

11. Michael S. Vaughn and Leo Carroll, "Separate and Unequal: Prison Versus Free-World Medical Care," *Justice Quarterly*, Vol. 15 (1998), pp. 3–40.

12. Center on Addiction and Substance Abuse, *Behind Bars: Substance Abuse and America's Prison Population* (New York: Columbia University, 1998). Online, available: http://www.casacolumbia.org.

13. Ibid.

14. Federal Bureau of Prisons, *Triad Drug Treatment Evaluation, Six-Month Report, Executive Summary* (Washington: Federal Bureau of Prisons, no date. Online, available: http://www.bop.gov/triad.html.

15. Allen J. Beck and Christopher J. Mumola, *Prisoners in 1998* (Washington: Bureau of Justice Statistics, August 1999).

16. Federal Bureau of Investigation, *Crime in the United States 1997* (Washington: Federal Bureau of Investigation, 1998).

17. Thomas P. Bonczar and Allen J. Beck, *Lifetime Likelihood of Going to State or Federal Prison* (Washington: Bureau of Justice Statistics, 1997).

18. James J. Stephan, *Census of State and Federal Correctional Facilities, 1995* (Washington: Bureau of Justice Statistics, August 1997).

19. For a complete listing of organization names, sizes, budgets, personnel, responsibilities and appointments, and list of all correctional facilities, see American Correctional Association, *1999 Directory of Juvenile and Adult Correctional Departments, Institutions, Agencies and Paroling Authorities* (Lanham, MD: American Correctional Association, 1999).

20. James J. Stephan, *State Prison Expenditures, 1996* (Washington: Bureau of Justice Statistics, August 1999).

21. Federal Bureau of Prisons, "Monday Morning Highlights" (Washington: Federal Bureau of Prisons, October 18, 1999).

22. Online at http://www.wa.gov/doc/.

23. Charles Dickens, *American Notes and Pictures From Italy* (London: Chapman & Hall, 1842), Vol. I, p. 238.

8 The Staff World
Managing the Prison Population

CHAPTER OBJECTIVES

After completing this chapter you should be able to:

1. List the staff roles within the organizational hierarchy of correctional institutions.
2. Define *custodial staff*.
3. Identify the types of power available to correctional officers.
4. Explain what structured conflict is and how it applies to correctional institutions.
5. Define the word *subculture,* and identify some of the essential features of correctional officer subculture.
6. Summarize correctional officer demographics.
7. List and describe the most common correctional officer personality types.
8. List and describe the seven correctional officer job assignments.
9. Describe how female correctional officers differ from males in their approach to the workplace.
10. Explain why stress is a problem in corrections work, and list some techniques for reducing stress.

Teaching Tip

Emphasize that prison security is the number one staff concern. Staff members are guided by a philosophy that stresses the safety and security of the institution first, the staff second, and the inmates third. Do students think anything else should be considered more important?

roles The normal patterns of behavior expected of those holding particular social positions.

staff roles The patterns of behavior expected of correctional staff members in particular jobs.

Corrections is not a business where only one sex, race, religion, or type of person can succeed. It takes men and women of all races, religions, and color to create a dynamic and effective workforce to manage diverse inmates and solve the problems we face.

—Dora Schriro, former Missouri Director of Corrections

On a calm Saturday afternoon in April 1998 at the Everglades Correctional Institute, a maximum-security prison in Florida, correctional officers staffing guard towers were shocked to see a big-rig truck heading toward prison fences and beginning to accelerate.[1] The truck rammed through four security fences and stopped in the middle of the prison yard. The driver, later identified as 31-year-old John Beaston, pulled out a shotgun and started firing at officers in the towers and the yard. Two officers were injured. Other officers returned fire.

A car, allegedly driven by 58-year-old Sandra Sigler, then drove through the hole the truck had ripped in the prison fences, picked up Beaston and inmate Jay Junior Sigler, 31, and sped away. Jay Sigler, son of Sandra Sigler, had served 8 years of a 20-year sentence for armed robbery.

Prison superintendent Joe T. Butler spoke to reporters shortly after the prison break. "I guess we were blessed, but my officers did respond appropriately and got the inmates to their respective dormitories," he said. "This happened in the daytime and there are a lot of activities in the prison at that time, both recreation and visitation."

The Everglades Correctional Institute is a state-of-the art facility, incorporating a number of high-technology security systems. The institution houses more than 1500 prisoners. Butler said the breakout did not raise new security concerns. "I think anyone would think this was a very unusual situation," he noted. "How often do you hear about a semi truck . . . crashing through your security system?"

The Staff Hierarchy

Although planned escapes with outside help are rare, correctional personnel must be constantly alert for possible threats to institutional security. Ever since prisons began, one observer after another has noted that security is the number one concern of correctional staff. Barnes and Teeters, for example, wrote more than half a century ago: "Above all else, the main purpose of the prison is to keep the prisoners from escaping."[2]

Practically speaking, a prison of any size has a number of different staff roles—each with its own unique set of tasks. **Roles** are the normal patterns of behavior expected of those holding particular social positions. **Staff roles** are the patterns of behavior expected of correctional staff members in particular jobs. Eventually, many people internalize the expectations others have of them, and such expectations can play an important part in their self-perceptions.

The Staff World: Managing the Prison Population

Ideally, today's correctional staff members have four main goals:

1. To provide for the security of the community by incarcerating those who break the law.
2. To promote the smooth and effective functioning of the institution.
3. To ensure that incarceration is secure but humane.
4. To give inmates the opportunity to develop a positive lifestyle while incarcerated and to gain the personal and employment skills they need for a positive lifestyle after release.[3]

Prison staff are organized into a hierarchy, or multilevel categorization, according to responsibilities. An institution's hierarchy generally has the warden or superintendent at the top and includes a level for correctional officers. A typical correctional staff hierarchy includes:

- Administrative staff (wardens, superintendents, assistant superintendents, and others charged with running the institution and its programs and with setting policy)
- Clerical personnel (record keepers and administrative assistants)
- Treatment and educational staff (psychologists, psychiatrists, medical doctors, nurses, medical aides, teachers, counselors, caseworkers, and ministers—many of whom contract with the institution to provide services)
- Custodial staff (majors, captains, lieutenants, sergeants, and correctional officers charged primarily with maintaining order and security)
- Service and maintenance staff (kitchen supervisors, physical plant personnel, and many outside contractors)
- Volunteers (prison ministry, speakers, and other volunteers in corrections)

Organizational charts graphically represent the staff structure and the chain of command within an institution. An organizational chart for a typical medium-to-large correctional institution is shown in Figure 8–1. **Custodial staff** are most directly involved in managing the inmate population, through daily contact with inmates. Their role is to control prisoners within the institution. **Program staff**, on the other hand, are concerned with encouraging prisoners to participate in educational, vocational, and treatment programs. Custodial staff, who make up over 60 percent of prison personnel, are generally organized in a military-style hierarchy, from assistant or deputy warden down to correctional officer (see Figure 8–1). Program staff generally operate through a separate organizational structure and have little in common with custodial staff.

Prison management involves to a great extent managing relationships—among employees, between employees and inmates, and between inmates. Prisons are unique in that most of the people in them (the inmates) are forced to live there according to the terms of their sentence; they really do not want to be there. Such a situation presents tremendous challenges. The people on the front lines dealing around the clock with such challenges are the correctional officers.

custodial staff Those staff members most directly involved in managing the inmate population.

program staff Those staff members concerned with encouraging prisoners to participate in educational, vocational, and treatment programs.

FIGURE 8–1

Organizational Chart of a Typical Midsize or Large Correctional Institution

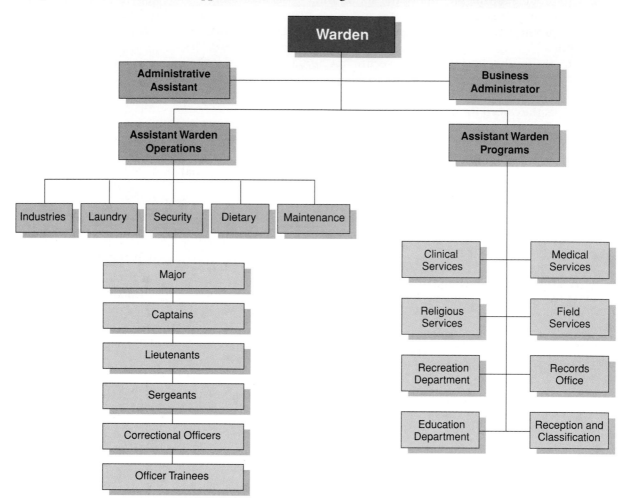

Teaching Tip
Tell students that although security remains the number one concern of correctional officers today, a number of other correctional responsibilities can be identified, such as counseling, arbitration, protection, discipline, supervision, and crisis management. Point out that such complex responsibilities can lead to role ambiguity and on-the-job stress.

The Correctional Officer— The Crucial Professional

Although security is still the major concern, correctional officers today are expected to perform a variety of other tasks. As one commentator has said,

Correctional officers have more responsibilities [now] than in the past and their duty is no longer to merely watch over the prisoners. They now have to play several roles in keeping prisoners in line. They have to be "psychiatrists" when prisoners come to them with their problems and they have to be "arbitrators and protectors" when inmates have complaints or problems with each other, while still watching out for their own safety. In these situations, the wrong decision could offend someone and start a riot. This makes correctional officers "prisoners" of the daily emotional and physical moods of the inmates.[4]

Don Josi and Dale Sechrest explain it this way:

> Correctional officers today must find a balance between their security role and their responsibility to use relationships with inmates to change their behavior constructively. They routinely assume numerous essential yet sometimes contradictory roles (e.g., counselor, diplomat, caretaker, disciplinarian, supervisor, crisis manager), often under stressful and dangerous conditions."[5]

Josi and Sechrest then go on to say, "These divergent and often incompatible goals can prove problematic; role conflict, role diffusion, and role ambiguity may be difficult if not impossible to avoid."[6]

Bases of Power

Correctional officers rely on a variety of strategies to manage inmate behavior. After surveying correctional officers in five prisons, John Hepburn identified five bases of officers' power: legitimate power, coercive power, reward power, expert power, and referent power.

Legitimate Power Correctional officers have power by virtue of their positions within the organization. That is, they have formal authority to command. As Hepburn says, "the prison guard has the right to exercise control over prisoners by virtue of the structural relationship between the position of the guard and the position of the prisoner."[7]

Coercive Power Inmates' beliefs that a correctional officer can and will punish disobedience give the officer coercive power. Many correctional officers use coercive power as a primary method of control.

Reward Power Correctional officers dispense both formal and informal rewards to induce cooperation among inmates. Formal rewards include assignment of desirable jobs, housing, and other inmate privileges. Correctional officers are also in a position to influence parole decisions and to assign good-time credit and **gain time** to inmates. Informal rewards correctional officers use include granting special favors and overlooking minor infractions of rules.

Expert Power Expert power results from inmates' perceptions that certain correctional officers have valuable skills. For example, inmates seeking treatment may value treatment-oriented officers. Inmates who need help with ongoing interpersonal conflicts may value officers who have conflict-resolution skills. Such officers may be able to exert influence on inmates who want their help.

gain time Time taken off an inmate's sentence for participating in certain activities such as going to school, learning a trade, working in prison, etc.

Referent Power   Referent power flows from "persuasive diplomacy." Officers who win the respect and admiration of prisoners—officers who are fair and not abusive—may achieve a kind of natural leadership position over inmates.

Some years before Hepburn's study, Gresham Sykes wrote that correctional officers' power can be corrupted through inappropriate relationships with inmates.[8] Friendships with prisoners, as well as indebtedness to them, can corrupt. According to Sykes, staff members who get too close to inmates and establish friendships are likely to find their "friends" asking for special favors. Similarly, officers who accept help from inmates may one day find that it's "payback time." In difficult or dangerous situations, help may be difficult to decline. In such cases, staff members must be careful not to let any perceived indebtedness to inmates influence their future behavior.

The Staff Subculture

Prison life is characterized by duality. An enormous gap separates those who work in prisons from those who live in them. This gap has a number of dimensions. One is that staff members officially control the institution and enforce the rules by which inmates live. Other formal and informal differences exist, including differences in background, values, and culture. Primarily, however, the relationship between correctional officers and inmates can be described as one of structured conflict.[9]

structured conflict   The tensions between prison staff members and inmates that arise out of the correctional setting.

Structured conflict is a term that describes the tensions between prison staff members and inmates that arise out of the correctional setting. In one sense, the prison is one large society—in which the worlds of inmates

and staff bump up against one another and intermingle. In another sense, however, the two groups keep their distance from each other—a distance imposed by both formal and informal rules. Conflict arises because staff members have control over the lives of inmates while inmates often have little say over important aspects of their own lives. The conflict is structured because it occurs within the confines of an organized institution and because, to some extent, it follows the rules—formal and informal—that govern institutional life.

Both worlds—inmate and staff—have their own cultures. Those cultures are generally called *subcultures* to indicate that both are contained within and surrounded by a larger culture. One writer has defined **subculture** as the beliefs, values, behavior, and material objects shared by a particular group of people within a larger society.[10] That is the definition we will use. The subcultures of inmates and correctional officers exist simultaneously in any prison institution. The beliefs, values, and behavior that make up the **staff subculture** differ greatly from the inmate subculture. Additionally, staff members possess material objects of control, such as keys, vehicles, weapons, and security systems.

Kauffman has identified a distinct correctional-officer subculture within prisons.[11] This set of beliefs, values, and behaviors sets correctional officers apart from other prison staff and from inmates. Their beliefs and values form an "officer code," which includes the following:

- Always go to the aid of an officer in distress.
- Don't "lug" drugs (bring them in for inmate use).
- Don't rat on other officers.

- Never make a fellow officer look bad in front of inmates.
- Always support an officer in a dispute with an inmate.
- Always support officer sanctions against inmates.
- Don't be a "white hat" or a "goody two-shoes."
- Maintain officer solidarity in dealings with all outside groups.
- Show positive concern for fellow officers.

Gender and Ethnicity of Correctional Officers

According to the American Correctional Association (ACA), state and local adult correctional facilities employed 337,736 custodial and administrative staff members as of September 30, 1997.[12] According to the ACA, most correctional personnel at state and local levels are white males. Of 105,975 female staff members, almost two-thirds (64.5%) are white (see Figure 8–2). Thirty percent of corrections personnel are members of minority groups. Of these, most are black (20%).

Ideally, the ethnic breakdown of correctional staff should closely approximate the ethnic breakdown of the population of the United States. According to the U.S. Census Bureau,[13] out of a 1995 population of about 265 million people, 33 million persons (12.7%) were black, 22.8 million (8.9%) were Hispanic, and 9.5 million (4%) were members of other minor-

Teaching Tip
Refer students to Figure 8–2. Point out that women are underrepresented within the ranks of correctional officers. Initiate a discussion about *why* women are underrepresented.

FIGURE 8–2

Profile of Correctional Personnel in Adult State and Local Correctional Facilities

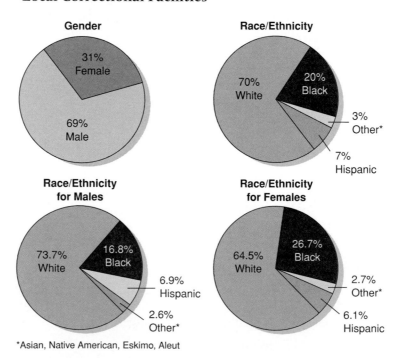

*Asian, Native American, Eskimo, Aleut

Source: Preliminary data (1996) from the table "Personnel in Adult and Juvenile Corrections," American Correctional Association, *Vital Statistics in Corrections.* Courtesy of the American Correctional Association.

The Staff World: Managing the Prison Population

FIGURE 8-3

Ethnic Groups as a Proportion of the U.S. Population and as a Proportion of Prison Staff

Teaching Tip
Refer students to Figure 8–3. Ask them to study the graph to compare the two sets of data. What conclusions can they draw?

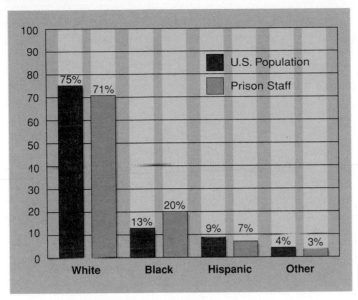

Sources: Staff statistics provided by David M. Wakefield, American Correctional Association, fax transmission June 12, 1998; preliminary data for the table "Personnel in Adult and Juvenile Corrections," American Correctional Association, *Vital Statistics in Corrections* (forthcoming). Population statistics derived from U.S. Bureau of the Census, *Population Profile of the United States:1995*, Current Population Reports, Series P23–189 (Washington: U.S. Government Printing Office, 1995); available online: http://www.census.gov/prod/1/pop/profile/95, access· July 20, 1998.

ity groups. Figure 8–3 above compares ethnic groups as a proportion of prison personnel and as a proportion of the U.S. population.

From Figure 8–3, it is easy to see that blacks are overrepresented among correctional personnel. While only 12.7 percent of the U.S. population, they account for 20 percent of the correctional workforce. Hispanics are slightly underrepresented (accounting for 8.9 percent of the country's population and 7 percent of the correctional workforce), as are other minorities (4 percent of the population, 3 percent of correctional staff). Whites, on the other hand, are almost evenly represented.

In addition, the federal Bureau of Prisons employs another 15,239 administrative and custodial personnel, of which 5,118 (33%) are female.[14] About 30 percent of correctional staff members in federal institutions are black. In juvenile facilities, females make up slightly more than 40 percent of a correctional workforce of 30,825.[15]

The American Correctional Association also says that approximately 10 percent of all correctional staff positions are supervisory (i.e., above the level of sergeant). Females hold 22.5 percent of all supervisory positions but only 18 percent of those at the level of warden or superintendent. Blacks fill approximately 21 percent of positions at the level of warden or superintendent. Members of other minority groups hold 5 percent of the top-level positions.[16]

Correctional Officer Personalities

correctional officer personalities The personal characteristics of officers as well as their modes of adaptation to their jobs, institutional conditions, the requirements of staff subculture, and institutional expectations.

The staff subculture contributes to the development of **correctional officer personalities**. Those personalities reflect the personal characteristics of the officers as well as their modes of adaptation to their jobs, institutional conditions, the requirements of staff subculture, and institutional expectations.[17] Common personality types that have been identified include those described in the following paragraphs.[18]

The Dictator   The dictator likes to give orders and seems to enjoy the feeling of power that comes from ordering inmates around. Correctional officers with dictator personalities are often strongly disliked by prisoners and may face special difficulties if taken hostage during a prison uprising.

The Friend   The correctional officer who tries to befriend inmates is often a quiet, retiring, but kind individual who believes that close friendships with inmates will make it easier to control the inmates and the work environment. Inmates, however, usually try to capitalize on friendships by asking for special treatment, contraband, and the like.

The Merchant   Merchant-personality correctional officers set themselves up as commodity providers to the inmate population. If an inmate needs something not easily obtained in prison, the merchant will usually procure it—at a cost. Often, such behavior is a violation of institutional rules, and it can lead to serious violations of the law as the merchant–correctional officer smuggles contraband into the institution for the "right price."

The Turnkey   Turnkey officers do little beyond the basic requirements of their position. A turnkey usually interacts little with other officers and does the minimum necessary to get through the workday. Unmotivated and bored, the turnkey may be seeking other employment. Some turnkey officers have become disillusioned with their jobs. Others are close to retirement.

The Climber   The correctional officer who is a climber is set on advancement. He or she may want to be warden or superintendent one day, and is probably seeking rapid promotion. Climbers are often diligent officers who perform their jobs well and respect the corrections profession. Climbers who look down on other officers, however, or attempt to look good by making coworkers look bad, can cause many problems within the institution.

The Reformer   The reformer constantly finds problems with the way the institution is run or with existing policies and rules. He or she always seems to know better than anyone else and frequently complains about working conditions or supervisors.

The Do-Gooder   The do-gooder is another type of reformer—one with a personal agenda. A devoutly religious do-gooder may try to convert other correctional officers and inmates to his or her faith. Other do-gooders actively seek to counsel inmates, using personal techniques and philosophies that are not integrated into the prison's official treatment program.

Teaching Tip
Review the correctional officer personality types described in the text. Suggest that some correctional officers may exhibit a blend of types. Ask students to speculate how each personality type might affect the nature and quality of a correctional officer's job performance.

Professional Issue
Abuse of Power Ask students what correctional officer personality types are most likely to be associated with abuse of power. Discuss the potential consequences of abuse of power and possible ways to curtail it.

Student Involvement
After students have reviewed the section on correctional officer personalities, have them devise a set of student personalities or a set of faculty personalities. Are there similarities between the sets? If so, what conclusions could students draw?

Charles D. Walston
Correctional Trainer
North Carolina
Department of
Correction

"Looking back, the majority of what I did was to guide people (offenders) and deal with unacceptable behavior. Even though I tried to be a positive influence on the inmates, the decision to change was all theirs. Now, I am in a position to encourage and motivate new employees. It is extremely rewarding to see students come into a training program with limited knowledge and leave as Certified Correctional Officers, beaming with confidence and professionalism."

Charles D. Walston is a Correctional Trainer with the North Carolina Department of Correction, Office of Staff Development and Training. He spent almost 12 years working in a close-custody state prison facility with 540 prisoners. Prior to leaving that facility, Charles was the Assistant Commander of the Institutional Prison Emergency Response Team and the First Shift Commander.

His duties currently include the development and delivery of certification training to new correctional employees throughout the state. In North Carolina, successful completion of a four-week basic training results in participants being certified as State Correctional Officers by the state Criminal Justice Training and Standards Commission.

Charles recently received an Associate Degree from a local community college and is currently working to complete a B.S. degree in criminal justice. He enjoys training new employees and helping them get their careers off the ground.

Although the personalities described may be exaggerated, their variety suggests that correctional officer personalities result from many influences, including:

- General life experiences
- Biological propensities
- Upbringing
- Staff subculture
- Working conditions
- Institutional expectations and rules

Correctional Officer Job Assignments

Seven different correctional officer roles or job assignments have been identified.[19] They are classified by their location within the institution, the duties required, and the nature of the contact with inmates.

Teaching Tip
If possible, have a correctional officer speak to the class about his or her job responsibilities.

block officers Those responsible for supervising inmates in housing areas.

Block Officers   **Block officers** are responsible for supervising inmates in housing areas. Housing areas include dormitories, cell blocks, modular living units, and even tents in some overcrowded prisons. Safety and security are the primary concerns of block officers. Conducting counts, ensuring the orderly movement of prisoners, inspecting personal property, overseeing inmate activity, and searching prisoners are all part of the block officer's job. Block officers also lock and unlock cells and handle problems that arise within the living area. Block officers are greatly outnumbered by the inmates they supervise. Hence, if disturbances occur, block officers usually withdraw quickly to defensible positions within the institution.

work detail supervisors Those that oversee the work of individual inmates and inmate work crews.

Work Detail Supervisors   **Work detail supervisors** oversee the work of individual inmates and inmate work crews assigned to jobs within the institution or outside it. Jobs assigned to inmates may include laundry, kitchen, and farm duties, as well as yard work and building maintenance. Work detail supervisors must also keep track of supplies and tools and maintain inventories of materials. Prison buildings are sometimes constructed almost exclusively with the use of inmate labor—creating the need for large inmate work details. On such large projects, supervising officers usually work in conjunction with outside contractors.

industrial shop and school officers Those that ensure efficient use of training and educational resources within the prison.

Industrial Shop and School Officers   **Industrial shop and school officers** work to ensure efficient use of training and educational resources within the prison. Such resources include workshops, schools, classroom facilities, and associated equipment and tools. These officers oversee inmates who are learning trades, such as welding, woodworking, or automobile mechanics, or who are attending academic classes. Ensuring that students are present and on time for classes to begin, protecting the school and voca-

THE OFFENDER SPEAKS

Ms. Eagle, a teacher in the Delaware Prison Life Skills Program, invited family members twice to come to the prison. On one occasion, she had the family members and students break into small groups—I wasn't in the same group with my mom— to discuss what various family members should do when someone comes home very late at night. Then each group reported its solutions to the whole class. In my group, a mom actually had a son who was going through this problem. The groups help each family to see how other families would solve the problem, and they also help everyone to see that everyone has the same problems.

An inmate in the Life Skills Program

tional instructors, and securing the tools and facilities used in instruction are all part of the job of these officers. The officers work with civilian instructors, teachers, and counselors.

Yard Officers   **Yard officers** supervise inmates in the prison yard. They also take charge of inmates who are (1) moving from place to place, (2) eating, or (3) involved in recreational activities. Like other officers, yard officers are primarily concerned with security and order maintenance.

Administrative Officers   **Administrative officers** are assigned to staff activities within the institution's management center. They control keys and weapons. Some administrative officers oversee visitation. As a result, they have more contact with the public than other officers do. Many administrative officers have little, if any, contact with inmates.

Perimeter Security Officers   **Perimeter security officers** (also called *wall post officers*) are assigned to security (or gun) towers, wall posts, and perimeter patrols. They are charged with preventing escapes and detecting and preventing intrusions (such as packages of drugs or weapons thrown over fences or walls from *outside*). Perimeter security can become a routine job because it involves little interaction with other officers or inmates and because relatively few escape attempts occur. Newer institutions depend more heavily on technological innovations to maintain secure perimeters, requiring fewer officers for day-long perimeter observation.

Relief Officers   **Relief officers** are experienced correctional officers who know and can perform almost any custody role in the institution. They are used to temporarily replace officers who are sick or on vacation or to meet staffing shortages.

Correctional Staff Issues

Female Officers

On a pleasant Sunday morning a few years ago, a high-custody female inmate at the Chillicothe (Missouri) Correctional Center was sitting in a dormitory, drinking her morning coffee. Having a good time, surrounded by friends, the inmate began laughing. Soon, however, the laughter turned to choking. Unable to breathe, she turned blue. Correctional officer Lisa Albin rushed to her side, and found her hanging onto her bed, unable to speak. Albin remained calm as she applied the Heimlich maneuver to the inmate. After three attempts, the trapped coffee cleared the inmate's windpipe and she began breathing again. After the incident, the inmate wrote a letter of thanks to the superintendent, saying, "If it had not been for Mrs. Albin I could have very well died in that room. She literally saved my life and I will be forever grateful to her and for the training she received."[20]

Literature and films almost invariably portray correctional officers as "tobacco-chewin', reflective-sunglass-wearin', chain-gang-runnin', good ol' boys."[21] Today's officer generally defies this stereotype, and women working in corrections have helped erode this otherwise persistent myth.

yard officers   Those that supervise inmates in the prison yard.

administrative officers   Those that control keys and weapons and sometimes oversee visitation.

perimeter security officers   Those assigned to security (or gun) towers, wall posts, and perimeter patrols. These officers are charged with preventing escapes and detecting and preventing intrusions.

relief officers   Experienced correctional officers who know and can perform almost any custody role within the institution, used to temporarily replace officers who are sick or on vacation or to meet staffing shortages.

Student Involvement
After students have reviewed all the correctional officer job assignments, ask them which job most appeals to them and which appeals least. Have them explain why.

Like most women working in male-dominated professions, female correctional officers face special problems and barriers—many of which are rooted in sexism. Prisons are nontraditional workplaces for women. As a consequence, female correctional officers—especially those working in men's prisons—often find themselves in a confusing position. As one author explains it: "On the one hand, to be female is to be different, an outsider. On the other hand, female guards have much in common with, and are sympathetic to, their male peers as a result of their shared job experience."[22]

According to studies, female correctional officers typically say that they perform their job with a less aggressive style than men.[23] This difference in style seems due mostly to differences in life experiences and to physical limitations associated with women's size and strength. Life experiences prepare most women for helping roles rather than aggressive ones. As a consequence, women are more likely to rely heavily on verbal skills and intuition. Female correctional officers use communication rather than threats or force to gain inmate cooperation. They tend to talk out problems. Studies have also found that female correctional officers rely more heavily than male correctional officers on established disciplinary rules when problems arise. Male staff members, on the other hand, are more likely to bully or threaten inmates to resolve problems.

According to research, 55 percent of female officers indicate that their primary reason for taking a job in corrections was an interest in human service work or in inmate rehabilitation.[24] In striking contrast, only 20 percent of male officers give this as their primary reason for working in corrections.

As the number of women who work in corrections increases, more men must confront the unfamiliar situation of a female authority figure. What kinds of skills do female correctional officers tend to rely on to resolve problems?

Perhaps as a result of such attitudes, gender makes a dramatic difference in the number of assaults on correctional officers. One national survey of maximum-security prisons in 48 states, the District of Columbia, and the federal Bureau of Prisons showed that female officers were assaulted only 27.6 percent as often as male officers.[25]

Though female correctional officers may take a different approach to their work, the skills they use complement those of male staff members. "Women may humanize the workplace in small ways by establishing less aggressive relationships with inmates."[26]

Studies also show that male officers, by and large, believe that female officers competently perform day-to-day custodial tasks. Most male staff members are "pro-woman," meaning that they applaud the entry of women into the corrections profession.[27] Many male correctional officers do express concerns about women's ability to provide adequate backup in a crisis. It is important to note, however, that the need to use force in prison is relatively rare and that officers generally do not respond to dangerous situations alone. Nonetheless, some female correctional officers report that in emergencies some male officers adopt a protective, chivalrous attitude toward them. Women generally report that they resent such "special treatment," because it makes them feel more like a liability than an asset in an emergency.

Another issue concerning women in today's workplace is personal and sexual harassment. Studies show that few female correctional officers personally experience unwanted touching or other forms of sexual harassment. The forms of harassment women most commonly experience are physical (nonsexual) assaults, threats, unfounded graphic sexual rumors about them, and demeaning remarks from peers, inmates, and supervisors.[28]

A fair amount of harassment is tolerated in the correctional officer subculture. It is viewed as customary and is often accorded little significance. The response to any form of harassment, however, is up to the officer experiencing it. He or she can tolerate it, resist it, or report it. Female correctional officers, however, express a real fear of being ostracized if they complain.

One writer has made the following recommendations for improving the acceptance of women as correctional officers:[29]

1. Require managers and guards to undergo training to sensitize them to the concerns of women working in prisons.

Female correctional officers competently perform day-to-day custodial tasks. Are there any areas of a male prison that female correctional officers should be barred from supervising?

2. Establish a strong policy prohibiting sexual and personal harassment, with significant consequences for harassers.
3. Screen male job candidates for their ability and willingness to develop relationships of mutual respect with female colleagues.

Stress

In all occupational categories, employers estimate that more than 25 percent of all reported sick time is due to stress.[30] **Stress**—tension in a person's body or mind, resulting from physical, chemical, or emotional factors—appears to be more commonplace in prison work than in many other jobs. Nonetheless, it is often denied. As one early writer on correctional officers' stress observed, "Most officers . . . try to disguise the toll taken by the job and make the best of what is often a frustrating situation. Though not immune to the pressures of the workplace these officers project a tough, steady image which precludes sharing frustrations with other co-workers or family members. Some of these officers may be particularly vulnerable to stress."[31]

Correctional officers frequently deny that they are under stress. Many resort to self-medication or other tactics to deal with feelings that they may not readily admit, even to themselves. Unfortunately, ineffective methods of dealing with stress do not alleviate the pressure, but may instead make it worse.

Stress among correctional officers has a number of sources. Feelings of powerlessness, meaninglessness, social isolation, and self-estrangement all contribute to stress. Some authors have identified job alienation as the major source of stress among correctional officers.[32] Correctional officers rarely participate in setting the rules they work under and the policies they enforce; as a result, they may feel alienated from those policies and rules, and from those who create them.

Other factors that create stress include:

- Work overload
- Family conflict
- Lack of autonomy or control over one's life
- Threat of job loss
- Role conflict or role ambiguity
- Conflicts with coworkers
- Conflicts with supervisors
- The organizational culture
- The working environment
- Insufficient resources to reach one's goals
- Inadequate job training
- Overqualification for one's current position
- Supervisors' attitudes
- Changes in the work environment

Symptoms of stress can be psychological, behavioral, and physical. Psychological symptoms of stress include anxiety, irritability, mood swings, sadness or depression, low self-esteem, emotional withdrawal, and hypersensitivity (to others and to what others say). Behavioral symptoms of stress

Always read the supervision file or pretrial services bond report before making a field contact. If possible, talk to the prior supervision officer before any contact. If the Bureau of Prisons or another district does not provide sufficient background material, make them do their job by requiring this information before making any field contact.

After reviewing the material, determine what precautions need to be taken. Decide whether to make contact at a certain place or time of day, to take a partner, or to make some other arrangement. If you find you are still not comfortable, and no precaution can assuage this feeling, don't make the contact.

Consciously consider possible risks and what actions to take before making a field contact. After you have done this, there is still the unexpected. For this possibility, all you can do is be aware, have your safety equipment, and heed your sixth sense.

1. Things happen fast. Have a plan, and mentally rehearse various scenarios in advance.
2. Have a plan that includes immediate rapid movement to a place of cover.
3. Don't think you can talk yourself out of every situation. Sometimes immediate action is called for.
4. Listen to your instincts. If things don't feel right, leave.
5. Most of the time acting firmly helps you to control the situation. It creates the impression you are not an easy target.
6. Remain professional, but act firm. (Note: May not be the best course in a very few mental health cases.)

Ben Bridgman
Federal Supervision Probation Officer
Middle District of Florida

include an inability to make decisions, increased interpersonal conflict, blocked creativity and judgment, poor memory, lowered productivity, and difficulty in concentrating. The physical symptoms of stress include insomnia, headaches, backaches, gastrointestinal disturbances, fatigue, high blood pressure, and frequent illnesses.

Poorer job performance and exhaustion are the results of stress. When stress reaches an unbearable level, burnout can occur. Burnout, a severe reaction to stress, "describes a state of physical and emotional depletion that results from the conditions of one's occupation."[33]

Studies have shown that a person's ability to tolerate stress depends on the frequency, severity, and types of stressors confronted.[34] Stress tolerance also depends on a number of personal aspects, including past experiences, personal values and attitudes, sense of control, personality, residual stress level, and general state of health.

Authorities suggest a number of techniques for avoiding or reducing job stress. Among them are the following:[35]

1. Communicate openly. Tell people how you feel.
2. Learn not to harbor resentment, not to gossip, and to complain less often.
3. Learn to feel confident in your skills, your values and beliefs, and yourself.
4. Develop a support system. Close friends, pets, social activities, and a happy extended family can all help alleviate stress.
5. Be a good and conscientious worker, but don't become a workaholic.
6. Learn to manage your time, and do not procrastinate.
7. Make it a habit to get a good night's sleep.
8. Exercise regularly.
9. Watch your diet. Avoid excessive fat, sugars, salt, red meat, and caffeine.
10. Learn some relaxation exercises such as self-affirmation, mental imaging, deep breathing, stretching, massage, or yoga.
11. Try to have fun. Laughter can combat stress quite effectively.
12. Spend time cultivating self-understanding. Analyze your feelings and your problems—and recognize your accomplishments.
13. Set goals and make plans. Both bring order and direction to your life.

One especially effective strategy for coping with job stress is to develop clear and favorable role definitions. According to J. T. Dignam and coauthors, "officers who have more opportunities for receiving assistance and goal clarification from supervisors and coworkers [are] less likely to experi-

As more and more prison staff develop a professional perspective, the structural organization of prisons and interactions among staff and inmates may significantly change. What characteristics may help correctional officers adjust to a changing environment?

ence role ambiguity than those for whom such support is not available or sought. Further, the risk of burnout or other deleterious consequences of occupational stress may be reduced for those who are 'insulated' by social support."[36]

Similarly, another group of researchers found that "support from colleagues or supervisors may be one of the most important factors ameliorating stress in the workplace."[37] The same researchers also found that when correctional officers felt "rewarding companionship" with fellow correctional officers, they reported fewer stressful events (even when objective measures showed an actual rise in such events). Most researchers agree that officers need more extensive and thorough training to prepare them for the psychological and sociological consequences of becoming a correctional officer.

Job Satisfaction

Teaching Tip
Ask students to list the techniques they think would be the most effective for increasing correctional officer job satisfaction.

High levels of stress reduce the satisfaction correctional officers get from their jobs. In a sad indictment of the corrections field, a 1996 study found that correctional officers were significantly different from most other groups of correctional employees. "They showed the lowest levels of organizational commitment, possessed the highest levels of skepticism about organizational change, were the least positive about careers in corrections and the rehabilitation of offenders, possessed the lowest levels of job satisfaction, were the least involved in their jobs, and were described as having the poorest work habits and overall job performance."[38] In a separate study, correctional supervisors and managers were found to have much higher levels of job satisfaction and professionalism.[39]

One reason for the difference in job satisfaction between supervisory personnel and those on the front lines of corrections work is that correctional officers often feel alienated from policy making.[40] As one writer puts it, "when looking at the atmosphere and environment of a state or federal prison, it would seem obvious what correction personnel like least about working there: surveys of personnel who resign or quit show that their biggest problems are with supervisory personnel rather than inmates."[41]

Correctional officers' job satisfaction appears to be tied to the amount of influence they feel they have over administrative decisions and policies. Officers who feel they have some control over the institution and over their jobs seem much more satisfied than officers who believe they have no control. Hence, it appears that correctional officers' job satisfaction can be greatly enhanced by caring administrators who involve the officers in policy making.

There is evidence that job satisfaction among correctional officers is rising. The rise may be partly due to increasing awareness of what correctional officers find most important in the work environment. Recent studies have identified the most important determinants of job satisfaction among correctional officers as (1) working conditions, (2) the level of work-related stress, (3) the quality of working relationships with fellow officers, and (4) length of service.[42]

In one of the most significant studies to date, treatment-oriented correctional staff reported far higher levels of job satisfaction than custody-

Tutorial CD-ROM
Refer students to the Tutorial With Simulation Applications CD-ROM. The tutorial is a comprehensive interactive study tool that reinforces and reviews the concepts in Chapter 8. Also included are two simulations that apply concepts presented in Chapter 8.

oriented staff.[43] The study was of survey data collected from 428 Arizona correctional service officers (CSOs) and 118 correctional program officers (CPOs). Job satisfaction was significantly greater among the human-services-oriented CPOs than among the traditional-custody-oriented CSOs. The findings suggest that additional attention should be given to enhancing and enriching the duties of correctional officers, extending their control over and involvement in prisoners' activities, and redefining their roles more as service workers than as control agents.

Determinants of job satisfaction appear to differ for male and female correctional officers. One study found that the quality of working relationships with other officers, the amount of stress experienced at work, the length of service as a correctional officer, and educational level were all positively related to job satisfaction for males.[44] Women officers, on the other hand, appeared to place more emphasis on the quality of working relationships with all other correctional officers (not just the ones with whom they worked) and tended to be happier in prisons at lower security levels. Other studies have related higher job satisfaction among white female officers to the officers' positive evaluation of the quality of supervision. In other words, white female correctional officers tend to be happier in prisons that they believe are well run.[45]

Professionalism

On October 29, 1994, correctional officer Ken Davis was instantly catapulted to the forefront of national attention when he tackled White House shooter Francisco Martin Duran. Without warning, Duran had leveled a Chinese-made AK-47 assault rifle at the White House from outside the iron gates and had begun firing. While most other bystanders either fled or stood stunned, Davis ran toward Duran and wrestled him to the ground, holding him until police and White House security officers arrived. Duran was later sentenced to 40 years in prison with no chance of parole on charges of attempting to assassinate President Clinton.

Davis, a correctional officer at the Victor Cullins Academy[46] in Maryland, was honored for his quick actions. During the ceremony, he noted a few lifestyle principles that could benefit all correctional officers. "Correctional officers serve and survive better," said Davis, "if they adopt the capacity for balance as a personal philosophy."[47] Balance means understanding themselves, knowing when they can handle a situation and when they cannot, and admitting when they need help. It also means having a clear sense of their roles and keeping a clear view of their purpose and their career goals. A good sense of balance, said Davis, reduces job stress and "improves officer-officer relations" by leading to good teamwork and by ensuring that correctional officers understand the importance of positive peer relationships in maintaining high morale. Officer Davis observed that inmates look for correctional officers without a personal sense of balance and "systematically and continuously work to manipulate the human frailties of correctional officers."

Student Involvement
Ask students what they think correctional officer Ken Davis meant when he said, "Correctional officers serve and survive better if they adopt the capacity for balance as a personal philosophy." Then ask what "the capacity for balance as a personal philosophy" means for correctional officers.

"There is danger in ignorance," Davis said. "Learning is a lifelong process. True knowledge is knowing what you do not know! Don't worry about sounding stupid. Know when to call for help. Don't be afraid to say, 'I need help,' 'I don't understand this duty post,' or 'This approach seems wrong.'"

Davis also noted that "listening is the heart of communication. Good listening practices shape a successful officer. Effective officers strive to perfect both active and passive listening skills, by exploring innovative ways to improve communication with peers and supervisors, inmates, visitors, and the public."

"One way for officers to accomplish the achievement of their personal career goals," noted Davis, "is to constantly groom themselves early in their career for higher rank and responsibility by learning from their experienced supervisors and by keeping a journal of lessons learned. This process will provide dividends for years to come. It will give you a bank of positive experiences to draw on in future times of career decisions and in times of crisis."

The International Association of Correctional Officers has published a Correctional Officer's Creed (see Exhibit 8–1), which summarizes the duties and responsibilities of a correctional officer.

Teaching Tip
Refer to Chapter 8 of the *Instructor's Resource Manual* for additional activities and for answers to the end-of-chapter exercises.

Professional Issue
Ethics Have students read The Correctional Officer's Creed. Then ask which parts of the creed they think would be most useful in guiding the job performance of correctional officers.

EXHIBIT 8–1

International Association of Correctional Officers

The Correctional Officer's Creed

To speak sparingly...to act, not argue...to be in authority through personal presence...to correct without nagging...to speak with the calm voice of certainty...to see everything, and to know what is significant and what not to notice...to be neither insensitive to distress nor so distracted by pity as to miss what must elsewhere be seen...

To do neither that which is unkind nor self-indulgent in its misplaced charity...never to obey the impulse to tongue slash that silent insolence which in time past could receive the lash...to be both firm and fair...to know I cannot be fair simply by being firm, nor firm simply by being fair...

To support the reputations of associates and confront them without anger should they stand short of professional conduct...to reach for knowledge of the continuing mysteries of human motivation...to think; always to think...to be dependable...to be dependable first to my charges and associates, and thereafter to my duty as employee and citizen...to keep fit...to keep forever alert...to listen to what is meant as well as what is said with words and with silences.

To expect respect from my charges and my superiors yet never to abuse the one for abuses from the other...for eight hours each working day to be an example of the person I could be at all times...to acquiesce in no dishonest act...to cultivate patience under boredom and calm during confusion...to understand the why of every order I take or give...

To hold freedom among the highest values though I deny it to those I guard...to deny it with dignity that in my example they find no reason to lose their dignity...to be prompt...to be honest with all who practice deceit that they not find in me excuse for themselves...to privately face down my fear that I not signal it...to privately cool my anger that I not displace it on others...to hold in confidence what I see and hear, which by telling could harm or humiliate to no good purpose...to keep my outside problems outside...to leave inside that which should stay inside...to do my duty.

SUMMARY BY CHAPTER OBJECTIVES

CHAPTER OBJECTIVE 1
There is a hierarchy of staff positions, from warden (or superintendent) at the top, down to correctional officer and correctional officer trainee. A typical correctional staff includes (1) administrative staff, (2) clerical personnel, (3) treatment and educational staff, (4) custodial staff, (5) service and maintenance staff, and (6) volunteers.

CHAPTER OBJECTIVE 2
The custodial staff consists of correctional officers only—not correctional administrators, treatment or educational staff, or other staff members.

CHAPTER OBJECTIVE 3
The types of power available to correctional officers are legitimate power, coercive power, reward power, expert power, and referent power.

CHAPTER OBJECTIVE 4
In correctional institutions, structured conflict refers to the tensions between prison staff members and inmates that arise out of institutional arrangements.

CHAPTER OBJECTIVE 5
A subculture is the beliefs, values, behavior, and material objects shared by a particular group of people within a larger society. The subculture of correctional officers reinforces group solidarity and cohesion among correctional personnel.

CHAPTER OBJECTIVE 6
State prisons and local jails employed 337,736 corrections personnel (including administrative staff) in late 1997. One-third were women. About 30 percent were minorities.

CHAPTER OBJECTIVE 7
Common correctional officer personality types include (1) the dictator, (2) the friend, (3) the merchant, (4) the turnkey, (5) the climber, (6) the reformer, and (7) the do-gooder.

CHAPTER OBJECTIVE 8
The seven correctional officer assignments are (1) block officers, (2) work detail supervisors, (3) industrial shop and school officers, (4) yard officers, (5) administrative officers, (6) perimeter security officers (also called wall post officers), and (7) relief officers.

CHAPTER OBJECTIVE 9
Female correctional officers tend to differ from male ones in their approach to workplace problem solving because they are generally less aggressive than male officers. They are more likely to resolve disputes through nonconfrontational means and tend to rely more heavily on verbal skills and interpersonal communication than do male officers. Studies have also found that female correctional officers depend more on established disciplinary rules when problems arise.

CHAPTER OBJECTIVE 10
Feelings of powerlessness, meaninglessness, social isolation, self-estrangement, and alienation are all sources of correctional officer stress. Techniques for reducing stress include open communication, self-confidence, a support system, conscientious work performance, effective time management, adequate sleep, exercise, a wholesome diet, relaxation techniques, laughter, self-understanding, realistic goals and plans, and avoidance of resentment.

roles, p. 222
staff roles, p. 222
custodial staff, p. 223
program staff, p. 223
gain time, p. 225
structured conflict, p. 226
subculture, p. 227
staff subculture, p. 227
correctional officer personalities, p. 230

block officers, p. 232
work detail supervisors, p. 232
industrial shop and school officers, p. 232
yard officers, p. 233
administrative officers, p. 233
perimeter security officers, p. 233
relief officers, p. 233
stress, p. 236

QUESTIONS FOR REVIEW

1. What staff roles does the hierarchy of a typical correctional institution include?
2. What is the role of a prison's custodial staff?
3. According to John Hepburn, what are five bases of the power correctional officers have to gain inmate compliance?
4. What is meant by *structured conflict*?
5. What elements make up the staff subculture?
6. According to the ACA, what percentage of corrections personnel are members of minority groups?
7. List common personality types of correctional officers.
8. What are the seven correctional officer job assignments?
9. List and explain some challenges facing women who work as correctional officers.
10. What are some sources of stress for correctional officers?

CRITICAL THINKING EXERCISES

ON-THE-JOB ISSUE

You are an experienced correctional officer, assigned to yard duty. As you patrol the prison yard, watching inmates milling around and talking, a fellow officer named Renée approaches you. Renée was hired only a week ago, and she has gained a reputation for being inquisitive—asking experienced correctional officers about prison work.

Renée walks up and says, "You know, I'm wondering what I should do. Yesterday I saw an officer push an inmate around because the guy didn't do what he asked. I don't know if the inmate didn't hear what was being said, or if he was just ignoring the officer."

Renée looks at the ground. "What am I supposed to do in a situation like that? Should I have said something right then? Should I talk to the officer privately? Should I suggest to the officer that maybe the inmate didn't hear him? He knows we aren't supposed to use force on inmates unless it's really necessary. If I see him do this kind of thing again, should I report him?" Looking up, Renée says, "I know we're supposed to support each other in here. But what would you do?" How should you respond to Renée's questions?

CORRECTIONS ISSUE

The staff culture is generally instilled in correctional officer trainees by more experienced officers and by work experiences. Socialization into the staff subculture begins on the first day of academy training or the first day of work (whichever comes first). One of the most important beliefs of the staff subculture is that officers should support one another.

Some people argue that the staff subculture is dangerous because it can sustain improper and even illegal behavior, while forcing correctional officers to keep to themselves what they know about such behavior. Others, however, suggest that the staff subculture is a positive element in the correctional world. It is important to correctional officer morale, they claim. They also suggest that it "fills the gaps" in formal training by establishing informal rules to guide staff behavior and decision making in difficult situations. The staff subculture can provide informal "workarounds" when the formal requirements of a correctional officer's position seem unrealistic.

1. Do you think the staff subculture contributes to or detracts from meeting the goals of institutional corrections? Why?
2. Do you think the staff subculture benefits or harms the lives and working environment of correctional officers? Explain.
3. What functions of the staff subculture can you identify? Rate each of those functions as positive or negative for its role in meeting the goals of institutional corrections.

CORRECTIONS ON THE WEB

Access the Arizona Peace Officer Standards and Training Board at **http://www.azpost.state.az.us/**. Click on "Correctional Officer Rules," and then read all eight sections of the state code relating to correctional officers. After reading the state code sections, write a short paragraph summarizing the expectations the state of Arizona has of its correctional officers.

ADDITIONAL READINGS

American Correctional Association. *The State of Corrections: Proceedings—ACA Annual Conferences 1995.* Lanham, MD: ACA, 1996.

Farkas, Mary Ann, and P. K. Manning. "The Occupational Culture of Corrections and Police Officers." *Journal of Crime and Justice,* Vol. 20, No. 2 (1997), pp. 51–68.

Josi, Don A., and Dale K. Sechrest. *The Changing Career of the Correctional Officer: Policy Implications for the 21st Century.* Boston: Butterworth-Heinemann, 1998.

Kantrowitz, Nathan. *Close Control: Managing a Maximum Security Prison.* Guilderland, NY: Harrow and Heston, 1996.

Price, Barbara Raffel, and Natalie J. Sokoloff. *The Criminal Justice System and Women: Offenders, Victims, and Workers,* 2d ed. New York: McGraw-Hill, 1995.

ENDNOTES

1. CNN Online, "Truck Rams Prison Fence in Florida Breakout," Web posted April 11, 1998.
2. Harry Elmer Barnes and Negley K. Teeters, *New Horizons in Criminology,* 3d ed. (Englewood Cliffs, NJ: Prentice Hall, 1959), p. 463.
3. See Sylvia G. McCollum, "Excellence or Mediocrity: Training Correctional Officers and Administrators," *The Keeper's Voice,* Vol. 17, No. 4 (Fall 1996).
4. Anthony R. Martinez, "Corrections Officer: The 'Other' Prisoner," *The Keeper's Voice,* Vol. 18, No. 1 (Spring 1997).
5. Don A. Josi and Dale K. Sechrest, *The Changing Career of the Correctional Officer: Policy Implications for the 21st Century* (Boston: Butterworth-Heinemann, 1998), p. 11.
6. Ibid., p. 12.
7. John Hepburn, "The Exercise of Power in Coercive Organizations: A Study of Prison Guards," *Criminology,* Vol. 23, No. 1 (1985), pp. 145–164.
8. Gresham Sykes, *The Society of Captives* (Princeton, NJ: Princeton University Press, 1958).
9. See, for example, James B. Jacobs and Lawrence J. Kraft, "Integrating the Keepers: A Comparison of Black and White Prison Guards in Illinois," *Social Problems,* Vol. 25, No. 3 (1978), pp. 304–318.
10. Adapted from John J. Macionis, *Society: The Basics,* 2d ed (Englewood Cliffs, NJ: Prentice Hall, 1994), p. 405.
11. Kauffman, Kelsey, *Prison Officers and Their World* (Cambridge, MA: Harvard University Press, 1988), pp. 85–86.
12. David M. Wakefield, American Correctional Association, fax transmission June 12, 1998. Preliminary data for the table "Personnel in Adult and Juvenile Corrections," in ACA, *Vital Statistics in Corrections* (forthcoming).
13. U.S. Bureau of the Census, *Population Profile of the United States: 1995,* Current Population Reports,

Series P23–189 (Washington: U.S. Government Printing Office, 1995); available online: http://www.census.gov/prod/1/pop/profile/95, access: July 20, 1998.

14. Preliminary data for ACA, *Vital Statistics in Corrections*.

15. Ibid.

16. Ibid.

17. See, for example, E. Poole and R. M. Regoli, "Work Relations and Cynicism Among Prison Guards," *Criminal Justice and Behavior*, Vol. 7 (1980), pp. 303–314.

18. Adapted from Frank Schmalleger, *Criminal Justice Today: An Introductory Text for the 21st Century*, 5th ed. (Upper Saddle River, NJ: Prentice Hall, 1999).

19. Lucien X. Lombardo, *Guards Imprisoned: Correctional Officers at Work*, 2d ed. (Cincinnati, OH: Anderson, 1989).

20. Adapted from Dora B. Schriro, "Women in Prison: Keeping the Peace," *The Keeper's Voice*, Vol. 16, No. 2 (Spring 1995).

21. Ibid.

22. M. I. Cadwaladr, "Women Working in a Men's Jail," *FORUM*, Vol. 6, No. 1 (1994).

23. Ibid.

24. N. C. Jurik and J. Halemba, "Gender, Working Conditions, and the Job Satisfaction of Women in a Non-Traditional Occupation: Female Correctional Officers in Men's Prisons," *Sociological Quarterly*, Vol. 25 (1984), pp. 551–66.

25. Joseph R. Rowan, "Who Is Safer in Male Maximum Security Prisons?" *The Keeper's Voice*, Vol. 17, No. 3 (Summer 1996).

26. Ibid.

27. See, for example, Stephen Walters, "Changing the Guard: Male Correctional Officers' Attitudes Toward Women as Co-workers," *Journal of Offender Rehabilitation*, Vol. 20, No. 1 (1993), pp. 47–60.

28. Cadwaladr.

29. Ibid.

30. Public Service Commission (of Canada), "Stress and Executive Burnout," *FORUM*, Vol. 4, No. 1 (1992). Much of the material in this section is taken from this work.

31. B. M. Crouch, "The Guard in a Changing Prison World," in B. M. Crouch (ed.), *The Keepers: Prison Guards and Contemporary Corrections* (Springfield, IL: Charles C. Thomas, 1980).

32. Lombardo.

33. Public Service Commission.

34. Ibid.

35. "Not Stressed Enough?" *FORUM*, Vol. 4, No. 1 (1992). Adapted from C. C. W. Hines and W. C. Wilson, "A No-Nonsense Guide to Being Stressed," *Management Solutions*, October 1986, pp. 27–29.

36. J. T. Dignam, M. Barrera, and S. G. West, "Occupational Stress, Social Support, and Burnout Among Correctional Officers," *American Journal of Community Psychology*, Vol. 14, No. 2 (1986), pp. 177–193.

37. M. C. W. Peeters, B. P. Buunk, and W. B. Schaufeli, "Social Interactions and Feelings of Inferiority Among Correctional Officers: A Daily Event-Recording Approach," *Journal of Applied Social Psychology*, Vol. 25, No. 12 (1995), pp. 1073–1089.

38. David Robinson, Frank Porporino, and Linda Simourd, "Do Different Occupational Groups Vary on Attitudes and Work Adjustment in Corrections?" *Federal Probation*, Vol. 60, No. 3 (1996), pp. 45–53. See also Francis T. Cullen et al., "How Satisfying Is Prison Work? A Comparative Occupational Approach," *The Journal of Offender Counseling Services and Rehabilitation*, Vol. 14, No. 2 (1989), pp. 89–108.

39. Timothy J. Flanagan, Wesley Johnson, and Katherine Bennett, "Job Satisfaction Among Correctional Executives: A Contemporary Portrait of Wardens of State Prisons for Adults," *Prison Journal*, Vol. 76, No. 4 (1996), pp. 385–397.

40. Lombardo.

41. Martinez.

42. Stephen Walters, "The Determinants of Job Satisfaction Among Canadian and American Correctional Officers," *Journal of Crime and Justice*, Vol. 19, No. 2 (1996), pp. 145–158.

43. John R. Hepburn and Paul E. Knepper, "Correctional Officers as Human Services Workers: The Effect on Job Satisfaction," *Justice Quarterly*, Vol. 10, No. 2 (1993), pp. 315–337.

44. Stephen Walters, "Gender, Job Satisfaction, and Correctional Officers: A Comparative Analysis," *The Justice Professional*, Vol. 7, No. 2 (1993), pp. 23–33.

45. Dana M. Britton, "Perceptions of the Work Environment Among Correctional Officers: Do Race and Sex Matter?" *Criminology*, Vol. 35, No. 1 (1997), pp. 85–105.

46. The Victor Cullins Academy is a facility operating under contract with the Youth Services Division of the state of Maryland.

47. The material in this section comes from Jess Maghan, "Ken Davis: The Complete Correctional Officer," *The Keeper's Voice*, Vol. 16, No. 2 (Spring 1995).

9 The Inmate World
Living Behind Bars

CHAPTER OBJECTIVES

After completing this chapter you should be able to:

1. Profile state inmate populations.
2. Explain what the inmate subculture is.
3. Distinguish among deprivation theory, importation theory, and the integration model as they explain the development of the inmate subculture.
4. Know what is meant by the prison code, and be able to list some elements of the prison code.
5. Explain what is meant by *prison argot*.
6. List some common roles that male inmates assume.
7. Describe some major differences between women's and men's prisons.
8. Compare some of the characteristics of female inmates with those of male inmates.
9. Explain how the social structure in women's prisons differs from that in men's prisons.

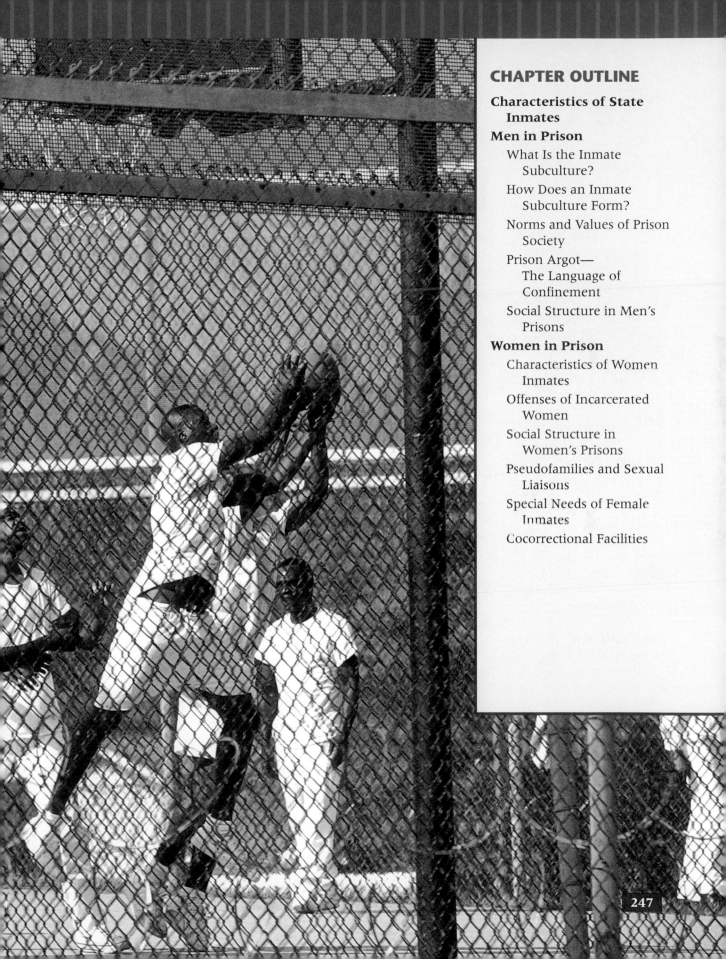

IPSAS CD-ROM

The Instructor's Presentation and Student Assessment Software CD-ROM contains the following:

- A PowerPoint presentation for Chapter 9. The presentation includes over 100 illustrated lecture screens for introducing or reinforcing chapter content and two topical simulations for applying concepts presented in the chapter.
- The ExamView Pro Test Generator and a 100-item question bank for Chapter 9.

Teaching Tip

Refer students to Figure 7–2 in Chapter 7 to review the characteristics of inmates in federal and state prisons. Point out that Chapter 9 concentrates on state inmates, who make up most of the U.S. prison population.

total institution A place where the same people work, play, eat, sleep, and recreate together on a continuous basis. The term was developed by the sociologist Erving Goffman to describe prisons and other facilities.

Teaching Tip

Write out Hans Toch's statement or read it aloud. Ask students if they agree with the statement, and have them explain their responses.

In prison, those things withheld from and denied to the prisoner become precisely what he wants most of all.

— Eldridge Cleaver

In 1997, Rebecca Lynn Thornton pulled open a section of the chain link fence surrounding the prison in Florence, South Carolina, and opened fire. Her husband, a death row inmate, was working in a prison vegetable garden. A hail of gunfire followed, as correctional officers staffing prison towers returned fire. When the smoke cleared, Thornton, 38, and her husband, Floyd Bennet Thornton, Jr., 36, were both dead. Officials were unsure whether the woman meant to kill her husband or was trying to spring him from the institution. Floyd Thornton had been sentenced to die for the 1993 slaying of a 74-year-old man. Thornton was a fugitive at the time. He had escaped from Arizona's Cochise County Jail while awaiting trial for a 1991 slaying.[1]

As this story shows, prison inmates are not as isolated as they may sometimes seem in popular culture. Not only do inmates interact with one another, but they also have relationships that extend beyond prison walls. This chapter will describe prison life, the inmate subculture, and the prison experience in general.

Characteristics of State Inmates

As we have already seen, most state inmates are male, belong to racial or ethnic minority groups, are relatively young, and have been incarcerated for a violent offense. A recent Bureau of Justice Statistics study examined the social, economic, and other characteristics of all state inmates.[2] Highlights of that study are shown in Figure 9–1.

Men in Prison

In his classic work *Asylums*, Erving Goffman used the phrase **total institution** to describe a place where the same people work, eat, sleep, and engage in recreation together day after day.[3] Prisons, concentration camps, mental hospitals, and seminaries are all total institutions, said Goffman. They share many of the same characteristics—even though they exist for different purposes and house different kinds of populations. His words were echoed years later by Hans Toch, who noted that "prisons are 24-hour-a-day, year-in-and-year-out environments in which people are sequestered with little outside contact."[4]

Prisons and other total institutions are small, self-contained societies with their own social structures, norms, and rules. Physically, emotionally, and socially, prison inmates are almost completely cut off from the larger society. As a consequence, they develop their own distinctive lifestyles, roles, and behavioral norms.

The Inmate World: Living Behind Bars

FIGURE 9–1

Profile of State Prison Inmates

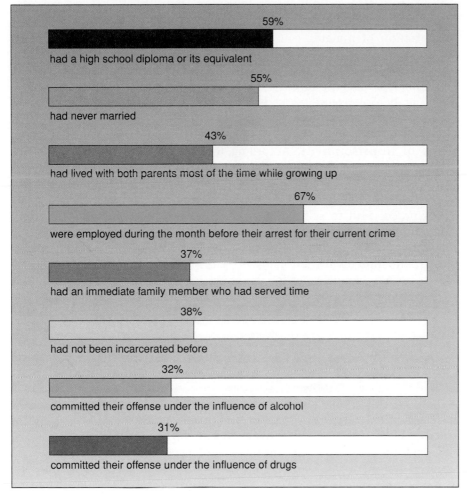

59%
had a high school diploma or its equivalent

55%
had never married

43%
had lived with both parents most of the time while growing up

67%
were employed during the month before their arrest for their current crime

37%
had an immediate family member who had served time

38%
had not been incarcerated before

32%
committed their offense under the influence of alcohol

31%
committed their offense under the influence of drugs

Source: Allen Beck, et al., *Survey of State Prison Inmates*, 1991, Bureau of Justice Statistics (Washington: U.S. Department of Justice, March 1993).

What Is the Inmate Subculture?

Although any prison has its own unique way of life or culture, it is possible to describe a general inmate subculture that characterizes the lives of inmates in correctional institutions nationwide. The **inmate subculture** (also called the *prisoner subculture*) can be defined as "the habits, customs, mores, values, beliefs, or superstitions of the body of inmates incarcerated in correctional institutions."[5]

Prisoners are socialized into the inmate subculture through a process known as prisonization. The concept of **prisonization** was developed by Donald Clemmer in his book *The Prison Community.*[6] Clemmer defined prisonization as the process by which inmates adapt to prison society, and he described it as "the taking on of the ways, mores, customs, and general cul-

pains of imprisonment

Major problems new inmates face, such as loss of liberty and personal autonomy, lack of material possessions, loss of heterosexual relationships, and reduced personal security.

ture of the penitentiary." When the process of prisonization is complete, Clemmer noted, prisoners have become "cons."

In a further study of prisonization, Stanton Wheeler examined how prisoners adapted to life at the Washington State Reformatory.[7] Wheeler found that prisonization has greater impact with the passage of time. The prisonization of inmates, said Wheeler, can be described by a U-shaped curve. When an inmate first enters prison, the conventional values of the outside society still hold sway in his life. As time passes, however, he increasingly adopts the prison lifestyle. Wheeler also found that within the half-year before release, most inmates begin to demonstrate a renewed appreciation for conventional values.

In *The Society of Captives*,[8] Gresham Sykes described what he called the **pains of imprisonment**. According to Sykes, new inmates face major problems, including the loss of liberty, a lack of material possessions, deprivation of goods and services, the loss of heterosexual relationships, the loss of personal autonomy, and a reduction in personal security. These deficits, Sykes noted, lead to self-doubts and reduced self-esteem. Prison society compensates for such feelings and reduces the pains of imprisonment for the prison population as a whole. It also meets the personal and social needs induced in inmates by the pains of imprisonment. In short, said Sykes, inmate society compensates for the losses caused by imprisonment, and it offers varying degrees of comfort to those who successfully adjust to it.

THE OFFENDER SPEAKS

When I was in school and didn't have any homework, my parents would give me some. I was always encouraged and questioned about current events by them. It was a must that we watch the news instead of cartoons on television, and then they would quiz me about what I saw. My parents would come up to school uninvited to check things out. It was embarrassing. My behavior was perfect. Then I joined a gang! They had no control over me after that. I did as I wished. That's why I think that families have little impact on the behavior of a kid. They could be great parents, but once the kid is running the streets with a gang, anything goes.

I'll get out in the year 2002, I think. When I do and I'm with my own kids, there ain't no way they'll run with a gang. I don't care if I gotta quit my job and watch 'em day and night. If the gang don't corrupt 'em, the cops will, 'cause they see the boy with the gang and they think he's bad. They arrest him. They rough him up. They set him up to fail. Prison life? Hell is better. Here it's fight, push, and violate—that's the code. Those who don't keep it can die a thousand different ways.

Michael L. Johnson, N71961
Joliet Correctional Institution
Illinois Department of Corrections

The inmate subculture can vary from one institution to another. Variations are due to differences in the organizational structure of prisons. Maximum-security institutions, for example, are decidedly more painful for inmates because security considerations require greater restriction of inmate freedoms and access to material items. As a result, the subcultures in maximum-security institutions may be much more rigid in their demands on prisoners than those in less secure institutions.

How Does an Inmate Subculture Form?

Early students of inmate subcultures, particularly Clemmer and Sykes, believed that such subcultures developed in response to the deprivations in prison life. This perspective is called **deprivation theory**. It suggests that inmates' values arise in response to the prison environment and its deprivations. Shared deprivation gives inmates a basis for solidarity.[9]

A more recent perspective is that an inmate subculture does not develop in prison, but is brought into prison from the outside world. Known as **importation theory**, this point of view was popularized by John Irwin and Donald R. Cressey.[10] It was further supported by the work of James Jacobs.[11] Importation theory holds that inmate society is shaped by factors outside prison—specifically, preprison life experiences and socialization patterns. Inmates who lived violent lives outside tend to associate with other violent inmates and often engage in similar behavior in prison.[12]

More realistic is the **integration model**, which acknowledges that both theories have some validity. According to the integration model, people undergo early socialization experiences. In childhood, some persons develop leanings toward delinquent and criminal activity, acquiring—from peer groups, parents and other significant adults, television, movies, other mass media, and even computer and video games—values that support law-

Teaching Tip
Review the formation of inmate subcultures, noting the three major theories of subculture development: deprivation theory, importation theory, and the integration model. Ask students which perspective makes the most sense to them and why.

deprivation theory
The belief that inmate subcultures develop in response to the deprivations in prison life.

importation theory
The belief that inmate subcultures are brought into prisons from the outside world.

integration model   A combination of importation theory and deprivation theory. The belief that in childhood, some inmates acquired, usually from peers, values that support law-violating behavior, but that the norms and standards in a prison also affect an inmate.

In some prisons, the inmate subculture is being fragmented as inmates form competing gangs and other groups along ethnic, racial, and geographic lines. How could the differences among such groups affect the order and stability of a prison?

violating behavior. Those who become inmates are also likely to have experienced juvenile court proceedings and may have been institutionalized as juveniles. As a consequence, such persons are likely to have acquired many of the values, much of the language, and the general behavioral patterns of deviant or criminal subcultures before entering adult prison.

The integration model also recognizes, however, the effects that the norms and behavioral standards of inmates in a particular prison have on those who are imprisoned. If a new inmate has already been socialized into a criminal lifestyle, the transition into the inmate subculture is likely to be easy. For some persons, however—especially white-collar offenders with little previous exposure to criminal subcultures—the transition can be very difficult. The language, social expectations, and norms of prison society are likely to be foreign to them.

Norms and Values of Prison Society

Central to prison society is a code of behavior for all inmates. The **prison code** is a set of inmate rules antagonistic to the official administration and rehabilitation programs.[13] Violations of the code result in inmate-imposed sanctions, ranging from ostracism to homicide. Sykes and Messinger have identified five main elements of the prison code:[14]

1. Don't interfere with the interests of other inmates. Never rat on a con. Don't have loose lips.
2. Don't lose your head. Don't quarrel with other inmates. Play it cool. Do your own time.
3. Don't exploit other inmates. Don't steal. Don't break your word. Pay your debts.
4. Don't whine. Be tough. Be a man.
5. Don't be a sucker. Don't trust the guards or staff. Remember that prison officials are wrong and inmates are right.

Prison Argot—The Language of Confinement

Prison argot is the special language of the inmate subculture. *Argot* is a French word meaning "slang." Prison society has always had its own unique language, illustrated by the following argot-laden paragraph:

> The new con, considered fresh meat by the screws and other prisoners, was sent to the cross-bar hotel to do his bit. He soon picked up the reputation through the yard grapevine as a canary-bird. While he was at the big house, the goon squad put him in the freezer for his protection. Eventually, he was released from the ice-box and ordered to make little ones out of big ones until he was released to the free world. Upon release he received $100 in gate money, vowing never to be thrown in the hole or be thought of as a stool-pigeon again.[15]

Prison argot originated partly as a form of secret communication. Gresham Sykes, however, believes that it serves primarily as "an illustrative symbol of the prison community"—or as a way for inmates to mark them-

prison code A set of norms and values among prison inmates. It is generally antagonistic to the official administration and rehabilitation programs of the prison.

prison argot The special language of the inmate subculture.

Teaching Tip
Have students try their hand at translating the argot in the paragraph into standard English.

selves as outlaws and social outcasts.[16] Sykes's work brought prison argot to the attention of sociologists and criminologists. Since Sykes's time other authors have identified a number of words, terms, and acronyms in prison argot. Some of these terms are presented in Table 9–1 on page 254.

Social Structure in Men's Prisons

Inmate societies, like other societies, have a hierarchy of positions. Inmates assume or are forced into specific social roles, and some inmates—by virtue of the roles they assume—have more status and power than others.

Early writers often classified prisoners by the crimes they had committed or their criminal histories. Irwin, for example, divided prisoners into such categories as thieves (those with a culture of criminal values), convicts (time doers), square johns (inmates unfamiliar with criminal subcultures), and dope fiends (drug-involved inmates).[17]

Other writers have identified **inmate roles**, defining them as prison lifestyles or as forms of ongoing social accommodation to prison life. Each role has a position in the pecking order, indicating its status in the prison society.

inmate roles   Prison lifestyles; also, forms of ongoing social accommodation to prison life.

Frank Schmalleger recently developed a contemporary typology of male inmate roles.[18] It is based on actual social roles found among inmates in prison, and it uses contemporary prison argot to name or describe each type. Each type can be viewed as a prison lifestyle either chosen by inmates or forced on them. Some of the types were previously identified by other writers. The twelve inmate types are discussed in the following paragraphs.

The Real Man   Real men do their own time, don't complain, and don't cause problems for other inmates. They see confinement as a natural consequence of criminal activity, and view time spent in prison as an unfortunate cost of doing business. Real men know the inmate code and abide by it. They are well regarded within the institution and rarely run into problems with other inmates. If they do, they solve their problems on their own. They never seek the help of correctional officers or the prison administration. Although they generally avoid trouble within the institution, they usually continue lives of crime once released.

The Mean Dude   Some inmates are notorious for resorting quickly to physical power. They are quick to fight and, when fighting, give no quarter. They are callous, cold, and uncaring. Mean dudes control those around them through force or the threat of force. The fear they inspire usually gives them a great deal of power in inmate society. At the very least, other inmates are likely to leave the mean dude alone.

The Bully   A variation of the mean dude is the bully. Bullies use intimidation to get what they want. Unlike mean dudes, they are far more likely to use threats than to use actual physical force. A bully may make his threats in public so that others see the victim's compliance.

The Agitator   The agitator, sometimes called a "wise guy," is constantly trying to stir things up. He responds to the boredom of prison life by causing

Teaching Tip
Ask students if they are already familiar with some of the examples of argot presented in Table 9–1. If so, how did they learn the expressions?

Professional Issue
Communication Refer to Table 9–1 on page 254. Ask students if it would be useful and appropriate for correctional personnel to manage inmates by using prison argot to communicate with them. Why or why not?

Teaching Tip
Ask students to describe if counterparts for the prisoner types described on these pages are found in free society.

TABLE 9–1

Prison Argot: The Language of Confinement

Argot in Men's Prisons

ace duce: best friend

badge (or bull, hack, "the man," or screw): a correctional officer

ball busters: violent inmates

banger (or burner, shank, sticker): a knife

billys: white men

boneyard: conjugal visiting area

cat-J (or J-cat): a prisoner in need of psychological or psychiatric therapy or medication

cellie: cellmate

center men: inmates who are close to the staff

chester: child molester

dog: homeboy or friend

fag: a male inmate believed to be a natural (preprison) homosexual

featherwood: a peckerwood's "woman"

fish: a newly arrived inmate

gorilla: an inmate who uses force to take what he wants from others

hipsters: young, drug-involved inmates

homeboy: a prisoner from one's hometown or neighborhood

ink: tattoos

lemon squeezer: an inmate who has an unattractive "girlfriend"

man walking: phrase used to signal that a guard is coming

merchant (or peddler): one who sells when he should give; or one who sells goods and services to other inmates illegally

nimby: not in my back yard

peckerwood (or wood): a white prisoner

punk: male inmate who is forced into a submissive or feminine role during homosexual relations

rat (or snitch): an inmate who squeals (provides information about other inmates to the prison administration)

real men: inmates respected by other inmates

schooled: knowledgeable in the ways of prison life

shakedown: search of a cell or a work area

shu (pronounced shoe)**:** special housing unit

toughs: those with a preprison history of violent crimes

tree jumper: rapist

turn out: to rape or make into a punk

wolf: a male inmate who assumes an aggressive masculine role during homosexual relations

Argot in Women's Prisons

cherry (or cherrie): an inmate not yet introduced to lesbian activities

fay broad: a white inmate

femme (or mommy): an inmate who plays the feminine role during lesbian relations

safe: the vagina, especially when used for hiding contraband

stud broad (or daddy): an inmate who assumes the role of a male during lesbian relations

Sources: Gresham Sykes, *The Society of Captives* (Princeton, NJ: Princeton University Press, 1958); Rose Giallombardo, *Society of Women: A Study of Women's Prison* (New York: John Wiley, 1966); Richard A. Cloward et al., *Theoretical Studies in Social Organization of the Prison* (New York: Social Science Research Council, 1960). For a more contemporary listing of prison slang terms, see Reinhold Aman, *Hillary Clinton's Pen Pal: A Guide to Life and Lingo in Federal Prison* (Santa Rosa, CA: Maledicta Press, 1996); Jerome Washington, *Iron House: Stories from the Yard* (Ann Arbor, MI: QED Press, 1994); Morrie Camhi, *The Prison Experience* (Boston: Charles Tuttle Co., 1989); Harold Long, *Survival In Prison* (Port Townsend, WA: Loompanics Unlimited, 1990).

problems for others. An agitator may point out, for example, how a powerful inmate has been wronged by another inmate or that an inmate seen talking to a "rat" must be a snitch himself.

The Hedonist   The hedonist adapts to prison by exploiting the minimal pleasures it offers. Hedonists always seek the easy path, and they plot to win the "cushiest" jobs. They may also stockpile goods to barter for services of various kinds. Hedonists live only in the now, with little concern for the future. Their lives revolve around such activities as gambling, drug running, smuggling contraband, and exploiting homosexual opportunities.

The Opportunist   The opportunist sees prison as an opportunity for personal advancement. He takes advantage of the formal self-improvement opportunities of the prison, such as schooling, trade training, and counseling. Other inmates generally dislike opportunists, seeing them as selfish "do-gooders." Staff members, however, often see opportunists as model prisoners.

The Retreatist   Some inmates, unable to cope with the realities of prison life, withdraw psychologically from the world around them. Depression, neurosis, and even psychosis may result. Some retreatists lose themselves in drugs or alcohol. Others attempt suicide. Isolation from the general prison population, combined with counseling or psychiatric treatment, may offer the best hope for retreatists to survive the prison experience.

The Legalist   Legalists are known as "jailhouse lawyers," or simply "lawyers," in prison argot. They are usually among the better-educated prisoners, although some legalists have little formal education. Legalists fight confinement through the system of laws, rules, and court precedent. Legalists file writs with the courts, seeking hearings on a wide variety of issues. Although many legalists work to better the conditions of their own confinement or to achieve early release, most also file pleas on behalf of other prisoners.

The Radical   Radicals see themselves as political prisoners of an unfair society. They believe that a discriminatory world has denied them the education and skills needed to succeed in a socially acceptable way. Most of the beliefs held by radical inmates are rationalizations that shift the blame for personal failure onto society. The radical inmate is likely to be familiar with contemporary countercultural figures.

The Colonist   Colonists, also referred to as "convicts," turn prison into home. Colonists know the ropes of prison, have many "friends" on the inside, and often feel more comfortable in prison than outside it. They may not look forward to leaving prison. Some may even commit additional offenses to extend their stay. Colonists are generally well regarded by other prisoners. Many are old-timers. Colonists have learned to take advantage of the informal opportunity structure in prisons, and they are well versed in the inmate code.

The Religious Inmate   Religious inmates profess a strong religious faith and may attempt to convert both inmates and staff. Religious inmates frequently form prayer groups, request special meeting facilities and special diets, and may ask for frequent visits from religious leaders. Religious inmates are often under a great deal of suspicion from inmates and staff, who tend to think they are faking religious commitment to gain special treatment. Those judged sincere in their faith may win early release, removal from death row, or any number of other special considerations.

The Punk   The punk is a young inmate, often small, who has been forced into a sexual relationship with an aggressive, well-respected prisoner. Punks are generally "turned out" through homosexual rape. A punk usually finds a protector among the more powerful inmates. Punks keep their protectors happy by providing them with sexual services.

Violence and victimization occur in men's prisons. A good deal of prison violence has sexual overtones. One person who has contributed significantly to the study of sexual violence in men's prisons is Daniel Lockwood.[19] Using interviews and background data from prison files, Lockwood identified and studied 107 "targets" of aggressive sexual threats and 45 inmate "aggressors" in New York state male prisons. He also conducted a general survey, which revealed that 28 percent of all male prisoners had been targets of sexual aggressors in prison at least once. Lockwood found that only one of the inmates he interviewed had actually been raped—an indication that the incidence of prison rape is quite low relative

CAREER PROFILE

*Jack Osborn
Custody Utility Officer
Jefferson City
Correctional Center
Jefferson City, MO*

"What makes a good custody officer? Being firm, fair, and consistent—clear, concise actions with the inmates and the other prison staff. Being honest goes far. If you don't know the answer, say so. If you say you will find out, do it. Learn to say no, too. You can change it to a yes easier than changing a yes to a no."

Jack Osborn is a custody utility officer at the Jefferson City Correctional Center in Missouri. As a utility officer, he may be assigned to any area or department that needs an additional staff member. Before becoming a correctional officer, Jack was a deputy sheriff for 10 years. He has completed two years of community college coursework.

Jack advises knowing the inmates and being able to interpret behavioral changes. "Know what silence means. Communicate— listen," says Jack. "Learn who runs drugs and gambling, who the punks are. That's where your trouble will come from." Jack believes that if you follow this advice and know the mechanics of the job, you should have a great career in corrections.

to other types of harm that may accompany sexual incidents, such as physical abuse, verbal abuse, threatening gestures, and threatening propositions.

Targets, when compared with nontargets, were found to be physically slight, young, white, nonviolent offenders from nonurban areas. They generally had a higher rate of psychological disturbance than other inmates and were more apt to attempt suicide while in prison. Shown here is a note found by a new inmate in his cell at a New York state prison unit. The new inmate was young and not prison-wise. After discovering the note, the inmate asked to be moved to the prison's isolation area. His request was granted.[20]

The typical incident of sexual aggression, Lockwood found, is carried out by a group. About half the incidents Lockwood identified included physical violence, and another third involved threats. The incidents studied showed patterns of escalation from verbal abuse to physical violence.

Lockwood also found that prison rapes generally occur when gangs of aggressors circumvent security arrangements and physically control their victims. Fear, anxiety, suicidal thoughts, social disruption, and attitude changes develop in many victims of homosexual rape.

> Yo S
> Check this out if you don't give me a peace of your ass I am going to take you off the count and that is my word.
> I be down a very long time So I need It very Bad I will give you 5 Pack's of Smokes If you do it OK That is my word So if you Want to live you Better do it and get it over with there are Three of us who need it. OK. . . .

Women in Prison

In America today, there are far fewer women's prisons than men's prisons, and men in prison outnumber women in prison 16 to 1.[21] A state usually has one women's prison, housing a few hundred women. The size of a women's prison generally depends on the population of the state. Some small states house women prisoners in special areas of what are otherwise institutions for men.

Women's prisons are generally quite different from men's. Here's how one writer describes them:

> Often, there are no gun towers, no armed guards and no stone walls or fences strung on top with concertina wire. Neatly pruned hedges, well-kept flower gardens, attractive brick buildings and wide paved walkways greet the visitor's eye at women's prisons in many states. Often these institutions are located in rural, pastoral settings which may suggest tranquility and well-being to the casual observer.[22]

Such rural settings, however, make it hard for female inmates to maintain contact with their families, who may live far from the correctional facility.

Many prisons for women are built on a cottage plan. Cottages dot the grounds of such institutions, often arranged in pods. A group of six or so cottages constitutes a pod. Each cottage is much like a traditional house, with individual bedrooms; a day room with a television, chairs, couches, and tables; and small personal or shared bathrooms.

Teaching Tip
Direct attention to the "Letter to a Punk." Point out that besides the aggressive sexual threats, the letter shows the black market economy of the prison at work, with cigarettes the preferred medium of exchange for a high-demand service.

Student Involvement
If any of your students are currently employed in a women's correctional facility or a women's area of a coed prison, ask them to describe the physical environment of the prison.

FIGURE 9–2

Sample Regulations at a Women's Prison

RULES AND REGULATIONS
SYBIL BRAND INSTITUTE FOR WOMEN
LOS ANGELES, CALIFORNIA

Appearance—Cleanliness—Neatness

Cells and Dormitories. Each inmate is required to keep her own cell or bed area and surrounding area neat and clean at all times.

Lockers. Only cup and ashtray on outside locker shelf in Dorms. There are to be no liners on the inside locker shelves. Locker contents must be orderly and not excessive. Any amount over five (5) of each cosmetic item is considered excessive and will NOT be returned to you. Dresses, etc. to be hung on rack inside locker. Do NOT hang anything on doors of locker.

Beds. Must be made prior to breakfast and kept neat during the day.

Floors and Walls. Nothing is to be left on the floor during the night except one (1) pair of shoes or thongs per person. Do NOT deface or paste pictures on walls or lockers. No blankets or pillows on floor.

Trash. All trash which will burn is to be placed in the trash can. There are to be NO individual trash receptacles (boxes, paper bags, etc.) in bed areas or lockers. Soiled napkins must be wrapped securely in newspaper and placed in trash cans. Glass and metal are to be turned in to the officer.

Personal Appearance. Each inmate is required to keep herself neat and clean at all times. You must be fully dressed and presentable when leaving your housing area for any reason: do NOT walk around in stocking feet or barefooted.

Showers. Shower is to be taken daily. You are allowed ten (10) minutes to shower. No showers one-half hour prior to any meal line or after lights out.

Headscarves or Pin Curls. Headscarves or pin curls are not permitted from 7:00 A.M. to 5:30 P.M. unless special permission is granted.

Nightcaps. May be worn after 5:30 P.M. only if hair is in curlers. May be worn from bedtime to 7:00 A.M. whether or not hair is in curlers. Are to be worn above eyebrows.

Source: Kathryn Watterson, *Women in Prison* (Boston, MA: Northeastern University Press, 1996), appendix (p. 365).

Security in women's prisons is generally more relaxed than in men's, and female inmates may have more freedom within the institution than their male counterparts. Practically speaking, women—even those in prison—are seen as less dangerous than men and less prone to violence or escape. Despite the more relaxed nature of women's prisons, certain rules govern the behavior of inmates (see Figure 9–2 on page 258 for sample regulations at a women's prison).

Treatment, education, recreation, and other programs in women's prisons have often been criticized as inferior to those in men's prisons. Recent research has uncovered continuing disparities in many areas.[23] For example, men's institutions often have a much wider range of vocational and educational training programs and services, and larger and better-equipped law libraries. Similarly, exercise facilities—including weight rooms, jogging areas, and basketball courts—are often better equipped and larger in men's institutions today than in women's.

Prison administrators have often found it impractical to develop and fund programs at the same level in women's and men's prisons, because of differences in interest, participation, space, and so on. Nonetheless, it is important to strive for parity of opportunity as an ideal. The American Correctional Association, for example, through its Guidelines for Women's Prison Construction and Programming,[24] insists that the same level of services and opportunities be available in women's prisons as in men's prisons in the same jurisdiction.

In some instances, women may be placed in an institution housing inmates with a range of security levels. Consequently, women who are low security risks may have less personal freedom than their male counterparts. Women may also not have the opportunity to transfer to a less secure institution as they become safer risks.

Activity Therapy Administrator

Helps confined clients help themselves through personal activities developed by the administrator and other human services professionals working in each unit. Qualifications: completion of graduate school core program in recreation (physical education) or a specialty area (art, music, dance, theater), or an undergraduate degree and one year's experience in activity therapy. All applicants must pass a civil service examination and tests assessing knowledge, skills, and abilities related to the job classification.

Characteristics of Women Inmates

Many of our conceptions of female inmates derive more from myth than reality. Two recent BJS surveys provide a more realistic picture of female inmates.[25] In 1998, women were 6.5 percent of the prisoners in the nation. Female prisoners largely resembled male prisoners in race, ethnic background, and age. However, they were substantially more likely to be serving time for a drug offense and less likely to have been sentenced for a violent crime. Women were also more likely than men to be serving time for larceny or fraud.

Female inmates had shorter criminal records than male inmates. They generally had shorter maximum sentences than men. Half of all women had a maximum sentence of 60 months or less, while half of all men had a sentence of 120 months or less. Significantly, more than 4 in 10 of the women prisoners responding to the BJS survey reported prior physical or sexual abuse. One of the major factors distinguishing male inmates from female is that the women have experienced far more sexual and physical abuse than the men. Figure 9–3 is a comparison of selected characteristics of female and male state prisoners.

Student Involvement
Have students review the rules in Figure 9–2. Do they think the rules are too strict, not strict enough, or just right? Are there any differences of opinion between men and women in the class?

FIGURE 9–3

Characteristics of Women and Men in State Prisons

Women in Prison

Criminal Offense
- 35% were in prison for drug offenses
- 28% were in prison for violent offenses
- 27% were in prison for property offenses

Criminal History
- 46% were nonviolent recidivists
- 28% had no previous sentence
- 26% were violent recidivists

Family Characteristics
- 78% had children
- 42% had lived with both parents most of time growing up
- 33% had a parent/guardian who abused alcohol or drugs
- 17% were married at the time they committed the offense for which they were incarcerated
- 45% had never married
- 47% had a family member who had been incarcerated

Drug and Alcohol Use
- 41% had used drugs daily in the month before the current offense
- 36% were under the influence of drugs at the time of the offense
- 12% were under the influence of alcohol at the time of the offense

Men in Prison

Criminal Offense
- 48% were in prison for violent offenses
- 22% were in prison for property offenses
- 20% were in prison for drug offenses

Criminal History
- 50% were violent recidivists
- 31% were nonviolent recidivists
- 19% had no previous sentence

Family Characteristics
- 64% had children
- 43% had lived with both parents most of time growing up
- 26% had a parent/guardian who abused alcohol or drugs
- 18% were married at the time they committed the offense for which they were incarcerated
- 56% had never married
- 37% had a family member who had been incarcerated

Drug and Alcohol Use
- 36% had used drugs daily in the month before the current offense
- 31% were under the influence of drugs at the time of the offense
- 18% were under the influence of alcohol at the time of the offense

Source: Allen J. Beck and Christopher J. Mumola, *Prisoners in 1998,* Bureau of Justice Statistics (Washington: U.S. Department of Justice, August 1999) and Allen Beck et al., *Survey of State Prison Inmates, 1991,* Bureau of Justice Statistics (Washington: U.S. Department of Justice, March 1993).

The Inmate World: Living Behind Bars

Offenses of Incarcerated Women

Drug offenses account for a large percentage of the women behind bars. Two-thirds of all women in federal prisons, for example, are serving time on drug charges.[26] Some sources estimate that, together, drug crimes and other crimes indirectly related to drug activities account for the imprisonment of around 95 percent of today's women inmates. In short, drug use and abuse, or crimes stimulated by the desire for drugs and drug money, are what send most women to prison. (See Figure 9–4.) This has been true for at least a decade. According to an American Correctional Association report, the primary reasons incarcerated women most frequently gave for their arrest were (1) trying to pay for drugs, (2) attempts to relieve economic pressures, and (3) poor judgment.[27]

According to the BJS, before arrest, women in prison used more drugs than men and used those drugs more frequently.[28] About 54 percent of imprisoned women had used drugs in the month before the offense for which they were arrested, compared with 50 percent of the men. Female inmates were also more likely than male inmates to have used drugs regularly (65 percent versus 62 percent), to have used drugs daily in the month preceding their offense (41 percent versus 36 percent), and to have been under the influence at the time of the offense (36 percent versus 31 percent). Nearly 1 in 4 female inmates surveyed reported committing the offense to get money to buy drugs, compared with 1 in 6 males.

Female inmates who used drugs differed from those who did not in the types of crimes they committed. Regardless of the amount of drug use, users were less likely than nonusers to be serving a sentence for a violent offense.

FIGURE 9–4

Imprisoned Inmates by Offense Category and Gender

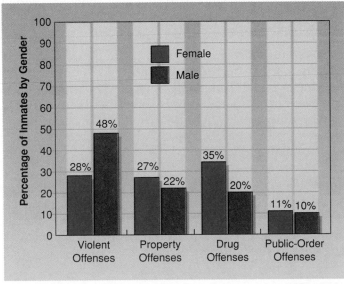

Source: Allen J. Beck and Christopher J. Mumola, *Prisoners in 1998*, Bureau of Justice Statistics (Washington: U.S. Department of Justice, August 1999).

Social Structure in Women's Prisons

As might be expected, the social structure and the subcultural norms and expectations in women's prisons are quite different from those in men's prisons. Unfortunately, however, relatively few studies of inmate life have been conducted in institutions for women.

One early study, of women at the Federal Reformatory for Women in Alderson, West Virginia, was an effort to compare subcultural aspects of women's prisons with those of men's. Rose Giallombardo reached the conclusion that "many of the subcultural features of the institution are imported from the larger society."[29] Giallombardo believed that male and female inmate subcultures are actually quite similar, except that women's prisons develop "a substitute universe," a world "in which inmates may preserve an identity which is relevant to life outside the prison."

Giallombardo was unable to find in the women's prison some of the values inherent in a male inmate subculture, such as "Do your own time." The inmate subculture in a women's prison, she said, tended to encourage relationships rather than isolation. Hence, women were expected to share their problems with other inmates and to offer at least some support and encouragement to others. On the other hand, she observed, women prisoners tend to see each other as conniving, self-centered, and scheming. Hence, a basic tenet of the inmate subculture in a women's prison is "You can't trust other women." As Giallombardo put it, women prisoners tend to believe that "every woman is a sneaking, lying bitch."

Giallombardo concluded that the social structure of women's prisons and the social role assumed by each inmate were based on three elements:

1. The individual woman's level of personal dependence and her status needs (which were said to be based upon cultural expectations of the female role).
2. The individual's needs arising from incarceration, combined with the institution's inability to meet female inmates' emotional needs.
3. Needs related to the individual's personality.

A more recent study was of inmates in the District of Columbia Women's Reformatory at Occoquan, Virginia.[30] Esther Heffernan identified three roles that women commonly adopt when adjusting to prison. According to Heffernan, women's roles evolved partly from the characteristics the women brought with them to prison and depended partly on the ways the women chose to adapt to prison life. The roles she described are discussed in the following paragraphs:

The Cool Inmate   Cool women usually had previous records, were in the know, were street-wise, and did not cause trouble for other inmates while in prison. Cool women were seen as professional or semiprofessional criminals who worked to win the maximum number of prison amenities without endangering their parole or release dates.

The Square Inmate   Square women were not familiar with criminal lifestyles and had few, if any, criminal experiences other than the one for

THE STAFF SPEAKS

Oftentimes, my prison clients tell me that prison rehab providers like myself have few clues about the needs of people in prison rehabilitation programs. I think that many prisoners believe that educated people who have never used drugs have difficulty in developing and implementing drug rehab programs that really work. Many of my clients say they would design the program differently. I usually listen to their ideas, and sometimes I incorporate some of their thoughts in my work. But I realize that they would water a program down so much that other inmates who want to save themselves wouldn't have an opportunity to do so. Sometimes these clients argue that drug rehab providers should be former addicts—as if any knowledge gained in school, many years of experience, and dedication to helping others are worthless. I don't say that to them, but I do remind them that dentists don't need rotten teeth to be good dentists.

John McNerney
Correctional Counselor
Willard-Cybulski Correctional Institution
Enfield, CT

which they were imprisoned. They tended to hold the values and roles of conventional society.

The Life Inmate   Life inmates were habitual or career offenders, and were generally well socialized into lives of crime. They supported inmate values and subculture. Life inmates typically were in and out of prison from an early age and had developed criminal lifestyles dedicated to meeting their political, economic, familial, and social needs outside conventional society.

One writer, summarizing the results of studies such as those discussed here, found two features that distinguish women's prisons from men's prisons:[31]

1. The social roles in women's prisons place greater emphasis on homosexual relations as a mode of adaptation to prison life.
2. The mode of adaptation a female inmate selects is best assessed by studying the inmate's preinstitutional experiences.

Pseudofamilies and Sexual Liaisons

One of the most serious deprivations women in prison experience is isolation from family and loss of contact with loved ones, especially children.

Student Involvement
Have students compare Esther Heffernan's female inmate roles with the male inmate roles presented earlier in the chapter. Are there any matches?

A BJS study of women in prison showed that two-thirds of imprisoned women had at least one child younger than 18.[32] The children usually stayed with their maternal grandmothers or with other relatives, although some were placed in foster homes. Worry about children affects female inmates' physical and emotional well-being.

A unique feature of women's prisons is pseudofamilies. **Pseudo-families** are familylike structures, common in women's prisons, in which inmates assume roles similar to those families in free society. Pseudofamilies appear to provide emotional and social support for the women who belong to them. Courtship, marriage, and kinship ties formed with other women inmates provide a means of coping with the rigors of imprisonment. One inmate has explained pseudofamilies this way: "It just happens. Just like on the outside, you get close to certain people. It's the same in here— but we probably get even closer than a lot of families because of how lonely it is otherwise."[33]

Some authors suggest that pseudofamilies are to women's prisons what gangs are to men's.[34] Men establish social relationships largely through power, and gang structure effectively expresses such relationships. Women relate to one another more expressively and emotionally. Hence, family structures are one of the most effective reflections of women's relationships in prison, just as they are in the wider society. At least one study of prison coping behavior found that new female inmates, especially those most in need of support, advice, and assistance in adjusting to the conditions of incarceration, are the women most likely to become members of prison pseudofamilies.[35]

pseudofamilies
Familylike structures, common in women's prisons, in which inmates assume roles similar to those in families in free society.

The kinship of substitute families plays a major role in the lives of many female inmates, who take the relationships very seriously. How might these relationships supplant values such as "do your own time" commonly found in the subculture of men's prisons?

To a large extent, the social and behavioral patterns of family relationships in prison mirror their traditional counterparts in the community. Moreover, homosexual relationships, marriage alliances, and the larger informal familylike groupings that emerge within the social structure of women's prisons fulfill women's social and emotional needs during incarceration.

Families in women's prisons come in all sizes and colors. They can be virtual melting pots of ethnicity and age. A member of a family may be young or old and may be black, white, or Hispanic. As in families in free society, there are roles for husbands and wives, sisters, brothers, grandmothers, and children. Roles for aunts and uncles don't exist, however.

"Stud broads," in prison argot, assume any male role, including husband and brother. Other inmates think of them as men. "Men" often assume traditional roles in women's prisons, ordering women around, demanding to be waited on, expecting to have their rooms cleaned and their laundry done, and so forth. Most women who assume masculine roles within prison are said to be "playing" and are sometimes called "players." Once they leave, they usually revert to feminine roles. A "femme" or "mommy" is a woman who assumes a female role in a family, and during homosexual activity.

Most women in prison, including those playing masculine roles, were generally not lesbians before entering prison. They resort to lesbian relations within prison because relationships with men are unavailable. The lesbian, in contrast, prefers homosexual relationships to heterosexual ones, even in the outside world.

Though gender roles and family relationships within women's prisons appear to have an enduring quality, women can and sometimes do change gender. When a woman playing a masculine role, for example, reverts to a feminine one, she is said to have "dropped her belt." A stud broad who drops her belt may wreak havoc on relationships within her own family and in families related to it.

Food Services Coordinator

This position is responsible for all matters relating to a seven-day-a-week, 365-days-a-year institutional food service operation: diet planning; menu publication; food ordering and purchasing; inventory control; scheduling, supervising, training, directing, and evaluating full- and part-time food service staff. Qualified candidates must possess a degree in food service, dietetics, or other related field or at least five years' work experience in food service, with a minimum of two years' supervisory or management experience preferred.

Special Needs of Female Inmates

Rarely are the special needs of imprisoned women fully recognized—and even less frequently are they addressed. Many of today's prison administrators and correctional officers still treat women as if they were men. Nicole Hahn Rafter, for example, says that many prisons have an attitude akin to "just add women and stir."[36]

Susan Cranford is division director of the Community Justice Assistance Division of the Texas Department of Criminal Justice. Rose Williams is warden of Pulaski State Prison in Hawkinsville, Georgia. Cranford and Williams wrote in a 1998 article that "correctional staff should keep the unique needs of women offenders in mind."[37] They say that the effective running of a women's prison requires consideration of those needs.

A critical difference between male and female prisoners, say Cranford and Williams, is "the manner in which they communicate." Female offenders, they note, are usually much more open, more verbal, more emotional,

Student Involvement
Ask students to write position papers detailing the special needs of women offenders and offering creative ways of addressing them. Students who don't think women offenders have special needs should support their positions.

Most children of incarcerated mothers have little contact with their mothers. The lack of contact often upsets their emotional development. How might prisons contribute to the development of positive relationships between incarcerated mothers and their children?

and more willing to share the intimacies of their lives than men are. Male prisoners, like most men in free society, are guarded about the information they share and the manner in which they share it. "For men, information is power. For women, talking helps establish a common ground, a way to relate to others."

Gender-specific training is vital for COs who work in women's prisons, say Cranford and Williams. Proper training, they write, can head off the development of inappropriate relationships (especially by male staff members), which could lead to sexual misconduct. Moreover, staff members who work with women should receive additional training in negotiating and listening skills.

Finally, say Cranford and Williams, it is important to realize that a woman's children are usually very important to her and that many imprisoned women have children on the outside. Even more significant is that children of offenders are about eight times as likely as children of nonoffenders to become criminals. Hence, parenting skills should be taught to imprisoned mothers, since most imprisoned mothers will rejoin their children and will be with the children during critical stages in their development.

Cocorrectional Facilities

In 1971, a disturbance at the federal women's prison at Alderson, West Virginia, led to calls for ways to expand incarceration options for women. The federal Bureau of Prisons responded by moving low-security female prisoners from the crowded Alderson institution to a federal minimum-security prison at Morgantown, West Virginia. The Morgantown facility had been built for young males but had not reached its design capacity. With this move, the modern era of coed prisons, or cocorrections, was born.

A **coed prison** is a facility housing both men and women, and **cocorrections** is the incarceration and interaction of female and male offenders under a single institutional administration.[38] It is estimated that as many as 52 adult correctional institutions in the United States are coed and that they confine almost 23,000 men and 7,000 women.[39]

Since its inception, cocorrections has been cited as a potential solution to a wide variety of corrections problems. The rationales in support of cocorrections are that it

1. Reduces the dehumanizing and destructive aspects of incarceration by permitting heterosocial relationships.
2. Reduces problems of institutional control.
3. Creates a more "normal" atmosphere, reducing privation.
4. Allows positive heterosocial skills to emerge.
5. Cushions the shock of release.
6. Increases the number of program offerings and improves program access for all prisoners.
7. Expands career opportunities for women.

An examination of the cocorrections literature from 1970 to 1990, however, found no evidence that cocorrections benefits female prisoners.[40] A former warden of a coed prison contends that "going coed" has often been done to appease male egos and smooth the running of men's prisons. Warden Jacqueline Crawford tells us that most women in prison have generally been exploited by the men in their lives. A coed prison, she says, furthers this experience because male prisoners continue the abuse women have come to expect from men.[41]

Others have found that all too often women's prisons have been turned into coed prisons, thus limiting correctional options for women. Overall, researchers have concluded, "Co-corrections offers women prisoners few, if any, economic, educational, vocational, and social advantages."[42] Whether prisoners released from coed prisons adjust better to the community or experience less recidivism has not been sufficiently studied.

Although the literature on single-sex prisons[43] has repeatedly shown poor overall performance in prisoner rehabilitation and public safety, correctional decision makers, policy makers, legislators, and the public are not calling for an end to one-sex imprisonment. If cocorrections is to become more than window dressing, however, it requires more attention to planning, implementation, and evaluation. Contrary to some early claims, coed prisons are not a quick fix for problems of prison administration.

coed prison A prison housing both female and male offenders.

cocorrections The incarceration and interaction of female and male offenders under a single institutional administration.

Teaching Tip
Have students volunteer what they consider the pros and cons of coed prisons. List their replies in separate columns. Then initiate a discussion of which type of prison students would prefer to work in—all male, all female, or coed.

Teaching Tip
Refer to Chapter 9 of the *Instructor's Resource Manual* for additional activities and for answers to the end-of-chapter exercises.

9

Review and Applications

SUMMARY BY CHAPTER OBJECTIVES

CHAPTER OBJECTIVE 1
Most state inmates are male, belong to racial or ethnic minority groups, are relatively young, and have been incarcerated for a violent offense.

CHAPTER OBJECTIVE 2
Prison inmates live their daily lives in accordance with the dictates of the inmate subculture. The inmate subculture consists of the customs and beliefs of those incarcerated in correctional institutions.

CHAPTER OBJECTIVE 3
Deprivation theory holds that prisoner subcultures develop in response to the pains of imprisonment. Importation theory claims that inmate subcultures are brought into prisons from the outside world. A more realistic approach might be the integration model, which uses both theories to explain prisoner subcultures.

CHAPTER OBJECTIVE 4
An important aspect of the male inmate subculture is the prison code. The prison code is a set of norms for the behavior of inmates. Central elements of the code include notions of loyalty (to prison society), control of anger, toughness, and distrust of prison officials. Because the prison code is a part of the inmate subculture, it is mostly opposed to official policies.

CHAPTER OBJECTIVE 5
The inmate subculture also has its own language, called prison argot. Examples of prison argot include "fish" (a new inmate), "cellie" (cellmate), and "homeboy" (a prisoner from one's hometown).

CHAPTER OBJECTIVE 6
Inmate roles are prison lifestyles. They include the real man, the mean dude, the bully, the agitator, the opportunist, the retreatist, the legalist, and the punk.

CHAPTER OBJECTIVE 7
There are far fewer women's prisons than men's in the United States. Women's prisons often have no gun towers or armed guards and no stone walls or fences topped by barbed wire. They tend to be more attractive and are often built on a cottage plan. Security in most women's prisons is more relaxed than in institutions for men, and female inmates may have more freedom within the institution than their male counterparts. Even so, gender-based disparities exist. A lack of funding and inadequate training have been cited to explain why programs available to women inmates are often not on a par with those available to male prisoners.

CHAPTER OBJECTIVE 8
Female prisoners largely resemble male prisoners in race, ethnic background, and age. However, they are substantially more likely to be serving time for a drug offense and less likely to have been sentenced for a violent crime.

CHAPTER OBJECTIVE 9
While there are many similarities, the social structure and the subcultural norms and expectations in women's prisons differ from those in men's prisons in a number of important ways. One important difference can be found in the fact that the prisoner subculture in a women's prison tends to encourage relationships rather than isolation. As a consequence, pseudofamilies arise, with fully developed familial relationships and roles.

KEY TERMS

total institution, p. 248
inmate subculture, p. 249
prisonization, p. 249
pains of imprisonment, p. 250
deprivation theory, p. 251
importation theory, p. 251
integration model, p. 251

prison code, p. 252
prison argot, p. 252
inmate roles, p. 253
pseudofamilies, p. 264
coed prison, p. 267
cocorrections, p. 267

QUESTIONS FOR REVIEW

1. What did Erving Goffman mean when he wrote that prisons are *total institutions*?
2. What is the *inmate subculture*, and how is it central to understanding society in men's prisons?
3. What is *prisonization*?
4. According to Gresham Sykes, what are the pains of imprisonment?
5. Explain how inmate subcultures develop, according to deprivation theory, importation theory, and the integration model.
6. What is the *prison code*? How does it influence behavior in men's prisons?
7. Explain what is meant by inmate roles, and give some examples.

8. Compare female and male inmates by their criminal histories, their family characteristics, and the offenses for which they were incarcerated.
9. In what ways do women's prisons differ from men's prisons?
10. What are *pseudofamilies*, and why are they important to the society of women's prisons?
11. What is the most common type of offense for which women are imprisoned?
12. What are some issues relating to cocorrectional facilities?

CRITICAL THINKING EXERCISES

ON-THE-JOB ISSUE

You are a correctional officer assigned to a women's prison. Six months ago, the superintendent of your institution ordered an investigation to determine the proper role of male officers within the facility. The investigation centered on charges by a handful of inmates that they had been sexually harassed by male COs. The alleged harassment included requests for sexual favors in return for special privileges, observation of female inmates in various states of undress while in their rooms and in shower facilities, and inappropriate touching during cell and facility searches (policy allowed only female COs to conduct body searches).

Although the investigation was inconclusive, the activities of male COs have been restricted. They are no longer permitted to have any physical contact with inmates unless an emergency demands that they restrain or search inmates. They have been reassigned to areas of the facility where they cannot view shower and toilet facilities. They are expected to announce their presence in living areas, and they have been ordered to take special classes on staff-inmate interaction.

Unfortunately, however, there are not enough female COs for all of the reassignments required by the recent shift in policy. As a result, the routines of female officers are being significantly disrupted. Female officers are being asked to work shifts that are inconvenient for their personal lives (many are mothers or college students and had come to count on predictable shift work). Most female COs also feel that their work load has increased, since they have to cover areas of the institution and assume tasks that male officers would previously have handled.

A few female COs have already left for jobs elsewhere, citing difficulties created in the work environment by the new policies. The talk among the correctional staff is that many of the remaining female staff members might also soon leave. If more female COs leave the facility, it will be impossible for those who remain to keep the facility running under the new rules.

1. Did the superintendent make the right decision in limiting the activities of male COs? Why or why not?

2. Might there be other ways to resolve the issues raised by the investigation into sexual harassment? If so, what might they be?

CORRECTIONS ISSUE

A woman who gives birth in prison may lose her child to state authorities or may have her parental rights severely restricted. In most cases, the child is removed from the inmate mother shortly after birth. Do you think this is fair? Why or why not?

CORRECTIONS ON THE WEB

Access the Bureau of Justice Statistics at **http://www.ojp.usdoj.gov/bjs**, and click on "Criminal offenders." Review the following topics: Lifetime Likelihood of going to state or federal prison, Intimate victimizers, and Use of alcohol by convicted offenders. Write a summary of the information you find under each topic.

ADDITIONAL READINGS

American Correctional Association. *The Female Offender: What Does the Future Hold?* Washington: St. Mary's, 1990.

Flanagan, Timothy J. (ed.). *Long-Term Imprisonment: Policy, Science, and Correctional Practice.* Thousand Oaks, CA: Sage, 1995.

Johnson, Robert. *Hard Time: Understanding and Reforming the Prison,* 2d ed. Belmont, CA: Wadsworth, 1996.

Morris, Allison, et al. *Managing the Needs of Female Prisoners.* London: Home Office, 1995.

Rafter, Nicole. *Partial Justice: Women, Prisons and Social Control.* Brunswick, NJ: Transaction, 1990.

Pollock-Byrne, Joycelyn. *Women, Prison and Crime.* Pacific Grove, CA: Brooks-Cole, 1990.

Watterson, Kathryn. *Women in Prison: Inside the Concrete Tomb,* 2d ed. Boston: Northeastern University Press, 1996.

ENDNOTES

1. Adapted from "Inmate, Wife Killed in Prison Shootout," *The Keeper's Voice,* Vol. 18, No. 2–3 (Summer-Fall 1997), citing the *Arizona Tribune,* July 10, 1997.

2. Allen Beck et al., *Survey of State Prison Inmates, 1991* (Washington: U.S. Department of Justice, March 1993) online, available: http://www.ojp.usdoj.gov/bjs/pub/ascii/sospi91.txt.

3. Erving Goffman, *Asylums: Essays on the Social Situation of Mental Patients and Other Inmates* (Garden City, NY: Anchor Books, 1961).

4. Hans Toch, *Living in Prison: The Ecology of Survival,* reprint ed. (Washington: American Psychological Association, 1996), p. xv.

5. "Inmate Subculture," in Virgil L. Williams (ed.), *Dictionary of American Penology: An Introductory Guide* (Westport, CT: Greenwood, 1979).

6. Donald Clemmer, *The Prison Community* (Boston: Holt, Rinehart, Winston, 1940).

7. Stanton Wheeler, "Socialization in Correctional Communities," *American Sociological Review,* Vol. 26 (October 1961), pp. 697–712.

8. Gresham M. Sykes, *The Society of Captives: A Study of a Maximum Security Prison* (Princeton, NJ: Princeton University Press, 1958).

9. Stephen C. Light, *Inmate Assaults on Staff: Challenges to Authority in a Large State Prison System,* dissertation, State University of New York at Albany (Ann

Arbor, MI: University Microfilms International, 1987).

10. John Irwin and Donald R. Cressey, "Thieves, Convicts and the Inmate Culture," *Social Problems*, Fall 1962 (Vol. 10), pp. 142–155.

11. James Jacobs, *Statesville: The Penitentiary in Mass Society* (Chicago: University of Chicago Press, 1977).

12. Miles D. Harer and Darrell J. Steffensmeier, "Race and Prison Violence," *Criminology*, Vol. 34, No. 3 (1996), pp. 323–355.

13. John M. Wilson and Jon D. Snodgrass, "The Prison Code in a Therapeutic Community," *Journal of Criminal Law, Criminology, and Police Science*, Vol. 60, No. 4 (1969), pp. 472–478.

14. Gresham M. Sykes and Sheldon L. Messinger, "The Inmate Social System," in Richard A. Cloward et al. (eds.), *Theoretical Studies in Social Organization of the Prison* (New York: Social Science Research Council, 1960), pp. 5–19.

15. Peter M. Wittenberg, "Language and Communication in Prison," *Federal Probation*, Vol. 60, No. 4 (1996), pp. 45–50.

16. Sykes.

17. John Irwin, *The Felon* (Englewood Cliffs, NJ: Prentice Hall, 1970).

18. Adapted from Frank Schmalleger, *Criminal Justice Today*, 5th ed. (Upper Saddle River, NJ: Prentice Hall, 1999).

19. Daniel Lockwood, *Sexual Aggression Among Male Prisoners*, dissertation, State University of New York at Albany (Ann Arbor, MI: University Microfilms International, 1978); Daniel Lockwood, "Issues in Prison Sexual Violence," *The Prison Journal*, Vol. 58, No. 1 (1983), pp. 73–79.

20. Adapted from Toch, p. 274.

21. See American Correctional Association, Task Force on the Female Offender, *The Female Offender: What Does the Future Hold?* (Washington: St. Mary's, 1990).

22. Phyllis J. Baunach, "Critical Problems of Women in Prison," in Imogene L. Moyer, ed., *The Changing Roles of Women in the Criminal Justice System* (Prospect Heights, IL: Waveland Press, 1985), pp. 95–110.

23. See John W. Palmer, *Constitutional Rights of Prisoners* (Cincinnati: Anderson, 1997).

24. American Corrections Association, *Standards for Adult Correctional Institutions* (Lanham, MD: ACA, 1990).

25. Tracy L. Snell, *Women in Prison*, Bureau of Justice Statistics Bulletin NCJ-145321 (Washington: Bureau of Justice Statistics, March 1994); Allen J. Beck and Christopher J. Mumola, *Prisoners in 1998* (Washington: Bureau of Justice Statistics, August 1999).

26. Bureau of Justice Statistics, "Comparing Federal and State Prisoners," press release, October 2, 1994.

27. American Correctional Association.

28. Bureau of Justice Statistics.

29. Rose Giallombardo, *Society of Women: A Study of a Women's Prison* (New York: John Wiley, 1966).

30. Esther Heffernan, *Making It in Prison: The Square, the Cool, and the Life* (New York: Wiley-Interscience, 1972).

31. Williams, p. 109.

32. Snell, op. cit.

33. Kathryn Watterson, *Women in Prison: Inside the Concrete Tomb*, 2d ed. (Boston: Northeastern University Press, 1996), p. 291.

34. For example, John Gagnon and William Simon, "The Social Meaning of Prison Homosexuality," in David M. Petersen and Charles W. Thomas (eds.), *Corrections: Problems and Prospects* (Englewood Cliffs, NJ: Prentice Hall, 1980).

35. Doris Layton MacKenzie, James Robinson, and Carol Campbell, "Long-Term Incarceration of Female Offenders: Prison Adjustment and Coping," *Criminal Justice and Behavior*, Vol. 16, No. 2 (1989), pp. 223–238.

36. Nicole Hahn Rafter, *Partial Justice: Women, Prisons and Social Control* (New Brunswick, NJ: Transaction, 1990).

37. Susan Cranford and Rose Williams, "Critical Issues in Managing Female Offenders," *Corrections Today*, Vol. 60, No. 7 (December 1998), pp. 130–135.

38. John Ortiz Smykla, "Coed Prison: Should We Try It (Again)?" in Charles B. Fields (ed.), *Controversial Issues in Corrections* (Boston: Allyn and Bacon, 1999), pp. 203–218.

39. John Ortiz Smykla and Jimmy J. Williams, "Co-Corrections in the United States of America, 1970–1990: Two Decades of Disadvantages for Women Prisoners," *Women & Criminal Justice*, Vol. 8, No. 1 (1996), pp. 61–76.

40. Ibid.

41. Jacqueline K. Crawford, "Two Losers Don't Make a Winner: The Case Against the Co-correctional Institution," in John Ortiz Smykla (ed.), *Coed Prison* (New York: Human Sciences Press, 1980), pp. 263–268.

42. Smykla and Williams, p. 61.

43. Lawrence W. Sherman, et al, *Preventing Crime: What Works, What Doesn't, What's Promising* (Washington: NIJ, 1997).

10 Legal Aspects
Prisons and the Courts

CHAPTER OBJECTIVES

After completing this chapter you should be able to:

1. Explain what is meant by the *hands-off doctrine*.
2. Identify the sources of prisoners' rights.
3. List the five ways in which inmates can challenge their conditions of confinement.
4. Describe the major changes that took place during the Prisoner Rights Era.
5. List and explain the four amendments to the U.S. Constitution on which most prisoners' claims are based.
6. Explain how the development of rights for female prisoners has differed from that of male prisoners.
7. Describe which special-needs inmates have been the subject of court decisions regarding their confinement.

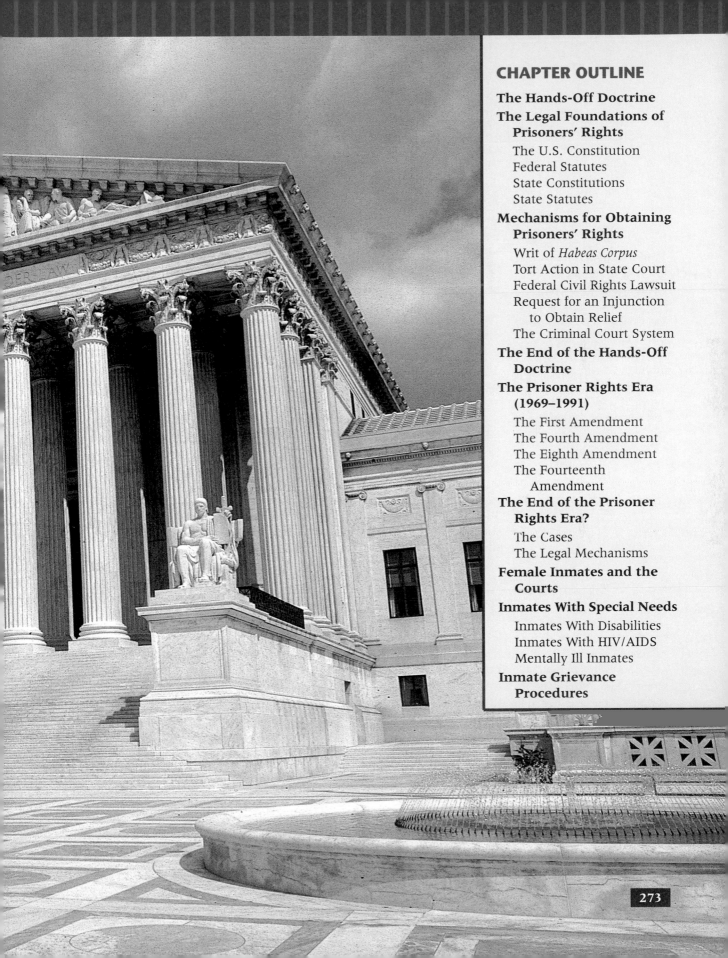

> *The federal courts traditionally have adopted a broad hands-off attitude toward problems of prison administration. . . . Suffice it to say that the problems of prisons in America are complex and intractable, and, more to the point, they are not readily susceptible of resolution by decree.*
>
> —*Procunier* v. *Martinez* (1974)

Student Involvement
In 1974, U.S. Supreme Court Justice Thurgood Marshall wrote in *Wolff* v. *McDonnell*: "A prisoner does not shed his basic constitutional rights at the prison gate." Ask students to write an essay contrasting what Justice Marshall said with what the judge said in *Ruffin* v. *Virginia* in 1871.

In 1871, in the case of *Ruffin* v. *Commonwealth*, a Virginia judge declared:

A convicted felon . . . punished by confinement in the penitentiary instead of with death . . . is in a state of penal servitude to the State. He has, as a consequence of his crime, not only forfeited his liberty, but all his personal rights except those which the law in its humanity accords to him. He is for the time being the slave of the State. He is *civiliter mortuus*; and his estate, if he has any, is administered like that of a dead man. The Bill of Rights is a declaration of general principles to govern a society of freemen, and not of convicted felons and men civilly dead.[1]

The judge in *Ruffin* was voicing what had long been believed: that prisoners had no rights. It was this kind of thinking that long supported a "hands-off" approach to prisoners' rights. If inmates were really civilly dead, the federal government and the federal courts certainly had no cause to tell the states how to run their prisons.

The Hands-Off Doctrine

hands-off doctrine
An historical policy of American courts not to intervene in prison management. Courts tended to follow the doctrine until the late 1960s.
Teaching Tip
Explain that the hands-off doctrine was based on a number of rationales operative at the time, and show how it supported an atmosphere rife with abuse potential.

Under the **hands-off doctrine**, American courts for many decades avoided intervening in prison management. The doctrine was based on two rationales: (1) that under the *separation of powers* inherent in the U.S. Constitution, the judicial branch of government should not interfere with the running of correctional facilities by the executive branch and (2) that judges should leave correctional administration to correctional experts.[2] For a very long time in our nation's history, states ran their prisons as they saw fit. Prison inmates were thought of as "nonpersons," and rights were things that only persons had. Pleas from prisoners based on allegations of deprivations of their rights were ignored.

The hands-off doctrine and the philosophy of the prisoner as a slave of the state began to change in the mid-1900s. Public attitudes about punishment versus rehabilitation changed, and more and more people became aware that inmates had *no* rights. As a result, the courts began to scrutinize the correctional enterprise in America.

Legal Aspects: Prisons and the Courts

The Legal Foundations of Prisoners' Rights

Prisoners' rights have four legal foundations: the U.S. Constitution, federal statutes, state constitutions, and state statutes. Most court cases involving prisoners' rights have involved rights claimed under the U.S. Constitution, even though state constitutions generally parallel the U.S. Constitution and sometimes confer additional rights. State legislatures and Congress can also confer additional prisoners' rights.

The U.S. Constitution

The U.S. Constitution is the supreme law of our land. At the heart of any discussion of prisoners' rights lies one question: What does the Constitution have to say? As scholars began to search the Constitution, they could find no requirement that prisoners give up all of their rights as American citizens (and human beings) after conviction.

It is important to remember, however, that **constitutional rights** are not absolute. Does freedom of speech mean that you have a protected right to stand up in a crowded theater and yell "Fire"? No, it does not (at least, not unless there *is* a fire). That's because the panic that would follow such an exclamation would probably cause injuries and would put members of the public at risk of harm. Hence, the courts have held that although freedom of speech is guaranteed by the Constitution, it is not an absolute right; in other words, there are limits to it.[3]

So the question seems to be, Which constitutional rights do you keep and which rights do you lose when you become a prisoner of the state? Answering that question has become a job of the courts. The results depend on the courts' interpretation of the U.S. Constitution, state constitutions, and federal and state laws. Generally speaking, the courts have recognized four legitimate **institutional needs** that justify some restrictions on the constitutional rights of prisoners:

1. The maintenance of institutional order
2. The maintenance of institutional security
3. The safety of prison inmates and staff and
4. The rehabilitation of inmates

According to the courts, *order* refers to calm and discipline within the institution, *security* is the control of individuals and objects entering or leaving the institution, *safety* means avoidance of physical harm, and *rehabilitation* refers to practices necessary for the health, well-being, and treatment of inmates.[4]

Federal Statutes

Laws passed by Congress can confer certain rights on inmates in federal prisons. In addition, Congress has passed a number of laws that affect the running of state prisons. The Civil Rights Act of 1871, for example, was enacted after the Civil War to discourage lawless activities by state officials. Section 1983 is as follows:

prisoners' rights
Constitutional guarantees of free speech, religious practice, due process, and other private and personal rights, as well as constitutional protections against cruel and unusual punishments, made applicable to prison inmates by the federal courts.

constitutional rights
The personal and due-process rights guaranteed to individuals by the U.S. Constitution and its amendments, especially the first ten amendments, known as the Bill of Rights. Constitutional rights are the basis of most inmate rights.

institutional needs
Prison administration interests recognized by the courts as justifying some restrictions on the constitutional rights of prisoners. Those interests are maintenance of institutional order, maintenance of institutional security, safety of prison inmates and staff, and rehabilitation of inmates.

Cross-Cultural Perspective
Have students rewrite Section 1983 of the Civil Rights Act of 1871 in contemporary language.

civil liability A legal obligation to another person to do, pay, or make good something.

Teaching Tip
Describe the legal basis of prisoners' rights, to include the U.S. Constitution, federal statutes, the Bill of Rights, and (specifically) the First, Fourth, Eighth, and Fourteenth Amendments to the Constitution.

Every person who, under color of any statute, ordinance, regulation, custom, or usage, of any State or Territory, subjects, or causes to be subjected, any citizen of the United States or other person within the jurisdiction thereof to the deprivation of any rights, privileges, or immunities secured by the Constitution and laws, shall be liable to the party injured in an action at law, suit in equity, or other proper proceeding for redress.

This section imposes **civil liability** (but not criminal blame) on any person who deprives another of rights guaranteed by the U.S. Constitution. The case of *Cooper* v. *Pate* (1964) established that inmates have protections under the Civil Rights Act of 1871. The act allows state prisoners to challenge conditions of their imprisonment in federal court. Most prisoner suits brought under this act allege deprivation of constitutional rights.

State Constitutions

Most state constitutions are patterned after the U.S. Constitution. However, state constitutions tend to be longer and more detailed than the U.S. Constitution and may contain specific provisions regarding corrections. State constitutions generally do not give prisoners more rights than are granted by the U.S. Constitution, except in a few states such as California and Oregon. Inmates in such a state may challenge the conditions of their confinement in state court under the state's constitutional provision.

State Statutes

Unlike the federal government, state governments all have inherent police power, which allows them to pass laws to protect the health, safety, welfare, and morals of their citizens. A state legislature can pass statutes to grant specific rights beyond those conferred by the state constitution. Often such legislation specifies duties of corrections officials or standards of treatment for prisoners. Prisoners who can show failure of officials to fulfill state statutory obligations may collect money damages or obtain a court order compelling officials to comply with the law.

Mechanisms for Obtaining Prisoners' Rights

Today, inmates have five ways to legally challenge prison conditions or the practices of corrections officials: (1) a state *habeas corpus* action, (2) a federal *habeas corpus* action after state remedies have been exhausted, (3) a state tort lawsuit, (4) a federal civil rights lawsuit, and (5) a petition for an injunction to obtain relief.[5]

Writ of *Habeas Corpus*

writ of *habeas corpus* An order that directs the person detaining a prisoner to bring him or her before a judge, who will determine the lawfulness of the imprisonment.

A **writ of *habeas corpus*** is an order from a court to produce a prisoner in court so that the court can determine whether the prisoner is being legally detained. A prisoner, or someone acting for a prisoner, files a *habeas corpus* petition asking a court to determine the lawfulness of the imprisonment. *Habeas corpus* is Latin for "you have the body." The petition for the writ is merely a procedural tool. If a writ is issued, it has no bearing on any issues to be reviewed. It only guarantees a hearing on those issues.

Federal and state prisoners may file *habeas corpus* petitions in federal courts. State prisoners must first, however, exhaust available state *habeas corpus* remedies. In 1995, out of 3,459 petitions that inmates filed in federal courts, 456 (13 percent) were *habeas corpus* actions; out of 11,533 petitions that inmates filed in state courts, 3,939 (34 percent) were *habeas corpus* actions.[6]

Tort Action in State Court

State inmates can file a tort action in state court. A **tort** is a civil wrong, a wrongful act, or a wrongful breach of duty, other than a breach of contract, whether intentional or accidental, from which injury to another occurs. In tort actions, inmates commonly claim that a correctional employee, such as the warden or a correctional officer, or the correctional facility itself failed to perform a duty required by law regarding the inmate. Compensation for damages is the most common objective. Tort suits often allege such deficiencies as negligence, gross or wanton negligence, or intentional wrong.

tort A civil wrong, a wrongful act, or a wrongful breach of duty, other than a breach of contract, whether intentional or accidental, from which injury to another occurs.

Federal Civil Rights Lawsuit

Federal and state inmates can file suit in federal court alleging civil rights violations by corrections officials. Most of these suits challenge the conditions of confinement, under Section 1983 of the Civil Rights Act of 1871, which is now part of Title 42 of the U.S. Code. Lawsuits may claim that officials have deprived inmates of their constitutional rights, such as adequate medical treatment, protection against excessive force by correctional officers or violence from other inmates, due process in disciplinary hearings, and access to law libraries. According to the Bureau of Justice Statistics, 1 out of 10 civil cases filed in U.S. district courts is Section 1983 litigation, as it is commonly called.

If inmates are successful in their civil suits, in state or federal courts, the courts can award three types of damages. **Nominal damages** are small amounts of money that may be awarded when inmates have sustained no actual damages, but there is clear evidence that their rights have been violated.

Compensatory damages are payments for actual losses, which may include out-of-pocket expenses the inmate incurred in filing the suit, other forms of monetary or material loss, and pain, suffering, and mental anguish. Some years ago, for example, a federal appeals court sustained an award of $9300 against a warden and a correctional commissioner. The amount was calculated by awarding each inmate $25 for each day he had spent in solitary confinement (a total of 372 days for all the inmates) under conditions the court found cruel and unusual.[7]

Punitive damages are awarded to punish the wrongdoer when the wrongful act was intentional and malicious or was done with reckless disregard for the rights of the inmate.

Student Involvement Review the five basic ways in which inmates may bring legal challenges in court concerning the conditions of imprisonment or the practices of correctional officials. Ask students to write a brief paper describing each of these options in some detail.

nominal damages Small amounts of money a court may award when inmates have sustained no actual damages, but there is clear evidence that their rights have been violated.

compensatory damages Money a court may award as payment for actual losses the inmates suffered, including out-of-pocket expenses the inmate incurred in filing the suit, other forms of monetary or material loss, and pain, suffering, and mental anguish.

punitive damages Money a court may award to punish the wrongdoer when a wrongful act was intentional and malicious or was done with reckless disregard for the rights of the inmate.

Request for an Injunction to Obtain Relief

injunction A judicial order to do or refrain from doing a particular act.

An **injunction** is a judicial order to do or refrain from doing a particular act. A request for an injunction might claim adverse effects of a health, safety, or sanitation procedure and might involve the entire correctional facility. It is important for anyone working in corrections to realize that a lack of funds cannot justify failure to comply with an injunction.[8]

The Criminal Court System

There is a dual court system in the United States: the federal and state court systems coexist. (See Figure 10–1.) The federal court system is nationwide, with one or more federal courts in each state. These courts coexist with state court systems. Whether a defendant is tried in a federal court or a state court depends on which court has jurisdiction over the particular case.

jurisdiction The power, right, or authority to interpret and apply the law.

The **jurisdiction** of a court is the power or authority of the court to act with respect to a case before it. The acts involved in the case must have taken place or had an effect in the geographical territory of the court, or a statute must give the court jurisdiction.

Professional Issue
Civil Liability Use the example of Section 1983 suits to show how correctional workers can be sued if they deny inmates their civil rights guaranteed by the U.S. Constitution. Emphasize that entire corrections departments, institutions, and even individual correctional officers can be held liable in such legal actions. Ask the class why individuals working within corrections may be held liable, and not just agencies.

Teaching Tip
Figure 10–1 shows the structure of the criminal court system in the United States. Have students research the names of the trial, intermediate appellate, and supreme courts in your state.

FIGURE 10–1

Criminal Court Structure

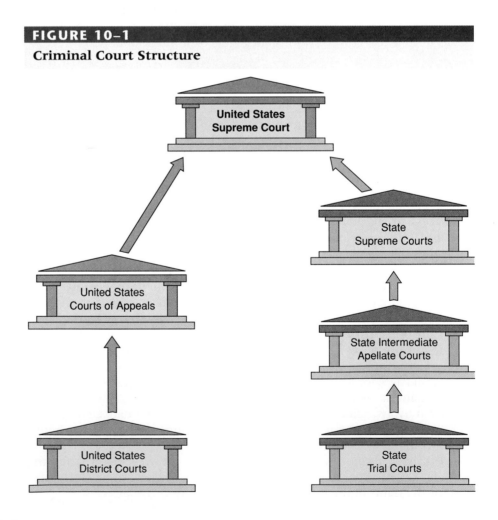

District courts are the trial courts of the federal system. They have original jurisdiction over cases charging defendants with violations of federal criminal laws. Each state has at least one United States district court, and some, like New York and California, have as many as four. There are also federal district courts in Puerto Rico, the District of Columbia, and the U.S. territories. There are currently 12 United States courts of appeals, arranged by circuit (11 numbered circuits, a District of Columbia circuit, and one federal circuit—see Table 10–1).

Each state has its own court system. Most state court structures are similar to the federal court structure—trial courts, intermediate appellate courts, and a top appellate court. In most states, the trial courts are organized by county.

TABLE 10–1

United States Courts of Appeal

Court of Appeals	District Courts Included in Circuit
Federal Circuit	United States
District of Columbia Circuit	District of Columbia
First Circuit	Maine, Massachusetts, New Hampshire, Rhode Island, and Puerto Rico
Second Circuit	Connecticut, New York, and Vermont
Third Circuit	Delaware, New Jersey, Pennsylvania, and the Virgin Islands
Fourth Circuit	Maryland, North Carolina, South Carolina, Virginia, and West Virginia
Fifth Circuit	Louisiana, Mississippi, and Texas
Sixth Circuit	Kentucky, Michigan, Ohio, and Tennessee
Seventh Circuit	Illinois, Indiana, and Wisconsin
Eighth Circuit	Arkansas, Iowa, Minnesota, Missouri, Nebraska, North Dakota, and South Dakota
Ninth Circuit	Alaska, Arizona, California, Hawaii, Idaho, Montana, Nevada, Oregon, Washington, Guam, and the Northern Mariana Islands
Tenth Circuit	Colorado, Kansas, New Mexico, Oklahoma, Utah, and Wyoming
Eleventh Circuit	Alabama, Florida, and Georgia

Source: Administrative Office of the United States Courts

Student Involvement
Direct attention to Table 10–1. Have students determine in which district court circuit your state is located.

HELP WANTED

Paralegal

Paralegal for the Travis County Attorney's Office. Provides legal research support and screens, reviews, analyzes, and organizes case-related material required for court presentation and/or case settlement in the criminal and civil courts. Drafts agreed, summary, and default judgment motions and orders. Drafts various pleadings, affidavits, and subpoenas. Coordinates the work of assigned secretarial support staff. Qualifications: bachelor's degree and three years' experience as a legal assistant/paralegal. Must be a certified paralegal or legal assistant. Background checks will be conducted on all interviewees.

Teaching Tip

Discuss the 1961 U.S. Supreme Court case of *Monroe* v. *Pape* as the single most significant step toward abandonment of the hands-off doctrine. Explain what novel legal interpretation by the Justices gave the case such special significance.

Though federal offenses are prosecuted in federal court and state offenses are prosecuted in state courts, the federal courts have supervisory jurisdiction over the administration of criminal justice in the state courts. The U.S. Supreme Court has ruled that constitutional requirements for criminal procedure in federal courts also apply to the states. Violation of these constitutional requirements can be the subject of both state appeals and federal suits by prisoners.[9]

The End of the Hands-Off Doctrine

In 1941, the hands-off doctrine began to wane. *Ex parte Hull*[10] established that no state or its officers may interfere with a prisoner's right to apply to a federal court for a writ of *habeas corpus*. Before that time, it had been common for corrections personnel to screen inmate mail, including prisoner petitions for writs of *habeas corpus*. Corrections officials often confiscated the petitions, claiming they were improperly prepared and not fit to submit to court. In *Ex parte Hull*, the Supreme Court ruled that no state or its officers may interfere with a prisoner's right to apply to a federal court for a writ of *habeas corpus*. Thus, court officials, not corrections officials, have the authority to decide whether such petitions are prepared correctly.

Though this seemed like a small step at the time, it would later enable a major leap in prisoners' rights. Three years later, *Coffin* v. *Reichard* (1944) brought the end of the hands-off era one step closer.[11] In *Coffin*, the Sixth Circuit Court of Appeals extended *habeas corpus* hearings to consideration of the conditions of confinement. Even more important, the *Coffin* case was the first in which a federal appellate court ruled that prisoners do not automatically lose their civil rights when in prison.[12]

Another important development in the abandonment of the hands-off doctrine occurred in 1961, with the Supreme Court's ruling in *Monroe* v. *Pape*.[13] Prior to *Pape*, it was believed that the phrase "under color of state law" in the 1871 statute meant that a Section 1983 suit could only involve actions authorized by state law. In *Pape*, however, the Court held that for activities to take place *under color* of state law, they did not have to be *authorized* by state law. The statute, said the Court, had been intended to protect against "misuse of power, possessed by virtue of state law and made possible only because the wrongdoer is clothed with the authority of state law."[14]

Officials "clothed with the authority of state law" seemed to include state corrections officials. Thus, state corrections officials who violated an inmate's constitutional rights while performing their duties could be held liable for their actions in federal court, regardless of whether state law or policy supported those actions.[15]

A third important case establishing inmates' rights to access to the courts was *Cooper* v. *Pate* (1964).[16] In *Cooper*, a federal circuit court clarified the *Pape* decision, indicating that prisoners could sue a warden or another correctional official under Title 42 of the United States Code, Section 1983, based on the protections of the Civil Rights Act of 1871.

Commenting on the importance of *Cooper*, one observer noted:

> Just by opening a forum in which prisoners' grievances could be heard, the federal courts destroyed the custodian's absolute power and the prisoners' isolation from the larger society. The litigation itself heightened prisoners' consciousness and politicized them.[17]

With prisoners' access to the courts now established, cases challenging nearly every aspect of corrections were filed. The courts, primarily the federal district courts, began to review prisoners' complaints and intervene on prisoners' behalf.

The hands-off era is said to have ended in 1970, when a federal district court, in *Holt* v. *Sarver*, declared the entire Arkansas prison system "so inhumane as to be a violation of the Eighth Amendment bar on cruel and unusual punishment."[18] Robert Sarver, the Arkansas commissioner of cor-

CAREER PROFILE

Tammy Waldrop
Inspector
Correctional Facilities
Palm Beach County, FL

"In corrections, the words care, custody, and control are repeatedly stated as your primary tasks. But remember three additional words in your interactions with inmates: fair, firm, and consistent. If you build your officer reputation on this foundation, you will not have any problems. Treat everyone with respect and the respect will come back to you. And never, never lie to an inmate."

Tammy Waldrop is an inspector with the Palm Beach County (Florida) Sheriff's Office, assigned to Corrections Administration. She's been in the position for almost one year. Quarterly, Tammy inspects all four correctional facilities in Palm Beach County to verify that each one complies with agency, local, state, and American Correctional Association standards. She investigates staff and inmate grievances and works with the Legal Advisors' office to resolve conflicts.

Tammy received her bachelor's degree in criminal justice from Florida Atlantic University in Boca Raton. She remembers that the undergraduate course that influenced her the most was a sociology course titled "Social Conflict." She says, "This course changed my perspective on life and my views on crime. It was the best preparation for my current job. It helped me understand the importance of changing conflict into occasions for problem solving."

In the future, Tammy would like to build on her present career, attend law school, concentrate on corrections law, and work in the Legal Advisors' office.

rections, admitted that, "the physical facilities at both [prison units named in the suit] were inadequate and in a total state of disrepair that could only be described as deplorable." Additionally, he testified that inmates with trustee status, some of them serving life or long-term sentences, constituted 99 percent of the security force of the state's prison system.

Commissioner Sarver continued, testifying that, "trustees sell desirable jobs to prisoners and also traffic in food, liquor and drugs. Prisoners frequently become intoxicated and unruly. The prisoners sleep in dormitories. Prisoners are frequently attacked and raped in the dormitories and injuries and deaths have resulted. Sleep and rest are seriously disrupted. No adequate means exist to protect the prisoners from assaults. There is no satisfactory means of keeping guns, knives and other weapons away from the prison population."

The *Holt* court declared:

> The obligation . . . to eliminate existing unconstitutionalities does not depend upon what the Legislature may do, or upon what the Governor may do. . . . If Arkansas is going to operate a Penitentiary System, it is going to have to be a system that is countenanced by the Constitution of the United States.[19]

Prisoner litigation had brought sad conditions to light, and the court had intervened to institute reforms for the prisoners in Arkansas.

The Prisoner Rights Era (1969–1991)

Many refer to the era following *Holt* v. *Sarver* as the Prisoner Rights Era. That title might give the impression that during that time, prisoners won virtually every case. That is far from true. Although prisoners won many cases involving their rights during this period, it was the turnaround in court attitudes toward prisoners that was most remarkable. As we shall see, courts went from practically ignoring prison systems to practically running those systems. It might be more appropriate to refer to the period as "the court involvement era." We will now review some of the most important cases won *and* lost by inmates, presented in order of the constitutional amendments on which they were based.

When we speak of prisoners' rights, we are generally speaking of the rights found in four of the amendments to the U.S. Constitution. Three of these—the First, Fourth, and Eighth Amendments—are part of the Bill of Rights (the first ten amendments to the Constitution). The fourth is the Fourteenth Amendment. Keep in mind that what we call inmate rights today are largely the result of federal court decisions that have interpreted constitutional guarantees and applied them to prisons and prison conditions. Often such a case sets a **precedent,** serving as an example or authority for future cases. Rulings in cases that find violations of inmate rights must be implemented by the administrators of affected correctional systems and institutions.

The First Amendment

Congress shall make no law respecting an establishment of religion, or prohibiting the free exercise thereof; or abridging the freedom of speech, or of the press; or the right of the people peaceably to assemble, and to petition the government for a redress of grievances.

Student Involvement Have students create a list of the various First Amendment cases discussed in this section. Put the list on the board or on your Web site. In a discussion of the significance of the First Amendment for prisoners' rights, have students identify the specific issues dealt with in each case.

First Amendment guarantees are important to members of free society. It is no surprise, then, that some of the early prisoners' rights cases concerned those rights. For example, in 1974, in *Pell* v. *Procunier*,[20] four California prison inmates and three journalists challenged the constitutionality of regulation 415.071 of the California Department of Corrections. That regulation specified that "press and other media interviews with specific individual inmates will not be permitted." The rule had been imposed after a violent prison episode that corrections authorities attributed at least in part to a former policy of free face-to-face prisoner-press interviews. Such interviews had apparently resulted in a relatively small number of inmates gaining disproportionate notoriety and influence among other prisoners.

The U.S. Supreme Court held that "in light of the alternative channels of communication that are open to the inmate appellees, [regulation] 415.071 does not constitute a violation of their rights of free speech." Significantly, the Court went on to say, "A prison inmate retains those first amendment rights that are not inconsistent with his status as prisoner or with the *legitimate penological objectives* of the corrections system." [Emphasis added.] **Legitimate penological objectives** are the permissible aims of a correctional institution and include the realistic concerns that correctional officers and administrators have for the integrity and security of the correctional institution and the safety of staff and inmates. The *Pell* ruling established a **balancing test** that the Supreme Court would continue to use, weighing the rights claimed by inmates against the legitimate needs of prisons.

legitimate penological objectives The realistic concerns that correctional officers and administrators have for the integrity and security of the correctional institution and the safety of staff and inmates.

balancing test A method the U.S. Supreme Court uses to decide prisoners' rights cases, weighing the rights claimed by inmates against the legitimate needs of prisons.

Freedom of Speech and Expression Visits to inmates by friends and loved ones are forms of expression. But prison visits are not an absolute right. In *Cruz* v. *Beto* (1972),[21] the Supreme Court ruled that all visits can be banned if they threaten security. Although *Cruz* involved short-term confinement facilities, the ruling has also been applied to prisons.

Another form of expression is correspondence. As a result of various court cases, prison officials can (and generally do) impose restrictions on inmate mail. Inmates receive mail, not directly from the hands of postal carriers, but from correctional officers. They place their outgoing mail, not in U.S. Postal Service mailboxes, but only in containers provided by the correctional institution.

Corrections officials often read inmate mail—both incoming and outgoing—in an effort to uncover escape plans. Reading inmate mail, however, is different from censoring it. In 1974, in *Procunier* v. *Martinez*,[22] the U.S. Supreme Court held that the censoring of inmate mail is acceptable only

TABLE 10–2

Selected U.S. Supreme Court Cases Involving Rights of Prisoners

Case Name	Year	Decision
Monroe v. *Pape*	1961	Individuals deprived of their rights by state officers acting under color of state law have a right to bring action in federal court.
Johnson v. *Avery*	1968	Inmates have a right to consult "jailhouse lawyers" when trained legal assistance is not available.
Cruz v. *Beto* (First Amendment)	1972	Inmates have to be given a "reasonable opportunity" to pursue their religious faiths. Also, visits can be banned if such visits constitute threats to security.
Pell v. *Procunier* (First Amendment)	1974	Inmates retain First Amendment rights that are not inconsistent with their status as prisoners, nor with the legitimate penological objectives of the corrections system.
Procunier v. *Martinez* (First Amendment)	1974	Censorship of inmate mail is acceptable only when necessary to protect legitimate governmental interests.
Wolff v. *McDonnell* (Fourteenth Amendment)	1974	Sanctions cannot be levied against inmates without appropriate due process.
Estelle v. *Gamble* (Eighth Amendment)	1976	Prison officials have a duty to provide proper inmate medical care.
Bounds v. *Smith*	1977	Resulted in creation of law libraries in many prisons.
Jones v. *North Carolina Prisoners' Labor Union, Inc.* (First Amendment)	1977	Inmates have no inherent right to publish newspapers or newsletters for use by other inmates.
Cooper v. *Morin*	1980	Neither inconvenience nor cost are acceptable excuses for treating female inmates differently from male inmates.
Rhodes v. *Chapman* (Eighth Amendment)	1981	Double-celling of inmates is not cruel and unusual punishment unless it involves the wanton and unnecessary infliction of pain, or conditions grossly disproportionate to the severity of the crime committed.

TABLE 10–2 (continued)

Selected U.S. Supreme Court Cases Involving Rights of Prisoners

Case Name	Year	Decision
Block v. *Rutherford* (First Amendment)	1984	State regulations may prohibit inmate union meetings and use of mail to deliver union information within the prison. Prisoners do not have a right to be present during searches of cells.
Hudson v. *Palmer* (Fourth Amendment)	1984	A prisoner has no reasonable expectation of privacy in his prison cell that entitles him to protections against "unreasonable searches."
Ponte v. *Real*	1985	Inmates have certain rights in disciplinary hearings.
Whitley v. *Albers* (Eighth Amendment)	1986	The shooting and wounding of an inmate was not a violation of that inmate's rights, since "the shooting was part and parcel of a good-faith effort to restore prison security."
O'Lone v. *Estate of Shabazz* (First Amendment)	1987	An inmate's right to practice religion was not violated by prison officials who refused to alter his work schedule so that he could attend Friday afternoon services.
Turner v. *Safley* (First Amendment)	1987	A Missouri ban on correspondence between inmates was upheld as "reasonably related to legitimate penological interests."
Washington v. *Harper* (Eighth Amendment)	1990	An inmate who is a danger to self or others as a result of mental illness may be treated with psychoactive drugs against his or her will.
Wilson v. *Seiter* (Eighth Amendment)	1991	Clarified the totality of conditions notion, saying that some conditions of confinement "in combination" may violate prisoners' rights when each would not do so alone.
Sandin v. *Conner* (Fourteenth Amendment)	1995	Perhaps signaling an end to the Prisoner Rights Era, this case rejected the argument that disciplining inmates is a deprivation of constitutional due-process rights.
Lewis v. *Casey*	1996	Earlier cases do not guarantee inmates the wherewithal to file any and every type of legal claim. All that is required is "that they be provided with the tools to attack their sentences."

Inmates have limited rights to send and receive mail. Restrictions on inmates' mail focus on maintaining institutional security. Judicial interpretations of which amendment have led to inmates' rights to send and receive mail?

when necessary to protect legitimate government interests. The case turned upon First Amendment guarantees of free speech.

Under a 1979 federal appeals court decision, in *McNamara* v. *Moody*, prison officials may not prohibit inmates from writing vulgar letters, or those that make disparaging remarks about the prison staff.[23] Similarly, while correctional administrators have a legitimate interest in curbing inmates' deviant sexual behavior, courts have held that viewing nudity is not deviant sexual behavior. Hence, prison officials may not ban mailed nude pictures of inmates' wives or girlfriends.[24] Nor may they prevent inmates from receiving, by mail direct from publishers, publications depicting nudity unless those publications depict deviant sexual behavior.[25]

In 1989, in the case of *Thornburgh* v. *Abbott*, in an effort to clear up questions raised by lower court rulings concerning mailed publications, the U.S. Supreme Court ruled as follows:

> Publications which may be rejected by a warden include but are not limited to publications which meet one of the following criteria: (1) It depicts or describes procedures for the construction or use of weapons, ammunition, bombs, or incendiary devices; (2) It depicts, encourages or describes methods of escape from correctional facilities, or contains blueprints, drawings, or similar descriptions of Bureau of Prisons institutions; (3) It depicts or describes procedures for the brewing of alcoholic beverages, or the manufacture of drugs; (4) It is written in code; (5) It depicts, describes, or encourages activities which may lead to the use of physical violence or group disruption; (6) It encourages or instructs in the commission of criminal activities; (7) It is sexually explicit material which by its nature or content poses a threat to

the security, good order, or discipline of the institution, or facilitates criminal activity.[26]

Prison officials haven't lost every mail case. In the case of *Turner* v. *Safley*, for example, the Supreme Court upheld a Missouri ban on correspondence between inmates.[27] Such a regulation is valid, the Court said, if it is "reasonably related to legitimate penological interests." *Turner* established that officials had to show only that a regulation was reasonably *related* to a legitimate penological interest. No clear-cut damage to legitimate penological interests had to be shown.

The U.S. Supreme Court sided with corrections officials in its 1977 decision in *Jones* v. *North Carolina Prisoner's Labor Union, Inc.*[28] In *Jones*, the Court upheld regulations established by the North Carolina Department of Correction that prohibited prisoners from soliciting other inmates to join the union and barred union meetings and bulk mailings concerning the union from outside sources. Citing *Pell* v. *Procunier*, the Court went on to say, "The prohibition on inmate-to-inmate solicitation does not unduly abridge inmates' free speech rights. If the prison officials are otherwise entitled to control organized union activity within the confines of a prison the solicitation ban is not impermissible under the First Amendment, for such a prohibition is both reasonable and necessary.[29]

Freedom of Religion   Lawsuits involving religious practices in prison have been numerous for at least 40 years. In 1962, for example, the court of appeals for the District of Columbia ruled that the Black Muslim faith must be recognized as a religion, and held that officials may not restrict members of that faith from holding services.[30]

In 1970 the U.S. Supreme Court refused to hear an appeal from inmate Jack Gittlemacker, who wanted the state of Pennsylvania to provide him with a clergyman of his faith.[31] The court held that although states must give inmates the opportunity to practice their religions, they are not required to provide clergy for that purpose.

In *Cruz* v. *Beto* (mentioned earlier), the Supreme Court also decided that inmates had to be given a "reasonable opportunity" to pursue their religious faiths.[32] Later federal court decisions expanded this decision, requiring officials to provide such a "reasonable opportunity" even to inmates whose religious faiths were not traditional.

In 1975, the U.S. Court of Appeals for the Second Circuit ruled in *Kahane* v. *Carlson* that an Orthodox Jewish inmate has the right to a kosher diet unless the government can show good cause for not providing it.[33] Similarly, the courts have held that "Muslims' request for one full-course pork-free diet once a day and coffee three times daily is essentially a plea for a modest degree of official deference to their religious obligations."[34]

On the other hand, courts have determined that some inmate religious demands need not be met. In a 1986 case, for example, Muslim prisoners had requested raw milk, distilled water, and organic fruits, juices, vegetables, and meats. The special diet was so costly that a federal court allowed the prison to deny the inmates' request.[35]

In 1986, a federal court of appeals considered the appeal of Herbert Dettmer, an inmate at Powhatan Correctional Center in Virginia.[36]

Student Involvement
Ask students to create a list of the cases discussed in this book that involve inmate claims of freedom of religion. Have them examine the outcome of each case, and ask them to tell whether they disagree with any of the decisions. If so, have them explain why.

Beginning in 1982, Dettmer had studied witchcraft through a correspondence course provided by the Church of Wicca. Within a year, he was holding private ceremonies for meditation as described in the course. Dettmer decided that he needed certain items to aid him in these ceremonies. Those items included a white robe with a hood, sea salt or sulfur to draw a protective circle on the floor around him, and candles and incense to focus his thoughts. Late in 1983, Dettmer requested permission to order the items he felt he needed for meditating. The prison property officer refused permission because the prison rules did not list the items as "authorized personal property." The Supreme Court concluded that "the security officer's concern about inmates' unsupervised possession of candles, salt, and incense is reasonable."

In *O'Lone* v. *Estate of Shabazz* (1987), the U.S. Supreme Court found that a Muslim inmate's right to practice religion was *not* violated by prison officials who refused to alter his work schedule so that he could attend Friday afternoon services.[37] The Court concluded that "even where claims are made under the First Amendment, this Court will not substitute its judgment on difficult and sensitive matters of institutional administration for the determinations of those charged with the formidable task of running a prison."

Student Involvement
Have students create a list of the various Fourth Amendment cases discussed in this section. Put the list on the board or on your Web site. In a discussion of the significance of the Fourth Amendment for prisoners' rights, have students identify the specific issues dealt with in each case.

The Fourth Amendment

The right of the people to be secure in their persons, houses, papers, and effects, against unreasonable searches and seizures, shall not be violated, and no Warrants shall issue, but upon probable cause, supported by Oath or affirmation, and particularly describing the place to be searched, and the persons or things to be seized.

The right to privacy is at the heart of the Fourth Amendment. Clearly, unreasonable searches without warrants are unconstitutional. Does this mean that an inmate has a right to privacy in his or her cell? When is it reasonable to search a cell without a warrant? Some suggest that the needs of institutional security prohibit privacy for inmates. Others argue that a prison cell is the equivalent of an inmate's house. Over the years, the courts have been fairly consistent in deciding that the privacy rights implied in this amendment must be greatly reduced in prisons to maintain institutional security.

In *United States* v. *Hitchcock* (1972), an inmate claimed that his Fourth Amendment rights had been violated by a warrantless search and seizure of documents in his prison cell.[38] Previously, courts had generally held that "constitutionally protected" places—such as homes, motel rooms, safe-deposit boxes, and certain places of business—could not be searched without a warrant. In *Hitchcock*, however, the U.S. Court of Appeals for the Ninth Circuit created a new standard: "first, that a person have exhibited an actual (subjective) expectation of privacy and second, that the expectation be one

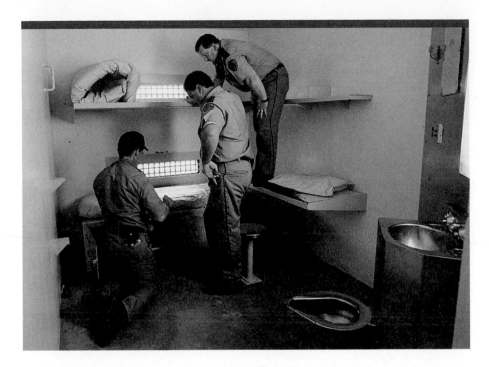

that society is prepared to recognize as reasonable." The court concluded that although Hitchcock plainly expected to keep his documents private, his expectation was not reasonable. In the words of the court:

> [It] is obvious that a jail shares none of the attributes of privacy of a home, an automobile, an office, or a hotel room. In prison, official surveillance has traditionally been the order of the day. . . . [Hence], we do not feel that it is reasonable for a prisoner to consider his cell private.

In *Hudson* v. *Palmer* (1984), a Virginia inmate claimed a correctional officer had unreasonably destroyed some of his permitted personal property during a search of his cell.[39] The inmate also claimed that under the Fourth Amendment, the cell search was illegal. Echoing *Hitchcock*, the U.S. Supreme Court ruled that "a prisoner has no reasonable expectation of privacy in his prison cell entitling him to the protection of the Fourth Amendment against unreasonable searches." Similarly, in *Block* v. *Rutherford* (1984), the Court ruled that prisoners do not have the right to be present during searches of their cells.[40]

In 1985, the Ninth Circuit Court of Appeals decided a case involving inmates at San Quentin State Prison.[41] The inmates had brought a class action lawsuit against prison administrators, objecting to the policy of allowing female correctional officers to view nude or partly clothed male inmates. Women officers, complained the inmates, could see male inmates while they were dressing, showering, being strip-searched, or using toilet facilities. Such viewing, said the inmates, violated privacy rights guaranteed by the United States Constitution.

At the time of the suit, approximately 113 of the 720 correctional officers at San Quentin were female. Both female and male correctional officers

cruel and unusual punishment A penalty that is grossly disproportionate to the offense or that violates today's broad and idealistic concepts of dignity, civilized standards, humanity, and decency. In the area of capital punishment, cruel and unusual punishments are those that involve torture, a lingering death, or unnecessary pain.

consent decree A written compact, sanctioned by a court, between parties in a civil case, specifying how disagreements between them are to be resolved.

were assigned to patrol the cell block tiers and gun rails. Both were also assigned to supervise showering from the tiers and from the gun rails, but only male officers were permitted to accompany inmates to the shower cells and lock them inside to disrobe and shower. Female officers were allowed to conduct pat-down searches that included the groin area.

The court found that prison officials had "struck an acceptable balance among the inmates' privacy interests, the institution's security requirements, and the female guards' employment rights." According to the court:

> The female guards are restricted in their contact with the inmates, and the record clearly demonstrates that at all times they have conducted themselves in a professional manner, and have treated the inmates with respect and dignity. . . . Routine pat-down searches, which include the groin area, and which are otherwise justified by security needs, do not violate the Fourteenth Amendment because a correctional officer of the opposite gender conducts such a search.

The Eighth Amendment

Excessive bail shall not be required, nor excessive fines imposed, nor cruel and unusual punishments inflicted.

Many prisoners' rights cases turn upon the issue of **cruel and unusual punishment.** Defining such punishment is not easy. A working definition, however, might be: punishments that are grossly disproportionate to the offense, as well as those that transgress today's broad and idealistic concepts of dignity, civilized standards, humanity, and decency.[42] Cases concerning constitutional prohibition of cruel and unusual punishment have centered on prisoners' need for decent conditions of confinement. In one case, *Ruiz* v. *Estelle* (1980),[43] the conditions of confinement in the Texas prison system were found unconstitutional, and a **consent decree** was imposed on the system. Inmate rights cases involving the Eighth Amendment cover areas as diverse as medical care, prison conditions, physical insecurity, psychological stress, and capital punishment.

Medical Care   The right to adequate medical care was one of the issues in *Holt* v. *Sarver* (1970), a case in which the Arkansas prison system was declared inhumane and a violation of the Eighth Amendment ban on cruel and unusual punishment.[44]

In one case, medical personnel in state prisons had given inmates injections of apomorphine without their consent, in a program of "aversive stimuli." The drug caused vomiting, which lasted from fifteen minutes to an hour. The state justified it as "Pavlovian conditioning." The federal courts, however, soon prohibited the practice.[45]

Another decision, that of *Estelle* v. *Gamble* (1976), spelled out the duty of prison officials to provide inmates medical care.[46] The Court held that prison officials could not lawfully demonstrate **deliberate indifference** to the medical needs of prisoners.

Prison Conditions   The 1976 federal court case of *Pugh* v. *Locke* introduced the **totality of conditions** as a standard.[47] That standard, said the court, is to be used in evaluating whether prison conditions are cruel and unusual. The *Pugh* court held that "prison conditions [in Alabama] are so debilitating that they necessarily deprive inmates of any opportunity to rehabilitate themselves or even maintain skills already possessed." The totality-of-conditions approach was also applied in a 1977 federal case in which officials in overcrowded Oklahoma prisons had forced inmates to sleep in garages, barbershops, libraries, and stairwells. Oklahoma prison administrators were found in violation of the cruel-and-unusual-punishment clause of the U.S. Constitution.[48]

The U.S. Supreme Court ruled on the use of solitary confinement in *Hutto* v. *Finney* (1978).[49] The Court held that confinement in Arkansas's segregation (solitary-confinement) cells for more than 30 days was cruel and unusual punishment. It then went on to exhort lower courts to consider the totality of the conditions of confinement in future Eighth Amendment cases. Where appropriate, it said, a court should specify the changes needed to remedy the constitutional violation.

In the 1991 case *Wilson* v. *Seiter*, the U.S. Supreme Court clarified the totality-of-conditions standard.[50] The Court noted that:

> Some conditions of confinement may establish an Eighth Amendment violation "in combination" when each would not do so alone, but only when they have a mutually enforcing effect that produces the deprivation of a single, identifiable human

deliberate indifference
Intentional and willful indifference. Within the field of correctional practice the term refers to calculated inattention to unconstitutional conditions of confinement.

totality of conditions
A standard to be used in evaluating whether prison conditions are cruel and unusual.

Teaching Tip
Explain the totality-of-conditions concept as it relates to prison overcrowding. Show how the 1991 U.S. Supreme Court case of *Wilson* v. *Seiter* helped clarity this concept.

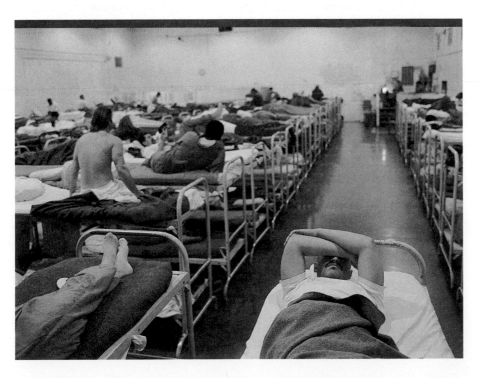

The Eighth Amendment's prohibition of cruel and unusual punishment has been tied to prisoners' need for decent conditions of confinement. In determining if conditions such as overcrowding and inadequate diet constitute a denial of such protection, courts have used the concept of totality of conditions. What is meant by the totality of conditions?

need such as food, warmth, or exercise—for example, a low cell temperature at night combined with a failure to issue blankets. . . . To say that some prison conditions may interact in this fashion is a far cry from saying that all prison conditions are a seamless web for Eighth Amendment purposes. Nothing so [shapeless] as "overall conditions" can rise to the level of cruel and unusual punishment when no specific deprivation of a single human need exists.

Several rulings have addressed inmate claims that overcrowding was cruel and unusual punishment. A U.S. Supreme Court case, *Rhodes* v. *Chapman* (1981), decided the issue of double-celling (housing two inmates in a cell designed for one) in long-term correctional facilities.[51] In response to rising prison populations, Ohio authorities had begun double-celling. There was no evidence that Ohio authorities had wantonly inflicted pain through the practice, and double-celling had not resulted in food deprivation, a lower quality of medical care, or a decrease in sanitation standards. For those reasons, the Court denied the inmates' claims.

In *Rhodes*, the Court also emphasized that the Eighth Amendment prohibition of cruel and unusual punishments is a fluid concept that "must draw its meaning from the evolving standards of decency that mark the progress of a maturing society." In other words, what is considered cruel and unusual, changes as society evolves.

In 1982, the U.S. Court of Appeals for the Seventh Circuit ruled, in *Smith* v. *Fairman*, that double-celling in a short-term facility (a jail) was not cruel and unusual punishment.[52] The court said that government officials did not intend to punish inmates by double-celling. The double-celling was innocent overcrowding required by circumstances.

Many conditions of confinement that violate prisoners' Eighth Amendment rights can be remedied by changes in prison rules, by special training for correctional personnel, or by educational programs for prisoners. The remedies can be implemented through everyday administrative policies in the prison, once prisoners' court petitions have brought violations to light. Relief of overcrowding, however, is not always within the power of prison administrators. Prison officials have little control over the sizes of their prisons or the numbers of inmates the courts assign to them. New prison facilities are expensive and take time to build.

The Fourteenth Amendment

When the Constitution and the Bill of Rights became law, the people of many states thought the document applied only to federal courts and to federal law. This attitude prevailed at least until the end of the Civil War. After the war, to clarify the status of the newly freed slaves and to apply the Bill of Rights to state actions, the Fourteenth Amendment was passed. The portion relevant to our discussion is as follows:

No State shall make or enforce any law which shall abridge the privileges or immunities of citizens of the United States;

Student Involvement

Have students create a list of the various Fourteenth Amendment cases discussed in this section. Put the list on the board or on your Web site. In a class discussion of the significance of the Fourteenth Amendment for prisoners' rights, have students identify the specific issues dealt with in each case. Make certain that they focus on due process as a central issue.

nor shall any State deprive any person of life, liberty, or property, without due process of law; nor deny to any person within its jurisdiction the equal protection of the laws.

Most cases involving prisoners' rights and the Fourteenth Amendment deal with issues of **due process**. Due process requires that laws and legal procedures be reasonable and be applied fairly and equally. The right to due process is a right to be fairly heard before being deprived of life or liberty.

To get their cases to court, prisoners need access to legal materials, and many of them need legal assistance. Without access to the courts, inmates have no due process. What if one inmate understands how to file cases with the court, but a second inmate does not? Does the second inmate have a right to enlist the aid of the first? "Yes," said the U.S. Supreme Court in *Johnson* v. *Avery* (1968).[53] Inmates have a right to consult "jailhouse lawyers" (other inmates knowledgeable in the law) when trained legal advisers are not available.

The case of *Wolff* v. *McDonnell* (1974) expanded the concept of due process by applying it to disciplinary actions within prisons.[54] Prior to *Wolff*, prison administrators had the discretion to discipline inmates who broke prison rules. Disciplinary procedures were often tied to vague or nonexistent rules of conduct and were exercised without challenge. A prisoner might be assigned to solitary confinement or might have good-time credits reduced because of misconduct. Because the prisoner was physically confined and lacked outside communication, there was no opportunity for the prisoner to challenge the charge. The *Wolff* court concluded that sanctions (disciplinary actions) could not be levied against inmates without appropriate due process, saying:

> [The state of Nebraska] asserts that the procedure for disciplining prison inmates for serious misconduct is a matter of policy raising no constitutional issue. If the position implies that prisoners in state institutions are wholly without the protection of the Constitution and the Due Process Clause, it is plainly untenable. Lawful imprisonment necessarily makes unavailable many rights and privileges of the ordinary citizen, a retraction justified by the consideration underlying our penal system. . . . But though his rights may be diminished by the needs and exigencies of the institutional environment, a prisoner is not wholly stripped of constitutional protections when he is imprisoned for a crime.

The *Wolff* Court imposed minimal due-process requirements on prison disciplinary proceedings that could lead to solitary confinement or reduction of good-time credits. The requirements included (1) advance notice by means of a written statement of the claimed violation, (2) a written statement by an impartial fact finder of the evidence relied on and the reasons for imposing punishment, and (3) an opportunity to testify and call witnesses unless the fact finder concluded such proceedings would undermine institutional security.[55]

due process A right guaranteed by the Fifth, Sixth, and Fourteenth Amendments to the U.S. Constitution and generally understood, in legal contexts, to mean the expected course of legal proceedings according to the rules and forms established for the protection of persons' rights.

In 1976 inmates lost three due-process appeals. First, in *Baxter* v. *Palmigiano*, the Supreme Court decided that due process for an inmate in a disciplinary hearing does not include a right to counsel, even when the consequences are potentially "serious."[56] In a second opinion issued that year (*Meacham* v. *Fano*), the Court held that prisoners have no right to be in any particular prison and therefore have no due-process protections before being transferred from one prison to another.[57] A third case (*Stone* v. *Powell*) denied prisoners the right in most instances to seek federal review of state court Fourth Amendment search-and-seizure decisions.[58]

Inmates' right to legal materials was formally recognized in 1977, in the U.S. Supreme Court decision in *Bounds* v. *Smith*.[59] In *Bounds* the Court held:

> The fundamental constitutional right of access to the courts requires prison authorities to assist inmates in the preparation and filing of meaningful legal papers by providing prisoners with adequate law libraries or adequate assistance from persons trained in the law.

As a result of the *Bounds* decision, law libraries were created in prisons across the nation.

As we saw in Chapter 8, one challenge facing corrections personnel is to find safe, humane ways to manage inmate populations. Inmates often have grievances regarding conditions of confinement or disciplinary actions for infractions. Those grievances must be dealt with to maintain the safety and security of the institution. The Supreme Court's decision in *Jones* v. *North Carolina Prisoners' Labor Union, Inc.* (1977) required prisons to establish and maintain formal opportunities for the airing of inmate grievances.[60] *Ponte* v. *Real* (1985) required prison officials to explain to inmates why their

Inmates must be allowed access to the courts and assistance in preparing their cases. Most states stock law libraries in each correctional institution. Under which clause of the Fourteenth Amendment does inmates' access to the courts fall?

Legal Aspects: Prisons and the Courts

requests to have witnesses appear on their behalf at disciplinary hearings were denied.[61]

The due-process clause protects against unlawful deprivation of life or liberty. When a prisoner sued for damages for injuries (*Daniels* v. *Williams*, 1986), the Supreme Court ruled that prisoners could sue for damages in federal court only if officials had inflicted injury intentionally.[62] According to the Court, "The due process clause is simply not implicated by a negligent act of an official causing unintended loss or injury to life, liberty or property."

As we have seen, federal and state inmates can file suits in federal court alleging civil rights violations by corrections officials. In 1988, the U.S. Supreme Court (in *West* v. *Atkins*) decided that private citizens who contracted to do work for prisons could be sued for civil rights violations against inmates.[63] The Court found that such contractors were acting "under color of state law," as required by Section 1983 of the Civil Rights Act of 1871.

As a result of Supreme Court decisions, most prisons now have rules that provide the due process required when prisoners must appear before disciplinary committees. The makeup of disciplinary committees varies among institutions. The committees may include both inmates and free citizens.

The End of the Prisoner Rights Era?

By the late 1980s, the Prisoner Rights Era seemed to be drawing to a close. The Justices sitting on the Supreme Court had become less sympathetic to prisoners' claims of denial of civil rights. As indicated in *Daniels* v. *Williams* (1986), discussed in the preceding section, due process was intended only to prevent abuse of power, not to protect against mere carelessness. Further, judicial and legislative officials began to realize that inmates frequently abused their access to the courts. As state costs of defending against **frivolous lawsuits** by inmates began to grow, federal courts began to take a new look at prisoners' rights.

Examples of abuse of the court system by prison inmates abound. One inmate sued the state of Florida because he got only one roll with dinner. He sued two more times because he didn't get a salad with lunch and because prison-provided TV dinners didn't come with drinks. He sued yet again because his cell wasn't equipped with a television. Another inmate claimed prison officials were denying him freedom of religion. His religion, he said, required him to attend prison chapel services in the nude. Still another inmate, afraid that he could get pregnant through homosexual relations, sued because prison officials wouldn't give him birth control pills.

As early as 1977, the U.S. Supreme Court refused to hear an appeal from Henry William Theriault, founder of the Church of the New Song (or CONS).[64] Theriault, an inmate at the federal penitentiary in Atlanta, had a mail-order divinity degree. Members of CONS celebrated communion every Friday night. They claimed that prison officials must supply them with steak and Harvey's Bristol Cream Sherry for the practice. Although "Bishop Theriault" admitted that he had originally created CONS to mock other reli-

Teaching Tip

Explain how inmates' filing of numerous frivolous lawsuits contributed to the end of the Prisoner Rights Era.

frivolous lawsuits

Lawsuits with no foundation in fact. They are generally brought for publicity, politics, or other reasons not related to law.

Student Involvement

Have students prepare and submit a paper identifying the constitutional amendments that are of special relevance to prisoners' rights. Have them describe how each amendment has affected prisoners' rights to date.

My name is Brian Pierce. I'm an ex-con.

Let me tell you about myself. I grew up in a small southern Minnesota river town. In an effort to bring our family closer together, my parents purchased a small family-run tourist business they hoped we could eventually run as a family. My parents have always been hard workers and Christians. I am not sure what got me started really, but by the time I was 14 I was using drugs heavily and starting to spin the revolving door of Minnesota's illustrious correctional system.

First, I was court-ordered into a drug treatment center called the Cannon Valley Center in Cannon Falls, Minnesota. From there I went to a halfway house in Winona named the East House. When the county ran out of funding, they told me I could leave despite the fact that the counselors did not think I was ready. Not long after getting home I was on the way to the Minnesota Correctional Facility at Red Wing, the end of the line for juveniles in Minnesota.

When I turned 18, I was moving too fast to slow down and was soon on my way to the Minnesota Correctional Facility at St. Cloud. I was sentenced to 38 months for third-degree burglary and received two shorter sentences that ran concurrently for theft charges. Under Minnesota's guidelines, I had to serve two thirds of that sentence inside and the remaining one third on parole.

St. Cloud is relatively old and made predominately out of dark gray granite. The wall is solid granite and somewhere around 20 feet high and several feet thick. It encompasses over 50 acres, including several cell houses, factories, maintenance facilities, and a yard for recreation. There are armed guard towers spaced evenly around the top of the wall.

Like most of my friends there, I got out and quickly got back into the same old routine. An Olmstead County judge gave me the option of pleading guilty to possession of a controlled substance but getting a stay of adjudication pursuant to Minnesota Statute Section 152.18 and being sentenced to treatment rather than a prison term. If I completed the recommended treatment, follow-up, and after-care, the charge would not appear on my record. Although it sounded good, I had already been in prison once and thought I would screw it up in the treatment program and end up doing the time anyway. I asked to have my sentence executed.

Teaching Tip
Beginning with the 1991 court case of *Wilson v. Seiter*, explain the role that various cases played in bringing the Prisoner Rights Era to a close. End your discussion with the 1996 case of *Lewis v. Casey.*

gions, he claimed that he became a serious believer as the religion developed and acquired more followers. The U.S. Supreme Court dismissed that argument and held that the First Amendment does not protect so-called religions that are obvious shams.

The Cases

In *Wilson* v. *Seiter* (1991),[65] the U.S. Supreme Court again sided with prison officials in a way uncharacteristic of the previous two decades. In *Wilson* the Court found that overcrowding, excessive noise, insufficient

A few months after being released from St. Cloud for the second time in four years, I jumped my parole and began wandering around the country with a group of misfits selling Dunn-EZ, a homemade chemical cleaner, to small businesses. Eventually, we ended up in Atlanta, Georgia, where I met my wife. She was a single mother with two young boys and was as wild as I was. Together, my wife, the boys, and I traveled the country treading water for the next several months until we found ourselves in the Lowndes County, Georgia, jail for credit card fraud. It was the most miserable time I have ever had in jail—first, because the woman I loved was in with me and, second, because the conditions were unbelievable. I slept on the floor of a very small one-man cell with two other guys. At night the guards would come by and for a Little Debbie snack or two, they would sell you a full bottle of Nyquil. One of my cellmates would drink it and get high.

With the help of my parents, my new wife and I rode the Greyhound back to Minnesota. I had to finish up about 30 days' worth of my last Minnesota sentence so that my parole would expire. Because the time left on my sentence was so short, Minnesota refused to extradite me from Georgia for the parole violation (leaving the state), but was ready and willing to incarcerate me for every day I had coming if I returned to Minnesota.

Once released and working odd jobs, I enrolled in the University of Minnesota, Duluth. I received my B.A. *magna cum laude* in criminology, with a minor in psychology, almost four years later. Graduating from college felt so unbelievably good to me. I was energized and committed to going on to law school. I applied to the University of Minnesota's law school, where I received my Juris Doctorate *cum laude*, May 10, 1997. Midway through my first year I hooked up with a law professor interested in computers, as I was. Together we created the Human Rights Library on the World Wide Web.

I completed a one-year judicial clerkship with a judge on the Court of Appeals and I am currently clerking for my second year with the Chief Judge of the Court of Appeals. In addition, I develop Web sites for law firms and nonprofit human-rights organizations, and I am writing a book. I also do public speaking about drugs, crime, corrections, and rehabilitation.

locker space, and similar conditions did not violate the Constitution if the intent of prison officials was not malicious. The Court ruled that the actions of officials did not meet the "deliberate indifference" standard defined in *Estelle* v. *Gamble* (1976).

After *Wilson*, inmates won very few new cases. The courts either reversed themselves or tightened the conditions under which inmates could win favorable decisions. Decisions supporting freedom of religion had been among the earliest and most complete victories during the Prisoner Rights Era. Even in that area, however, things began to change. The courts held that crucifixes and rosaries could legally be denied to inmates because of their possible use as weapons.[66] Although some jurisdictions had previously allowed certain Native American religious items within prisons,[67] the courts now ruled that prohibiting ceremonial pipes, medicine bags, and eagle claws did *not* violate the First Amendment rights of Native American inmates.[68]

The "deliberate indifference" standard was soon interpreted to require both actual knowledge *and* disregard of the risk of harm to inmates or others.[69] This tighter definition allowed federal courts to side more easily with state prison officials in cases where prisoners claimed there was deliberate indifference.

If there was any question that the Prisoner Rights Era had ended, that question was settled in 1995 by the case of *Sandin* v. *Conner*.[70] In *Sandin* the Supreme Court rejected the argument that by disciplining inmates, a state deprived prisoners of their constitutional right not to be deprived of liberty without due process. "The time has come to return to those due process principles that were correctly established and applied in earlier times," said the Court. A year later, the decision in *Lewis* v. *Casey*[71] overturned portions of *Bounds* v. *Smith*. The *Bounds* case had been instrumental in establishing law libraries in prisons. The Court in *Lewis* held, however, that "*Bounds* does not guarantee inmates the wherewithal to file any and every type of legal claim, but requires only that they be provided with the tools to attack their sentences."

The Legal Mechanisms

Changes in state and federal statutes have also slowed the pace of prisoners' rights cases. In 1980 Congress modified the Civil Rights of Institutionalized Persons Act.[72] It now requires a state inmate to exhaust all state remedies before filing a petition for a writ of *habeas corpus* in federal court. Inmates in federal prisons may still file *habeas corpus* petitions directly in federal court. In their petitions, federal inmates are now required to show (1) that they were deprived of some right to which they were entitled despite the confinement and (2) that the deprivation of this right made the imprisonment more burdensome.

Teaching Tip
Describe the various provisions of the 1996 Prison Litigation Reform Act. Explain how the act provides a legal mechanism for clamping down on frivolous inmate lawsuits.

The Prison Litigation Reform Act of 1996[73] (PLRA) was another legislative response to the ballooning number of civil rights lawsuits filed by prisoners. It restricts the filing of lawsuits in federal courts by:

1. Requiring inmates to pay $120 in federal filing fees unless they can claim pauper status.[74]
2. Limiting awards of attorneys' fees in successful lawsuits.
3. Requiring judges to screen all inmate lawsuits and immediately dismiss those they find frivolous.
4. Revoking good-time credit toward early release if inmates file malicious lawsuits.
5. Barring prisoners from suing the federal government for mental or emotional injury unless there is an accompanying physical injury.
6. Allowing court orders to go no further than necessary to correct the particular inmate's civil rights problem.
7. Requiring court orders to be renewed every two years or be lifted.
8. Ensuring that no single judge can order the release of federal inmates for overcrowding.

When inmates bring lawsuits against the Department of Corrections in behalf of their rights, those lawsuits are not a big-bucks undertaking for a lawyer. Most prisoners cannot afford to pay a retainer. When an attorney agrees to a contingency fee, there's always the likelihood that the state or federal government will prevail against the prisoner. After all, government agencies have more lawyers and more money than do prisoners. Also, judges tend to be more sympathetic to their own than to prisoners. It is true that prisoner litigants won more cases 20 years ago, but the political trends since then have resulted in judicial appointments more favorable to the corrections side of the scale. There's also been legislation limiting prisoners' access to the courts. I'm afraid the mood of the courts does not favor prisoners, and I believe that's true across the United States.

A Texas attorney

Female Inmates and the Courts

The prisoners' rights movement has been largely a male phenomenon. While male inmates were petitioning the courts for expansion of their rights, female inmates frequently had to resort to the courts simply to gain rights male inmates already had.

One early state case, *Barefield* v. *Leach* (1974),[75] demonstrated that the opportunities and programs for female inmates were clearly inferior to those for male inmates. In that case a court in New Mexico spelled out one standard for equal treatment of male and female inmates. The court said that the equal-protection clause of the Constitution requires equal treatment of male and female inmates, but not identical treatment. *Barefield*, however, was a state case—not binding on other states or the federal government.

In 1977, the Supreme Court of North Dakota ruled that a lack of funds was not an acceptable justification for unequal treatment of male and female prisoners.[76] Although this decision also came in a state court case, it would later be cited as a legal authority in a similar federal court case.

In *Glover* v. *Johnson* (1979), a U.S. district court case, a group of female prisoners in the Michigan system filed a class action lawsuit claiming that they were denied access to the courts and constitutional rights to equal protection.[77] The prisoners demanded educational and vocational opportunities comparable to those for male inmates. At trial, a prison teacher testified that while men were allowed to take shop courses, women were taught remedial courses at a junior-high-school level because the attitude of those in charge was "Keep it simple, these are only women." The court found that "the educational opportunities available to women prisoners in Michigan were substantially inferior to those available to male prisoners." Consequently, the court ordered a plan to provide higher education and vocational training for female prisoners in the Michigan prison system. *Glover* was a turning point in equal treatment for imprisoned women. Since 1979, female inmates have continued to win the majority of cases seeking equal treatment and the elimination of gender bias.

In the 1980 case of *Cooper* v. *Morin*, the U.S. Supreme Court accepted neither inconvenience nor cost as an excuse for treating female jail inmates differently from male inmates.[78] Female inmates at a county jail in New York had alleged that inadequate medical attention in jail violated their civil rights. Later that same year, a federal district court rejected Virginia's claims that services for female prison inmates could not be provided at the same level as those for male inmates because of cost-effectiveness issues.[79] Virginia authorities said that the much smaller number of women in prison raised the cost of providing each woman with services. The appellate court ordered the state of Virginia to provide equitable services for inmates, regardless of gender.

An action challenging the denial of equal protection and the conditions of confinement in the Kentucky Correctional Institution for Women was the basis of *Canterino* v. *Wilson*, decided in U.S. district court in 1982.[80] The district court held that the "levels system" used to allocate privileges to female prisoners, a system not applied to male prisoners, violated both the equal-protection rights and the due-process rights of female inmates. The court also held that female inmates in Kentucky's prisons must have the same

Many claims of female inmates have focused on the failure of correctional institutions to provide them with educational opportunities and medical care comparable to those provided male inmates. The equal protection clause of which amendment guarantees female inmates conditions of confinement comparable to those of male inmates?

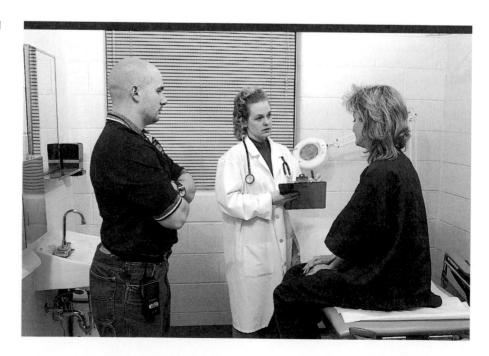

Legal Aspects: Prisons and the Courts

opportunities as men for vocational education, training, recreation, and outdoor activity.

In 1982, a district court in Louisiana ordered an end to the unequal treatment of female inmates in that state's jails.[81] (Recall that the federal courts have supervisory jurisdiction over state courts.) The next year, the Seventh Circuit Court of Appeals found that strip searches of female misdemeanor offenders awaiting bond in a Chicago lockup were unreasonable under the Fourth Amendment.[82] In addition, the court found that a policy of subjecting female arrestees to strip searches while subjecting similarly situated males only to hand searches violated the equal protection clause of the Constitution.

Women inmates have continued to win significant court cases regarding conditions of confinement. In 1994, for example, in a class action suit by female inmates, a federal district court held the District of Columbia Department of Corrections liable under the Eighth Amendment for inadequate gynecological examinations and testing, inadequate testing for sexually transmitted diseases, inadequate health education, inadequate prenatal care, and an inadequate overall prenatal protocol.[83]

Inmates With Special Needs

Inmates with special needs face numerous difficulties. This section focuses on the legal claims brought by such inmates.

Inmates With Disabilities

Ronald Yeskey was sentenced to 18 to 36 months in a Pennsylvania correctional facility. Yeskey was recommended for a motivational boot camp, which would have shortened his sentence to 6 months. He was, however, refused admission to the boot camp because of a physical disability—hypertension. He sued, claiming that the Americans with Disabilities Act (ADA) of 1990 prohibits any "public entity" from discriminating against a "qualified individual with a disability" because of that disability.[84] In a unanimous opinion, the U.S. Supreme Court held that state prisons fall squarely within the ADA's definition of a "public entity."[85] As a consequence, it is now recognized that the Americans with Disabilities Act applies to all prisons. Reacting to the decision, Yeskey's attorney noted, "The court's ruling means that prison officials cannot discriminate against prisoners with disabilities, and must make reasonable modifications to prison operations so that these prisoners will have reasonable access to most prison programs."[86]

Inmates With HIV/AIDS

Most suits by prisoners with HIV/AIDS are claims that officials have violated a prisoner's rights by revealing the condition or by segregating the prisoner because of the condition. In 1988, officials in Erie County, New York, placed an HIV-positive female prisoner in a segregated prison wing reserved for mentally ill inmates. They also placed on her possessions red

Teaching Tip

Discuss the provisions of the Americans with Disabilities Act. Show how they relate to the rights of confined individuals who are disabled.

stickers revealing her HIV-positive status. The inmate sued, claiming denial of her rights to privacy and due process. The district court agreed.[87] In the same year, however, the Eleventh Circuit Court of Appeals held that an Alabama policy of isolating all HIV-positive inmates did not violate the Fourth or Eighth Amendment.[88]

In 1994, the Ninth Circuit Court of Appeals ruled that California correctional officials could continue to bar HIV-positive inmates from working in prison kitchens.[89] The court made it clear that its decision was based more on the anticipated reactions of prisoners receiving the food than on any actual risk of infection. The court agreed that food service "has often been the source of violence or riots" because inmates "are not necessarily motivated by rational thought and frequently have irrational suspicions or phobias that education will not modify" and because prisoners "have no choice of where they eat." Correctional officials had based their policy, the court said, on "legitimate penological concerns."

Mentally Ill Inmates

The federal courts have recognized the right of mentally ill inmates to treatment. According to a district court in Illinois, this right is triggered when it becomes reasonably certain that (1) the prisoner's symptoms demonstrate a serious mental disease or brain injury, (2) the disease or injury is curable or at least treatable, and (3) delaying or denying care would cause substantially more harm to the inmate.[90]

In 1990, in *Washington* v. *Harper*, the U.S. Supreme Court ruled that an inmate who is dangerous to himself or others as a result of mental illness may be treated with psychoactive drugs against his will.[91] Such involuntary drug treatment, however, has to be in the best interest of the inmate's mental health, not just for the convenience of the correctional institution.

Inmate Grievance Procedures

Teaching Tip
Remind the class that inmate grievance procedures are formal institutional processes for hearing inmate complaints. Then review the requirements established by the U.S. Department of Justice for certification of grievance procedures.

Inmate grievance procedures are formal institutional processes for hearing inmate complaints. Grievance procedures are required under a U.S. Supreme Court ruling in 1977 in *Jones* v. *North Carolina Prisoners' Labor Union* (discussed earlier in this chapter). Federal law allows a federal judge to refer a state inmate's lawsuit back to the state correctional system.[92] For such a referral, court precedents require the state correctional agency to have an inmate grievance procedure certified by the U.S. Department of Justice. A referral can save the state correctional agency enormous amounts of time and money. Once the federal judge sends the case back to the state, correctional officials do not have to defend themselves in federal court, transport the inmate to and from federal court, or contend with the publicity that can go along with a court case. Hence, inmate grievance procedures are in the best interest of state correctional officials.

Certification of state grievance procedures by the U.S. Department of Justice requires that:[93]

1. Both inmates and employees of the institution have advisory roles in the development of the procedures.

2. Maximum time limits for responses to grievances be established.
3. Provisions exist for rapid processing of emergency inmate grievances when undue delay could result in harm to an inmate.
4. A mechanism exists for review of decisions by a person or committee not under the direct control of the prison in which the grievance originated.

Today most correctional systems use a three-step process for resolving grievances. First, a staff member or committee in each institution receives complaints, investigates them, and makes decisions. Second, if a prisoner is dissatisfied with that decision, the case may be appealed to the warden. Third, if the prisoner is still dissatisfied, the complaint may be given to the state's commissioner of corrections or the state's corrections board. This three-step procedure satisfies the requirements for U.S. Department of Justice certification.

Teaching Tip
Refer to Chapter 10 of the *Instructor's Resource Manual* for additional activities and for answers to the end-of-chapter exercises.

10

Review and Applications

SUMMARY BY CHAPTER OBJECTIVES

CHAPTER OBJECTIVE 1
The hands-off doctrine was a working philosophy of the courts in this country until the 1970s. It allowed corrections officials to run prisons without court intervention. The hands-off doctrine existed because courts were reluctant to interfere with activities of the executive branch and because judges realized that they were not experts in corrections.

CHAPTER OBJECTIVE 2
The sources of prisoners' rights are the U.S. Constitution, federal statutes, state constitutions, and state statutes.

CHAPTER OBJECTIVE 3
Inmates can challenge the conditions of their confinement through (1) a state *habeas corpus* action, (2) a federal *habeas corpus* action, (3) a state tort lawsuit, (4) a federal civil rights lawsuit, and (5) an injunction to obtain relief.

CHAPTER OBJECTIVE 4
During the Prisoner Rights Era (1969–1991), inmates won many court cases based on claims that conditions of their confinement violated their constitutional rights. Court decisions affected inmate rights concerning freedom of

expression, including free speech; personal communications; access to the courts and legal services; religious issues; the right to assembly and association; grievances and disciplinary procedures; personal and cell searches; health care, including diet and exercise; protection from violence; the physical conditions of confinement; and rehabilitation.

CHAPTER OBJECTIVE 5
Most prisoners' claims focus on denial of constitutional rights guaranteed by the First (freedom of expression and religion), Fourth (freedom from unlawful search and seizure), Eighth (freedom from cruel and unusual punishment), and Fourteenth (due process and equal protection of the law) Amendments.

CHAPTER OBJECTIVE 6
The prisoners' rights movement has been largely a male phenomenon. Female inmates have had to petition the courts to gain rights that male inmates already had.

CHAPTER OBJECTIVE 7
Claims involving conditions of confinement have been brought by inmates with disabilities, inmates with HIV/AIDS, and mentally ill inmates.

KEY TERMS

hands-off doctrine, p. 274
prisoners' rights, p. 275
constitutional rights, p. 275
institutional needs, p. 275
civil liability, p. 276
writ of *habeas corpus*, p. 276
tort, p. 277
nominal damages, p. 277
compensatory damages, p. 277
punitive damages, p. 277
injunction, p. 278

jurisdiction, p. 278
precedent, p. 282
legitimate penological objectives, p. 283
balancing test, p. 283
cruel and unusual punishment, p. 290
consent decree, p. 290
deliberate indifference, p. 291
totality of conditions, p. 291
due process, p. 293
frivolous lawsuits, p. 295

Legal Aspects: Prisons and the Courts

1. What constitutional rights were prisoners thought to have a hundred years ago?
2. Why was the hands-off doctrine so named? What was the basis for the doctrine?
3. Which statutes might have a bearing on the rights of prison inmates?
4. What are the legal mechanisms through which inmates have gained access to the courts?
5. To what degree are prison officials liable for their actions toward inmates?
6. What led to the end of the hands-off doctrine?
7. What First Amendment rights have been gained by inmates? What First Amendment rights do inmates *not* have?
8. What Fourth Amendment rights have been gained by inmates? What Fourth Amendment rights do inmates *not* have?
9. What Eighth Amendment rights have been gained by inmates? What Eighth Amendment rights do inmates *not* have?
10. How does the Fourteenth Amendment relate to prisoners' rights? Are there Fourteenth Amendment rights enjoyed by the average citizen but not by inmates? If so, what are they?
11. What caused the relatively recent slowdown in the granting of rights to inmates by the courts?
12. Do the rights of male inmates correspond to the rights of female inmates? Why or why not?
13. Have the courts given any direction to prisons regarding the treatment of inmates with disabilities? If so, what have the courts said?
14. Are there differences in legal status between HIV-negative inmates and HIV-positive inmates? If so, what are the differences?
15. What are the court-required obligations of prisons in their treatment of mentally ill prisoners?
16. What are inmate grievance procedures? Why do they exist? How do they function?

CRITICAL THINKING EXERCISES

ON-THE-JOB ISSUE

You are a prison administrator. The prison where you work has a rule that inmates may write letters in English only. This rule seems sensible. After all, if inmates could write in languages not understood by correctional officers, they could discuss plans to escape, riot, or smuggle drugs or weapons into the prison. Even though the courts allow the censoring of outgoing inmate mail, what good is that power if corrections personnel can't read the mail?

It occurs to you, however, that inmates who can't write in English will have difficulty communicating with the outside world and with their families. Inmates unable to write in English won't even be able to write to their attorneys. You also wonder what might happen if an inmate can write in English, but his parents read only a foreign language. If the inmate and his parents can't afford long-distance phone calls, they will not be able to communicate with each other at all. You begin to consider how the English-only rule might be changed to facilitate wholesome communications while still preventing communications that might endanger the safety of the institution and the inmate population.

1. Can the English-only rule be amended to meet the inmate needs discussed here, while still being consistent with legitimate institutional concerns? If so, how?
2. Does an inmate have a constitutionally protected right to communicate with his or her parents? What if that right conflicts with prison policy?

CORRECTIONS ISSUE

The right to freedom of nonverbal expression is said to be implied in the First Amendment. Hence, how people wear their hair and how they dress are expressions that some believe are protected by the First Amendment. Might there be modes of dress that interfere with a correctional institution's legitimate goals?

CORRECTIONS ON THE WEB

In 1996, the state of Ohio passed a law designed to limit frivolous lawsuits by state inmates. The law requires inmates to pay at least a portion of the filing fee from their prison accounts, sets up a process by which a court may declare a lawsuit frivolous, institutes sanctions for inmates whose claims are dismissed as frivolous, and requires screening of new cases by inmates who file multiple cases in one year. Search the Internet for other ways in which states have attempted to limit frivolous inmate lawsuits. Write a report summarizing the techniques and laws that states employ to limit inmates to filing valid lawsuits.

ADDITIONAL READINGS

del Carmen, Rolando, Susan Ritter, and Betsy Witt. *Briefs of Leading Cases in Corrections*, 2d ed. Cincinnati: Anderson, 1998.

DiIulio, John J., Jr. (ed.). *Courts, Corrections and the Constitution*. New York: Oxford University Press, 1990.

Mushlin, Michael. *The Rights of Prisoners*, 2d ed. Colorado Springs: Shepard's/ McGraw-Hill, 1993.

Palmer, John W. *Constitutional Rights of Prisoners*, 5th ed. Cincinnati: Anderson, 1997.

ENDNOTES

1. *Ruffin* v. *Commonwealth*, 62 Va. 790 (1871).
2. Frances Cole, "The Impact of *Bell* v. *Wolfish* Upon Prisoners' Rights," *Journal of Crime and Justice*, Vol. 10 (1987), pp. 47-70.
3. *Schenk* v. *United States*, 249 U.S. 47 (1919).
4. Todd Clear and George F. Cole, *American Corrections*, 4th ed. (New York: Wadsworth, 1997).
5. R. Hawkins and G. P. Alpert, *American Prison Systems: Punishment and Justice* (Englewood Cliffs, NJ: Prentice-Hall, 1989).
6. John Scalia, *Prisoner Petitions in the Federal Courts, 1980–96* (Washington: U.S. Department of Justice, October 1997).
7. *Sostre* v. *McGinnis*, 442 F.2d 178 (1971).
8. *Smith* v. *Sullivan*, 553 F.2d 373 (5th Cir. 1977).
9. Adapted from Norman M. Garland and Gilbert B. Stuckey, *Criminal Evidence for the Law Enforcement Officer*, 4th ed. (Columbus: Glencoe/McGraw-Hill, 1999), pp. 14–16.
10. *Ex parte Hull*, 312 U.S. 546 (1941).
11. *Coffin* v. *Reichard*, 143 F.2d 443 (1944).
12. Cole.
13. *Monroe* v. *Pape*, 365 U.S. 167 (1961).
14. Ibid.
15. D. J. Gottlieb, "The Legacy of *Wolfish* and *Chapman*: Some Thoughts About 'Big Prison Case' Litigation in the 1980s," in I. D. Robbins (ed.), *Prisoners and the Law* (New York: Clark Boardman, 1985).
16. *Cooper* v. *Tate*, 382 F.2d 518 (1964).
17. James B. Jacobs, *New Perspectives on Prisons and Imprisonment* (Ithaca, NY: Cornell University Press, 1983).
18. *Holt* v. *Sarver*, 300 F.Supp. 825 (D.C. 1969); see also *Holt* v. *Sarver*, 309 F.Supp. 362 (E.D. Ark. 1970), aff'd, 442 F.2d 304 (8th Cir. 1971).
19. *Holt* v. *Sarver*, 309 F.Supp. 362 (E.D. Ark. 1970).
20. *Pell* v. *Procunier*, 417 U.S. 817 (1974).
21. *Cruz* v. *Beto*, 405 U.S. 319, 321 (1972).
22. *Procunier* v. *Martinez*, 416 U.S. 396 (1974).
23. *McNamara* v. *Moody*, 606 F.Supp.2d 621 (5th Cir., 1979).
24. *Peppering* v. *Crist*, 678 F.Supp.2d 787 (1981).
25. *Mallery* v. *Lewis*, 106 Idaho 227 (1983).
26. *Thornburgh* v. *Abbott*, 490 U.S. 401 (1989).
27. *Turner* v. *Safley*, 482 U.S. 78, 94–99 (1987).
28. *Jones* v. *North Carolina Prisoners' Labor Union, Inc.*, 433 U.S. 119 (1977).
29. *Pell* v. *Procunier*, 417 U.S. 817, 822 (1974).
30. *Fulwood* v. *Clemmer*, 206 F.Supp. 370, 373 (D.D.C., 1962).
31. *Gittlemacker* v. *Prasse*, 428 F.2d 1 (3rd Cir., 1970).
32. *Cruz* v. *Beto*, 405 U.S. 319 (1972).
33. *Kahane* v. *Carlson*, 527 F.2d 492 (2nd Cir., 1975).
34. *Kahane* v. *Carlson*, elaborating on *Barnett* v. *Rodgers*, 133 U.S. App. D.C. 296, 410 F.2d 995 (1969).
35. *Udey* v. *Kastner*, 805 F.2d 1218 (1986).
36. *Dettmer* v. *Landon*, 799 F.2d 929 (1986).

37. *O'Lone* v. *Estate of Shabazz*, 482 U.S. 342 (1987).
38. *United States* v. *Hitchcock*, 467 F.2d 1107 (9th Cir., 1972).
39. *Hudson* v. *Palmer*, 468 U.S. 517 (1984).
40. *Block* v. *Rutherford*, 486 U.S. 576 (1984).
41. *Grummett* v. *Rushen*, 779 F.2d 491 (9th Cir., 1985).
42. See *Estelle* v. *Gamble*, 429 U.S. 97, 102 (1976), and *Hutto* v. *Finney*, 437 U.S. 678, 681 (1978).
43. For a complete history of this case, see *Ruiz* v. *Estelle*, 503 F. Supp. 1265, 1385–1390 (S.D.Tex., 1980), and *Ruiz* v. *Estelle*, 679 F.Supp.2d 1115 (1982).
44. *Holt* v. *Sarver*, 309 F.Supp. 362 (E.D. Ark., 1970). See also, *Holt* v. *Sarver*, 300 F.Supp. 825 (D.C. 1969).
45. *Knecht* v. *Gillman*, 488 F.2d 1136 (8th Cir., 1973).
46. *Estelle* v. *Gamble*, 429 U.S. 27 (1976).
47. *Pugh* v. *Locke*, 406 F.Supp. 318, 332 (M.D.Ala., 1976).
48. *Battle* v. *Anderson*, 564 F.2d 388 (10th Cir., 1977).
49. *Hutto* v. *Finney*, 437 U.S. 678 (1978).
50. *Wilson* v. *Seiter*, 501 U.S. 294 (1991).
51. *Rhodes* v. *Chapman*, 452 U.S. 337 (1981).
52. *Smith* v. *Fairman*, 690 F.2d 122 (7th Cir., 1982).
53. *Johnson* v. *Avery*, 393 U.S. 483 (1968).
54. *Wolff* v. *McDonnell*, 418 U.S. 539 (1974).
55. Ibid.
56. *Baxter* v. *Palmigiano*, 425 U.S. 308 (1976).
57. *Meacham* v. *Fano*, 427 U.S. 215, 228 (1976).
58. *Stone* v. *Powell*, 96 S.Ct. 3037 (1976).
59. *Bounds* v. *Smith*, 430 U.S. 817 (1977).
60. *Jones* v. *North Carolina Prisoners' Labor Union, Inc.*, 433 U.S. 119 (1977).
61. *Ponte* v. *Real*, 471 U.S. 491 (1985).
62. *Daniels* v. *Williams*, 474 U.S. 327 (1986).
63. *West* v. *Atkins*, 487 U.S. 42, 48 (1988).
64. See *Theriault* v. *Carlson*, 339 F.Supp. 375 (N.D.Ga., 1972), vacated, 495 F.2d 390 (5th Cir., 1973), cert. denied 419 U.S. 1003 (1974). In 1977, Theriault's appeal to the U.S. Supreme Court was denied. See 434 U.S. 953 (November 14, 1977).
65. *Wilson* v. *Seiter*, 501 U.S. 294 (1991).
66. See *Mark* v. *Nix*, 983 F.2d 138 (1993), and *Escobar* v. *Landwehr*, 837 F.Supp. 284 (1993).
67. *Sample* v. *Borg*, 675 F.Supp. 574 (E.D. Cal., 1987).
68. *Bettis* v. *Delo*, 14 F.3d 22 (1994).
69. *Hudson* v. *McMillan*, 503 U.S. 1 (1992).
70. *Sandin* v. *Conner*, 515 U.S. 472 (1995).
71. Electronic citation: *Lewis* v. *Casey*, S.Ct. 131 (1996). (http://www.versuslaw.com).
72. Civil Rights of Institutionalized Persons Act, 42 U.S.C. § 1997 et seq. (1976 ed., Supp. IV), as modified 1980 (see especially Sec. 1997e). In section 1997e, Congress created a specific, limited exhaustion requirement for adult prisoners bringing actions pursuant to section 1983.
73. Prison Litigation Reform Act, Pub. L. No. 104-134, 801-10, 110 Stat. 1321 (1996).
74. If a prisoner wishes to proceed as an indigent on appeal, the prisoner must file in the district court, with the notice of appeal, a motion for leave to proceed as an indigent, a certified copy of a prison trust account statement, and Form 4 from the Appendix of Forms found in the *Federal Rules of Appellate Procedure*.
75. *Barefield* v. *Leach*, New Mexico Civil Action No. 10282 (1974).
76. *State, ex rel. Olson* v. *Maxwell*, 259 N.W.2d 621 (Supreme Ct. of N.D., 1977).
77. *Glover* v. *Johnson*, 478 F.Supp. 1075 (1979).
78. *Cooper* v. *Morin*, 446 U.S. 984 (1980).
79. *Bukhari* v. *Hutto*, 487 F.Supp. 1162 (E.D. Va., 1980).
80. *Canterino* v. *Wilson*, 546 F.Supp. 174 (W.D.Ky., 1982).
81. *McMurray* v. *Phelps*, 535 F.Supp. 742 (W.D.La., 1982).
82. *Mary Beth G.* v. *City of Chicago*, 723 F.2d 1263 (7th Cir., 1983).
83. *Women Prisoners of the District of Columbia Department of Corrections* v. *District of Columbia*, 877 F.Supp. 634 (D.D.C., 1994).
84. 42 U.S.C. Section 12132.
85. *Pennsylvania Dept. of Corrections* v. *Yeskey*, U.S. Supreme Court Case No. 97-634 (1998).
86. The Associated Press, "Supreme Court Upholds Rights of Disabled Inmates," June 15, 1998.
87. *Nolley* v. *County of Erie*, 776 F.Supp. 715 (W.D.N.Y., 1991).
88. *Harris* v. *Thigpen*, 941 F.2d 1495 (11th Cir., 1991). See also *Austin* v. *Pennsylvania Dept. of Corr.*, 876 F.Supp. 1437 (11th Cir., 1991).
89. *Gates* v. *Rowland*, 39 F.3d 1439 (9th Cir., 1994).
90. *Parte* v. *Lane*, 528 F.Supp. 1254 (N.D. Ill., 1981).
91. *Washington* v. *Harper*, 494 U.S. 210, 1990.
92. Title 42 U.S.C., Section 1997.
93. Hans Toch, "Democratizing Prisons," *Prison Journal*, Vol. 74 (1995), pp. 62–72.

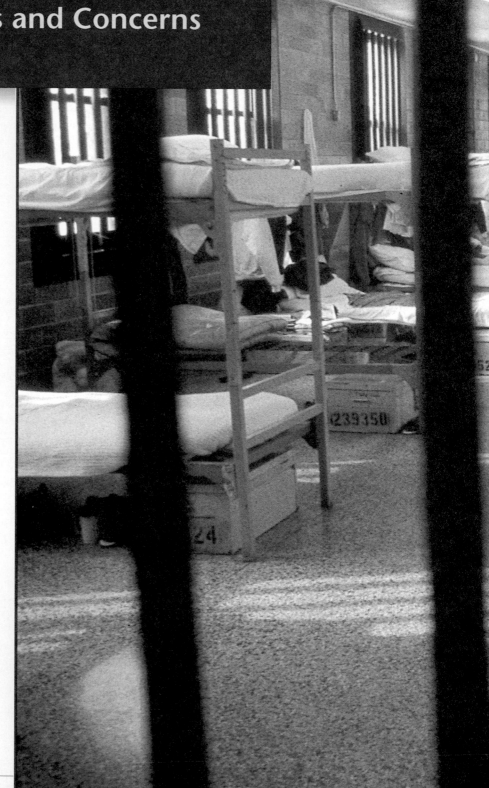

11 The Prison Environment
Issues and Concerns

CHAPTER OBJECTIVES

After completing this chapter you should be able to:

1. List the three main reasons why prisons are overcrowded.
2. Identify six methods of controlling prison overcrowding.
3. Identify six causes of prison riots.
4. Describe what can be done to prevent prison riots.
5. Outline the emergence of supermax housing and its impact.
6. Describe "no-frills" jails and prisons and their impact on corrections.
7. Summarize the issues that special needs inmates raise for corrections professionals.

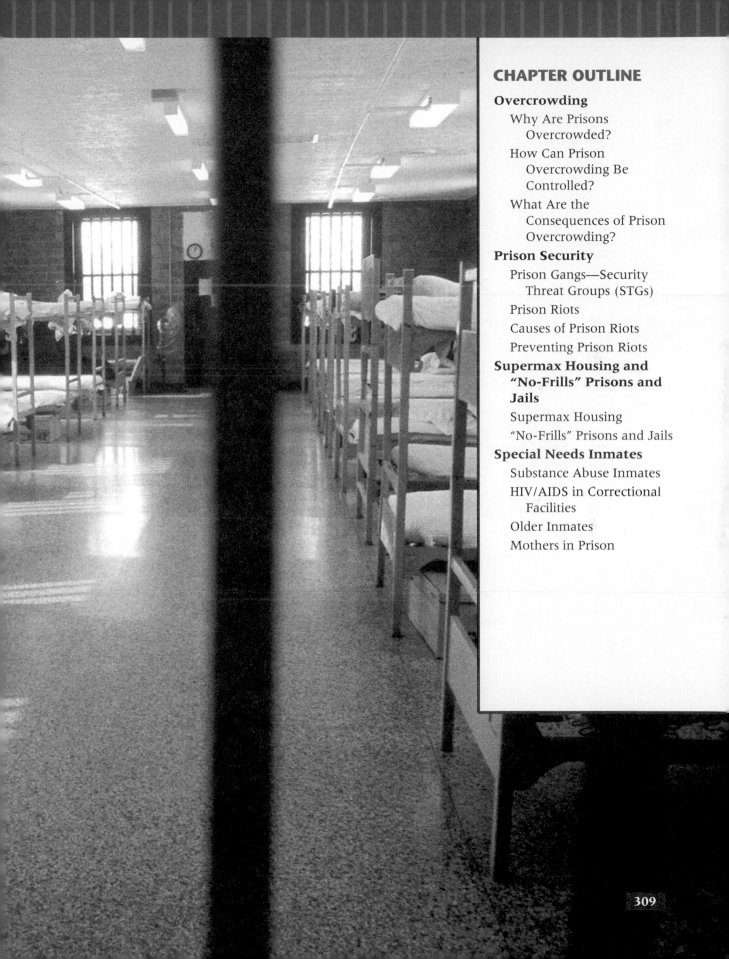

> *Those of us on the outside [of prisons] do not like to think of wardens and guards as our servants. Yet they are, and they are intimately locked in a deadly embrace with their human captives behind the prison walls. By extension so are we. A terrible double meaning is thus imparted to the original question of human ethics: Am I my brother's keeper?*
>
> —Jessica Mitford

The Happy Valley Redirection Institution was in the midst of a riot. Warden Batman shook his head in disbelief as he tried to figure out how this had happened. Prison riots, common in the 1980s, were a thing of the past. Maybe, he thought, the robot correctional officers malfunctioned; they were overdue for tune-ups. Robots were so complex. Fortunately, he still had 25 human correctional officers.

One clear mistake was his decision to forego the inmates' serotonin for one night. He wanted them to have a fun night—it didn't occur to him that things might get out of hand. Serotonin—the master chemical of mood, appetite, and memory—controls aggression; he should not have forgotten.

He imagined explaining the riot to his superiors. He would tell them that the riot only proved that land prisons were a thing of the past. The decision in late 2005 to build prisons on the floors of oceans or on orbiting space stations had proven to be the proper direction for corrections. He also knew, regrettably, that the old excuse of riots resulting from improper food would not fly in 2010. All inmates were tested for chemical imbalances that might cause deficiencies, dependencies, or toxicity. Furthermore, vitamin mega-doses were standard treatment.

On a positive note, no property damage could occur; all furniture was fireproof and unbreakable. Also, human staff would remain unharmed; inmates had received drug-induced amnesia treatments to forget violent learned behaviors.

Suddenly the solution hit him like a bolt of lightning. He would simply end the riot—which was nothing more than inmates running aimlessly around the institution—by pressing the sound alarm. This modern device produced high intensity sound waves that would render the inmates unconscious for several minutes. He pressed the activator, and the inmates fell to the floor. Fortunately, all the human correctional officers wore riot helmets to protect their eardrums. As a precaution, they sprayed the more aggressive of the unconscious inmates with sticky foam; they would not escape, or move, for that matter.

The riot was over. As the inmates were returned to their temperature-controlled cellular units, he relaxed. Perhaps his career was not over.[1]

Sound far out? It may not be as unimaginable as you think. Imagine reporting a crime to a "software agent" police officer at your local police department via the Internet. Imagine probation officers using electronically transmitted smells to monitor the lifestyles of convicted drug offenders. Imagine virtual courtrooms, digitally displayed evidence, and virtual tours of crime scenes. Don't imagine. They're already here.

The Prison Environment: Issues and Concerns

But what are the issues and concerns of the prison environment today? In this chapter we shall consider four aspects of the prison environment: overcrowding; riots and violence; supermax housing and "no-frills" prisons; and special needs inmates.

Overcrowding

A prison was often referred to as "the big house" in the past. Today, however, a more appropriate description is "the full house." Over the past 25 years prison population has increased six-fold—from 240,000 to 1.3 million. Some say that prisons are "capacity-driven"; that is, cut the ribbon and they're full. Saying exactly how full, though, is difficult, because each state has its own method for measuring prison capacity. Some use **rated capacity** (the number of beds in a facility); others **operational capacity** (the number of inmates that can be accommodated based on a facility's staff and existing programs and services); still others **design capacity** (the number of inmates that planners intended the facility to house). The problem is compounded because some states have their own definitions. In spite of the differences, by any measure, today's prisons are overcrowded.

On January 1, 1999, 36 states and the Federal Bureau of Prisons (BOP) were operating above capacity, most by 15 percent. That would suggest that as many as 195,302 (15%) of the 1,302,019 million adult prisoners on January 1, 1999, were housed in overcrowded facilities. Eliminating the present overcrowding would require building 150 new prisons at a cost of $7.2 billion (assuming that each has a capacity of 1,300 and costs approximately $48 million to build), then staffing and maintaining the new facilities. Even if this were possible, the relief from overcrowding would be short-term; the prisoner population continually grows. The increase in prisoner population in 1998 was 4.8 percent over 1997—58,090 more prisoners in 1998. Based on the forementioned assumptions and averaging 58,000 more prisoners each year, keeping up with the increase would require adding 45 new prisons each year.

Why Are Prisons Overcrowded?

There are three main reasons why prisons are crowded. The first is a continuous increase in the number of persons imprisoned. This number increased significantly between 1990 and 1998—almost 64,000 per year; from 743,382 in 1990 to almost 1.3 million in 1998, an increase of almost 75 percent. Nearly 1 of every 150 people in the United States is incarcerated.

The second reason is that offenders are serving a larger portion of their sentences. Sentencing laws changed, reducing the difference between the sentence imposed and the actual time served, and restricting the possibility of early release from prison. Jurisdictions began to depart from the prevailing approach, known as indeterminate sentencing (broad authorized sentencing ranges, parole release, and case-by-case decision making), in the mid-1970s (see Chapter 2). Today the trend in many jurisdictions is toward determinate sentencing—a fixed term of incarceration and no possibility of parole. In addition, most jurisdictions have adopted one or more of the fol-

rated capacity The number of beds in a facility.

operational capacity The number of inmates that can be accommodated based on a facility's staff and existing programs and services.

design capacity The number of inmates that planners intended the facility to house.

Student Involvement Ask a student to volunteer to contact your state's corrections department to obtain information about prison construction and operating costs and report to the class, or invite someone from the corrections department to visit your class and present the information.

Student Involvement Have interested students research the imprisonment increase in your state between 1990 and the current year. Suggest that they check with your state's corrections department or obtain the data online at **www.ncjrs.org**.

THE STAFF SPEAKS

D o you want to know why Louisiana has the second highest incarceration rate in this country? Our sentences are too long, our sentences are too tough! You're doing more time for every crime than you do in most any other state. The problem with Louisiana? We don't ever let 'em go. Once you break the law, you don't get another chance. If it were up to me I'd say let's not keep dying old men in prison. They're too old to pull an armed robbery or be a ski-mask rapist. They ought to do about twenty years on most any serious crime and when they turn about fifty years old—when those two come together on a graph—they pretty well should have a good shot at going free.

Burl Cain, Warden
Louisiana State Penitentiary
at Angola

Student Involvement
Have students contact the local prosecuting or district attorney's office to find out if and when your state implemented mandatory minimum sentences, three-strikes laws, or truth-in-sentencing laws and how the prison population changed after implementation.

Student Involvement
Ask a group of students to research the number and percentage of persons imprisoned in your state each year for the last 10 years, for drug-related crimes and for violent offenses. Then ask the students to compare the changes. What conclusions about your state's sentencing laws can they draw from these changes?

lowing sentencing approaches: mandatory minimum sentences, three-strikes laws, or truth-in-sentencing laws requiring offenders to serve mandated percentages of imposed sentences (see Chapter 2). As a result, between 1990 and 1998 the number of offenders held in state prisons grew annually by an average of almost 7 percent.

The goal of sentencing policies such as mandatory minimums or three-strikes laws is to curtail repeat offenses. Research, however, suggests that time spent in prison or jail actually increases the risk of future crime.[2] Thus, while a strong case can be made for lengthier prison sentences, legislators and prison administrators may find little evidence to support the theory that longer sentences deter crime.

The third reason why prisons are overcrowded is that many incoming prisoners are drug users, not the drug dealers the tougher drug laws were designed to capture. Today, more than 400,000 people are behind bars for drug crimes; nearly one-third of these are for simple possession. Nearly 60 percent of all federal prisoners and 22 percent of state prisoners are doing time for drug offenses; triple the percentages of 15 years ago. The goal of tougher drug laws was more convictions, putting more people in jail and prison and reducing the drug-related crime rate. This goal has not been achieved. At least 22 percent of the federal prison population consists of nonviolent drug offenders; their continued incarceration is extremely costly and wasteful of precious prison space.

How Can Overcrowding Be Controlled?

In most jurisdictions across the United States today we find at least six methods of controlling prison overcrowding:

1. Reduce the number of people going to prison.
2. Release the less dangerous to make room for the more dangerous.
3. Change prison or jail sentences to community-related sentences.
4. Increase the number of releases.
5. Expand existing prison capacity or build new prisons.
6. Implement an overall program of structured sentencing.

The first four methods are referred to as front-end, trap-door, side-door, and back-door strategies, respectively (see Chapter 6).

The fifth method of controlling prison overcrowding is the most commonly considered—in 1996, the United States spent $859 million on prison expansion and $2.5 billion on new prison construction. Prison overcrowding, however, continues to worsen. Some experts believe that legislators will one day have to choose between new prison construction and funding for other areas, such as health care or education.

The sixth method refers to sentencing guidelines that are designed to save prison beds for more serious crimes and violent offenses, using community and intermediate sanctions for lesser offenses. Structured sentencing is a compromise between indeterminate sentencing and mandatory determinate sentencing (see Chapter 2). Under **structured sentencing**, a commission creates a set of guidelines that consider both the offense and a few personal characteristics of the offender (notably, a prior criminal record). The guidelines for the type and duration of sentence are normally determined by deciding what type of punishment a particular crime deserves and calculating the probable cost of the sentence. Under a structured sentencing system, sentences are more uniform and less subject to the individual discretion of judges or parole board members. Structured sentencing makes it possible to anticipate and meet correctional resource needs on an ongoing basis rather than reacting after an overcrowding problem develops.

A jurisdiction establishing structured sentencing might consider implementing non-prison options such as interchangeability of punishments, also called **exchange rates.** A sentencing commission might, for example, decide that three days under house arrest or 40 community service hours is equivalent to one day of incarceration, or that three years under intensive supervision is equivalent to one year in prison.

What Are the Consequences of Overcrowding?

Researchers and prison administrators routinely observe the consequences of overcrowding. These include increases in idleness, drug trafficking, predatory sexual behavior, safety risks, gang confrontations, arguments, fights, assaults, murders, suicides, riots, medical and mental health problems, staff turnover, and stress. Other consequences include decreases in program opportunities; inappropriate housing assignments; judicial intervention to counteract illegal conditions; fines by state governments for operating over capacity; excessive wear and tear on prison facilities and

structured sentencing
A set of guidelines for determining an offender's sentence.

exchange rates An approach to sentencing, implemented by a sentencing commission, that emphasizes interchangeability of punishments; for example, three days under house arrest might be considered equal to one day of incarceration.

equipment; and negative publicity about conditions in overcrowded facilities. Researchers have also linked overcrowding to higher rates of recidivism.[3]

Prison Security

Prison gang confrontations and riots inspire frightening images. For prisoners, staff, and their families on the outside, nothing is more frightening than a prison gang confrontation or riot, regardless of where it occurs.

Prison Gangs—Security Threat Groups (STGs)

Prison gangs are one of the most significant developments in American prisons since the existence of the Gypsy Jokers Motorcycle Club was first recorded at the Walla Walla, Washington, penitentiary in 1950. The problem of prison gangs is so pervasive today that experts now refer to them as **security threat groups** (STGs). The American Correctional Association (ACA) reports that there are 1,153 different STGs having over 46,000 members in U.S. prisons.[4] Most STGs are founded along racial and ethnic boundaries. STGs commonly found across the United States are the Aryan Brotherhood, Black Disciples, Black Guerrilla Family, Bloods, Crips, Latin Kings, Mexican Mafia, Nuestra Familia, Skinheads, Texas Syndicate, and Vice Lords. The STGs most tracked because of violent behavior are the Aryan Brotherhood, Black Guerrilla Family, Mexican Mafia, Nuestra Familia, and Texas Syndicate.

STGs have a profound impact on prison security. STG members are five times more likely to incite or be involved in prison violence than nonmembers.[5] In an attempt to control STG influence, some prison administrators transferred known STG members from one institution to another only to find that this practice actually increased STG organization and activity—it extended the STG's influence throughout a state's prison system. Other states enacted "gang enhancement" statutes that imposed severe sentences

Teaching Tip
Review with students the definition of STGs (security threat groups). Ask students if they are familiar with any of the STGs mentioned in the text.

security threat groups (STGs) The current term for prison gangs.

Teaching Tip
Discuss with students different methods of controlling STGs and the pros and cons of each.

Correctional institutions may use identifiable tattoos as one of the ways to designate that an inmate is a member of a security threat group. Once an STG member is identified, what restrictions might prison administrators place on such an individual?

The Prison Environment: Issues and Concerns

on STG activity. Today, many states are adopting a new strategy—segregate known STG members to highly restrictive supermax housing, correctional facilities that are designed to house the "worst of the worst" prisoners under complete lockdown and total isolation. Advocates of this approach contend that removing STG leaders from the general prison population reduces the amount of control that STG leaders exert. Critics of the approach argue that violence actually may increase because conditions within supermax housing are so harsh that they emotionally damage inmates who may one day be returned to the general prison population or released or paroled into the community.

Teaching Tip
Review with students the two explanations for why STGs develop (deprivation and importation). Then ask students how prison policies might be changed to control STGs.

Two explanations for STG development are deprivation and importation. As we saw in Chapter 9, the basic premise of deprivation theory is that inmates develop a social system as a way to adapt to the pains of imprisonment. Because inmates are deprived of liberty, autonomy, goods and services, sexual relations, and security, they develop a culture that helps them get back what imprisonment has taken. Importation theory, on the other hand, emphasizes that inmates' pre-prison attitudes and values guide their reactions and responses to the internal conditions of prison. Both theories are valid; most major STGs can be traced to pre-prison attitudes and values, but prison conditions influence when and to what extent STG activity and violence occur.

Prison Riots

Prison disturbances occur in a variety of forms, not all of which are violent. A hunger strike or refusal to work is a disturbance because it is a defiance of prison authority and could disrupt prison routine. A prison **riot** involves seizure of control by inmates over all or part of a correctional facility, violence against staff and/or other prisoners, and demands for administrative changes in the facility.[6]

riot Seizure of control by inmates over all or part of a correctional facility with violence against staff and/or other prisoners.

On Wednesday, February 23, 2000, the worst prison riot in more than a decade in California broke out when correctional officers permitted white, Black, and Hispanic inmates in the maximum-security unit at the Pelican Bay State Prison to enter the exercise yard together for the first time since racial tension had flared in August 1999. (The maximum-security unit is one of three units in the Pelican Bay prison complex. The complex also includes a super-maximum housing unit for 1,500 inmates and a minimum-security housing unit for 200 inmates.)

Correctional officers used pepper spray, tear gas, rubber bullets, and lethal force to break up the riot. Sixteen inmates were shot, one was killed, and another was critically wounded. Prisoners stabbed 32 inmates. No correctional officers were injured. Observers believed that the riot was caused by overcrowding (the maximum-security unit was built to house 2,280 prisoners but was overcrowded with 3,326) and mismanagement (in 1995 a federal judge found prison officials had endorsed the use of excessive force). An FBI investigation of alleged civil rights violations followed the disturbance.

There is no agreement on what constitutes a prison riot. What some call a riot, others downplay and call a disturbance. For example, in 1993 there were over 186 disturbances in 21 corrections systems—only 7 were classified as riots.[7] In Connecticut, a gang fight involving over 300 inmates

Teaching Tip
Ask students to describe their perceptions of what occurs in riot situations. Compare their responses to the information in the text book. What are the similarities and differences?

and causing over $100,000 in damage was called a riot. At Leavenworth, a racial fight involving 427 inmates that caused significant damage to the prison's auditorium, chapel, and industry buildings was called a disturbance. Correctional administrators label most incidents disturbances because the term is less sensational.

How many prison riots have there been in the United States? Nobody knows for sure. Not only do we have different opinions as to what constitutes a riot, but wardens and state officials are reluctant to publicize loss of control. Scholars estimate that almost 500 prison riots have taken place in the United States since 1855.[8]

Prison violence and riots are as old as prisons themselves. There were riots and mass escapes at the Walnut Street Jail in Philadelphia, at Newgate Prison in New York, and almost everywhere, from the beginning of prisons in this country.[9] One particularly eventful year was 1952, when riots erupted in 25 of the 152 U.S. prisons. Although no lives were lost, prison staff and inmates were in danger and damage ran into the millions. Reasons for the riots included absence of inmate programs and work, idleness, unqualified staff who were poorly trained and poorly paid, old facilities (one-third were more than 70 years old), absence of policies to hear inmate grievances, crowding, insufficient prison budgets, absence of inmate classification, philosophical conflicts about the nature of prisoners (treat them as human beings who will one day rejoin society or "treat them rough"), and the presence of a new generation of prisoners.[10]

In 1954, reformers advocated overhauling and modernizing prison programs, replacing old prisons, hiring more and better staff, and developing an integrated state system. They advocated the creation of:

- professionally staffed classification centers;
- prisons no larger than 500 beds;
- professionally trained, well-paid correctional officers;
- inmate self-governance;
- procedures that allow inmate grievances to be aired;
- prison work programs with fair wages paid to prisoners;
- periodic review of sentencing patterns and parole board decisions;
- dissemination of statistics on commitments and releases;
- pre-release orientation and job-finding assistance for discharged prisoners; and
- statewide prison leadership headed by nonpolitical, nationally recruited, and professionally trained individuals.[11]

Despite reformers' calls for overhauls of prison programs and management, violence-provoking conditions continue to exist in many prisons. One might wonder if anything has changed since the storm of prison riots in 1952. Three of the bloodiest and most violent prison riots in the United States occurred in severely overcrowded prisons in New York in 1971, in New Mexico in 1980, and in Ohio in 1993.

Student Involvement
Assign students to four groups. Direct the groups to prepare brief presentations, using library and Internet resources, on the riots at Attica, Santa Fe, Lucasville, and any prison riots in your state.

In the 1971 riot at the Attica Correctional Facility, New York, where 2,225 inmates were incarcerated in a prison designed for 1,200, 43 lives were lost: four inmates were killed during the riot as part of inmate "justice," and when police stormed in to retake the prison, they killed 10 civilian hostages and 29 prisoners. The New York State Special Commission that investigated the riot wrote, "With the exception of Indian massacres in the late 19th century, the State Police assault which ended the four-day prison uprising was the bloodiest one-day encounter between Americans since the Civil War."[12]

In the 1980 riot at the Penitentiary of New Mexico in Santa Fe, where 1,136 inmates were confined in space designed for 900 inmates, the taking of human life was brutal. Thirty-three inmates were tortured, dismembered, decapitated, burned alive, and killed by fellow inmates. Although staff were held hostage, none was killed.

The longest prison riot in United States history occurred at the Southern Ohio Correctional Facility in Lucasville in 1993, where 1,820 inmates were held in a prison built for 1,540. Inmates killed nine of their fellow inmates and one correctional officer in the 11-day siege.

The riot at Lucasville cost an estimated $15 million in property damage. At Santa Fe, the estimate was $28.5 million. At Attica, the cost was more than $3 million.

Causes of Prison Riots

The causes of prison riots today are no different than they were in the 1950s: overcrowding, racial antagonism, environmental factors, administrative factors, individual factors, and prison social structure.

Overcrowding   Overcrowding is the most important cause of heightened prison tension and potential violent disruption. Overcrowding is responsible for curtailing or even eliminating opportunities for education, vocational training, and recreation. When the ratio of correctional officers to inmates becomes too low, something has to give. At Attica, Santa Fe, and Lucasville, overcrowding raised tensions, interfered with prisoner classification, reduced living space, and restricted access to programs. Restlessness and boredom grew.

Racial Antagonism   Outside prison the ratio of racial minorities to whites is about one to five. In prison, however, whites are the minority. That disproportion, in addition to overcrowding, close living quarters, and lack of space, adds to racial antagonism. Antagonism is heightened when inmates separate themselves along racial or ethnic lines for self-protection. Researchers have discovered that as inmates' perception of overcrowding increases, their antagonism toward other racial and ethnic groups also increases.[13]

Environmental Factors   Environmental factors refer to the ability of the physical structure to withstand a riot situation. At Attica, a faulty weld joint in a metal gate gave way and allowed prisoners access to most areas of the institution. At Santa Fe, "shatter-proof" glass broke. At Lucasville, inmates collected master keys from staff hostages and opened cell doors.

Administrative Factors   Poor prison management and administration are linked to prison riots. Poor management can result from frequent staff

Program Analysts
Adult Correctional Services Section seeks program analysts to develop, monitor, and evaluate grant projects funded by the agency, including jail and prison-based drug treatment, drug courts, community justice, and local pretrial services. Candidates must have a degree in criminal justice, public administration, or a related field, or equivalent experience. Applicants should have experience with criminal justice intervention strategies, drug treatment programming, and grants administration.

turnover, low correctional officer qualifications, inadequate training, poor staff-inmate communication, and low staff pay. At Attica, Santa Fe, and Lucasville, inmates' complaints about living conditions, lack of programs, and officers' excessive use of force and harassment went unheard by administration. Rumors of riots were not taken seriously.

Individual Factors   Prisoners at Attica, Santa Fe, and Lucasville were young, violence-prone and poorly classified. Most were undereducated, underemployed, and uncommitted to society's means for achieving social goals. The racial and ethnic minority imbalance, together with these individual factors, prompted many inmates to adopt tough attitudes and join STGs for self-protection.

Social Structure   The social structure in prison is often cited as a key cause of violence and incidents that may escalate into a riot. The social structure consists of racial, political, and ideological tensions; deprivation of inmate goods and services; confusion over prison goals; and a natural desire by prisoners to challenge authority. Controlling this social structure requires strong and consistent leadership from the prison administration. When inmates sense little likelihood of improvement in prison conditions and inconsistent and unpredictable shifts in administration and prison policies, they may feel as if there is little to lose in inciting a disturbance.

Preventing Prison Riots

Prison violence provokes more violence. Measures to prevent prison riots must become a national priority, and change must occur. Three years before the Attica riot, the U.S. National Advisory Commission on Civil Disorders (the Kerner Commission) warned that the only effective way to prevent riots, whether in or out of prison, was to eliminate sources of tension by making good "the promises of American democracy to all citizens, urban and rural, white and black, Spanish surname, American Indian, and every minority group."[14] While that change is long-range, corrections officials can implement immediate measures to reduce the likelihood of inmate aggression including:

- formal inmate grievance procedures;
- ombudsmen to mediate disputes;
- an improved classification system;
- smaller institutions;
- meaningful prison school and work programs;
- alternatives to incarceration;
- professional corrections staff who are trained and well paid;
- administrators who are visible and available to staff and inmates; and
- clearly written and understood policies on the use of force when necessary.

To assure that the use of force is appropriate and justifiable, the American Correctional Association recommends establishing polices and procedures that govern its use (see Exhibit 11–1).

EXHIBIT 11–1

American Correctional Association

Policy on Use of Force

Use of force consists of physical contact with an offender in a confrontational situation to control behavior and enforce order. Use of force includes use of restraints (other than for routine transportation and movement), chemical agents, and weapons. Force is justified only when required to maintain or regain control, or when there is imminent danger of personal injury or serious damage to property. To assure the use of force is appropriate and justifiable, correctional agencies should:

A. Establish and maintain policies that require reasonable steps be taken to reduce or prevent the necessity for the use of force, that authorize force only when no reasonable alternative is possible, that permit only the minimum force necessary, and that prohibit the use of force as a retaliatory or disciplinary measure;

B. Establish and enforce procedures that define the range of methods for and alternatives to the use of force, and that specify the conditions under which each is permitted. The procedures must assign responsibility for authorizing such force, assure appropriate documentation and supervision of the action;

C. Establish and maintain procedures that limit the use of deadly force to those instances where it is legally authorized and where there is an imminent threat to human life or a threat to public safety that cannot reasonably be prevented by other means;

D. Maintain operating procedures and regular staff training designed to anticipate, stabilize and defuse situations that might give rise to conflict, confrontation, and violence;

E. Provide specialized training to ensure competency in all methods of use of force, especially in methods and equipment requiring special knowledge and skills such as defensive tactics, weapons, restraints, and chemical agents; and

F. Establish and maintain procedures that require all incidents involving the use of force be fully documented and independently reviewed by a higher correctional authority. A report of the use of force, including appropriate investigation and any recommendations for preventive and remedial action, shall be submitted for administrative review and implementation of recommendations when appropriate.

Supermax Housing and "No-Frills" Prisons and Jails

In an effort to control the behavior of violence-prone inmates, two new types of prisons are emerging—supermax housing and "no-frills" prisons. Both alter the conditions of confinement for thousands of U.S. prisoners, raising important issues for the prisoners and staff who must live and work in them and the society that must accept the prisoners when they are released.

Supermax Housing

Teaching Tip
Discuss similarities and differences of routine maximum security and supermax housing facilities in terms of physical structure and prisoner movement.

Prison systems have always needed a way to deal with inmates whose violent behavior makes it impossible for them to live with the general prison population. Segregation and solitary confinement have been the most widely used methods of dealing with this issue. You may recall from Chapter 4 that in 1829, the Eastern State Penitentiary in Cherry Hill, Pennsylvania, was built on the principle of solitary confinement. However, in 1913 the Pennsylvania legislature dropped "solitary" from sentencing statutes and housing arrangements at Eastern State became congregate. From that point forward, specialized housing units were developed for management and control of troublesome inmates.

The BOP returned to the idea of controlling the most violent and disruptive inmates in indefinite solitary confinement when it opened Alcatraz in 1934. Alcatraz, which had a capacity of 275, did not offer any treatment program; its sole purpose was to incarcerate and punish the federal prison system's most desperate criminals and worst troublemakers. "Alcatraz, it was charged, was America's Devil's Island, it was 'Hellcatraz'—a place where convicts slowly went insane from the tedium and hopelessness of endless years on 'the Rock.'"[15] By 1963, Alcatraz was judged an expensive failure; it symbolized a penal philosophy that was outdated in an era that espoused rehabilitation, not punishment, as the goal of incarceration.[16] Alcatraz closed in the early 1960s under orders from U.S. Attorney General Robert Kennedy. During the era of rehabilitation that followed the Alcatraz closing, prison officials used the *dispersal model*—problem prisoners were distributed to a number of prisons. Prison officials hoped that dispersal among populations of generally law-abiding inmates would dilute the influence of problem prisoners. Inmates from Alcatraz were moved to federal prisons in Atlanta and Leavenworth.

By the 1970s, the goal of incarceration had shifted back to punishment. Disturbances, violence, and riots at state and federal prisons convinced the BOP to try again to control the most troublesome federal inmates in one location. The BOP reverted to the *concentration model*—all problem prisoners are housed together in a separate facility. The federal prison at Marion, Illinois, was chosen for this purpose. The construction features at Marion, however, made it difficult for staff to maintain complete control over recalcitrant inmates. Open cell-fronts were a major limitation in Marion's design to control the toughest prisoners. Through their cell bars, inmates threw trash, urine, and feces at corrections officers; passed contraband; set fires; and verbally harassed and lunged at staff and other prisoners as they walked by. Tension, hostility, violence, and murder were all too common. On October 23, 1983, a state of emergency was declared and the Marion facility was placed on lockdown status. Over the next few years, the BOP conceived plans to build a supermax facility that would implement construction features for controlling difficult inmates.

Teaching Tip
Have willing students roleplay a supermax housing unit for one class period. Assign various roles: inmates, correctional officers, etc. After the roleplay, discuss with students their reactions.

In 1994, the BOP opened its first supermax housing facility at Florence, Colorado, for the 400 most dangerous, violent, escape prone, and STG federal inmate leaders. Construction cost totalled $60 million ($150,000 per cell). Annual operating cost per cell per year may be as much as another $40,000, or $19.2 million total. Cell design resists vandalism. Each prisoner's bed, desk, stool, and bookcase are made of reinforced concrete and anchored in place. Each cell has a shower stall with flood-proof plumbing and a 12-inch black-and-white television set. Cell windows deny prisoners all views of the outside except the sky above. A simple hole-in-the-wall apparatus for lighting cigarettes has replaced matches and cigarette lighters. Meals are dispensed through cell slots in separate heated trays from airline-style carts pulled by small tractors. Cells are staggered so that inmates cannot make eye contact with other inmates. Each cell has a double entry door; an interior barred cage door backed up by a windowed steel door that prevents voice contact among prisoners.

The new prison has 1,400 electronically-controlled gates, 168 television monitors, and two mirrored-glass gun towers. The 400 cells are subdivided into nine units—each unit is self-contained and includes a sick-call room, law library, and barber chair. After three years of good behavior, an inmate gradually regains social contact. "What puts a man in is his behavior, and what gets a man out is his behavior," said John M. Vanyur, the associate warden.[17]

This type of super-controlled environment is taking hold across the United States. California opened Pelican Bay State Prison in Crescent City in 1990. Construction cost was $133,653 per cell. The supermax housing unit of Pelican Bay has a capacity of 1,500 inmates, all of whom are isolated in windowless cells and denied access to prison work and group exercise yards.

Pelican Bay, like the federal supermax housing facility in Florence, Colorado, is entirely automated. Inmates in the supermax housing unit have no face-to-face contact with staff or other inmates. Cell doors are solid stainless steel with slots for food trays. Cell doors open and close electronically. Officers can talk with or listen in on inmates through a speaker system. These inmates do not work. They have no recreational equipment. They don't mix with other inmates. They are not permitted to smoke. They eat all meals in their cells. They leave their cells only for showers and 90 minutes of daily exercise in small cement areas enclosed by 20-foot cement walls. An inmate who leaves his cell to go to the exercise pen must strip naked in front of a control booth; the door to the exercise pen is then opened electronically.

In 1997, the National Institute of Corrections (NIC) conducted a nationwide survey to determine the number of supermax housing facilities and the policies and procedures of each.[18] NIC defined **supermax housing** as a free-standing facility, or a distinct unit within a facility, that provides for the management and secure control of inmates who have been officially designated as exhibiting violent or serious and disruptive behavior while incarcerated. This includes STG leaders. Supermax housing controls inmate behavior through separation, movement restriction, and limited access to staff and other inmates. Supermax housing does not include maximum or close custody facilities that are designated for routine housing of inmates with high custody needs, inmates in disciplinary segregation or protective custody, or other inmates requiring segregation or separation for other routine purposes.

What NIC found is that a common definition of supermax housing is problematic. The many states that provided information had different reasons and needs for supermax housing. They consider different factors in their inmate classification systems and facility operations procedures. What is considered supermax housing in one jurisdiction may not be considered supermax housing in another. NIC's conclusion is, "Supermax as defined in the survey may exist in relatively few agencies."[19]

Criminologists and psychiatrists who have studied the effects of long-term solitary confinement report evidence of acute sensory deprivation, paranoid delusion belief systems, irrational fears of violence, little ability to control rage, and mental breakdowns.[20] The vast majority of inmates in long-term solitary confinement remain anxious, angry, depressed, insecure, and confused. Some commit suicide. Others fail to adjust upon release and become recidivists.

Some inmates in supermax housing facilities have challenged the conditions of their confinement. In 1995, inmates at Pelican Bay's supermax unit challenged the constitutionality of extreme isolation and environmental deprivation. They claimed that the degree of segregation was so extreme and the restrictions so severe, the inmates confined there were psychologically traumatized and, in some cases, deprived of sanity. The federal court agreed. The court ruled that "conditions in security housing unit did impose cruel and unusual punishment on mentally ill prisoners"[21] and "those who were at particularly high risk for suffering very serious or severe injury to their mental health."[22] The court declared that the state of California cannot continue to confine inmates who are already mentally ill or those who are at an unreasonably high risk of suffering serious mental illness in the supermax unit. The court also appointed a **special master** (a person appointed to act as the representative of the court) to work with the state of California to

supermax housing
A free-standing facility, or a distinct unit within a facility, that provides for management and secure control of inmates who have been officially designated as exhibiting violent or serious and disruptive behavior while incarcerated.

Student Involvement
Invite interested students to research and analyze segregation and/or long-term solitary confinement and present a report to the class.

special master   A person appointed by the court to act as its representative to oversee remedy of a violation and provide regular progress reports.

The Prison Environment: Issues and Concerns

develop a satisfactory remedial plan and provide a progress report to the court.

"No-Frills" Prisons and Jails

The image of prisons and jails as "country clubs" and "mini-resorts" is not new. That description continues to make for great speeches, but it is erroneous. It ignores the harsh realities of imprisonment. Having only the information that appears on television and in newspapers and magazines, the public still believes that inmates are living the good life, lounging on recliners and channel surfing. In 1995, an NBC television poll found that 82 percent of Americans felt that prison life was too easy.[23]

Public perception has influenced reality as corrections reform has focused on the conditions of confinement. **"No-frills" prisons and jails** that take away prisoner amenities and privileges are the latest fad on the corrections landscape. New policies are designed to make jail and prison life as brutal as possible in the belief that such conditions deter even the most hardened criminals. Proponents of "no-frills" jails and prisons believe that criminals will shun future illegal activity to avoid returning. Mississippi representative Mark McInnis said it clearly: "The people who run the prisons want happy prisoners. I want prisoners to be so miserable that they won't even think of coming back."[24] However, that sentiment is not supported by research and may actually be causing a backlash. Violent offenders do not think about the consequences beforehand. They think they'll never get caught.

For the past few years state legislatures, governors, corrections commissioners, and county sheriffs have been eliminating or reducing the availability of certain amenities and privileges that prisoners previously enjoyed. They've justified their positions publicly by arguing that pleasures of any kind contribute to the crime rate by making prison a tolerable way of life and claiming that more austere prison and jail conditions will reduce crime. Others claim that it's what inmates deserve. Skeptics wonder if the driving force behind these new "no-frills" statutes and bills is the belief that they help get legislators and others elected or reelected by offering the impression that they are tough on crime.[25]

The amenities and privileges that have been reduced or eliminated include smoking, weightlifting equipment, long hair and beards, hot meals, personal clothing, recreation, telephone calls, television, family days, funeral furloughs, and unrestricted access to medical care. Proponents of "no-frills" incarceration argue that punishing offenders in "no-frills" environments is not vindictive revenge. They argue that reducing or eliminating amenities and privileges is deserved—the offender committed a serious crime that warrants incarceration, and incarceration is intended to be punitive. The "no-frills" movement is catching on, but not everybody agrees with it.

To date, no court case has been heard on "no-frills" prisons and jails. Unless the eliminated or reduced amenity or privilege results in serious harm to the inmate, the "no-frills" movement will continue.

At present, there is no evidence that making prisons and jails more unpleasant has any effect on crime. Legislators claim that inmates will not want to be incarcerated or reincarcerated under such harsh conditions.

"no-frills" prisons and jails Correctional institutions that take away prisoner amenities and privileges.

Teaching Tip

If possible, take the class to a local jail or prison. Have students discuss with staff prisoner amenities and privileges. If the institution you're visiting is a "no-frills" facility, ask the staff members if they think that this environment deters crime.

Teaching Tip

Invite volunteers to read James Finckenauer, *Scared Straight and the Panacea Phenomenon*, and report on his conclusions about whether "no-frills" prisons deter crime.

Professional Issue
Correctional Officer Safety
Many wardens and correctional officers have reservations about the "no-frills" prison concept. Those groups are concerned that, if amenities and privileges are eliminated, the staff will have nothing with which to motivate cooperative inmate behavior. (They are concerned about correctional officers' safety.) Write a "letter to the editor" as a correctional officer explaining how the "no-frills" prison concept might put correctional officers at risk.

However, over 200 years of prison history has not proven that making a prison austere deters offenders. In a recent survey, state wardens, corrections experts, and attorneys said that they did not believe that eliminating privileges would reduce crime.[26] Correctional officers, on the other hand, cringe at the idea of trying to maintain civility without amenities and privileges. "What some outside the corrections profession perceive as privileges, we in the profession see as vital prison and jail management tools to insure the safety of the facility," said Bobbie Huskey, former president of the American Correctional Association.[27]

Others have wondered what impact "no-frills" may have on institutional security. "The elimination of privileges theoretically could increase disturbances, either in the short term if inmates react violently to the loss or in the long term if inmates have more idle time, resent the perceived vindictiveness of corrections managers, or conclude they have nothing more to lose by misbehaving."[28] A corrections official in Florida concluded, "From a correctional administrator's standpoint, there is a point at which further reductions create an undue risk to a safe and orderly operation." A 27-year veteran corrections administrator in the New Jersey Department of Corrections fears that the "take-back trend," as he calls it, might result in inmate retaliation on staff.[29] Sufficient time has not passed to study the long-term impact of "no-frills" incarceration. However, there is concern that eliminating privileges (such as weightlifting, television, and recreation) that keep inmates busy may encourage inmates to spend more time planning or causing trouble.

If privileges are eliminated, what positive incentives will correctional staff have with which to motivate appropriate inmate behavior? A July 1995 survey of 823 wardens of state adult prisons indicates that programs and amenities serve a critical control function.[30] Correctional officers can grant access to privileges and amenities in exchange for adherence to rules and restrict access as punishment for rule violation. "The entire prison disciplinary structure is founded on punishments that amount to restriction of privileges," report the survey's authors.[31] Chances are, prison administrators will not completely eliminate or abolish privileges or amenities; they will curtail availability and offer the privileges or amenities as reward for good behavior.

Special Needs Inmates

Prison inmates have disproportionately high rates of substance abuse, high-risk sexual activity, and other health problems. Because thousands of these inmates return to the general population each month, correctional health and public health are becoming increasingly intertwined. Health care and disease prevention in correctional facilities must become a top priority for correctional managers and all correctional personnel.

Substance-Abusing Inmates

Teaching Tip
Eighty percent of America's jail and prison population—some 1.4 million prisoners at year-end 1996—were seriously involved with drug/alcohol abuse and addiction; ask students to research the percentage of drug/alcohol abusers in your state's prisons and jails.

Substance abuse takes a toll on users, the community, and the criminal justice system. In January 1998, the National Center on Addiction and Substance Abuse at Columbia University (CASA) released its findings from a

3-year study on substance abuse and the prison population.[32] According to this study, 80 percent of America's jail and prison population—some 1.4 million prisoners at year-end 1996—were seriously involved with drug and/or alcohol abuse and addiction and the crimes it spawns. Those 1.4 million offenders had violated drug/alcohol laws, were high at the time they committed their crimes, stole property to buy drugs, had a history of drug/alcohol abuse and addiction, or had some combination of these characteristics.

Treatment for Offenders   Research shows that drug/alcohol treatment can result in reduced substance abuse, criminal activity, and associated problems. When substance abusers are incarcerated, the correctional system becomes a potential point of intervention to reduce or eliminate their abuse. What most concerns CASA is the low priority given to dealing with inmates' drug/alcohol addictions. From 1993 to 1996, the number of inmates who needed substance abuse treatment climbed from 688,000 to 840,000. The number of inmates receiving treatment remained the same—about 150,000. From 1995 to 1996, the number of inmates in treatment decreased by 18,360 as the number of inmates who needed treatment rose by 39,578. CASA estimates that states spend 5 percent of their prison budget on drug/alcohol treatment; the BOP spends less than 1 percent.

Alcohol: The Real Culprit   According to CASA, alcohol is linked more closely with violent crimes than drugs. More widely available than illegal drugs, alcohol is connected with rape, assault, child and spouse abuse, and most homicides arising from disputes or arguments. Over 20 percent of inmates in state and federal prisons for violent crimes were under the influence of alcohol—and no other substance—when they committed their crimes; in contrast, at the time of their crimes, 4 percent of violent offenders were under the influence of drugs.

CASA also reports a link between alcohol abuse and addiction and property crime. Among state prisoners, 17 percent of property offenders were under the influence of alcohol (and no other substance) at the time of their crime; among federal prisoners, 9 percent.

Consequences of No Treatment   Lack of treatment for substance-abusing prisoners endangers the public. Releasing substance abusers from prison without treatment maintains the market for illegal drugs and keeps drug dealers in business; untreated substance abusers are likely to return to substance abuse and crime upon release. As CASA put it, "Release of untreated drug and alcohol addicted inmates is tantamount to visiting criminals on society."[33] Brooklyn, New York, district attorney Charles Hynes calls releasing untreated drug/alcohol-addicted inmates "lunacy."[34]

Recidivism also is related to drug/alcohol abuse. "The more often an individual is imprisoned," CASA wrote, "the likelier that inmate is to be a drug or alcohol addict or abuser."[35] Over 40 percent of first-time offenders have a history of drug use. The proportion increases to over 80 percent for offenders with five or more prior convictions. Regardless of the crimes committed, offenders who test positive for drugs at the time of arrest have longer criminal records and have been imprisoned more often than those who do not. The cost to society of their recidivism is enormous.

Teaching Tip
To illustrate the impact of the lack of prison substance abuse treatment programs (only about one out of every five prisoners who need substance abuse treatment is receiving it), ask your students to stand up and count off by fives. When the students finish counting, ask the fives to sit down. Explain that the fives are an approximate proportion of the inmates who receive treatment. Those standing need substance abuse treatment but do not receive it. Ask students for their reactions to this situation.

Teaching Tip
Review the consequences of lack of substance abuse treatment for inmates (endangers the public, maintains the market for illegal drugs, keeps drug dealers in business, misses opportunity to get offenders into recovery programs, and the likelihood that the more often an individual is imprisoned, the likelier that inmate will be a drug or alcohol addict or abuser). Then ask students: If we know these consequences, what should we do to change them?

therapeutic community (TC) A highly structured residential treatment program within a prison or jail involving resocialization, intensive counseling, and an increasing level of inmate responsibility.

Treatment Works Why should prisoners receive drug treatment? According to Jeremy Travis, Director of the National Institute of Justice, there are two powerful reasons.[36] First, drug offenders consume a staggering volume of illegal drugs, and any reduction in their drug use represents a significant reduction in the nation's demand for illegal drugs. About 60 percent of the cocaine and heroine consumed by the entire nation in a year is consumed by individuals arrested in that year. Drug treatment has the potential for significantly reducing the nation's demand for illegal drugs.

The second reason we should provide drug treatment to prisoners is we now know that we can reduce drug use in the offender population. In other words, treatment works, with the important corollary that we can reduce the new crimes offenders commit. Treatment programs that start 9 months to a year before prison release, provide community-based aftercare services in the community (housing, education, employment, and health care), attract and retain staff that demonstrate concern for the offender's welfare, and give offenders a clear understanding of the program's rules and the penalties for breaking them provide the greatest chances for success.[37] Such programs have success rates as high as 80–90 percent. Community aftercare services are particularly important for substance abusers because they tend to have medical problems such as cirrhosis of the liver, diabetes, and HIV/AIDS.

One successful prison-based substance treatment program is a therapeutic community. A **therapeutic community (TC)** is a residential treatment program under which inmates are housed in a separate unit within a prison or jail facility, characterized by highly structured treatment involving resocialization, intensive counseling, and an increasing level of responsibility as the inmate progresses through the program. Recent evaluations of prison-based TCs offer solid evidence of their effectiveness. The TC treatment program at the R. J. Donovan Correctional Facility near San Diego, California was recognized by the U.S. Department of Justice as a model program.[38]

Donovan's TC inmates participate in group meetings, seminars, group and individual counseling, video feedback, relapse prevention, and urine testing. Pre-parole planning is also provided to assist inmates in return to their communities. Seminars, workshops, and group meetings are also provided for the TC inmates' families and friends. After release, TC inmates are paroled to a community residential facility where full treatment services and community-based aftercare services are available. The average stay in a community residential facility is 5.3 months; the participant then makes the transition to independent living.

Most treatment programs are successful when offenders attend often and stay in contact with treatment counselors over long periods. Also important to successful program completion is effective aftercare. CASA reports on the success of other prison-based substance abuse programs followed by community aftercare services. For example, the California Department of Corrections operates Forever Free, a prison-based substance abuse treatment program followed by community aftercare for women offenders. Graduates of the prison-based treatment program alone had a 62 percent success rate. When women completed the community aftercare phase, their success rate climbed even higher: 90 percent for women who completed an average of 5 months in the community residential treatment setting versus 72 percent for those who did not. There is ample evidence that offenders who participate in in-prison treatment and post-release community aftercare treatment are more likely to remain drug- and arrest-free after release from prison.

Costs and Benefits of Treatment CASA estimates that the cost of proven treatment programs for inmates, accompanied by appropriate education, job training, and health care, averages $6,500 per year per offender. The annual economic benefit to society—in terms of avoided incarceration and health care costs, salary earned, taxes paid, and contribution to the economy—is $68,000 for every prisoner who successfully completes such treatment and becomes a taxpaying, law-abiding person. Excluding over 200,000 drug dealers who don't use drugs, if only 10 percent of the 1.2 million abusers and addicts are successfully treated (120,000), the economic benefit in the first year of work after release would be $8.256 billion. CASA says that's $456 million more than the $7.8 billion cost of providing training and treatment (at a cost of $6,500 each) for the entire 1.2 million inmates with drug and/or alcohol problems.

Recommendations for Managing Substance-Abusing Offenders
Controlling the revolving door of drug and alcohol abusers and addicts going in and out of prison is an important aspect of management for corrections officials. In its report, CASA offers pre-prison, prison, and post-prison recommendations designed to cut taxpayer costs and protect the public safety by reducing recidivism:[39]

Pre-Prison:
1. Assess the substance abuse involvement of offenders at the time of arrest—perform drug tests and thoroughly evaluate substance abuse history. This can form the basis for decisions about pretrial supervision, sentencing, and treatment.
2. Encourage development, implementation, and evaluation of treatment alternatives to prison, such as diversion and drug courts, and expand diversion programs for nonviolent first offenders who are drug/alcohol abusers and addicts.
3. Provide police, prosecutors, and judges with the training and assistance required to effectively deal with substance-related crime, including counselors and public health experts experienced in evaluating substance abuse and addiction.
4. Get rid of mandatory sentences that eliminate the possibility of alternative sentencing and/or parole. Judges and prosecutors need the flexibility to divert substance-abusing offenders into treatment, drug courts, coerced abstinence, or other alternatives to prison when appropriate. Corrections officials need every possible carrot and stick to encourage inmates to seek treatment, including the carrot of reduced prison time for substance-abusing inmates who successfully complete treatment and the stick of getting sent back to jail for parolees who fail to participate in required post-release treatment or aftercare.

In Prison:
1. Train corrections officers and other personnel in treating substance abuse and addiction so that they can better prevent the use

Teaching Tip
Have students review the pre-prison recommendations by CASA. Which do they think is most important? Would they add any?

Teaching Tip
Have students review the in-prison recommendations by CASA. Which recommendations would they support if they were corrections officers? If they were the warden or assistant warden?

of alcohol and drugs in prison and better assist inmates in the recovery process.

2. Keep jails and prisons tobacco-, alcohol-, and drug-free. This means enforcing prohibitions against alcohol and drugs, promoting smoke-free prisons and local jails to enhance inmate health, and eliminating distribution of tobacco products to inmates.

3. Expand random testing of prisoners to corrections officers and deter drug and alcohol use; refer inmates for substance abuse treatment and monitor their progress.

4. Provide treatment in prison for all who need it: every alcohol- or drug-involved offender, including property offenders, violent offenders, and drug sellers. Tailor treatment to the special needs of inmates, such as women or children of alcoholics and drug addicts.

5. Encourage participation in literacy, education, and training programs. Such programs should be widely available, and inmates should be encouraged to enroll in them—participation in these programs will increase inmates' chances of securing gainful employment upon release.

6. Provide substance-abusing prisoners with a range of support services including medical care, mental health services, prevention services (including confidential HIV testing), counseling, and other services they need.

7. Increase the availability of religious and spiritual activity and counseling in prison and provide an environment that encourages such activity.

Post-Prison:

1. Provide pre-release planning for treatment and aftercare services for individuals who need them. Help parolees find services they need to remain substance-free after leaving prison, such as drug-free housing, literacy training, job placement, and social services.

2. Train parole and probation officers to deal with alcohol and drug abuse and assist parolees and probationers with locating addiction services and staying in treatment.

HIV/AIDS in Correctional Facilities

HIV/AIDS continues to be far more prevalent among prison inmates than in the total U.S. population (see Table 11–1). The Northeast region has the highest number and percentage of inmates with HIV/AIDS. Generally, the prevalence of HIV/AIDS is higher among Hispanic and black inmates than among white inmates and higher among female inmates than among males. High-risk behaviors for transmitting HIV—sex, drug use, sharing needles, and tattooing—occur in correctional facilities. Also, some transmission of HIV among inmates has been shown to occur.[40] Thus, prisons and jails are places to reach a large concentration of persons who are HIV-positive or infected with AIDS and provide them treatment, education, and behavior modification techniques prior to release to the community.

TABLE 11-1

Percent of Population With Confirmed AIDS

Year	U.S. General Population	Inmates in State and Federal Prisons
1991	0.03%	0.21%
1992	0.03	0.33
1993	0.06	0.50
1994	0.07	0.52
1995	0.08	0.51
1996	0.09	0.54

Source: Theodore M. Hammett, Patricia Harmon, and Laura M. Maruschak, *1996–1997 Update: HIV/AIDS, STDs, and TB in Correctional Facilities* (Washington: National Institute of Justice, July 1999), p. 5.

Student Involvement
Refer students to Table 11–1. Ask them to study the data provided, then write a brief paragraph to explain what the data show.

HIV Testing and Treatment Most correctional systems test their inmates for HIV, but testing policies vary widely.

- 45 jurisdictions test inmates if they have HIV-related symptoms or if the inmates request a test
- 24 states test inmates after they are involved in an incident
- 15 states test inmates who belong to specific "high-risk groups"
- 16 states test all inmates who enter their facilities
- 3 states and the BOP test inmates upon their release
- 3 states test all inmates currently in custody
- 2 states and the BOP test inmates selected at random

Treating HIV in prison is difficult for at least five reasons. [41] The first is the issue of privacy. Inmates, like other people infected with HIV, do not want to disclose their condition. The therapeutic regimen often involves taking multiple drugs several times a day. Going to the prison medication line often compromises a prisoner's privacy and increases the risk of stigmatization by other inmates and staff. Stigmatization can range from isolation and shunning to more overt forms of abuse. This is true even when high-quality health care is available. Anti-retroviral therapies (ART) can effectively treat HIV, but only if corrections officials help inmates overcome the obstacles to obtaining the treatment.

A second reason focuses on the frequency of taking medication and the prison routine. Some drugs must be taken with food and others in a fasting state. As the therapeutic regimen increases to five or six times a day, it strains the routine of most prisons to dispense medication frequently and to provide food as required.

The third reason is distrust of the medical and legal system. Not surprisingly, many inmates distrust the legal and health care system. This may be especially true for women and minorities who have a documented history of being experimented on without consent and being denied appropriate legal and medical care.

Professional Issue
Universal Precautions
Some correctional officers' unions and some individual officers assert their "right to know" about all HIV-positive inmates so that they can take special precautions when dealing with such inmates. Problems of identifying and remembering HIV-infected individuals have led to a policy of confidentiality with systematic practice of *universal precautions.* That is, correctional officers treat all offenders as if they were HIV-infected, avoiding unprotected contact with body fluids that are considered potentially infective, especially blood and semen.

Teaching Tip

Organize the class into five groups. Ask each group to consider one of the five reasons why treating HIV in prison is difficult. Direct each group to develop three to five recommendations for overcoming the difficulty and present their recommendations orally to the class.

Student Involvement

Ask students if they agree with the National Institute of Corrections' recommended age of 50 as the starting point to define older inmates. Why or why not?

The fourth reason is fear of side effects. The HIV drug regimen is known to make patients feel worse than they already do. Consequently, inmates will be less likely to adhere to the strict dosages and timing.

The final reason it is difficult to treat HIV-infected prisoners is a legal one. The courts have rejected the idea that the level and quality of health care available to prisoners must be the same as is available to society at large.[42] You may recall the *principle of least eligibility* from Chapter 7—the belief that prison conditions, including the delivery of health care, be a step below those of the working class and people on welfare. Thus, prisoners are denied access to medical specialists, timely delivery of medical services, technologically advanced diagnostic techniques, the latest medication and drug therapies, up-to-date surgical procedures, and second opinions.[43]

Overcoming these obstacles will not be easy. The key is developing trust between HIV-infected prisoners and the prison health-care team, extending the regimen when inmates are discharged, and building collaboration between correctional institutions and public health agencies. If an inmate undergoes complex drug therapy in prison but cannot obtain the same therapy upon release, his/her health is threatened and he or she may transmit the virus to others.

Incarceration offers opportunities to provide HIV and sexually-transmitted disease education as well as prevention programs for high-risk inmates. Such programs benefit not only the inmate but also the health and well-being of the community to which the inmate returns. The types of education and prevention programs provided vary among correctional systems and may include instructor-led programs, peer-led programs, pre-/post-test counseling, multi-session prevention counseling, and audiovisual and written materials. Within programs, high-risk inmates may learn basic disease information, safer sex practices, tattooing risks, self-perception of risk, and triggers for behavior relapse. Education and prevention programs are becoming more common in correctional facilities, but only 10 percent of state/federal prison systems offer comprehensive education and prevention programs.[44]

Older Inmates

Most of us imagine prisoners as young and aggressive. However, elderly and passive describes a significant portion of the prison population. Defining *elderly* is subject to debate. Some define *elderly* as 65 years of age and older, some suggest 60 years, others suggest 55, and still others 50. There are some who do not consider chronological age at all. Rather, they believe that, because of the impact of prison lifestyle, including lower socioeconomic status and limited access to medical care, a prisoner's physiological age may be higher than his or her chronological age. Simply put, the declining health of many prisoners makes them appear old before their time. In addition, some say prison life can age an inmate 10 years beyond chronological age.

Mark A. Molesworth
Substance Abuse Unit
Manager
North Dakota

"My philosophy is that all staff have two important roles regardless of their profession. First, 30 percent of our job is to make sure individuals who are incarcerated do not escape, hurt staff, hurt other inmates or themselves. Second, 70 percent of our role is directed toward rehabilitating inmates who will live in society after they leave our care. It is everyone's responsibility to provide appropriate role modeling and opportunities (treatment, education, employment, social, and cognitive) which permit residents to make the necessary changes which will enable them to live productively in society after their release. We cannot force people to change. But, if we do not provide the opportunity for change, we are a part of the problem."

Mark A. Molesworth is a unit manager for a long-term residential substance abuse facility for convicted male and female felons in North Dakota. He began his career as a temporary correctional officer during summer vacations. When he graduated from Minot State University with a B.S. degree in criminal justice, he was promoted to the rank of lieutenant and made director of the Adult Services Program at a minimum security unit. Mark is the single custodial father of two young children and is the past president of the board of directors of the Bismarck School of Hope (a nonprofit learning center for disabled preschool-age children). He is currently involved in the MPA program through the University of North Dakota.

Despite the differences in defining *elderly,* it is important to establish a common chronological starting point to define *older* inmates for purposes of comprehensive planning, programming, evaluation, and research within and among prison systems. After careful study of the issue, the NIC recommended that correctional agencies nationwide adopt age 50 as the chronological starting point to define **older inmates**.[45] In 1998, 7.2 percent (almost 84,000) of the 1.2 million state and federal prisoners were over age 50.[46] Experts believe that by the year 2010, inmates over the age of 50 will comprise 33 percent of the total prison population.[47]

older inmates   Inmates age 50 and older, as defined by the National Institute of Corrections.

Health Issues   Physical health, mental health, and medical care for older inmates have implications for prison policymakers, administrators, and staff. It is estimated that an elderly prisoner suffers from an average of three chronic illnesses.[48] Incarcerating older prisoners with impaired eyesight, physical handicaps, cancer, arthritis, diabetes, heart disease, hypertension, or Alzheimer's disease and treating these illnesses raises many concerns. For example, providing surgery, physical therapy, and daily medication for elderly prisoners raises ethical questions about providing health care to prisoners when persons outside prison are unable to receive similar medical treatment. In addition, new laws such as the Americans With Disabilities Act

THE OFFENDER SPEAKS

In October 1997, journalist Anne Seidlitz and National Prison Hospice Association representative Nancy Craig spent five days at the Louisiana State Penitentiary (LSP) at Angola, observing training sessions for the inmate volunteers who would be part of the interdisciplinary team of the LSP Hospice. Together with Carol Evans, they interviewed five of the volunteers at the R. J. Barrow Treatment Center. The following excerpt has been edited.

Anne Seidlitz: I'd like to know why you decided to join the volunteer group, what your experience has been with this kind of work, and what you expect to get out of it.

Charles Buie: The way the hospital used to be here, before they changed it to the Treatment Center, inmates would more or less die alone, with only the hospital staff around. So some of us came up with the idea of doing some kind of hospice work. We used to come over here and visit our friends. The administration used to let us do that, but then they stopped it, and that really worried some of us, because we had friends who were really ill or even dying. So that's how the idea got started. We sent the idea to Warden Cain, and he sent it to someone else and this hospice program came about. This all really came out of love for our fellow inmates. The important thing is that now when we get sick, we won't be afraid to come to the hospital. Some of us were terrified of coming to the hospital because of the perception that if you came here you died. Now we are working on changing that perception in the larger prison population.

Claude Donald: This program is really needed here at Angola. I'm an orderly on this ward and for a long time, I've thought about how wonderful it would be for guys to get involved in this type of program, not only for the patients but for the inmates themselves. You've got to sit back and imagine: how would it be—and this is deep—when a prisoner is dying? You never know what state of mind that prisoner is in. But you do know that he doesn't even have a family member around; he doesn't even have a close friend around. That's where you come in—you be that family member, you be that friend. You know, I've gotten so tied up in this ward, with these guys, that I've often told myself, I'm not going to get involved anymore. I've been through it over and over, with guys dying on me. But it's something you can't avoid; you've got to get attached to these guys and their families. To know that someone is dying, and take care of him like this and he says, "I appreciate that"—well, that's more to me than anything I could get in a material way. In the end it's just a joy to be able to do that.

AS: Were there any times when you felt that you could have used some help in dealing with the patients' needs?

Claude Donald: Well, I was reading this hospice volunteer manual and I saw things in there that really could have helped me over the year. This morning on the [training video], I saw that when a person is in his last stages and he don't want to eat, you don't force that eating upon him. When he don't want to sleep, you don't force that sleep upon him. That little bit of information right there was a great help. In the past, I've tried to persuade a guy to eat, but I learned today to let them do whatever they want to do, and whatever is comfortable for them. This program is giving us some first-class knowledge.

David Veal: I agree that the knowledge of hospice is very important for us to hear. Like Claude said, now we know what to do for the patients. Our desire is to help them, but without the right information we got to figure out things by ourselves. Like the food issue, it would have been easier for Claude to relax and talk to the fellow—to where that brother would have felt comfortable about eating or not eating—rather than trying to convince him to do it.

Michael Singletary (a patient as well as a volunteer): The thing about being in prison for any length of time is that you begin to lose family members, or they forget about you. I've got one friend who is dying on the ward right now; he's been my friend for my fifteen years of incarceration, and I can be there for him. My family and friends are now at Angola. I've been over here for twelve days and I've had numerous cards from my friends down the Walk since I have been sick. And that's my strength; that's where it comes from.

Charles Buie: "What will happen to me in years to come if I don't get parole or a pardon, when I get old, sick?" That's a question we're asking ourselves. We see so many of our friends, people we are growing old with, getting sick. Who takes care of them? We have to become our own family, and believe me that happens. Even if someone is in one of the outcamps, he's still my friend; I can still send messages and letters to him because we've bonded together. But if he's in the hospital—it used to be that you might not know that for a while. Then you find out and worry about him. Before, there was no way to make contact with him. That set-up is going to change with the hospice program. The volunteers come from every area of the institution, and we can take information back to friends, so it becomes like a big family network. Someone is in the hospice program from every area.

I can tell you this: from attending last night's meeting and from talking to some of the guys in my dormitory that saw us on the Walk and wanted to know what was going on, everybody is excited. The inmates are happy because someone is here who cares about them; the myth and the concept we have about the treatment in the hospital is fading away. That especially goes for the inmates who live where David lives in Camp F, where most of the elderly people live.

David Veal: Those guys in Camp F are maybe 74 years old; they haven't seen their families for 25 years or so, and they've got life sentences. This one guy the other day was shooting horseshoes. He was from Baton Rouge, and he started talking about life there in the '50s, way before I was around! I found out that he really needed to share the things that he knew and had experienced. I gave him so much ear play, that it burnt my ears up! But it was a learning experience for me, to help me understand that talking was what he needed to do. And right now, today, with this hospice program, people are being trained to provide just this type of attention and caring. We understand the social workers' position, but we have to come along and make it work for one another. We've got to really do it. It's not that we want to push for the staff to do it, because these folks don't live with you at night. At eleven or twelve at night, they are not there—we are there. We are right there next to one another. This guy sleeping next to me, if he's in a bad way, I've got to wake up and understand.

AS: People on the outside think that kind of sensitivity would be very hard to develop in this environment.

Larry Landry: I've been in trouble all my life. This is my second time at Angola. In the early seventies, there was no such thing as this program. You had to lead a macho life; no matter how much fear you had, you couldn't show it. You couldn't have compassion for another guy, because they would take it as weakness. Over the years it changed. Now my feeling is that this is my community, this is my life, I want to put something back.

In 1995, I had to come in here and be operated on. I saw a friend I hadn't seen in ten years because he was in an outcamp. He was dying of AIDS. His leg was smaller than my arm, and I just felt so hurt 'cause I couldn't do nothing for him. [Starts to cry.] Even if I could have come back to see him after I left the hospital, I couldn't get to him 'cause he had AIDS. I heard that he would ask for me to come and see him, but I couldn't. I said to myself, "My God, that could be me." I would want somebody to care for me; so now I try to do that, to show that somebody cares. My family gave up on me, and most of the guys in here—nobody cares for them, so who's gonna care for them? This is our community. If we don't take care of each other, who's going to take care of us? I have friends in the infirmary right now. I want them to know that I care. Just to see their faces, I can tell it means a lot to them.

Charles Buie: It has a lot to do with our Warden Cain. He genuinely cares about human beings even though his job is to keep us here. If you explain things to him and show him a need, where it makes sense he'll do something. He's changed this penitentiary. Now sometimes people don't like to hear that, but he has changed this institution and I've been here a long time. Some hardened criminals are changing, going to church more. Now security can take you to church almost any time. And that was once unheard of. Now we would like to have a wake service in the chapel when somebody dies. But that's another project.

Carol Evans: One of the greatest needs of family is a funeral service of some type, some sort of ritual in which they can say good-bye to their friends, at least at the burial site.

(ADA) affect not only mainstream society but also prisons and jails. Designing prison spaces that are accessible for elderly prisoners, with ramps, handrails, good lighting, and subtle grades is now law under ADA.

Cost Issues The economic consequences of incarcerating older prisoners are huge. The estimated national costs per year to confine an inmate over 55 years old is $70,000.[49] In North Carolina it costs $37,000 per year to keep elderly prisoners at the McCain Correctional Facility. In Maryland, it's $69,000 per year. In California, it's $80,000 per year.

Could elderly prisoners who are considered harmless be released early to go back to their families or to independent care living and thereby save prisons money? Systematic research on how elderly prisoners adapt after prison release is sketchy, although it's known that recidivism drops with age. According to the U.S. Parole Commission, older federal prisoners show lower recidivism rates. The U.S. Department of Justice reported that only 2 percent of inmates who are 55 or older when paroled return to prison.[50] It is doubtful that when mandatory sentencing laws, "three-strikes" laws, and "truth-in-sentencing" laws were enacted the economic impact of incarcerating elderly prisoners for long periods of time was actually considered. Unless legislatures give courts and prison administrators more leeway to interchange prison sentences with community sentences, states will find themselves in economic crisis providing for the 33 percent of the inmate population that is projected to be elderly by the year 2010.

Geriatric Prison Facilities   An increasing number of states are beginning to house their older prisoner population away from the general population, in nursing-home-like settings. Alabama, Arizona, Georgia, Illinois, Kansas, Kentucky, Maryland, Michigan, Minnesota, Mississippi, North Carolina, New Jersey, Ohio, Pennsylvania, South Carolina, Tennessee, Texas, Virginia, West Virginia, and Wisconsin have special prisons for the elderly, often called "aged/infirm," "medical/geriatric," "disabled," or simply "geriatric." The facility itself accommodates special needs of the elderly. Few stairs, reduced distances, more crafts and leisure activities, and staff trained in gerontological issues make these facilities unique. The majority confine only elderly male prisoners. Older female prisoners, who constitute only a small percentage of the total elderly prisoner population, are generally kept in the state's only women's prison.

A number of states are also opening prison **hospices** as a compassionate way to deal with dying inmates.[51] A hospice is an interdisciplinary, comfort-oriented care facility that allows seriously ill and dying patients to die with dignity and humanity in an environment where they have mental and spiritual preparation for the natural process of dying. Hospice programs provide a wide array of services, including pain management, spiritual support, and psychological counseling, as well as grief counseling for bereaved families.

In 1998, the NIC looked at prison care for terminally ill prisoners across the United States.[52] Of the slightly more than 1,000 inmates diagnosed as terminally ill, 800 were in regular prison hospitals, 150 in formal prison hospice settings, and 100 on parole or another form of compassionate release. The same survey found that 11 states and the BOP have started formal prison hospice programs and 20 states are developing such programs.

Often, one of the challenges in starting a prison hospice is educating the prison staff in caring for the terminally ill and making a psychological adjustment—getting over the resentment that prisoners are getting this level of care. According to Elizabeth Craig, executive director of the National Prison Hospice Association (NPHA) in Boulder, Colorado, "In my view, inmates are being punished by being incarcerated; we don't need to create more suffering for them. It can only be helpful for ill inmates to see that people care for them, which might be the starting point for some kind of transformation."[53]

Teaching Tip
If your state has a prison hospice and the facility is not far from campus, arrange to visit it. Prior to the visit discuss issues about inmates' death and dying. If your state does not have a prison hospice, have a group of students contact your state corrections department and ask how many terminally ill persons are in prison and how they are being cared for (prison hospital, compassionate parole, etc.).

hospice   An interdisciplinary, comfort-oriented care unit that allows seriously ill and dying prisoners to die with dignity and humanity in an environment that provides mental and spiritual preparation for the natural process of dying.

Mothers in Prison

According to a recent BJS study,[54] an estimated 6.7 percent of black women, 5.9 percent of Hispanic women, and 5.2 percent of white women are pregnant at the time of incarceration.

An estimated 4,000 women prisoners give birth each year, even though most women's prisons have no special facilities for pregnant inmates.[55] Some experts recommend that women's prisons should routinely make counseling available to pregnant inmates, and that they should fully inform these women of the options available to them, including abortion and adoption.[56]

The ACA[57] recommends that institutions provide counseling for pregnant inmates, that "prenatal care" should be offered, and that deliveries should be made at community hospitals.[58] Similarly, the American Public Health Association's standards for health services in correctional institutions say that pregnant inmates should be provided with prenatal care, including medical exams and treatment, and that pregnant prisoners should be allowed a special program of housing, diet, vitamin supplements, and exercise.[59]

Once inmates give birth, other problems arise—including the critical issue of child placement. Some states still have partial civil death statutes, which mean that prisoners lose many of their civil rights upon incarceration. In such states women may lose legal custody of their children. Children either become wards of the state or are placed for adoption.

Although there is some historical precedent for allowing women inmates to keep newborns with them in the institutional setting, very few women's prisons permit this practice. Overcrowded prisons lack space for children, and the prison environment is a decidedly undesirable environment for children. A few women's prisons allow women to keep newborns for a brief period. Most, however, arrange for foster care until the mother is able to find relatives to care for the child or is released. Others work with services which place prison-born infants up for adoption. Some facilities make a special effort to keep mother and child together. Even relatively progressive prisons which allow mother-child contact usually do so only for the first year.

Many women are already mothers when they come to prison. BJS statistics[60] show that more than three-quarters of all women in prison in the United States have young children (i.e., those under the age of 18). Black (69%) and Hispanic (72%) female inmates are more likely than white (62%) women to have young children. Also, black women are more likely than other women to have lived with their young children before being imprisoned.

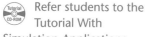
Twenty-five percent of women inmates with children under age 18 have children living with the other parent. More than a third of white female inmates report that their children are living with their fathers, compared to a quarter of Hispanic women and less than a fifth of black women. Regardless of race, grandparents were the most common caregivers: 57 percent of black mothers, 55 percent of Hispanic mothers, and 41 percent of white mothers. Nearly 10 percent of the inmate mothers reported that their children were in a foster home, agency, or institution.

The Prison Environment: Issues and Concerns

According to BJS, nearly 90 percent of women with children under age 18 have had contact with their children since entering prison. Half of all women inmates surveyed had been visited by their children, four-fifths had corresponded by mail, and three-quarters had talked with children on the telephone. Female inmates with children under age 18 were more likely than those with adult children to make daily telephone calls to their children.

Understandably, inmate mothers frequently express concern about possible alienation from their children due to the passage of time associated with incarceration. They often worry that their children will develop strong bonds with new caretakers and be unwilling to return to their mothers upon release.[61]

Finally, it is important to note that a number of women's prisons operate programs designed to develop parenting skills among inmates. Included here are the Program for Caring Parents at the Louisiana Correctional Institute for Women; Project HIP (Helping Incarcerated Parents) at the Maine Correctional Center; and Neil J. Houston House, a program for non-violent female offenders in Massachusetts.[62]

Teaching Tip
Refer to Chapter 11 of the *Instructor's Resource Manual* for additional activities and for answers to the end-of-chapter exercises.

11

Review and Applications

SUMMARY BY CHAPTER OBJECTIVES

CHAPTER OBJECTIVE 1

Prisons are overcrowded for three main reasons. First, over the past decade there has been an increase in imprisonment. Second, changes in federal and state sentencing laws require more offenders to serve longer periods. The third is an increase in imprisonment for drug and violent offenses.

CHAPTER OBJECTIVE 2

This chapter presented six methods of controlling prison overcrowding. First, reduce the number of persons who go to prison by making more use of front-end strategies such as diversion, community corrections, and intermediate sanctions. Second, put a cap or ceiling on the prison population, sometimes called trap-door strategies. Third, use what are called side-door strategies, such as giving sentenced offenders the opportunity to apply to the sentencing court for release to intensive community corrections programs, usually six months after imprisonment. Fourth, use more parole and halfway houses, called back-door strategies. Fifth, build more prisons and/or expand existing facilities. Sixth, use structured sentencing guidelines that are designed to save prison space for serious crimes and violent offenses while using community corrections and intermediate sanctions for lesser offenses.

CHAPTER OBJECTIVE 3

Prison riots occur for a number of reasons. Sometimes they are a result of spontaneous outburst; others are planned. Most experts believe that the primary causes of prison riots are overcrowding, racial antagonism, environmental factors, weak prison administration, young and violence-prone prisoners, and control of the inmate social structure.

CHAPTER OBJECTIVE 4

Preventing prison riots requires changes both outside and inside the prison. It is important for other social institutions to reduce sources of tension that contribute to crime. Experts recommend formal inmate grievance procedures, ombudsmen, improved classification systems, smaller institutions, meaningful educational and work programs, alternatives to incarceration, professional prison staff who are well trained and well paid, and clearly written and well-understood policies on the use of force.

CHAPTER OBJECTIVE 5

A supermax housing facility is a free-standing facility, or a distinct unit within a facility, that provides for management and secure control of inmates who have been officially designated as violent or who exhibit serious and disruptive behavior while incarcerated. It is not yet known what impact conditions of extreme isolation will have on the prisoner or on the public when prisoners released from these facilities return to the community.

CHAPTER OBJECTIVE 6

"No-frills" prisons and jails eliminate prisoner privileges and amenities in the belief that this process will deter criminals from future criminal activity. It appears, however, that "no-frills" correctional facilities may actually produce the results they were designed to avert. Corrections professionals tell us that what outsiders perceive as privileges and amenities, they consider to be important management tools. They also suggest that eliminating privileges and amenities may increase the number of prison disturbances and make it more difficult for corrections staff to motivate appropriate inmate behavior.

CHAPTER OBJECTIVE 7

Special needs inmates in prison include substance abusers, HIV-positive and AIDS-infected inmates, elderly prisoners, pregnant inmates, and female prisoners with children. Eighty percent of the U.S. prison and jail population is seriously involved with drug/alcohol abuse and addiction. Comprehensive prison-based treatment programs that provide community-based aftercare services are most likely to succeed. Prison-based treatment, education, and prevention programs can also help reduce the risk of becoming HIV-positive or acquiring AIDS. The rate of confirmed prison AIDS cases is over six times that of the general population, and the AIDS-related death rate in prison is three times higher. Finally, projections indicate that older prisoners will comprise 33 percent of the prison population by the year 2010. The cost of treating older inmates' health problems is enormous—an estimated $70,000 per year per person. States are beginning to confine the oldest prisoners in nursing-home-like facilities and provide a prison hospice environment for those who are dying. Adding to the pain of imprisonment is the frustration and conflict felt by female inmates at being separated from and unable to care for their children. Pregnant inmates are an additional concern for correctional facilities. Few of them offer adequate medical care to fulfill the needs of pregnant inmates.

KEY TERMS

rated capacity, p. 311
operational capacity, p. 311
design capacity, p. 311
structured sentencing, p. 313
exchange rates, p. 313
security threat groups (STGs), p. 314
riot, p. 315

supermax housing, p. 322
special master, p. 322
"no-frills" prisons and jails, p. 323
therapeutic community (TC), p. 326
older inmates, p. 331
hospices, p. 335

QUESTIONS FOR REVIEW

1. Explain the differences among *rated capacity, operational capacity,* and *design capacity.*
2. How has the increase in convicted offenders affected prisons?
3. What changes in federal and state sentencing laws have affected prison populations?
4. How have arrests for drug offenses affected prison populations?
5. What are the six methods of controlling prison overcrowding?
6. How does *structured sentencing* work?
7. What is meant by *exchange rates*?
8. Compare and contrast the causes of prison riots in the 1950s and the 1990s.
9. What are *security threat groups*?
10. What are some factors that can lead to a prison riot?
11. What are some ways to prevent prison riots?
12. Distinguish between a supermax housing facility and a prison built for maximum-security prisoners.
13. What are some of the psychological effects of long-term solitary confinement?
14. What is a "no-frills" prison or jail and why are they emerging?
15. What impact can we expect "no-frills" prisons and jails to have on recidivism, institutional security, and inmate behavior control?
16. According to the National Center on Addiction and Substance Abuse (CASA), what percentage of America's jail and prison population at yearend 1996 was involved in substance abuse?
17. Why is alcohol more closely linked with violent crimes than drugs?
18. What is a *therapeutic community*?
19. How does lack of treatment for substance-abusing inmates endanger the public?
20. What are some CASA recommendations for managing substance-abusing inmates?
21. What in-prison recommendations does CASA offer?

22. What post-prison recommendations does CASA offer?

23. How does the number of people in the general population with HIV/AIDS compare with the number of prisoners with HIV/AIDS?

24. What are five reasons that it is difficult to treat HIV in prison?

25. Define what is meant by *older inmate*. What are some issues concerning older prisoners?

26. How does a geriatric prison differ from a regular prison?

27. What is a prison *hospice*?

28. What are two issues that corrections officials face in regard to female inmates?

CRITICAL THINKING EXERCISES

ON-THE-JOB ISSUES

1. You are the state corrections department's public information officer. Write a press release that explains to an angry public the reasons why the corrections department pays for older prisoners' medical treatment.

2. It's 2010 and you are the director of your state's Department of Corrections and Rehabilitation. Predictions from the year 2000 that older inmates would comprise 33 percent of the state's prison population were wrong. It's actually 42 percent because twice earlier in the decade the state legislature changed the habitual offender law from "three-strikes" to "two-strikes," and mandated that offenders sentenced under the new law serve all their sentence, not just 85 percent. It's difficult to find reliable figures on what it is costing to care for older inmates' health, yet there are signs all around that it's expensive. For example, your state is now building its third geriatric prison. You are currently working on the department's budget for next year. What issues should you consider when determining what monies to request for the incarceration of older offenders?

CORRECTIONS ISSUES

1. Under the Violent Offender Incarceration and Truth-in-Sentencing Incentive Grants Program passed by Congress in 1994, to qualify for federal funds to build new prisons and jails, states must require persons convicted of a Part I violent offense to serve not less than 85 percent of their prison sentences. Do you think such a requirement is appropriate? Why or why not?

2. In the district court case *Madrid* v. *Gomez*,[63] the court said: "It is clear that confinement in the Pelican Bay SHU severely deprives inmates of normal human contact and substantially reduces their level of environmental stimulation."[64] The court further said, "Based on studies undertaken in this case, and the entirety of the record bearing on this claim, the court finds that many, if not most, inmates in the SHU experience some degree of psychological trauma in reaction to their extreme social isolation and the severely restricted environmental stimulation in the SHU."[65] Do you agree with the court that the conditions in the supermax unit imposed cruel and unusual punishment on mentally ill prisoners? Explain.

CORRECTIONS ON THE WEB

1. The Publications section of the Centers for Disease Control and Prevention maintains a Web site at **http://www.cdc.gov/nchstp/od/cccwg/publications.htm** that discusses HIV, AIDS, and TB in correctional institutions. Go to the site and find and report on a document that discusses HIV, AIDS, or TB in corrections.

2. Access the National Prison Hospice Association at **www.npha.org**. Read the Association's Mission Statement. Then access the Newsletter and read one of the articles. Summarize the article in light of the Association's mission statement.

ADDITIONAL READINGS

Braswell, Michael C., Reid H. Montgomery, and Lucien X. Lombardo. *Prison Violence in America, 2d ed.* Cincinnati, OH: Anderson Publishing Co., 1994.

Finn, Peter. "No-Frills Prisons and Jails: A Movement in Flux," *Federal Probation*. Volume 60, Number 3, September 1996, pp. 35–44.

Hammett, Theodore M. *Public Health/Corrections Collaboration: Prevention and Treatment of HIV/AIDS, STDs, and TB.* Washington, DC: National Institute of Justice Centers for Disease Control and Prevention Research in Brief, NCJ 169590, July 1998.

Irwin, John, and James Austin. *It's About Time: America's Imprisonment Binge, 2d ed.* Belmont, CA: Wadsworth Publishing Company, 1997.

LIS, Inc. *Supermax Housing.* Longmont, CO: National Institute of Corrections, March 1997.

Logan, Charles H. *Private Prisons: Cons and Pros.* New York: Oxford University Press, 1990.

Morton, Joann B. *An Administrative Overview of the Older Inmate.* Washington, DC: National Institute of Corrections, August 1992.

Belenko, Steven. *Behind Bars: Substance Abuse and America's Prison Population.* New York: National Center on Addiction and Substance Abuse, Columbia University, January 1998.

National Institute of Corrections. *Hospice and Palliative Care in Prison.* Longmont, CO: National Institute of Corrections, September 1998.

Shichor, David. *Punishment for Profit: Private Prisons/Public Concerns.* Thousand Oaks, CA: Sage Publications, Inc., March 1995.

ENDNOTES

1. Adapted from Reid H. Montgomery, "Bringing the Lessons of Prison Riots Into Focus," *Corrections Today,* Volume 59, Number 1 (February 1997), pp. 28–33. Reprinted with permission.

2. James M. Byrne and Linda Kelly, *Restructuring Probation as an Intermediate Sanction, An Evaluation of Massachusetts' Intensive Probation Supervision Program, Final Report,* (Washington, DC: National Institute of Justice, 1989).

3. David P. Farrington and C. P. Nuttal, "Prison Size, Overcrowding, Prison Violence, and Recidivism," *Journal of Criminal Justice,* Volume 8, Number 4 (1980), pp. 221–231.

4. Victoria G. Putnam, *Gangs in Correctional Facilities: A National Assessment,* NCJ 173076. (Washington, DC: National Institute of Justice, 1993).

5. Mary E. Pelz, "Gangs," In Marilyn D. McShane and Frank P Williams III (eds.), *Encyclopedia of American Prisons.* (New York: Garland Publishing, Inc., 1996), p. 213.

6. Bert Useem and Peter Kimball, *States of Siege: U.S. Prison Riots, 1971-1986* (New York: Oxford University Press, 1991).

7. J. Lillis, "Prison Escapes and Violence Remain Down," *Corrections Compendium*, Volume 19, Number 6 (1994), pp. 6–21.

8. Vernon B. Fox, *Violence Behind Bars: An Explosive Report on Prison Riots in the United States,* (New York: Vantage Press, 1956) and Reid H. Montgomery, Jr.,

"Bringing the Lessons of Prison Riots Into Focus," *Corrections Today.*

9. Negley K. Teeters, "The Dilemma of Prison Riots," *The Prison Journal,* Volume 33, Number 1 (April 1953), p. 14.

10. "Prison Riots. . . Why?" *The Prison Journal,* Volume 33, Number 1 (April 1953) and "Aftermath of Riot," *The Prison Journal,* Volume 34, Number 1 (April 1954).

11. Negley K. Teeters, "The Dilemma of Prison Riots," pp. 19–20.

12. New York State Special Commission on Attica [McKay Commission], *Attica: The Official Report of the New York State Special Commission on Attica* (New York: Bantam Books, 1972), p. xi.

13. Sue Mahan, Richard Lawrence, and Deanna Meyer, "Riots," in Marilyn D. McShane and Frank P. Williams III (eds.), *Encyclopedia of American Prisons* (New York: Garland Publishing, Inc., 1996), pp. 406–412.

14. U.S. National Advisory Commission on Civil Disorders [Kerner Commission], *Report,* (Washington DC: The Commission, 1968), p. 2.

15. David A. Ward and Allen F. Breed, *The U.S. Penitentiary, Marion, Illinois: Consultants' Report Submitted to the Committee on the Judiciary, U.S. House of Representatives, Ninety-Eighth Congress, Second Session,* (Washington, DC: U.S. Government Printing Office, 1985), p. 1.

16. Ibid., pp. 1–2.
17. As quoted in Francis X. Clines, "A Futuristic Prison Awaits the Hard-Core 400," *The New York Times* (October 17, 1994), Section A, p. 1.
18. LIS, Inc., *Supermax Housing*, (Longmont, CO: National Institute of Corrections, March 1997).
19. Ibid., p. 1.
20. Richard H. McCleery, "Authoritarianism and the Belief System of Incorrigibles," in Donald R. Cressy (ed.), *The Prison: Studies in Institutional Organization and Change*, (New York: Holt, Rinehart and Winston, 1961), pp. 260–306 and *Wright* v. *Enomoto* (July 23, 1980), pp. 5, 15.
21. *Madrid* v. *Gomez*, 889 F.Supp. 1146 (N.D. Cal. 1995).
22. Ibid., p. 1151.
23. Mark Curriden, "Hard Time: Chain Gangs Are In and Exercise Rooms Are Out in the Prisons of the 90s," *ABA Journal*, Volume 81 (July 1995), pp. 72–76.
24. As quoted in Garry Boulard, "What's Tough Enough," *State Legislatures*, Volume 21, Number 10 (December 1995), p. 26.
25. Peter Finn, "No-Frills Prisons and Jails: A Movement in Flux," *Federal Probation*, Volume 60, Number 3 (September 1996), pp. 35–44.
26. As quoted in "5 Florida County Jails Make It Real Hard Time: No Television," *The New York Times* (August 14, 1994, Section L), p. 27.
27. As quoted in Brett Pulley, "Always a Good Sound Bite: The 'Good Life' Behind Bars," *The New York Times* (September 22, 1996, Section 13), p. 2.
28. "5 Florida County Jails Make It Real Hard Time: No Television."
29. John J. Rafferty, "Prison Industry: The Next Step," *Corrections Today*, Volume 60, Number 4 (July 1998), p. 22.
30. W. Wesley Johnson, Katherine Bennett, and Timothy J. Flanagan, "Getting Tough on Prisoners: Results From the National Corrections Executive Survey, 1995," *Crime and Delinquency*, Volume 43, Number 1 (January 1997), pp. 24–41.
31. Ibid., p. 38.
32. National Center on Addiction and Substance Abuse, *Behind Bars: Substance Abuse and America's Prison Population*, (New York: National Center on Addiction and Substance Abuse, Columbia University). Online at http://www.casacolumbia.org/pubs/jan98. Accessed August 1998.
33. National Center on Addiction and Substance Abuse, *Behind Bars: Substance Abuse and America's Prison Population*.
34. As quoted in Joseph A. Califano, "Foreword," National Center on Addiction and Substance Abuse, *Behind Bars: Substance Abuse and America's Prison Population* (Columbia University, NY: National Center on Addiction and Substance Abuse, January 1998). Online at http://www.casacolumbia.org/pubs/jan98. Accessed August 1998.
35. Ibid.
36. Jeremy Travis, *Framing the National Agenda: A Research and Policy Perspective. Speech to National Corrections Conference on Substance Abuse*, April 23, 1997.
37. Marcia R. Chaiken, *Prison Programs for Drug-Involved Offenders*, (Washington, DC: National Institute of Justice, October 1989); D. A. Andrews, Ivan Zinger, Robert D. Hoge, James Bonta, Paul Gendreau, and Francis T. Cullen, "Does Correctional Treatment Work? A Clinically Relevant and Psychologically Informed Meta-Analysis," *Criminology*, Volume 28, Number 3 (1990), pp. 369–404; and Donald Lipton and Frank Pearson, "The CDATE Project: Reviewing Research on the Effectiveness of Treatment Programs for Adults and Juvenile Offenders," Paper presented at the annual meeting of the American Society of Criminology, Chicago, IL, 1996.
38. Bureau of Justice Statistics, *Improving the Nation's Criminal Justice System: Findings and Results From State and Local Program Evaluations*, (Washington, DC: Bureau of Justice Statistics, December 1997).
39. National Center on Addiction and Substance Abuse, *Behind Bars: Substance Abuse and America's Prison Population*.
40. Theodore M. Hammett, Patricia Harmon, and Laura M. Maruschak, *1996–1997 Update: HIV/AIDS, STDs, and TB in Correctional Facilities* (Washington, DC: National Institute of Justice, July 1999), pp. xiii–xiv.
41. *Management of the HIV-Positive Prisoner*, (New York: World Health CME), no date.
42. Michael S. Vaughn and Leo Carroll, "Separate and Unequal: Prison Versus Free-World Medical Care," *Justice Quarterly*, Volume 15, Number 1 (March 1998), pp. 3–40.
43. Ibid., pp. 31–32.
44. Hammett, et al., op. cit., pp. 25–44.
45. Joann B. Morton, *An Administrative Overview of the Older Inmate*, (Washington, DC: National Institute of Corrections, August 1992). Online at http://www.nicic.org. Accessed November 1998.
46. Ronald H. Aday, "Responding to the Graying of American Prisons: A National Perspective Update." Paper presented to the annual meeting of the Academy of Criminal Justice Sciences, March 13, 1999, Orlando, FL.
47. Connie L. Neeley, Laura Addison, and Delores Craig-Moreland, "Addressing the Needs of Elderly

Offenders," *Corrections Today,* Volume 59, Number 5 (August 1997), pp. 120–124.

48. Ronald H. Aday, "Golden Years Behind Bars: Special Programs and Facilities for Elderly Inmates," *Federal Probation,* Volume 58, Number 2 (June 1994), pp. 47–54.

49. Jurgen Neffe, "The Old Folks' Slammer: Aging Prison Population in the United States," *World Press Review,* Volume 44, Number 6 (June 1997), pp. 30–32; Irina R. Soderstrom and W. Michael Wheeler, "Is It Practical to Incarcerate the Elderly Offender? Yes and No," in Charles B. Fields, *Controversial Issues in Corrections* (Boston: Allyn and Bacon, 1999), pp. 72–89.

50. Alexandra Pelosi, "Age of Innocence: A Glut of Geriatric Jailbirds," *The New Republic,* Volume 216, Number 18 (May 5, 1997), pp. 15–18.

51. Anne Seidlitz, "National Prison Hospice Association Facilities Deal With Inmate Deaths," *CorrectCare,* Volume 12, Number 1 (Spring 1998), p. 10.

52. National Institute of Corrections, *Hospice and Palliative Care in Prisons,* (Longmont, CO: National Institute of Corrections, September 1998).

53. Seidlitz, op. cit., p. 10.

54. Tracy L. Snell, "Women in Prison," *Bureau of Justice Statistics Bulletin,* NCJ 145321 (March, 1994).

55. As estimated by Vesna Markovic, "Pregnant Women in Prison: A Correctional Dilemma?" *The Keepers' Voice* (Summer 1995).

56. Ibid.

57. American Correctional Association, *Standards for Adult Correctional Institutions,* 3d ed. American Correctional Association, January, 1990.

58. Gerald Austin McHugh, "Protection of the Rights of Pregnant Women in Prison and Detention Facilities," *New England Journal of Prison Law,* Vol. 6, No. 2 (Summer 1980), pp. 231–263.

59. Ibid., p. 246.

60. Snell, op. cit.

61. Phyllis Jo Baunach, "Critical Problems of Women in Prison," in Imogene L. Moyer (ed.), *The Changing Roles of Women in the Criminal Justice System* (Prospect Heights, IL: Waveland Press, 1985), p. 16.

62. John J. Sheridan, "Inmates May Be Parents, Too," *Corrections Today,* Volume 58, Number 5 (August 1996), p. 100.

63. *Madrid* v. *Gomez,* 889 F.Supp. 1146 (N.D. Cal. 1995).

64. Ibid., p. 1232.

65. Ibid., p. 1235.

12 Parole
Early Release and Reintegration

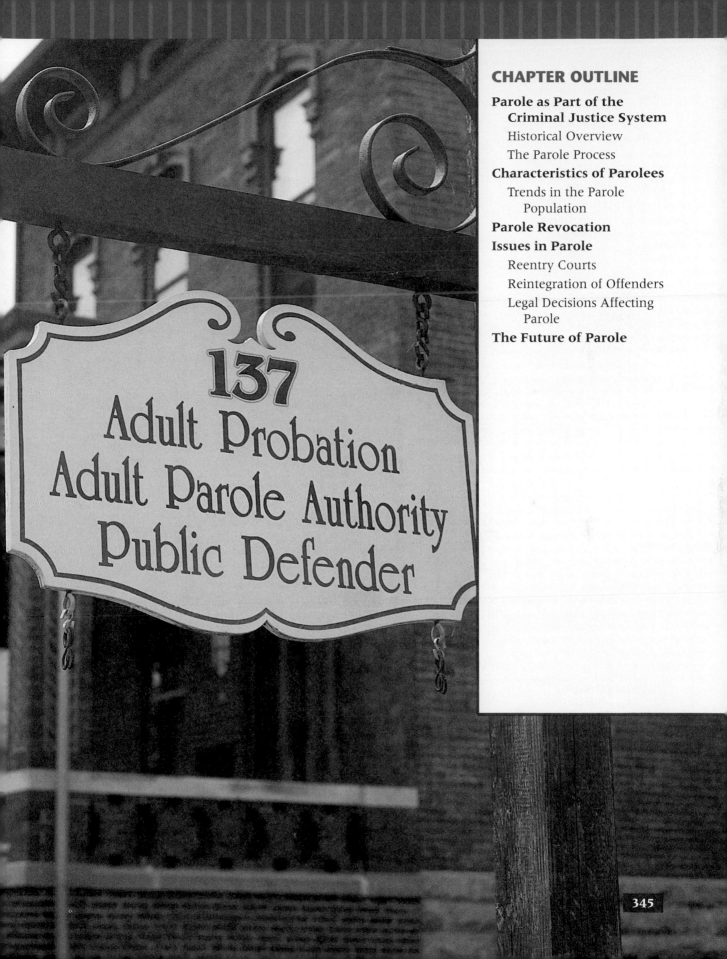

137
Adult Probation
Adult Parole Authority
Public Defender

Sorry it's taken so long to write, but I do have a good excuse. I'm working 7 days a week, 14 hours a day, driving for an appliance store. I deliver appliances for $15 a trip, and I try to do as much as possible each day. I average about $100 a day, saving every cent for a new truck.

When I went for my job interview I told the interviewer up front that I was on parole, but it made no difference at all to him. And for anyone who is interested, Project RIO works. Not only does it help you find a job, they call and talk to the company before you have your interview. Get involved with Project RIO.

When I went to the employment office under Project RIO, it made finding a job easy. I went for two interviews and got one job [with the second company]. But the first company I applied with has already called me for a second interview and [also] wants to hire me. It starts out at less money, but within a year I'll be making about $35,000 a year, working 5 days a week, 8 hours a day. Once I get enough money together to buy a new truck I may switch jobs.

—Peter Finn, Texas' Project RIO (Re-Integration of Offenders)

The letter above, written by a Texas parolee to a friend still in a Texas prison, is indicative of the success of a program designed to help parolees find jobs. Project RIO (Re-Integration of Offenders) is a major initiative the state of Texas has undertaken to help keep parolees from returning to prison. Inmates who find decent jobs soon after release are less likely to return to a life of crime. In 1996, 16,000 Texas parolees participated in Project RIO.

For more than a century, parole has been used for early release from prison—inmates are released from some type of institutional custody but remain in the legal custody of the government. A parolee who violates one or more of the conditions of parole may be returned to custody to serve the remainder of the original sentence plus any additional sentence imposed for the parole violation.

Parole as Part of the Criminal Justice System

People often confuse parole, probation, and pardon. All three place offenders in the community, but they are very different.

Parole: Early Release and Reintegration

Parole is the release of a prison inmate, prior to sentence expiration, with supervision in the community. A parole usually comes from authorities in the correctional system—responsibility for offenders passes from the judicial system to the correctional system upon imprisonment. In those states that permit parole, state laws give correctional officials the authority to change, within certain limits, the length of a sentence. Correctional officials may, therefore, change the conditions under which convicted offenders are supervised—they may release offenders from prison to supervision in the community or in an outside facility.

As we saw in Chapter 5, **probation** is a judge's sentence that allows a convicted offender to continue to live in the community, with restrictions on activities and with supervision for the duration of the sentence.

A **pardon** is an executive act that legally excuses a convicted offender from penalty. It is granted by a governor or the President. Those who are pardoned are excused from any further supervision.

Historical Overview

The parole concept has its roots in an 18th century English penal practice—banishment. Judges transferred custody of physically fit condemned felons to independent contractors, paying those contractors a fee to transport the prisoners to the American colonies and sell their services, for the duration of their sentences, to the highest bidder. This practice, known as indentured servitude, was similar to today's parole in that the indentured servant had to comply with certain conditions to remain in supervised "freedom." This practice was discontinued in 1787 because of the Revolutionary War—English offenders were joining colonial forces against England.

From 1787 through 1879, English offenders were sent to Norfolk Island, Australia, a British penal colony. In 1840, British Navy Captain Alexander Maconochie was appointed superintendent of the penal colony. He developed a "ticket of leave" system, which moved inmates through stages: imprisonment, conditional release, and complete restoration of liberty. Inmates moved from one stage to the next by earning "marks" for improved conduct, frugality, and work habits.

In 1854, Sir Walter Crofton, director of the Irish prison system, implemented a system that was based on Maconochie's "ticket of leave" system. Crofton's version required that, upon conditional release, a former inmate:

1. Report immediately to the constabulary on arrival and once a week thereafter.
2. Abstain from any violation of the law.
3. Refrain from habitually associating with notoriously bad characters.
4. Refrain from leading an idle and dissolute life, without means of obtaining an honest living.
5. Produce the "ticket of leave" when asked to do so by a magistrate or police officer.
6. Not change locality without reporting to the constabulary.[1]

The former inmate who did not comply with the conditions of release was re-imprisoned. Crofton's system of conditional release is considered the forerunner of modern American parole.

parole The conditional release of a prisoner, prior to completion of the imposed sentence, under the supervision of a parole officer.

probation The conditional release of a convicted offender into the community under the supervision of a probation officer as a sentence for conviction of a crime.

pardon An executive act that legally excuses a convicted offender from a criminal penalty.

Captain Alexander Maconochie, who became superintendent of the British penal colony on Norfolk Island, Australia in 1840, implemented a "ticket of leave" system to ease inmate transition from custody to freedom. Later, Sir Walter Crofton, director of the Irish prison system, implemented a system based on Maconochie's ideas. How did their systems influence current parole procedures?

Teaching Tip

Direct students' attention to the quotation in the text from Dr. S. G. Howe. Ask students how they think Dr. Howe's use of the word *parole* might have led to use of the term *parole* for a prisoner's conditional release.

Teaching Tip

Elmira Reformatory was credited with several "firsts." Assign a group of students to research those "firsts" and report to the class.

Use of the term *parole* for early release from prison began with a letter from Dr. S. G. Howe of Boston to the Prison Association of New York in 1846. Howe said, "I believe there are many (prisoners) who might be so trained as to be left upon their parole (a promise made with or confirmed by a pledge of one's honor) during the last period of their imprisonment with safety."[2]

Early American Parole Development   The first legislation authorizing parole in the United States was enacted in Massachusetts in 1837. However, the Elmira Reformatory in New York, opened in 1876, was the first U.S. correctional institution to implement an extensive parole program. Zebulon Brockway, the institution's first superintendent, implemented a system of upward classification. The first grade was Brockway's personal interview with the new inmate. The second grade was the prison regime that Brockway established for the prisoner: a mix of labor (in the iron foundry or factories, on the farm, or on the maintenance crew), formal schooling, mandatory religious service, and military drill. An inmate who earned three marks each for labor, education, and behavior each month for six months in the second grade was promoted to the third grade. Six months after achieving the third grade promotion, the inmate was granted a parole hearing before Brockway and five other Elmira staff members. Paroled inmates made their own living and work arrangements. Elmira employees and community volunteers provided parole supervision. Failure to comply with conditions of parole meant parole revocation and return to Elmira's second grade.[3]

By 1889, twelve states had implemented parole programs; by 1944 all 48 states had enacted parole legislation.

Parole Development in the Early 20th Century   The 1920s and early 1930s were turbulent. During Prohibition, organized crime increased, street gang warfare escalated, and the media became obsessed with coverage of notorious criminals. Prison riots became all too familiar. Prisoner idleness, arbitrary rules and punishment, and failure of prison and parole to rehabilitate were recurring themes.

The Wickersham Commission, a commission on law enforcement and observance appointed by President Herbert Hoover, issued a report in 1931 that recommended that states establish a centralized policy-making board to write standards and guidelines for parole practices, advocating uniformity in state parole practices.[4] This report included a list of the "essential elements" of a good parole system:

1. Indeterminate sentence law permitting the offender to be released (conditionally) at the time when he or she is most likely to successfully make the transition back to society.
2. Provision of quality release preparation—in the institution—for the offender who is reentering the community.
3. Familiarity by the parole officer with the home and environmental conditions of the offender before he or she leaves the institution.
4. Sufficient staffing levels to ensure an adequate number of parole officers to supervise parolees.[5]

The Wickersham Commission reported that parole was logical because it was an inexpensive way to supervise offenders. Moreover, the Commission reported, the parolee earns money, whereas the prisoner cannot support him- or herself, and cannot contribute financially to his or her family. Parole advocates advised the public that more parole was the answer. By 1944, all of the states had passed enabling legislation for parole.[6]

Despite the fact that all the states had enacted parole legislation, opposition was strong. The attitude that parole boards were turning hardened criminals loose on society sparked a series of angry attacks, through national and state commissions, investigatory hearings, editorials and cartoons, press releases, and books.[7] Opponents claimed that parole had a dismal performance record, its goals were never realized, parole board members and parole officers were poorly trained, and that parole hearings were little more than hastily conducted, almost unthinking interviews.

In spite of the gap between goals and reality, parole fulfilled important functions for officials in the criminal justice system. Wardens supported parole—the possibility of parole served as an incentive, making it easier to keep peace. Wardens also used parole to control prison overcrowding by keeping the number of persons being released on parole about equal to the number of new prisoner admissions.

Legislators supported parole because it cost less than incarceration. District attorneys supported parole because they felt it helped with plea bargaining. Without parole, district attorneys argued, there was little motivation for defendants, particularly those facing long prison sentences, to plead guilty to lesser crimes. District attorneys also supported parole because parolees could be returned to prison without new trial proceedings.

Together, these groups made a claim to the public that parole actually extended state control over offenders—parolees were supervised. The public accepted the claim that parole was tough on criminals and that abolishing parole ended state control over dangerous persons.

Student Involvement

Ask students to research the Wickersham Commission and answer these questions: Why was the Commission formed? What major issues did it address? What major parole recommendations did the Commission make?

Teaching Tip

Review with students how parole benefits the criminal justice system.

Parole: Early Release and Reintegration

Parole Development in the Late 20th Century Opposition to parole resurfaced in the 1960s and 1970s, this time as part of a larger political debate about crime, the purposes of sanctioning, and the appropriateness of the unlimited discretion afforded various sectors of the criminal justice system (paroling authorities in particular). During this period, the debate on correctional policy addressed both the assumptions of the rehabilitative ideal and the results of indeterminate sentencing and parole.

In the 1970s, research indicated that prison rehabilitation programs had few positive benefits. Parolees were not rehabilitated as parole advocates claimed.[8] This position was supported on all sides of the political spectrum, including those who believed that prisons "coddled" dangerous criminals and those who questioned the ethics of coercing offenders into submitting to unwanted treatment as a condition of release.[9] These research findings led to many of the sentencing reforms of the 1970s and 1980s, when political rhetoric implied that parole meant a "soft" stance on crime. During a time when crime rates and recidivism were up, the public did not want prisoners released on parole.

In 1987, the American Probation and Parole Association (APPA), the nation's largest association of probation and parole professionals, voiced its support of parole and objected to efforts to abolish it. However, in that same year, six states abolished discretionary parole-board release. By the year 2000, 15 states and the federal government had abolished it. The APPA position statement on parole is presented in Exhibit 12–1.

Cross-Cultural Perspective

Emphasize that a relationship exists between society's cultural values and crime control. Ask students what they think about parole, then ask them how cultural values may have influenced their perceptions.

Teaching Tip

Have students read the APPA's position statement on parole, then have them explain, in their own words, the mission of parole.

EXHIBIT 12–1

American Probation and Parole Association

Position Statement on Parole

The mission of parole is to prepare, select, and assist offenders who, after a reasonable period of incarceration, could benefit from an early release while, at the same time, ensuring an appropriate level of public protection through conditions of parole and provision of supervision services. This is accomplished by:

- Assisting the parole authority in decision making and the enforcement of parole conditions;
- Providing pre-release and post-release services and programs that will support offenders in successfully reintegrating into the community;
- Working cooperatively with all sectors of the criminal justice system to ensure the development and attainment of mutual objectives.

Parole: Early Release and Reintegration

The Parole Process

Eligibility   An inmate's eligibility for parole is determined by the sentence received from the court, as set by law. The **parole eligibility date** is the earliest date on which an inmate might be released. State statutes usually dictate parole eligibility dates and specify what portion of a sentence an offender must serve before being considered for release. Generally, state statutes apply formulas to deduct amounts of time from sentences to determine when an inmate might be eligible for release. The state statutes vary but, in general, reduce the sentence based on the number of days the inmate serves without disciplinary problems. The parole eligibility date, then, is determined by subtracting the maximum number of good-time days that could be earned from the length of the sentence. For example, a state statute might allow one day of good-time credit for every five days of good behavior. In this instance, an inmate could be eligible for parole after serving 292 days of a one-year sentence.

Although parole eligibility is ordinarily based on time served, some states have additional requirements, such as maintaining good conduct for a specific time period preceding the parole hearing.

Release Preparation   Most correctional systems recognize the importance of planning for early release. A good institution encourages inmates to participate in an established release preparation program that is designed to ensure successful reintegration into the community.

Release preparation should begin at incarceration and continue through release. A well-designed release preparation program requires participation by parole officers and the institution's staff, as well as various community resources. It may include training and/or information in the following areas:

1. Release—requirements for early release, types of release, the parole hearing, conditions of release, and post-release supervision.
2. Information/Community Resources—finding and using local resources such as social service agencies.
3. Health—mental health counseling, stress management, disease prevention, AIDS awareness, holistic health, nutrition, sexuality, weight management, and physical fitness.
4. Personal Growth and Development—anger management, marriage counseling, parenting classes, drug education, decision-making skills development, speech and communication classes, and general education classes.
5. Employment—basic job readiness, job search techniques, state employment services, interview skills, keeping a job, resume writing techniques, and dressing for interviews.
6. Personal Finance/Consumer Skills—maintaining and balancing checking and savings accounts, managing money and credit, buying a car and/or home, and living on a budget.

Granting Parole—The Paroling Authority   Every jurisdiction in the United States has a paroling authority. A **paroling authority** is a correc-

---

parole eligibility date
The earliest date on which an inmate might be paroled.

Student Involvement
Ask a volunteer to contact your state's paroling authority to find out what method your state uses to determine parole eligibility and present the information to the class.

Professional Issue
Pre-release Planning
Among the many factors that contribute to a parolee's successful adjustment is pre-release planning. Invite students to imagine that they are parole officers and write a brief paragraph describing their participation in the pre-release process. Ask volunteers to read their paragraphs for class discussion.

paroling authority
A person or correctional agency (often called a parole board or parole commission) that has the authority to grant parole, to revoke parole, and to discharge from parole.

Teaching Tip
Invite a member of your state's paroling authority to discuss with students the history of your state's parole board, its size, membership, functions, issues, and future. If a guest speaker is not available, investigate the possibility of a telephone conference with a paroling authority staff member.

salient factor score (SFS) Scale, developed from a risk-screening instrument, used to predict parole outcome.

Teaching Tip
Ask interested students to find out if your state's paroling authority uses a risk-assessment instrument similar to the Salient Factor Score, and, if so, obtain a copy of it. Make and distribute photocopies of the instrument and have students review the scoring mechanism.

Teaching Tip
Call a parole officer and ask if one of his or her parolees might visit your class and talk about parole from the parolee's perspective.

parolee A person who is conditionally released from prison to community supervision.

tional agency (often called a parole board or parole commission) that has the authority to grant parole, set conditions of parole, supervise parolees, revoke parole, and discharge from parole.

Parole boards vary in size from 3 members (Alabama, Hawaii, Montana, North Dakota, Washington, and West Virginia) to 10 or more (Connecticut, 11; Illinois,12; Michigan, 10; New York, 19; Ohio, 11; and Texas, 18). Of the 52 jurisdictions—the 50 states, the District of Columbia, and the federal government—34 have full-time salaried parole board members and 18 do not. Minnesota's paroling authority is its Commissioner of Corrections.[10]

The paroling authority's decision to grant or deny parole is partially based on its assessment of potential risk to the community. Risk assessment factors may include: the nature and circumstance of the crime; the offender's criminal record and prison record; and input from court officials, victims, and other interested parties. Some states use scoring instruments for risk assessment—the most commonly used are based on the U.S. Parole Commission's **salient factor score (SFS)**.[11] The salient factors are: (1) number of prior convictions/adjudications, (2) number of prior commitments of more than 30 days, (3) age at current offense, (4) recent commitment-free period (three years), (5) probation/parole/confinement/escape violation at time of current offense or during present confinement, (6) heroin/opiate dependence, and (7) if an older offender. The SFS places the offender in one of four risk categories: very good, good, fair, or poor. Parole officials consider this score in deciding whether parole is to be granted and, if so, what level of supervision will be required.

Policymakers differ on which criteria are the most important, and each parole board member brings to the release decision a variety of assumptions, values, and different views on the purpose of imprisonment (rehabilitation, incapacitation, or deterrence). The information used to make the parole decision varies significantly, depending on the goal or goals of the decision-maker.[12]

State statutes also specify factors that paroling authorities must consider when making their decisions. These considerations generally include likelihood of recidivism, welfare of the community into which the inmate will be released, the inmate's prison conduct, and any treatment or rehabilitation plans developed for the inmate.

Parole plays a key role in criminal justice administration, and that puts a parole board in a powerful position. The majority of state parole boards determine the actual duration of incarceration and exercise discretionary release and revocation powers, specifying conditions of release and terms of supervision. The parole board's release policies can have a direct impact on institutional management. For example, parole boards can help reduce prison population by increasing the number of parolees.

Granting Parole—The Hearing In general, parole hearings are attended by the applicant, the institutional representative, and hearing examiners or parole board members. The final decision to grant or deny parole considers both eligibility guidelines and the interview. If parole is granted, a contract that defines the release plan is executed and the inmate is given a release date. The inmate who is conditionally released to community supervision is called a **parolee**.

"I like being a parole agent because the job allows me to help people who got caught up in the criminal justice system and assist them with a smooth transition from prison back into society by providing a range of services. The most exciting thing about my job is I get to help parolees perform acceptably in the community and remove those who cannot."

Kenneth Wong
State Parole Agent
California Department
of Corrections

Kenneth Wong is a state parole agent with the California Department of Corrections. Before joining the San Francisco parole office in 1990, Ken worked three and one-half years as a correctional officer at the California State Prison at San Quentin and one and one-half years as an auto mechanic. Ken completed the automotive program at the College of Alameda and later enrolled in courses in human behavior at the University of California at Hayward.

As a parole officer, Ken works closely with police and social service agencies. He conducts anti-narcotic testing, refers parole violators to the State Board of Prison Terms, and helps parolees make a smooth transition from prison to the community. His paramount concern is community protection.

Ken's advice to persons interested in corrections is simple: "If you like working with people who've been in prison and if you have the patience to listen to their problems and make positive referrals and provide advice, then you should apply. The job is challenging and there is always something new."

In 1996, the California Probation, Parole, and Correctional Association recognized Ken Wong as Parole Agent of the Year. The Association said Wong's job performance was exemplary and he made a significant contribution to the field of corrections.

Ken plans to spend his career with the California Department of Corrections. He'd like to pursue management positions, beginning with parole unit supervisor.

If parole is denied, the inmate remains in prison and a date is set for the next review. The waiting period between hearings depends on the jurisdiction and the inmate's offense.

Conditions of Parole Paroling authorities set specific conditions for parole, on a case-by-case basis (see Figure 12–1). Parolees must comply with these conditions, which may include restitution, substance abuse aftercare, electronic monitoring, and/or house arrest, among others.

Parole requires supervision. Parole officers, who work closely with the parolee and the paroling authority, carry out this supervision and can return parolees to prison if they threaten community safety or otherwise violate the conditions of release. Depending on the severity of the crime and the risk

Student Involvement
Refer students to Figure 12–1. What are the specific conditions of release this parolee must meet?

FIGURE 12–1

Sample Order for Release on Parole

MARYLAND PAROLE COMMISSION

No. 028239

ORDER FOR RELEASE ON PAROLE

The Parole Commission, by virtue of the authority conferred upon it by the laws of the State of Maryland, does hereby grant parole to:

(True Name) _____ Travis Glen Hardin, #273843, DOB November 24, 1950 _____
(Commitment Name/s)

who was convicted of: _____ Distribution of cocaine; Violation of probation _____

Court: Talbot County Circuit Court #6903

Sentenced: May 18, 1996

Term: 6 years;   2 years, 6 months

From: March 10, 1996;   consecutive

Therefore, the said Commission does hereby order the release on parole of the said prisoner from

_____ Eastern Correctional Institution _____
(Correctional Institution or Jail)

The Parolee, upon release, shall be deemed to remain in legal custody until the expiration of the full, undiminished term and upon violation of any condition of his parole shall be remanded to the authority from which paroled, where a hearing shall be conducted by the Parole Commission. If parole is revoked, the Commission shall determine the amount of time spent on parole, if any, which shall be credited to the parolee.

This order is subject to the rules, regulation, and conditions of this parole as set forth below and on page 2 of this agreement, and such further conditions as the Commission may impose at any time during the period of parole.

Upon being released, report to the Division of Parole and Probation office located at

_____ 301 Bay Street, Suite 302, Easton, MD 21601   (410-555-1212) _____

MARYLAND PAROLE COMMISSION

Parole Expiration Date: September 2004

By: _____ Patricia K. Cushwa _____
Commissioner

Special Condition(s):   substance abuse therapy,
     subject to curfew as directed by parole agent,   March 20, 2000
     community service if agent directs, employment within 30 days   Date

Home/Employment Plan: _____ live with mother - Lynn Fortney, 2055 Sokol Drive,
Tilghman, MD 21671   (410-822-5555) _____

Anyone serving a sentence for a crime committed on or after May 1, 1991, must pay supervision and/or drug testing fees as prescribed in Article 41, Section 4.519 of the Annotated Code of Maryland.

Date(s) of Offense(s): _____ January 6, 1999 _____

MPC - 14 - (Revised 8/15/96)

WHITE – Parolee • PINK – Parole Commission Copy • YELLOW – Institution Copy • BLUE – Certified Copy • GREEN – Court Copy presented by the offender, parole supervision can incorporate several types of contact with and "examination" of the parolee, including drug testing, curfew, electronic monitoring, and employment verification.

The conditions under which parolees must live are very similar in form and structure to those for probationers. Sometimes the rules are established by law, but more often they are established by the paroling authority. The paroling authority can require any of the following forms of release: standard parole supervision, parole with enhanced treatment and programming conditions, halfway house placement, intensive supervision, parole with electronic monitoring and/or voice and location tracking, or release with follow-up drug testing and payment of supervision fees and restitution.

Parolees are technically still in state custody. They have been granted the privilege of living in the community rather than in prison. The paroling authority, therefore, has at least three responsibilities:

1. Help a parolee with employment, residence, finances, or other personal issues that often present difficulties for a person trying to readjust to life in the community.
2. Protect the community by helping parolees avoid situations that might encourage recidivism.
3. Expedite parole for those who meet the criteria established by the paroling authority and are unlikely to commit another crime.

Types of Parole   Release on parole may be mandatory or discretionary. **Mandatory release** requires that the correctional authority grant parole after a specific period of time, as specified by law—the inmate serves the time that is mandated by the sentence minus good-time credits. Mandatory release is generally associated with determinate sentencing or parole guidelines. **Discretionary release** is at the paroling authority's discretion, within boundaries established by the sentence and by law. Discretionary release, associated with indeterminate sentencing, requires that a paroling authority certify eligibility for release. The effective date of release may be contingent upon completion of a satisfactory plan for parole supervision.

Characteristics of Parolees

According to the U.S. Department of Justice, 704,964 American adults were on parole on January 1, 1999—an increase of 1.5 percent over January 1, 1998.[13] Ninety-one percent of those adults were state parolees; the rest were federal. The typical adult parolee was a white, non-Hispanic male, on mandatory parole, and under active parole supervision. Women made up 12 percent of the parole population. The region with the highest number of parolees was the South, followed by the Northeast, West, and Midwest (see Figure 12–2, on page 356).

Not all who are sent to prison are released on parole. Those who are the most serious offenders (those who have life sentences or are facing the death penalty) or have disciplinary problems while incarcerated generally are not paroled. Instead, they live out their lives in prison or are released when they have served their entire sentences.

Teaching Tip
Initiate a discussion on why it is important for offenders to plan early for post-prison employment. Ask interested students to contact your state corrections department and ask what your state institutions do in terms of planning for post-prison employment. Does your state have a network of job placement services for parolees? How do your state's job placement services for parolees work?

mandatory release
Early release after a time period specified by law.

discretionary release
Early release based on the paroling authority's assessment of eligibility.

Student Involvement
Ask interested students to contact your state's paroling authority to determine if parole in your state is mandatory, discretionary, or both, and what eligibility requirements must be met for parole.

Student Involvement
Direct students' attention to Figure 12–2 on page 356. Have students offer opinions as to the significance of the data.

FIGURE 12–2

Selected Characteristics of Adults on Parole

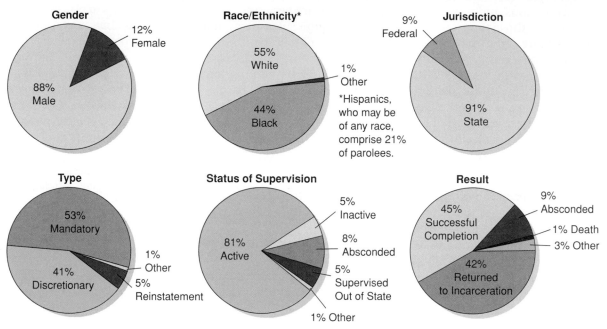

Source: Thomas P. Bonczar and Lauren E. Glaze, *Probation and Parole in the United States, 1998* (Washington: Bureau of Justice Statistics), August 1999, revised 10/13/99.

Student Involvement
Have students identify trends in Table 12–1.

Trends in the Parole Population

The estimated number of adults under community supervision and incarceration from 1990 through 1998 is shown in Table 12–1. As you can see, except for 1995, the parole population has continually increased.

TABLE 12–1

Adults on Probation, in Jail or Prison, and on Parole, 1990–1998

	Total Estimated Correctional Population	Probation	Jail	Prison	Parole
1990	4,348,000	2,670,234	403,019	743,382	531,407
1991	4,535,600	2,728,472	424,129	792,535	590,442
1992	4,762,600	2,811,611	441,781	850,566	658,601
1993	4,944,000	2,903,061	455,500	909,381	676,100
1994	5,141,300	2,981,022	479,800	990,147	690,371
1995	5,335,100	3,077,861	499,300	1,078,542	679,421
1996	5,475,000	3,161,996	510,400	1,127,528	679,733
1997	5,726,200	3,296,513	557,974	1,176,922	694,787
1998	5,890,300	3,417,613	584,372	1,232,900	704,964

Sources: Sourcebook of Criminal Justice Statistics 1998 Online, Bureau of Justice Statistics (October 1999), p. 462; Thomas P. Bonczar and Lauren E. Glaze, *Probation and Parole in the United States, 1998,* Bureau of Justice Statistics (August 1999), p. 1.

Table 12–2 defines parole populations among the states in 1998. Texas had the largest number of adults on parole, followed by California and Pennsylvania. Pennsylvania also had the highest rate of parole supervision (910 parolees supervised per 100,000 adult residents), which means it used parole more than any other state per capita residents; Maine used parole the least per capita residents (7 per 100,000 adult residents).

TABLE 12–2

Selected Parole Populations Among the States, 1998

10 States with the largest parole populations	Number supervised	10 States with the highest rates of supervision	Persons supervised per 100,000 adult U.S. residents	10 States with the lowest rates of supervision	Persons supervised per 100,000 adult U.S. residents
Texas	112,022	Pennsylvania	910	Maine	7
California	110,617	Texas	793	Washington	9
Pennsylvania	83,168	Oregon	703	North Dakota	37
New York	59,548	Louisiana	590	Connecticut	48
Illinois	30,432	California	466	Nebraska	51
Georgia	20,482	New York	436	Oklahoma	62
Louisiana	18,759	Maryland	404	Rhode Island	62
Oregon	17,270	Georgia	364	Florida	65
Maryland	15,528	Illinois	344	West Virginia	69
Michigan	15,331	Arkansas	338	Mississippi	75

Source: Adapted from Thomas P. Bonczar and Lauren E. Glaze, *Probation and Parole in the United States, 1998,* Bureau of Justice Statistics (August 1999), p. 2.

Parole Revocation

Parole may be revoked for two reasons. A **technical violation** occurs when any of the technical conditions of parole (e.g., find and keep a job, live at home, sign no contracts, pay restitution and fees, perform community service, attend drug and alcohol abuse counseling) are violated. Alaska's standard conditions of parole are presented in Figure 12–3 on page 358. The second type of violation is a **new offense violation**. This involves arrest for the commission of a new crime. A new offense violation might involve a technical violation. For example, an arrest for selling drugs and a positive test for drug use would be a violation for a new offense and a technical violation. When a violation occurs, a revocation hearing date is set. The purpose of a **revocation hearing** is to determine whether the violation warrants the parolee's removal from the community. During a revocation hearing, the parolee has certain rights of due process because he or she could lose conditional freedom; but he or she is not entitled to a full adversary

technical violation
Failure to comply with conditions of parole (e.g., nonreporting).

new offense violation
Arrest and prosecution for the commission of a new crime by a parolee.

revocation hearing
Administrative review to determine whether a violation of the conditions of parole warrants return to prison.

FIGURE 12-3

Sample State Conditions of Parole

STATE OF ALASKA

STANDARD CONDITIONS OF PAROLE

The following standard conditions of parole apply to all prisoners released on mandatory or discretionary parole, in accordance with AS 33.16.150(a).

1. REPORT UPON RELEASE: I will report in person no later than the next working day after my release to the parole officer located at the PAROLE OFFICE and receive further reporting instructions. I will reside at _____ .

2. MAINTAIN EMPLOYMENT/TRAINING/TREATMENT: I will make a diligent effort to maintain steady employment and support my legal dependents. I will not voluntarily change or terminate employment without receiving permission from my parole officer to do so. If discharged or if employment is terminated (temporarily or permanently) for any reason, I will notify my parole officer the next working day. If I am involved in an education, training, or treatment program, I will continue active participation in the program unless I receive permission from my parole officer to quit. If I am released, removed, or terminated from the program for any reason, I will notify my parole officer the next working day.

3. REPORT MONTHLY: I will report to my parole officer at least monthly in the manner prescribed by my parole officer. I will follow any other reporting instructions established by my parole officer.

4. OBEY LAWS/ORDERS: I will obey all state, federal, and local laws, ordinances, orders, and court orders.

5. PERMISSION BEFORE CHANGING RESIDENCE: I will obtain permission from my parole officer before changing my residence. Remaining away from my approved residence for 24 hours or more constitutes a change in residence for the purpose of this condition.

6. TRAVEL PERMIT BEFORE TRAVEL OUTSIDE ALASKA: I will obtain the prior written permission of my parole officer in the form of an interstate travel agreement before leaving the state of Alaska. Failure to abide by the conditions of the travel agreement is a violation of my order of parole.

Source: State of Alaska Board of Parole, *Parole Handbook, Appendix II; Conditions of Parole,* June 1998.

FIGURE 12-3 (continued)

Sample State Conditions of Parole

7. NO FIREARMS/WEAPONS: I will not own, possess, have in my custody, handle, purchase, or transport any firearm, ammunition, or explosives. I may not carry any deadly weapon on my person except a pocket knife with a 3" or shorter blade. Carrying any other weapon on my person such as a hunting knife, axe, club, etc. is a violation of my order of parole. I will contact the Alaska Board of Parole if I have any questions about the use of firearms, ammunition, or weapons.

8. NO DRUGS: I will not use, possess, handle, purchase, give, or administer any narcotic, hallucinogenic, (including marijuana/THC), stimulant, depressant, amphetamine, barbiturate, or prescription drug not specifically prescribed by a licensed medical person.

9. REPORT POLICE CONTACT: I will report to my parole officer, no later than the next working day, any contact with a law enforcement officer.

10. DO NOT WORK AS AN INFORMANT: I will not enter into any agreement or other arrangement with any law enforcement agency which will place me in the position of violating any law or any condition of my parole. I understand the Department of Corrections and Parole Board policy prohibits me from working as an informant.

11. NO CONTACT WITH PRISONERS OR FELONS: I may not telephone, correspond with, or visit any person confined in a prison, penitentiary, correctional institution or camp, jail, halfway house, work release center, community residential center, restitution center, juvenile correctional center, etc. Contact with a felon during the course of employment or during corrections-related treatment is not prohibited if approved by my parole officer. Any other knowing contact with a felon is prohibited unless approved by my parole officer. I will notify my parole officer the next working day if I have contact with a prisoner or felon.

12. CANNOT LEAVE AREA: I will receive permission from my parole officer before leaving the area of the state to which my case is assigned. My parole officer will advise me in writing of limits of the area to which I have been assigned.

13. OBEY ALL ORDERS/SPECIAL CONDITIONS: I will obey any special instructions, rules, or order given to me by the Alaska Board of Parole or by my parole officer. I will follow any special conditions imposed by the Alaska Board of Parole or my parole officer.

Source: State of Alaska Board of Parole, *Parole Handbook, Appendix II; Conditions of Parole,* June 1998.

One frequent reason for revoking parole is the parolee's arrest for a criminal offense. What are others reasons for which parole may be revoked?

Student Involvement

Refer students to Figure 12–3. Ask students which of the conditions they consider the most strict, the most surprising, and the least strict.

Teaching Tip

Review with students the difference between a technical violation and a new offense violation, then ask if they think both deserve incarceration and why or why not.

Teaching Tip

Explain that, generally speaking, parolees are returned to prison with new sentences if they commit a new crime while on parole. Parolees are also returned to prison if they violate the technical conditions of parole. Technical violations, generally speaking, do not yield a new sentence but rather a return to prison to serve more of the original sentence.

reentry court A court that manages the return to the community of individuals released from prison.

hearing, as would be the case in a new criminal proceeding. If the parolee violates his or her conditions of parole, a revocation hearing could return the offender to prison to serve the remainder of the original sentence, plus any new sentence that might be given because of new violations.[14]

The primary difference between a criminal trial and a revocation hearing is the threshold of evidence that the hearing body needs to convict. In a criminal trial, a conviction may be obtained only if the government proves its facts beyond a reasonable doubt. In a revocation hearing, the panel need only find that a violation is shown by a preponderance of the evidence.[15] In addition, there is a more relaxed rule of what constitutes evidence—a rule that permits letters, affidavits, and reports to be presented in lieu of direct testimony.

Issues in Parole

Over the past few decades, the face of parole has changed. We conclude this chapter with a discussion of several innovative programs in parole, court rulings that have changed the parole revocation process, and the future of parole.

Reentry Courts

The latest innovation in helping offenders released from prison make a successful adjustment to the community is reentry courts. A **reentry court** manages the return to the community of individuals released from prison, using the authority of the court to apply graduated sanctions and positive reinforcement and to marshal resources to support the prisoner's reintegration. The U.S. Attorney General has proposed that reentry courts operate like drug courts or other problem-solving courts (domestic violence court, community court, family court, gun court, and DWI court).[16] In drug court, for example, a judge is limited to managing a caseload of drug-involved offenders. The judge requires the offender to make regular court appearances and participate in drug treatment and testing. If the drug offender violates the conditions of release, the judge administers a predetermined range of graduated sanctions that do not automatically require return to prison (except for new crimes or egregious violations). The frequent appearances before the court with the offer of assistance, coupled with the knowledge of a predetermined range of sanctions for violations of the conditions of release, assist the offender in getting back on track. Research on drug courts is still new, but already studies show that recidivism among all drug court participants has ranged between 5 and 28 percent and less than 4 percent for program graduates.[17]

The U.S. Department of Justice proposes that a reentry court have six core elements:

- **Assessment and Planning** Correctional administrators and the reentry judge meet with inmates who are near release to explain the reentry process, assess inmates' needs, and begin building links to a range of social services, family counseling, health and mental health services, housing, job training, and work opportunities that support reintegration.

- **Active Judicial Oversight** The reentry court sees all prisoners released into the community with a high degree of frequency, maybe once or twice a month. Also involved are the parole officer and others responsible for assessing the parolee's progress. In court, offender progress is praised, and offender setbacks are discussed.

- **Case Management of Support Services** The reentry court acts as a service broker and advocates on behalf of parolees for substance abuse treatment, job training, private employment, faith instruction, family member support, housing, and community services.

- **Accountability to the Community** Reentry courts appoint broad-based community advisory boards to develop and maintain accountability to the community. Advisory boards also help courts negotiate the sometimes difficult task of brokering services for parolees and advocating on their behalf.

- **Graduated Sanctions** Reentry courts establish a predetermined range of graduated sanctions for violations of the conditions of release that do not automatically require return to prison.

- **Rewarding Success** Reentry courts incorporate positive judicial reinforcement actions after goals are achieved. Examples include negotiating early release from parole or conducting graduation ceremonies similar to those used in drug courts.

Student Involvement
Ask students if they have had any experience with any special courts such as family court, DWI court, or community court. If so, invite them to share their experiences. Ask students if they think reentry courts could be successful.

I work in a city of 80,000, which currently has no supervised accommodations for parolees who have been serving sentences of two years or more in a federal facility. Currently, there are 30–40 such individuals in unsupervised conditions. There are also many more who are assigned to halfway houses in nearby communities, making life unnecessarily difficult on some of these individuals.

We are trying to bring a 12-bed facility into the community. We are facing strenuous resistance, including death threats—ironic, isn't it—of both the NIMBY (not in my back yard) and the NOPE (not on planet earth) variety. Some of the resistance, I'm sure, is based on fear that we are bringing criminals into the community. One obvious answer is that many of these individuals came from the community in the first place.

One really hard question to answer is whether the local property values will be negatively affected. That's a realistic concern for everyone. Yet, the most recent material that I have been able to find is from the early 1980s. It suggests that there is no clear effect on property values, and that most people on a street are unaware that such accommodations are there, once they have been there a while. Of course, if these former offenders are released into the community without any preparation or socialization, they won't have a chance, let alone a halfway chance, of following the rules and becoming a positive contributor to the very community that denies them.

Linda Deutschmann
Halfway House Worker
Brookhaven, KS

According to the U.S. Department of Justice, "The successful completion of parole should be seen as an important life event for an offender, and the court can help acknowledge that accomplishment. Courts provide powerful public forums for encouraging positive behavior and for acknowledging the individual effort in achieving reentry goals."[18]

Reentry court is still a concept, not a reality. The U.S. Department of Justice is promoting the idea and asking communities to experiment with it, depending upon statutory framework, caseload considerations, administrative flexibility, levels of collaboration among the judiciary, corrections, parole, police, business community, religious institutions, community organizations, and the like. Whichever form a reentry court takes, developing new ways that communities can manage and support offenders after release from prison with assistance in securing employment, housing, substance abuse treatment, family counseling, and other services, is essential to our ability to reduce crime and keep communities safe.

Reintegration of Offenders

The institution where the offender is incarcerated and the paroling authority play a large part in the parolee's return to society. An important part of reintegration into society is the opportunity to earn a living. Institution and parole personnel must actively seek opportunities to further parolees' chances of securing employment.

Texas' Project RIO (Re-Integration of Offenders) is one of the most ambitious state programs for parolee job placement in the United States. From its beginnings in 1985, RIO has grown to more than 100 staff members, serving 92 Texas cities and towns, and provides job placement services to nearly 16,000 parolees each year. To date, over 12,000 companies throughout Texas have hired RIO participants.[19]

Project RIO involves close collaboration between the Texas Workforce Commission and two divisions of the Texas Department of Criminal Justice—Institutional Division (prisons) and the Parole Division. Project RIO's principal presence in prisons is through the Windham School District, which is a school operating within the state's prisons. The Windham/Project RIO team provides inmates with the following services:

- **Assessment and Testing** A Project RIO assessment specialist evaluates each participant's skills and work history and devises an employability development plan that reflects availability of jobs and occupational demands in the community where the inmate will be released.
- **Documentation** Assessment specialists gather birth certificates, social security cards, diplomas, and school records to provide documentation for employment applications.

THE OFFENDER SPEAKS

I got out of prison April 22, 1996, after being locked up for 10 years for robbing a bank at gunpoint. For three weeks, I just hung out, reacclimating to society. I got restless the fourth week and tried to get a job, but nobody called me back. My parole officer kept asking me, "Have you gone to RIO yet?" I thought the program would get me only menial jobs, like heavy cleanup work, but finally I went just to appease my parole officer. After I completed RIO's five-day job preparation course I got the first job I interviewed at, a sales agent at a hotel.

Project RIO Participant

- **Job Readiness Training** A specialist meets with every RIO enrollee who is within 2 years of release every 90 days to hone the inmate's job interviewing skills.
- **Employability and Life Skills Projects** Inmates work at their own pace to complete a series of skill-building projects under a specialist's supervision.
- **Changes Program** The Windham School offers a life-skills program to RIO participants who are within 6 months of release; the course includes self-concept, family relationships, civic and legal responsibilities, victim awareness, personal health and hygiene, and job preparation.

As you can see, Project RIO works with offenders while they are still in prison, helping them develop the skills and attitudes they need to find and keep a job and giving them a head start in their search for employment. Evaluations of Project RIO have come from several sources and focus on a number of important questions for policymakers, legislators, and the general public. Project RIO has a high placement rate (almost 75%) of participants. Also, Project RIO participants are much more likely to get jobs than ex-offenders who do not participate in the program. Participation in RIO while in prison is a statistically significant predictor of post-release employment. Minority offenders do especially well in RIO: 66 percent of black participants and 66 percent of Hispanic participants found employment, compared with only 30 percent of blacks and 36 percent of Hispanics who were not enrolled in the program. Does Project RIO prevent recidivism? According to a Texas A&M study, the answer is yes. Ex-offenders who found jobs through RIO had lower recidivism rates than unemployed ex-offenders who did not enroll in RIO, with demographic factors and reoffending risk taken into account. These findings suggest that employment and participation in Project RIO have been of greatest benefit to ex-offenders whom prison and parole personnel consider most likely to reoffend.

Can other states duplicate RIO's success? Although other states may not have the same circumstances as Texas, they can implement a Project RIO-type program. Georgia is using aspects of the Project RIO model; local employment security offices and staff provide job placement services for ex-offenders. The state of Washington uses a different model; the state contracts with local community-based organizations throughout the state to provide integration services to offenders.

Legal Decisions Affecting Parole

As we saw in Chapter 10, numerous challenges to the correctional system have brought about changes in prisoners' rights. You may recall that due process guarantees that a person has a right to be fairly heard before being deprived of liberty. Three of the most widely cited cases affecting parolees' and probationers' rights are *Morrissey* v. *Brewer* (1972), *Gagnon* v. *Scarpelli* (1973), and *Greenholtz* v. *Inmates of the Nebraska Penal and Correctional Complex* (1979).

In *Morrissey* v. *Brewer*, John Morrissey pled guilty to writing bad checks in 1967. He was sentenced to not more than 7 years of confinement in the Iowa State Prison and paroled in June 1968. Seven months later he was arrested for parole violation and incarcerated in the county jail. One week later, at the direction of the parole officer's written report, the Iowa Board of Parole revoked his parole and he was returned to the penitentiary.

Morrissey's complaint stated that he received no counsel and no hearing prior to parole revocation. The Supreme Court agreed and overturned the Iowa parole board's decision. The Court ruled that due process establishes a parolee's right to a preliminary and a final hearing before parole can be revoked. According to the Court, a preliminary hearing must be held at the time of arrest and detention to determine whether there is probable cause to believe that the parolee has violated the conditions of supervision. If probable cause is established, "a more comprehensive hearing prior to making of the final revocation decision" determines guilt or innocence and extends to the parolee certain minimum due process rights: written notification of the alleged violation, disclosure of evidence, opportunity for a hearing to present witnesses and evidence, the right to confront and cross-examine adverse witnesses, a neutral hearing body, and a written statement by the hearing authority as to the evidence relied upon and the reasons for revocation.[20]

Morrissey did not extend to parolees the right to legal representation in parole revocation hearings. This issue was addressed one year later, in *Gagnon* v. *Scarpelli*.

In a Wisconsin court in July 1965, Gerald Scarpelli pled guilty to a robbery charge. He was sentenced to 15 years; the judge suspended the sentence and placed him on probation for 7 years. One month later, Scarpelli was arrested and charged with burglary. His probation was revoked. He was sent to the Wisconsin state reformatory to serve a 15-year prison term and was paroled after 3 years. Before he was paroled, however, Scarpelli filed a *habeas corpus* petition. He alleged that his right to due process had been denied—he had no access to counsel and no hearing prior to probation rev-

Student Involvement
Ask students to go online (http://www.findlaw.com/casecode/supreme.html) and read the U.S. Supreme Court opinions in *Morrissey*, *Gagnon*, and *Greenholtz*. When was each case argued and decided? What did the petitioner claim? What did the Court rule? Which Justice delivered the opinion of the Court?

Daniel Savasta, a U.S. probation officer, demonstrates an alcohol breath analyzer. The technology uses voice verification and allows probation/parole officers to monitor an offender's alcohol use from his or her home. Testing can be scheduled at regular intervals, randomly, or on demand. Voice verification technology reduces the likelihood of an imposter taking the test. What are the advantages of such technology in supervising parolees?

Parole: Early Release and Reintegration   CHAPTER 12   365

Parole Officer

Supervises offenders pursuant to agency policies and procedures. Provides counseling, work referrals, and services related to offender's risk and needs. Works with Common Pleas Court judges, prosecutors, and other law enforcement personnel. Conducts investigations and writes reports. Makes arrests and transports violators. Testifies at violation hearings. Qualifications: Bachelor's degree in criminal justice, law enforcement, or social service; no legal prohibition against carrying firearms; successful project managerial skills.

Student Involvement
Have students look at the list of states that have abolished discretionary release in Table 12–3. Determine your state's status. Then organize students into small groups. If you live in a state that abolished discretionary release, instruct each group to find out when and why the change was made and what duties the parole board had before and after the change.

ocation. The Court ruled in favor of Scarpelli. It applied the fundamental due process and two-stage hearing requirements that it had laid out one year earlier in *Morrissey*, thus equating probation with parole. In *Gagnon*, the Court ruled that state officials may be required to assign counsel at the hearing under "special circumstances" and that decisions should be made on a case-by-case basis, depending on the offender's competence, case complexity, and mitigating evidence.

In *Greenholtz* v. *Inmates of the Nebraska Penal and Correctional Complex* (1979), a case involving a routine parole board hearing, the U.S. Supreme Court ruled that parole is a privilege—the full complement of due process rights need not be afforded at parole hearings. The Court also said that the parole board is not required to specify the evidence used in deciding to deny parole. As a result of this case, states are deciding what inmate privileges are appropriate at parole hearings.

The Future of Parole

We read earlier in this chapter that there was strong opposition to parole in the 1930s and that opponents wanted to abolish it. They argued that parole boards were turning hardened criminals loose on society, that parole had a dismal performance record, its goals were never realized, parole board members and parole officers were poorly trained, and that parole hearings were little more than hastily conducted, almost unthinking interviews. In spite of the gap between goals and this 1930s reality, parole fulfilled important functions for wardens, legislators, and district attorneys. Parole continued.

The movement to abolish parole resurfaced in the 1970s, when the concept of "just deserts"—the idea that offenders deserve punishment for what they did to society—was being discussed.[21] However, states did not do away with parole; they restructured parole. In a number of states, discretionary release was replaced with mandatory release, with or without supervision, after a certain amount of time served. As the data in Table 12–3 show, discretionary release has been on the decline for some time.

The backdrop for the debate on just deserts was an extraordinary increase in the nation's crime rate that began in the mid-1960s and continued through the 1970s. Legislatures were growing anxious about crime and were willing to try new options in correctional approaches to the crime problem. They felt that rehabilitation and indeterminate sentencing were not working. Hence, their answer was determinate sentencing and abolition of discretionary release.

Why did some states abolish discretionary parole? There are at least four reasons. First, scholars concluded that indeterminate sentencing and discretionary parole did not achieve offender rehabilitation and that was unfair, since it was based solely on parole board judgment, without explicit standards of fairness and equity in sentencing.

TABLE 12–3

Postrelease Practices in States That Have Abolished Parole

State	Year Discretionary Parole Was Abolished	Postrelease Supervision Available After Abolishment of Discretionary Release by Parole Board
Arizona	1994	Community supervision
Delaware	1990	Administrative supervision, field supervision, intensive supervision, electronic monitoring, and halfway houses
Florida	1983	Conditional release and controlled release
Illinois	1978	Mandatory supervised release
Maine	1976	Probation term can be imposed by the court after prison term is completed
Minnesota	1982	Supervised release
Mississippi	1995	Earned release supervision
North Carolina	1994	Postrelease supervision for most serious offenses
Ohio	1996	Judicial release, shock incarceration, and furlough with judicial approval
Oregon	1989	Community supervision
Virginia	1995	Probation term can be imposed by the court after prison term is completed
Washington	1984	Community custody and community supervision

Additional jurisdictions that abolished discretionary release include California, Indiana, New Mexico, and the federal government.

Source: 1996 National Survey of State Sentencing Structures, Bureau of Justice Assistance (September 1998), p. 15.

Second, eliminating discretionary parole appeared to be tough on crime.

Third, parole boards' lack of openness in the decision-making process—making all their parole decisions on a case-by-case basis without benefit of a written set of policies and procedures—prompted criticism.

Finally, state politicians were able to convince the public that parole was the cause of the rising crime problem and abolition was the solution.

Teaching Tip
Refer to Chapter 12 of the *Instructor's Resource Manual* for additional activities and for answers to the end-of-chapter exercises.

12

Review and Applications

SUMMARY BY CHAPTER OBJECTIVES

CHAPTER OBJECTIVE 1

Early English judges spared the lives of condemned felons by exiling them to America as indentured servants. Captain Alexander Maconochie, superintendent of the British penal colony on Norfolk Island, devised a "ticket of leave" system that moved inmates through stages. Sir Walter Crofton used some of Maconochie's ideas for his early release system in Ireland. In the United States, Zebulon Brockway implemented a system of upward classification.

CHAPTER OBJECTIVE 2

Paroling authorities have powerful roles in the criminal justice system. They determine the length of incarceration for many offenders and can revoke parole. The paroling authority's policies have a direct impact on an institution's population. Paroling authorities use state laws and information from courts and other criminal justice agencies to make release decisions.

CHAPTER OBJECTIVE 3

Parole is serving part of a sentence under supervision in the community following a period of incarceration. The parole process of release begins in the courtroom when the judge sentences an offender to either a determinate or indeterminate sentence. After serving a certain portion of his or her sentence an offender is eligible for parole release. That portion varies from state to state. If an inmate does maintain good conduct for a certain amount of time preceding the parole hearing and is granted parole, he or she must live in accordance with specified rules and regulations in the community. If a parolee violates either the technical conditions of parole or commits a new crime, he or she may have parole revoked. For the past few decades, the parole decision making pro-cess has become standardized in most states through the use of parole guidelines. Guidelines ensure that each parole decision is based on limited factors that are considered important to the parole decision.

CHAPTER OBJECTIVE 4

The majority of the American parole population consists of state parolees in the South. Nine out of ten are male. More than half are white. The parole sector of the correctional population has the highest growth rate. Texas has the largest number of persons on parole. Pennsylvania has the highest rate of parole supervision.

CHAPTER OBJECTIVE 5

Parole may be revoked for a technical violation (failure to comply with one of the conditions of parole) or for a new offense violation (commission of a crime).

CHAPTER OBJECTIVE 6

The reentry court concept, designed to manage parolee return to the community, requires that the parolee make regular court appearances for progress assessment.

CHAPTER OBJECTIVE 7

Three important U.S. Supreme Court decisions significantly affected parole. In *Morrissey* v. *Brewer* (1972), the U.S. Supreme Court said that parole, once granted, becomes a right and that parolees are to have certain due process rights in any revocation hearing. In *Gagnon* v. *Scarpelli* (1973), the U.S. Supreme Court held that a probationer has a limited right to counsel in a revocation hearing and that the hearing body must decide whether counsel should be provided on a case-by-case basis. In *Greenholtz* v. *Inmates of the Nebraska Penal and Correctional Complex* (1979), the U.S. Supreme Court ruled that parole is a privilege; therefore, the full complement of due process rights need not be afforded at parole hearings. As a result, states are deciding what inmate privileges are appropriate at parole hearings.

CHAPTER OBJECTIVE 8

Between 1976 and February 1996, 15 states and the federal government abolished or restricted parole. Many states added statutes that require mandatory minimum sentences and a mandatory incarceration period for each crime.

KEY TERMS

parole, p. 347
probation, p. 347
pardon, p. 347
parole eligibility date, p. 351
paroling authority, p. 351
salient factor score (SFS), p. 352
parolee, p. 352

mandatory release, p. 355
discretionary release, p. 355
technical violation, p. 357
new offense violation, p. 357
revocation hearing, p. 357
reentry court, p. 360

QUESTIONS FOR REVIEW

1. What are the similarities among indenture and parole?
2. Who were Captain Alexander Maconochie and Sir Walter Crofton, and what were their contributions to the parole development?
3. What did the Elmira Reformatory contribute to the history of American parole?
4. What is parole?
5. What is the difference between parole and probation? Between parole and pardon?
6. What is parole eligibility?
7. What is the paroling authority's role in the parole decision-making process?
8. How does parole affect the criminal justice system?
9. What are conditions of parole?

10. Explain the difference between mandatory release and discretionary release.
11. What is a revocation hearing and when is it used?
12. What are the typical parolee's characteristics?
13. Which state has the largest parole population? The highest rate of parole supervision? The lowest?
14 What are reentry courts?
15. What is Project RIO? What results has it achieved?
16. What are three U.S. Supreme Court decisions that affected parole?
17. Why did some states and the federal government abolish or limit discretionary release?

CRITICAL THINKING EXERCISES

ON-THE-JOB ISSUE

You have just learned that one of your parolees tested positive in a drug test. The positive drug test, a technical violation of parole, requires a revocation hearing. You have long wished that your state had a set of informal guidelines for responding to such technical violations so that you could handle the violation without waiting for a hearing. In this case, you could immediately place the parolee in a substance abuse program rather than waiting for a decision that might have the same result. Draft a proposal for such a technical violation response policy. First, formulate the basic expectations of the policy (for example, "The least restrictive response to the behavior should be used."). Then determine what components the policy should include (for example, "Define clear goals and understand the agency's concept of supervision.").

CORRECTIONS ISSUE

1. Paroling authorities generally maintain a low profile, and their work is often known only to the offenders seeking release and the victims of their crimes. This is changing as the public demands to know more about paroling authorities' actions. In some states, legislatures and sentencing commissions replaced

the case-by-case decision-making process with a policy-driven decision-making process. A policy-driven decision-making process implements a written set of policies and procedures in the parole decision-making process. Such a process standardizes the procedure and the information used to make a paroling decision. What are the advantages and disadvantages of a policy-driven decision-making process?

2. In *The Prison Reform Movement* (1990), Larry E. Sullivan suggests that prison reforms have always failed because they never addressed the "carceral problem." That is, is it possible to instill free society values in a caged population? What do you think about Sullivan's premise in terms of preparing prisoners for early release?

CORRECTIONS ON THE WEB

The United States Parole Commission maintains a Web site at **http://www.usdoj.gov/uspc/ overview.htm.** It describes the Commission's mission, organization, jurisdiction, and procedures. It gives background information on all the commissioners and lists federal conditions of parole and mandatory release supervision. It also presents the 54 most frequently asked questions (FAQs) and answers about federal parole procedures. Visit the site and look at the FAQs. Compare federal parole procedures with your state's by asking a member of your state's paroling authority similar questions. Compare and contrast the differences.

ADDITIONAL READINGS

Abadinsky, Howard. *Probation and Parole: Theory and Practice,* 2d ed. Englewood Cliffs, NJ: Prentice-Hall, 1982.

Burke, Peggy B. *Abolishing Parole: Why the Emperor Has No Clothes.* Lexington, KY: American Probation and Parole Association, 1995.

Hoffman, Peter B. "History of the Federal Parole System, Part I (1910–1972)." *Federal Probation,* Vol. 61, NCJ 172978, September 1997, pp. 23–31, and "History of the Federal Parole System, Part II (1973–1997)," *Federal Probation,* Vol. 61, December 1997, pp. 49–57.

McGarry, Peggy. *Handbook for New Parole Board Members,* Philadelphia: Center for Effective Public Policy, NCJ 124111, 1989.

ENDNOTES

1. Charles L. Newman, *Sourcebook on Probation, Parole and Pardons,* 3d ed. (Springfield, IL: Charles C. Thomas Publisher Ltd., 1968), 1970, pp. 30–31.

2. Philip Klein, *Prison Methods in New York State* (New York: Columbia University Press), 1920, p. 417. Cited in U.S. Department of Justice, *Attorney General's Survey of Release Procedures, Vol. 4* (Washington: U.S. Government Printing Office), 1939–1940, p. 5.

3. M. W. Calahan, *Historical Corrections Statistics in the United States, 1850–1984* (Washington: Bureau of Justice Statistics), 1986.

4. G. W. Wickersham, *Reports of the United States National Commission on Law Observance and Enforcement: Wickersham Commission, Report on Penal Institutions, Probation and Parole* (Washington: U.S. Government Printing Office), 1930–1931, p. 324.

5. Ibid., p. 325.

6. Edwin H. Sutherland and Donald R. Cressey, *Principles of Criminology* (Chicago: J. B. Lippincott), 1955, p. 568.

7. David J. Rothman, *Conscience and Convenience: The Asylum and Its Alternatives in Progressive America* (Boston: Little, Brown), 1980, pp. 159–161.

8. Douglas R. Lipton, Robert Martinson, and Judith Wilks, *The Effectiveness of Correctional Treatment: A Survey of Treatment Evaluation Studies* (New York: Praeger), 1975.

9. Peggy McGarry, *Handbook for New Parole Board Members* (Philadelphia: Center for Effective Public Policy), NCJ 124111, 1989, p. 4.

10. Camille Graham Camp and George M. Camp, *The Corrections Yearbook 1997* (Middletown, CT: Criminal Justice Institute), 1997, p. 181.

11. Peter B. Hoffman and Lucille K. DeGostin, "Parole Decision-Making: Structuring Discretion," *Federal Probation*, Vol. 38, Issue 1, 1974, NCJ 19232, pp. 24–28.

12. McGarry, op. cit., p. 4.

13. Thomas P. Bonczar and Lauren E. Glaze, Bureau of Justice Statistics, *Probation and Parole in the United States, 1998* (Washington: U.S. Department of Justice), NCJ 178234, October 1999.

14. Peggy B. Burke, *Abolishing Parole: Why the Emperor Has No Clothes* (Lexington, KY: American Probation and Parole Association), 1995.

15. U.S. Parole Commission, *Notes and Procedures Manual* (Chevy Chase, MD: U.S. Government Printing Office), 1989, p. 143.

16. "Reentry Courts: Managing the Transition from Prison to Community" (Washington: Office of Justice Programs), September, 1999.

17. Ibid., p. 5.

18. Ibid., p. 9.

19. Material for this section was extracted from Peter Finn, *Texas' Project RIO (Re-Integration of Offenders)*, (Washington: National Institute of Justice), June 1998 [Online at http://www.ncjrs.org/txtfiles/168637.txt].

20. Edward J. Latessa and Harry E. Allen, *Corrections in the Community*, 2d ed. (Cincinnati, OH: Anderson Publishing Co.), 1999, p. 221.

21. Andrew von Hirsch, *Doing Justice: The Choice of Punishments, Report of the Committee for the Study of Incarceration* (New York: Hill and Wang), 1976.

22. Bureau of Justice Assistance, 1996 National Survey of State Sentencing Structures (Washington: U.S. Department of Justice), NCJ 169270, September 1998 [Online at http://www.ncjrs.org/txtfiles/169270.txt].

Privatizing Corrections

Privatization

In 1998 the California Senate's Public Safety Committee killed a bill that would have stopped the growth of private prisons in that state.[1] The bill, which called for an amendment to the state constitution, had the backing of the California Correctional Peace Officers Association (CCPOA), the state's correctional officers' union. Had the bill passed, it would have forbidden most privatization in state and local law enforcement, correctional, and firefighting agencies throughout the state of California. In rejecting the measure by a 5–2 vote, the committee kept alive state Department of Corrections proposals to add 5000 for-profit beds to the system before the year 2000.

At about the same time, Ohio lawmakers were mulling the idea of closing a private prison near Youngstown.[2] Six prisoners had escaped in July 1998 from the Northeast Ohio Correctional Center, run by Corrections Corporation of America (CCA). The 1500-bed facility had been open only since May 1997. Other problems plagued the CCA prison as well. In the 15 months after it opened, 13 stabbings and 2 murders were reported there. An inmate lawsuit in federal court alleged unfit conditions at the facility, and a federal judge had ordered hundreds of inmates removed and had halted transfers into the prison from Washington, D.C.[3]

As these two state examples illustrate, the privatization of jails, prisons, and other correctional programs is and will continue to be controversial. **Privatization**—a term that refers to privately-owned correctional facilities or private operation of government-owned facilities—has increased dramatically as local, state, and federal government agencies have sought ways to cut costs while still meeting their mandated responsibilities. Expected savings and speedy implementation are the most common reasons for privatization.

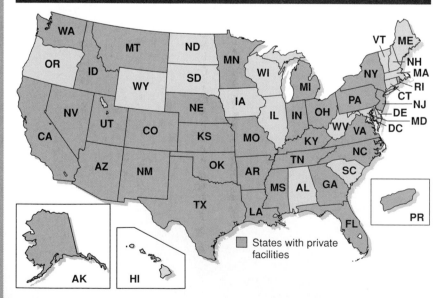

States With Private Correctional Facilities

States with private facilities

Over 65 percent of the states have private correctional facilities.

Opportunities for Growth

Almost 2 million people are incarcerated in the United States, and the inmate population is growing at about 5 to 7 percent per year. Experts estimate that two 1000-bed facilities must be built each week just to keep up with demand. Contracts with private prison firms cover less than 5 percent of the inmate population, but that percentage is increasing. In April 2000, private corrections in the United States included 158 facilities with a rated capacity of 122,871 inmates. The capacity of private prisons is expected to more than double within the next few years. Already, 31 states (see map), the District of Columbia, the Federal Bureau of Prisons, the Immigration and Naturalization Service, Puerto Rico, and the U.S. Marshals Service have private correctional facilities.[4] Privatization of prisons and jails is gaining support in other nations, which are closely following the experiences of the United States. In July 1999, private correctional facilities were in operation in Australia, England, the Netherlands Antilles, New Zealand, Scotland, and South Africa.

Pros and Cons

Largely because there has been no conclusive research, arguments continue to rage over the merits of privately run correctional facilities. Most advocates of privatization rely on information showing that private facilities are less costly to run than public ones. Such arguments are based on budgetary concerns and the results of account audits. Proponents also suggest that privately run correctional facilities can be economic boons for the areas in which they are located, providing many jobs and feeding public coffers with increased tax revenues. Among groups supporting privatization are the American Correctional Association and the President's Commission on Privatization.

Opponents of privatization, on the other hand, build their arguments on mostly philosophical grounds. One writer says that the fundamental issue is a moral one: Should private parties make a profit from inflicting pain on others?[5] Most opponents of privatization argue that the practice is inherently flawed by the profit motive of private corporations. The corporate interest in maximizing profits, they claim, can have numerous negative consequences for inmates, correctional employees, and society. Some claim, for example, that the need to maintain healthy profit margins may preclude the cost of rehabilitation and recreational programs for inmates. Other opponents of privatization say that privately run companies save money by paying lower wages and benefits than states do.[6]

Some critics note that, while the administration of punishment may, in fact, be delegated to the private sector, the government retains ultimate responsibility for it. Among the groups opposing privatization are the American Jail

---

Privatization

Arguments For Privatization

Proponents claim that private companies will:
- Provide better service at lower cost
- Save taxpayers' money
- Use the latest technologies and management techniques
- Reduce costly, time-consuming red tape
- Implement innovative strategies
- Build prisons cheaply and more quickly
- Have greater flexibility in labor policies

Arguments Against Privatization

Opponents of privatization charge that private companies will:
- Profit from the misery of others
- Lobby for legislation to increase the use of incarceration
- Have no incentive to lower recidivism rates, as doing so would threaten their livelihood
- Reduce the number, quality, and training of personnel
- Abuse inmate civil rights
- Skim the "cream of the crop" inmates, leaving those with behavioral or costly medical problems for publicly operated prisons
- Be more concerned about profit than the well-being of inmates

---

Source: Linda L. Zupan, "The State of Knowledge on the Privatization of Prison and Jail Operations," (April 1996), Web posted at: http://codc.nmu.edu/progs/ppjo.html.

Association, the National Sheriffs' Association, and the American Federation of State, County, and Municipal Employees.

Some opponents discount the alleged savings of privatization. Proponents counter that public prisons are not without their problems and that governments almost always renew contracts with private operators—proving such contracts worthwhile. The table summarizes the arguments for and against privatization.

Private Corrections Companies

A number of private companies operate prisons and jails. The pie graph[7] shows the market shares held by the major providers of private prison and jail management. Some are well known and even offer shares of their companies to the public.

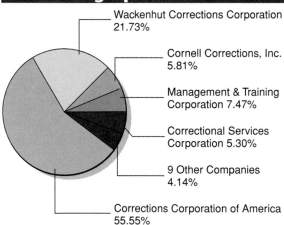

Slicing Up the Market

Wackenhut Corrections Corporation
21.73%

Cornell Corrections, Inc.
5.81%

Management & Training
Corporation 7.47%

Correctional Services
Corporation 5.30%

9 Other Companies
4.14%

Corrections Corporation of America
55.55%

Two companies dominate the market. Percentage of market share based on U.S. contracts.

Privatizing Community Supervision

We also find movement toward privatization in community corrections, including offender assessment, drug testing and treatment, electronic monitoring, halfway houses, and probation field services. Two states—Connecticut and Colorado—have successfully privatized community supervision. In both states, the impetus for privatizing community supervision was similar: staffing and resources were not keeping pace with increasing caseloads. Community supervision officials felt they had exhausted the use of interns and volunteers, and funding for new staff was not possible. They used risk management principles to assign staff and resources in direct proportion to the risk level of a case. Both states partnered with the private sector to monitor the low risk offender population, a group that generally has few needs, whose past records reflect little or no violence, and who successfully complete probation about 90 percent of the time.

In Connecticut, the privatization initiative to monitor low risk offender populations by the private sector allowed scarce resources to be used to better monitor offenders with higher levels of risk. Private case management responsibilities in Connecticut included sending an introductory letter to the probationer, monitoring restitution payments and compliance with conditions of probation, responding to probationer's inquiries, preparing standardized reports for probation officers, providing verification of condition compliance, and providing statistical reports. Robert J. Bosco, Director of Connecticut's Office of Adult Probation, says that the "success" of this privatization initiative "is in the agency's ability to use its resources to control recidivism of the highest risk offender population."[8]

The situation in Colorado was similar. When Colorado officials adopted risk management and looked at how treatment and supervision were matched with levels of risk, they found more probation officers were needed than the Colorado General Assembly would fund. The result was a directive that allowed probation departments to contract with private agencies for the supervision of low risk probationers. Thirteen of Colorado's 22 judicial districts have entered into such contracts. The private agencies directly bill the probationers for their supervision services, eliminating public expenditures for community supervision. According to Suzanne Pullen, Management

Analyst with Colorado's Judicial Department, Office of Probation Services, "The diversion of these low-risk offenders allows local probation departments to focus more clearly on the supervision and case management of medium and high risk offenders that are burdening their caseloads."[9]

Issues

Private companies offer increasingly attractive alternatives for financing and building new correctional facilities. Those alternatives may be less expensive than traditional financing through the selling of government bonds. They can be secured more quickly, thus reducing delays when new facilities are desperately needed. They allow government officials to bypass voters who want tough treatment for criminals but are unwilling to pay for it. A disadvantage is that these alternatives avoid citizen input into decisions that have far-reaching consequences.

According to Reginald A. Wilkinson, Director of the Ohio Department of Rehabilitation and Correction:

> The next ten years will reveal whether the privatization of prisons will succeed. If so, the evolution from public to private management may prove to be painful to correctional traditionalists. Debate on the pros and cons, rights and wrongs, of "punishment for profit" will rage back and forth. In the end, the profit margin and public opinion may be the determining factors on how much of the corrections profession will be outsourced to for-profit providers.[10]

Notes

1. See "Effort to Block Private Prisons Dies in Senate," *The Sacramento Bee,* ed., June 17, 1998.
2. Ann Fisher, "Lawmakers Mull Prison's Future," *The Columbus Dispatch,* August 5, 1998.
3. Ibid.
4. Charles W. Thomas, "Frequently Asked Questions," Private Corrections Project, April 23, 2000 (accessed at http://web.crim.ufl.edu/pcp/html/questions.html).
5. David Shichor, *Punishment for Profit: Private Prisons/Public Concerns* (Thousand Oaks, CA: Sage Publications, 1995).
6. Material in this paragraph is adapted from Maeve McMahon, review of *Punishment for Profit: Private Prisons/Public Concerns,* by David Shichor, *Canadian Journal of Criminology,* Vol. 39, No. 1 (January 1997), p. 115.
7. Thomas.
8. Robert J. Bosco, "Connecticut Probation's Partnership with the Private Sector," *Topics in Community Corrections: Privatizing Community Supervision,* p. 12.
9. Suzanne Pullen, "An Evaluation of Private Probation Supervision and Case Management in Colorado," *Topics in Community Corrections: Privatizing Community Supervision,* p. 15.
10. Reginald A. Wilkinson, "The Future of Adult Corrections," *Corrections Management Quarterly,* Vol. 1, Issue 1 (Winter 1997).

13 Death
The Ultimate Sanction

CHAPTER OBJECTIVES

After completing this chapter you should be able to:

1. Discuss the history of capital punishment in the United States.
2. Describe the characteristics of death row inmates.
3. List and summarize the major U.S. Supreme Court decisions that influenced capital punishment legislation.
4. Summarize the arguments for and against the death penalty.
5. Discuss death penalty issues to be faced in the 21st century.

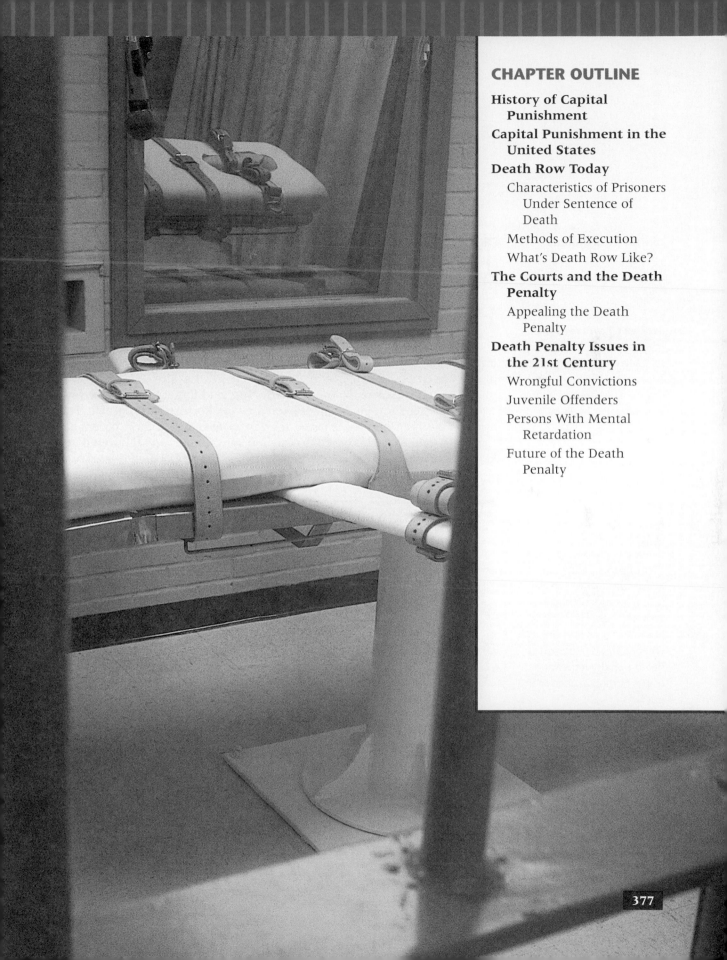

For centuries the death penalty, often accompanied by barbarous refinements, has been trying to hold crime in check; yet crime persists. Why? Because the instincts that are warring in man are not, as the law claims, constant forces in a state of equilibrium.

—Albert Camus

capital punishment
Legal infliction of the death penalty.

N o current corrections issue sparks more passionate debate than **capital punishment**—the death penalty. The debate is a difficult one, with thought-provoking arguments on both sides.

History of Capital Punishment

Capital punishment was once common throughout the world and imposed for many crimes, including murder, rape, stealing, witchcraft, piracy, desertion, sodomy, adultery, concealing the birth or death of an infant, aiding runaway slaves, counterfeiting, and forgery. Death, however, was not the harshest punishment—torture was. Torture, so cruel that death came as a relief, sometimes lasted for days. Death was a form of leniency. Criminals were boiled, burned, roasted on spits, drawn and quartered, broken on wheels, disemboweled, torn apart by animals, gibbeted (hung from a

Student Involvement
Invite interested students to research the changes in types of punishment during the Enlightenment and to share their findings with the class.

Teaching Tip
Refer to Figure 13–1. Determine your state's death penalty status and that of surrounding states. Invite students to use the resources of your state attorney general's office or the Internet to find out when your state passed death penalty legislation or how long it's been without it.

FIGURE 13–1

States With Death Penalty Statutes

- ■ Death Penalty
- □ No Death Penalty

Source: Adapted from *Death Row, U.S.A., Winter 2000*, NAACP Legal Defense and Educational Fund, New York, January 1, 2000. Reprinted with permission.

post with a projecting arm and left to die), bludgeoned (beaten to death with sticks, clubs, or rocks), or pressed (crushed under a board and stones).

Capital punishment began changing in the 18th century during the Enlightenment. This philosophical movement led to many new theories on crime and punishment. One of these theories proposed that the punishment fit the crime. Penalties involving torture began to disappear, and the use of the death penalty diminished.

As of January 1, 2000, the majority of countries (106) had abolished the death penalty in law or in practice.[1] In the United States, 40 jurisdictions allowed capital punishment and 13 did not (see Figure 13–1).

Capital Punishment in the United States

Although research on executions in the United States has been hampered by a lack of official records, almost 15,000 executions, beginning in the 1600s and continuing through 1999, have been confirmed.[2]

Executions stopped in 1968, pending a U.S. Supreme Court decision on the constitutionality of certain aspects of capital punishment. By 1977 the Court ruled that capital punishment itself was not unconstitutional and did not violate the Eighth Amendment to the U.S. Constitution, and executions resumed. The first person to be executed after the moratorium ended was Gary Gilmore, who gave up his right to appeal and was executed by firing squad on January 17, 1977, by the State of Utah.

The number of executions from 1930–1999 is shown in Figure 13–2. Note that in 1999 more inmates were executed than in any other year since the early 1950s.

Cross-Cultural Perspective

As of January 1, 2000, 82 foreign nationals (tourists, visitors, migrant workers, etc.) were on death row in the United States. Ask students if they think foreign nationals, particularly those from countries that have abolished the death penalty, should be executed in the United States. Why or why not?

FIGURE 13–2

Persons Executed, 1930–99

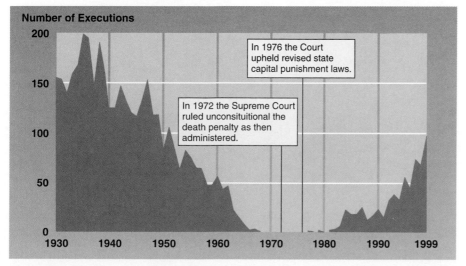

Sources: *Death Row U.S.A., Winter 2000* (New York: NAACP Legal Defense and Educational Fund), January 1, 2000 and Tracy L. Snell, *Capital Punishment 1998*, Bureau of Justice Statistics (Washington: U.S. Department of Justice) December 1999, pp. 7, 11.

Student Involvement

Refer to Figure 13–2. Point out that executions peaked in the 1930–40 decade. Ask students what they think the reason might have been.

capital crime A crime for which the death penalty may, but need not necessarily, be imposed.

Today in the United States, what constitutes a **capital crime**—a crime that is punishable by death—is defined by law. This definition varies among jurisdictions. In Louisiana, for example, first-degree murder, aggravated rape of a victim under age 12, and treason are capital crimes; in Nevada, first-degree murder with 13 aggravating circumstances is a capital crime; and in New Jersey, purposeful or knowing murder by one's own conduct, contract murder, or solicitation by command or threat in furtherance of a narcotics conspiracy are capital crimes.[3]

Death Row Today

Characteristics of Prisoners Under Sentence of Death

On January 1, 2000, 40 jurisdictions (38 states, the federal government, and the U.S. military) held a total of 3,652 prisoners under sentence of death. Thirty-nine percent of the nation's death row population was in three states: California (561), Texas (462), and Florida (389). Ninety-nine percent of all prisoners sentenced to death were male, with whites predominating (47%).[4] Figure 13–3 shows additional characteristics of inmates under sentence of death.

Student Involvement
Refer to Figure 13–3. Ask students to study the data presented and write a brief paragraph generalizing the data. Ask volunteers to share their paragraphs with the class. Ask members of the class whether they agree or disagree with the statements.

FIGURE 13–3

Characteristics of Prisoners Under Sentence of Death, 2000

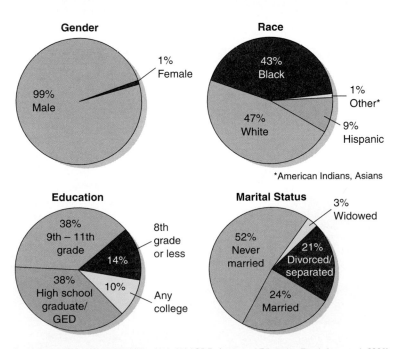

Sources: *Death Row U.S.A., Winter 2000* (New York: NAACP Defense and Education Fund, January 1, 2000), p. 1 and Tracy L. Snell, *Capital Punishment 1998*, Bureau of Justice Statistics (Washington: U.S. Department of Justice), December 1999, p. 8.

Death: The Ultimate Sanction

TABLE 13-1

Clemency Process by State

Governor Has Sole Authority (14)

Alabama	New Jersey	South Carolina
California	New Mexico	Virginia
Colorado	New York	Washington
Kansas	North Carolina	Wyoming
Kentucky	Oregon	

Governor: Must Have Recommendation of Clemency from Board or Advisory Group (9)

Arizona	Indiana	Oklahoma
Delaware	Louisiana	Pennsylvania
Florida*	Montana	Texas

Governor: After Non-binding Recommendation of Clemency from Board or Advisory Group (9)

Arkansas	Mississippi	Ohio
Illinois	Missouri	South Dakota
Maryland	New Hampshire	Tennessee

Board or Advisory Group Makes Determination (3)

Connecticut	Georgia	Idaho

Governor Sits on Clemency Board Which Makes the Determination (3)

Nebraska	Nevada	Utah

*Florida's Governor must have recommendation of Board, on which s/he sits.

For Federal Death Row inmates, the President alone has pardon power.

Source: "Exccutive Clemency Process and Execution Warrant Procedure In Death Penalty Cases," National Coalition to Abolish the Death Penalty (1993), with updates by DPIC through January 2000.

Teaching Tip

Refer to Table 13–1. If you live in a death penalty state, invite a criminal defense attorney who has clemency experience to explain the clemency process to your class. If you live in one of the 13 jurisdictions that does not permit capital punishment, initiate a discussion about the advantages and disadvantages of the five clemency models presented in Table 13–1.

Prisoners spend an average of 10 years and 5 months on death row. They may leave death row by means other than execution—between 1973 and January 1, 2000, 54 persons on death row committed suicide; 157 died of natural causes or were killed; 1,697 had their convictions/sentences reversed;[5] and 90 were granted **clemency** and received a **commutation**. Table 13–1 shows the clemency process by state.

Methods of Execution

Five methods of execution are used in the United States: (1) lethal injection, (2) electrocution, (3) lethal gas, (4) hanging, and (5) firing squad. As you can see in Table 13–2, lethal injection is the predominant method.

clemency Kindness, mercy, forgiveness, or leniency, usually relating to criminal acts.

commutation A change of a legal penalty to a lesser one; e.g., from death to life imprisonment.

TABLE 13–2

Method of Execution, by Jurisdiction, 2000

Lethal Injection		Electrocution	Lethal Gas	Hanging	Firing Squad
Arizona[a,b]	New Hampshire[a]	Alabama	Arizona[a,b]	Delaware[a,c]	Idaho[a]
Arkansas[a,d]	New Jersey	Arkansas[a,d]	California[a]	New Hampshire[a,e]	Oklahoma[f]
California[a]	New Mexico	Florida[a]	Maryland[a,j]	Washington[a]	Utah[a]
Colorado	New York	Georgia	Missouri[a]		
Connecticut	North Carolina	Kentucky[a,g]	Wyoming[a,h]		
Delaware[a,c]	Ohio[a]	Nebraska			
Florida[a]	Oklahoma[a]	Ohio[a]			
Idaho[a,j]	Oregon	Oklahoma[f]			
Illinois	Pennsylvania	South Carolina[a]			
Indiana	South Carolina[a]	Tennessee[a,i]			
Kansas	South Dakota	Virginia[a]			
Kentucky[a,g]	Tennessee[a,i]				
Louisiana	Texas				
Maryland[a,k]	Utah[a]				
Mississippi	Virginia[a]				
Missouri[a]	Washington[a]				
Montana	Wyoming[a]				
Nevada	U.S. Military				

Note: The method of execution of Federal prisoners is lethal injection, pursuant to 28 CFR, Part 26. For offenses under the Violent Crime Control and Law Enforcement Act of 1994, the method is that of the State in which the conviction took place, pursuant to 18 U.S.C. 3596. If the state has no death penalty, the inmate will be transferred to another state.

[a]Authorizes 2 methods of execution.

[b]Arizona authorizes lethal injection for persons whose capital sentence was received after 11/15/92; for those sentenced before that date, the condemned may select lethal injection or lethal gas.

[c]Delaware authorizes lethal injection for those whose capital offense occurred after 6/13/86; for those whose offense occurred before that date, the condemned may select lethal injection or hanging.

[d]Arkansas authorizes lethal injection for those whose capital offense occurred on or after 7/4/83; for those whose offense occurred before that date, the condemned may select lethal injection or electrocution.

[e]New Hampshire authorizes hanging only if lethal injection cannot be given.

[f]Oklahoma authorizes electrocution if lethal injection is ever held to be unconstitutional, and firing squad if both lethal injection and electrocution are held unconstitutional.

[g]Kentucky authorizes lethal injection for persons whose capital sentence was received on or after 3/31/98; for those sentenced before that date, the condemned may select lethal injection or electrocution.

[h]Wyoming authorizes lethal gas if lethal injection is ever held to be unconstitutional.

[i]Tennessee authorizes lethal injection for those whose capital offense occurred after 1/1/99; those whose offense occurred before that date may select lethal injection or electrocution.

[j]Idaho authorizes firing squad only if lethal injection is "impractical."

[k]Maryland authorizes lethal injection for those whose capital sentence was received on or after 3/25/94; for those sentenced before that date, the condemned may select lethal injection or lethal gas.

Sources: Bureau of Justice Statistics Bulletin NCJ 179012, *Capital Punishment 1998* (U.S. Department of Justice, Office of Justice Programs), December 1999. Update from DPIC online at http://www.essential.org/dpic/methods.html.

Some states authorize more than one method. Arizona, for example, uses lethal injection for persons sentenced after November 15, 1992; those sentenced before that date may select lethal injection or lethal gas. Oklahoma authorizes electrocution if lethal injection is ever held unconstitutional, and firing squad if both lethal injection and electrocution are held unconstitutional. The federal government authorizes a method of execution under two different laws; the method of execution for federal prisoners prosecuted under the *Code of Federal Regulations*, Volume 28, Part 26 is lethal injection; for those offenses prosecuted under the Violent Crime Control and Law Enforcement Act of 1994, the method is that of the state in which the person was convicted. If the state has no death penalty, the inmate will be transferred to another state.

What's Death Row Like?

Prisoners who are sentenced to death are held on **death row**, a prison within a prison. Death row inmates are segregated from the general prison population; they receive no rehabilitation, treatment, or work programs. Death row existence has been called "living death" to convey a prisoner's loneliness, isolation, boredom, and loss of privacy.[6]

What many people forget is that a death row inmate's living environment is a correctional officer's workplace. The concrete and steel construction materials and furnishings that guarantee security and durability in death row amplify normal sounds within its hard walls. It takes little effort to imagine what effect shouting, flushing toilets, opening and closing steel doors, doing janitorial work, the blaring of televisions and radios, and voices wailing on the bars has not only on those who live there but also on those who work there. In summer the oppressive heat and in winter the freezing cold are trapped in the walls of steel and concrete. The quality of life experienced by inmates depends on the work environment created by the corrections officers who guard them.

Death row cells usually have steel bunks, toilets, and sinks. These are bolted to concrete floors and cinder block walls. Small lockers or wall shelves hold prisoners' personal property, which may include toiletries, books, pictures, a clock, and usually a television. The television is the death row inmate's most valued possession, not only because of its entertainment value, but also because it makes available the world that the death row inmate has lost. Revoking television or telephone privileges is sometimes used by correctional officers as a threat to control behavior on death row. Generally, though, corrections officers say that death row inmates seldom exhibit disciplinary problems. Alabama's death row warden, Charlie Jones, described death row inmates as "the group who causes the least trouble."[7]

Most death row inmates spend 22–23 hours a day in five-by-eight- or six-by-nine-foot cells. They receive their meals through slots in the cell doors. Generally twice a week, they are handcuffed, escorted to, and locked in shower stalls for five- or ten-minute showers. In some jurisdictions, death row inmates may visit the prison library; in others, books are taken to them.

Most death row inmates slowly lose their ties with the outside world. Although some states permit contact visits, most allow only noncontact visits. Every time death row inmates leave death row for visits—whether

Cross-Cultural Perspective
Refer students to Table 13–2 on page 382. Have them review the methods of execution used among the states. Do students see the reflection of cultural values in the type of execution that prevails among the states?

death row A prison area housing inmates sentenced to death.

Professional Issue
Duty Assignments Refer to Table 13–2. Have students find the method of execution used in your state, if any. Do any special circumstances apply? Ask students how they would feel about being the correctional officer assigned to carry out an execution by one of the methods presented in the table.

Teaching Tip
Have students read the description of life on death row presented in the text. Ask them what changes, if any, they think should be made.

THE OFFENDER SPEAKS

I am a 29-year-old death row inmate, and I want to talk to you about death row. I want to tell you that if you look, you will find people! We are small, tall, fat, skinny, and different races living together. I am very happy to say that there is a brotherhood here, but I call it my family, because they know when I am happy or sad.

I get help with schoolwork, law study, hobby crafts, and most of all my feelings. I will not hesitate to speak about my feelings because there are so many people here that are willing to talk about them with me. What I have learned in my five years on the Row is the people here are not mean or crazy like everyone thinks. I see happiness and friendships here.

We do not fight against each other; nor do we disrespect each other. We share birthdays and holidays together. I myself had a birthday party this year. I believe that was the happiest time for me, because all these people sang happy birthday to me. It is the first time so many people did that for me.

I am not going to give an excuse for you to save my life. I am not going to say I am retarded or an ex-drug user or that I was beaten in my childhood. What I will say is, I am a person! An American, of the United States of America. The world looks at America with respect. We go help other countries with food and medicine. We are against violence and aggression. However, having the death penalty does not set a very good example! Executing our people puts a deep scar that will not go away until we stop this madness.

I invite you to visit a state's death row and see for yourself. Meet a death row inmate, talk to him or her, and see what they are like. Society has put an X on our foreheads because they are made to believe that we do not care about the country. That is not true. We do care about this country of ours, and this world, too.

I get really sad when I see news about people starving or dying with AIDS. It really hits home! I am not smart, I did not go to high school or college. But what I do know is street smarts. I know what it feels like to go hungry and not have anything. I know about goals and dreams because I have them too.

I do not want to die in the electric chair. And with your help I will not have to. Violence exists across the world because we want it to be there, just like executions! We can stop all the violence and suffering by pulling together and helping each other. Please come together and stop this madness. Restore the American Dream. Stop executions, help the poor, give medical care to people that need it, go into those cities and neighborhoods, help those families, give them jobs. Let them know you care.

Mark Allen Jenkins
#Z527, Holman Prison
Atmore, AL

contact or noncontact—they are strip-searched before and after the visit. Over the years, visitors and mail are less frequent, and sometimes cease altogether. Corrections officers assigned to death row are instructed not to estab-

The men in the red jumpsuits—dead men walking! I don't judge them, I don't disrespect them, I just protect them from other inmates and themselves. I work on death row and have for three and a half years. Death row inmates sleep in cell blocks which consist of sixteen individual cells with solid electronic steel doors. Some talk to everybody all the time, some don't talk to anyone and others act as if they have multiple personalities. If they aren't talking, they're playing cards, checkers, or doing push-ups. They get outside two times a day to exercise. Law says they can't work.

Some act like they are your buddies, and some act as if they can't stand you. For the most part, the ones that act like your buddy are usually trying to get you to do something for them.

As a group, they are very manipulative in every exchange they have with everyone, including each other.

Most of the inmates say they are innocent. A few say they actually committed the crime, and others say they were framed. I know a lot about most of their cases and it seems to me that they belong here—on death row. But, a few of the cases seem questionable. That's a private thought and I don't let it change the way I deal with these offenders in red jumpsuits.

John Juehrs
Correctional Officer
Death Row
Central Prison
Raleigh, NC

lish relationships with inmates because it may make it more difficult to carry out their duties. Pennsylvania's policy manual for death row corrections officers reads, "Employees must not be too familiar or discuss personal items of interest with the inmates."[8]

Preparing for an execution is a correctional officer's toughest job. "We begin to dread electrocutions weeks before they take place," former corrections officer Lynch Alford, Sr., said. "We're almost glad when someone is commuted, regardless of what crime he committed. We just sit around and wait. We drink coffee. We don't talk about anything. We don't talk about the electrocution. We just get it over with as soon as possible and then go home immediately." A death row inmate who refuses to walk to the death chamber is carried by corrections officers, sometimes screaming and kicking. "Guards have been known to go all to pieces during episodes such as these. Their nerves just don't hold up. In my opinion it is something you never become accustomed to. It's the most gruesome job I've come in contact with

Cross-Cultural Perspective

Have students research a recent execution in your state or a neighboring state to determine how local cultural values for and against the death penalty were expressed in the media.

Death: The Ultimate Sanction

EXHIBIT 13–1

American Correctional Association
Policy Statement on Capital Punishment

Correctional professionals have a fundamental responsibility to support participation in the public dialogue concerning capital punishment, and to make available to the public and their policymakers the unique perspectives of persons working in the profession. Toward this end, correctional agencies should:

A. Support conducting research on capital punishment, to inform the public debate with accurate information about all aspects of capital punishment.

B. Support full public discussion of capital punishment, focusing on the morality, purposes, and efficacy of this form of punishment.

C. Accept and encourage a diversity of opinion within the field, assuring that employment, promotion, and retention are never affected by the expression of opinion either in support of or opposition to capital punishment.

D. Encourage correctional professionals to fully consider this issue, and permit them to present their opinions within the profession and in appropriate public forums.

during my 35 years with the department. The more you see, the more you hate it."[9]

The American Correctional Association (ACA), in its Policy Statement on Capital Punishment (see Exhibit 13–1), encourages corrections professionals to support and participate in the debate about capital punishment.

The Courts and the Death Penalty

"Death is different [from other punishments]," said U.S. Supreme Court Justice William Brennan. For that reason, every phase of a capital crime proceeding, from jury selection to sentencing instructions, has been

Death: The Ultimate Sanction

influenced by court rulings. The legal history of today's death penalty can be traced through several landmark cases. In the June 29, 1972 decision in *Furman* v. *Georgia*,[10] the U.S. Supreme Court ruled that the death penalty, as imposed and carried out under the laws of Georgia, was cruel and unusual punishment in violation of the Eighth and Fourteenth Amendments. According to the Court, Georgia's death penalty statute gave the sentencing authority (judge or trial jury) complete freedom to impose a death or life imprisonment sentence without standards or guidelines; the death penalty had been imposed arbitrarily, discriminatorily, and selectively against minorities and was therefore "cruel and unusual punishment in violation of the Eighth and Fourteenth Amendments." It is important to note that the Court majority did not rule that the death penalty itself was unconstitutional, only the way in which it was being administered at that time.

About two-thirds of the states responded to the *Furman* decision by rewriting their capital punishment statutes to limit discretion and avoid arbitrary and inconsistent results. The new penalty laws took two forms. Some imposed a **mandatory death penalty** for certain crimes, and others permitted **guided discretion** that sets standards for judges and juries to use when deciding whether to impose the death penalty.

In 1976, the U.S. Supreme Court rejected mandatory death penalty statutes in *Woodson* v. *North Carolina* and *Roberts* v. *Louisiana*, but approved guided discretion statutes in *Gregg* v. *Georgia* and two companion cases.[11]

In *Gregg*, the Court also approved automatic appellate review, a proportionality review whereby state appellate courts compare the sentence with similar cases, and a **bifurcated**, or special two-part, **trial**. The first part, the *guilt phase*, decides the issue of guilt. If the defendant is found guilty, the second part of the trial, the *penalty phase*, takes place. The penalty phase includes presentation of facts that mitigate or aggravate the circumstances of the crime. **Mitigating circumstances** are factors that may be considered as reducing the culpability of the crime. **Aggravating circumstances** are factors that may increase the penalty. A list of mitigating and aggravating circumstances associated with the death penalty in the state of Pennsylvania is shown in Figure 13–4 on the following pages.

Appealing the Death Penalty

Execution of death row inmates takes an average of 10 years and 5 months. Death penalty cases may pass through up to ten courts, across three stages: trial and direct appeal, state post-conviction appeals, and federal *habeas corpus* appeals.

In stage one, trial and direct appeal, a death sentence is imposed. In a death penalty case, legal issues about the trial and sentence are automatically appealed to the state appellate courts. Some states have a dual level of appellate review; this means that the legal issues may be heard first in the state court of criminal appeals (court 1) before reaching the state supreme court (court 2). These courts evaluate the trial for legal or constitutional errors at trial and determine if the death sentence is consistent with sentences imposed in similar cases. State appellate courts seldom overturn a conviction or change a death sentence. The defendant then petitions the U.S. Supreme Court (court 3) to grant a petition for a **writ of** *certiorari*—

Teaching Tip
Direct students' attention to Figure 13–4 and ask if they think that any of the circumstances listed should be removed or if any should be added and why.

mandatory death penalty A death sentence that the legislature has required to be imposed upon persons convicted of certain offenses.

guided discretion Decision-making bounded by general guidelines, rules, or laws.

bifurcated trial Two separate hearings for different issues in a trial; one for guilt and the other for punishment.

mitigating circumstances Factors that, although not justifying or excusing an action, may be considered as reducing the culpability of the offender.

aggravating circumstances Factors that may be considered as increasing the culpability of the offender.

writ of *certiorari* The written order a superior court issues to a lower court requiring provision of a certified copy of a particular case record.

FIGURE 13–4

Sample Aggravating and Mitigating Circumstances

Aggravating and Mitigating Circumstances in Pennsylvania

The Commonwealth of Pennsylvania must prove aggravating circumstances beyond a reasonable doubt. Mitigating circumstances must be proved by the defendant by a preponderance of the evidence.

The verdict must be a sentence of death if the jury unanimously finds at least one aggravating circumstance and no mitigating circumstances or if the jury unanimously finds one or more aggravating circumstances which outweigh any mitigating circumstances.

The court shall instruct the jury that if it finds at least one aggravating circumstance and at least one mitigating circumstance, it shall consider, in weighing the aggravating and mitigating circumstances, any evidence presented about the victim and about the impact of the murder on the victim's family. The court shall also instruct the jury on any other matter that may be just and proper under the circumstances.

Aggravating circumstances shall be limited to the following:

1. The victim was a firefighter, peace officer, public servant concerned in official detention, as defined in 18 Pa.C.S. § 5121 (relating to escape), judge of any court in the unified judicial system, the Attorney General of Pennsylvania, a deputy attorney general, district attorney, assistant district attorney, member of the General Assembly, Governor, Lieutenant Governor, Auditor General, State Treasurer, State law enforcement official, local law enforcement official, Federal law enforcement official or person employed to assist or assisting any law enforcement official in the performance of his duties, who was killed in the performance of his duties or as a result of his official position.

2. The defendant paid or was paid by another person or had contracted to pay or be paid by another person or had conspired to pay or be paid by another person for the killing of the victim.

3. The victim was being held by the defendant for ransom or reward, or as a shield or hostage.

4. The death of the victim occurred while the defendant was engaged in the hijacking of an aircraft.

5. The victim was a prosecution witness to a murder or other felony committed by the defendant and was killed for the purpose of preventing his testimony against the defendant in any grand jury or criminal proceeding involving such offenses.

6. The defendant committed a killing while in the perpetration of a felony.

7. In the commission of the offense the defendant knowingly created a grave risk of death to another person in addition to the victim of the offense.

8. The offense was committed by means of torture.

9. The defendant has a significant history of felony convictions involving the use or threat of violence to the person.

10. The defendant has been convicted of another Federal or State offense, committed either before or at the time of the offense at issue, for which a sentence of life imprisonment or death was imposable or the defendant was undergoing a sentence of life imprisonment for any reason at the time of the commission of the offense.

11. The defendant has been convicted of another murder committed in any jurisdiction and committed either before or at the time of the offense at issue.

12. The defendant has been convicted of voluntary manslaughter, as defined in 18 Pa.C.S. § 2503 (relating to voluntary manslaughter), or a substantially equivalent crime in any other jurisdiction, committed either before or at the time of the offense at issue.

- 1 -

Source: Pennsylvania Consolidated Statutes, Section 9711 (1997).

FIGURE 13–4 (continued)

Sample Aggravating and Mitigating Circumstances

13. The defendant committed the killing or was an accomplice in the killing, as defined in 18 Pa.C.S. § 306(c) (relating to liability for conduct of another; complicity), while in the perpetration of a felony under the provisions of the act of April 14, 1972 (P.L.233, No.64), known as The Controlled Substance, Drug, Device, and Cosmetic Act, and punishable under the provisions of 18 Pa.C.S. § 7508 (relating to drug trafficking sentencing and penalties).

14. At the time of the killing, the victim was or had been involved, associated, or in competition with the defendant in the sale, manufacture, distribution, or delivery of any controlled substance or counterfeit controlled substance in violation of The Controlled Substance, Drug, Device, and Cosmetic Act or similar law of any other state, the District of Columbia or the United States, and the defendant committed the killing or was an accomplice to the killing as defined in 18 Pa.C.S. § 306(c), and the killing resulted from or was related to that association, involvement, or competition to promote the defendant's activities in selling, manufacturing, distributing, or delivering controlled substances or counterfeit controlled substances.

15. At the time of the killing, the victim was or had been a nongovernmental informant or had otherwise provided any investigative, law enforcement, or police agency with information concerning criminal activity, and the defendant committed the killing or was an accomplice to the killing as defined in 18 Pa.C.S. § 306(c), and the killing was in retaliation for the victim's activities as a nongovernmental informant or in providing information concerning criminal activity to an investigative, law enforcement, or police agency.

16. The victim was a child under 12 years of age.

17. At the time of the killing, the victim was in her third trimester of pregnancy or the defendant had knowledge of the victim's pregnancy.

18. At the time of the killing, the defendant was subject to a court order restricting in any way the defendant's behavior toward the victim pursuant to 23 Pa.C.S. Ch. 61 (relating to protection from abuse), or any other order of a court of common pleas or of the minor judiciary designed in whole or in part to protect the victim from the defendant.

Mitigating circumstances shall include the following:

1. The defendant has no significant history of prior criminal convictions.

2. The defendant was under the influence of extreme mental or emotional disturbance.

3. The capacity of the defendant to appreciate the criminality of his conduct or to conform his conduct to the requirements of law was substantially impaired.

4. The age of the defendant at the time of the crime.

5. The defendant acted under extreme duress, although not such duress as to constitute a defense to prosecution under 18 Pa.C.S. § 309 (relating to duress), or acted under the substantial domination of another person.

6. The victim was a participant in the defendant's homicidal conduct or consented to the homicidal acts.

7. The defendant's participation in the homicidal act was relatively minor.

8. Any other evidence of mitigation concerning the character and record of the defendant and the circumstances of his offense.

- 2 -

Teaching Tip
Point out that when the U.S. Supreme Court denies a petition for a writ of *certiorari*, in effect the judgment of the court below stands unchanged.

a written order to the lower court whose decision is being appealed to send the records of the case forward for review.

If the defendant's direct appeals are unsuccessful, stage two—state post-conviction appeals—begins. At this point, many death row inmates allege ineffective or incompetent trial counsel, and new counsel is engaged or appointed. The new counsel petitions the trial court (court 4) with newly discovered evidence; questions about the fairness of the trial; allegations of jury bias, tainted evidence, incompetence of defense counsel, and prosecutorial or police misconduct. If the trial court denies the appeals, they may be filed with the state's appellate courts (either directly to the state supreme court, or, if there exists a dual level of appellate review, a petition first to the state court of criminal appeals (court 5) followed by a petition to the state supreme court (court 6). Most often, the state appellate courts deny the petition. Defendant's counsel then petitions the U.S. Supreme Court (court 7). If the U.S. Supreme Court denies the petition for a writ of *certiorari*, stage two ends and stage three begins.

CAREER PROFILE

Rodge Wood
Prison Chaplain
Western Penitentiary
Pittsburgh, PA

"My work is difficult to describe. I meet weekly with a group of men sentenced to life in prison. The group has met with me since 1977 and I have come to understand the benefits of long-term work with people inside. We work toward building trust that allows their stories to be told. The object is to work toward forgiveness and finding life in a life sentence. I work alone, though, and I wonder what it is about prisons that keeps prison chaplains so isolated."

Rodge Wood is the prison chaplain at Western Penitentiary in Pittsburgh, Pennsylvania. He holds a bachelor's degree in psychology from the University of Pittsburgh and a Master of Divinity from Virginia Theological Seminary at Alexandria. Before going to seminary school, Rodge spent a number of years in secular employment, in radio and television, always with a nagging desire to enter the ministry.

After beginning parish ministry, he discovered that his life had become integrated in ways that it never had been before. According to Rodge, he has a passion for the Gospel—the good news that Jesus Christ has for those who are sick, poor, in prison, outcast, or strangers—the marginalized of our society. He says, "There is a Gospel preference for these people. That is why I go into the prison."

In prison, Rodge's duties include giving sermons, counseling, and advising of high-custody inmates. He has come to believe in restorative justice—to move people beyond the crime and back into life. His group members are all lifers, have each killed somebody, and carry the burden of that daily. "I believe that God forgives and receives people back with eagerness. I talk about that a lot, with varying degrees of acceptance among group members," he says.

In stage three, the federal *habeas corpus* stage, a defendant files a petition in U.S. District Court (court 8) alleging violations of constitutional rights. Such rights include the right to due process (Fourteenth Amendment), prohibition against cruel and unusual punishment (Eighth Amendment), and the right to effective assistance of counsel (Sixth Amendment). If the District Court denies the petition, defense counsel submits it to the U.S. Court of Appeals (court 9) for the circuit representing the jurisdiction. If the Court of Appeals denies the petition, defense counsel asks the U.S. Supreme Court (court 10) to grant a writ of *certiorari*. If the U.S. Supreme Court denies *certiorari*, the office of the state attorney general asks the state supreme court to set a date for execution.

In 1996, in an effort to reduce the time persons spent on death row and the number of federal appeals, the U.S. Congress passed the Anti-Terrorism and Effective Death Penalty Act (AEDPA). The AEDPA defines filing deadlines and limits reasons for second, or successive, federal appellate reviews to (1) new constitutional law, (2) new evidence that could not have been discovered at the time of the original trial, or (3) new facts that, if proven, would be sufficient to establish the applicant's innocence. Under the AEDPA, if the U.S. Supreme Court denies the petition for a writ of *certiorari* in the final federal *habeas corpus* appeal, defense counsel may once again petition the federal courts; however, before a second, or successive, application for a writ of *habeas corpus* may be filed in U.S. District Court, defense counsel must petition the appropriate U.S. Court of Appeals for an order authorizing the District Court to consider the application. The petition to the U.S. Court of Appeals is decided by a three-judge panel; the panel must grant or deny the authorization to file the second, or successive, application within 30 days after the petition is filed. If the panel approves the petition, the District Court must render a decision regarding the application within 180 days. If the motion is appealed to the Court of Appeals representing the jurisdiction, the court must render its decision within 120 days. If the petition is filed with the U.S. Supreme Court, the Court may grant the petition for *certiorari* or let the lower court's decision stand.

Death Penalty Issues in the 21st Century

Current issues on capital punishment include questions about executing the innocent, juveniles, and the mentally retarded.

Wrongful Convictions

Execution is irreversible. The most extensive safeguards cannot ensure an infallible legal system because human beings are fallible. False testimony, mistaken identification, misinterpretation of evidence, or community prejudices and pressures can result in wrongful conviction and sometimes execu-

Student Involvement

Have a group of students find and photocopy the section of the Anti-Terrorism and Effective Death Penalty Act that describes the appeals process and present it to the class. Ask students what kinds of evidence they think might qualify as recently discovered proof of innocence that would be sufficient "to establish by clear and convincing evidence that, but for constitutional error, no reasonable fact finder would have found the person guilty of the offense."

tion of the innocent. From 1973 through 1999, 84 death row inmates were released as a result of new evidence. Some might consider this statistic as evidence that the legal system's elaborate procedural protections work; others consider it evidence of the likelihood that innocent people have been or will be executed. Most of the new evidence in these 84 cases was not evidence discovered through the normal appeals process, but rather evidence made available as a result of new scientific discoveries such as DNA testing, or investigations by journalists, professors, students, or attorneys. These 84 people sat on death row for an average of six and a half years before their innocence was established and they were released. At least 23 people were not so fortunate; they were executed between 1900 and 1987, before their innocence was proved.[12]

Some professionals and researchers believe that mistakes are more likely in capital cases than in other criminal matters due to the following:[13]

1. Pressure on law enforcement officials to quickly arrest and prosecute the most notorious murders.
2. Lack of eyewitness testimony.
3. Publicity that may influence jurors.
4. Inadvertent conveyance of guilt during jury selection—establishing that jurors can recommend the death penalty may imply that they should.
5. Limited defense resources.
6. Heinousness of the crime—the details of the crime may cause the jury to ignore reasonable doubt and return a guilty verdict.

On January 31, 2000, Governor George Ryan of Illinois announced a temporary halt to executions, saying he had grave concerns about convicting innocent people and putting them on death row. The state of Illinois

The death penalty issue generates public controversy. In some states, there are movements to end the death penalty, while in others the move is to speed up death row appeals and complete the sentence of execution. Do demonstrations such as these influence the public policy implemented by state legislatures?

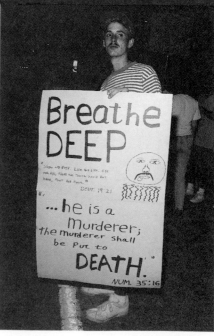

released 13 persons who were wrongfully sentenced to die, outnumbering the 12 who had been executed by lethal injection since the state reinstated the death penalty in 1977. The governor also appointed a special commission to study the state's capital punishment system and determine why 13 persons were wrongfully convicted of capital crimes. Other states are considering similar moratoriums.

Juvenile Offenders

As youth violence increases, the question of how to deal with juvenile offenders guilty of capital offenses becomes more urgent. International human rights treaties and standards recommend that juveniles not be sentenced to death because they lack adult judgment. Legislators in 24 U.S. jurisdictions disagree (See Table 13–3.): eight do not specify a minimum age

Student Involvement
Refer to Table 13–3. Ask students for their opinions about executing a person under 18. Ask students if they think justice is achieved if where one lives determines the minimum age at execution.

TABLE 13–3

Minimum Age Authorized for Capital Punishment, 1998

Age 16 or less	Age 17	Age 18	None specified
Alabama (16)	Georgia	California	Arizona
Arkansas (14)[a]	New Hampshire	Colorado	Idaho
Delaware (16)	North Carolina[b]	Connecticut[c]	Louisiana
Florida (16)	Texas	Federal system	Montana
Indiana (16)		Illinois	Pennsylvania
Kentucky (16)		Kansas	South Carolina
Mississippi (16)[d]		Maryland	South Dakota[e]
Missouri (16)		Nebraska	Utah
Nevada (16)		New Jersey	
Oklahoma (16)		New Mexico	
Virginia (14)[f]		New York	
Wyoming (16)		Ohio	
		Oregon	
		Tennessee	
		Washington	

Note: Reporting by states reflects interpretations by state attorneys general's offices and may differ from previously reported ages.
[a]See Ark. Code Ann. 9-27-318(b)(2)(Repl. 1991).
[b]Age required is 17 unless the murderer was incarcerated for murder when a subsequent murder occurred; then the age may be 14.
[c]See Conn. Gen. Stat. 53a-46a(g)(1).
[d]The minimum age defined by statute is 13, but the effective age is 16 based on interpretation of U.S. Supreme Court decisions by the Mississippi Supreme Court.
[e]Juveniles may be transferred to adult court. Age can be a mitigating factor.
[f]The minimum age for transfer to adult court by statute is 14, but the effective age is 16 based on interpretation of U.S. Supreme Court decisions by the state attorney general's office.

Source: Bureau of Justice Statistics Bulletin NCJ 179012, *Capital Punishment 1998* (U.S. Department of Justice, Office of Justice Programs), December 1999.

Teaching Tip

Take a confidential poll (Yes/No) of your students' opinions: "Should we execute mentally retarded persons who have committed a crime?" Reserve the poll results. Create a two-column table with space to write "Yes" reasons and space to write "No" reasons. Ask students to come forward and supply the reasons. Initiate a discussion on the topic.

Teaching Tip

Designate half of the students "supporters" and the other half "opponents" for a debate on the death penalty. Have each team present its position, then one rejoinder. After the debate, ask the class which side was most convincing and why.

Teaching Tip

Take a confidential poll of your students using the arguments presented in Table 13–4 on page 395. Does capital punishment deter crime? (Yes/No, etc.) Share the results with your students.

for the death sentence; four specify an age of 17; and twelve specify an age between 13 and 17.

From January 1973 through March 2000, 182 convicted juvenile offenders were sentenced to death. Ninety-seven (54%) of these sentences have been reversed; sixteen have been carried out.

Currently there are 69 death row inmates (all males) sentenced as juveniles. All of them were age 16 or 17 when they committed their crimes. One-third (26) of these juveniles are on death row in Texas.

Persons With Mental Retardation

Most of the opposition to executing mentally ill prisoners is based on the premise that killing people who do not comprehend the nature or purpose of their punishment serves no legitimate purpose. Thirty-four people who were diagnosed as mentally retarded were executed in the United States between 1983 and January 1, 2000. Thirteen of the 40 jurisdictions in the United States that allow the death penalty do not permit execution of the mentally retarded. These states include:

Arkansas
Colorado
Georgia
Indiana
Kansas
Kentucky
Maryland
Nebraska
New Mexico
New York
Tennessee
Washington
the federal government

Future of the Death Penalty

Capital punishment has always been a subject of debate, and the debate will continue into the 21st century. There are many arguments favoring capital punishment and many arguments opposing it. Some of the arguments—pro and con—are summarized in Table 13–4. The debate over capital punishment is complex and emotional. It has always inspired passionate, partisan feelings and will continue to do so as decisions about how to strike the right balance of justice and social utility are made.

TABLE 13–4

Arguments Favoring and Opposing the Death Penalty

The Death Penalty Debate

PRO	CON
Deters people from crime through fear of punishment; exerts a positive moral influence by stigmatizing crimes of murder and manslaughter.	Does not deter crime; no evidence exists that the death penalty is more effective than other punishments.
Is a just punishment for murder; fulfills "just deserts" principle of a fitting punishment; life in prison is not a tough enough punishment for a capital crime.	Violates human rights; is a barbaric remnant of an uncivilized society; is immoral in principle, and ensures the execution of some innocent people.
Is constitutionally appropriate; 8th Amendment prohibits cruel and unusual punishment, yet 5th Amendment implies that with due process of law one may be deprived of life, liberty, or property.	Falls disproportionately on racial minorities; those who murdered whites are more likely to be sentenced to death than those who murdered blacks.
Reduces time spent on death row to reduce costs of capital punishment and its attendant costs of post-conviction appeals, investigations, and searches for new evidence and witnesses.	Costs too much; $2 million to $4 million are poured into each execution while other criminal justice components such as police and the courts lack funding.
Protects society from the most serious and feared offenders; prevents the reoccurrence of violence.	Boosts the murder rate following an execution; this is known as the *brutalizing effect*; the state is a role model, and when the state carries out an execution, it shows that killing is a way to solve problems.
Is more humane than life imprisonment because it is quick; making the prisoner suffer by remaining in prison for the rest of his/her life is more torturous and inhumane than execution.	Not everyone wants vengeance; many people favor alternative sentences such as life without parole.
Almost impossible for an innocent person to be executed; slow execution rate results from process of appeals, from sentencing to execution.	Is arbitrary and unfair; offenders who commit similar crimes under similar circumstances receive widely differing sentences; race, social and economic status, location of crime, and pure chance influence sentencing.

Teaching Tip
Refer to Chapter 13 of the *Instructor's Resource Manual* for additional activities and for answers to the end-of-chapter exercises.

SUMMARY BY CHAPTER OBJECTIVES

CHAPTER OBJECTIVE 1

Capital punishment has been imposed throughout history, for crimes ranging from horse stealing and witchcraft to crimes against humanity and murder. Before the 18th century, torture often preceded death. Researchers have confirmed almost 15,000 executions in the United States from 1608 through 1999.

CHAPTER OBJECTIVE 2

Most death row inmates are male. Only 48 percent of death row inmates completed high school. Only 24 percent of death row inmates were married at the time of incarceration. Whites and minorities are executed in about equal proportion.

CHAPTER OBJECTIVE 3

Two landmark cases that influenced capital punishment were *Furman* v. *Georgia* (1972) and *Gregg* v. *Georgia* (1976). In *Furman* v. *Georgia*, the U.S. Supreme Court ruled that capital punishment, as imposed by Georgia, constituted cruel and unusual punishment—Georgia's death penalty statute gave the sentencing authority (judge or trial jury) complete freedom to impose a death sentence without standards or guidelines. As a result of the *Furman* ruling, state death penalty statutes took two forms—mandatory death penalty or sentencing based on guided discretion. In *Woodson* v. *North Carolina* and

Roberts v. *Louisiana*, the Court rejected mandatory statutes. However, in *Gregg* v. *Georgia*, the Court ruled that Georgia's new guided discretion death penalty legislation was not unconstitutional.

CHAPTER OBJECTIVE 4

Arguments in favor of the death penalty include the following: it deters rational people from becoming habitual killers; it is "just" punishment for taking someone's life; it is constitutional as long as it is achieved with due process of law; it reduces the amount of time a person spends on death row; it protects society from feared offenders; it is more humane than life imprisonment; and it is almost impossible for an innocent person to be executed. Arguments against the death penalty include the following: it violates human rights; it does not deter violent crime; it is implemented arbitrarily and unfairly; it falls disproportionately on racial minorities; it actually boosts the murder rate by promoting homicides in the months following an execution; not everyone wants vengeance; and it costs too much to support a capital trial, appeals, and execution.

CHAPTER OBJECTIVE 5

In the 21st century issues that the debate on capital punishment addresses will include execution of the wrongfully convicted, juveniles, and the mentally ill.

KEY TERMS

capital punishment, p. 378
capital crime, p. 380
clemency, p. 381
commutation, p. 381
death row, p. 383
mandatory death penalty, p. 387

guided discretion, p. 387
bifurcated trial, p. 387
mitigating circumstances, p. 387
aggravating circumstances, p. 387
writ of *certiorari*, p. 387

1. What is *capital punishment*?
2. How many jurisdictions in the United States permit capital punishment? How many do not?
3. What is a *capital crime*?
4. What are the characteristics of death row inmates?
5. What is the average length of time spent on death row?
6. What execution methods are used in the United States today? Which is used most?
7. What are the two landmark U.S. Supreme Court cases that most affected capital punishment legislation? What impact did they have?
8. What is a *bifurcated trial*?
9. What are *aggravating* and *mitigating circumstances*?
10. What is the process for appealing a death sentence?
11. What is the Anti-Terrorism and Effective Death Penalty Act? What is its purpose?
12. List and explain at least four arguments in favor of capital punishment.
13. List and explain at least four arguments against capital punishment.
14. What are the primary causes of wrongful convictions?
15. How many jurisdictions permit execution of juveniles?
16. How many jurisdictions permit execution of the mentally ill?

CRITICAL THINKING EXERCISES

ON-THE-JOB ISSUES

1. Capital murder trials are longer and more expensive at every step than other murder trials. The irreversibility of the death sentence requires courts to follow heightened due process in the preparation and course of the trial. Defendants are much more likely to insist on a trial when they are facing a possible death sentence. Crime investigations, pre-trial preparations and motions, expert witness investigations, jury selection, and the necessity for two trials—one on guilt and one on sentencing—makes capital cases extremely costly, even before the appeals process begins. After conviction, there are constitutionally mandated appeals that involve both prosecution and defense costs. In addition, should the jury recommend life over death or end as a hung jury, or if the condemned person's sentence is commuted after he or she has served time on death row, the state has already paid the cost of a capital trial. These are the unsuccessful capital trials in which the death penalty was sought (and paid for) but not achieved. Assume that you are the prosecuting attorney in a rural county of 7,500 people in a southern state. A capital case is coming up for trial. Estimates of costs for the case begin at $500,000. How will you justify paying for the prosecution of the case?

2. According to a study at Kentucky's University of Louisville, blacks who killed whites in Kentucky were more likely to be charged with a capital offense and receive a death penalty than others. As a result of this study, the Kentucky Senate passed the Kentucky Racial Justice Act, which states, in part, "no person shall be subject to or given a death sentence that was sought on the basis of race." This legislation permits introduction of statistical evidence of racial bias in Kentucky's capital sentencing process in cases sentenced after July 15, 1998.[14] What impact do you think this law might have on your life as a corrections professional in Kentucky?

CORRECTIONS ISSUES

1. Daryl Mease was scheduled to die by lethal injection in Missouri's death chamber on Wednesday, January 27, 1999, at 12:01 A.M. Pope John Paul II, who was visiting St. Louis at the time, called upon Americans to renounce capital punishment and made a personal appeal to Missouri Governor Mel

Carnahan. "The Pope asked me to have mercy on Mr. Daryl Mease," said the Governor. "I continue to support capital punishment, but because of a deep and abiding respect for the pontiff and all that he represents, I decided last night to grant his request." Mease's lawyers were overjoyed and somber. "I'm sort of torn," said Kent Gipson, Mease's lawyer. "I'm happy for Daryl, but it underscores how arbitrary the death penalty is. Daryl gets spared just because his number was up while the Pope was in town. It was the luck of the draw." Do you agree with Mease's lawyer that the death penalty is arbitrary? Why or why not?

2. Ted Bundy's 10-year stay on Florida's death row until he was executed on January 24, 1989, cost in excess of $6 million. Do you think this was an appropriate use of public funds? Why or why not?

3. The majority of death penalty states have higher murder rates than non-death penalty states. The average murder rate among death penalty states was 7.1 per 100,000 population in 1996; for non-death penalty states the rate was 3.6. The South executes the largest percentage of offenders who are convicted of a capital crime (over 80%) and records the highest murder rate (8.4 murders per 100,000 people); the Northeast executes the fewest (less than 1%) and records a murder rate of 4.8. What conclusions might you draw from these data?

4. Research shows that execution costs more than life imprisonment. Do you think there is a point at which the economic consequence of execution outweighs its value to the public? Explain.

CORRECTIONS ON THE WEB

1. The Death Penalty Information Center, a source of current information on the death penalty, maintains a Web site at **http://www.essential.org/dpic**. Test your knowledge of capital punishment by taking the DPIC "Death Penalty Quiz." Click on "Information Topics," then "Death Penalty Quiz."

2. Use the FindLaw Web site to compare the aggravating and mitigating circumstances different states consider in determining the sentence for a capital crime. See Figure 13–1 on page 378 for the list of jurisdictions that permit the death penalty. For example, if you want to find the aggravating circumstances for the state of Alabama, go to **http://www.findlaw.com/casecode/state.html**, click on "Alabama," then under "Primary Materials" on "Code." Click "Criminal Code," then "Punishments and Sentences." Scroll down and click the link (Section 13A-5-49) to the left of "aggravating circumstances."

ADDITIONAL READINGS

Bedau, Hugo Adam. *The Death Penalty in America: Current Controversies.* New York: Oxford University Press, 1997.

Bohm, Robert M. *Deathquest: An Introduction to the Theory and Practice of Capital Punishment in the United States.* Cincinnati: Anderson Publishing Company, 1999.

Costanzo, Mark. *Just Revenge: Costs and Consequences of the Death Penalty.* New York: St. Martin's Press, 1997.

Johnson, Robert. *Death Work: A Study of the Modern Execution Process,* 2d ed. Belmont, CA: Wadsworth Publishing, 1998.

Marquart, James W., Sheldon Ekland-Olson, and Jonathan R. Sorensen. *The Rope, The Chair, and the Needle: Capital Punishment in Texas, 1923–1990.* Austin: University of Texas Press, 1994.

Paternoster, Raymond. *Capital Punishment in America.* New York: Lexington Books, 1991.

ENDNOTES

1. See the Death Penalty Information Center Web site for current international death information. Online at http://www.essential.org/dpic/dpicintl.html.

2. Victoria Schneider and John Ortiz Smykla, "A Summary Analysis of Executions in the United States, 1608–1987: The Espy File," Robert M. Bohm (ed.), *The Death Penalty in America: Current Research* (Cincinnati: Anderson Publishing Company, 1991), pp. 1–19.

3. Tracy L. Snell, *Capital Punishment 1998,* Bureau of Justice Statistics (Washington: U.S. Department of Justice, NCJ 179012, December 1999), p. 3.

4. *Death Row U.S.A., Winter 2000* (New York: NAACP Defense and Education Fund, January 1, 2000), p. 1.

5. Ibid.

6. Robert Johnson, "Under Sentence of Death, The Psychology of Death Row Confinement," *Law and Psychology Review,* Vol. 5 (Fall 1979), pp. 141–192.

7. As quoted in Bonnie Bartel Latino and Bob Vale, "Welcome to Death Row," *The Birmingham News,* January 16, 2000, pp. 1C, 4C.

8. Mark Costanzo, *Just Revenge: Costs and Consequences of the Death Penalty* (New York: St. Martin's Press, 1997), p. 51.

9. As quoted in John Ortiz Smykla, "The Human Impact of Capital Punishment," *Journal of Criminal Justice,* Vol. 15, Number 4 (1987), pp. 331–347.

10. *Furman* v. *Georgia,* 408 U.S. 238 (1972).

11. *Woodson* v. *North Carolina,* 428 U.S. 280 (1976); *Roberts* v. *Louisiana,* 428 U.S. 325 (1976); *Gregg* v. *Georgia,* 428 U.S. 153 (1976); *Jurek* v. *Texas,* 428 U.S. 262 (1976); and *Proffitt* v. *Florida* 428 U.S. 242 (1976).

12. Hugo Adam Bedau and Michael L. Radelet, "Miscarriages of Justice in Potentially Capital Cases," *Stanford Law Review,* Vol. 40 (1987), pp. 21–179.

13. See, for example, Michael L. Radelet, Hugo Adam Bedau, and Constance E. Putnam, *In Spite of Innocence: Erroneous Convictions in Capital Cases* (Boston: Northeastern University Press, 1992); Samuel Gross, "The Risks of Death: Why Erroneous Convictions are Common in Capital Cases," *Buffalo Law Review,* Vol. 44 (Fall 1996), pp. 469–500; and Richard C. Dieter, *Innocence and the Death Penalty: The Increasing Danger of Executing the Innocent* (Washington: Death Penalty Information Center, 1997).

14. Gennaro F. Vito, "Presidential Address. Research and Relevance: Role of the Academy of Criminal Justice Sciences," *Justice Quarterly,* Vol. 16, Number 1 (March 1999), pp. 10–13.

14 Juvenile Corrections
End of an Era?

CHAPTER OBJECTIVES

After completing this chapter you should be able to:

1. Explain *parens patriae*.
2. Describe Houses of Refuge, reform schools, and industrial schools.
3. Discuss the history of the juvenile court.
4. Summarize five U.S. Supreme Court cases that changed modern day juvenile court proceedings.
5. Discuss the two types of juvenile crime.
6. List the characteristics of the typical juvenile delinquent.
7. List and explain the three stages of the juvenile justice process.
8. List disposition options for adjudicated juvenile offenders.
9. List and explain four teen court models.
10. Explain how youth gangs affect juvenile correctional institutions.

FRANKLIN COUNTY JUVENILE DETENTION CENTER

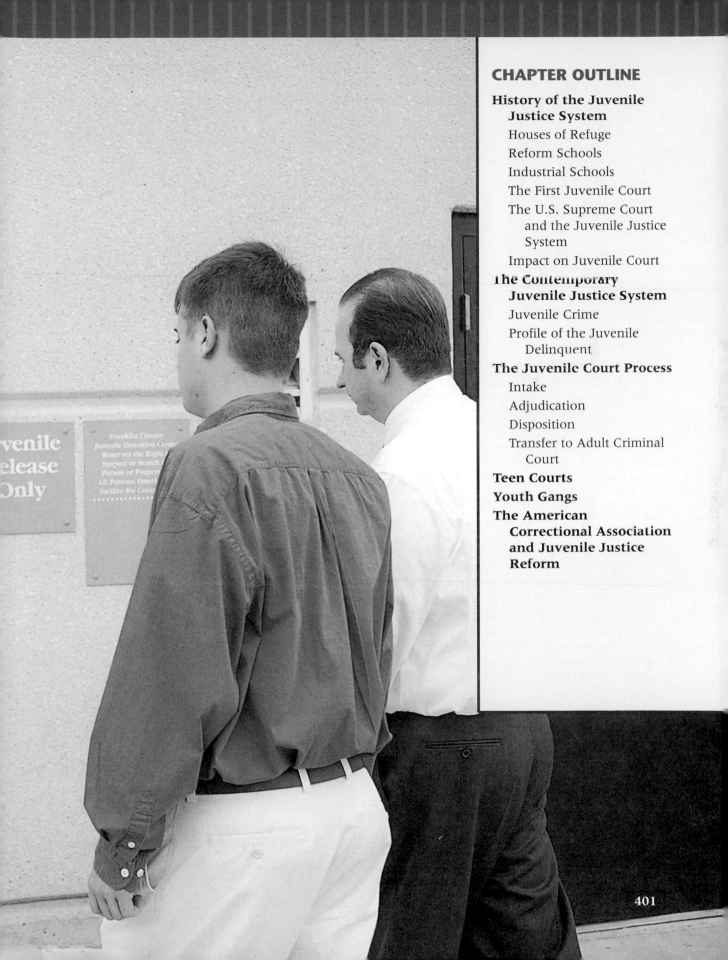

The vast majority of youth are good citizens who have never been arrested for any type of crime.

—Shay Bilchik

Here is a portion of a story that recently appeared in a midwestern city newspaper:[1]

> A teen-ager accused of killing his father and stepmother disliked his stepmother and used disparaging terms to describe her to his buddies, one of the youth's friends testified yesterday.
>
> "Brandon never really liked Becky," Trevor Howe said during a hearing in Hardin County Juvenile Court. "He also called her the 'B' word."
>
> Howe, 16, testified at a hearing to determine whether Brandon Grigaliunas, 16, should be tried as an adult for the October slayings of his father, Scott, 39, and stepmother, Rebecca, 42, in their home in Kenton, about 50 miles northwest of Columbus.
>
> Grigaliunas is charged with two delinquency counts each of aggravated murder and murder. In juvenile court, the most serious penalty he could face is juvenile detention until age 21. As an adult, he could face life in prison.
>
> He was 15 at the time of the shootings, and County Prosecutor Lora Manon made the request to have him tried as an adult.

Although the majority of juvenile offenders are charged with property offenses rather than violent offenses, the majority of juvenile offenses reported by the media involve violent crime, which overstates the violence issue and unduly alarms the public. High-profile juvenile violence—such as the shootings at Columbine High School on April 20, 1999 and the National Zoo in Washington on April 24, 2000—is changing juvenile corrections from treatment to punishment. As a result, attention and scarce resources focus on a small portion of juvenile offenders, neglecting the vast majority.

Juvenile justice will face other challenges in its second century of existence. The United States Congress, the Department of Justice, the American Bar Association, the NAACP, think-tanks, academic researchers, and others are revealing a juvenile justice system that disproportionately arrests, prosecutes, and sentences minority youth. Data from several sources show that minority youth are more likely than white youth who commit comparable crimes to be arrested, be referred to juvenile court, be detained, face trial as adults, be jailed with adults, and sentenced to correctional institutions.

Some argue that minority youth are victims of racial bias built into the justice system. Others maintain that juvenile justice policies discriminate against low-income youth, who are overwhelmingly minority, from single-parent homes, or in foster care. Still others claim that overrepresentation simply means that minority youth are committing more crimes or more serious crimes. Whatever the explanation, significant change is underway. In 1992, the U.S. Congress strengthened its commitment to end disproportionate juvenile minority confinement by elevating the issue as a core requirement in federal juvenile justice legislation. The Office of Juvenile Justice and Delinquency Prevention (OJJDP) has taken the lead to develop solutions in partnership with the states.

History of the Juvenile Justice System

The historical origins of America's juvenile justice system can be traced to early England, where bridewells (the first houses of corrections) confined both children and adults until 1704, when John Howard brought to England a model of a Roman institution for juvenile offenders (see Chapter 3). Colonists brought these ideas with them to America, and reformers tailored the ideas to their experiences, creating Houses of Refuge, reform schools, and industrial schools for juveniles. Both the English and American juvenile justice systems utilize the doctrine of *parens patriae*, the state as parent. The first known application of *parens patriae* in America was in 1636. Bridget Fuller was ordered by the governor of Plymouth Colony to take Benjamen Eaton, keep him in school for two years, and keep him employed.[2] By the end of the 19th century, every American state had affirmed its right to act as guardian of minors.

Houses of Refuge

The New York House of Refuge, the first legally chartered American custodial institution for juvenile offenders, was founded in 1825 by penal reformer Thomas Eddy, educational reformer John Griscom, and the Society for the Prevention of Pauperism. Its purpose was to provide poor, abused, and orphaned youths with food, clothing, and lodging in exchange for hard work, discipline, and study. The concept spread, and Houses of Refuge were established throughout America.

Living conditions in Houses of Refuge were not as generous as the term *refuge* might imply. Administrators of these institutions subjected juveniles to hard physical labor and were known to use corporal punishment. Residents were expected to earn their keep and comply with strict institutional rules. Guards and superintendents, who replaced parents or guardians, exhibited little tolerance or understanding.

Despite the path-breaking role the House of Refuge played in the development of the American juvenile justice system, the original institutions were short-lived. The movement as a whole died out by the middle of the 19th century.

Teaching Tip
Point out to students that *parens patriae* refers to guardianship of minors and those adults who are deemed mentally incompetent, then ask them to list situations in which they think *parens patriae* is or might be applied by the juvenile justice system.

parens patriae   A Latin term that refers to the state as guardian of minors and incompetent people.

Teaching Tip
Investigate the possibility of taking your class to a group home or inviting a group home house parent and/or resident to visit your class to describe life in the group home.

Reform Schools

The nation's first state-sponsored **reform school** opened in Massachusetts in 1848. Named the Lyman School, for Theodore Lyman, a former mayor of Boston, the institution resembled a prison. The school was designed to house 300 boys. Because of liberal admissions policies and unregulated commitment procedures, the reformatory was filled within a few years. The Massachusetts legislature authorized an addition, doubling the structure's capacity.

In the late 1800s, with the school again becoming overcrowded, a ship in Boston Harbor was designated an annex. Any boy under age 14 could be committed to either Lyman School or its Nautical Branch. Boys who were housed at the Nautical Branch were trained in navigation and the duties of seamen, then transferred to passing vessels that needed cabin boys or young laborers.

Because the Lyman School housed only boys, the Massachusetts legislature voted to create a separate institution for girls. Belief that the physical and emotional make-up of girls was inherently more delicate than that of boys led reformers to focus on a new European model for the girls school.

European-style reform schools introduced a small residential arrangement, breaking down structural barriers so that staff and inmates could interact, providing a more intimate setting for treatment. Advocates of the European-style reform school believed that personal contact with youth was the cornerstone of the rehabilitative effort. Under the new design, as many as thirty inmates with similar personality traits were placed in separate small homes or cottages and supervised by paid "cottage parents." Residents of each house or cottage lived, worked, and attended school together, meeting with inmates in other living quarters only infrequently.

The first of the European-style reform schools was the Lancaster Industrial School for Girls in Massachusetts, established in 1854. The Lancaster cottages had features associated with both school and home, and provided academic classes and domestic training programs. Lancaster's cottage plan gained national attention as prison reform advocates encouraged adoption of this system for youthful offenders throughout the United States.

Industrial Schools

After the Civil War, state welfare services expanded and began to require that juvenile reform schools and adult penal institutions help pay operating costs by contracting inmate labor to local manufacturers. The use of juvenile contract labor hindered the growth of reform schools. Manufacturers controlled the children during working hours, and exploitation and brutality were common. Some reform schools were converted into housing units to better serve manufacturers' labor needs.

Concerned citizens and elected officials recognized the inadequacies of reform schools. Public efforts were made to improve institutional life and to reduce the number of children being incarcerated. Special state committees investigated abuses in contract labor systems, and reform schools were added to the list of public institutions that were subject to annual inspection by regulatory agencies.

The First Juvenile Court

The movement toward establishing a separate juvenile court began in 1870, when the Illinois Supreme Court heard *People ex rel O'Connell* v. *Turner*.[3] Daniel O'Connell was committed to the Chicago Reform School for vagrancy. His parents protested the confinement and petitioned the court for Daniel's release. In its decision, which ordered Daniel's release, the Illinois Supreme Court:

- recognized that Daniel's parents genuinely wanted to care for their son;
- held that vagrancy was a matter of misfortune, not a criminal act;
- viewed Daniel's commitment to the Chicago Reform School as a punishment, not merely placement in a school for troubled children; and
- deemed Daniel's incarceration imprisonment—the doctrine of *parens patriae* did not apply and formal due process protections were required.

By the end of the 19th century, debate about juvenile facilities had established the need for differentiating between juveniles and adults in court procedures. Some states had even established children's aid societies to represent juveniles in court and to supervise them in the community.

The first completely separate juvenile court was established in Illinois in 1899. The Illinois legislature passed a law called "An Act to Regulate the Treatment and Control of Dependent, Neglected and Delinquent Children," which established a juvenile court in Cook County that had jurisdiction over any youth who committed an act that would be a crime if committed by an adult. However, young criminal offenders were not the only juveniles who needed help or supervision—the legislation was revised to also give the juvenile court jurisdiction over:

> . . . any child who for any reason is destitute or homeless or abandoned; or dependent on the public for support; or has not proper parental care or guardianship; or who habitually begs or receives alms; or who is found living in any house of ill fame or with any vicious or disreputable person; or whose home, by reason of neglect, cruelty or depravity on part of its parents, guardian or other person in whose care it may be, is an unfit place for such a child; and any child under the age of 8 years who is found peddling or selling any article or singing or playing any musical instrument upon the street or giving any public entertainment.[4]

The intent of the new legislation was to give the juvenile court jurisdiction when the child's best interests would be served.

The Illinois act was a prototype for legislation in other states, and juvenile courts were quickly established in Wisconsin (1901), New York (1901), Ohio (1902), Maryland (1902), and Colorado (1903). By 1945, all states had established separate juvenile courts. New terminology accompanied the establishment of the juvenile court, to differentiate it from adult criminal court. Juvenile offenders are "delinquents" rather than "criminals," they are

Teaching Tip
Point out to students that the public perception of reform school inadequacy was reinforced by the Illinois Supreme Court's *People ex rel O'Connell* v. *Turner* decision. Discuss with students possible reasons why reform schools failed to accomplish their goals.

Professional Issue
Treatment of Juveniles
Invite a juvenile court judge or magistrate to visit your class to discuss with students your state's juvenile justice system. If a judge or magistrate is not available, invite the director of juvenile court services or an intake officer.

Teaching Tip
Remind students that the juvenile court was established to protect children from unjust punishment or imprisonment, then ask for their opinions as to why an adult criminal court trial might be inappropriate for a juvenile.

Teaching Tip

Explain that social and legal movements often result in new language. Draw two columns. Title the first "adult justice" and the second "juvenile justice." List the terms presented in the chapter in the appropriate columns, then point out to students that some people consider the juvenile terms *euphemisms*; that is, words that mean the same thing but are less distasteful. Ask students to think of other criminal justice terms that could be modified for juveniles.

Student Involvement

Organize students into five groups. Assign each of the following cases to a group for review: *Kent, Gault, Winship, McKeiver,* and *Breed.* Ask each group to create a table, recording the following information for each case: date heard, original jurisdiction, issue before the U.S. Supreme Court, facts presented, the Court's decision, and date decided. Encourage students to copy and share the tables with the class for use as study guides.

"taken into custody" rather than "arrested," a "petition" is filed rather than a "charge," juveniles are "held on petition" rather than "indicted," there is an "adjudicatory hearing" rather than a "trial," the court returns a "finding" rather than a "verdict" and imposes a "disposition" rather than a "sentence," the offender is "adjudicated" rather than "convicted," sent to a "training school" rather than a "prison," and put on "aftercare" rather than "parole."

The U.S. Supreme Court and the Juvenile Justice System

For most of the 20th century, all juvenile hearings were considered civil proceedings—rules of criminal procedure did not apply. Juveniles had no constitutional protections, and there were no challenges to the admissibility of evidence or the validity of testimony.

Five landmark U.S. Supreme Court decisions dramatically changed the juvenile justice system, establishing due process rights for juvenile offenders.

***Kent v. United States* (1966)**[5] In 1959, Morris A. Kent, Jr., age 14, was arrested in Washington, D.C. on charges of burglary and attempted purse snatching. He was placed on juvenile probation and returned to his mother's custody. In September 1961, an intruder entered a woman's apartment, raped her, and stole her wallet. Police found Kent's fingerprints at the crime scene. Kent, now age 16 and still on probation, was arrested and charged with rape and robbery. He confessed to these offenses and several similar incidents. Kent's mother retained an attorney, who, anticipating that the case would be transferred to an adult criminal court, filed a motion to oppose the transfer.

The juvenile court judge did not rule on this motion; instead, he waived jurisdiction and remanded Kent to the jurisdiction of the adult criminal court system. Kent was tried in U.S. District Court, found guilty of six counts of housebreaking, and found "not guilty by reason of insanity" on the rape charge. He received indeterminate sentences of 5 to 15 years on each count of housebreaking.

Kent's lawyer appealed the conviction, citing that the juvenile court judge failed to hear motions filed on Kent's behalf before waiving the case to adult criminal court and that Kent's due process rights had been denied. The U.S. Supreme Court heard the case, and Kent's conviction was reversed.

In *Kent*, the Court ruled that, in a case involving transfer of jurisdiction, the juvenile defendant is entitled to certain essential due process rights: (1) a hearing; (2) representation by an attorney; (3) access to records involved in the transfer; and (4) a written statement of reasons for the transfer.

***In re Gault* (1967)**[6] On June 8, 1964, Gerald F. Gault, age 15, was arrested for making a crank telephone call to an adult neighbor and taken to a detention home by the sheriff of Gila County, Arizona. At the time, Gault was on juvenile probation for involvement in the theft of a lady's wallet in February 1964.

The complainant was not present at the juvenile court hearing on the following day. No one was sworn at the hearing, no transcript or recording of the proceedings was made, and no decision was issued. Gault was returned to the detention home—where he remained for several days—then released. At a second hearing, on June 15, the judge committed Gault to the Arizona State Industrial School "for the period of his minority." Gault's attorney filed a petition for a writ of *habeas corpus* that was heard by the U.S. Supreme Court in December 1966.

In its May 1967 *Gault* decision, the U.S. Supreme Court ruled that, in proceedings that might result in commitment to an institution, juveniles have the right to: (1) reasonable notice of charges; (2) counsel; (3) question witnesses; and (4) protection against self-incrimination.

In re Winship (1970)[7] Samuel Winship, age 12, was charged with stealing $112 from a woman's purse. Winship's attorney argued that there was "reasonable doubt" of Winship's guilt. The court agreed, but, because New York juvenile courts operated under the civil court standard of "preponderance of the evidence," adjudicated Winship delinquent and committed him to a training school for 18 months.

The U.S. Supreme Court, in *Winship*, ruled that the reasonable doubt standard should be required in all delinquency adjudications.

McKeiver v. Pennsylvania (1971)[8] Joseph McKeiver, age 16, was charged with robbery, larceny, and receiving stolen property in Philadelphia, when he and 20 or 30 other juveniles took 25 cents from three boys. McKeiver had no prior arrests, was doing well in school, and was employed. McKeiver's attorney requested a jury trial; his request was denied and McKeiver was adjudicated and put on probation.

McKeiver's attorney appealed to the state supreme court on the grounds that the juvenile court violated the 6th Amendment's guarantee of the right to an impartial jury and the 7th Amendment's guarantee of the right to a trial by jury. The state supreme court affirmed the lower court, arguing that, of all due process rights, a trial by jury is the one most likely to destroy the traditional non-adversarial character of juvenile court proceedings.

The U.S. Supreme Court, in *McKeiver*, held that the due process clause of the 14th Amendment did not require jury trials in juvenile court (although a state could provide a jury trial if it wished), that juries are not necessarily more accurate than judges, and that juries could be disruptive and therefore adversarial to the informal atmosphere of the juvenile court.

Breed v. Jones (1975)[9] In February 1971, Gary S. Jones, age 17, was charged with armed robbery and adjudicated delinquent in a Los Angeles juvenile court. The judge deferred sentencing, pending receipt of a predisposition report and a recommendation from the probation department. Jones was returned to detention. When the court reconvened for the disposition hearing, the judge waived jurisdiction to adult criminal court. Counsel for Jones filed a petition for a writ of *habeas corpus*, arguing that waiver to

Juvenile Probation Counselor
Responsibilities include developing, coordinating, and enforcing the supervision and treatment of juveniles placed on probation. Requires skills in case management, assessment, counseling, crisis intervention, ability to think creatively and to work as part of a treatment team. Requires a bachelor's degree in social work, behavioral science, or criminal justice. Master's degree preferred. Extraordinary growth opportunity for motivated person.

Tutorial CD-ROM
Refer students to the Tutorial With Simulation Applications CD-ROM. The tutorial is a comprehensive interactive study tool that reinforces and reviews the concepts in Chapter 14. Also included are two simulations that apply concepts presented in Chapter 14.

criminal court violated the double jeopardy clause of the 5th Amendment. The U.S. District Court denied the petition, saying that Jones had not been tried twice because juvenile adjudication is not a trial. Jones was tried in adult criminal court, convicted of robbery, and committed to the California Youth Authority for an indeterminate period.

The U.S. Supreme Court, in *Breed*, ruled that juvenile adjudication for violation of a criminal statute is equivalent to a criminal court trial; therefore, the double jeopardy clause applied. The Court ordered that Jones be released or remanded to the original juvenile court for a disposition hearing. Jones, now over 18, was released.

Impact on Juvenile Court

The U.S. Supreme Court's decisions in these cases affirmed juvenile due process rights. As a result, the "best interests of the child" is no longer the only concern for juvenile courts; they also are required to protect the juvenile's constitutional rights.

The Contemporary Juvenile Justice System

Age limits for juvenile court jurisdiction are defined by state statutes. In most states, the juvenile court has original jurisdiction over all youths under age 18 at the time of offense, arrest, or referral to court (see Table 14–1).

TABLE 14–1

Oldest Age for Original Juvenile Court Jurisdiction in Delinquency Matters

Age	State
15	Connecticut, New York, North Carolina
16	Georgia, Illinois, Louisiana, Massachusetts, Michigan, Missouri, New Hampshire, South Carolina, Texas, Wisconsin
17	Alabama, Alaska, Arizona, Arkansas, California, Colorado, Delaware, District of Columbia, Florida, Hawaii, Idaho, Indiana, Iowa, Kansas, Kentucky, Maine, Maryland, Minnesota, Mississippi, Montana, Nebraska, Nevada, New Jersey, New Mexico, North Dakota, Ohio, Oklahoma, Oregon, Pennsylvania, Rhode Island, South Dakota, Tennessee, Utah, Vermont, Virginia, Washington, West Virginia, Wyoming

Juvenile Corrections: End of an Era?

Juvenile Crime

U.S. law enforcement agencies arrested approximately 2.6 million juveniles in 1998.[10] According to the Federal Bureau of Investigation (FBI), juveniles accounted for 18 percent of all 1998 arrests, and 17 percent of all 1998 violent crime arrests. Most juvenile arrests were for property crime offenses (see Figure 14–1).

More than 90 percent of the cases handled by juvenile courts are for **delinquent offenses**—acts committed by a juvenile that, if committed by an adult, could result in criminal prosecution. The remaining cases are for **status offenses**—acts that are offenses only when committed by juveniles (e.g., running away, truancy, ungovernability, and liquor law violations). In 1996, liquor law violations accounted for 28 percent of status offense cases; truancy, 24 percent; runaway, 16 percent; ungovernability, 12 percent; and miscellaneous other status offenses, 20 percent.[11]

delinquent offenses
Acts committed by juveniles which, if committed by adults, could result in criminal prosecution.

status offenses   Acts that are law violations only for juveniles: e.g., running away, truancy, or ungovernability (sometimes referred to as incorrigibility or beyond parental control).

FIGURE 14–1

Percent of Arrests Involving Juveniles in 1998

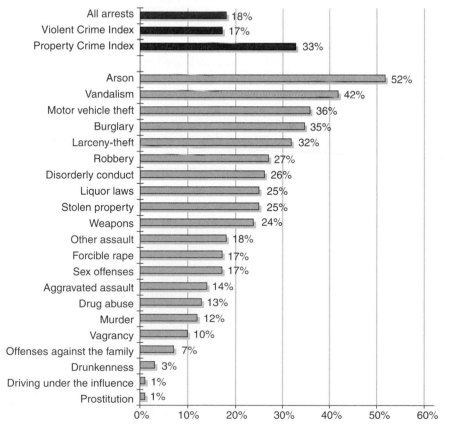

Source: Adapted from Federal Bureau of Investigation, *Crime in the United States 1998* (Washington, DC: U.S. Government Printing Office, 1999), table 38.

Teaching Tip
Before reviewing the data presented in Figure 14–1, ask students what they think might be the top 10 delinquent offenses, then compare their answers with the data presented.

Student Involvement
Organize students into small groups. Instruct each group to assume the role of a task force assigned to determine how the number of juvenile crimes might be reduced. Have each group make a list of five suggestions. Then ask the class to select, by vote, the three that are most likely to have the desired effect.

Sophia Nelson
Drug Counselor and
Parent Educator
West Palm Beach, FL

"Be ready for a roller-coaster ride of emotions. Every day your clients are up and down. Your personality has to be able to adjust to that for you to be successful."

Sophia Nelson is a drug counselor and parent educator in West Palm Beach, Florida. She's been in her job for four years. As a drug counselor, she carries a caseload of 55 clients and conducts intake assessments and provides treatment. As a parent educator, she facilitates group counseling for children and single mothers. She assists the children in her groups with improving their communication and interaction skills and building confidence techniques. She helps single moms improve their life skills that provide them with the knowledge, skills, and attitudes they need to maintain strong family ties, find and keep good jobs, manage their finances, and lead productive lives.

Sophia graduated from Bethune-Cookman College in Daytona Beach, Florida, with a degree in criminal justice. The courses she recalls enjoying the most were those where there was a lot of classroom discussion, especially courses in prisoners' rights, correctional counseling, and social policy. She says she knew from these courses that she wanted a career working with people. Now that she's a drug counselor and parent educator, she feels she contributes to her community by helping people avoid drugs and develop more healthy lifestyles. She says, "I see lives change each day."

For now, Sophia wants to stay working with drug offenders and teaching life skills to parents and children. But one day she hopes to be a prison warden and influence correctional policy on a large scale.

Teaching Tip
Have students review the juvenile delinquent profile presented in the chapter, then ask them if these statistics match their perception of the typical juvenile offender.

Profile of the Juvenile Delinquent

Of the estimated 1.8 million delinquency cases handled by U.S. juvenile courts in 1996:

- Fifty-nine percent involved a juvenile under age 16.
- Seventy-seven percent involved boys.
- Sixty-six percent involved white juveniles, 30 percent black.
- Fifty percent were drug property offenses.

The Juvenile Justice Process

Juvenile offenders are processed through one or more of three phases of the juvenile justice process: intake, adjudication, and disposition. Figure 14–2 shows that U.S. juvenile courts processed almost 1.8 million delinquency cases in 1996. Juvenile courts also processed 162,000 status offense cases. Fifty-two percent of these status offense cases were adjudicated; the disposition was probation in almost 60 percent of the cases.

FIGURE 14–2

Juvenile Court Processing of Delinquency Cases, 1996

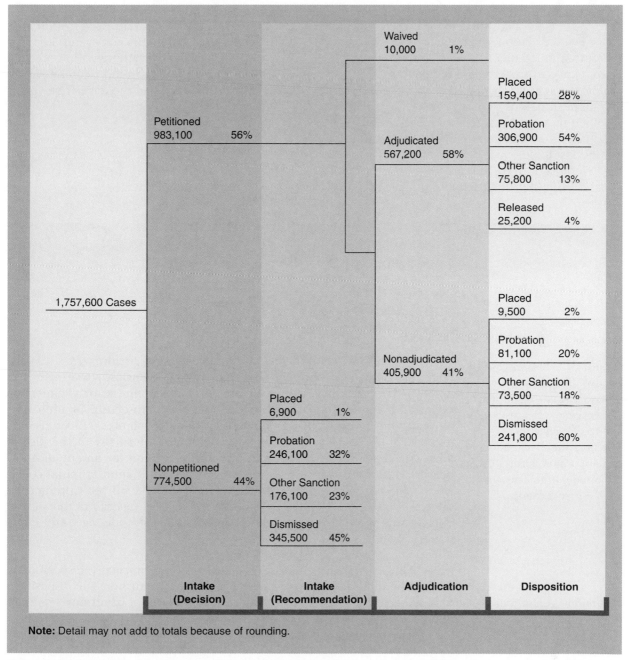

Note: Detail may not add to totals because of rounding.

Source: Anne L. Stahl, Melissa Sickmund, Terrence A. Finnegan, Howard N. Snyder, Rowen S. Poole, and Nancy Tierney, *Juvenile Court Statistics 1996* (Washington, DC: U.S. Department of Justice, Office of Juvenile Justice and Delinquency Prevention, July 1999), p. 9.

Working with teens is especially challenging for me because—being a recent college graduate—I am not that much older than youths who are expected to do what I tell them, whether they want to or not. There are a lot of situations that can get sticky. When they do, I just remind myself to be patient and that I am many of these kids' last hope.

Most of these kids are 180-day expulsion cases from their high schools. If I give up on them, the only alternative is dropping out altogether. Each time I think of giving up I ask myself: "If this student dropped from school today could my conscience be clear that I did everything within my power to work with them?" You know what? I have not had the answer be yes yet.

Julie Judge
Teacher
Alternative Learning Center
Florissant, Missouri

Intake

intake The first stage of the juvenile justice process. A court-appointed officer reviews the case and recommends a course of action—dismissal, informal disposition, formal disposition, or transfer to adult criminal court.

In the first phase of the juvenile justice process, **intake**, cases that are referred to juvenile court (by law enforcement agencies, social agencies, school personnel, parents or guardians, probation officers, or victims) are reviewed by a court-appointed officer (usually a prosecutor or probation officer), who recommends a course of action. The intake officer recommends that the case be: (1) dismissed, (2) resolved informally (no petition is filed with the court), (3) resolved formally (a petition for an adjudication hearing is filed with the court), or (4) transferred to adult criminal court. The juvenile court establishes guidelines for the intake officer. Criteria considered in the decision in many jurisdictions include: severity of the alleged offense, any prior history of delinquent behavior, attitude, age, and emotional stability.

diversion A non-judicial juvenile sanction.

Informal Disposition In cases that are resolved informally, disposition is decided by the intake officer, and the case goes no further. The disposition imposed is usually informal probation or some form of **diversion**—requiring the youth to make restitution or referring the youth to a local social service agency. Diversion is generally an option only for status offenders or low-risk delinquent offenders.

Formal Disposition   In cases that are to be resolved formally, the intake officer files a petition for an adjudicatory hearing and decides whether the youth should be confined while awaiting the hearing.

Detention Hearing   If the intake officer decides that secure placement is advisable, the youth is taken to a **juvenile detention facility**. In general terms, a juvenile detention facility serves to keep juvenile offenders in secure custody through various stages of the juvenile justice process, to protect the community and the juvenile, and to ensure appearance at scheduled hearings.

A juvenile who is placed in a detention facility by an intake officer must have a **detention hearing**, usually within 48 hours. During this hearing, the court reviews the intake officer's confinement decision and orders either release or continued detention pending adjudication and disposition.

Also during the detention hearing, the court determines whether the youth has legal representation and, if not, appoints defense counsel. The court may also appoint a **guardian** *ad litem*, who serves as a special guardian for the youth throughout the court proceedings. In many jurisdictions, defense counsel also serves as guardian.

Adjudication

In the second phase of the juvenile justice process, **adjudication**, a juvenile court hears the case. A **juvenile court** is any court that has original jurisdiction over matters involving juveniles.

Adjudicatory Hearing   During the adjudicatory hearing, attorneys typically present physical evidence, examine and cross-examine witnesses, and argue on behalf of their clients. If, after hearing arguments, the court rules that the evidence supports the allegations, a predisposition report is ordered and a disposition hearing scheduled.

Disposition

In the third phase of the juvenile justice process, the juvenile court decides on a **disposition**.

Predisposition Report   The court's disposition decision is based on its review of the intake report (information regarding the current offense and any previous delinquent behavior—crime severity and prior adjudication greatly influence the decision) and the **predisposition report**, a document, usually prepared by a probation officer, similar to the PSI discussed in Chapter 5. A predisposition report typically includes (1) medical and psychological background; (2) educational history; (3) information gathered from interviews with the juvenile, family members, and other people who know the youth; (4) availability of appropriate placement options; and (5) recommendations for suitable disposition. Any treatment "needs" of the youth are also considered.

juvenile detention facility   A facility for keeping juvenile offenders in secure custody, as necessary, through various stages of the juvenile justice process.

detention hearing   A judicial review of the intake officer's detention decision.

guardian *ad litem*   A person appointed by the juvenile court, often defense counsel, to serve as a special guardian for the youth being processed through the juvenile justice system.

adjudication   The second stage of the juvenile justice process—the court decides whether or not the offender is responsible for (guilty of) the alleged offense.

juvenile court   Any court that has jurisdiction over matters involving juveniles.

disposition   The third stage of the juvenile justice process—the court decides the disposition (sentence) for a juvenile case.

predisposition report   A report that documents: (1) the juvenile's background; (2) educational history; (3) information gathered from interviews with the juvenile, family members, and others; (4) available placement options; and (5) recommended dispositions.

Juvenile probation officers play an important role in the juvenile justice process, beginning with intake and continuing through the period in which a juvenile is under court supervision. Why is writing the predisposition report such an important part of the probation officer's responsibilities?

Teaching Tip
Ask students to find out what is involved in your state's juvenile disposition hearings and adult sentencing hearings, including any rules for procedure, then identify ways in which the two differ. For example, disposition hearings are likely to be private unless the state permits open proceedings for selected offenses, while adult sentencing hearings are usually public.

group home   A non-secure residential facility for juveniles.

Student Involvement
Ask students if the conditions in Figure 14–3 are appropriate, too harsh, or not harsh enough.

Disposition Hearing   At the disposition hearing the court imposes the appropriate sanction. In some jurisdictions, the youth is remanded either to the state correctional system or to a social service agency. Many juvenile courts ensure that adjudicated juveniles receive an appropriate disposition by establishing predefined sanctions based on type of offense, past delinquency, effectiveness of previous interventions, and assessment of special treatment, counseling, or training needs. Some of the more widely used sanctions are juvenile probation, group homes, residential treatment centers, boot camps, and commitment to juvenile correctional institutions.

If the sanction imposed is probation, the youth is permitted to remain in the community under the supervision of a court services officer. Figure 14–3 shows a supervision agreement used by the juvenile court of Topeka, Kansas.

If a youth poses a threat to public safety but incarceration is not warranted, the court may impose Intensive Supervised Probation (ISP). The major differences between regular probation and ISP are (1) more rigid conditions, and (2) more frequent contact between the probation officer and the probationer—more face-to-face interaction, closer monitoring of the juvenile's activities, and more frequent evaluation of the juvenile's progress.

Another sanction that may be imposed is referral to a **group home**. Group homes are operated by private agencies, under contract with local or state government; or by the public corrections unit, under direction of the juvenile court. Typically, group homes accommodate 15 to 30 residents. They provide living quarters, recreational and leisure areas, kitchen and dining room, and meeting room space. Youths attend school in the community, participate in field trips, and may be granted special passes to visit family, attend religious services, or participate in activities. The range of services provided by the group home often depends on the type of offender usually

FIGURE 14-3

Sample Juvenile Court Supervision Agreement

SUPERVISION AGREEMENT

Name _____ Andrea Johnson _____ Case Number _____ 00JV2751 _____

In accordance with authority conferred by the laws of the state of Kansas, you have been placed under the supervision of Court Services It is the order of the Court that you comply with any special conditions, programs, or counseling as set forth by the supervision Court Services Officer.

The following conditions will apply:

___X___ 1.   You will attend all regularly scheduled appointments with the Court Services Officer and comply with their directions. If you are ill, it is your responsibility to make other arrangements.

___X___ 2.   You will obey all laws of the State and ordinances of the City. You are to immediately report any contacts with law enforcement to your Court Services Officer.

___X___ 3.   You are to obey the rules of your home. Persistent disobedience will be considered a violation of your supervision.

___X___ 4.   You are not to leave the state of Kansas nor change residence without permission of your Court Services Officer. You are to notify the officer of any change in address prior to moving. You will reside in the home of your parent(s) or approved guardian and will not be permitted to spend the night away from home without prior permission of said parent(s) or guardian.

___X___ 5.   You will attend school every day and obey all school regulations. Suspension, truancies, and tardies could result in further court action. If you are home due to illness or school suspensions, you are to consider yourself on a form of house arrest. This means if you are ill, you are only permitted to leave to attend verifiable doctors appointments. If you are on suspension, you are not to leave your home unless you are with a parent or guardian.

_____ 6.   If you have been excused form attending school, you will obtain employment (get a job) and work faithfully at that job in order to maintain it. You will not quit any job without first discussing it with your Court Service Officer. If you are fired or laid off from a job, you are required to report that fact to your Court Service Officer by the end of the next business day.

___X___ 7.   You will neither possess nor carry firearms or other weapons.

___X___ 8.   You will neither use nor possess any alcohol, narcotics, or other controlled substances.

_____ 9.   Your are to submit to chemical tests of blood, breath, or urine.

___X___ 10. You have a curfew. If you are under the age of 15, your curfew is 9:00 p.m. Sunday through Thursday, and 10:30 p.m. Friday and Saturday. If you are 15 or older, your curfew is 10:00 p.m. Friday and Saturday. If your are 15 or older, your curfew is 10:00 Sunday through Thursday, and 12:00 midnight Friday and Saturday, Curfew means that you will be inside your own residence by the stated time. With parent or guardian's permission, you may attend a school or church sponsored function at the school or church you attend, but must be home not later than 30 minutes after the end of the event.

- 1 -

FIGURE 14-3 (continued)

Sample Juvenile Court Supervision Agreement

_____11.   It will be considered a violation of your supervision if you display clothing or insignia indicating membership in a gang, or carry a beeper, pager, or cellular telephone equipment.

_X_ 12.   You will not be discharged from supervision until all costs, fees, and restitution has been paid in full.

Traffic/City Ordinance   District Court   Guardian Ad Litem

Fines: _____   Costs: $25.00   Fees: _____   Restitution: $299.95

_X_ Payment Plan $54.16/month for 6 months _____

_X_ I will complete _20_ hours Community Service Work (X) in addition to, or ( ) in lieu of the above.

SPECIAL CONDITIONS:

_X_ a). Do not go into Electronics Plus for 6 months.

_X_ b). Within two weeks, write a letter of apology to Ms. Valerie Carte, owner of Electronics Plus.

_X_ c). Do not quit your weekend job at Bruno's grocery store until court costs and restitution are paid.

_X_ d). Write a three page paper on why shoplifting is wrong and hand deliver it to Judge Gray in three weeks.

I have read, understood, initialed and agreed to abide by all terms and special conditions of my supervision as explained by the assigned Court Services Officer. I understand fully that my failure to comply could result in the imposition of additional condition, revocation and/or out of home placement.

DATE: May 17, 2000   SIGNED: _Andrea Johnson_
                                    Respondent

                                     Rosalind Johnson
                                     Parent or Guardian

                                     Larry Bayens
                                     Court Services Officer

cc: Working File
    Respondent
    Parents or Guardian

- 2 -

referred. Some group homes are treatment-oriented, providing individual and/or group counseling to youths with problems such as substance abuse or lack of self-control.

Another community-based program is the **residential treatment center**. Residential treatment centers often provide long-term care and intensive treatment services.

Today, most states have juvenile boot camps. Boot camp programs vary in size, requirements, and structure. For the most part, juvenile corrections officials have been slow to accept the boot camp concept; they consider the amount of time devoted to military drill, ceremony, and exercise an encroachment on the time available for education or rehabilitation programs.

The most restrictive sanction that a juvenile court may impose is commitment to a juvenile correctional institution. Although the juvenile justice system is different from the adult criminal justice system, many juvenile correctional institutions resemble adult correctional institutions. Access to the facilities is restricted, and perimeter fences are equipped with razor wire. Surveillance cameras, located throughout the complex, are monitored from a central security location. Housing units are austere physical structures that emphasize security.

Characteristics of the estimated 73,000 juvenile offenders confined in juvenile correctional facilities are similar to those of adult prisoners: 90 percent are male, 46 percent are black, 40 percent have committed property offenses (larceny, burglary, auto theft, or vandalism), and 29 percent have committed violent crimes (murder, rape, robbery, or assault).[12] The average age of confined youths is 15.[13] The average time served is eight months.[14]

A few states have responded to violent juvenile crime by enacting **blended sentencing** legislation: the juvenile court may impose both a juvenile sentence and an adult criminal sentence. In 1996, the Kansas legislature passed a blended sentencing law that created a new category, referred to as "extended jurisdiction juvenile prosecution," for serious and violent offenders.[15] Under this legislation, two sentences are imposed, but the adult criminal sentence is waived if the juvenile offender does not violate any of the provisions of the juvenile sentence.

Transfer to Adult Criminal Court

All states and the District of Columbia allow adult criminal prosecution of juveniles under certain circumstances. Juveniles may be transferred to adult criminal court under one of three provisions: waiver, direct file, or statutory exclusion. Under **waiver provisions**, the juvenile court orders transfer of the case to adult criminal court. In all but four states (Massachusetts, Nebraska, New Mexico, and New York), a juvenile court judge is authorized to waive the juvenile court's original jurisdiction over cases that meet certain criteria and to refer them to criminal court for prosecution. Under **direct file provisions**, the prosecutor determines whether to initiate a case against a juvenile in juvenile court or in adult criminal court. Fifteen states have statutes that specify circumstances in which the prosecutor may make the transfer decision. Under **statutory exclusion provisions**, state law specifies adult criminal court jurisdiction for certain juvenile cases. An increasing number of states (28 in 1996) automatically

residential treatment center A residential facility that provides intensive treatment services to juveniles.

Student Involvement Have interested students research several juvenile boot camps and report their findings to the class. Organize a debate about juvenile boot camps. Allow each side 5–7 minutes to present arguments and 2–3 minutes for rejoinders, then open the debate to discussion.

blended sentencing A two-part (juvenile and adult) sentence—the adult sentence may be waived if the offender complies with all provisions of the juvenile sentence.

waiver provisions Provisions under which the juvenile court orders transfer of the case to adult criminal court.

direct file provisions Provisions under which the prosecutor determines whether to initiate a case against a juvenile in juvenile court or in adult criminal court.

statutory exclusion provisions Provisions under which adult criminal court jurisdiction for certain juvenile cases is established by state law.

exclude from juvenile court any cases that meet specific age and offense criteria. In 1996, 10,000 juvenile cases were transferred to adult criminal court. Of these, 43 percent involved a crime against a person; 37 percent involved property crime; 14 percent involved a drug law violation; and 6 percent involved a public order offense.[16]

Teen Courts

teen courts Courts in which youths adjudicate and impose disposition for a juvenile offense.

Teen courts, also called peer and youth courts, have become a popular alternative to the traditional juvenile court for relatively young or first-time offenders. The teen court was first used in Grand Prairie, Texas, in 1976.[17] Since then the number of teen courts has grown, to between 400 and 500 nationwide in 1998.[18] Teen courts handled approximately 65,000 cases in 1998.

Teen courts use one of four models: Adult Judge, Youth Judge, Tribunal, or Peer Jury. In the Adult Judge model, an adult serves as judge, ruling on legal terminology and courtroom procedure, and youth serve as attorneys, jurors, clerks, bailiffs, etc. The Youth Judge model parallels the Adult Judge model, with the exception that a youth serves as judge. In the Tribunal model, youth attorneys present the case to a panel of three youth judges. The Peer Jury model uses no attorneys—the case is presented to a youth jury by

THE OFFENDER SPEAKS

What about kids? Most juvenile delinquents often show hostile attitudes and are rebellious toward authority because the media shows that it's okay, and these children without adequate supervision will do damn well what they please. A lot of people commit crimes and get away with it, reports the media, and it's cool. The juvenile thinks he can get away with it too, and wants to be cool.

In a broken or poor home, the parent(s) are working all the time so that no one is around the child to give him guidance. Improving family life and enhancing educational systems to make education an exciting and growth-producing experience for juveniles is half the step to crime control.

But is all that what "the man" wants to hear? It's easier to lock those kids up than to put a brake on the media and reduce the opportunities for kids to be alone. When I get out of this hell hole, I hope that somebody will listen! Our children are our future, and if those children are running wild on the streets of Chicago or Columbia, they are going to be here with me, before you know it.

William Geer
Broad River Correctional Institution
Columbia, SC

a youth or adult and the jury questions the defendant directly. Forty-seven percent of teen courts use the Adult Judge model, 12 percent the Peer Jury, 10 percent the Tribunal, and 9 percent the Youth Judge. The remaining 22 percent use more than one model.

Most teen courts require that the defendant plead guilty before participating in the program; only a small number determine guilt or innocence. In teen courts, offenders are sentenced by their peers.

Teen courts are particularly effective in jurisdictions where disposition of misdemeanor offenses is given low priority because of heavy caseloads and focus on more serious offenders. Teen courts also teach young people valuable life skills and provide positive peer influence. Volunteers serve as jurors, attorneys, court clerks, bailiffs, and, in some cases, judges.

According to the Office of Juvenile Justice and Delinquency Prevention (OJJDP), community service was the most common disposition imposed in teen court cases in 1998. Other dispositions included victim apology letters, apology essays, teen court jury duty, drug/alcohol classes, and monetary restitution.

Tammy Hawkins, Teen Court Coordinator for Odessa, Texas, says that teen court makes quite an impact when you give a teenaged jury sole discretion in handing down sentences. "The juvenile defendant receives this sentence from his peers and sees that they are saying, 'We as your peers do not agree with your actions and breaking the law is not acceptable.' A child is more likely to listen to one of their own, as opposed to an adult or the system. After all, as one defendant put it, 'Your peers are the ones that you want to accept you.'"[19]

HELP WANTED

Juvenile Detention Officer

Duties: Maintaining security; Supervising youth; Inspecting for contraband, damage, and repairs; Implementing emergency procedures; Escorting youth to activities, Maintaining an accurate count of residents; Providing non-physical crisis intervention and resolution; Completing logs, security checks, and reports. Requirements: Two years of college in criminology, corrections, law enforcement, or related field. Experience working with youth in a supervised setting.

Youth Gangs

In a 1999 OJJDP National Youth Gang Center (NYGC) survey, 3,024 law enforcement agencies reported that an estimated 30,818 gangs, with an estimated 846,428 members, were active across the United States.[20] About half of these agencies reported worsening gang problems. All states, and nearly all large cities, reported youth gang problems.[21]

The youth gang problem is one of the most important issues for juvenile corrections today. Many of the youths confined for serious crimes commit violent acts as gang members. For some correctional institutions, a primary housing consideration is a youth's gang affiliation—rival gang members must be housed separately. Juvenile correctional personnel regularly deal with problems that stem from gang-related activity within the institution: extortion, violence, and attempts to smuggle in contraband.

One of the more pressing gang-related issues facing today's juvenile corrections agencies is identification of youth gangs. A **gang** is a group of individuals involved in continuing criminal activity. The group need not wear similar clothing ("colors") or tattoos, have hand signs, initiation rituals, or even a specific name (e.g., "Crips" or "Bloods") to be a gang—participation in criminal activity is what distinguishes community groups or social clubs from gangs.

gang A group of individuals involved in continuing criminal activity.

Graffiti is a common method of communication for gangs;[22] the gang "newspaper" or "bulletin board," graffiti communicates many messages, including challenges, warnings, and pronouncements. Juvenile corrections professionals must become familiar with gang language, graffiti, and symbols to be able to deal with gang power and control. A partial listing of gang slang is shown in Table 14–2.

TABLE 14–2

Selected Terms Commonly Associated with Gangs

A-K	An assault rifle
All That	Something that possesses good qualities
Ay Yo Trip	To gain another's attention
Bag Up	To be arrested by the police
Baller	A gang member who makes money
Bama	A person who can't dress
Bang	To fight to kill
Battle	To compete, i.e., freestyle rapping
Blood	A member of a Los Angeles gang whose color is red
Blunt	A marijuana cigarette
Crab	A derogatory name for a Crip
Crip	A member of a Los Angeles gang whose color is blue
Cuz	A greeting, primarily used for Crip members
Down	To meet expectations
Five-O	The police
Fly Girl	A very attractive female
Gangbanging	To participate in gang activity
Gat	A gun
Hay Shen	A term for crack cocaine
Head Up	To fight one-on-one
Hezee	A home or house
Highroller	A Crip term for someone in the gang who makes much money
Homeboy/Homie	Someone from the neighborhood or gang
Hood	The neighborhood or turf
Jet	To go or leave
Jumped In	To be initiated into a gang, usually by getting beat up
Kickin' It	To hang out with the gang
Knockin Boots	To have sex
Loco	A crazy person
No Diggity	To accept as the truth
OG	An original gangster; considered when you have killed someone
Peel	To kill
Rifa	To rule
Salty (You)	To think you know everything
Set	An individual gang
Smoke	To kill
Snaps	A term for money
Whadup Dawg	A way of greeting friends
Yash	A greeting used on the telephone to attract attention

Source: Adapted from several online sources [http://www.cus.wayne.edu/u_safety/gang_slang01.html; http://www.leevalley.co.uk/yush/rewind/yush0111/slang.htm]

One reason that gangs successfully recruit members within the correctional setting is that the transition to a confined existence can be traumatic. Residents often challenge new arrivals, usually within the first few days, threatening physical harm to intimidate and exploit the youth. A youth who is the object of such an encounter may believe that joining a gang is the only way to survive.

Another reason that incarcerated juveniles join gangs is boredom. Their typical daily routine includes eating meals, exercise, and schoolwork. Leisure activities, family visitation, social programs, and other special services are intermittent, and are permitted only if the juvenile complies with institution rules. Involvement in gang activity may represent excitement and adventure for confined juveniles.

The American Correctional Association and Juvenile Justice Reform

Since it was founded in 1870, the American Correctional Association (ACA) has advocated juvenile justice reform. In a 1997 campaign for juvenile justice reform, the ACA called for:

- Legislative and community action to fund and operate early-intervention strategies;
- Support of continued research, and responsible action based on the results of research already available, on prevention programs that work;
- Support of system reforms that allow juvenile justice officials, family, social, educational and other agencies and institutions to relate to a specific child, and to work together for the best interests of the child, including accountability or shared use of confidential information about children at risk;
- Support of programs that address the causes of violent and delinquent activity in communities;
- Opposition to efforts to establish automatic certification of juvenile offenders to adult status for certain offenses;
- Opposition to determinate sentencing for juvenile offenders;
- Support of the use of confidential systems for information-sharing about juvenile offenders.[23]

Juvenile justice officials and the courts rely on the ACA for guidance. The ACA responds to more than 20,000 members, disseminating information, establishing advisory standards for juvenile corrections, providing technical assistance, and training juvenile corrections personnel.

Cross-Cultural Perspective
Gangs, both juvenile and adult, often form along racial and/or ethnic lines. Have students review Chapter 11's discussion about adult prison gangs, then ask if they think the strategies mentioned for controlling gang-related violence in adult institutions might be applied in juvenile institutions. What other strategies do they think might be used to control juvenile gang-related violence?

Teaching Tip
Review with students the list of juvenile justice reform measures advocated by the ACA. Which are short-term strategies? Long-range reform strategies? Which do students think are most likely to be implemented?

Teaching Tip
Refer to Chapter 14 of the *Instructor's Resource Manual* for additional activities and for answers to the end-of-chapter exercises.

SUMMARY BY CHAPTER OBJECTIVES

CHAPTER OBJECTIVE 1

Parens patriae is a legal philosophy that is used to justify intervention in children's lives when their parents are unwilling or unable to care for them.

CHAPTER OBJECTIVE 2

Houses of Refuge, the first legally chartered custodial institutions for juvenile offenders, were established in the early 19th century. Reform schools, which were established in the middle of the 19th century, sought to reform rather than punish young offenders through vocational (especially trade and industrial), physical, and military education. Reform schools for girls used "cottage-like" residential units. Industrial schools emerged in the latter part of the 19th century and emphasized vocational training for youthful offenders.

CHAPTER OBJECTIVE 3

The first completely separate juvenile court in the United States was established in Cook County (Chicago), Illinois, in 1899 and had jurisdiction over youth who committed acts that would be crimes if committed by adults and youth who were in danger of growing up to be paupers or in need of supervision. By 1945, separate juvenile courts had been established in all states.

CHAPTER OBJECTIVE 4

Five U.S. Supreme Court decisions established due process rights for juvenile offenders:

- *Kent* v. *United States* (1966)—a juvenile who is to be transferred to adult criminal court is entitled to a hearing, representation by an attorney, access to records being considered by the juvenile court, and a statement of reasons for the transfer.
- *In re Gault* (1967)—in a proceeding that might result in commitment to an institution, a juvenile is entitled to: reasonable notice of

charges; counsel; question witnesses; and protection against self-incrimination.

- *In re Winship* (1970)—proof beyond a reasonable doubt, not simply a preponderance of the evidence, is required during the adjudicatory stage for a delinquent offense.
- *McKeiver* v. *Pennsylvania* (1971)—trial by jury is not a constitutional requirement for juvenile adjudication.
- *Breed* v. *Jones* (1975)—transfer to adult criminal court after juvenile court adjudication constitutes double jeopardy.

CHAPTER OBJECTIVE 5

Most cases handled by the juvenile courts are for delinquent offenses—acts committed by a juvenile that, if committed by an adult, could result in criminal prosecution. The remaining cases are for status offenses—acts that are offenses only when committed by juveniles. Such offenses include running away, truancy, ungovernability, and liquor law violations.

CHAPTER OBJECTIVE 6

Juvenile delinquents are young persons, usually under age 18, who commit acts which, if committed by an adult, could result in criminal prosecution. The typical juvenile offender is a 16-year-old white male property offender.

CHAPTER OBJECTIVE 7

The three stages of the juvenile justice process are intake, adjudication, and disposition. During the intake stage, a court-appointed officer recommends a course of action—dismissal, informal disposition, formal disposition, or, in some instances, transfer to adult criminal court—for a juvenile who has been referred to the juvenile court. Adjudication is judicial determination of guilt or innocence. Disposition is judicial imposition of the most appropriate sanction.

CHAPTER OBJECTIVE 8

Disposition for the majority of juvenile offenders is probation. Other dispositions include placement in group homes, residential treatment centers, juvenile boot camps, or juvenile correctional institutions.

CHAPTER OBJECTIVE 9

Teen court, an alternative to the traditional juvenile court, operates under one of four models: adult judge (an adult serves as judge); youth judge (a youth serves as judge); tribunal (youth attorneys present the case to youth judges); or peer jury (a youth or adult presents the case to a youth jury). Common teen court dispositions are apologies, educational and/or counseling programs, restitution, and community service.

CHAPTER OBJECTIVE 10

A gang is a group of individuals involved in continuing criminal activity. Youth gangs are a serious problem for juvenile correctional professionals. For some juvenile institutions, gang affiliation is an important consideration in housing arrangements.

KEY TERMS

parens patriae, p. 403
reform school, p. 404
delinquent offenses, p. 409
status offenses, p. 409
intake, p. 412
diversion, p. 412
juvenile detention facility, p. 413
detention hearing, p. 413
guardian ad litem, p. 413
adjudication, p. 413
juvenile court, p. 413

disposition, p. 413
predisposition report, p. 413
group home, p. 414
residential treatment center, p. 417
blended sentencing, p. 417
waiver provisions, p. 417
direct file provisions, p. 417
statutory exclusion provisions, p. 417
teen courts, p. 418
gangs, p. 419

QUESTIONS FOR REVIEW

1. Explain the principle of parens patriae.
2. Distinguish among Houses of Refuge, reform schools, and industrial schools.
3. Where and when was the first completely separate juvenile court established?
4. What five U.S. Supreme Court rulings established due process rights for juveniles? What impact did each have on juvenile court proceedings?
5. What is a delinquent offense? A status offense?
6. What is the typical juvenile delinquent's age? Gender? Race?
7. Identify and explain the three stages of the juvenile justice process.
8. What are the three provisions for transferring juveniles to adult criminal court?
9. What is blended sentencing?
10. What is a guardian ad litem?

11. What is a predisposition report? To what does it compare in adult criminal court?
12. What is the most common sanction imposed by a juvenile court?
13. What is a group home? A residential treatment center?
14. What are the characteristics of the typical offender confined in a juvenile correctional institution?
15. What is teen court? How does it operate?
16. What is a gang? What impact do youth gangs have on juvenile correctional institutions?
17. Why is it important for juvenile corrections professionals to stay informed about gang affiliation, membership, and graffiti?
18. What is the American Correctional Association's position on juvenile justice reform?

ON-THE-JOB ISSUE

Read the following case.

IN THE MATTER OF: BETH LEONARD

CHARGES: Three (3) counts of retail theft. Hoover police were summoned to the Hoover Mall branch store of Fancy This on March 17, 2000, at 11:20 a.m. regarding a shoplifter. Beth Leonard was arrested at 11:52 a.m. for three (3) counts of retail theft.

An employee noticed Beth entering the dressing room with a blue short outfit and a swimsuit. Beth exited the dressing room carrying only her purse. After a quick scan of the room, the attendant, unable to locate the clothes, called security. Beth was led to the manager's office, where she confessed to putting the items on under her clothing and attempting to leave.

When the police arrived, they asked for identification and discovered a bottle of Spring Musk Perfume bearing a new, undamaged sales sticker in Beth's purse. When the officer asked if Beth had a receipt, she stated she had purchased the perfume but upon further prompting admitted that she had taken this item from the Perfumeria, a mall perfume store.

A further search of Beth's purse revealed two pairs of earrings with sales stickers from Carters, a mall accessory shop. Beth admitted to taking these items without purchasing them.

While searching Beth's purse, the officer located her wallet and found $85 in cash. When asked why she didn't just pay for the items, Beth stated she was planning to purchase a gift for her parents' wedding anniversary.

Beth was questioned as to why she had taken these items and she stated she did not know. She was then transported to the Hoover police department and her parents were called.

When Beth's parents arrived, a conference was held between the parents, Beth, and the arresting officer. During this conference, Beth stated that all her girlfriends did this and they never got caught. She was dared by one to bring certain items to her with the sales tags still intact to prove that she had not paid for them. It was dumb, but she did it, and she was sorry.

ITEMS:

Tank top		Perfume	$12
short set	$25	Two pairs of	
Swimsuit	$38	earrings	$32

PERSONAL DATA:

Beth Leonard is 16 years old and resides at 612 Mockingbird Lane in Hoover. She has a younger brother who is in junior high and an older sister who is just ready to start college. Her parents have been married 20 years.

Beth started working at Pizza House after volleyball season. During the school year, she works 20 hours a week; during the summer, she works 35 hours a week.

Beth is a straight A student. She plans to pursue a college degree in teaching Spanish. Beth is an active member of Spanish Club and is a member of Spanish Honor Society. She has played on her high school volleyball team for two years.

If you were the intake officer handling this case, would you recommend that it be handled by a teen court? Why or why not?

CORRECTIONS ISSUES

1. The Sentencing Project reports that abuse (physical and sexual) and suicide rates are higher for children who serve time in adult correctional institutions than for those held in juvenile correctional institutions—youths held in adult institutions are 7.7 times more likely to commit suicide, 5 times more likely to be sexually assaulted, twice as likely to be beaten by staff, and 50 percent more likely to be attacked with a weapon.[24] What conclusions might you draw from this report?

2. Juvenile court proceedings are becoming more accessible to the public. At least 21 states now permit open juvenile court proceedings for serious or violent crime charges or repeat offenses. In 1995, Georgia passed a law allowing the public admission to adjudicatory hearings for youths who have been charged with delinquent offenses. Do you think juvenile court proceedings should be open to the public? Why or why not?

CORRECTIONS ON THE WEB

1. Go to the FBI Web page at **http://www.fbi.gov** and in the search box type "gang." Then scroll to the document *Law Enforcement True Story, Gang Alert*. Read the scenarios and decide which the FBI would classify as a gang.

2. Access the National Youth Court Center at its Web site (**http://www.appa-net.org**). Determine the status of teen courts in your state.

ADDITIONAL READINGS

Leonard, Kimberly Kempf, Carl E. Pope, and William H. Feyerherm (eds.). *Minorities in Juvenile Justice*. Thousand Oaks, CA: Sage Publications, 1995.

Watkins, Jr., John C. *The Juvenile Justice Century: A Socio-Legal Commentary on American Juvenile Courts*. Durham, NC: Carolina Academic Press, 1998.

ENDNOTES

1. Tom Sheehan, "Buddy testifies teen didn't like his stepmother," *The Columbus Dispatch*, February 2, 2000, p. 1B.
2. Ken Wooden, *Weeping in the Playtime of Others* (New York: McGraw-Hill, 1976), pp. 23–24.
3. *People ex rel. O'Connell* v. *Turner*, 55 Ill.280, 8 Am. Rep. 645.
4. R. M. Mennel, *Thorns and Thistles: Juvenile Delinquency in the United States, 1825-1940* (Hanover, NH: University Press of New England, 1973), p. 131.
5. *Kent* v. *United States*, 383 U.S. 541 (1966).
6. *In re Gault*, 387 U.S. 1, 55 (1967).
7. *In re Winship*, 397 U.S. 358 (1970).
8. *McKeiver* v. *Pennsylvania*, 403 U.S. 528 (1971).
9. *Breed* v. *Jones*, 421 U.S. 519 (1975).
10. Howard N. Snyder, *Juvenile Arrests 1998* (Washington, DC: Office of Juvenile Justice and Delinquency Prevention, December 1999), p. 1.
11. Anne L. Stahl, Melissa Sickmund, Terrence A. Finnegan, Howard N. Snyder, Rowen S. Poole, and Nancy Tierney, *Juvenile Court Statistics 1996* (Washington, DC: Office of Juvenile Justice and Delinquency Prevention, July 1999).
12. S. Rudenstine, *Juvenile Admissions to State Custody, 1993* (Washington, DC: Office of Juvenile Justice and Delinquency Prevention, 1995). American Correctional Association, *1997 Directory, Juvenile and Adult Correctional Departments, Institutions, Agencies, and Paroling Authorities* (Lanham, MD, 1997), p. xxiv.
13. American Correctional Association, op. cit., p. 39.
14. Melissa Sickmund, Howard N. Snyder, and Eileen Poe-Yamagata, *Juvenile Offenders and Victims: 1997 Update on Violence* (Washington DC: Office of Juvenile Justice and Delinquency Prevention, 1997).
15. Gerald Bayens, *Assessing the Impact of Judicial Waiver Laws in Kansas: Implications for Correctional Policy* (Ann Arbor, MI: University Microfilms International, 1998).
16. Anne L. Stahl, *Delinquency Cases Waived to Criminal Court, 1987–1996* (Washington, DC: Office of Juvenile Justice and Delinquency Prevention, April 1999).
17. Tammy Hawkins (personal communication, September 21, 1998).
18. "A Second Chance," *TIME*, August 2, 1999, p. 100.
19. Tammy Hawkins (personal communication, September 21, 1998).
20. *1996 National Youth Gang Survey* (Washington, DC: Office of Juvenile Justice and Delinquency Prevention, 1999).
21. James H. Burch and Betty M. Chemers, *A Comprehensive Response to America's Youth Gang Problem* (Washington, DC: Office of Juvenile Justice and Delinquency Prevention, 1997).
22. Jeff Ferrell, "Criminological Verstehen: Inside the Immediacy of Crime," *Justice Quarterly*, Volume 14, Number 1, 1997, pp. 3–23.
23. James Turpin, "Juvenile Justice in the Spotlight," *Corrections Today*, Volume 59, Number 3, 1997, p. 124.
24. *Briefing Paper: Prosecuting Juveniles in Adult Court* (Washington, DC: The Sentencing Project, 1999).

15 The Victim
Role in the Correctional Process

CHAPTER OBJECTIVES

After completing this chapter you should be able to:

1. Briefly summarize the history of America's victims' rights movement.
2. Identify and describe important federal victims' rights legislation.
3. Understand why a victims' rights amendment to the U.S. Constitution may be considered necessary.
4. List and describe crime victims' costs.
5. Understand how corrections agencies participate in meeting victims' needs and list victim services provided by correctional agencies.
6. Explain crime victim compensation programs.
7. List the three avenues available to victims to recover financial losses due to crime.
8. Understand the nature of victim impact statements, and explain why they are useful.

427

As a victim you're amazed that no one will ask you about the crime, or the effect that it has on you and your family. You took the . . . defendant's blows, heard his threats, listened to him brag that he'd "beat the rap" or "con the judge." No one ever hears these things. They never give you a chance to tell them.

—A victim

Student Involvement
Ask students if they are aware of any victim support groups in your area and, if so, whether any of them have participated in these groups. Invite those who have participated to share their experiences with the class.

Teaching Tip
Review with students the BOP's definition of *victim*. Point out that, as indicated by the second half of the definition, more than one person could be a *victim*.

victim Someone who suffers direct or threatened physical, emotional, or financial harm as the result of the commission of a crime. The term *victim* also includes the immediate family of a minor or homicide victim.

victims' rights The fundamental rights of victims to be equitably represented throughout the criminal justice process.

In 1985, Ralph Hubbard's 23-year-old son was shot and killed in New York City. After years of feeling angry, frustrated, and powerless, Hubbard resolved to help himself by helping others work through their suffering. He began to speak out in a New York Victim Services support group for families of homicide victims, telling his story to police, criminal justice officials, social service providers, and the public.

Hubbard started a self-help group for men who had lost family members to violence. He found that telling his story helped him cope with his own pain and anger, and inspired other victims to express their feelings. He also became an adviser to New York's Crime Victims' Board, vice president of Justice For All (a victims' rights advocacy group), and a board member of the National Organization for Victim Assistance (NOVA). A leading spokesperson for victims' rights in New York state, Hubbard felt no less compelled to advocate victims' rights 10 years after his son's murder: "It's something I need to do. This is therapeutic for me."[1]

The efforts that Hubbard and other crime victims have made toward their own recoveries have led to reforms in the criminal justice system and new crime prevention programs.

A Brief History of America's Victims' Rights Movement

According to the federal Bureau of Prisons (BOP), a **victim** is "someone who suffers direct or threatened physical, emotional, or financial harm as the result of the commission of a crime. The term 'victim' also includes the immediate family of a minor or homicide victim."[2]

Victims were rarely recognized in the laws and policies that govern our nation until the 1970s. From a legal perspective, crimes were offenses against the state (the state made the law), not against the individual. Victims merely set the wheels of justice in motion (by filing charges), and, if necessary, helped carry out justice (by testifying in court). The victim had little or no status within the justice system, and victims' rights were virtually nonexistent.[3]

Tremendous strides have since been made in **victims' rights** legislation and victims' services. Few movements in American history achieved as much success in prompting legislative response as did victims' rights activists' campaigns through the 1980s and 1990s.

The 1980 enactment of Wisconsin's Victims' Bill of Rights, the nation's first state bill of rights for crime victims, launched an era of dramatic progress in the victims' rights movement.[4] Passage of the federal Victim and Witness Protection Act of 1982[5] (VWPA) and release of the *Final Report* by the President's Task Force on Victims of Crime in the same year, brought national visibility to crime victims' concerns.

The VWPA and the *Final Report* were catalysts for a decade of significant advances in victims' rights. At the date of release of the *Final Report*, four states had legislated victims' basic rights;[6] today, all states have laws, modeled after the VWPA, that establish, protect, and enforce victims' rights. There are now more than 27,000 victim-related state statutes and 29 state victims' rights constitutional amendments.

Although no standard has been defined for victims' rights, most states' victims' bills of rights include basic provisions for treatment with dignity and compassion, ongoing access to information about the status of the case and the offender, notification of hearing and trial dates, attendance at judicial proceedings involving the case, input at sentencing and parole hearings (through victim impact statements), and restitution. (See Figure 15–1.)

Most states have legislated victims' rights to notification of events and proceedings at various stages of the judicial process; 35 have legislated victims' rights to attend criminal justice proceedings, and 24 constitutionally protect these rights.[7] All states permit consideration of victim impact information at sentencing, with most permitting victim presentation of the information during the sentencing hearing. The majority of states require that victim impact information be included in the presentencing report, and at least half require that the court consider this information in its sentencing decision.

Teaching Tip

Draw students' attention to the fact that the interests of victims were rarely recognized by the American criminal justice system until the late 1970s and early 1980s. Ask interested students to research victims' rights legislation in your state and report to the class.

FIGURE 15–1

Victim's Rights

- THE RIGHT TO INFORMATION about the case as it progresses through the justice system;

- THE RIGHT TO NOTIFICATION of many different types of justice proceedings;

- THE RIGHT TO PARTICIPATE in court proceedings related to the offense;

- THE RIGHT TO BE REASONABLY PROTECTED from the accused offender;

- THE RIGHT TO INFORMATION about the conviction, sentencing, imprisonment, and release of the offender; and

- THE RIGHT TO RECEIVE RESTITUTION from the offender.

Source: Office for Victims of Crime

Student Involvement

Ask students to refer to Figure 15–1 and write a brief paragraph explaining which of the victims' rights listed they think is most important and why.

Despite the advances in victims' rights legislation, there remain serious deficiencies, in the laws and in implementation of the laws. Crime victims' rights, which vary significantly at both the federal and state levels, are often ignored, and many victims are still denied the right to participate in the justice process. Implementation of state-enacted constitutional victims' rights is often arbitrary and based on judicial preference. Many states make no provision for victims' rights in cases involving juvenile offenders.

Legislation

Congressional concern for crime victims was evident in the VWPA; its stated purpose was "to enhance and protect the necessary role of crime victims and witnesses in the criminal justice process; to ensure that the federal government does all that is possible to assist victims and witnesses of crime, within the limits of available resources, without infringing on the constitutional rights of the defendant; and to provide model legislation for state and local governments."[8]

A subsection of the Crime Control Act of 1990,[9] known as the Victims' Rights and Restitution Act of 1990 (Victims' Rights Act), established a Bill of Rights for federal crime victims.[10] The Victims' Rights Act requires that federal law enforcement officials use their "best efforts" to ensure that victims receive basic rights and services, as specified by law, including:

- fair and respectful treatment by authorities,
- reasonable protection from the accused,
- notification of court proceedings,
- presence at public court proceedings unless the court specifies otherwise,
- conference with the prosecutor,
- restitution, and
- updates to information about the offender, including conviction, sentencing, imprisonment, and release.

best efforts standard

A requirement of the federal Victims' Rights and Restitution Act of 1990 (also known as the Victims' Rights Act) which mandates that federal law enforcement officers, prosecutors, and corrections officials use their best efforts to ensure that victims receive basic rights and services during their encounter with the criminal justice system.

The **best efforts standard** made the federal law weaker than many state victims' rights laws in which provision for victims' rights and services is mandatory.

The Violent Crime Control and Law Enforcement Act,[11] passed in 1994, established new rights for victims of sexual assault, domestic violence, sexual exploitation, child abuse, and telemarketing fraud. This legislation also designated significant funding for combating domestic violence and sexual assault, placed more than 100,000 community police officers on the street, and launched a number of other crime prevention initiatives.

In 1996, the federal Community Notification Act, known as Megan's Law, was enacted to ensure community notification of the locations of convicted sex offenders.[12]

In the Victims' Rights Clarification Act of 1997, Congress asserted victims' rights to attend proceedings and deliver victim impact statements within the federal system. This act was passed to ensure that victims and survivors of the Alfred P. Murrah Federal Building bombing in Oklahoma City, Oklahoma, could observe the trial and provide input at sentencing.

Table 15–1 summarizes the victims' rights defined by federal legislation.

TABLE 15–1

Federal Victims' Rights Legislation

Legislation	Provisions
Victims' Rights Clarification Act, 1997	Ensured that victims of federal crimes should have the right both to attend proceedings and to deliver or submit a victim impact statement.
Mandatory Victim Restitution Act, 1996	Made restitution mandatory on the federal level in all violent crime cases and in certain other cases.
Community Notification Act (also known as Megan's Law), 1996	Ensured that communities are notified of the release and location of convicted sex offenders.
Violent Crime Control and Law Enforcement Act, 1994	Created new rights for victims of sexual assault, domestic violence, sexual exploitation, child abuse, and telemarketing fraud.
Victims' Rights and Restitution Act (also called the Victims' Rights Act), 1990	Created the first federal bill of rights for victims of crime, and required federal law enforcement officers, prosecutors, and corrections officials to use their *best efforts* to ensure that victims receive basic rights and services.
Victims of Crime Act (VOCA), 1984	Established the federal Office for Victims of Crime (OVC) to provide federal funds in support of victim assistance and compensation programs around the country, and to advocate for the fair treatment of crime victims. Also established the federal Crime Victims' Fund to assist states in paying victim benefits.
Victim and Witness Protection Act (VWPA),1982	Enacted a set of basic rights for crime victims, and became a national model for state victims' rights laws.

Student Involvement
Direct students' attention to Table 15–1. Ask volunteers to research the laws and expand on the information provided in the table.

Professional Issue
Best Efforts Divide students into seven groups, assigning to each one of the basic rights and services specified by the Victims' Rights Act. Ask each group to create a checklist that corrections officials might use to be sure they meet the "best efforts" standard in implementing the right or service.

The Proposal for a Federal Victims' Rights Constitutional Amendment

The 1982 President's Task Force on Victims of Crime made 68 recommendations for protection of victims' rights, including a recommendation that the Sixth Amendment to the U.S. Constitution be amended to guarantee specific rights to crime victims. Although the recommendation has not yet been implemented, NOVA, Mothers Against Drunk Driving (MADD), the National Center for Victims of Crime (NVC—formerly the National Victim Center), and other national victims' organizations joined together to create, in 1987, the National Victims' Constitutional Amendment Network (NVCAN). NVCAN provides leadership and coordinates ongoing efforts to amend the federal constitution in recognition of victims' rights.[13] NVCAN spent the next decade assisting state legislators in their efforts to pass amendments. Efforts to pass state constitutional amendments produced impressive results. Each of the 29 state victims' rights amendment votes won by an overwhelming majority—80 to 90 percent in most states.[14]

The Costs and Consequences of Victimization

According to a two-year National Institute of Justice (NIJ) study,[15] personal crimes result in costs of about $105 billion annually in medical expenses, lost earnings, and public victim assistance programs. For victims, crime costs may include: (1) out-of-pocket expenses, such as medical bills and property losses; (2) reduced productivity at work, home, or school; and (3) non-monetary losses, such as fear, pain, suffering, and reduced quality of life.

Unlike **tangible losses** (such as medical expenses or lost wages), **intangible losses** (such as pain, suffering, and reduced quality of life) do not have a market price and cannot be bought or sold. Nevertheless, these losses are real and can be valued in dollars—victims would pay dearly to avoid them.

Tangible losses do not represent the true cost of victimization. Intangible losses, including pain, suffering, and reduced quality of life, place the annual cost of crime at an estimated $450 billion (see Figure 15–2). Violent crime (including drunk driving) accounts for $426 billion of this total; property crime, $24 billion. These estimates exclude several other types of crime such as white collar crime, personal fraud, and drug crime.

The cost of crime victimization is far greater when its impact on society is considered. Such costs include: (1) monies spent by the criminal justice system to find, prosecute, and confine offenders; (2) social costs associated with fear of crime (e.g., changed behavior, the fear of being outside at night, moving to a safer neighborhood, etc.); (3) mental health costs associated with healing "scars" from victimization; (4) private security expenditures by the general population concerned about crime; (5) monies spent by employers to train temporary or new employees; (6) the costs of lost productivity borne by employers; (7) insurance claims processing costs (for example, life insurance claims for fatalities and workers' compensation claims); (8) workers' compensation and disability payments, especially those made to workers

Student Involvement

Ask interested students to research the work of NOVA, MADD, NVC, and NVCAN and report their findings to the class.

Student Involvement

Assign a group of students to find out if your state has passed a victims' rights amendment and, if so, what rights it specifies. Initiate a discussion of what changes students think could be made. If your state has no amendment, work with the class to draft one.

tangible losses Costs such as medical expenses, lost wages, and property losses that accrue to crime victims as a result of their victimization.

intangible losses Costs such as fear, pain, suffering, and reduced quality of life that accrue to crime victims as a result of their victimization.

FIGURE 15-2

Annual Cost of Crime in the United States

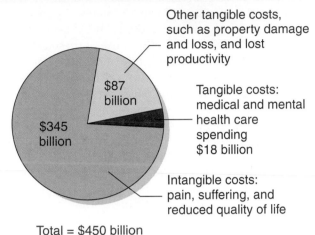

Other tangible costs, such as property damage and loss, and lost productivity

$87 billion

Tangible costs: medical and mental health care spending $18 billion

$345 billion

Intangible costs: pain, suffering, and reduced quality of life

Total = $450 billion

Source: Ted R. Miller, Mark A. Cohen, and Brian Wiersema, *Victim Costs and Consequences: A New Look,* U.S. Department of Justice, National Institute of Justice Research Report (Washington, DC: GPO, February 1996), p. 17.

Teaching Tip
Direct students' attention to Figure 15–2 and ask them to think of other examples of tangible and intangible losses.

victimized while on the job; and (9) legal expenses incurred in recovering productivity losses from offenders and insurance companies (e.g., drunk drivers and their insurers). The National Crime Victimization Survey (NCVS) data include estimates of the number of hours of work and earnings lost due to medically related problems associated with victimization. Some specifics from the NIJ study show that:

- Violent crime necessitates 3 percent of all U.S. medical spending, and 14 percent of all injury-related medical spending.
- Violent crime results in wage losses equivalent to 1 percent of American earnings.
- Violent crime is a significant factor in mental health care usage. As much as 10 to 20 percent of mental health care expenditures in the United States may be attributable to crime, primarily for victims treated as a result of their victimization.
- Personal crime reduces the average American's quality of life by 1.8 percent. Violence alone causes a 1.7 percent loss. These estimates include only costs to victimized households, ignoring the broader impact of crime-induced fear on our society.

NIJ also reports the estimated total annual cost of crime to victims in the United States, including the value of intangible losses, and victim losses due to crimes.

Teaching Tip
Review with students the nine costs of crime victimization listed in the text and ask them what other costs, if any, might be added.

Who Pays the Bill?

Victims and their families pay the bill for some crimes, while the public largely pays the bill for others. Insurers pay $45 billion in crime-related claims annually.[16] That's $265 per American adult. Government pays $8 billion annually for restorative and emergency services to victims, plus about one-fourth of the $11 billion in health insurance claim payments.

The Victim: Role in the Correctional Process

Taxpayers and insurance purchasers cover almost all the tangible victim costs of arson and drunk driving. They cover $9 billion of the $19 billion in tangible nonservice costs of larceny, burglary, and motor vehicle theft.

Victims pay about $44 billion of the $57 billion in tangible non-service expenses for violent crimes—murder, rape, robbery, assault, and abuse and neglect. Employers pay almost $5 billion because of these crimes, primarily in health insurance bills. (This estimate excludes sick leave and disability insurance costs other than workers' compensation.) Government bears the remaining costs, through lost tax revenues and Medicare/Medicaid payments. Crime victim compensation accounts for 38 percent of homeowner insurance premium costs and 29 percent of automobile insurance premium costs.

Criminologists and public policy researchers are now using crime cost estimates to help assess the desirability of various policy options. Reported costs can be used to assess the wisdom of early offender release and diversion programs.

The Role of Corrections

Professional Issue

Victims Remind students that correctional agencies are beginning to recognize victims' needs, then ask what services they think different corrections professionals—from probation officers to prison staff—might provide to help meet these needs.

In the past, correctional agencies were viewed only as facilities for punishing and rehabilitating offenders. Today, they also serve crime victims—protecting them from intimidation and harassment, notifying them of offender status, providing avenues for victim input into release decisions, and collecting restitution.[17]

Correctional agencies are also beginning to recognize the important role that victims can play in helping them develop policies, procedures, and programs that consider victims as well as correctional staff and offenders. Across the nation, crime victims are being asked to join advisory committees and agency boards, become official members of parole commissions, and serve as teachers in innovative classes that sensitize offenders to the impact of their offenses.

Teaching Tip

Victim notification of an offender's impending release is considered critically important. Ask students if they can think of any situations in which a victim might not want to be notified of an impending release.

Correctional agencies are beginning to acknowledge victims' needs in their mission statements. In Oregon, for example, the state board of parole recently issued the following statement: "The Board's mission is to work in partnership with the Department of Corrections and local supervisory authorities to protect the public and reduce the risk of repeat criminal behavior through incarceration and community supervision decisions based on applicable laws, victims' interests, public safety, and recognized principles of offender behavioral change." Many state corrections departments have now issued similar mission statements.

Crime victims' involvement with correctional agencies helps ensure priority for victim safety and services within correctional agencies. Victim advisory committees now exist in a number of correctional agencies for that purpose.

Victim Notification

victim notification

Notification to victims of the release or pending release of convicted offenders who have harmed them.

Victim notification of the release or pending release of convicted offenders is an important service. Without notification, victims are denied an opportunity to take precautions to ensure their own safety.

The importance of providing offender release information to crime victims has long been recognized. In 1982, it was one of the primary recommendations of the President's Task Force on Victims of Crime. In the *Final Report*, the Task Force recommended that parole boards notify victims and their families in advance of parole hearings if victims provide the paroling authority with their names and addresses. In addition, the Task Force called on parole boards to allow victims of crime, their families, or their representatives to attend parole hearings and to provide information about the impact of the crime. According to the recent National Victim Services Survey, marked improvements have occurred in this area over the last decade or so.[18]

There is, however, no consistent victim notification procedure. Some correctional agencies notify victims of only certain types of inmate releases (such as the release of sex offenders). Others notify victims of changes in offender classification. Some notify victims of an inmate's escape, while others notify victims of an inmate's clemency or death. At the federal level, the BOP has created one of the nation's first comprehensive victim notification programs, which has served as a model to the states for over a decade. The BOP notifies victims of any major change in an inmate's status.

Innovative technologies have emerged in recent years that augment victim access to notification and information. At least 10 state correctional agencies utilize automated voice notification systems that place telephone calls to victims, upon request, and inform them of offenders' pending release or release hearings. Victims can also contact a centralized call center, 24 hours a day, 7 days a week. Call center operators confirm offender status and provide referrals to community-based victim services. Many state correctional agencies are following the example of the Illinois Department of Corrections, which provides current updates on inmate status and location and relevant upcoming hearings to victims and the general public via the Internet.[19]

In most jurisdictions, victims must request certain types of notification. Many victims do not request notification simply because they have not been informed that they have a right to do so.

Victim and Witness Protection

Every day in the United States, victims and witnesses are harassed, intimidated, and retaliated against by incarcerated offenders, through intimidating phone calls, mail, or threatened visits from friends and associates. Many correctional agencies have responded creatively to this problem. Today, when such problems occur, 37 states revoke an offending inmates' privileges, 36 transfer the inmate to a more restrictive level, 28 allow the filing of a new criminal charge, and 21 allow enhancement of the inmate's sentence. In addition, 40 state correctional agencies document such harassment and threats in the offender's case file, 35 recommend investigation for additional prosecution, and 31 recommend revocation of parole when a

Student Involvement
Ask students if they think that victim notification procedures should be consistent among the states. Why or why not?

Professional Issue
Prison Management Ask students to assume that they are prison wardens. How would they respond to a report of victim or witness harassment by a prisoner in their facility?

The Victim: Role in the Correctional Process

*Karen Taylor George
Victim Services
Administrator
Department of
Corrections
Raleigh, North Carolina*

"I am often asked how I can handle working with the devastation that offenders leave in the wake of their crimes. What most people don't realize is that victim services allows me the privilege to work with the amazing strength exhibited by survivors and to offer services that support the reconstruction of their emotional and physical lives."

Upon the governor's recommendation that victims of violent crimes receive information and notification, the North Carolina Post-Release Supervision and Parole Commission hired Karen Taylor George as its first victim services coordinator. To assist victims in understanding the system, she created easily understood educational materials that explained the parole process, and victims' rights and opportunities to be notified and involved. To overcome the long distances that victims had to travel to meet with the Parole Commission, she created a video conferencing program through grant funding by the Governor's Crime Commission.

In 1998, North Carolina had pending legislative requirements for all criminal justice agencies to comply with a new victims' rights amendment to the state's constitution. With 32,000 offenders in prison and 105,000 offenders on probation or parole, Ms. Taylor George recognized the need for additional victim services to meet the upcoming legal mandates. She won two grants to fund three full-time positions to develop and implement victim services and to provide victim training to correctional staffs. The victim services program was expanded from the North Carolina Parole Commission to service all of the North Carolina Department of Corrections, and Ms. Taylor George was named the Victim Services Administrator for the department.

Ms. Taylor George has a bachelor's degree in psychology and is completing her master's degree in social work. She is committed to helping reconstruct the lives of survivors who have suffered at the hands of offenders and to educating those who work to assist them. In addition to her work with the correction department, she has often been called upon to deliver victim sensitivity training to various organizations across the state, such as MADD chapters, Parents of Murdered Children, district attorneys' offices, and the North Carolina Victim Assistance Network. Through her creative vision and innovative approaches, she has made great strides within the department in meeting victims' needs and raising the level of awareness for the importance of ongoing victim services within corrections in North Carolina.

parolee harasses, intimidates, or attempts retaliation.[20] California authorities are using an innovative method to stop the increasing number of instances in which inmates use telephones or letters to threaten and harass victims. The California Department of Corrections has created a program to block victims' phone numbers from inmate access and check inmates' outgoing mail.

In managing offenders who are ordered by the court to community supervision or released early from prison with supervision, probation and parole officers need to ensure the safety of victims and the public. Officers will generally use surveillance to identify offenders who pose a continued threat and make monitoring efforts such as checking with contacts at the offender's home and employment and with neighbors to ensure that he or she is meeting the conditions of probation or parole.

Just as there are special units in law enforcement and prosecutors' offices, probation and parole departments have begun to establish special units, such as sex offender and domestic violence units, to provide intensive probation or parole to reduce the safety risks to victims and society as a whole. Agents in these units have smaller caseloads and have received specialized training in intensive supervision.

Correctional agencies also use intermediate sanctions to ensure victim safety. Such sanctions include electronic monitoring, house arrest, random alcohol and drug testing, parole to a location other than the victim's community, mandatory restitution, and increased surveillance.

Community Notification

Most states have passed laws that either provide for community notification of sexual offender releases or authorize the general public or certain individuals or organizations to access sexual offender registries. Often referred to as Megan's laws, in memory of seven-year-old Megan Kanka, who was murdered by a twice-convicted sex offender paroled to her New Jersey neighborhood, community notification laws recognize that a community has a compelling interest in being informed of offenders' whereabouts. In 1996, a federal Megan's law was enacted that requires states to release relevant registration information when necessary to protect the public.[21]

To be truly effective, **community notification** laws require coordination among law enforcement officials, courts, correctional agencies, victim service providers, the news media, and other key stakeholders. Correctional agencies play a major role in providing this service by determining when and to where sex offenders will be paroled and by conducting community outreach and public education projects.

A promising practice in planning and implementing community notification programs emerged in 1990 in the state of Washington.[22] The Washington approach considers the rights and interests of victims, the community, and offenders. The strategy incorporates the following elements: establishing requirements for registration, requiring registration information for offenders, implementing guidelines for failure to register, implementing guidelines for a preliminary offender risk assessment, compiling offender information packets for distribution to the county prosecutor where the offender plans to reside; distributing special bulletins to law enforcement agencies, developing notification policies, creating guidelines concerning who should have access to sex offender registry information, and conducting community outreach efforts that involve victims and address their rights and needs.

Crime Impact Classes

Student Involvement

Ask interested students to find out if your state has a victim-offender program and, if so, what services it provides.

Over the past decade, the number of educational programs in correctional institutions that involve both offenders and victims has greatly increased. The purpose of such programs is to help offenders understand the devastating impact their crimes have on victims and their families and friends, on their communities, and on themselves and their own families. For victims, participation in programs with offenders is useful because, although the harm they have suffered cannot be undone, they may prevent others from being victimized. Studies also show that participation in impact panels helps heal victims' emotional scars.[23]

Notable among victim-offender programs is the Impact of Crime on Victims (IOC) program, initiated by the California Youth Authority in 1986. The program has been replicated in more than 20 juvenile and adult correctional agencies and numerous diversion programs. IOC programs include a 40-hour curriculum that is designed to educate offenders about how different crimes affect victims and society.[24]

The U.S. Department of the Navy's Corrections and Programs Division took an important step in integrating victims into its corrections process when it issued guidelines in 1996 instructing U.S. Naval correctional facilities to implement impact-of-crime classes for prisoners before releasing them from custody. Information from inmates and correctional staff indicate that, after completing the classes, offenders have a greater understanding of the impact of their criminal conduct.

Victim-Offender Dialogue

Student Involvement

Invite willing students to role play a victim-offender dialogue. Then ask students for opinions as to who might benefit from the dialogue and in what way.

During the past two decades, a number of victim-offender dialogue programs have been developed in juvenile and criminal justice agencies, predominantly in juvenile probation agencies. These programs, primarily used in property crime cases, give victims an opportunity to engage in a structured dialogue with their offenders, who have already admitted their guilt or been convicted/adjudicated. When conducted with sensitivity to the victim and with care to ensure that participation by both victim and offender is voluntary, the victim-offender dialogue process can be very effective in helping victims overcome feelings of trauma and loss.[25] The program gives victims greater satisfaction with the justice system, increases their likelihood of being compensated, and reduces fear of future victimization.

In recent years, correctional agencies have begun to experiment with victim-offender dialogue in violent crime cases. In 1995, for example, the Texas Department of Criminal Justice initiated a victim-offender mediation/dialogue program for victims of severe violence and their incarcerated offenders. Under this program, the contact is initiated by the victim.

THE STAFF SPEAKS

As government has become increasingly centralized, a major source of citizen frustration is the inability to define what is being achieved by the justice system, both on an individual case basis and from the perspective of the community. As the media focus on the spectacular failures and the extremes of the normal spectrum, government is caught between overwhelming caseloads of minor criminals and the need to target resources to protect the public from the dangerous ones. In the rush to efficiency, the government bypasses the most effective agents, the community and the family, instead focusing on the individual cases that squeak the loudest.

In the Reparative Probation program, ordinary citizens of the State of Vermont make sentencing decisions about adult criminal offenders from their community. Board members meet with offenders and victims, resolving their disputes by providing the offenders with the opportunity to acknowledge their wrong-doing, apologize to their victim, and make amends to their community. The offenders are sentenced by the court, having pled guilty to a non-violent crime. The sentence is then suspended, pending their completion of a reparative agreement.

Direct involvement in decisionmaking about individual cases forces citizens to look at the offenders not as strangers, not as numbers, and not as monsters. The offenders are forced to confront the reality of their offense and its impact on the community and their victims. This confrontation, with a restorative outcome, shifts the paradigm from punishment to reintegration. The offender is held accountable, the victim is restored, and the community is repaired. Perhaps even more important, the dispute is resolved by the community, and the community is empowered.

John G. Perry
Director of Planning
Vermont Department of Corrections

The Victimization of Correctional Staff

Correctional agencies have begun to recognize the impact of victimization on their employees. Correctional professionals are exposed to a wide range of victimization, including verbal harassment by inmates, sexual harassment by inmates or colleagues, physical or sexual assaults, hostage situations, and murder. To respond to the acute and chronic trauma this violence has on employees, many adult correctional agencies have developed written policies and procedures to respond to staff victimization and critical incidents.[26]

Most institutions have standard procedures for dealing with correctional staff victimization that focus on prevention. Many prison management departments, including California, South Carolina, and Texas have developed procedures for helping victimized staff. Guidelines for response to employee victimization have also been developed, under a national training and technical project funded by the Office for Victims of Crime (OVC).[27] The OVC project provides a comprehensive model for correctional agencies that is based on victims' rights laws, either state or federal.

Victim Compensation

victim compensation
A form of victim assistance in which state-funded payments are made to victims to help them recover financial losses due to crime.

Victims generally have three potential options for recovering crime-related financial losses: (1) state-sponsored compensation programs; (2) court-ordered restitution; and (3) civil remedies. **Victim compensation** programs, which exist in every state, may pay for medical care, mental health counseling, lost wages, funeral expenses, and/or crime scene cleanup.

Restitution, the subject of the next section in this chapter, can be ordered in juvenile and criminal courts as a way to hold offenders financially accountable for their crimes.[28] The potential financial as well as preventative remedies that crime victims can seek through the civil justice system are not discussed in this text, but you should know that they represent one more avenue that victims can pursue in order to be financially compensated for their injuries. At the very least, correctional offices should consider implementing a policy of informing victims and victim service providers of the legal rights of crime victims to pursue reparations through the civil justice system.

The first victim compensation programs were established in New Zealand and Great Britain in 1964. These programs were based on a concept suggested by British Magistrate Margery Fry in the late 1950s. The first victim compensation program established in the United States was California's, created in 1965. By the time the President's Task Force on Victims of Crime released its *Final Report* in 1982, 36 states had victim compensation programs.[29] Today, all 50 states, the District of Columbia, and the Virgin Islands operate victim compensation programs.[30]

Victim compensation programs provide assistance to victims of almost all types of violent crime: rape, robbery, assault, sexual abuse, drunk driving, and domestic violence. These programs, as a rule, pay expenses but do not pay for lost, stolen, or damaged property. Eligibility and specific benefits vary from state to state.

In a typical year, state compensation programs pay approximately $240 million, to more than 110,000 victims, nationwide.[31] The amounts paid by each state vary considerably. Ten states pay less than $500,000 annually, and about 15 pay more than $3 million. The two states with the largest programs, California and Texas, pay nearly one-half of the total benefits paid in the United States.

Benefit maximums, which also vary from state to state, generally range from $10,000 to $25,000, although maximums are lower or higher for a few states. For example, California, Maryland, Minnesota, Ohio, Texas, and Wisconsin allow benefits of $40,000–$50,000. Some states, New York, for example, set no limit on payment of medical expenses; other states, Washington, for example, pay medical expenses up to a predetermined maximum. Many states also set limits for other types of expense, such as

Teaching Tip
Review with students the potential options that victims have for recovering financial losses: compensation, restitution, and civil suits. Ask students to identify situations in which each alternative might apply.

Student Involvement
Ask interested students to research your state's eligibility requirements for state-funded victim compensation. Ask students if they think the requirements are reasonable and why or why not.

The Victim: Role in the Correctional Process

funerals and mental health counseling. Nationally, the average amount paid to each victim applying for compensation is $2,000.

President's Task Force on Victims of Crime

In 1982 the President's Task Force recommended federal funding to help support state victim compensation programs. It also documented problems in several state victim compensation programs: absence of a system for emergency compensation to cover immediate need for food, shelter, and/or medical assistance; insufficient maximum reimbursement levels; lack of coverage for domestic violence, and differences in residency requirements for eligible crime victims. Many of these problems have since been remedied, through federal and state legislation and increased federal and state funding.

State-operated victim compensation programs have improved dramatically since 1982, in benefits provided and to whom. However, some of the concerns raised by the President's Task Force, such as emergency compensation and insufficient maximums, have not been fully addressed by all states.

Victims of Crime Act

The Task Force's recommendation for federal support of state victim compensation programs was implemented through the Victims of Crime Act (VOCA),[32] passed in 1984. VOCA established the federal Office for Victims of Crime, which administers the federal Crime Victims' Fund, reimbursing states for up to 40 percent of victim compensation payments and providing technical assistance to state compensation programs.

Victims must apply for compensation in the state where the crime occurs. Prior to VOCA, many states' programs provided compensation only to residents unless a reciprocal agreement had been made with the victim's state of residence. States are now required, by federal law, to cover residents, non-residents, and victims of federal crimes. Two states still restrict eligibility to U.S. citizens.

Recent Trends

Due to increases in publicity concerning victim compensation programs and new laws mandating that rights, services, and information be provided to victims, the number of victims applying for financial assistance increased. As a result, many victim compensation program budgets were inadequate, and victims did not receive the compensation that they should have. Today, although a few states are still unable to pay all eligible claims, most do.

Eligibility Requirements

Each state has victim eligibility requirements for compensation benefits. Although states' requirements vary, most programs require that the victim:

- Report the crime promptly, usually within 72 hours. A few states allow more time or less, but most have "good cause exceptions"

Student Involvement
Assign a group of students to research the payments made by your state's victim compensation program over the last five years. Initiate a class discussion about changes in the amounts and crimes involved.

Tutorial CD-ROM

Refer students to the Tutorial With Simulation Applications CD-ROM. The tutorial is a comprehensive interactive study tool that reinforces and reviews the concepts in Chapter 15. Also included are two simulations that apply concepts presented in Chapter 15.

that apply to children, incapacitated victims, and others with special circumstances.

■ Cooperate with law enforcement agencies in investigation and prosecution of the crime.

■ Submit a timely application for compensation, generally within one year. Again, a few states allow more time or less, and most may waive the deadline under certain circumstances.

■ Provide other information, as needed by the program.

■ Not file claims for compensation of victimization that resulted from claimant criminal activity or misconduct.

The VOCA Victim Compensation Final Program Guidelines encourage state compensation program staff members to meet with victims and victim service providers, to review state statutes, program guidelines, and policies for responsiveness to crime victims' needs; and to identify potential barriers to victim cooperation with law enforcement agencies, such as apprehension about personal safety and fear of offender retaliation. Victims tend to be reluctant to cooperate if offenders threaten violence or death. Age and psychological, cultural, or linguistic barriers may also influence the amount of victim cooperation. For instance, a young child, senior citizen, or foreign national may have difficulty communicating. Embarrassment or shame may delay or prevent reporting of a sexual assault.

Compensation programs are the victim's last resort. All other potential sources, such as the offender's insurance or public benefits, must be exhausted before state victims' compensation may be paid. If, however, payment from another source is delayed, the program may provide funds to the victim, which must be repaid if and when the victim receives other payment.

The victim cannot have been engaged in criminal activity. Dependents' eligibility depends largely on the victim's eligibility. Dependents or relatives of a homicide victim, for example, who was committing a crime at the time of death are generally not eligible for benefits.

Benefit Criteria

All compensation programs cover the same major expenses, although limits vary. The primary costs covered by all states are medical expenses, mental health counseling, wages lost as a result of a crime-related injury, lost support (for dependents of homicide victims), and funeral expenses. Nationwide, medical fees represent well over half of all compensation awards, with lost wage and support payments comprising the next highest payment percentage. In a few states, 20 to 40 percent of awards are for counseling; compensation payment in this area is increasing rapidly throughout the country. Twenty-five to 30 percent of claim payment recipients are children age 17 and under.[33]

Many compensation programs also may pay for:

■ Moving or relocation expenses, when a victim may be in danger or relocation becomes medically necessary as a result of victimization.

■ Transportation for medical services when the provider is located far from the victim's residence or when other special circumstances exist.

- Services, such as child care and/or housekeeping, that the victim cannot perform due to a crime-related injury.
- Essential lost or damaged personal possessions. Eleven states pay for medically necessary equipment, such as eyeglasses or hearing aids, but only a few cover other such items.
- Crime-scene cleanup—securing or restoring a home to its pre-crime condition.
- Rehabilitation—physical or job therapy, ramps, wheelchairs, and/or home or vehicle modification and/or driving instruction.

Restitution

Restitution is repayment to the victim, by the offender, for losses, damages, or expenses that result from the crime. Restitution is a form of victim compensation that holds the offender liable for the victim's financial losses. Restitution is generally seen not as a punishment or an alternative to fines or sanctions, but as a debt owed.[34]

Criminal courts often order restitution to compensate victims for expenses that are the direct result of a crime. It is most often ordered in cases of property crime, such as a burglary. It may also be ordered to reimburse victims for expenses related to physical and/or mental health recovery, and, for survivors of homicide victims, to make up for loss of support. Restitution is also common for cases of theft of services (e.g., restaurant bills), fraud, forgery, and traffic or vehicle law violation. Judges have also begun to order community restitution in which convicted offenders pay back the community through service.

Restitution, as a significant remedy for crime victims, was first imposed on the federal level in 1982, when the VWPA required federal judges to order full restitution in criminal cases or state their reasons for not doing so on the record.[35] That same year, the *Final Report* of the President's Task Force on Victims of Crime reinforced the VWPA by recommending that judges order restitution in all cases in which the victim suffered financial loss, or state compelling reasons for a contrary ruling in the case record.[36]

The importance of restitution was emphasized in 1994, with enactment of the federal Violent Crime Control and Law Enforcement Act, which made restitution mandatory in cases of sexual assault or domestic violence. The Mandatory Victim Restitution Act made restitution mandatory in all violent crime cases and in certain other cases on the federal level in 1996.[37]

In the decade that followed VWPA, every state enacted statutes that addressed restitution, most following the lead of the federal model. However, states continue to amend their statutes, creating a patchwork of financial reparations for victims across the country. As of 1995, 29 states had mandated restitution in all cases. Some states, however, mandate restitution only in cases involving violent crimes, while others mandate restitution only in cases involving property crimes. A number of states require that offenders be on probation or parole before victims may collect restitution, and many do not require restitution from juvenile offenders. Probationers who fail to make restitution payments may have their probation revoked.

Despite the developments in legislation, restitution remains one of the most underenforced of victims' rights in terms of ordering and in monitoring,

restitution The practice of requiring an individual who has harmed another to repay the victim for the harm caused. Also, a court requirement that an alleged or convicted offender pay money or provide services to the victim of the crime or provide services to the community.

Teaching Tip
Point out to students that restitution, although court-ordered, is often not made. Ask interested students to find out if your state enforces payment of restitution and, if so, how.

Teaching Tip

Ask volunteers to contact your state's correctional agencies to find out if they have restitution collection programs and, if so, how they work.

Student Involvement

Ask students if they think community restitution is an appropriate way for indigent offenders to pay restitution debts and why or why not.

collecting, and dispersing payments. A recent BOJ study of recidivism among probationers reported that, of 32 counties surveyed,[38] only half required restitution in at least one-third of all felony probation cases. Of felony probationers who had completed their sentences, only 54 percent had fully satisfied restitution orders.[39] Even so, national research studies indicate that restitution is one of the most significant factors affecting the satisfaction of victims with the criminal justice process.[40]

Collecting Restitution in Institutions Many correctional agencies encourage inmates to fulfill restitution obligations. These agencies increase collections by offering incentives (such as increased visitation and prison commissary services or priority enrollment in education programs) for compliance and by denying privileges for failure or refusal to participate.

The California Department of Corrections (CDC) has implemented an Inmate Restitution Fine Collections System, supported by state law, that allows deduction of up to 50 percent of inmate wages for payment of court-ordered restitution. These funds are transferred to the State Board of Control Restitution Fund for disbursement. This system collected over $9 million from its inception in November 1992 through early 1998. CDC's Victim Services Program staff coordinate voluntary inmate and parolee restitution payments as well.

Community Restitution Offenders who are truly indigent may be given the option to perform community service in lieu of monetary restitution. According to OVC, however, this option should be offered only with victim consent. Some victims prefer that the monetary restitution order stand until such time, if any, that the offender is able to fulfill it. Other victims may feel somewhat compensated if they participate in the decision about type and location of the service to be performed. Payment of victim restitution does not necessarily preclude an order for community restitution. In many instances the offender has done damage not only to the victim but to the community as well.

The Office for Victims of Crime

Established by VOCA, OVC's mission is to:[41]

- Help ensure that justice is done and that the victim achieves a sense of personal healing.
- Administer the Crime Victims' Fund. Nearly 90 percent (about $500 million) of the monies collected each year, all from fines and penalties paid by federal criminal offenders, is distributed to state victim assistance and compensation programs, helping to support more than 2,500 local victim services agencies (such as domestic violence shelters, children's advocacy centers, and rape treatment programs) and provide expense reimbursement to victims.
- Advocate fair treatment of crime victims.

- Develop and administer projects for enhancing victims' rights and services.
- Provide training, on a number of victim issues, for many different professions—victim service providers, law enforcement personnel, prosecutors, clergy, and medical and mental health personnel.
- Provide training on victim-witness issues for 70 federal law enforcement agencies, including the Federal Bureau of Investigation (FBI), the Department of Defense (DOD), and the National Park Service.
- Provide services to people victimized on tribal or federal lands, such as military bases and national parks.
- Maintain a fund to provide emergency services such as temporary shelter and travel to court for victims of federal crimes.
- Establish **victim assistance programs** on Indian reservations to recruit and train multidisciplinary teams to handle child sexual abuse cases and provide comprehensive victim services.

Victim Impact Statements

Victim impact statements are assertions—by victims and/or friends or relatives of the victim—about the crime's impact on the victim and the victim's family. Victim impact statements, now permitted at all sentencing hearings,[42] may be verbal or written, depending on the jurisdiction. Many states and the federal government now require that victim impact statements be included in pre-sentencing reports (see Figure 15–3 on page 446). The Crime Control and Law Enforcement Act of 1994 gave federal victims of violent crime or sexual assault a federal **right of allocution**—the right to make a statement at sentencing. Another federal law, the Child Protection Act of 1990, provides that victim impact statements from young children might take the form of drawings or models.

Victim impact statements typically include a tally of the physical, financial, psychological, and emotional impact of crime. As such, they provide information for courts to use in assessing the human and social cost of crime. Of equal significance, they also provide a way for victims to take part in the justice process. In most states, the right to make an impact statement is available to the direct victim, to family members of homicide victims, to the parents or guardians of a victimized minor, and to the guardian or legal representative of an incompetent or incapacitated victim.

According to OVC, the first victim impact statement was made in 1976 in Fresno County, California, by James Rowland,[43] who was then the county's chief probation officer. Mr. Rowland's contributions, which detailed the harm suffered by victims in that case, led Fresno County to make victim impact statements a part of all presentence reports.

In 1991, the U.S. Supreme Court case of *Payne* v. *Tennessee*[44] upheld the constitutionality of victim impact statements. Additionally, the *Payne* decision specifically permitted victim impact statements in cases involving potential application of the death penalty.

Victim impact statements are also frequently provided by victims or their survivors to parole hearing bodies. Statements are sometimes made in

victim assistance program An organized program which offers services to victims of crime in the areas of crisis intervention and follow-up counseling, and which helps victims secure their rights under the law.

victim impact statement An assertion made by victims (and sometimes by friends or relatives of the victim) about the impact of the crime in question upon the victim and the victim's family. Also, a written document which describes the losses, suffering, and trauma experienced by a crime victim or by the victim's survivors.

right of allocution A statutory provision permitting crime victims to speak at the sentencing of convicted offenders. A federal right of allocution was established for victims of federal violent and sex crimes under the Violent Crime Control and Law Enforcement Act of 1994.

FIGURE 15–3

Sample Victim Impact Statement

VICTIM IMPACT STATEMENT

If you need more space to answer any of the following questions, please feel free to use as much paper as you need, and simply attach these sheets of paper to this impact statement. Thank you.

Your Name
Defendant's Name(s)

1. How has the crime affected you and those close to you? Please feel free to discuss your feelings about what has happened and how it has affected your general well-being. Has this crime affected your relationship with any family members, friends, co-workers, and other people? As a result of this crime, if you or others close to you have sought any type of victim services, such as counseling by either a licensed professional, member of the clergy, or a community-sponsored support group, you may wish to mention this.

2. What physical injuries or symptoms have you or others close to you suffered as a result of this crime? You may want to write about how long the injuries lasted, or how long they are expected to last, and if you sought medical treatment for these injuries. You may also want to discuss what changes you have made in your life as a result of these injuries.

3. Has this crime affected your ability to perform your work, make a living, run a household, go to school, or enjoy any other activities you previously performed or enjoyed? If so, please explain how these activities have been affected by this crime.

Student Involvement

Direct attention to Figure 15–3. Ask students if victim impact statements help judges better appraise the seriousness of a crime and choose a sentence that best serves both offender and victim.

person; at other times they are submitted on audiotape or videotape, by tele-conferencing, via computerized forms of communication, or in writing. Such statements give the paroling authority crucial information about the financial, physical, and emotional impact of crime upon the individuals most affected by it. In the past two decades, the passage of laws requiring victim input at parole has been seen as one of the greatest advances in victims' rights, with 43 states now providing this right.[45] This right loses its meaning, however, if paroling authorities don't notify victims of crime and their families of hearings in advance, or don't schedule time during the hearing to allow them to describe the impact of crime on their lives.

The Future of Victims' Rights

The OVC report, *New Directions from the Field*,[46] summarizes hundreds of recommendations from the field and from listening to victims, their advocates, and allied professionals who work with crime victims throughout the nation. In the course of compiling the hundreds of recommendations, certain key recommendations emerged. The following five global challenges for responding to victims of crime in the twenty-first century form the core of the ideas and recommendations presented in the report.

- To enact and enforce consistent, fundamental rights for crime victims in federal, state, juvenile, military, and tribal justice systems, and administrative proceedings.
- To provide crime victims with access to comprehensive, quality services regardless of the nature of their victimization, age, race, religion, gender, ethnicity, sexual orientation, capability, or geographic location.
- To integrate crime victims' issues into all levels of the nation's educational system to ensure that justice and allied professionals and other service providers receive comprehensive training on victims' issues as part of their academic education and continuing training in the field.
- To support, improve, and replicate promising practices in victims' rights and services built upon sound research, advanced technology, and multidisciplinary partnerships.
- To ensure that the voices of crime victims play a central role in the nation's response to violence and those victimized by crime.

15 Review and Applications

CHAPTER OBJECTIVE 1

Victims were rarely recognized in the laws and policies that govern our nation until the 1970s. Since then, tremendous strides have been made in victims' rights legislation and victim services.

CHAPTER OBJECTIVE 2

The 1980 enactment of Wisconsin's Victims' Bill of Rights, the nation's first state bill of rights for crime victims, began an era of dramatic progress in the victims' rights movement. Passage of the federal Victim and Witness Protection Act (VWPA) of 1982 brought national visibility to crime victims' concerns. In 1990, the Victims' Rights and Restitution Act (Victims' Rights Act) established a bill of rights for federal crime victims. The Violent Crime Control and Law Enforcement Act of 1994 established new rights for victims of sexual assault, domestic violence, sexual exploitation, child abuse, and telemarketing fraud. In 1996, the Community Notification Act, know as Megan's law, was enacted to ensure community notification of the locations of convicted sex offenders. In 1997, The Victims' Rights Clarification Act of 1997 asserted victims' rights to attend proceedings and deliver victim impact statements.

CHAPTER OBJECTIVE 3

Many believe that a victims' rights amendment to the U.S. Constitution is needed to establish clear rights for crime victims and to protect those rights to the same degree that the rights of criminal suspects are already protected.

CHAPTER OBJECTIVE 4

The costs that crime victims suffer can be divided into two major categories: (1) tangible losses, including medical bills, lost property, and lost wages; and (2) intangible losses, such as lost quality of life, fear, pain, and suffering.

CHAPTER OBJECTIVE 5

Correctional agencies play an important role in meeting victims' needs. Services provided by correctional agencies include: (1) victim and community notification of offender release or change in status; (2) victim and witness protection services; (3) classes for offenders on the impact of crime; (4) opportunities for victim-offender dialogue.

CHAPTER OBJECTIVE 6

Crime victim compensation programs pay for medical and mental health care, lost wages, funeral expenses, and crime-scene cleanup.

CHAPTER OBJECTIVE 7

The three options available to victims for recovering crime-related financial losses are compensation, restitution, and civil remedies.

CHAPTER OBJECTIVE 8

Victim impact statements are assertions by victims and/or friends or relatives of victims about the crime's impact on the victim and the victim's family. These statements are considered by judicial authorities in decisions regarding sentencing and parole.

KEY TERMS

victim, p. 428
victims' rights, p. 428
best efforts standard, p. 430
tangible losses, p. 432
intangible losses, p. 432
victim notification, p. 434

community notification, p. 437
victim compensation, p. 440
restitution, p. 443
victim assistance program, p. 445
victim impact statement, p. 445
right of allocution, p. 445

1. Briefly outline the history of the American victims' rights movement.
2. Explain and date five federal laws that have significantly impacted victims' rights.
3. Why do some people consider a victims' rights amendment to the U.S. Constitution necessary?
4. What costs do crime victims suffer as a result of their victimization?
5. What can correctional agencies do to assist crime victims?
6. What are crime victim compensation programs and what do they do?
7. What three avenues are available to victims to recover financial losses due to crime?
8. Describe victim impact statements. In what ways are they useful?

CRITICAL THINKING EXERCISES

ON-THE-JOB ISSUE

You work in a state correctional facility. A month ago you were promoted from yard supervisory work into a program position that tasks you with conducting classes for offenders and their victims. Classes are held within the institution, and usually about 5 or 6 victims show up at each session to confront inmates. Many of the victims come from a local victims' rights group and, although they have all been victims of violent crime, they are not the people who have been victimized by the inmates involved in the class.

Classes usually involve victims telling inmates about the personal impact of their crimes, and about the personal burdens crime places upon victims everywhere. What strategies could you implement to ensure that inmates express true remorse for what they have done and that victims do not use the class as an opportunity to demean inmates?

CORRECTIONS ISSUES

1. In 1996, resolutions were introduced in the U.S. House and Senate to amend the Constitution to include crime victims' rights. A proposed federal constitutional amendment was reintroduced in modified form in 1999 with bipartisan support. A federal constitutional amendment for victims' rights, say supporters, is needed for many different reasons, including:

   a. to establish consistency in the rights of crime victims in every state and at the federal level;
   b. to ensure that courts engage in careful balancing of the rights of victims and defendants;
   c. to guarantee crime victims the opportunity to participate in criminal justice proceedings;
   d. to further enhance the participation of victims in the criminal justice process.

   Do you agree or disagree that the U.S. Constitution should be amended to include victims' rights? Why?

2. While correctional services for victims exist today in many correctional agencies and institutions across the country, some people believe that correctional agencies have enough to do without worrying about victims. Dealing with offenders is a full-time job, say such critics, and the time and expense required to meet the needs of victims are just not available. Besides, they say, corrections is about controlling and rehabilitating offenders, not about making victims "whole again."

   a. Should correctional agencies and correctional personnel be involved in victims' support programs? Why or why not?
   b. If you were a corrections professional, how would you feel about being called upon to assist crime victims?

1. Access the National Center for Victims of Crime at **http://www. nvc.org.** Click on the link to the "Victim Offender Reconciliation Program." Go to "Mediating the Victim-Offender Conflict" and click on "Case Studies." Read the case studies and decide whether or not the victims' needs and concerns were met through the reconciliation process.

2. All 50 states operate victim compensation programs. Some states have crime victim support agencies attached to the office of the state's attorney general. Access the Texas crime victims' page at **http://www.oag.state.tx.us/victims/victims.htm**, then search the Web to see if your state has a similar victim support organization and, if so, what information and services it provides.

ADDITIONAL READINGS

Alexander, Ellen K. and Janice Harris Lord. *Impact Statements—A Victim's Right to Speak, A Nation's Responsibility to Listen.* (Washington, DC: Office for Victims of Crime), 1994.

Beatty, D.L. Frank, A. J. Lurigio, A. Seymour, M. Paparozzi, and B. Macgargle. *A Guide to Enhancing Victim Services Within Probation and Parole.* (Lexington, KY: American Probation and Parole Association), 1994.

Bureau of Justice Statistics. *Criminal Victimization in the United States,* 1998. (Washington, DC: U.S. Department of Justice), 1999.

National Institute of Justice. *Victim Costs and Consequences: A New Look.* (Washington, DC: NIJ), January 1996.

National Victim Center. *1996 Victims' Rights Sourcebook: A Compilation and Comparison of Victims' Rights Laws.* (Arlington, VA: NVC), 1997.

ENDNOTES

1. Office for Victims of Crime, *From Pain to Power: Crime Victims Take Action* (Washington, DC: U.S. Department of Justice, 1998).

2. Federal Bureau of Prisons, Program Statement number 1490.03, December 14, 1994.

3. Much of the material in this chapter is adapted from Office for Victims of Crime, *New Directions from the Field: Victims Rights and Services for the 21st Century* (Washington, DC: U.S. Department of Justice, 1998).

4. National Organization for Victim Assistance, *1988 NOVA Legislative Directory* (Washington, DC: National Organization for Victim Assistance, 1988), p. 191.

5. Victim and Witness Protection Act of 1982, Pub. L. No. 97-291.

6. Office of Justice Programs, *President's Task Force on Victims of Crime: Four Years Later* (Washington, DC: U.S. Government Printing Office, May 1986), p. 4.

7. National Victim Center, *1996 Victims' Rights Sourcebook: A Compilation and Comparison of Victims'*

Rights Laws (Arlington, VA: National Victim Center, 1997).

8. Victim and Witness Protection Act of 1982, Pub. L. No. 97-291, section 2(b).

9. Crime Control Act of 1990, Pub. L. No. 101-647.

10. Op. cit., Title V, Section 502-503.

11. Violent Crime Control and Law Enforcement Act of 1994, Pub. L. No. 103-322.

12. Megan's Law amendment to the Jacob Wetterling Crimes Against Children and Sexual Violent Offender Act, 42 U.S.C. Section 14071.

13. NVCAN was created following a meeting sponsored by the National Organization for Victim Assistance (NOVA) and Mothers Against Drunk Driving (MADD) in 1985.

14. See the National Victims' Constitutional Amendment Network (NVCAN), *1996 Constitutional Amendment Action Kit.*

15. National Institute of Justice, *Victim Costs and Consequences: A New Look* (Washington, DC: NIJ, January 1996).

16. Ibid.
17. Much of the material in this section comes from Office for Victims of Crime, *New Directions*.
18. A. Seymour, *National Victim Services Survey of Adult and Juvenile Correctional Agencies and Paroling Authorities, 1996* (Arlington, VA: National Victim Center, April 1997).
19. Office for Victims of Crime, *New Directions*.
20. A. Seymour, op. cit., p. 5.
21. Megan's Law, Pub. L. No. 104-145, 110 Stat. 1345.
22. See Office for Victims of Crime, *New Directions*.
23. See Dorothy Mercer, R. Lord, and J. Lord, "Sharing Their Stories: What are the Benefits? Who is Helped?," paper presented at the Annual Meeting of the International Society for Traumatic Stress Studies, Chicago, IL, November 8, 1994.
24. Office for Victims of Crime, *New Directions*.
25. Ibid.
26. A. Seymour, op. cit.
27. A. Seymour, *Promising Practices and Strategies for Victim Services in Corrections* (Washington, DC: Office for Victims of Crime, 1999).
28. Office for Victims of Crime, *New Directions*.
29. President's Task Force on Victims of Crime, *Final Report* (Washington, DC: U.S. Government Printing Office, December 1982), p. 39.
30. National Association of Crime Victim Compensation Boards, *Crime Victim Compensation: An Overview* (Washington, DC: National Association of Crime Victim Compensation Boards, 1997), p. 1.
31. *Nationwide Analysis, Victims of Crime Act: 1996 Victims of Crime Act Performance Report, State Compensation Program* (Washington, DC: U.S. Department of Justice, Office of Justice Programs, Office for Victims of Crime, April 14, 1997).
32. Victims of Crime Act of 1984, Pub. L. No. 104-235.
33. President's Task Force on Victims of Crime, *Final Report*.
34. Much of the material is this section is taken from the Office for Victims of Crime fact sheet on the World Wide Web, http://www.ncjrs.org/ovcfs. htm. Accessed September 1, 1998.
35. Victim and Witness Protection Act of 1982, Pub. L. No. 97-291, Sec. 4.
36. President's Task Force on Victims of Crime, *Final Report* (Washington, DC: U.S. Government Printing Office, December 1982), p. 72.
37. The Mandatory Victim Restitution Act, Title II of the Antiterrorism and Effective Death Penalty Act of 1996, Pub. L. No. 104-132 (1996), 18 U.S.C. Section 3663A (1996).
38. P. A. Langan and M. A. Cunniff, *Recidivism of Felons on Probation, 1986-89* (Washington, DC: U.S. Department of Justice, Bureau of Justice Statistics, February 1992).
39. R. L. Cohen, *Probation and Parole Violators in State Prison, 1991* (Washington, DC: Bureau of Justice Statistics, 1995).
40. Ibid.
41. Much of the material in this section is taken from the office for victims of crime fact sheet, op. cit.
42. The National Victim Center, "INFOLINK: Victim Impact Statements," Web posted at http://www. nvc.org/infolink/info72.htm. Accessed January 2, 1999.
43. See Ellen K. Alexander and Janice Harris Lord, *Impact Statements: A Victim's Right to Speak, A Nation's Responsibility to Listen* (Washington, DC: Office for Victims of Crime, 1994).
44. *Payne v. Tennessee*, 501 U.S. 808, 111 S. Ct. 2597, 115 L. Ed. 2d 720.
45. National Victim Center, *1996 Victims' Rights Sourcebook*.
46. Office for Victims of Crime, *New Directions*.

16 Careers
Your Future in Corrections

CHAPTER OBJECTIVES

After completing this chapter you should be able to:

1. List the six steps of career planning.
2. Explain self-assessment.
3. List sources of information on careers and job opportunities.
4. Explain networking.
5. Explain informational interviewing.
6. Explain the purpose of a resume.
7. List and describe the two most widely used resume formats.

One's philosophy is not best expressed in words: it is expressed in the choices one makes . . . In the long run, we shape our lives and we shape ourselves. The process never ends until we die. And the choices we make are ultimately our responsibility.

—Eleanor Roosevelt

C areer development experts tell us that career development is a lifelong process that involves continual and consistent maintenance. Your interests, skills, and preferences change throughout your life. Thus, it is important that you know the steps involved in career planning, developing employability and job readiness, and finding the right job.[1]

Career Planning

Successful career planning is a continual process of self-assessment, occupational research, decision making, contacting potential employers, working at a job, and reevaluating your situation (see Figure 16–1).

Self-Assessment

Career planning begins with **self-assessment**—learning who you are and what you can and want to do by evaluating your interests, skills, and values. Self-assessment tools, which pose a series of questions and identify potential career choices based on your answers, are available from most col-

self-assessment

A method of enhancing self-understanding—identifying your unique characteristics: what you do well (skills), what is important to you (values), and what you like to do (interests)—clearly and accurately.

FIGURE 16–1

Steps to Career/Life Planning Success

STEPS TO CAREER/LIFE PLANNING SUCCESS

Begin at the bottom and work up.
Periodically reevaluate your career/life plans by starting again at step 1.

Self-Assessment					

					Planning
					Re-evaluation
				Work	
				Work Offers/Acceptance	Success at Work
			Employment Contacts		
			Job/Work Search	Resumes/Letters	Job/Work Interviews
		Decision Making			
		Career Objectives	Personal Objectives	Community Service	Lifelong Learning
	Occupational Research				
	Information Search	Information Interview	Job Shadow	Hands-on Experience	Trends
Self-Assessment					
Personality/Attitudes	Skills/Achievements	Knowledge/Learning Style	Values	Interests	Entrepreneurism

You may need to move from an upper step to a lower one; e.g., from step 4 to step 2, should a lack of openings in a particular field require research into a different one.

Source: Career Services at University of Waterloo

lege and university career counselors, as well as in book stores and on the Internet. The questions involved pertain to: (1) personal information—education, experience, achievements, personality factors, and interest in various activities; (2) skills—abilities in such areas as athletics, analysis, management, communication, and persuasion; and (3) values—ranking work-related issues (such as job location, pressure, security, responsibility, teamwork, and wages) in order of importance.

Occupational Research

The second step in career planning is research. Make a list of the potential career choices identified by your self-assessment, as well as any additional careers that you would like to know more about. Research job requirements (training, education, certification, licensure), job characteristics, working conditions, duties, employment outlook, salary, and methods of entry for each of the career alternatives: read everything you can find and talk to people.

Reading Information on careers and job opportunities is available in libraries (public, school, and special), career development centers, and on the Internet. Among others, three U.S. Department of Labor publications—*Dictionary of Occupational Titles, Occupational Outlook Handbook,* and *Guide for Occupational Exploration*—provide information on more than 20,000 jobs, and cross-reference each career field with others that are similar in nature. The U.S. Department of Labor also publishes two periodicals, *Occupational Outlook Quarterly* and *Monthly Labor Review,* that are excellent sources of information about occupational trends and salaries.

Talking to People **Networking** is meeting new people (often through people that you know) who can give you information about careers, the job market, and specific positions. Broadening your acquaintance base to include solid professional contacts, through networking, builds long-term professional relationships that facilitate job hunting and professional development and enhance personal growth.

networking An ongoing process of building professional contacts.

Developing a network is an integral part of job hunting; networking is considered the most effective method of job searching and is the number one way people obtain jobs. It has no time limit, nor does it end when you secure a position. Start developing contacts before you begin your career planning, and keep in touch with those contacts—they might hear of a job opening for you. Continue to keep in touch after you get a job—you may need to use your network again.

How do you begin networking? How do you establish contacts if you do not have any? Anyone can be a contact: the student who sits next to you in class, your parents' next-door neighbor, your doctor, your professor, previous supervisors, people with whom you have something in common (attending the same school, working out at the same gym, membership in the same professional association, etc.). Join organizations and participate in local programs that are related to your area of interest.

One of the key elements of networking is talking to people about your career interests and goals. Most people are more than willing to share information; in fact, the majority are flattered by the attention and truly want to help. Talk to the people you meet about what they do, their backgrounds, and their perspectives on the job market for their specialties, and ask if they know anyone else you might speak with. Take advantage of any and every opportunity to build your network—talk to people while you are waiting in line, riding the bus, attending a seminar, playing golf. The other key element is follow-up—keep your contacts apprised of your career status; let them know about your latest career move or your progress in a new job.

informational interviewing A process for obtaining firsthand information about a particular job or career.

Informational interviewing, talking to people who are currently employed in a career field that you are interested in exploring, is an excellent means of researching a particular job or position. Introduce yourself to the person you wish to talk to, either by calling or writing, and ask if you might have 30 minutes of time to discuss the job or position. Explain that you're gathering career information, and ask for an appointment. An informational interview can provide:

- An accurate portrayal of the career field you are investigating.
- Specifics about necessary skills, entry level positions, employment trends, etc.
- Information about related volunteer, part-time, or internship opportunities.
- Additional professional contacts.
- Increased confidence in interacting with professionals.
- Information about possible job openings.
- A good chance of "being at the right place at the right time."
- Information about concerns that should not be discussed in a job interview (e.g., salaries, hours, and minority issues).

Decision Making

The third step in career planning is making your career decision. Carefully review all of the information that you have gathered. For which of the careers that you researched are you best qualified? Which are most appealing? Which are most likely to enhance your career development? List career choices in order of preference, then begin your job search (see Figure 16–2).

Seeking Employment

Finding a job can be a tough process that requires an overwhelming amount of thought, time, and energy. Make the job search part of your everyday routine; decide how much time you will devote to the search and when, and stick with that decision.

Be creative in your job search; utilize all of the resources available to you—classified ads, Internet ads, professional associations, advisors, employment services (local and Internet), etc.—to identify available positions.

resume A written summary of your education, interests, skills, achievements, and goals.

Writing Your Resume

A good **resume** may not necessarily get you the job, but a bad resume can ensure that you don't get the job. Your resume is not meant to convey

Careers: Your Future in Corrections

FIGURE 16–2

Job Search Checklist

JOB SEARCH CHECKLIST

✓ Establish specific goals. Determine two or three potential career areas that are compatible with your values, skills, and interests.

✓ Prepare your search tools. Write a resume and sharpen your interviewing skills. Are you ready for your interview?

✓ Identify and research potential employers by utilizing different resources, such as:

- Career Development Center
- Professional Associations
- Newspaper Classifieds
- Internet Sites
- Deans/Professors/Other Advisors
- Trade Organizations
- Career Library Resources/Texts
- State/County Employment Offices

✓ Conduct informational interviews, which differ from job interviews—they provide you with an excellent opportunity to meet with individuals in a specific career field and obtain up-to-date information on that field. This can help your career decision making and develop a network of contacts.

✓ Initiate contact with employers. Establish a mailing list of potential employers within the targeted fields you identified from your earlier research. Mail your resume with a focused cover letter and then follow up with telephone calls to request interview appointments.

✓ Follow up with each contact. Remember, follow-up is your responsibility.

✓ Get organized, and stay on schedule. Devote at least 20 hours a week to your job search. Develop a schedule and create a list of organizations, contact people, contact dates, and outcomes.

✓ Accept an offer—consider these factors when deciding on which:

- size of the organization
- job security
- travel/relocation requirements
- hours
- formal training arrangements
- people you met with
- advancement potential
- entry level salary
- salary potential
- geographical factors
- education/fringe benefits
- name recognition of employer

your complete life history. Through your resume, you convey your capability for a particular position; it must be clear, directed, and persuasive—its objective is to secure an interview.

Your resume should (1) support a career direction and (2) be selective. Career direction gives the resume focus; all of the information included in the resume should support the career direction that you are trying to convey. Career guidance experts tell us, "You should make yourself as attractive as possible on paper so that the employer feels as though she would be missing out by not interviewing you."[2] Your resume should project you as someone who produces, accomplishes, and is results-oriented. Use active verbs and descriptive terms; i.e., "researched and drafted reports" rather than "responsible for research and reports." What works best today is a conservative style and a focus on key achievements—particularly those that relate to the position for which you are applying; find out as much as you can about the prospective employer, then modify the resume to highlight those items that will most benefit the company or organization. The most effective resume is one that is tailored to a specific job; the results are well worth the extra effort. According to Tom Jackson, "The Perfect Resume is a written communication that clearly demonstrates your ability to produce results in an area of concern to selected employers, in a way that motivates them to meet you."[3]

FIGURE 16–3

Tips for Writing Resumes

RESUME WRITING–QUICK TIPS

- One Page
- Font Size: 10 (minimum)–12 (preferred)
- Paper Weight: recommended, 24 lb; acceptable, 21 lb.
- Paper Color: white or off-white
- GPA is required dependent upon major
- Margins: .5–1.5 inch, portrait
- Include your objective
- Do not use personal pronouns
- Use action verbs
- Use conventional English, preferably one- or two-syllable words
- Use short paragraphs—preferably no longer than five lines
- Use a chronological or functional format
- Use "bullet" format where appropriate
- Proofread and have others proofread for you
- "References available upon request" ends your resume

When creating your resume, keep the following in mind:

- The "one page rule"—one page is ideal; two is acceptable (however, do not add a second page simply to expand content); three is unacceptable.
- Your resume should be easily scanned: effectively organized to carry the reader's eye from major point to major point (a prospective employer will look for words and phrases that convey the necessary qualifications).
- The eye is drawn to eye-catching type; **bold,** CAPITALIZE, or underscore to emphasize a particular item.
- Bullets break job and skill descriptions into easy-to-read component parts that begin with eye-catching verbs.
- Talents, skills, and experience should be highlighted to some extent, but don't overdo.
- Word processing allows great flexibility in the selection of fonts, but choose something simple. Avoid ornateness, and avoid combining several fonts.
- Employers want employees who can set goals and complete tasks; present yourself as someone who gets things done.
- You must identify your strengths and convey them on paper; this is not arrogance or boasting. The person who is reading your resume wants to know that you are exceptional.
- You should always honestly summarize your work experience and skills, including any technologies you are familiar with (such as computers, calculators, fax machines, telephone systems, word processing, spreadsheet or database software, etc.).
- Personal pronouns should not be used; "I" is implied.
- Complete sentences are not necessary.
- Abbreviations should be avoided.

Your resume is a primary tool in obtaining more attractive positions; thus, extra time spent on its preparation is a good investment. All resumes should be accurate and truthful, but each should highlight different strengths, as they relate to the potential job. The resume should go through several stages of drafting and editing until it is as perfect as it can be.

Resume Format

The selected resume format should establish a natural flow of information that simplifies the review process, and should incorporate a consistent pattern of information placement, allowing the reader to anticipate where certain information will be found. An employer usually reviews information on the left side first—names of employers, job titles, etc., should be placed on the left. Less important information (dates, locations, etc.) should be placed on the right. No resume format is universally preferred, although the **chronological resume** and the **functional resume** are the most widely used. (See Figures 16–4 and 16–5.)

Chronological Resume The chronological resume format is the most widely accepted and preferred resume style. It is most effectively used by

chronological resume
An historical resume, in which work experience and personal history are presented, in reverse chronological order.

functional resume
A qualitative resume, in which work experience and abilities are presented by major area of involvement, usually with dates.

people who have established or are establishing credentials within a particular field, or whose credentials show career growth and direction within one particular employment environment. To be effective, the chronological resume should project a sense of quality by emphasizing skills and accomplishments, and should be carefully organized (in terms of layout) to most effectively present a particular background. In this format, your education and work experience are presented in reverse time sequence, with the most recent degrees and jobs appearing first. In developing a chronological resume:

- de-emphasize history for the sake of content; place dates and other less relevant information on the right-hand side of the page;
- devote more space to the most recent position;
- fully describe the three or four positions most supportive of the career direction—summarize other work experience unless it is exceptionally meaningful;
- avoid excessive repetition in detail and substance; and
- emphasize career growth.

Functional Resume The functional resume emphasizes abilities over work history by organizing information according to skills, results accomplished, contributions made, or functions successfully performed. It is best used by those who are changing careers or have been out of the work force for some time. In developing a functional resume:

- select functions that describe job-related abilities (versatile abilities, if possible);
- list functions in order of importance and relevance to your career direction, emphasizing accomplishment and achievement while illustrating specific abilities;
- avoid including employment detail (employer names, dates of employment, job titles) within the functional descriptions; include a work history section that sets forth this information.

What To Include Regardless of which resume format you use, your resume should include:

1. Identification—name (first, middle initial, last), address (permanent and/or present), telephone numbers (work and/or home, fax), and e-mail address (if applicable). Accurate information is critical; a prospective employer who is unable to reach you with the information provided is not likely to try to verify contact information. If the information changes, correct your resume and reprint it.
2. Objective/Career Interest—your career objective specifies the type of work you want to do, the position you want, or the skills/attributes you anticipate utilizing, and the employment sector in which you wish to establish a career; a career interest statement is a broader, long-range career direction, which simply lists the field or occupation in which you wish to be employed.

Careers: Your Future in Corrections

FIGURE 16–4

Reverse Chronological Resume Format

Derrick A. Salyer
1555 Campus Lake Drive, Richmond, KY 40477
(606) 555-1212

OBJECTIVE

To secure a position as a juvenile court probation officer.

EDUCATION

Bachelor of Science, August 1999
Eastern Kentucky University, Richmond, KY
Major: Correctional Services
GPA: 3.20/4.00
Dean's List, Distinguished Undergraduate Award

Associate of Arts, December 1995
Houston Community College, Houston, TX
Major: General Studies

Self-financed 50% of education through work, loans, and scholarships

EXPERIENCE

Intern, January–May 1999
Kentucky Department of Juvenile Justice, Richmond, KY
- Assisted department staff with hosting of three live national satellite videoconferences
- Served as liaison to downlink sites
- Attended all planning sessions

Intern, August–December 1998
Richmond Juvenile Court Services, Richmond, KY
- Assisted intake officer with predisposition investigation and report writing
- Attended detention and adjudication hearings
- Answered questions relating to the predisposition report

Sales Associate, March 1996–July 1998
Just For Feet, University Mall, Richmond, KY
- Coordinated sales associates' schedules
- Managed evening cashier sales associates
- Achieved and maintained Best Shift/Least Checkout Errors monthly in 1998

ACTIVITIES

Criminal Justice Student Association, 1998 President, 1997 Vice President
Alpha Phi Sigma (Criminal Justice Honor Society) Spirit Award, 1996

REFERENCES

Available upon request.

FIGURE 16–5

Functional Resume Format

Tanisha Williams

1500 Maplewood Drive, Palmdale, CA 93510

(213) 555-1212

CAREER INTERESTS:

   Correctional industry managment

SKILLS:

PLANNING/ORGANIZATION

- Successfully established and operated a T-shirt design shop
- Developed market/trade survey programs to determine customer interest
- Initiated radio T-shirt give-away contests
- Established connection with local homeless shelter to employ the homeless

ADMINISTRATION/MANAGEMENT/SALES MARKETING

- Supervised team of 20 sales associates
- Hired and delegated supervision of 18-person T-shirt design shop to two associate managers
- Approved corporate sales contracts
- Increased corporate sales 32%
- Managed commercial sales advertisements—three radio, one television, and one newspaper—averaging $32,000 annually

EMPLOYMENT EXPERIENCE

OWNER AND OPERATOR   1990–Present

TANISHA'S SHIRTS AND DESIGNS

Lancaster, California

SALES ASSOCIATE AND MANAGER   1987–1990

HUTTON'S TEES

Lancaster, California

EDUCATION

BACHELOR OF SCIENCE, CRIMINAL JUSTICE ADMINISTRATION, 1999

Califormia State University

Northridge, California

REFERENCES AVAILABLE UPON REQUEST

3. Education—schools attended, degrees received, dates of graduation, majors and other concentrations of study, and academic achievement (class rank and grade point average for an undergraduate or graduate program). The education section can also include extracurricular activities of particular significance and academic honors and awards.

4. Skills/Accomplishments/Qualifications—descriptions, grouped by major functional skill area. Choose three to five functional skill areas that correspond to your career objective.

5. Experience—for a chronological resume, list experience in reverse chronological order, beginning with your current or most recent position.

6. Optional—Other information that can be included in your resume includes: personal statements (relatively neutral comments about personal interests such as foreign language, community activity, travel, sports, public speaking, unique hobbies, and military experience); honors and awards (academic honors, memberships in national honor societies, scholarships, etc.); curricular and cocurricular activities (those that demonstrate leadership), community activities or volunteer experiences (demonstrates personal work habits, leadership potential, and level of motivation/commitment); professional associations and licenses, and publications.

References should always be listed on a separate page, not on the resume. Do not approach the selection of references casually; your references are critical to the strength of your employment credentials.

The resume copy should be meticulously reviewed before it is forwarded to a potential employer (you might have a friend or a qualified professional critique it):

- Is the resume easily scanned?
- Does the resume immediately project a career direction and provide supporting evidence?
- Is the resume neat, clean, and professional? Is the layout attractive?
- Are the margins wide enough?
- Are there typos? Check and recheck spelling, punctuation, and grammar—proofread by reading the resume backward.
- Is the highlighting (bold, capitalization, underscore) excessive?
- Is the language direct and concise?
- Is the resume action- and results-oriented?
- Is the resume free of jargon that the reader may not understand?
- Are sentences short? Are paragraphs short? Are they vivid and descriptive?
- Is all repetition eliminated?
- Are there time gaps that the employer might question?
- Is all irrelevant information excluded?
- Is the verb tense consistent?
- Are there any personal pronouns?
- Does the resume represent you at your very best?

Many employers and employment services now encourage online job application. Be aware, though, that if you used a word-processing program or desktop publishing program to create your resume, it may not look the same to the online recipient as it did on your computer—a resume that is to be submitted online should be translated to text format. Here are some guidelines:

- Line length—line lengths in excess of 80 characters have a very good chance of wrapping prematurely, creating an annoying double-spaced window.
- Vertical alignment—vertical alignment is achieved by using an equal number of spaces from the left-hand margin; to ensure that all characters are the same size (including spaces), use a fixed-width font such as 10-point Courier and use spaces rather than tabs to indent text.
- Other issues—if your resume design includes columns or bullets, take advantage of ASCII characters such as dashes (-), asterisks (*), and arrows (>).

The Cover Letter

A cover letter (see Figures 16–6 and 16–7) should always accompany your resume. Like the resume, the cover letter should be direct, persuasive, descriptive, and attractive. Remember, the cover letter is specific to the potential employer; it should emphasize credentials and experience that apply to the position. Your cover letter can differentiate you significantly from others competing for the same position. The following is the basic format for the cover letter:

1. First paragraph—serves to get the attention of the person receiving the letter and answers the question: "Why are you writing?" This can be as simple as stating that you are "a graduating student seeking employment at [name of employer]," or that you are "responding to a job posting from [name of source]." If (in the ideal situation) you are referred by a professional or personal contact, use it to your advantage—begin your letter with "John Smith recommended that I contact you regarding employment."
2. Second paragraph—details your interest in and your fit with the company or organization. Keep in mind that employers are more interested in what you can do for them than in what they can give you. Answer implied questions, such as:
   a. "Why are you interested in working for this firm or organization?" This part need only be a sentence or two, but should include reference to specifics about the organization—its mission, type of work, geographic location, size, reputation in the community, and/or types of positions available. Employers' hiring decisions are often based not only on qualifications, but also on level of interest in the firm or organization. Be genuine. This is an opportunity to show that you researched the employer.

Careers: Your Future in Corrections

FIGURE 16–6

Tips on Writing Cover Letters

WRITING A COVER LETTER

Your Street Address
City, State Zip Code

Today's Date

Contact Person's Name
Contact Person's Title (if applicable)
Company/Organization Name
Street Address
City, State Zip Code

Dear (Contact Person's Name, or Contact Person's Title if name is unknown):

OPENING PARAGRAPH: Clearly state why you are writing, name the position or type of work for which you are applying, and mention how you heard of the opening. If you are writing without prior knowledge of an available opening, say that you are interested in openings that may currently be available.

MIDDLE PARAGRAPH: Explain why you are interested in working for this employer, and/or your reasons for desiring this type of work. Describe applicable experience, achievements, or other qualifications in this environment or type of employment.

MIDDLE PARAGRAPH: Refer the reader to your enclosed resume, which positively illustrates your training, skills, and experience. DO NOT DUPLICATE RESUME INFORMATION IN THE COVER LETTER—"highlight," and elaborate on how you can make a tangible contribution to this company/organization.

CLOSING PARAGRAPH: Use a closing appropriate to acquiring an interview. If you know the contact person's name and telephone number, use a pro-active strategy—say that you will call to request an appointment in the very near future. If you do not know the contact person's name, ending your letter with a question often encourages a response. (e.g., May we meet soon to discuss this matter further?)

Sincerely,

Your signature

Your Full Name (typewritten)

Enclosure

FIGURE 16–7

Sample Cover Letter

1500 Maplewood Drive
Palmdale, CA 93510
January 12, 2000

Ms. Caroline Butterworth
Human Resources
State of California
Department of Corrections
Sacramento, CA 94283-0001

Dear Ms. Butterworth:

I am applying for the position of Supervisor of Correctional Industries in your Southeast Region. I am a graduate of California State University, Northridge, with a bachelor's degree in criminal justice administration. I believe that my work experience and education make me a strong candidate for this position.

My degree in criminal justice administration has given me an excellent understanding of the criminal justice field, particularly institutional corrections and the corrections industry. I completed a 15-week internship at the Chino, California Institution for Men, where I gained considerable insight into prison industry operations—especially security—and the importance of helping prisoners to develop and maintain job skills prior to release.

My work experience spans 10 years, which includes self-employment (in T-shirt design and sales—I hired and supervised a staff of 20) and industry organization and management.

I look forward to speaking with you about utilizing my business skills and criminal justice qualifications in the position of Supervisor of Correctional Industries. I will contact you next week to arrange an interview. Please call me if you have questions.

Sincerely,

Tanisha Williams

Tanisha Williams

Enclosure

b. "Why are you the right person for the job?" In two or three sentences, tell the prospective employer what skills you will bring to the job without reiterating details included in your resume. Give specific examples of skills and accomplishments related to this position that you emphasized in your resume. You might consider a wrap-up sentence commenting on how the organization might benefit from your skills and experience.

3. Last paragraph—express appreciation for the prospective employer's time and consideration, and provide details about what you plan to do next—how you will follow up (e.g., a telephone call) and when (either a specific date or within a certain number of weeks; wait at least two weeks). If you do not know whom to call to follow up, you might ask the employer to contact you at a particular telephone number or by e-mail. If a job listing says, "No phone calls, please," state in the cover letter that you look forward to hearing from the employer soon.

The Job Interview

The **job interview** plays a very important role in your job search. To interview successfully, you must understand the interview process and prepare well. Do not assume that the interview is, or should be, one-sided. During an interview, you must project your most impressive qualities. In other words, you must sell yourself to the prospective employer. As part of the evaluation process, the interviewer will be deciding how you will function as an employee. Therefore, it is essential to demonstrate how your skills, knowledge, and experience match the requirements of the position for which you are interviewing.

It is essential that you speak confidently (not arrogantly) about your skills, knowledge, and experience. In preparing, take time to think about answers to potential interview questions (see Figure 16–8). When the interviewer asks a question for which you are unprepared, think before you speak; take a second or two and organize your thoughts, then answer as best you can.

Reread your resume before every interview—chances are the interviewer did just that, too. In addition, review your resume for possible questions you might be asked. Formulating answers ahead of time will allow you to be more relaxed and articulate during the interview.

Job interview attire can be summed up in two words: "conservative" and "businesslike." Proper dress will give you confidence and enhance your professional image. For most professional-level jobs, the standard dark suit is appropriate for both men and women; less formal clothing may be more appropriate for some jobs. Use common sense. College faculty and career planning counselors can help, as well as someone you may know who is employed in the same field as the position for which you are interviewing. Keep perfume or cologne and jewelry to a minimum. Do not chew gum or other food during the interview.

Take with you to the interview copies of your resume, your list of references (or reference letters), any other relevant papers, and your transcripts(s), as well as a pen or pencil and notebook and a list of questions.

job interview A meeting between two or more people for a mutual exchange of information regarding employment.

FIGURE 16–8

Sample Interview Questions

FIFTY QUESTIONS MOST OFTEN ASKED BY EMPLOYERS DURING AN INTERVIEW

1. Tell me about yourself.
2. What personal goals, other than those related to your occupation, have you established for yourself for the next ten years?
3. What do you see yourself doing five years from now?
4. What do you really want to do in life?
5. What are your short-range and long-range career objectives?
6. How do you plan to achieve your career goals?
7. What are the most important rewards you expect in your career?
8. What do you expect to be earning in five years?
9. Why did you choose the career for which you are preparing?
10. Which is more important to you, the money or the type of job?
11. What do you consider your greatest strengths and weaknesses?
12. How would you describe yourself?
13. How do you think a friend or professor who knows you well would describe you?
14. What motivates you to put forth your greatest effort?
15. How has your college experience prepared you for your career?
16. Why should I hire you?
17. What qualifications do you have that makes you think that you will be successful in this environment/setting?
18. How do you determine or evaluate success?
19. What do you think it takes to be successful in an organization like ours?
20. In what ways do you think you can make a contribution to this organization?
21. What qualities should a successful supervisor possess?
22. Describe the relationship that should exist between a supervisor and those reporting to him or her.
23. What two or three accomplishments have given you the most satisfaction? Why?

A typical first job interview usually lasts 30–60 minutes, although it may be longer. Often called a screening interview, the first interview is often used to shorten a long list of candidates. You also may be asked to complete a job-related questionnaire that may serve to shorten the list of candidates (see Figure 16–9). Those who make a positive impression are invited back for second interviews.

Remain alert for indications that you are on track. If the interviewer seems relaxed, is following closely, and encouraging you with comments and nods, you are probably on target. If the interviewer appears puzzled, stop and restate your reply. If the interviewer has obviously lost interest, try getting back on track by asking if you covered the point adequately. Maintain eye contact when answering questions, but do not be afraid to avert your eyes when thinking about an answer.

FIGURE 16–8 (continued)

Sample Interview Questions

24. Describe your most rewarding college experience.
25. If you were hiring a graduate for this position, what qualities would you look for?
26. Why did you select your college or university?
27. What led you to choose your field or major?
28. What college subjects did you like best? Why?
29. What college subjects did you like least? Why?
30. If you could do so, how would you plan your academic study differently?
31. What changes would you make in your college or university? Why?
32. Do you have plans for continued study? An advanced degree?
33. Do you think that your grades are a good indication of your academic achievement/ability?
34. What have you learned from participation in extracurricular activities?
35. In what kinds of environments are you most comfortable?
36. How do you work under pressure?
37. In what part-time or summer job have you been most interested? Why?
38. How would you describe the ideal job for you following graduation?
39. Why did you decide to seek a position with this organization?
40. What do you know about this organization?
41. What three things are most important to you in your career/job?
42. Are you seeking employment in an organization of a certain size? Why?
43. What criteria are you using to evaluate the organization/employer for which you hope to work?
44. Do you have a geographical preference? Why?
45. Will you relocate? Do relocations bother you?
46. Are you willing to travel?
47. Are you willing to spend at least six months in training?
48. Why do you think you might like to live in the area in which our organization is located?
49. Describe a major problem you have encountered and how you dealt with it.
50. What have you learned from your mistakes?

A prospective employer may request a second interview, either because initial interviews indicated that more than one of the applicants might qualify for the position or because others are involved in the hiring decision. Keep in mind when preparing for the second interview that you may now be in direct competition with others whose qualifications are as appropriate as yours; prepare carefully:

- Engage in a more extensive study of the organization to gain in-depth knowledge.
- Evaluate your skills, knowledge, and experience and how they are applicable to the position for which you are applying.
- Review general interview skills.
- Gather appropriate documents: resumes, references, transcripts, etc.

FIGURE 16-9

Sample Job Screening Questionnaire

SUPPLEMENTAL QUESTIONNAIRE
SELF-SCREENING
PROBATION AND PAROLE OFFICER I

The following requirements are needed by all candidates for this position. If you answer "yes" to all requirements listed, sign below and return this form with your completed application. If you answer "no" to any of the requirements, do not complete the rest of the form and do not submit an application. An answer "no" in any one area will result in a rating of "not qualified" for this position.

1. Are you willing and able to cope with unmotivated and hostile individuals who have committed all types of crimes?

    Yes _____   No _____

2. Are you willing to do field checks knowing that you will be going into areas where you may be subject to threats or physical danger?

    Yes _____   No _____

3. Are you willing to testify before the court, parole board, and other judicial hearings to answer questions, present progress reports, and make recommendations?

    Yes _____   No _____

4. Are you willing to be trained in the use of firearms and deadly force?

    Yes _____   No _____

5. Are you willing to be trained in the use of defensive tactics which involve physical contact?

    Yes _____   No _____

6. Are you willing to participate in the arrest of criminal offenders?

    Yes _____   No _____

The answers I have given are true and correct to the best of my knowledge, and I understand that I must be willing and able to perform tasks requiring physical strength and agility.

SIGNATURE _____ DATE _____

- Compare your personal agenda with the organization's agenda.
- Make additional copies of pertinent records.
- Prepare a list of questions.

Remember, interviewing is a two-way street. Not only is it an opportunity for the organization to ask questions of you, it is also your opportunity to learn more about the organization. Get answers to your questions; this information will help you decide which of the job offers you receive you should accept, and asking the same question of different individuals will allow you to compare responses. Whatever the outcome of any job interview, bear in mind that the employer is thinking first of organizational needs, not of you. Don't let rejections weaken your self-confidence.

The Thank-You Letter

A thank-you letter (see Figure 16–10 on page 472) should always immediately follow a job interview; in fact, you should start thinking about the thank-you letter as soon as the interview is over, and mail it within 24 hours of the interview. The thank-you letter is not just "a nice thing to do"; it's also a sales opportunity—another opportunity for you to "sell" yourself. The thank-you letter should be simple; the following is the basic format:

1. First paragraph—Thank the reader for the interview and restate the position for which you are applying and your interest in it.
2. Second paragraph—restate your qualifications and reiterate what you have to offer to the company. Refer to specific points discussed during the interview.
3. Last paragraph—restate the first paragraph.

Securing Employment

Job offers are not typically made on the spot. However, if an offer is made, you should delay acceptance until you have had an opportunity to evaluate all of your job opportunities. When evaluating your options, be sure to consider all aspects of the position—type of work, location, salary, benefits, opportunity for growth, co-workers. Again, the job hunting process can be tough; choose a job that you will want to keep for a long while.

Re-evaluation

Because your interests, skills, and preferences change, you should periodically re-evaluate your career choice to determine if you could more effectively utilize your skills, abilities, and talents in a different occupation or at a different organization. Correspond with your contacts on a fairly regular basis and investigate available positions, but be careful not to take steps that may jeopardize your present position—you may find that it is still the best job for you.

FIGURE 16–10

Sample Thank You Letter

1500 Maplewood Drive
Palmdale, CA 93510
March 16, 2000

Ms. Caroline Butterworth
Human Resources
State of California
Department of Corrections
Sacramento, CA 94283-0001

Dear Ms. Butterworth:

Thank you for taking the time to meet with me on Wednesday and giving me the opportunity to learn more about California's prison industries program. The materials you gave me were very informative and interesting.

As we discussed during our interview, my education and work experience have prepared me for many of the duties of the Supervisor of Correctional Industries, and, based on the additional knowledge that I gained during that interview, I am certain that my performance in this position will exceed the requirements.

As you requested, I have asked the California State University records office to forward a copy of my transcript to your office; you should receive it within a few days.

Thank you again for your time and interest. I look forward to hearing from you.

Sincerely,

Tanisha Williams

Tanisha Williams

THE STAFF SPEAKS

In the past two years, The Corrections Connection has received thousands of e-mails with questions about getting hired in corrections. So, we thought it would be helpful to get advice from two corrections practitioners in different parts of the country, who frequently conduct job interviews and review applications for employment. We interviewed Warden George F. Wagner from the Hunterdon County Jail in Flemington, New Jersey and Captain Ken E. Richardson from the Licking County Jail in Licking, Ohio.

Both were very willing to share their experiences, the dos and don'ts of interviewing, and the types of interview questions most frequently asked. Although they have two very different styles of interviewing, you can see that they both seek the same type of qualities in an employee: loyalty, dedication, honesty, and integrity. In fact, in an independent survey of 20 other facilities, we found these overall qualities to be important to most corrections employers, even more so than problem solving skills, writing and communication skills. Here is what else we discovered.

Q: What do you think are the basics that every job applicant should know?

Warden George F. Wagner: Arrive on time and dress appropriately.

Captain Ken E. Richardson: "Be on time! It shows dependability and that's critical."

Q: What are you looking for in the interview room?

Wagner: By the time they come in for the interview, I already know everything about them from their application and background checks. Now, I want to know if they can articulate their goals. Why do they want to work in corrections? What I usually find is that the conversation is one-way; I do all the talking. They should be asking me questions, taking an active interest.

Richardson: I am looking for people who are able to express themselves. I want people who are proud of where they work. Proud of their employer. Proud of their profession. It makes a difference in their level of performance. I am looking for dedication and, above all, loyalty.

Q: What is one big mistake applicants should avoid?

Wagner: Don't come too early. Arriving at 8:00 a.m. for a 9:00 a.m. appointment is not good. You are actually impeding the process because now we have to figure out what to do with you while you are here. Being too early is actually a bad decision.

Q: What should an applicant wear to an interview?

Wagner: You should take the interview seriously and wear something appropriate. I'll tell you a true story. Last summer we were conducting interviews. I looked out into the lobby and saw this guy in shorts, a tee-shirt, flip flops, and a hat with the brim turned to the back. I asked my Lieutenant who he was, and he said, "That's your 10 o'clock. Should I bring him in for the interview?" My response was simple: "He just had his interview!" So sorry I interrupted his day at the beach.

Richardson: You should look professional (a suit or sports jacket and tie; a nice tailored dress or suit). You want to make a nice first impression.

Q: If someone is currently working in law enforcement or is in the armed forces, would you recommend that he or she wear the uniform to the interview?

Wagner: No, I would not. It just reminds me that you are working for someone else while you are looking for another job. I want to know that you're interested in me. Plus, as employers, you can't trust that the uniform is real. I once had a man come in a uniform, saying that he was a veteran. In reality, he

continued

had picked up the uniform in a local thrift shop. I'm going to do a thorough background check on you, check your references, meet with you, read your application, so I am going to know all that I have to know about you anyway. I don't need the uniform.

Q: What should an applicant bring to the interview?

Wagner: You need to look prepared and be prepared. If there are documents that you think we need, bring copies so we don't have to make the copies ourselves. Otherwise, I have to get up, get my secretary, have her make the copies and bring them back to you. Show a little planning on your part. I like it when someone has everything prepared.

Q: Do you always conduct a background check?

Wagner: We always check background. You can't trust documents, i.e., college records, certificates, etc. We are getting into scannable documents, where you can create anything with a computer and say it's real. An applicant may say he or she has a Ph.D. and have documents and certificates, but they are not authentic. We always do background checks.

Richardson: Absolutely. We do a thorough background check on every applicant.

Q: What kind of information should be included in a background check?

Wagner: We want to know everything. Where you were born, siblings, boyfriends, girlfriends. Financial obligations you have, financial obligations you've had, education, all employers from day 1, any interaction with any law enforcement agency, any judgments of any kind. I have had people come in to the office for an interview who have a criminal record, and they just don't put it on the application. People think if they don't list it, nobody is going to find out. That is simply not true.

Richardson: Everything should go on the application. To me, silence is a form of deception.

Q: What kind of preparation should applicants do prior to the interview?

Wagner: Do a little research on the institution to which they are going for the interview. Contact government authorities and find out how the position being interviewed for fits into the organizational chart. Know a little bit about the facility. It shows initiative to do that. On my end, I like to give them the tour before the interview. They need to know the kind of inmates they are dealing with, as well as our set-up and procedures.

Q: What about political and moral philosophies? How important is that?

Wagner: Their personal feelings don't matter because their professional behavior is guided by policy. It doesn't matter to me whether they are liberal, conservative, democratic, pro-choice, pro-life, right-wing, left-wing, or pro capital punishment. We formulate their professional conduct via policy and procedure. As long as they are following our procedures, I don't care what their personal views are. I think that's the way it usually is.

Q: What is the procedure for testing and applying?

Wagner: Well, it is going to depend a lot on the individual requirements of your state. We are a civil service state so applicants test and are ranked according to their scores and by their residence. We run a county jail, so people who live in Hunterdon County would be ranked first; then bordering counties in New Jersey; then state wide; then nationwide. We do give veterans preference. You should find out what your state requires. Of course, we do background checks; conduct oral interviews; require you to provide three references (vouchers) signed by a notary; take a physical which includes a drug test; then take a psychological test. Then you're hired . . . if you pass all that.

Richardson: In addition to the tests, the background checks and the interview, we do a writing

exercise. We tell applicants to write about the most important day of their life. This serves many purposes. One, we have in their own words what is important to them. Two, it shows us their report writing abilities and how well they can spell, etc. It's just one or two pages, but it gives us great insight into the way they think.

Q: Does military experience help? What about a B.A.?

Wagner: We are making a 25-year investment in this person, and, based on the pool of applicants we've been seeing, we can afford to be picky. Does military experience count? Is a BA going to help? Absolutely. Not just because the applicant pool is bigger, but because it shows the willingness of the individual to commit and complete things, and that is very important to an employer.

Q: What kinds of questions do you like to ask?

Wagner: Employees aren't prepared to ask any questions; it always seems to be a one- way conversation. I am going to look at the background packet. I am going to know about you before you come in. Then I want to hear your answers to the following questions:

1. Why do you want to work here?
2. How did you end up in corrections?

I have yet to find anyone who grew up wanting to work in a state jail or a prison. I have no problem with someone being honest and saying "I am graduating from college and I want to work for the FBI, but I saw you had openings and thought this would be a good segue." I would rather know from the employee what his or her career aspirations are.

3. What are your career goals?

Be able to articulate your career aspirations. I find it confounding that people don't know how to interview. You are given the opportunity to sell yourself. Why do I want to pick you as opposed to the other

328 people? Based on turnovers, I have done a lot of interviews. A majority of interviewees now have bachelor's degrees, but they don't know how to interview.

4. What would you do in the event of a riot? How would you prepare for such an event?
5. Are you prepared for the hours of work and varied scheduling?

   This place runs 24 hours a day, 7 days a week. You might have to work 8 hours, plus be required to stay and work mandatory overtime when you were planning to go to a family picnic on July 4th.

   Richardson: Our questions are subjective by some standards, but I think the responses are very useful to determine the person's psychological make up. We are looking for persons with substance to them. I want to know the answers to the following questions:

1. What motivates you?
2. What values are important to you?
3. What is the most significant problem you have ever had to contend with and how did you deal with it?

What is a problem to the interviewee and how he or she perceives it shows problem-solving abilities.

4. What is the most important personal quality you have? What is of value to you? If a person responds "defend myself," that is not really a value. However, responses such as "I have a lot of personal integrity," "I am a compassionate caring person" "People respect me for being honest" show important personal values.
5. Why do you want to work here?

We want to know if this a career to them or just a job. We just started using these kinds of questions in the past year or so. The last bunch of people we hired is about 10 notches above anyone before it.

CHAPTER OBJECTIVE 1

Successful career planning is a continual process of self-assessment, occupational research, decisionmaking, employment contacts, work, and re-evaluation.

CHAPTER OBJECTIVE 2

Self-assessment is learning who you are and what you can and want to do by evaluating your interests, skills, and values. Self-assessment tools pose a series of questions and identify potential career choices based on your answers.

CHAPTER OBJECTIVE 3

Information on careers and job opportunities is available in libraries (public, school, and special), career development centers, and on the Internet.

CHAPTER OBJECTIVE 4

Networking is meeting new people who can give you information about careers, the job market, and specific positions. Broaden your acquaintance base by networking—talk with people you know, join organizations, and participate in local programs that are related to your area of interest.

CHAPTER OBJECTIVE 5

Informational interviewing, talking to people who are currently employed in a career field that you are interested in exploring, is an excellent means of researching a particular job or position.

CHAPTER OBJECTIVE 6

Through your resume, you convey your capability for a particular position. It must be clear, directed, and persuasive—its objective is to secure an interview.

CHAPTER OBJECTIVE 7

The two most widely used resume formats are the chronological resume and the functional resume. The chronological resume emphasizes skills and accomplishments; the functional resume emphasizes abilities.

KEY TERMS

self-assessment, p. 454
networking, p. 455
informational interviewing, p. 456
resume, p. 456

chronological resume, p. 459
functional resume, p. 459
job interview, p. 467

QUESTIONS FOR REVIEW

1. What is self-assessment?
2. What is networking?
3. What is the reason for establishing contacts?
4. What is an informational interview?
5. In what ways does an informational interview differ from a job interview?
6. What is a resume?
7. Describe the chronological resume format.
8. Describe the functional resume format.
9. What information should be included in a resume?
10. What information should be included in a cover letter?
11. What information should be included in a thank-you letter?
12. How do you prepare for a job interview?

CORRECTIONS ON THE WEB

Access The Corrections Connection's Web site, at **http://www.corrections.com**. Click on "Careers," then "Job Openings." Review several openings for like positions and compare the requirements.

ADDITIONAL READINGS

Ackerman, Thomas H. *Guide to Careers in Federal Law Enforcement.* Traverse City, MI: Sage Creek Press, 1999.

DeLucia, Robert C., and Thomas J. Doyle. *Career Planning in Criminal Justice,* 2d ed. Cincinnati, OH: Anderson Publishing, 1994.

Harr, J. Scott, and Karen M. Hess. *Seeking Employment in Criminal Justice and Related Fields,* 2d ed. Minneapolis/St. Paul: West Publishing Co., 1996.

Henry, Stuart, ed. *Inside Jobs: A Realistic Guide to Criminal Justice Careers for College Graduates.* Salem, WI: Sheffield Publishing Co., 1994.

Stephens, W. Richard, Jr. *Careers in Criminal Justice.* Needhan Heights, MA: Allyn and Bacon, 1999.

ENDNOTES

1. John Barker and Jim Kellen, *Career Planning: A Developmental Approach* (Upper Saddle River, NJ: Merrill, 1998).
2. Ibid., p. 75
3. Tom Jackson, *The Perfect Resume* (New York: Doubleday, 1990).

Glossary

Numbers in parentheses indicate the chapters in which the terms are defined.

A

Adjudication ■ The process by which a court arrives at a final decision in a case. (1)

Adjudication ■ The second stage of the juvenile justice process—the court decides whether or not the offender is responsible for (guilty of) the alleged offense. (14)

Administrative officers ■ Those that control keys and weapons and sometimes oversee visitation. (8)

Aggravating circumstances ■ Factors that may be considered as increasing the culpability of the offender. (13)

Auburn system ■ The congregate style of prison discipline that began with the opening of the prison at Auburn, New York, in 1819. This system allowed inmates to work silently together during the day. At night, however, prisoners were isolated in small sleeping cells. With time, even sleeping cells became congregate. (7)

B

Back-end programs ■ Sanctions that move offenders from higher levels of control to lower ones for the final phase of their sentences. (6)

Balancing test ■ A method the U.S. Supreme Court uses to decide prisoners' rights cases, weighing the rights claimed by inmates against the legitimate needs of prisons. (10)

Benefit of clergy ■ Practiced in England from the thirteenth century through the early nineteenth century, the release of clergymen and women from capital punishment when they proved their literacy by reading in court the text of the Fifty-first Psalm. (5)

Best efforts standard ■ A requirement of the federal Victims' Rights and Restitution Act of 1990 (also known as the Victims' Rights Act) which mandates that federal law enforcement officers, prosecutors, and corrections officials use their best efforts to ensure that victims receive basic rights and services during their encounter with the criminal justice system. (15)

Bifurcated trial ■ Two separate hearings for different issues in a trial; one for guilt and the other for punishment. (13)

Blended sentencing ■ A two-part (juvenile and adult) sentence—the adult sentence may be waived if the offender complies with all provisions of the juvenile sentence. (14)

Block officers ■ Those responsible for supervising inmates in housing areas. (8)

Boot camp ■ A short institutional term of confinement, usually followed by probation, that includes a physical regimen designed to develop self-discipline, respect for authority, responsibility, and a sense of accomplishment. (6)

Bridewell ■ A workhouse. The word came from the name of the first workhouse in England. (3)

C

Capital crime ■ A crime for which the death penalty may, but need not necessarily, be imposed. (13)

Capital punishment ■ Legal infliction of the death penalty. (13)

Chronological resume ■ An historical resume, in which work experience and personal history are presented, in reverse chronological order. (16)

Citation ■ A type of nonfinancial pretrial release similar to a traffic ticket. It binds the defendant to appear in court on a future date. (4)

Civil liability ■ A legal obligation to another person to do, pay, or make good something. (10)

Clemency ■ Kindness, mercy, forgiveness, or leniency, usually relating to criminal acts. (13)

Client-specific plan (CSP) ■ A privately prepared presentence investigation report that supplements the PSI prepared by the probation department. (5)

Cocorrections ∎ The incarceration and interaction of female and male offenders under a single institutional administration. (9)

Coed prison ∎ A prison housing both female and male offenders. (9)

Community corrections acts (CCAs) ∎ State laws that give economic grants to local communities to establish community corrections goals and policies and to develop and operate community corrections programs. (6)

Community corrections ∎ A philosophy of correctional treatment that embraces (1) decentralization of authority, (2) citizen participation, (3) redefinition of the population of offenders for whom incarceration is most appropriate, and (4) emphasis on rehabilitation through community programs. (6)

Community notification ∎ Notification to the community of the release or pending release of convicted offenders. (15)

Community service ∎ A sentence to serve a specified number of hours working in unpaid positions with nonprofit or tax-supported agencies. (6)

Commutation ∎ A change of a legal penalty to a lesser one; e.g., from death to life imprisonment. (13)

Compensatory damages ∎ Money a court may award as payment for actual losses the inmates suffered, including out-of-pocket expenses the inmate incurred in filing the suit, other forms of monetary or material loss, and pain, suffering, and mental anguish. (10)

Concurrent sentences ∎ Sentences served together. (2)

Conditional diversion ∎ Diversion in which charges are dismissed if the defendant satisfactorily completes treatment, counseling, or other programs ordered by the justice system. (5)

Conditional release ∎ Pretrial release under minimal or moderately restrictive conditions with little monitoring of compliance. It includes ROR, supervised pretrial release, and third-party release. (4)

Consecutive sentences ∎ Sentences served one after the other. (2)

Consent decree ∎ A written compact, sanctioned by a court, between parties in a civil case, specifying how disagreements between them are to be resolved. (10)

Constitutional rights ∎ The personal and due-process rights guaranteed to individuals by the U.S. Constitution and its amendments, especially the first ten amendments, known as the Bill of Rights. Constitutional rights are the basis of most inmate rights. (10)

Contract system ∎ A system of prison industry in which the prison advertised for bids for the employment of prisoners, whose labor was sold to the highest bidder. (7)

Convict lease system ∎ A system of prison industry in which a prison temporarily relinquished supervision of its prisoners to a lessee. The lessee either employed the prisoners within the institution or transported them anywhere in the state. (7)

Corporal punishments ∎ Physical punishments, or those involving the body. (3)

Correctional clients ∎ Prison inmates, probationers, parolees, offenders assigned to alternative sentencing programs, and those held in jails. (1)

Correctional econometrics ∎ The study of the cost-effectiveness of various correctional programs and related reductions in the incidence of crime. (2)

Correctional officer personalities ∎ The personal characteristics of officers as well as their modes of adaptation to their jobs, institutional conditions, the requirements of staff subculture, and institutional expectations. (8)

Corrections professional ∎ A dedicated person of high moral character and personal integrity who is employed in the field of corrections and takes professionalism to heart. (1)

Corrections ∎ All the various aspects of the pretrial and postconviction management of individuals accused or convicted of crimes. (1)

Counter performance ∎ The defendant's participation, in exchange for diversion, in a treatment, counseling, or educational program aimed at changing his or her behavior. (5)

Crime index ∎ An annual statistical tally of major crimes known to law enforcement agencies in the United States. (1)

Crime rate ■ The number of index offenses reported for each unit of population. (1)

Criminal justice system ■ The collection of all the agencies that perform criminal justice functions, whether operations or administration or technical support. The basic divisions of the criminal justice system are police, courts, and corrections. (1)

Criminal justice ■ The process of achieving justice through the application of the criminal law and through the workings of the criminal justice system. Also, the study of the field of criminal justice. (1)

Criminal law (also called penal law) ■ That portion of the law that defines crimes and specifies criminal punishments. (1)

Cruel and unusual punishment ■ A penalty that is grossly disproportionate to the offense or that violates today's broad and idealistic concepts of dignity, civilized standards, humanity, and decency. In the area of capital punishment, cruel and unusual punishments are those that involve torture, a lingering death, or unnecessary pain. (10)

Custodial staff ■ Those staff members most directly involved in managing the inmate population. (8)

Customer model ■ An approach to private business partnerships with prisons. In this model, a company contracts with a correctional institution to provide a finished product at an agreed-upon price. The correctional institution owns and operates the business that employs the inmate workforce. (7)

D

Day fine ■ A financial penalty scaled both to the defendant's ability to pay and to the seriousness of the crime. (6)

Day reporting center (DRC) ■ A community correctional center where an offender reports each day to file a daily schedule with a supervision officer, showing how each hour will be spent. (6)

Death row ■ A prison area housing inmates sentenced to death. (13)

Deliberate indifference ■ Intentional and willful indifference. Within the field of correctional practice the term refers to calculated inattention to unconstitutional conditions of confinement. (10)

Delinquent offenses ■ Acts committed by juveniles which, if committed by adults, could result in criminal prosecution. (14)

Deprivation theory ■ The belief that inmate subcultures develop in response to the deprivations in prison life. (9)

Design capacity ■ A measure of prison capacity. It is the number of inmates that planners or architects intended for the facility. (7) (11)

Detention hearing ■ A judicial review of the intake officer's detention decision. (14)

Determinate sentence (also called fixed sentence) ■ A sentence to a fixed term of incarceration, which can be reduced by good time. Under determinate sentencing, for example, all offenders convicted of the same degree of burglary are sentenced to the same length of time behind bars. (2)

Deterrence ■ The discouragement or prevention of crimes similar to the one for which an offender is being sentenced; a goal of criminal sentencing. (2)

Direct file provisions ■ Provisions under which the prosecutor determines whether to initiate a case against a juvenile in juvenile court or in adult criminal court. (14)

Discretionary release ■ Early release based on the paroling authority's assessment of eligibility. (12)

Disposition ■ The third stage of the juvenile justice process—the court decides the disposition (sentence) for a juvenile case. (14)

Diversion ■ Referring defendants to noncriminal-justice agencies for services instead of processing them through the courts; also, "the halting or suspension, before conviction, of formal criminal proceedings against a person, conditioned on some form of counter performance by the defendant." (4) (5)

Diversion ■ A non-judicial juvenile sanction. (14)

Due process ■ A right guaranteed by the Fifth, Sixth, and Fourteenth Amendments to the U.S. Constitution and generally understood, in legal contexts, to mean the expected course of legal proceedings according to the rules and forms established for the protection of persons' rights. (10)

E

Electronic monitoring (EM) ■ The tracking of an offender's location by means of electronic signals from a small transmitter on the offender's wrist or ankle to a monitoring unit. (6)

Employer model ■ The most common approach to private business partnerships with prisons. The prison provides a company space in which to operate and a labor pool from which to hire. The company supervises its inmate employees and makes all decisions. (7)

Equity ■ The sentencing principle that similar crimes and similar criminals should be treated alike. (2)

Exchange rates ■ An approach to sentencing, implemented by a sentencing commission, that emphasizes interchangeability of punishments; for example, three days under house arrest might be considered equal to one day of incarceration. (11)

F

Fair sentencing ■ Sentencing practices that incorporate fairness for both victims and offenders. Fairness is said to be achieved by implementing principles of proportionality, equity, social debt, and truth in sentencing. (2)

Felony ■ A serious criminal offense; specifically, one punishable by death or by incarceration in a prison facility for more than a year. (1)

Fine ■ A financial penalty used as a criminal sanction. (6)

First-generation jail ■ A jail with multiple-occupancy cells or dormitories that line corridors arranged in spokes. Inmate supervision is sporadic or intermittent; staff must patrol the corridors to observe inmates in their cells. This linear design dates back to the eighteenth century. (4)

Flat sentences ■ Those that specify a given amount of time to be served in custody and allow little or no variation from the time specified. (2)

Folkways ■ Time-honored ways of doing things. Although they carry the force of tradition, their violation is unlikely to threaten the survival of the social group. (1)

Frivolous lawsuits ■ Lawsuits with no foundation in fact. They are generally brought for publicity, politics, or other reasons not related to law. (10)

Front-end programs ■ Punishment options for initial sentences more restrictive than traditional probation but less restrictive than jail or prison. (6)

Functional resume ■ A qualitative resume, in which work experience and abilities are presented by major area of involvement, usually with dates. (16)

G

Gain time ■ Time taken off an inmate's sentence for participating in certain activities such as going to school, learning a trade, working in prison, etc. (8)

Gang ■ A group of individuals involved in continuing criminal activity. (14)

General deterrence ■ The use of the example of individual punishment to dissuade others from committing crimes. (2)

Good time ■ The number of days or months prison authorities deduct from a sentence for good behavior and for other reasons. (2)

Group home ■ A non-secure residential facility for juveniles. (14)

Guardian *ad litem* ■ A person appointed by the juvenile court, often defense counsel, to serve as a special guardian for the youth being processed through the juvenile justice system. (14)

Guided discretion ■ Decision-making bounded by general guidelines, rules, or laws. (13)

H

Habitual offender statute ■ A law that (1) allows a person's criminal history to be considered at sentencing or (2) allows a person convicted of a given offense, and previously convicted of another specified offense, to receive a more severe penalty than that for the current offense alone. (2)

Hands-off doctrine ■ An historical policy of American courts not to intervene in prison management. Courts tended to follow the doctrine until the late 1960s. (10)

Hedonistic calculus ■ The idea that people are motivated by pleasure and pain and that the proper amount of punishment can deter crime. (3)

Hospice ■ An interdisciplinary, comfort-oriented care unit that allows seriously ill and dying prisoners to die with dignity and humanity in an environment that provides mental and spiritual preparation for the natural process of dying. (11)

House arrest ■ A sanction that requires an offender to remain in his or her home except for approved absences, such as work, school, or treatment programs. (6)

I

Importation theory ■ The belief that inmate subcultures are brought into prisons from the outside world. (9)

Incapacitation ■ The use of imprisonment or other means to reduce an offender's capability to commit future offenses; a goal of criminal sentencing. (2)

Indeterminate sentence ■ A sentence in which a judge specifies a maximum length and a minimum length, and an administrative agency, generally a parole board, determines the actual time of release. (2)

Industrial shop and school officers ■ Those that ensure efficient use of training and educational resources within the prison. (8)

Informational interviewing ■ A process for obtaining firsthand information about a particular job or career. (16)

Infraction ■ A minor violation of state statute or local ordinance punishable by a fine or other penalty, but not by incarceration, or by a specified, usually very short term of incarceration. (1)

Injunction ■ A judicial order to do or refrain from doing a particular act. (10)

Inmate roles ■ Prison lifestyles; also, forms of ongoing social accommodation to prison life. (9)

Inmate subculture ■ (also prisoner subculture) The habits, customs, mores, values, beliefs, or superstitions of the body of inmates incarcerated in correctional institutions; also, the inmate social world. (9)

Institutional corrections ■ That aspect of the correctional enterprise that "involves the incarceration and rehabilitation of adults and juveniles convicted of offenses against the law, and the confinement of persons suspected of a crime awaiting trial and adjudication." (1)

Institutional needs ■ Prison administration interests recognized by the courts as justifying some restrictions on the constitutional rights of prisoners. Those interests are maintenance of institutional order, maintenance of institutional security, safety of prison inmates and staff, and rehabilitation of inmates. (10)

Intake ■ The first stage of the juvenile justice process. A court-appointed officer reviews the case and recommends a course of action—dismissal, informal disposition, formal disposition, or transfer to adult criminal court. (14)

Intangible losses ■ Costs such as fear, pain, suffering, and reduced quality of life that accrue to crime victims as a result of their victimization. (15)

Integration model ■ A combination of importation theory and deprivation theory. The belief that in childhood, some inmates acquired, usually from peers, values that support law-violating behavior, but that the norms and standards in a prison also affect an inmate. (9)

Intensive-supervision probation (ISP) ■ Control of offenders in the community, under strict conditions, by means of frequent reporting to a probation officer, whose caseload is generally limited to 30 offenders. (6)

Intermediate sanctions ■ New punishment options developed to fill the gap between traditional probation and traditional jail or prison sentences and to better match the severity of punishment to the seriousness of the crime. (6)

J

Jail accreditation ■ The formal approval of a jail by a national accrediting body such as the American Correctional Association and the Commission on Accreditation. (4)

Jails ■ Locally operated correctional facilities that confine persons before or after conviction. Persons sentenced to jail usually receive a sentence of a year or less. (4)

Job interview ■ A meeting between two or more people for a mutual exchange of information regarding employment. (16)

Judicial reprieve ■ A nineteenth-century English forerunner of probation; a temporary suspension, or delay, of sentence. The suspended sentence was adopted in the United States and was used frequently until the Supreme Court found it unconstitutional in 1916. (5)

Jurisdiction ■ The power, right, or authority to interpret and apply the law. (10)

Just deserts ■ The punishment deserved. A just-deserts perspective on criminal sentencing holds that criminal acts are deserving of punishment and that justice is best served by the imposition of appropriate punishments on criminal-law violators. (2)

Juvenile court ■ Any court that has jurisdiction over matters involving juveniles. (14)

Juvenile detention facility ■ A facility for keeping juvenile offenders in secure custody, as necessary, through various stages of the juvenile justice process. (14)

L

Legitimate penological objectives ■ The realistic concerns that correctional officers and administrators have for the integrity and security of the correctional institution and the safety of staff and inmates. (10)

M

Mandatory death penalty ■ A death sentence that the legislature has required to be imposed upon persons convicted of certain offenses. (13)

Mandatory minimum sentencing ■ The imposition of sentences required by statute on those convicted of a particular crime or a particular crime with special circumstances, such as robbery with a firearm or selling drugs to a minor within 1000 feet of a school, or on those with a particular type of criminal history. (2)

Mandatory release ■ Early release after a time period specified by law. (12)

Mandatory sentences ■ Those that are required by law under certain circumstances—such as conviction of a specified crime or of a series of offenses of a specified type. (2)

Manpower model ■ An approach to private business partnerships with prisons in which the prison's role is similar to that of a temporary personnel service. (7)

Maximum-security prison ■ A prison designed, organized, and staffed to confine the most dangerous offenders for long periods. It has a highly secure perimeter, barred cells, and a

high staff-to-inmate ratio. It imposes strict controls on the movement of inmates and visitors, and it offers few programs, amenities, or privileges. (7)

Medical model ■ A philosophy of prisoner reform in which criminal behavior is regarded as a disease to be treated with appropriate therapy. (7)

Medium-security prison ■ A prison that confines offenders considered less dangerous than those in maximum security, for both short and long periods. It is also designed, organized, and staffed to prevent violence, escape, and disturbance but places fewer controls on inmates' and visitors' freedom of movement than a maximum-security facility. It, too, has barred cells and a fortified perimeter. The staff-to-inmate ratio is generally lower than in a maximum-security facility, and the level of amenities and privileges is slightly higher. (7)

Minimization of penetration ■ A form of diversion that keeps an offender from going further into the system. (5)

Minimum-security prison ■ A prison that confines the least dangerous offenders for both short and long periods. It allows as much freedom of movement and as many privileges and amenities as are consistent with the goals of the facility, while still following procedures to avoid escape, violence, and disturbance. It may have dormitory housing, and the staff-to-inmate ratio is relatively low. (7)

Misdemeanor ■ A relatively minor violation of the criminal law, such as petty theft or simple assault, punishable by confinement for one year or less. (1)

Mitigating circumstances ■ Factors that, although not justifying or excusing an action, may be considered as reducing the culpability of the offender. (13)

Model of criminal sentencing ■ A strategy or system for imposing criminal sanctions. (2)

Mores ■ Cultural restrictions on behavior that forbid serious violations of a group's values—such as murder, rape, and robbery. (1)

N

Net-widening ■ Increasing the number of offenders sentenced to a greater level of restriction. It results in the sentencing of offenders to more restrictive sanctions than their offenses and characteristics warrant. (6)

Networking ■ An ongoing process of building professional contacts. (16)

New offense violation ■ Arrest and prosecution for the commission of a new crime by a parolee. (12)

"No-frills" prisons and jails ■ Correctional institutions that take away prisoner amenities and privileges. (11)

Nolo contendere ■ A plea of "no contest." A no-contest plea may be used where a defendant does not wish to contest conviction. Because the plea does not admit guilt, however, it cannot provide the basis for later civil suits. (1)

Nominal damages ■ Small amounts of money a court may award when inmates have sustained no actual damages, but there is clear evidence that their rights have been violated. (10)

Noninstitutional corrections (also community corrections) ■ That aspect of the correctional enterprise that includes pardon, probation, and parole activities, correctional administration not directly connectable to institutions, and miscellaneous activities not directly related to institutional care. (1)

O

Older inmates ■ Inmates age 50 and older, as defined by the National Institute of Corrections. (11)

Open institution ■ A minimum-security facility that has no fences or walls surrounding it. (7)

Operational capacity ■ A measure of prison capacity. It is the number of inmates that a facility's staff, existing programs, and services can accommodate. (7) (11)

P

Pains of imprisonment ■ Major problems new inmates face, such as loss of liberty and personal autonomy, lack of material possessions, loss of heterosexual relationships, and reduced personal security. (9)

Pardon ■ An executive act that legally excuses a convicted offender from a criminal penalty. (12)

Parens patriae ■ A Latin term that refers to the state as guardian of minors and incompetent people. (14)

Parole eligibility date ■ The earliest date on which an inmate might be paroled. (12)

Parole ■ The conditional release of a prisoner, prior to completion of the imposed sentence, under the supervision of a parole officer. (12)

Parolee ■ A person who is conditionally released from prison to community supervision. (12)

Paroling authority ■ A person or correctional agency (often called a parole board or parole commission) that has the authority to grant parole, to revoke parole, and to discharge from parole. (12)

Penitentiary ■ A place for reform of offenders through repentance and rehabilitation. The earliest form of large-scale incarceration, it punished criminals by isolating them so that they could reflect on their misdeeds, repent, and reform. (7)

Pennsylvania system ■ The first style of prison discipline, begun at the Walnut Street Jail to punish offenders with confinement instead of corporal punishment. Conceived by the American Quakers in 1790, it emphasized solitary confinement in silence. (7)

Perimeter security officers ■ Those assigned to security (or gun) towers, wall posts, and perimeter patrols. These officers are charged with preventing escapes and detecting and preventing intrusions. (8)

Pleasure-pain principle ■ The idea that actions are motivated primarily by a person's desire to seek pleasure and avoid pain. (2)

Policy-centered approach ■ A method of thinking about and planning for intermediate sanctions that draws together key stakeholders from inside and outside the corrections agency that will implement the sanction. (6)

Precedent ■ A previous judicial decision that judges should consider in deciding future cases. (10)

Predisposition report ■ A report that documents: (1) the juvenile's background; (2) educational history; (3) information gathered from interviews with the juvenile, family members, and others; (4) available placement options; and (5) recommended dispositions. (14)

Presentence investigation report (PSI) ■ A report, prepared by the probation department of a court, that provides a social and personal history as well as an evaluation of an offender as an aid to the court in determining a sentence and/or outlining a treatment plan. (2) (5)

Principle of least eligibility ■ The requirement that prison conditions—including the delivery of health care—must be a step below those of the working class and people on welfare. (7)

Prison argot ■ The special language of the inmate subculture. (9)

Prison code ■ A set of norms and values among prison inmates. It is generally antagonistic to the official administration and rehabilitation programs of the prison. (9)

Prisoners' rights ■ Constitutional guarantees of free speech, religious practice, due process, and other private and personal rights, as well as constitutional protections against cruel and unusual punishments, made applicable to prison inmates by the federal courts. (10)

Prisonization ■ The process by which inmates adapt to prison society; the taking on of the ways, mores, customs, and general culture of the penitentiary. (9)

Probation ■ The conditional release of a convicted offender into the community, under the supervision of a probation officer. It is conditional because it can be revoked if certain conditions are not met. The judge or the probation department usually imposes a set of restrictions on the offender's freedom. (5) (12)

Profession ■ An occupational group granted high social status by virtue of the personal integrity of its members. (1)

Professional associations ■ Organized groups of like-minded individuals who work to enhance the professional status of members of their occupational group. (1)

Program staff ■ Those staff members concerned with encouraging prisoners to participate in educational, vocational, and treatment programs. (8)

Program-centered approach ■ A method of planning intermediate sanctions in which planning for a program is usually undertaken by a single agency, which develops and funds the program. (6)

Property crime ■ Burglary, larceny, automobile theft, and arson as reported in the FBI's Uniform Crime Reports. (1)

Proportionality ■ The sentencing principle that the severity of punishment should match the seriousness of the crime for which the sentence is imposed. (2)

Pseudofamilies ■ Familylike structures, common in women's prisons, in which inmates assume roles similar to those in families in free society. (9)

Public-accounts system ■ The earliest form of prison industry, in which the warden was responsible for purchasing materials and equipment and for the manufacture, marketing, and sale of prison-made items. (7)

Public-works system ■ A system of prison industry in which prisoners were employed in the construction of public buildings, roads, and parks. (7)

Punitive damages ■ Money a court may award to punish the wrongdoer when a wrongful act was intentional and malicious or was done with reckless disregard for the rights of the inmate. (10)

R

Rabble management ■ The control of persons whose noncriminal behavior is offensive to the community (for example, public nuisances, derelicts, junkies, drunks, vagrants, the mentally ill, and street people). According to John Irwin, rabble management is the purpose of jails. (4)

Rated capacity ■ A measure of prison capacity. It is the number of beds or inmates a rating official has assigned to a prison. (7) (11)

Recidivism ■ The repetition of criminal behavior; generally defined as re-arrest. The primary outcome measure for probation, as it is for all corrections programs. (5)

Reentry court ■ A court that manages the return to the community of individuals released from prison. (12)

Reform school ■ A penal institution to which especially young or first-time offenders are committed for training and reformation. (14)

Rehabilitation ■ The changing of criminal lifestyles into law-abiding ones by "correcting" the behavior of offenders through treatment, education, and training; a sentencing goal. (2)

Reintegration ■ The process of making the offender a productive member of the community. (2)

Release on bail ■ The release of a person upon that person's financial guarantee to appear in court. (4)

Release on own recognizance (ROR) ■ Pretrial release on the defendant's promise to appear for trial. It requires no cash guarantee. (4)

Relief officers ■ Experienced correctional officers who know and can perform almost any custody role within the institution, used to temporarily replace officers who are sick or on vacation or to meet staffing shortages. (8)

Residential community center (RCC) ■ A medium-security correctional setting that resident offenders are permitted to leave regularly—unaccompanied by staff—for work, for educational or vocational programs, or for treatment in the community. (6)

Residential treatment center ■ A residential facility that provides intensive treatment services to juveniles. (14)

Restitution ■ The practice of requiring an individual who has harmed another to repay the victim for the harm caused. Also, a court requirement that an alleged or convicted offender pay money or provide services to the victim of the crime or provide services to the community. (2) (15)

Restoration ■ The process of returning to their previous condition all those involved in or affected by crime—including victims, offenders, and society; a recent goal of criminal sentencing. (2)

Resume ■ A written summary of your education, interests, skills, achievements, and goals. (16)

Retribution ■ A sentencing goal that involves revenge against a criminal perpetrator. (2)

Revocation hearing ■ Administrative review to determine whether a violation of the conditions of parole warrants return to prison. (12)

Right of allocution ■ A statutory provision permitting crime victims to speak at the sentencing of convicted offenders. A federal right of allocution was established for victims of federal violent and sex crimes under the Violent

Crime Control and Law Enforcement Act of 1994. (15)

Riot ■ Seizure of control by inmates over all or part of a correctional facility with violence against staff and/or other prisoners. (11)

Roles ■ The normal patterns of behavior expected of those holding particular social positions. (8)

S

Salient factor score (SFS) ■ Scale, developed from a risk-screening instrument, used to predict parole outcome. (12)

Second-generation jail ■ A jail where staff remain in a secure control booth surrounded by inmate housing areas called pods. Bars are replaced with reinforced glass. Although visual surveillance increases, verbal interaction with inmates is reduced. This design emerged in the 1960s. (4)

Security threat groups (STGs) ■ The current term for prison gangs. (11)

Self-assessment ■ A method of enhancing self-understanding—identifying your unique characteristics: what you do well (skills), what is important to you (values), and what you like to do (interests)—clearly and accurately. (16)

Sentence ■ The penalty a court imposes on a person convicted of a crime. (2)

Sentencing commission ■ A group assigned to create a schedule of sentences that reflect the gravity of the offenses committed and the prior record of the criminal offender. The commission often includes private citizens as well as representatives of the criminal justice system, including law enforcement, courts, and corrections. (2)

Sentencing ■ The imposition of a criminal sanction by a sentencing authority, such as a judge. (2)

Social debt ■ The sentencing principle that the severity of punishment should take into account the offender's prior criminal behavior. (2)

Social order ■ The smooth functioning of social institutions, the existence of positive and productive relations between individual members of society, and the orderly functioning of society as a whole. (2)

Special master ■ A person appointed by the court to act as its representative to oversee remedy of a violation and provide regular progress reports. (11)

Special-needs inmates ■ Prisoners who require special treatment or care because they suffer from mental illness, chemical dependency (drug or alcohol abuse), or communicable disease (especially HIV/AIDS and TB). (4)

Specific deterrence ■ The deterrence of the individual being punished from committing additional crimes. (2)

Staff roles ■ The patterns of behavior expected of correctional staff members in particular jobs. (8)

Staff subculture ■ The beliefs, values, and behavior of staff. They differ greatly from those of the inmate subculture. (8)

State-use system ■ A system of prison industry that employs prisoners to manufacture products consumed by state governments and their agencies, departments, and institutions. (7)

Status offenses ■ Acts that are law violations only for juveniles: e.g., running away, truancy, or ungovernability (sometimes referred to as incorrigibility or beyond parental control). (14)

Statutory exclusion provisions ■ Provisions under which adult criminal court jurisdiction for certain juvenile cases is established by state law. (14)

Stress ■ Tension in a person's body or mind, resulting from physical, chemical, or emotional factors. (8)

Structured conflict ■ The tensions between prison staff members and inmates that arise out of the correctional setting. (8)

Structured sentencing ■ A set of guidelines for determining an offender's sentence. (11)

Subculture ■ The beliefs, values, behavior, and material objects shared by a particular group of people within a larger society. (8)

Supermax housing ■ A free-standing facility, or a distinct unit within a facility, that provides for management and secure control of inmates who have been officially designated as exhibiting violent or serious and disruptive behavior while incarcerated. (11)

Supervised pretrial release ■ Nonfinancial pretrial release with more restrictive conditions (for example, participating in therapeutic or rehabilitative programs, reporting to a pretrial officer, and checking in regularly). (4)

Supervision ■ The second major role of probation officers, consisting of intervention, surveillance, and enforcement. (5)

T

Tangible losses ■ Costs such as medical expenses, lost wages, and property losses that accrue to crime victims as a result of their victimization. (15)

Technical violation ■ A failure to fulfill the conditions of probation—attending counseling, paying restitution, contacting the probation officer—rather than the commission of a new offense. (5) (12)

Teen courts ■ Courts in which youths adjudicate and impose disposition for a juvenile offense. (14)

Therapeutic community (TC) ■ A highly structured residential treatment program within a prison or jail involving resocialization, intensive counseling, and an increasing level of inmate responsibility. (11)

Third-generation jail, sometimes called direct-supervision jail ■ A jail where inmates are housed in small groups in pods staffed 24 hours a day by specially trained officers. Officers interact with inmates to help change behavior. Bars and metal doors are absent, reducing noise and dehumanization. This approach to jail construction and inmate management emerged in the 1970s. (4)

Tort ■ A civil wrong, a wrongful act, or a wrongful breach of duty, other than a breach of contract, whether intentional or accidental, from which injury to another occurs. (10)

Total institution ■ A place where the same people work, play, eat, sleep, and recreate together on a continuous basis. The term was developed by the sociologist Erving Goffman to describe prisons and other facilities. (9)

Totality of conditions ■ A standard to be used in evaluating whether prison conditions are cruel and unusual. (10)

True diversion ■ A form of diversion that keeps an offender out of the system and avoids formal prosecution and labeling. (5)

Truth in sentencing ■ The sentencing principle that requires an offender to serve a substantial portion of the sentence and reduces the discrepancy between the sentence imposed and actual time spent in prison. (2)

U

Unconditional diversion ■ The termination of criminal processing at any point before adjudication with no threat of later prosecution. It generally means that treatment, counseling, and other services are offered voluntarily. (5)

Unit management system ■ A method of controlling prisoners in self-contained living areas that include office space for unit staff, making staff and inmates accessible to each other. A unit team—typically composed of the unit manager, one or more case managers, two or more correctional counselors, and a unit secretary—is responsible for the inmates living in that unit. (7)

Utilitarianism ■ The principle that the highest objective of public policy is the greatest happiness for the largest number of people. (3)

V

Victim assistance program ■ An organized program which offers services to victims of crime in the areas of crisis intervention and follow-up counseling, and which helps victims secure their rights under the law. (15)

Victim compensation ■ A form of victim assistance in which state-funded payments are made to victims to help them recover financial losses due to crime. (15)

Victim-impact statement ■ An assertion made by victims (and sometimes by friends or relatives of the victim) about the impact of the crime in question upon the victim and the victim's family. Also, a written document which describes the losses, suffering, and trauma experienced by a crime victim or by the victim's survivors. The judge considers it when sentencing the offender. (2) (5) (15)

Victim notification ■ Notification to victims of the release or pending release of convicted offenders who have harmed them. (15)

Victim ■ Someone who suffers direct or threatened physical, emotional, or financial harm as the result of the commission of a crime. The term victim also includes the immediate family of a minor or homicide victim. (15)

Victims' rights ■ The fundamental rights of victims to be equitably represented throughout the criminal justice process. (15)

Violent crime ■ Interpersonal crime that involves the use of force by offenders or results in injury or death to victims. In the FBI's Uniform Crime Reports, violent crimes are murder, forcible rape, robbery, and aggravated assault. (1)

W

Waiver provisions ■ Provisions under which the juvenile court orders transfer of the case to adult criminal court. (14)

Work detail supervisors ■ Those that oversee the work of individual inmates and inmate work crews. (8)

Writ of *certiorari* ■ A writ issued by an appellate court to obtain from a lower court the record of its proceedings in a particular case. (1) (13)

Writ of *habeus corpus* ■ An order that directs the person detaining a prisoner to bring him or her before a judge, who will determine the lawfulness of the imprisonment. (10)

Y

Yard officers ■ Those that supervise inmates in the prison yard. (8)

Case Index

Subject Index

Photo Credits

Text Credits

2 P.H. Hahn, "Standardized Curriculum for Correctional Officers: History and Rationale," *The Keepers Voice*, Vol., 15, no. 4 (Fall 1994), pp. 8–10;
15 Reprinted with permission;
21 Reprinted with permission of the American Correctional Association;
24 Reprinted with permission;
26 Reprinted with permission;
27 Reprinted with permission of the Federal Bureau of Prisons;
38–39 Reprinted with permission;
54 Reprinted with permission;
55 Reprinted with permission;
66 Reprinted with permission;
67 Reprinted with permission.
77 Reprinted with permission;
87 Reprinted with permission;
92 Reprinted with permission of the American Jail Association; **95–97** W. Raymond Nelson, Cost Savings in New Generation Jails: The Direct Supervision Approach (Washington, DC: National Institute of Justice, June 1988), pp. 2–3; **98** Rocky Finocchio, "Oxbow Jail Division: Accepting the Challenge," *American Jails*, Vol. 10, No. 6, January-February 1997, p. 69, reprinted with permission; **105** Peter Finn, *The Orange County, Florida, Jail Educational and Vocational Programs* (Washington, DC: National Institute of Justice), p. 2; **109** Reprinted with permission; **117** Reprinted with permission of the American Jail Association;
132 Reprinted with permission of the American Correctional Association;
134 Reprinted with permission.
136 Reprinted with permission;
141-45 Reprinted with permission;
149 Reprinted with permission;

156 H.G. Wells (1866–1946), *A Modern Utopia,* chapter 5, section 2 (1905), reprinted in *The Works of H.G. Wells*, Vol. 9 (1925); **158** Reprinted with permission of the American Jail Association;
161 Reprinted with permission;
169 Reprinted with permission;
171 Reprinted with permission;
173 Reprinted with permission;
197 Reprinted with permission of the American Correctional Association;
201 Reprinted with permission;
205 Peter Finn, *The Delaware Department of Correction Life Skills Program*, National Institute of Justice, Washington, DC, August 1998, p. 13; **214** Reprinted with permission; **222** Dora B. Schriro, "Women in Prison Keeping the Peace," *The Keeper's Voice,* Vol. 16, No. 2 (Spring 1995); **231** Reprinted with permission;
232 Peter Finn, *The Delaware Department of Correction Life Skills Program, National Institute of Justice,* Washington, DC, August 1998, p.9; **237** Reprinted with permission; **241** Reprinted with permission of the International Association of Correctional Officers; **248** Eldridge Cleaver, *Soul on Ice,* "On Becoming" (1968), written from Folsom Prison, June 25, 1965; **250** Reprinted with permission; **256** Reprinted with permission; **263** Reprinted with permission; **274** *Procunier* v. *Martinez,* 416 U.S. 396 (1974); **281** Reprinted with permission; **296–97** Reprinted with permission; **299** Reprinted with permission; **310** Jessica Mitford, *Kind and Usual Punishment: The Prison Business,* 1971; **312** Reprinted with permission; **319** Reprinted with permission of the American Correctional Association;

331 Reprinted with permission;
332–34 Excerpted from an interview with Ann Seidlitz in "Fixin' to Die: Hospice Program Operates at LSP," National Prison Hospice Association, reprinted with permission; **346** Peter Finn, *Texas' Project RIO (Re-Integration of Offenders)* (Washington, DC: 1998), p. 3; **350** Reprinted with permission of the American Probation and Parole Association; **353** Reprinted with permission; **354** Reprinted with permission; **362** Reprinted with permission; **363** Peter Finn, *Texas' Project RIO (Re-Integration of Offenders)* (Washington, DC: 1998), p. 9; **378** Albert Camus (1913–1960), *Resistance, Rebellion and Death,* "Reflections on the Guillotine" (1961); **384** Mark Allen Jenkins, "Stop All the Violence," *On Wings of Hope,* Vol. 2, No. 1, Winter 1997, p. 3, reprinted with permission; **385** Reprinted with permission; **386** Reprinted with permission of the American Correctional Association; **390** Reprinted with permission; **402** Shay Bilchik, Administrator, Office of Juvenile Justice and Delinquency Prevention, U.S. Department of Justice; **410** Reprinted with permission; **412** Reprinted with permission; **415–16** Reprinted with permission; **418** Reprinted with permission; **428** President's Task Force on Victims of Crime, Final Report (Washington, D.C., U.S. Government Printing Office, December 1982).
436 Reprinted with permission;
439 Reprinted with permission;
473–75 "Getting Hired in Corrections," *Corrections Connection,* reprinted with permission.